HEMORHEOLOGY

HEMORHEOLOGY

Proceedings of the First International Conference

The University of Iceland, Reykjavik

10th–16th July 1966

Edited by

A. L. COPLEY

Chief, Hemorrhage and Thrombosis Research Laboratories,
Veterans Administration Hospital, East Orange

Research Professor, New York Medical College

THE QUEEN'S AWARD
TO INDUSTRY 1966

PERGAMON PRESS

OXFORD · LONDON · EDINBURGH · NEW YORK

TORONTO · SYDNEY · PARIS · BRAUNSCHWEIG

Pergamon Press Ltd., Headington Hill Hall, Oxford
4 & 5 Fitzroy Square, London W.1
Pergamon Press (Scotland) Ltd., 2 & 3 Teviot Place, Edinburgh 1
Pergamon Press Inc., 44–01 21st Street, Long Island City, New York 11101
Pergamon of Canada Ltd., 207 Queen's Quay West, Toronto 1
Pergamon Press (Aust.) Pty. Ltd., 19a Boundary Street, Rushcutters Bay, N.S.W. 2011, Australia
Pergamon Press S.A.R.L., 24 rue des Écoles, Paris 5ᵉ
Vieweg & Sohn GmbH, Burgplatz 1, Braunschweig

First edition 1968

Library of Congress Catalog Card No. 67–24996

FILMSET BY THE EUROPEAN PRINTING CORPORATION LIMITED, DUBLIN, IRELAND
PRINTED IN GREAT BRITAIN BY A. WHEATON & CO., EXETER
08 013171 9

First International Conference on Hemorheology

UNDER THE AUSPICES OF

Haskoli Islands · Universitas Islandiae · The University of Iceland

Rektor: Professor ÁRMANN SNAEVARR

CONFERENCE CHAIRMAN

Professor A. L. COPLEY
President, The International Society of Hemorheology

CHAIRMAN OF THE LOCAL ARRANGEMENTS COMMITTEE

Professor OLAFUR BJARNASON
President, The Icelandic Medical Association

EXECUTIVE ORGANIZING COMMITTEE

G. BUGLIARELLO   A. L. COPLEY (Chairman)   G. W. SCOTT BLAIR
R. E. WELLS   R. L. WHITMORE

EDITOR

A. L. COPLEY

ORGANIZING COMMITTEE

G. BUGLIARELLO, U.S.A., *Secretary*
A. C. BURTON, Canada
A. L. COPLEY, U.S.A., *Chairman*
L-E. GELIN, Sweden
M. JOLY, France
H. HARTERT, Germany
S. OKA, Japan
G. W. SCOTT BLAIR, England
A. SILBERBERG, Israel
R. E. WELLS, U.S.A., *Treasurer*
R. L. WHITMORE, England, *Secretary*

LOCAL ARRANGEMENTS COMMITTEE

Professor OLAFUR BJARNASON, *Chairman*
Department of Pathology
University of Iceland, Reykjavik

Dr. ASMUNDUR BREKKAN
Secretary, Icelandic Medical Association
Borgarspitalinn—City Hospital
Reykjavik

Dr. TOMAS JONASSON
Treasurer, Reykjavik Medical Society
Reykjavik

Professor SIGMUNDUR MAGNUSSON
Department of Medicine
University of Iceland, Reykjavik

Professor SIGURDUR SAMUELSSON
Department of Medicine
University of Iceland, Reykjavik

LADIES PROGRAM COMMITTEE

Mrs. VALBORG SNAEVARR, *Chairman*
Principal, School for Nursery School Teachers,
Reykjavik

Mrs. OLAFUR BJARNASON, Reykjavik

Mrs. ASMUNDUR BREKKAN, Reykjavik

Mrs. NINA TRYGGVADOTTIR COPLEY, New York and Reykjavik

Mrs. TOMAS JONASSON, Reykjavik

Mrs. SIGMUNDUR MAGNUSSON, Reykjavik

THE INTERNATIONAL SOCIETY OF HEMORHEOLOGY COUNCIL

A. OFFICERS
President

A. L. COPLEY, U.S.A.
Hemorrhage and Thrombosis Research Laboratories, VA Hospital, East Orange, New York Medical College, New York, N.Y., U.S.A.

Vice-President for Europe and Africa

H. HARTERT, Germany
Medizinische Klinik, Städtisches Krankenhaus, Kaiserslautern and Medizinische Fakultät, Universität Heidelberg, Heidelberg, Germany.

Vice-President for the Americas

S. G. MASON, Canada
Department of Chemistry, McGill University, Montreal and Pulp and Paper Research Institute of Canada, Montreal, Canada.

Vice-President for Asia and Australia

S. OKA, Japan
Department of Physics, Tokyo Metropolitan University, Tokyo, Japan.

Secretary

G. BUGLIARELLO, U.S.A.
Biotechnology Committee and Civil Engineering Department, Carnegie Institute of Technology, Pittsburgh, Pennsylvania, U.S.A.

Treasurer

S. WITTE, Germany
Medizinische Klinik und Poliklinik der Universität Erlangen-Nürnberg, Erlangen, Germany

B. COMMITTEE CHAIRMEN

Blood Cellular Elements	Professor A. C. BURTON, Department of Biophysics, University of Western Ontario, London, Ontario, Canada.
Clinical Hemorheology	Dr. J. DITZEL, Department of Medicine, Aalborg Municipal Hospital, Aalborg, Denmark.
Coagulation and Fibrinolysis	Professor K. M. BRINKHOUS, Department of Pathology, School of Medicine, University of North Carolina, Chapel Hill, N.C., U.S.A.
Instrumentation	Professor HAROLD WAYLAND, Division of Engineering and Applied Science, California Institute of Technology, Pasadena, California, U.S.A.
In Vivo Hemorheology	Professor S. ROWLANDS, Department of Medical Biophysics, Faculty of Medicine, University of Calgary, Calgary, Alberta, Canada.
Link with Hemodynamics	Professor M. G. TAYLOR, Department of Physiology, University of Sydney, Sydney, N.S.W., Australia.
Model Studies and *Extra Vivum* Hemorheology	Professor A. SILBERBERG, Polymer Department, The Weizmann Institute of Science, Rehovoth, Israel.
Plasma Components and Modifiers	Dr. M. JOLY, Service de Biophysique, Institut Pasteur, Paris, France.
Standards and Terminology	Dr. G. W. SCOTT BLAIR, Physics Department, National Institute for Research in Dairying, University of Reading, Shinfield, Berks., England.
Theoretical Hemorheology	Dr. R. L. WHITMORE, Department of Mining and Metallurgical Engineering, University of Queensland, St. Lucia, Brisbane, Queensland, Australia.
Vessel Wall Hemorheology	Professor C. A. WIEDERHIELM, Department of Physiology and Biophysics, University of Washington, Seattle, Washington, U.S.A.

SPONSORS OF THE CONFERENCE

THE Organizing Committee and the International Society of Hemorheology gratefully acknowledge the generous aid from the following sources:

SUSTAINING BENEFACTORS

Office of Naval Research, United States Department of the Navy, Washington, D.C., U.S.A.
Pergamon Press, Oxford, England and New York, N.Y., U.S.A.
Pharmacia Laboratories, Uppsala, Sweden and New Market, New Jersey, U.S.A.
The University of Iceland, Reykjavik, Iceland.

CONTRIBUTORS

The Nuffield Foundation, London, England.
Research Laboratory, Snow Brand Milk Products Co., Ltd., Tokyo, Japan.
The Wellcome Trust, London, England.
Hofmann-LaRoche, Nutley, New Jersey, U.S.A.

DONORS

Smith, Kline and French Laboratories, Philadelphia, Pennsylvania, U.S.A.
Benjamin and Phillip Faneuil, Boston, Massachusetts, U.S.A.
Brookfield Engineering Laboratories, Inc., Stoughton, Massachusetts, U.S.A.
Eli Lilly and Company, Indianapolis, Indiana, U.S.A.
Schering Corporation, Bloomfield, New Jersey, U.S.A.
Professor George Bugliarello, Pittsburgh, Pennsylvania, U.S.A.
Professor A. L. Copley, New York, N.Y., U.S.A.
Professor Roe E. Wells, Boston, Massachusetts, U.S.A.
Tokyo Metropolitan University, Tokyo, Japan.
Keirinkan Book Publishing Co., Ltd., Osaka, Japan.
Knoll AG, Ludwigshafen, Germany.
Schaper und Brünner, Ringelheim, Germany.
The Icelandic Medical Association, Reykjavik, Iceland.
The Reykjavik Medical Society, Reykjavik, Iceland.
Tokyo Iyakuhin Kogyo Kyokai, Tokyo, Japan.
Research and Development Division, Takeda Chemical Industries, Osaka, Japan.
Professor T. Arai, Tokyo, Japan.
Boehringer Ingelheim Ltd., Isleworth, Middlesex, England.

CONTENTS

CONTENTS

CLINICAL HEMORHEOLOGY

PART IV. CLOSING SESSION

A. APPRAISALS OF THE ACHIEVEMENTS OF THE CONFERENCE

B. CLOSING REMARKS   825

PREFACE

MORE than one hundred persons participated in the Conference from the following twelve countries: Australia, Canada, Denmark, France, Germany, Great Britain, Iceland, Israel, Italy, Japan, Sweden and the United States of America. Among the participants were both non-biologists and biologists; the former representing the fields of mathematics, physics, engineering mechanics, physical chemistry, polymer chemistry and organic chemistry; the latter representing those of physiology, biochemistry, biophysics, pharmacology, anatomy, pathology, and of clinical medicine, for instance, surgery, medicine, gynecology and pediatrics.

This volume contains eighty-three contributions by one hundred and thirty-two authors. Throughout the book it was necessary to maintain uniformity of presentation. This relates also to the references given for each contribution. Since complete references were not furnished by many authors, it was decided not to include those titles of papers, as listed by many other authors in their manuscripts, although these titles would have been useful to the reader. The names of the session chairmen appear below the headings prior to the proceedings of each session.

The Proceedings are sub-divided into four parts. Part I deals with the seven presentations at the Inaugural Session on 10 July. Part II contains an account of the Poiseuille Medal and of the Award Ceremony. Photographs of both sides of the gold medal are reproduced, one of which appears in Part II and the other as Frontispiece of this book. The biographical sketches of Jean-Léonard-Marie Poiseuille and of Robin Fåhraeus, given at the Ceremony, are followed by the text of the presentation of the Poiseuille Award.

Part III represents the sixty-six original scientific contributions presented at the eleven working sessions on each day of the Conference, from Monday, 11 July, to and including Saturday, 16 July. These sessions were usually held from 9.00 a.m. to 12.15 p.m., and from 1.30 p.m. to 4.45 p.m. Six papers were read by title and two others were presented, although they were not in the printed program. Of the sixty-six original contributions, four appear as abstracts. Two of these communications were fully presented by their authors; however, the final manuscripts did not meet with our dateline for this volume. All authors of papers for which only the abstract is available expressed the intention to submit their complete articles to the journal *Biorheology*.

Part III also contains all discussion remarks made during the scientific sessions. The discussions were taped and after they were transcribed, each discussant was asked to edit his remarks. This procedure was used to increase the value of the discussions, since, fortunately, nearly all participants corrected their statements. In the few exceptions, the text, as recorded on the tape, was used with only slight editorial changes. Each session was conducted by two chairmen and, occasionally, at their discretion, several papers were discussed together. In general, the discussion of each paper immediately followed its presentation. As a rule, twenty minutes were allotted to the speaker and ten minutes for the discussion.

Part IV pertains to the Closing Session on 16 July. Brief appraisals of the achievements of the Conference were given in eight fields of hemorheology. These appraisals, each lasting about ten minutes, were taped and the appraisers were asked to edit their contributions which will also be published in the journal *Biorheology*. Such revisions of the original texts were made by five of the eight speakers. Following the appraisals, two statements were made, one by Professor S. Oka, on the Biorheology Sessions planned for the Fifth International Congress on Rheology, Tokyo, Japan, 1968; and the other by Dr. M. Joly, on the Second International Conference on Hemorheology, to be held in France, in 1969. These statements are not included in this volume and our readers are advised to consult issues of the journal *Biorheology*, in which information regarding these two conferences will appear. The Closing Session ended with remarks by Professor Alex Silberberg on behalf of the participants, by Professor Olafur Bjarnason as Chairman of the Local Arrangements Committee, and by the Conference Chairman. These remarks conclude the text of this volume.

Since there was considerable interest in the two drawings by Mr. L. Alcopley of the harbor of Reykjavik, abstracted directly from nature, which appeared on the covers of the Provisional Program and the Final Program, it was thought to include them in this book. This will also serve to present these pictures in their original proportions, because, as they appeared on the above program covers, they were cut inadvertently and therefore were not fully representative of the originals. These with two more drawings appear on the pages heading each of the four parts of the book, while two other drawings appear on pages xx and 826.* All drawings, which originated in the summer of 1950, are meant to convey feelings about Reykjavik and the landscape of its surroundings.

The solume contains a Name Index, an Author Index and a Subject Index to increase the usefulness of this book, which, it is hoped, will serve as a handbook for the present status of knowledge in the field of hemorheology. During the past few years, hemorheology has grown extensively as a branch of the science of biorheology. It is doubtful whether the Second International Conference on Hemorheology, in 1969, can be arranged without simultaneous sessions so that participants will have the luxury of listening to each paper and of contributing to its discussion if they so desire.

Numerous reports about the Conference appeared in medical and scientific journals, as well as the press and other publications, in many countries in different parts of the globe. Among the earliest reports, which were published in leading scientific journals, was that of Dr. G. W. Scott Blair (*Nature, London,* 10 September 1966, pp. 1129–30). *The Medical Tribune and Medical News,* a medical newspaper in the United States, published in New York City, sent their special correspondent, Mr. W. K. Waterfall, to the Conference. He was the author of four articles on the Conference and The International Society of Hemorheology, which was founded at the University of Iceland prior to the Conference. They appeared on the front page of the issues of 3, 8 and 10 August 1966. The reader may wish to consult a special issue, devoted to the Conference, of the journal *Biorheology*. The abstracts of the scientific papers, which appeared originally in the Program and Abstracts of the Conference, are contained in this issue (Vol. 4, No. 3, 1967), with revisions made by some of the authors.

The members of the Local and Ladies Committees arranged a social program for

*On page 826 the drawing by Mr. L. Alcopley is reproduced in its actual size, while the actual size of his other five drawings is 12·4 cm × 17·8 cm.

each day of the Conference. Several receptions were given and we are grateful to His Excellency Dr. Gylfi Gislason, the Minister of Education, and his wife, His Excellency Mr. James K. Penfield, Ambassador of the United States of America, and his wife, The Honorable Mr. Geir Hallgrimsson, Mayor of Reykjavik, and to the City Health Commissioner, Dr. Jon Sigurdsson and his wife. We thank the performing artists for their Icelandic songs and other musical entertainment during the Inaugural Session, the receptions and the Banquet.

The Ladies Committee arranged a number of activities for the non-professional attendees of the Conference. These arrangements included sightseeing tours, visits to the National Gallery of Art and other museums, as well as visits to various social institutions, such as children's homes, hospitals, and an institution for the rehabilitation of handicapped people. The ladies among our attendees appreciated particularly the luncheons given in their honor in Icelandic homes and the visit to the studio of the sculptor Mr. Asmundur Sveinsson. The arrangements of the Ladies Committee were sponsored by Professor Ármann Snaevarr, Rektor of the University of Iceland.

Tours of the National Museum and the National Gallery of Art were conducted under the guidance of their Directors Dr. Kristjan Eldjarn and Dr. Selma Jonsdottir, respectively. A film and lecture on the birth of the island of Surtsey was given at the University by the geologist Dr. Sigurdur Thorarinsson, Director of the Museum of Natural History. His presentation was followed by a discussion.

An excursion was made in the evening of 13 July to Thingvellir, the original site of the world's oldest parliament. The Ministry for Foreign Affairs of the Government of Iceland delegated its Press Officer, Mr. Bjarni Gudmundsson, to address the Conference participants and members of their families at Thingvellir with a lecture on the history of the Icelandic parliament. Mr. Gudmundsson's lecture was followed by a discussion, conducted by the Conference Chairman, on the ancient and present Icelandic parliament, law and government.

We are also grateful to the three after-dinner speakers at the Banquet, held at the Saga Hotel after the Award Ceremony in the evening of 15 July. They were His Excellency Dr. Gylfi Gislason, the Minister of Education, Dr. Asmundur Brekkan and Dr. George W. Scott Blair. The participants and attendees of the Conference were honored at the Banquet by the presence of prominent leaders of the Icelandic nation in government, health, education and other cultural fields, among them Mr. Halldor Kiljan Laxness, 1955 Nobel Laureate in Literature, and his wife, as well as by the presence of the ambassadors of several countries.

In the Inaugural Address, as well as in the Closing Remarks which are included in this volume, I expressed my gratitude to the sponsors and to everyone who contributed to the success of the Conference. A complete list of the names of sources which provided financial assistance as Sustaining Benefactors, Contributors and Donors is included in this book. I am particularly grateful to Dr. Leonard M. Libber, Chief of the Physiology Branch, Office of Naval Research, United States Department of the Navy.

It is my pleasure to acknowledge the assistance and cooperation of several persons who were engaged in work pertaining to the preparation of the Information Booklet with Provisional Program, of the Program and Abstracts and of this book. Among them, my special thanks go to Miss Ruth M. Stein for her work on the programs and abstracts; to Miss Una Dora Copley, my daughter, who helped in the collection

and cataloguing of the many manuscripts which were handed to me in Reykjavik;
to Mrs. Ingrid T. Luchini for her transcription of the discussion remarks from the
tapes; to Miss Joanne Bonner and Miss Marilyn Thaller for their aid in transcribing
the corrections of these remarks made by the discussants; to Mr. George Hilliard
for secretarial assistance and to Mr. Peter Phelan for aid in proofreading. Dr. E. W. J.
Mardles (England) compiled the Subject Index while Mrs. Coty Blank and Mrs. Jean
Meyer prepared the Name Index and the Author Index, tasks which are greatly
appreciated.

I am indebted to Mr. Robert Maxwell, M.P. and Mr. Detlev J. Raymond of
Pergamon Press for their generous aid and keen interest in our Conference and in the
publication of its Proceedings.

Finally, I thank my wife, Mrs. Nina Tryggvadottir Copley, who introduced me to
Iceland, for her help in many local arrangements at Reykjavik which contributed
to make the social activities of this Conference so highly successful.

New York and East Orange   A. L. Copley
19 June 1967

Part I

INAUGURAL SESSION

10 July, p.m.

Chairmen: OLAFUR BJARNASON, Iceland
ALFRED L. COPLEY, U.S.A.

INTRODUCTION

OLAFUR BJARNASON

MR. MINISTER OF EDUCATION, Rector, Mr. Chairman, ladies and gentlemen:

On behalf of the Local Committee of this Conference, I welcome you to the Inaugural Session of the First International Conference on Hemorheology.

I find it most becoming that this island of the old Sagas has been selected as a location for the Founding Meeting of the International Society of Hemorheology and the First International Conference on Hemorheology. It certainly is a pleasure for us here to provide the facilities that are available for that occurrence.

It really is a privilege to have here with us today distinguished scientists from all over the world.

This also is a great event for Icelandic scientists, because although we do not take active part in the scientific program, I am sure that the conference will act as a stimulus to scientific endeavour in this country. For those of us attending the meetings the reward is obvious, and I do hope the personal connections that may be established these days between Icelandic scientists and our guests will be mutually stimulating and rewarding.

There is no doubt of the fundamental and practical importance of this field of science for medicine as a whole. As an example, I mention the atheromatous and sclerosing degenerations of arteries, pathological processes, which besides cancer are becoming major enemies of human health. These processes will be most actively dealt with by numerous hemorheologists. It is not for me to elucidate the different angles of approach from which hemorheologists can tackle these processes, in order to understand their etiology and pathogenesis. But it seems obvious that the thorough understanding of their natural history will not be revealed without entering the field of hemorheology. I only have mentioned this single example of a serious disease, threatening an increasing proportion of mankind today, a disease which is a primary object of study of many hemorheologists, in order to stress the utmost practical importance of this field of science.

Again it is a great pleasure to welcome all of you to this important meeting.

Thank you.

WELCOME ADDRESS

Ármann Snaevarr

Mr. Chairman, Mr. Minister of Education, Excellencies, ladies and gentlemen:

It is a great pleasure and a privilege for me on behalf of the University of Iceland — Háskóli Islands — to extend a warm and a most cordial welcome to the members of the First International Conference on Hemorheology. We at this University are very pleased to see here today a great number of distinguished scientists from a number of countries and we are greatly honored by the presence of these well-known scientists. For us it is a real pleasure to offer you the facilities of our University, and we sincerely hope that you will feel at home here during the conference. We are particularly pleased to see here the wives of the scientists and a special welcome is extended to them. Your conference is a very important one, marking the foundation of the international society of specialists in hemorheology and dealing with many subjects of utmost scientific interest. May I wish you every success in your work and a pleasant stay in our country.

On this occasion I find it appropriate to say a few words about the University which has the pleasure to act as your host.

Our University is a relatively young one, founded as it was in 1911, although the oldest part of it dates back to 1847. It is also a small one, one of the smallest in Europe, necessarily so because of the smallness of our nation. It is the only university in our country. Needless to say, this places a heavy responsibility on us and this fact *per se* is a great challenge. We have by now between 1100 and 1200 students, divided into six faculties or departments, those of Theology, Medicine, Law, Fine Arts and Philosophy, Economics and Engineering. Until recently, the emphasis has been placed on the humanities, but now we are turning in an ever-increasing degree to science, and in these days we are finishing a building for institutes for basic research in the fields of physics, chemistry, mathematics and geophysics. Plans have been worked out for a building, housing various medical research institutes and we very much hope that this building will be built in the near future. A building for Icelandic studies and research in our Manuscript tradition has been designed on our campus and the building activity will start in a few weeks. At present one building is under construction on the campus, the Nordic House designed by the world famous Finnish architect Professor Alvar Aalto. This house is built jointly by the governments of all the Scandinavian countries as a center of Nordic cultural activities in Iceland.

We fully realize that our University is under the optimal size of a university according to the standards generally accepted in Europe nowadays, but a small university has also some attractive features — we have for instance here a ratio of one to ten as far as the teachers–students are concerned, and the relationship between the teachers and the students is a very personal one, to the great benefit of both groups. We are in Justice Brandeis' words spared "the curse of bigness".

The motto of our University which you will find inscribed above the door of the Festival Hall is taken from a poem of one of our best known poets from the nineteenth century, and may be translated into English prose as follows: "Science and learning give strength to all good deeds". Behind these words is the optimism of the first half of the last century. In our lifetime we have experienced how science and learning can be misused by faulty political leaders. Let us hope that in the future scientific progress and inventions will be used as to truly benefit mankind in its search for peace, prosperity and personal happiness — and never will be misused.

The poem from which our motto is taken was written in order to welcome a well known scientist from abroad who visited our country. I find this symbolic. Still today — although our isolation is definitely broken — nothing can be a source of greater joy to us than visits of scientists from other countries. I can assure you that no visitors can be more welcome guests here than people of science and learning.

Distinguished members of the Conference:

Our University is pleased and proud to offer you its facilities. I have the pleasure to bring you cordial greetings from your fellow scientists and scholars at our University. I wish you a pleasant and successful conference and every success in your very important scientific work, and I would like to conclude my address by congratulating you on the newly founded International Society of Hemorheology.

WELCOME ADDRESS

Gylfi Gislason

I AM very pleased to welcome to Iceland the scientists from abroad who are assembled here today. It is an honor for my country that the first international conference to be held on hemorheology should take place here. I have an idea that the Chairman of the Conference, Professor Copley, has had a good deal to do with this. It is remarkable, I think, that the present scientific conference should to some extent owe its origin to the fact that a scientist of international repute is also linked by artistic ties to this small country. Fortunately, the gap between science and art is often not as wide as many people think.

A few days ago there was a conference here of Scandinavian pathologists. I said to one of the foreign professors that there was now also to be a conference of hemorheologists in Reykjavik. I had some difficulty in pronouncing the word correctly and apologized for this. The professor replied, however, that I had no need to be ashamed. He himself had had to get the word spelt for him the previous day. May I continue now — instead of resorting merely to the usual official words of politeness — to say a few words at this Conference on the subject of science and politics? I hope you will not object, partly because I was once a professor myself.

Everyone today fully realizes what a debt of gratitude mankind owes to science. And everyone knows, too, that without ever-increasing specialization science would never have provided man with the knowledge he has acquired and would never have achieved the results we see today. But I doubt whether people realize to the same extent the danger that accompanies all specialization. I am not here referring to the well-known assertion that man is gradually ceasing to know nothing about everything and beginning to know everything about nothing. The matter is not so simple that we can find its crux by means of such witticisms.

The tremendous achievements of science have led too many people to believe that all problems can be solved by scientific methods. But this is not true. I will merely refer to one field, in which I — as a university man — have some knowledge, social science. I should be the last to underrate the part played by science in efforts to solve social problems. On the other hand, I realize that there is in fact no final "solution" to them, and one will not therefore be found by scientific methods either. As many persons as possible who deal with social affairs should understand this. And it is not only politicians and scientists who deal with social affairs, but also the whole public in a democratic society.

What I should like to stress here is my fear that increasing specialization in all spheres is preventing people from realizing this as clearly as before. I am afraid that the scientists — who are of course bringing mankind untold benefits — are getting farther away from those who deal with social problems, and that the knowledge of the politicians of the scientists' conclusions and even their methods is getting less. If this is so, it is a serious question. What I fear is that, because of science's achievements, some scientists imagine that scientific methods can solve more problems than is the case, and that they do not therefore have the necessary appreciation of the work of politicians nor the patience in this respect that might be expected of them. And on the other hand, I fear that politicians are losing healthy and profitable contact with scientists and the scientific world because of the growing difficulty of assimilating more and more specialized knowledge. Furthermore, both scientists and politicians are—owing to the increasing complexity of their work—exposed to the risk that an ever-narrowing specialization will obsess them to the detriment of their knowledge of other branches of intellectual life, other kinds of intellectual endeavour, for example in art. Fortunately of course, there are many instances of the opposite happening, of which the Chairman of this Conference is tangible evidence. Nevertheless, the danger is there.

I once heard a story, which will perhaps illustrate this problem better than a long lecture could do. Saint Peter was standing at the Gate of Heaven receiving people who wished to enter, and he made everybody show his identity card. Then came a man who said he was a painter by the name Van Gogh, but he had no documents. Peter would not let him in. When the man was about to go away, Peter took pity on him and asked if he could prove in some other way that he was really Van Gogh. The man asked for paper and pencil and drew a splendid picture. Then Peter said—Only Van Gogh could do a picture like that. Please come in. Later another man arrived, who had no documents either. He said his name was Kreisler. He was very unassuming and was also going to turn back. Then Peter told him about the painter who had proved his identity and he asked Kreisler if he could not do something similar. Kreisler enquired if there was a violin in Heaven. He was given one and began to play with great artistry. So Peter said—Only Kreisler could play like that. Please come in. After that a famous politician knocked at Peter's gate. He had been a government minister for many years and was known throughout the world. When Peter asked him for documents he almost took offence. He said he was sure most people knew him. But when Peter remained firm the politician became very worried. Peter then wanted to help him and he told him how Van Gogh and Kreisler had proved who they were. Surely he could do something like that too, and then everything would be all right. The politician replied—What are you talking about? Van Gogh, Kreisler? Who on earth are they? At this Saint Peter said— Well, you must be a politician. Come in.

This is the danger to which we are all exposed in an age of specialization. And we must not think that scientific methods will solve all problems for us, either now or in the future. We must learn better than we have done so far to cope with problems that are basically of a moral nature, whether they are in the sphere of personal interests or feelings. Science must not follow one path, politics another, art a third and morals a fourth. None of these aspects of human thought, of human endeavour can by itself cope with the difficulties that arise from being a human being. Those who work in one or other of these fields must not follow separate paths but must, on the contrary, cooperate more closely with one another and learn to understand better one another's contribution to the whole. Perhaps nothing is more important than this to a wealthy and powerful, though at the same time somewhat aimless, mankind, if man is to merit the title of "Master of the Earth".

GREETINGS

Asmundur Brekkan

Mr. President, honored guests, distinguished delegates:

It is my privilege to convey to you the greetings of the Icelandic Medical Association. It was with extreme pride and pleasure that we learnt that Reykjavik had been chosen as a meeting-place for this very first International Conference on Hemorheology.

Clinical medicine in general may by its nature be classified as a deductive science, whereas the basic biological and medical sciences as well as research into various fields of physics and chemistry may be called inductive. The trend in modern medicine, however, is towards an increasing and ever closer association with the various branches of the basic sciences.

We are all aware of the tremendous strides made in biorheological and more specially hemorheological basic research during the past years and it is well known that several important results and data from that work have found widespread and important applications in clinical medicine, surgery and radiology.

It is equally gratifying to note that among the papers to be read and discussed at this Conference, there are many which open up still new scopes and aspects of practical use in diagnostics and therapeutics within the various branches of clinical medicine.

We are therefore confident that your work here will be a direct and indirect stimulus to our own activities as well as being of great universal value, and wish you a pleasant and rewarding week in Reykjavik.

ON HEMORHEOLOGY.
INAUGURAL ADDRESS

A. L. COPLEY

MR. CHAIRMAN, Excellencies, ladies and gentlemen:

I have the great pleasure in addressing you on behalf of the Organizing Committee of the First International Conference on Hemorheology here in Reykjavik, and to thank His Excellency, The Minister of Education, Professor Gislason, the Rector of the University of Iceland, Professor Snaevarr, the Chairman of this Session Professor Bjarnason, President of the Icelandic Medical Association, and Dr. Brekkan for their kind thoughts and good wishes.

It is my privilege to express the gratitude of the scientist members of this Conference to our host, the University of Iceland, its Senate and the Rector, Professor Snaevarr, to the Local Chairman Professor Bjarnason and the members of the Local Committee, to Mrs. Valborg Snaevarr and the other ladies for making this Conference possible. Our thanks go likewise to our financial sponsors. They include agencies of different governments, private foundations, firms and persons in different countries. Acknowledgments of their names, listed in part in the Program, will be fully given in the printed Proceedings of the Conference. Without this help, encouragement and assistance, many among us could not have come from different parts of the globe to Reykjavik. My hearty welcome goes to my fellow scientists, whose enthusiasm to hold the Conference here has been overwhelming and a guiding stimulant to the members of the Organizing Committee.

At this point I should like to convey to you the greetings and good wishes from many parts of the globe for the success of the Conference, among others, from Dr. William H. Stewart, Surgeon General of the United States Public Health Service in Washington, D.C., * and from Dr. P. A. Messerli, Executive Secretary of the Council of International Organizations of Medical Sciences, C.I.O.M.S. (Conseil des Organisations Internationales des Sciences Medicales), Paris, France, an organization established under the auspices of the World Health Organization and UNESCO.

My colleagues Professor Hartert and Dr. Scott Blair will elaborate on the significance of hemorheology to the practice of medicine and to the different sciences. I shall limit my remarks to a historical sketch which will lead us to the event of this Conference. Rheology is a physical science and denotes the deformation and flow of matter. It was founded as late as in 1929, although the pre-Socratic or pre-Platonic philosophers[1] appeared to be quite aware of some of its major problems, posed by Nature.

At the First International Congress on Rheology in 1948 in Scheveningen, Holland, the role of rheology in the biological sciences was stressed and, at that time, the term "biorheology" was introduced[2]. Three years later, in Chicago, at the 25th Anniversary Meeting of the American Institute of Physics[3], of which the Society of Rheology is

* The telegram was read.

11

a founding member, in a survey on the rheology of blood, the term hemorheology was first employed[4]. Hemorheology is concerned with the flow of blood and its relations, in general, to the vessel in which it is contained, and, in particular, to the blood vessel wall, through which the flowing blood is in contact with the surrounding tissues in different organs.

You will hear, in a little while, from Professor Hartert, to which extent the flow properties of blood and of the vessel wall affect the health of all of us, much more so than many among you may have realized. Dr. Scott Blair will then develop how the interchange of hemorheological phenomena and their rheological treatments affect many other scientific disciplines and, vice versa, how the latter affect hemorheology and, ultimately, can be applied towards the maintenance of our health.

This Conference is the first international one devoted entirely to hemorheology. The increasing interest of prominent physicists, mathematicians, engineers, chemists, physiologists and other medical scientists, as well as physicians and surgeons, in hemorheology is reflected by the meetings in which hemorheology sessions were held. In 1958, at the University of London, a one-day national meeting, entitled "The Flow of Blood in Relation to the Vessel Wall"[5], triggered off others to follow. The next year, at the University of Oxford, a meeting sponsored by the Faraday Society and the British Society of Rheology took place on "Flow Properties of Blood and Other Biological Systems"[6, 7]. Three years ago at Brown University, Providence, Rhode Island, U.S.A., the Symposium on Biorheology[8], as part of the 4th International Congress on Rheology, was held, at which time many sessions were devoted to hemorheology. Other national and international meetings, foremost the European Conference on Microcirculation, included, in their programs, papers and sessions on hemorheology. Hemorheology is developing now at such a rapid pace that it became necessary to organize this branch of science by the founding of the International Society of Hemorheology, which preceded this Conference by only a few hours. Thus today, the 10 July 1966, marks two historical events, here in Reykjavik at the University of Iceland, the birth of the International Society and the beginning of the First International Conference.

It was decided that these conferences will take place every three years and will be held in different parts of the globe. I am happy to announce that the Second International Conference on Hemorheology will be held in France in 1969. France was chosen, because we have in three years the 100th Anniversary of the death of Jean-Léonard-Marie Poiseuille, who may be considered the first hemorheologist.

Poiseuille was a prominent physiologist and physician who made classical observations on the flow of blood in capillary vessels in living animals[9, 10]. His discoveries impelled him to search for the underlying laws of flow which led to his work, of utmost possible precision, on the flow of water and other liquids in tubes of very small diameter. As a tribute to these observations, MAXWELL[11] and other physicists in the last century deduced from the fundamental equation of Newton a famous formula which was named after Poiseuille and Hagen. Although Hagen discovered the same law independently at about the same time, the work of POISEUILLE brought conviction[11].

Our Conference, here in Reykjavik, is honoring Jean-Léonard-Marie Poiseuille by the initiation of the Poiseuille Gold Medal Award[12]. This award, given by The International Society of Hemorheology, will have as its first recipient Dr. Robin

Fåhraeus, Professor Emeritus of Pathology of the University of Uppsala, Sweden[13]. The International Society and the Organizing Committee of the Conference extend to you all our cordial invitation to be here, at the University Festival Hall, next Friday at 6.30 p.m., when the Award Ceremony will be held, to honor a Scandinavian, the scientist, scholar and physician Robin Fåhraeus.

The question may be asked: "Why was Iceland chosen to be the meeting place for the First International Conference?" There are many answers to this question. One is that Iceland is situated geographically between Western Europe and North America, where, at present, most work on hemorheology is being pursued. Another answer is that the University of Iceland, although small in size, is a vigorous new institution of higher learning and eminent scholarship. It provides an atmosphere which is conducive to original thinking, which, I trust, this Conference will promote. The third answer, strangely enough, can be related to theology. This, I am sure, will surprise you. I am mentioning this, because three years ago one of the founders of rheology as an organized science, Professor MARCUS REINER of the Israel Institute of Technology in Haifa, proposed, in a talk given at the Fourth International Congress on Rheology, a relationship between *theology* and *rheology*[14]. He discovered that a passage in the Bible was poorly translated, over 300 years ago, from the Hebrew into English. The Song of the Prophetess Deborah, which she sang after the victory over the Philistines, should read: "The mountains *flowed* before the Lord", instead of: "The mountains *melted* before the Lord". Deborah must have known before Heraclitus that everything flows, including the mountains. Professor Reiner proposed therefore as a nondimensional number, the Deborah number (D). D = time of relaxation/time of observation. Thus, he could define the difference between solids and fluids by the magnitude of the Deborah number.

Reiner thought that "the Deborah number is destined to become the fundamental number of rheology, bringing solids and fluids under a common concept, and leaving Heraclitus' $\pi\alpha\nu\tau\alpha$ $\rho\epsilon\iota$ as a special case for infinite time of observation, or infinitely small time of relaxation. The greater the Deborah number, the more solid the material: the smaller the Deborah number, the more fluid it is."

Deborah must have been convinced also that the mountains flow before the Lord, but not before man, for the reason that man cannot see them flowing in his short lifetime, while the time of observation of the Lord is infinite. Here, I think, most Icelanders must have known quite differently, ever since the Vikings landed on this volcanic island in the ninth century. And this is still another answer to why Iceland was chosen as the site of our Conference. Twenty years ago everyone here could see the flow of lava and the deformation of Mt. Hekla. On 14 November, 1963, the emergence of the new island Surtsey occurred from the bottom of the ocean, not far from this city, at the south coast of Iceland[15]. It is a flowing mountain, as will be demonstrated to you on Tuesday evening by Dr. Thorarinsson in a film, which he will be kind enough to show us.

Rheology is manifested in still other ways here in Iceland, this geologically very young part of the globe, by the flow of the Gulf Stream which warms the land, by the sudden flow of geysers, by the flow of hot springs, which have been ingeniously channelled to warm houses and homes here; by the flow of glaciers, by the many waterfalls and numerous rivers.

Metaphorically, this large island is full and rich in all kinds of flow, including the flow of colors, shapes and forms over its poetic land, waters and skies, or the mysterious flow of the North Lights — aurora borealis.

As most of us were brought to this assembly from lands far away by our mechanical birds, we may wonder about the flow of birds, migrating to and from this isle, which our fellow scientists, the ornithologists, consider a bird's paradise and hence a heaven for the study of bird life.

To wonder about nature will continue to be the prerogative of man, regardless of his origin. It is assumed that there are today two opposing worlds, one of the sciences and the other of the arts and humanities. I think these are erroneous and untenable assumptions. As practicing scientists with different professional, national and cultural backgrounds and experiences, we owe a great deal to the arts and humanities. As scientists, we search for answers to troubling questions about phenomena and processes in nature with all the resourcefulness and productivity we can muster. Our endeavors are guided by a sense of adventure into unknown and uncharted parts of the world in all its dimensions, a sense akin to that of the Vikings who came to this land, or of the Icelander Leif Eirikson who, five centuries before Christopher Columbus, discovered America and, exulting in his find, named it Vinland, the land of grapes[16].

As scientists we gather in meetings to exchange freely — and often in opposition — our findings or ideas, similar to the Vikings who began to meet in the year 930 at the Althing, their parliament at Thingvellir[17] which we are going to visit next Wednesday evening.

As scientists, we wonder, as every man wonders, about man's existence and the world around him. And as such, we cherish the high attainments in the arts and other humanities.

Here in Iceland, we meet a people, deeply aware of its high achievements in literature — the sagas, old and new, the poems of the Edda and of our time — a people as proud of its contemporary painters, sculptors, poets, musicians, scholars and scientists, as it is of the great originators in its past.

To many non-Icelanders, Iceland means the land of poetry. The Welshman and English poet, Dylan Thomas, told me in New York, how much he hoped to visit, what he called "the land of poets", but his death in 1953 made an end to his dream.

Recently, in reading an English translation of the *Prose Edda,* written about 1320 by SNORRI STURLUSON[18], the unique Icelandic chieftain, statesman, historian and writer, I came across passages on deformation and flow of matter, which, I think, have never been stated more forcefully. These rheological thoughts relate to the origins of the world, as seen by the early Germanic peoples, prior to their conversion to Christianity in Iceland in the year 1000. The Edda, considered by the Icelandic scholar, Professor SIGURDUR NORDAL, as "a sort of ars poetica"[19], falls into three parts: mythology, skaldic diction and a metrical key.

I read from its mythology or first part "Gylfaginning" — The Deluding of Gylfi — where King Gylfi, a wise man, skilled in magic, who "ruled the lands that are now Sweden", got answers to many questions.

> In the beginning
> not anything existed,
> there was no sand nor sea
> nor cooling waves;
> earth was unknown

and heaven above
only Ginnungagap — Open Void —
was — there was no grass.

When those rivers which are called Élivágar — Rivers — whipped-by-passing-showers — came so far from their source that the yeasty venom accompanying them hardened like slag, it turned into ice. Then when that ice formed and was firm, a drizzling rain that arose from the venom poured over it and cooled into rime, and one layer of ice formed on top of the other throughout Ginnungagap.

... the southern part of Ginnungagap became light by meeting the sparks and glowing embers which flew out of the world of Muspell. (The first world to exist was Muspell in the southern hemisphere; it is light and hot and that region flames and burns so that those who do not belong to it and whose native land it is not, cannot endure it.)

... life appeared in the drops of running fluid and grew into the likeness of a man. He was given the name Ymir...

From Ymir's flesh
the earth was made
and from his blood the seas,
crags from his bones,
trees from his hair,
and from his skull the sky.

From his eyebrows
the blessed gods
made Midgard for the sons of men,
and from his brains
were created
all storm-threatening clouds.

These are surprises from ancient Iceland, but there are surprises from contemporary Iceland. One of them will await all those among you, in this audience, who have never been before in Reykjavik, where the first settler of Iceland, Ingolfur Arnarson from Firdir in West Norway settled in the year 874[20].

Your surprise will be that this city is truly cosmopolitan in spite of her tiny size, when compared to her giant sisters London, Paris, New York or Tokyo. Your amazement will grow, after making your own discoveries, in getting acquainted. Upon your return to the land and place you come from, you will ponder questions about this city, this land and the Icelanders. You will consider many answers to your questions, as you do, when pondering about science and art, or about life and human existence.

I trust that, at this First International Conference on Hemorheology, we shall learn a little more about an essential part of our existence and how it is going on in a miraculous network of a variety of vessels of minute and large sizes in each one of us — the flow of the wondrous fluid blood.

[1] COPLEY, A. L. In *Symposium on Biorheology*, A. L. COPLEY (Editor), *Proc. 4th Internat. Conf. on Rheology*, Providence, R.I., U.S.A., 1963. Interscience Publishers — John Wiley, New York, 1965, part 4, p. 3.

[2] COPLEY, A. L. *Proc. Internat. Congress on Rheology*, Scheveningen, Holland, 1948, North-Holland Publ. Co., Amsterdam, and Interscience Publishers, New York, 1949, Vol. 1, p. 47.

[3] COPLEY, A. L. *Rheology Bulletin* **20**, 7, 1951.

[4] COPLEY, A. L. *J. Colloid Science* **7**, 323, 1952.

[5] SCOTT BLAIR, G. W. *Nature* **182**, 90, 1958.

[6] SCOTT BLAIR, G. W. *Nature* **184**, 1539, 1959.

[7] SCOTT BLAIR, G. W. In *Flow Properties of Blood and Other Biological Systems*, A. L. COPLEY and G. STAINSBY (Editors), Pergamon Press, Oxford, New York, 1960, p. xiii.

[8] COPLEY, A. L. and SCOTT BLAIR, G. W. *Biorheol.* **1**, 261, 1963.

[9] POISEUILLE, J. L. M. *Compt. rend. Acad. Sci., Paris* **1**, 554, 1835.

[10] POISEUILLE, J. L. M. Récherches sur les causes du mouvement du sang dans les vaisseaux capillaires. Acad. Sci., Séance publique du 28 décembre 1835. Tome VII des *Savants étrangers*, Impr. Royale, Paris, 1839.

[11] BINGHAM, E. C. In J. L. M. POISEUILLE, *Experimental Investigations Upon the Flow of Liquids in Tubes of Very Small Diameter* (Translated by W. H. Herschel). *Rheological Memoirs*, Vol. 1, No. 1, E. C. Bingham, Easton, Pa., 1940.

[12] JOLY, M. This volume, p. 29.

[13] SKAGIUS, K. This volume, p. 33.

[14] REINER, M. *Physics Today* **17**, 62, 1964.

[15] THORARINSSON, SIGURDUR. *Surtsey. The New Island in the North Atlantic*, Almenna Bokafelagid, Reykjavik, 1964.

[16] ANON. *The Vinland Sagas—The Norse Discovery of America. Graenlendinga Saga and Eirik's Saga.* Translated with an introduction by Magnus Magnusson and Hermann Palsson. Penguin Classics L154. Penguin Books, Baltimore, Md., 1965.

[17] THORSTEINSSON, BJÖRN and JOSEPSSON, THORSTEINN. *Thingvellir—Birthplace of a Nation.* Heimskringla, Reykjavik, 1961.

[18] STURLUSON, SNORRI. *The Prose Edda. Tales from Norse Mythology.* Translated from Icelandic by J. I. Young. University of California Press, Berkeley and Los Angeles, 1964.

[19] NORDAL, SIGURDUR. Introduction to Ref. 18, *ibid.*, p. 7.

[20] EINARSSON, STEFÁN. *A History of Icelandic Literature.* The Johns Hopkins Press, Baltimore, Md., 1957.

THE SIGNIFICANCE OF HEMORHEOLOGY IN THE PRACTICE OF MEDICINE

H. Hartert

TODAY begins a conference in hemorheology. Some of you here will not be familiar with this word, which was invented by A. L. Copley to define the theory of blood flow. You are correct in asking whether this is not an already well-known branch of medical science. Indeed, we have been studying blood flow for centuries, yet the attention has always been directed toward the "circulation pump". The heart, as a "promoter" of life, was the centre of interest, yet the vessels leading to it or from were looked upon as a more or less passive system of tubes. In the beginning the behaviour of circulation was seen only in relation to the heart and the "acting force" behind the circulation. This function, which I have just mentioned, of vessels in circulation is summarized in the word hemodynamics. In contrast to this we have "hemorheology", which is concerned, in the proper sense, with the actual flow of blood. This depends not only on the condition of the vessels — their width and inner surface — but principally on the quality of the blood as a fluid.

I can best demonstrate the difference between hemodynamics and hemorheology by relating to you an incident which took place when I was a student.

During the war I lived in a small attic room of a large hotel. Early in the morning, when I was usually in a great hurry not to be late for a lecture, it often happened that while I was shaving the water would suddenly stop flowing from the tap. Apparently too many residents were using the water at the same time, and the tap would react by very noisily drawing in air. One morning when this happened, I stood there with my half-shaved face and became so impatient that I took an ink bottle, poured the contents into my tooth-mug and held the full mug under the tap. In two seconds the ink, gargling loudly, had disappeared into the tap. During lunch at the hotel, listening to the comments coming from the surrounding tables, I was astonished to discover that not all the guests on the lower floors had found themselves bathing, or rinsing their stockings, in blue water that morning! The ink had, in following the laws of hydrodynamics, preferred some pipes to others, and had distributed itself according to the flow and pressure conditions present in the pipes at that time. So this is an example of hemodynamics in so far as the flow is considered a result of motivation.

Now, if I had taken melted tar instead of ink this would have become first of all viscous, and then solid, changes caused by the cooling action of the pipes. This means that the flow from the tap would have at first been diminished, and would have finally ceased completely. This would not have been caused by the lessening of pressure or liquid intake, but by the changes in the fluid itself; this would then have become an example of hemorheology.

I admit that I did not have the ideal conditions under which to conduct a scientific experiment, so I therefore avoided confessing myself to be the author of the incident!

In some way venous thrombosis parallels the hemorheology shown in my experiment. It is a classic example of the influence of both the inner lining of the vessels and the blood itself on the flow of blood. Venous thrombosis is started by the attachment of platelets to the perhaps already deteriorated lining of the blood vessel. This causes a clotting activity in the platelets. These then produce a thrombus in the passing blood, which joins the platelets in adhering to the inner lining of the vessel. This clot will block the vessel and will increase in size until it covers an appreciable area. The pressure of the blood trying to pass the obstruction can force this clot away from its moorings, allowing it to travel via the right heart to the branches of the lung vessels. Finally, it is brought to a sudden halt. Depending on its size, it may obstruct more important or other smaller lung vessels. This is lung embolism.

A similar, but much more frequent event, is myocardial infarction. In most cases this is nothing more than a thrombus in a coronary artery. This arterial thrombosis usually develops in a place where the flow of blood is irregular, especially where a vessel divides. Often a coronary occlusion seems to appear with no apparent warning or reason. It is in these "sandbanks" that a coronary thrombosis may be forming.

Our knowledge of the origin of such deseases is still rather incomplete, as is our knowledge of the influence blood vessels and blood flow have upon each other's behaviour. It is a remarkable fact that blood is propelled through the vessels in a rather non-homogenous stream. In the centre move all the corpuscular elements, whereas towards the walls of the vessels a cell-free layer of plasma is found, as long as the blood is in constant movement and without physical disturbance.

The diameter of the capillaries is smaller than that of a red corpuscle. The corpuscles are squeezed through these narrow tubes by the force of blood pressure. This close contact between the corpuscles and capillaries is definitely advantageous to the exchange of oxygen and carbon dioxide. Yet it is remarkable that this movement and process is accomplished with such apparent ease! Moreover, as Scott Blair has found, this flow of blood through the capillaries is even easier than that of water under similar circumstances. On the other hand, a slight increase in the concentration of cells in the blood to above normal level would be enough to disturb the very fine equilibrium of the rate of flow. Understandably it would then slow down. The optimum for components in the blood is overreached, for example, in the case of so-called polycythemia, a condition in which there is an abnormal increase in red blood cells in the vessels. This will lead to an appreciable increase in flow resistance together with a relative decrease in the amount of plasma fluid, and to several other disturbances.

The physiological influences play a large part in so-called extra-corporeal circulation. During all heart operations that necessitate the arrest of circulation for some time, the blood has to be pumped artificially. In most cases this blood has also to be forced through an artificial lung to obtain the necessary oxygen. The flow in this artificial system of tubes involves far more difficult problems than at first thought. Up until now we have had no artificial material whose surface could even approximate the qualities of the normal inner lining of the vessels. All artificial surfaces induce dangerous alterations in the plasma and partial destruction of the blood cells. Constant close care, and complicated devices, are necessary to compensate as far as possible for the distortions and imperfections of the blood created by the extra-corporeal circulation.

A. L. Copley discovered that a thin coating of fibrin, when applied to these artificial surfaces, renders them harmless to the vital blood. Perhaps one could use this knowledge to improve on the present methods used in extra-corporeal circulation.

Fibrin is a fibrous substance formed in the coagulation of blood. It is responsible for the cessation of bleeding in wounds, the development of thrombosis, and it plays, apparently, a part in the permeability of the capillaries. The greater number of students in this field acknowledge this as a hypothesis, and Copley assumes it as well, on the basis of his experiments.

My friend Lasch has furnished us with the physiological basis for so-called latent clotting. This could be responsible for the development of such a natural fibrin film. Thus we have the remarkable fact that there is apparently an ever present very slow clotting process in the vessel, which is responsible for a fibrin layer on the inner lining without producing thrombosis. The thickness, on the other hand, of this fibrin film is regulated by the fibrinolysing processes. Also, the platelets, which play an important role in blood clotting, seem to participate in the sealing of the walls of the blood vessels.

Very similar processes in fibrin production are going on in blood vessel surgery, where, to replace destroyed vessels, artificial prostheses are inserted. To the layman such prostheses would appear totally impractical since they are made of finely woven, yet absolutely permeable, nylon or dacron tissue. Yet if the blood is flowing, very soon clotting products fill the meshes and render the wall of the prostheses totally impermeable. Also the inner surface is coated with a layer of clotting products which, under favourable circumstances, becomes similar to a natural vessel lining.

To avoid a surplus deposit of these products of clotting in a vessel that has been operated on, it is necessary to check, in all surgical entries into blood vessels, the blood clotting conditions. In all probability these deposits could lead to a new obstruction of the blood vessels.

The checking of blood clotting is one of the most important factors in influencing the rheology of the blood by drugs. Heparin is a naturally produced substance. It is found, for example, in the lungs of mammals, which inhibits some clotting enzymes. If given intravenously in proper doses and frequency, heparin will hinder the development of coagula in the circulation. Because it is necessary to inject heparin several times a day, it is usually only used for therapy over a short period of time. Lengthy treatments are undertaken with the use of cumarin derivatives. They are derived from a compound first discovered in spoiled sweet clover when cows, after eating the clover, hemorrhaged heavily. Many patients who have survived a myocardial infarction, severe thrombosis or embolism, will take such cumarin derivatives to avoid further attacks. With this therapy constant tests must be made to determine the adequate dosage. It varies with the individual. On the other hand, one has to avoid overdosage, which may cause spontaneous bleeding.

A relatively new therapeutical process used in treating acute obstructions of blood vessels in thrombosis or embolism, is fibrinolysis. The blood vessel inherits the ability to dissolve the fibrin strands through fibrinolytic enzymes in the blood. In this way an obstructed blood vessel occasionally becomes open again. This spontaneous fibrinolytic activity is usually rather weak and thus too slowly acting. Yet it can be increased appreciably by intravenous injection of a bacteria-derived activator. It is possible in this manner to clear obstructed vessels, under favourable conditions, in a comparably short time. This way a limb frequently can be saved from amputation. Myocardial infarctions may be arrested in their development with an early started fibrinolytic treatment and may become less harmful. Occasionally, a rapid resumption of the cerebral circulation, after a stroke caused by thrombosis or embolism in a cerebral artery, may result in a fast and far reaching restoration of the health of the patient.

These are only a few select examples of clinical hemorheology. They may show you that this branch of medicine has an important significance to both the physician and the patient. Continuing studies of hemorheological problems will enable us to combat, with increasing knowledge and success some of the frightening diseases of mankind.

REFERENCES

COPLEY, A. L. The Rheology of Blood. A Survey. *J. Colloid Sci.* 7, 323 (1952).

COPLEY, A. L. and SCOTT BLAIR, G. W. Hemorheology. An Introduction. *Proc. IX Congr. Internat. Soc. Blood Transfusion, Tokyo 1960*, Basel 1962.

FRASHER, W. G., JR. A Microcirculatory Physiologist looks at Rheology. *III. Europ. Confer. on Microcirculation, Jerusalem 1964.*

GROSS, R. Durchblutungsstörungen durch Blutveränderungen; in *Angiology*, RATSCHOW, M. (Editor), Thieme, Stuttgart, 1959, pp. 733.

SCOTT BLAIR, G. W. Rheology of Blood Coagula; in *Flow Properties of Blood and Other Biological Systems*, COPLEY, A. L. and STAINSBY, G. (Editors), Pergamon Press, Oxford, New York, 1960, pp. 63–83.

WAYLAND, H. A Rheologist looks at the Microcirculation. *III. Europ. Confer. on Microcirculation, Jerusalem 1964.*

WHITMORE, R. L. A Theoretical Treatment of the Differential Flow Velocities of Plasma and Corpuscles in Living Bodies; in *Flow Properties of Blood and Other Biological Systems*, COPLEY, A. L. and STAINSBY, G. (Editors), Pergamon Press, Oxford, New York, 1960, pp. 63–83.

HEMORHEOLOGY AND THE PHYSICIST

G. W. Scott Blair

Long ago, when I was a young man, it was my privilege to show the Physics Department at the Institute at which I then worked, to Mr. Bernard Shaw, the playwright. I started with the rather trite remark: "You have, I believe, just visited our Chemistry Department: now may I tell you something about our physics?" He looked me straight in the eyes (as was his wont) and said, "What is the difference between chemistry and physics?" I supposed that he knew the answer quite well and that this was a kind of test question for me; so I said, without much time for thought: "Chemistry is interested in what things are made of and physics is how they behave." It was crude but he seemed quite happy to accept this definition.

At greater leisure, I have since often thought about what physics really is. I suppose it is fairest to say that it is concerned with energy-matter (which we now know to be inter-convertible) and with the processes of emission, absorption, storage and conversion of the various forms of energy.

Hemorheology is a term invented for us by my old friend, Professor A. L. Copley [1] to describe the study of "the deformation and flow (i.e. rheological) properties of cellular and plasmatic components of blood, in macroscopic, microscopic and submicroscopic dimensions and the rheological properties of vessel structure with which blood comes in direct contact". The heart provides much of the energy needed to cause the blood to circulate, though other muscular structures also play their part. In so far as blood flows as a liquid, this energy is converted into heat, even in cold-blooded animals. In so far as some vessels distend and contract in pulsatile flow, it is, at least partially, alternately stored and recovered. When platelets stick to one another, "by strong hyaline bonds"[2] or to the surface of a vessel, surface energies come into play. Coagulation, especially in its earlier stages, involves the interchange of position of molecules having enough energy to cross potential barriers.

In the larder of my house we keep our stores of perishable food in a large metal box. It is extremely unlikely that the molecules of air within this box should decide to move around much more slowly than do those in the rest of the room; yet in fact they do just this. Such a situation can only be maintained by supplying energy (usually electrical) from outside. Within an enclosed system, molecules tend to behave in the most probable way. But probability is not a very easy concept to use. If the probability of some event a occurring is p_a and of some other event b is p_b, the probability of both events occurring is not $p_a + p_b$ but $p_a \times p_b$. Physicists generally prefer additive things; and, if we take the logarithms of the probabilities, it is clear that these will be additive, not multiplicative. These logarithms of probabilities are linearly related to what we call "entropy", or degree of disorder. We all know that, left to themselves, things tend to get into disorder.

Thus, in a closed system, the interchange of energy involves an increase in entropy; i.e. an increasing degree of disorder; but living things are not closed systems and they forestall, for a time, the deadly increase in entropy by means of an exchange with their surroundings. In old age, elastic extensions, involving localized low entropies, become more difficult: our arteries tend to harden. All this comes within the field of the comparatively new science of Irreversible Thermodynamics.

I have said enough to make it clear that hemorheology is a branch of physics. As with most biophysical studies, research may be done in two really very different ways. In other fields, these are labelled *in vivo* and *in vitro*. Experiments with native (i.e. untreated) blood can seldom be done literally "in glass", so the term "extra-corporeal" is sometimes used; but it is somewhat cumbersome and one often sees *ex vivo*. This would mean, I think, "coming out of life" and I should therefore prefer *extra vivum* (outside life).* (These distinctions of declension will be more easily appreciated by our Icelandic friends than by us, English-speaking people!)

Blood and for that matter blood vessels, will behave very differently under these two conditions. We all know that the structure of a blood-clot in a test-tube is very different from that of a thrombus, though the thrombus type of structure can be at least partly simulated by causing the blood in the test-tube to clot under certain conditions of shear. However, even when *extra vivum* studies do not simulate what happens in the body, they are far from valueless to medicine.

It always helps to know all you can about your materials. In many fields of industrial research, this is forgotten in the scramble to solve day-to-day problems. When Poiseuille found that the natural flow of blood is a very complicated business, he showed himself to be a good physicist (as well as a good physician) when he went back to solve first the simple problems of how water, alcohol, etc., flow in rigid, impermeable glass tubes of even, circular cross-section. Without his basic equation, (though he did not know that it could be derived theoretically from Newton's hypothesis and some simple boundary assumptions) it would have been almost impossible to study the complex *in vivo* phenomena of hemorheology which interest us here today.

Concerning the dimensions of the blood vessel the diameter is often reduced and sometimes increased by pathological conditions. It was almost simultaneously that SCHOFIELD and SCOTT BLAIR[3] found that clay and soil pastes flow relatively more easily through very narrow than through rather wider glass tubes; and that FÅHRAEUS and LINDQUIST[4] found the same phenomenon for blood. Such "sigma phenomena" are now well-known for many materials and may owe their origin to very different causes. Poiseuille, and even earlier workers, had commented on the presence of a "plasmatic zone" along the wall of a tube through which blood was flowing and it is now known that corpuscles do not flow parallel to the wall of a narrow tube. Their distribution affects their relative velocities and this may well have profound physiological significance.

Poiseuille's equation applies to steady streamline flow within an impermeable tube of even, cylindrical cross-section. Blood flow is, in general, pulsatile and more often turbulent than we used to think and the vessel walls are, or should be, both semi-permeable and elastic. COPLEY's findings[5] when we worked together some years ago, that heparinized blood flows relatively faster in a glass capillary whose wall has been lined with fibrin than in an untreated glass capillary raises all kinds of interesting problems for the physicist. The hematologist is concerned with the possibility of a fibrin-like layer on the surface of the wall of the living vessel (COPLEY[6]) and the

*I have consulted a classical scholar on this point and he is in agreement!

physicist with studies on the wetting properties of fibrin (COPLEY, GLOVER and SCOTT BLAIR[7]). Professor Oka will have something to say about this, I understand, at our present Conference.

Blood coagulation and fibrinolysis also provide a tempting field for the rheologist. HARTERT[8] has invented an instrument (the thrombelastograph) which records the gradual firming up and eventual softening of the clot. Our own torsiometer[9] works on much the same principle.

This is not the place to go into details about what these instruments measure but it should perhaps be pointed out that the use of the term "viscosity" has caused some confusion. As fibrin polymerizes, we have a system which starts as almost a liquid; and, unless or until fibrinolysis, retraction, etc., interfere, we end up with an elastic gel. Within the interstices of this gel structure, there is, of course, a liquid serum.

Now it is true that oscillatory instruments are comparatively uninfluenced by the viscosity of the original blood or of the subsequent serum; but it is also true that, as the solid structure is alternately strained and relaxed, part of the energy is momentarily stored and then recovered; and part is dissipated as heat. From this latter part is calculated what the rheologists call the "dynamic viscosity" or, in other terms (multiplying by a frequency) "the imaginary part of the complex modulus". Oscillatory instruments certainly measure this and, if the measured consistency is independent of frequency, the two components, elastic and viscous, can be independently determined even when the motion is not strictly sinusoidal. There is reason to believe that, in the case of the fibrin gel, the elastic component preponderates; but one should be careful not to deny that the viscous component is measured.

All these questions are of strong current interest to the general rheologist.

We are still puzzled by many problems in the microcirculation, where Poiseuille's equation is very far from applicable; but the work of KATCHALSKY et al.[10] in following the slow and rapid osmotic swelling of individual erythrocytes, has greatly helped to explain how such comparatively large corpuscles can pass through very narrow capillaries without requiring great pressures. In many diseases, especially malaria, and some say in all pathological conditions, the erythrocytes clump together into what KNISELY[11] calls "sludge" and there has been much controversy as to whether this phenomenon is connected with the tendency for the blood of some (but not all) species to form rouleaux. Their rate of settling ("E.S.R."), as originally proposed by our distinguished pioneer, Professor Fåhraeus, has for many years given physicians at least some indication of how seriously ill their patients were likely to be. In recent times, HARKNESS[12] has shown that very accurate measurements of the viscosity of plasma can give much the same information as the E.S.R. with less dependence on the precise procedure of the test and the skill of the operator.

I hope that I have been able to show some reasons, at least, why so many rheologists and other physicists, who had previously no connection with hematology, have found a new and deep interest in problems connected with blood. The flow and coagulation properties of blood have interested medical men from the earliest times and yet remain a constant source of discussion today. It is, therefore, very suitable that we should hold our First International Conference on Hemorheology in Iceland: a country with an ancient civilization combined with a very modern outlook which has provided this splendid University in which we have the privilege of meeting.

REFERENCES

[1] COPLEY, A. L. *J. Colloid Sci.* **7**, 323, 1952.

[2] SHARP, A. A. *Biological Aspects of Occlusive Vascular Disease*, CHALMERS, D. G. and GRESHAM, G. A. (Editors), Cambridge Univ. Press, 1964, p. 205.

[3] SCHOFIELD, R. K. and SCOTT BLAIR, G. W. *J. Phys. Chem.* **34**, 248, 1505, 1930.

[4] FÅHRAEUS, R. and LINDQUIST, T. *Amer. J. Physiol.* **96**, 562, 1931.

[5] COPLEY, A. L. In *Flow Properties of Blood and Other Biological Systems*, COPLEY, A. L. and STAINSBY, G. (Editors), Pergamon Press, Oxford, New York, 1960, p. 97.

[6] COPLEY, A. L. *Abstr. Communic.* 19th Internat. Physiol. Congr. Montreal, Canada, 1953, p. 280.

[7] COPLEY, A. L., GLOVER, F. A. and SCOTT BLAIR, G. W. *Biorheol.* **2**, 29, 1964.

[8] HARTERT, H. German Patent Spec. No. 845720, 1952.

[9] BURNETT, J. and SCOTT BLAIR, G. W. *Dairy Inds.* **28**, 220, 1963.

[10] KATCHALSKY, A., KEDEM, O., KLIBANSKY, C. and DE VRIES, A. *Flow Properties of Blood and Other Biological Systems,* COPLEY, A. L. and STAINSBY, G. (Editors), Pergamon Press, Oxford, New York, 1960, p. 155.

[11] KNISELY, M. H. *Acta Anatomica Suppl.* 41 (vol. 44), 1961, and many other papers.

[12] HARKNESS, J. *Lancet* No. 7302, 280, 10 August, 1963.

Part II

CEREMONY OF POISEUILLE AWARD

15 July, Evening

Presided by A. L. COPLEY

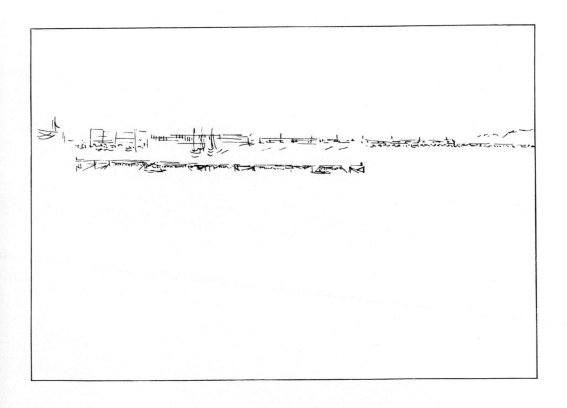

NOTES ON THE POISEUILLE MEDAL AND THE AWARD CEREMONY

A. L. COPLEY

THE Medal, of 18 carat gold, has on one side, in relief, a portrait of Jean-Léonard-Marie Poiseuille, the French physician and physiologist, who can be rightly called the first hemorheologist. The portrait was drawn by the Icelandic artist Nina Tryggvadottir from a photograph which was found in the archives of the Académie de Médecine in Paris, France[1]. The signature of Poiseuille, kindly furnished for the Medal by Dr. M. Joly and placed by the artist below the portrait, was also cast in relief, as shown in the photograph (Frontispiece). A photograph of the other side of the Medal shows the engraved citation.

The Poiseuille Award has been made possible through the generosity of Pharmacia Laboratories of Uppsala, Sweden and New Market, New Jersey, U.S.A. It was presented in the Ceremony honoring Dr. Robin Fåhraeus, Emeritus Professor of Pathology, University of Uppsala, on 15 July, 6.30 p.m. at the Festival Hall of the University of Iceland. The Ceremony was also attended by many dignitaries and leaders of the Icelandic Nation and the ambassadors and other diplomats of different countries. Their Excellencies, the Ambassadors of France and of Sweden represented the countries of the two hemorheologists Poiseuille and Fåhraeus, thus honored.

The Ceremony, presided by A. L. Copley, was so arranged that, prior to the actual presentation of the Award, two scientists who are working in the same cities as did Poiseuille and Fåhraeus, viz., Paris and Uppsala respectively, presented biographical sketches of the two hemorheologists. These biographies, given by Dr. M. Joly, Service de Biophysique, Institut Pasteur, Paris, and by Professor Kurt Skagius, Research Department, Pharmacia, Uppsala, and the subsequent presentation by the President of The International Society of Hemorheology constitute Part II of this volume, which also contains a photograph of Professor Fåhraeus taken after the Ceremony.

REFERENCE

[1] COPLEY, A. L., SCOTT BLAIR, G. W., BALÉA, T. and STAPLE, P. H. In *Flow Properties of Blood and Other Biological Systems,* COPLEY, A. L. and STAINSBY, G. (Editors), Pergamon Press, Oxford, New York, 1960, p. 422.

NOTICE BIOGRAPHIQUE SUR J. L. M. POISEUILLE

M. Joly

Dans un moment, un de nos plus éminents confrères va recevoir la première Médaille Poiseuille.

Les rhéologues francais ont été très touchés lorsque notre Président, le Professeur Copley, a eu l'idée de créer une Médaille Poiseuille pour récompenser et honorer, tous les trois ans, un hémorhéologiste de renommée mondiale. C'était en effet, par la même occasion, rendre un solennel hommage à un de leurs compatriotes dont ils ont parfois tendance à oublier injustement les mérites. Car, par un paradoxe fréquent dans l'histoire des sciences, c'est peut-être dans son propre pays que la notoriété de Poiseuille est la moins grande.

Certes, bon nombre de rhéologues et d'ingénieurs français connaissent les lois de Poiseuille. Mais, combien savent que Poiseuille fut un médecin et un physiologiste parisien du 19ème siècle?

Il faut dire que, comme beaucoup de précurseurs, Poiseuille ne connut pas les honneurs académiques. Il reçut seulement quelques très modestes récompenses. En 1835, il obtenait la moitié du prix de Physiologie expérimentale décerné par l'Académie des Sciences; en 1845, c'était une somme de 700 F qui lui était remise au titre du Prix de Médecine et Chirurgie; en 1860 une mention honorable lui était décernée par la même Académie. Il fut plusieurs fois candidat à l'Académie des Sciences de l'Institut de France, mais il ne fut jamais élu.

Et pourtant, des savants de très grande valeur, et qui ont laissé un grand nom dans la science du 19ème siècle, Arago, Babinet, Becquerel, Claude Bernard, Chevreul, Desprets, Dutrochet, Flourens, Magendie, Poncelet, Regnault, Savart, Velpeau, qui furent les rapporteurs de ses travaux devant l'Académie, louèrent toujours la haute qualité de ses recherches.

Mais à l'époque, la portée de l'œuvre de Poiseuille ne pouvait pas être comprise. C'est qu'en effet, bien avant que le mot n'existe, Poiseuille se trouvait être un des créateurs de la Biophysique.

Ce qui est passionnant dans le cas de Poiseuille, c'est qu'en suivant le développement de son œuvre, on assiste à une transformation fondamentale, je dirais presque une mutation, dans l'attitude de l'homme de science devant les faits.

De formation et de profession, Poiseuille est médecin et physiologiste, principalement préoccupé par les problèmes de la circulation pulmonaire et de ses anomalies pathologiques. Mais il se trouve qu'il a du génie.

En 1835, c'est un observateur extraordinairement perspicace qui, dans un mémoire couronné par l'Académie des Sciences, Recherches sur les causes du mouvement du sang dans les vaisseaux capillaires, décrit, avec une remarquable exactitude, ce qui deviendra plus tard l'effet sigma ou l'effet de couche plasmatique.

En 1840, devant la même Académie, c'est un expérimentateur de grande classe qui lit un mémoire intitulé Recherches expérimentales sur le mouvement des liquides dans les tubes de très petits diamètres. Avec une extrême précision sont établies et énoncées les lois de l'écoulement des liquides newtoniens dans les tubes capillaires. C'est ce qui, plus tard, sera universellement connu sous le nom de Lois de Poiseuille.

Par une bizarrerie du sort, ainsi que l'a fait remarquer naguère le Professeur Copley, les observations *in vivo* de Poiseuille sur le mouvement des globules sanguins dans les vaisseaux venaient infirmer par avance les lois qu'il allait établir quelques années plus tard pour un grand nombre de liquides. Dans cette contradiction étaient en germe tous les développements futurs de la rhéologie des liquides. Et c'est peut-être aussi l'origine de cet acharnement à faire varier systématiquement les conditions expérimentales qui est une des caractéristiques marquantes de l'œuvre de Poiseuille.

Ainsi, en quelques années, le physiologiste s'est transmué en physicien. Et pourtant, il restera physiologiste: ses préoccupations et ses travaux ultérieurs le prouvent. Mais dans toutes ses recherches, il apportera la tournure d'esprit du physicien, son souci de la définition précise des paramètres, sa rigueur dans l'expérimentation. Sans pour cela, bien entendu, perdre ce sens de la réalité vivante, sans lequel il n'y a pas de physiologiste digne de ce nom.

Nous sommes habitués maintenant à l'interpénétration des différentes disciplines scientifiques. Mais pour comprendre le grand mérite de Poiseuille, il faut essayer d'imaginer ce que pouvait représenter, dans la première moitié du 19ème siècle, un Médecin se livrant à des expériences de mécanique des liquides comme aurait pu les entreprendre un ingénieur hydraulicien, et prétendant expliquer par ce moyen les anomalies de la microcirculation. L'histoire des sciences nous a montré, en maintes circonstances, que créer un nouveau chapitre de la science n'est pas chose facile. Les seuls instruments pour cette création sont l'imagination expérimentale, la justesse de raisonnement et l'intuition des rapprochements, toutes qualités dont Poiseuille était riche, mais qui sont bien faibles pour lutter contre les habitudes de pensée d'une époque.

Si Poiseuille a, pendant de longues années (de 1840 à 1847), consacré une grande partie de son activité à l'étude de l'écoulement capillaire, en passant méthodiquement en revue les divers paramètres susceptibles d'intervenir, son œuvre n'en embrasse pas moins une grande diversité de sujets. Citons parmi ses travaux les plus originaux:

En 1844, des recherches expérimentales sur les médicaments, au moyen des techniques osmométriques de Dutrochet, et en considérant surtout l'action des médicaments sur la circulation. En 1845, un dispositif fort ingénieux pour assurer la ventilation des navires en vue de lutter contre la propagation des épidémies de peste. En 1855, des recherches sur la respiration où Poiseuille explique en faisant intervenir les actions mécaniques sur les capillaires alvéolaires, comment l'expiration succède à l'inspiration. En 1858, une série de travaux sur la recherche du glucose dans les différents tissus animaux, où est réfutée l'hypothèse d'une glycogénie intestinale. En 1859, des recherches sur le dosage de l'urée dans les organismes et son rôle physiologique. En 1860 et 1868, des travaux expérimentaux *in vitro* pour expliquer pourquoi la pression sanguine dans le système artériel ne varie pas notablement avec la distance au cœur.

Dans tous ces travaux, les mêmes qualités d'expérimentateur extrèment habile s'étaient manifestées, avec toujours une grande ingéniosité dans l'imagination d'appareils destinés à substituer à une nature changeante des modèles fidèles où les grandeurs deviennent mesurables.

Poiseuille était né à Paris le 22 avril 1799. Il mourut à Paris le 26 décembre 1869. Mais désormais, l'Hémorhéologie existait. Il n'y avait plus qu'à progresser. Un siècle plus tard, plusieurs centaines de chercheurs devaient, dans le monde entier, consacrer leurs efforts et leur enthousiasme à cette science aux multiples aspects. Une médaille, frappée à l'effigie de Jean-Léon-Marie Poiseuille allait être remise à l'un des plus éminents d'entre eux.

PRINCIPALES PUBLICATIONS DE J. L. M. POISEUILLE

[1] Recherches sur les causes du mouvement du sang dans les vaisseaux capillaires. *C.R.*, **1**, 554, 1835.
[2] De l'influence du froid sur la circulation capillaire. *C.R.*, **9**, 327, 1839.
[3] Recherches expérimentales sur le mouvement des liquides dans les tubes de très petits diamètres. *C.R.*, **11**, 961, 1041, 1840; **12**, 112, 1841; **15**, 1167, 1842.
[4] Recherches sur l'écoulement des liquides, considéré dans les capillaires vivants. *C.R.*, **16**, 60, 1843.
[5] Recherches expérimentales sur les médicaments. *C.R.*, **19**, 994, 1844.
[6] Ventilation des navires. *C.R.*, **21**, 1427, 1845.
[7] Recherches expérimentales sur le mouvement des liquides de nature différente, dans les tubes de très petits diamètres. *C.R.*, **24**, 1074, 1847.
[8] Recherches sur la respiration. *C.R.*, **41**, 1072, 1855.
[9] De l'existence du glycose dans l'organisme animal (avec J. Lefort). *C.R.*, **46**, 565, 677, 1858; **47**, 112, 1858.
[10] Détermination à l'aide de la fermentation de faibles quantités de glycose contenues dans des liquides de très petits volumes. *C.R.*, **47**, 906, 1058, 1858.
[11] Recherches sur l'urée. *C.R.*, **49**, 164, 1859.
[12] Sur la pression du sang dans le système artériel. *C.R.*, **51**, 238, 1860; **66**, 886, 1868.

BIOGRAPHICAL SKETCH OF
PROFESSOR ROBIN FÅHRAEUS

KURT SKAGIUS

YOUR Excellencies, Mr. Chairman, ladies and gentlemen,

1917 was an important year in the history of clinical symptomatology and hemorheology. In that year, one of the dramatic years of the First World War, Robin Fåhraeus was on duty at the delivery clinic of Karolinska Sjukhuset in Stockholm. He became interested in the factors regulating the delivery process and started collecting blood from his patients. He quickly recognized that blood from pregnant women differed remarkably from that of other patients—the suspension stability was much less and erythrocytes sedimented rapidly. The effect was pronounced and it was not necessary to label the test-tubes—the blood from pregnant women could easily be identified by the sedimentation rate.

It is a well-known fact in science, that a single observation like this may open whole fields of knowledge, if the investigator is skilled enough to realize the potentialities of the observation and curious enough to make further studies. Robin Fåhraeus was faced with these demands.

He collected blood from a large number of donors throughout Stockholm, and further studies revealed many details of the erythrocyte sedimentation velocity and the low suspension stability of blood from pregnant women was verified. In fact, E. S. R. was initially developed as a test of pregnancy.

Fåhraeus recognized, that the sedimentation velocity is subjected to physiological variations according to age and sex with the lowest figures obtained in newborns, and adult men showing considerably higher suspension stability than adult women.

On studying the literature, Fåhraeus found that his observation was by no means a new discovery. Already the ancient Greeks knew about the buffy coat, obtained in blood of low suspension stability, and for hundreds of years pregnant women were victims to blood letting in a formidable degree—often with fatal results. In his famous thesis, published in 1921[1], Fåhraeus gives us in about 70 pages, an excellent historical review of blood.

The rediscovery of the sedimentation reaction constitutes a milestone in the history of clinical symptomatology as Fåhraeus could demonstrate its utility as a nonspecific indication of a diseased body. The procedure has been modified in many ways, but the applicability of the basic principle has been demonstrated in thousands of papers all over the world.

Fåhraeus himself, however, was more interested in the theoretical explanation of the sedimentation reaction. He showed that the suspension stability was influenced by plasma factors, he studied the hydrodynamics of the sedimentation and made a series of interesting observations of the flow properties of blood—e.g. the Fåhraeus–Lindkvist effect. These studies are well known to you and it is not necessary to mention them all.

After his dissertation in Stockholm in 1921 he stayed there until he became professor of pathology in Uppsala in 1928. Of course, a man of his fighting spirit became very well known and the stories about him, told by the students in Uppsala, are numerous. His broad range of interests far beyond the fields of pathology and hemorheology has contributed to his good reputation. I have already mentioned his historical review of blood, which he has published separately in a Swedish book[2]. But he has also written *Läkekonstens historia* — the history of medicine — an impressive book covering 1200 pages[3].

Those of you, who have visited Uppsala may have seen "Rikssalen" — the large hall of Uppsala Castle. The reconstruction of this hall was inspired by Robin Fåhraeus, and it stands as a monument to the historical interests of a great man.

Fåhraeus' father was a well-known author and his mother an equally well-known actress. This fact may explain his skill in writing and lecturing. I think you will agree that the phenomenon of rouleaux formation cannot be better described than as by Fåhraeus.

It has been said that Robin Fåhraeus was born 35 years too early, that the scientific world was not prepared to receive his ideas at the time and that his work has been overlooked for several years. This may be true. It is not too late, however, to honour a scientist, who has made so many important contributions to hemorheology and I would like to congratulate the Executive Committee in having selected Robin Fåhraeus as the recipient of the first Poiseuille Gold Medal. I think that it would be hard to find a scientist who meets the requirements of this award better than him.

REFERENCES

[1] Fåhraeus, R. The suspension stability of the blood. *Acta Med. Scand.* **55**, 1, 1921.
[2] Fåhraeus, R. *Blodet i läkekonsten*, 1924.
[3] Fåhraeus, R. *Läkekonstens historia*. Albert Bonniers, Stockholm, Part I, 1944; part II, 1946; part III, 1950.

PRESENTATION OF POISEUILLE AWARD

A. L. COPLEY

PROFESSOR FÅHRAEUS, Excellencies, ladies and gentlemen:

In the name of The International Society of Hemorheology, it is my privilege to present to you, Professor Fåhraeus, the Jean-Léonard-Marie Poiseuille Award, in recognition of your pioneer work on blood flow and on the clumping and sedimentation of red blood cells.

PROFESSOR ROBIN FÅHRAEUS

35

We, the members of the Society and of this Conference, are happy to honor you as the first recipient of the gold medal, cast in honor of Poiseuille, the first hemorheologist. The citation, engraved on this medal, which bears the portrait of Jean-Léonard-Marie-Poiseuille and a replica of his signature, reads:

> To Robin Fåhraeus
> Nestor of Hemorheology
> For His Pioneering Research
> Presented at
> First International
> Conference on Hemorheology
> University of Iceland
> 10–16 July 1966
> Reykjavik
> The International Society of Hemorheology.

We all wish you to enjoy this Award in the best of health and in happiness, for many years to come, as a token of our gratitude, esteem and friendship. We thank you very much. Congratulations!

Part III

SCIENTIFIC SESSIONS

11–16 July

An asterisk behind a name denotes that the author was invited by the Organizing Committee to contribute the paper.

HEMORHEOLOGICAL THEORY I

11 July, a.m.

Chairmen: ALAN C. BURTON, Canada
R. S. RIVLIN, U.S.A.

RELATIONS ENTRE L'HÉMORHÉOLOGIE ET LA RHÉOLOGIE FONDAMENTALE

M. Joly*

Service de Biophysique, Institut Pasteur, Paris, France

INTRODUCTION

La nature de l'hémorhéologie et sa place dans l'ensemble des sciences ne sont pas toujours vues avec exactitude. Etant un chapitre de la biorhéologie qui est elle-même un chapitre de la biophysique, l'hémorhéologie est victime des mêmes erreurs de jugement que cette dernière. En effet, la biophysique est souvent considérée comme l'application des méthodes physiques à l'étude des phénomènes biologiques, donc comme une classe de techniques. Or, la vraie nature de la biophysique est tout autre: c'est une discipline scientifique, au sens plein du terme, dont le domaine propre est la physique des milieux et des systèmes biologiques, avec comme objectif la physique des organismes vivants. Pareillement, l'hémorhéologie n'est pas l'application des techniques rhéologiques à l'étude du sang, mais elle est la rhéologie du sang et des vaisseaux sanguins, c'est-à-dire la science de l'écoulement du sang, de la déformation de ses éléments constitutifs et des diverses parties du système circulatoire. Une telle conception de l'hémorhéologie est évidemment beaucoup plus riche et beaucoup plus féconde, tant pour son propre développement que pour ses conséquences dans les autres domaines de la biologie. Une conséquence immédiate de cette situation se manifeste dans les rapports entre l'hémorhéologie et la rhéologie fondamentale.

L'hémorhéologie, au lieu de n'être qu'une annexe de la rhéologie, en devient partie intégrante. Il en résulte que s'il y a apport de la rhéologie fondamentale à l'hémorhéologie, il y a aussi apport de l'hémorhéologie à la rhéologie fondamentale. L'hémorhéologie apparaît même comme un stimulant pour la rhéologie générale, du fait que nombre de problèmes qui se posent dans les divers domaines de l'hémorhéologie se présentent comme des cas particuliers de problèmes de rhéologie fondamentale qui n'ont pas encore été suffisamment approfondis ou qui, parfois même, n'ont été qu'à peine abordés.

Le liquide de nature très spéciale qu'est le sang, les particularités de son mouvement dans les gros vaisseaux, les phénomènes extrèmement complexes de la microcirculation, et la structure très compliquée du système vasculaire exigent le développement, sur le plan fondamental, d'une rhéologie d'un type fort différent de celui auquel les rhéologues classiques sont habitués. La diversité de forme, de dimension et de déformabilité des vaisseaux sanguins et des éléments constitutifs du sang, ainsi que la variabilité des uns et des autres dans le temps et dans l'espace, obligent à remettre en question la validité de certains modes de représentation courants et de certains modèles usuels, ou tout au moins à les généraliser considérablement.

Il faut, en fait, établir les bases théoriques d'une rhéologie nouvelle en ce sens qu'elle concerne des milieux et des conditions aux limites d'un niveau de complexité bien supérieur à celui que considère, en général, la rhéologie classique. Corrélativement, pour guider ces recherches théoriques, il est indispensable que les expérimentateurs, dans les divers domaines de l'hémorhéologie, apportent un très grand soin dans la définition rigoureuse de ce qu'ils observent ou de ce qu'ils mesurent. Ces objectifs sont loin d'être atteints, mais on peut dès maintenant entrevoir comment seront réalisables les premières étapes de cette coopération entre la rhéologie fondamentale et l'hémorhéologie, et dans quelles voies elle pourra vraisemblablement se développer.

LES RAISONS DE L'APPORT INSUFFISANT DE LA RHÉOLOGIE FONDAMENTALE

On peut se demander pourquoi l'hémorhéologie a relativement peu profité des progrès de la rhéologie fondamentale. La cause du raccord difficile entre ces deux domaines de la science des déformations et des écoulements tient essentiellement à la différence de complexité des systèmes étudiés.

La rhéologie fondamentale étudie principalement des milieux continus et homogènes, ou, tout au moins, d'hétérogénéité simple où les éléments constitutifs sont petits par rapport aux dimensions de l'éprouvette sur laquelle les mesures sont effectuées. Ces limitations tiennent au fait que les problèmes qui ont principalement préoccupé les rhéologues sont les questions de résistance des matériaux et de caractéristiques mécaniques des matières plastiques, ainsi que d'extrusion, de filage et de moulage de celles-ci. En outre la rhéologie classique n'étudie en général que des solides de forme géométrique simple ou des fluides contenus dans des enceintes de configuration simple et de symétrie élevée. De plus, ces corps, au sens mécanique du terme, sont soumis à des systèmes de contrainte également simples et il est presque toujours admis qu'ils ne subissent aucune évolution chimique au cours de leur écoulement ou de leur déformation. Il est bien évident qu'aucune de ces restrictions n'est valable dans le cas du sang et de l'appareil circulatoire. En particulier, l'ensemble sang et vaisseaux constitue un système ouvert dont les conditions aux limites sont variables. Le milieu circulant et les vaisseaux subissent des modifications qualitatives et quantitatives sous l'influence du milieu environnant.

Ce n'est que très exceptionnellement que la rhéologie classique prend en considération la structure moléculaire des systèmes qu'elle étudie. Elle se propose le plus souvent une représentation macroscopique des déformations en prenant comme base la mécanique du continu. En général, elle néglige l'analyse des processus rhéologiques à l'échelle moléculaire et des influences des structures fines sur les comportements globaux. Cependant la prise en considération de ces mécanismes a conduit à des développements fondamentaux très importants, en particulier en ce qui concerne la théorie de Eyring de la viscosité des liquides et son extension aux polymères[1–17]. Malheureusement, même cette orientation, qui a le mérite de commencer à faire passer la rhéologie du stade de la représentation à celui de l'explication, n'a pas apporté à l'hémorhéologie une très grande aide.

La raison de ces déficiences est liée à une question d'échelle d'hétérogénéité. Les dimensions des globules sanguins et des plaquettes sont macroscopiques par rapport à celles des molécules constitutives du plasma; elles sont du même ordre de grandeur que le diamètre des capillaires; mais elles sont microscopiques par rapport au diamètre des gros vaisseaux. Il n'est donc pas surprenant que la rhéologie de milieux continus et homogènes, dont les unités cinétiques sont infiniment petites par rapport aux dimensions du système qui se déforme, soit insuffisante pour décrire de façon satisfaisante les multiples aspects de la circulation du sang. Ce qu'il faut envisager, c'est la rhéologie d'un milieu extrèmement hétérogène. Or, dans ce domaine, il n'y a encore que peu de chose de fait du point de vue fondamental. En effet, les travaux théoriques sur l'écoulement des suspensions ou des émulsions se réfèrent à des schémas extrèment simples ou, par exemple, toutes les particules sont identiques, sphériques ou ellipsoîdales, indéformables ou de viscosité interne la même pour toutes. Il y est en outre supposé que le système est soumis à des conditions hydrodynamiques très simples, telles qu'écoulement laminaire dans un tube cylindrique ou entre cylindres coaxiaux de longueur infinie. Or, l'hétérogénéité du sang est d'un niveau de complexité beaucoup plus élevé, les vaisseaux sanguins constituent un édifice déformable extrèment compliqué, et les contraintes appliquées sont distribuées irrégulièrement et présentent un régime pulsé. D'où l'importance qu'aurait pour la rhéologie fondamentale l'élaboration d'un modèle satisfaisant pour représenter le sang et ses conditions de circulation. Une difficulté supplémentaire pour la caractérisation d'un tel modèle tient à la variation de la composition et de la structure du milieu circulant en fonction de la valeur locale des variables rhéologiques. Or, il n'y a encore eu que peu de travaux de rhéologie sur la corrélation écoulement-structure[18–28].

LE PROBLÈME GÉNÉRAL DE L'HÉMORHÉOLOGIE DU POINT DE VUE FONDAMENTALISTE

Le problème que pose aux rhéologues fondamentalistes l'hémorhéologie prise globalement apparaît pratiquement inextricable. Il s'agit, en effet, d'établir les bases théoriques d'une rhéologie qui soit valable à l'échelle microscopique pour un milieu hétérogène dont la composition et la structure varient au cours du temps et dont les constantes physiques des constituants dépendent de leur état de mouvement. De plus, ce milieu est soumis à un écoulement sous contrainte périodique dans un ensemble de vaisseaux ramifiés, de section variable, déformables, localement perméables à certains des constituants du fluide circulant, et dont les propriétés sont influencées par l'écoulement lui-même et par des facteurs extérieurs. On est donc en présence d'un système ouvert, au sens thermodynamique du terme, et la rhéologie théorique s'est jusqu'à maintenant peu développée dans cette voie. Il semble donc que le comportement rhéologique d'un tel système doive poser des problèmes à peu près insolubles. On serait même en droit de se demander s'il existe un régime d'écoulement défini qui corresponde à un tel ensemble de conditions fluctuantes. Or le fait biologique de la circulation du sang montre qu'il existe des solutions parfaitement définies dans des limites relativement étroites.

On peut donc espérer, par un choix convenable de modèles suggérés par les faits, trouver des voies d'approche théoriques permettant de comprendre de façon satisfaisante les phénomènes observés en hémorhéologie et, corrélativement, permettant de perfectionner les constructions abstraites de la rhéologie fondamentale. Il est bien évident que la caractérisation d'un tel modèle est très délicate. On a en effet affaire à une suspension non uniforme de particules visco-élastiques formant un système hétérogène compliqué à degré d'agrégation variable dont il est difficile de choisir les fonctions de distribution, surtout au niveau des capillaires, compte tenu de l'extrême complexité de la microcirculation réelle.

En règle générale, un modèle est représenté par un ensemble d'invariants, or la définition d'invariants dans les sytèmes vivants est en partie arbitraire[29]. Le choix ne pourra donc s'effectuer que par tâtonnement. L'arbitraire du choix des modèles se retrouve dans le choix des équations représentatives. De plus, on se heurte très vite au caractère inextricable des calculs dès qu'on ne se limite plus à des écoulements correspondant à des lois de distribution et à des conditions aux limites très simples. Même l'introduction des termes de gravitation complique considérablement les calculs. Or le recours aux simplifications et l'emploi de relations approchées présentent de grands dangers ainsi que le montrent, par exemple, les contradictions dans les calculs du déplacement radial des globules et de l'épaisseur de la couche périphérique dans les vaisseaux étroits[30–35].

Malgré cela, il est necessaire d'avoir recours à des simplifications, tout au moins dans une première étape, mais il faut prendre de grandes précautions dans le contrôle de leur validité. Pour progresser, il faut envisager des échelons successifs d'approxima-tion, ou de complexité[36], en utilisant des schématisations partielles et, pour ainsi dire, localisées. D'une facon plus précise, il faut délimiter dans le problème général des problèmes partiels faisant intervenir un nombre bien moindre de paramètres. Il faut s'efforcer de traiter chacun de ces problèmes partiels dans toute sa complexité, sans faire complètement abstraction des autres paramètres, c'est-à-dire, en tenant compte, mais sous une forme simplifiée, schématique. Un des moyens d'atteindre ce but est l'introduction de grandeurs apparentes, ou mieux, de grandeurs équivalentes convenablement choisies pour remplacer un ensemble complexe de données par un être fictif simple dont le comportement est le même relativement à un phénomène donné. C'est le cas, par exemple, des ellipsoïdes équivalents en biréfringence d'écoule-ment[37] ou des énergies de déformation équivalentes en viscosimétrie superficielle des macromolécules[38].

QUELQUES PROBLÈMES PARTIELS D'HÉMORHÉOLOGIE ET LEUR INCIDENCE EN RHÉOLOGIE FONDAMENTALE

Nous voudrions, très sommairement, énumérer un certain nombre de problèmes partiels de l'hémorhéologie, et indiquer, dans la mesure du possible, quels problèmes généraux ils incitent à traiter du point de vue de la rhéologie fondamentale.

De nombreux travaux ont mis en évidence la déformabilité des globules rouges, et en particulier les déformations qu'ils subissent lors du franchissement des capil-laires[39, 40]. Des tentatives ont été faites pour montrer indirectement l'effet de la viscosité propre des globules sur la viscosité du sang[41], mais l'étude directe de leur rhéologie ne semble pas avoir été entreprise. Des travaux théoriques et expérimentaux ont été faits sur la déformation de gouttelettes liquides et de filaments dans un écoule-ment[42–47]. Mais la structure des globules n'est pas si simple, et il serait très impor-tant d'étudier les lois de leur déformation en tant que phases organisées. Les recherches de rhéologie fondamentale sur les liquides organisés, structuralement anisotropes, seraient très utiles. Peu de travaux ont été poursuivis dans ce domaine en dehors des recherches expérimentales sur les phases des savons[48–51] et la déformation des tactoïdes[52]. L'aspect théorique du problème n'a pas été abordé à partir des données structurales, en tenant compte de l'anisotropie des fonctions de distribution. De tels milieux ne sont pas rares et l'étude théorique de leur déformabilité serait très utile pour préciser les aspects moléculaires de la rhéologie fondamentale.

Il est bien connu que les hématies ne sont pas réparties uniformément dans le sang mais groupées en agrégats dissymétriques labiles qui se dissocient sous l'effet du cisaillement[53, 54]. Il serait intéressant d'étudier les propriétés mécaniques des rouleaux de globules rouges. A défaut, des recherches ont été faites sur l'écoulement d'agglomérats de globules obtenus par centrifugation[55]. Des études de rhéologie fondamentale ont été développées sur des modèles beaucoup plus simples d'agrégats sphériques ou ellipsoïdaux, dissociables mais indéformables, constitués de particules toutes identiques, également sphériques ou ellipsoïdales et indéformables[21, 28, 56]. Un modèle d'agrégats en bâtonnets a été étudié[57]; sa validité pour le sang paraît assez satisfaisante[58–61]. Il serait très important de reprendre de telles études théoriques en tenant compte de la déformabilité des agrégats et de celle de leurs particules constitutives, en ne se limitant pas à des formes géométriques aussi régulières. Il faudrait aussi faire intervenir le fait, essentiel dans la microcirculation, que les dimensions des particules et des agrégats sont d'un ordre de grandeur comparable à celui des dimensions transversales des vaisseaux où s'écoulent leurs suspensions.

Un problème également important est celui du groupement des particules dans les dispersions sous l'effet de l'écoulement. Le phénomène a été étudié pour des suspensions de sphères[62]. Il est à rapprocher de celui de l'agrégation provoquée par l'écoulement[20, 24, 63], mais il serait intéressant d'en développer la théorie en envisageant des particules de formes différentes avec des distributions des potentiels d'interaction autour d'elles telles que, pour des valeurs convenables de la vitesse de cisaillement, la configuration de stabilité maximum ne corresponde pas à la formation d'agrégats mais à la formation d'essaims lâches librement perméables au solvant. La solution de ce problème suggéré par des observations d'hémorhéologie permettrait probablement de comprendre l'édification de structures quasi périodiques et, dans certains cas, l'apparition de microgels dans des systèmes en écoulement.

Mais ce que l'hémorhéologie devrait surtout inciter les rhéologues fondamentalistes à développer, c'est l'étude des systèmes dispersés de concentration très élevée. Dans ce domaine, il n'y a guère eu jusqu'à maintenant que des travaux de caractère empirique[64–76]. L'élucidation théorique du comportement des suspensions concentrées ne semble avoir été tentée que dans le cas de particules sphériques[11, 12, 77–80]. En partant d'un modèle géométrique suggéré par la structure du sang, et à partir d'une représentation des processus rhéologiques analogue à celle d'Eyring ou de Mooney, il faudrait essayer de décrire les propriétés rhéologiques globales des systèmes très concentrés et hautement hétérogènes en fonction des paramètres structuraux de ces systèmes. La solution d'un tel problème rendrait de grands services dans de nombreux domaines de la rhéologie fondamentale et de la rhéologie appliquée.

Les travaux relatifs à l'effet sigma et à la couche plasmatique ont été relativement nombreux et les faits sont expérimentalement bien établis[59, 81–86]. L'aspect théorique du problème a été envisagé par plusieurs auteurs. Nous avons signalé plus haut les contradictions auxquelles pouvaient conduire des calculs approchés, ce qui prouve que les processus qui sont à l'origine de ce comportement ne sont peut-être pas aussi simples qu'il pourrait sembler. Il y aurait intérêt à reprendre la théorie de ces phé-

nomènes sur une base générale, en précisant en particulier la signification des sépara-
tions de phases induites par l'écoulement[48, 87, 88] et en tenant compte de l'influence
des gradients de vitesse sur les fonctions de distribution[89].

En rhéologie classique, l'écoulement des liquides n'est en général considéré que dans
des conditions géométriques simples, telles que, par exemple l'écoulement dans un
tube cylindrique indéformable de section circulaire constante. On est donc très loin
des conditions qui se présentent avec le réseau des vaisseaux sanguins. Il est bien évident que l'établissement d'équations d'écoulement dans un système aussi complexe
présente de très grandes difficultés. Mais l'analyse rigoureuse des différents problèmes
qu'il soulève ne pourrait qu'être fructueuse, et il y aurait intérêt à poursuivre les
diverses tentatives qui ont déjà été faites.

L'écoulement d'un liquide incompressible de viscosité constante dans des tubes de
diamètre variable, et éventuellement curvilignes, a été abordé, soit à partir de l'analyse
dimensionnelle[90], soit à partir des équations générales de l'hydrodynamique[91].
Le cas des vaisseaux déformables a été traité à partir des lois générales de la mécanique
des fluides pour un liquide newtonien[92–94]. Les équations de l'écoulement d'un
liquide non newtonien ont été développées dans le cas de tubes de section constante
mais non circulaire[95–98]. Le cas particulièrement délicat des tubes ramifiés et des
tubes poreux ne semble pas avoir été abordé d'un point de vue théorique malgré un
début d'étude expérimentale[53, 99, 100] et la grande importance d'une telle étude
dans divers domaines de la rhéologie appliquée. Par contre, des tentatives ont été
faites pour tenir compte dans les équations de l'écoulement du régime pulsé de la circulation. Les calculs ont été conduits aussi bien à partir des lois générales de la mécanique des fluides[101, 102] que des principes de l'analyse dimensionnelle[103].

Les conditions de passage des régimes d'écoulement laminaire à des régimes tour-
billonnaires pour des fluides non newtoniens ont été étudiées expérimentalement[104–
106], mais l'étude théorique du processus en tenant compte des divers paramètres
intervenant dans la circulation sanguine ne semble pas avoir été entreprise. Cependant,
les phénomènes liés à la turbulence mériteraient une analyse détaillée car il semble que
les effets mécaniques de la turbulence puissent jouer un grand rôle aussi bien en ce
qui concerne la stabilité physico-chimique de divers constituants du plasma qu'en
ce qui concerne les variations de perméabilité des vaisseaux. Les recherches sur les
phénomènes d'écoulement secondaire des fluides[95, 96, 107–110] pourraient peut-
être fournir les éléments d'un modèle pour l'étude théorique précise du mouvement
turbulent du sang et des divers types d'amortissement des perturbations de la circulation sanguine.

Nous avons rappelé plus haut qu'une des complications de l'hémorhéologie tenait à
ce que le système circulatoire ne pouvait pas être considéré comme un système fermé,
et que des flux chimiques modifiant les propriétés intrinsèques du sang se superposaient
à l'écoulement purement mécanique. Ceci conduit à envisager une rhéologie où les
paramètres ne sont pas exclusivement des paramètres mécaniques. Des développements théoriques ont été apportés récemment dans cette voie, à partir des conceptions
de la magnétohydrodynamique[111–112], ou à partir des principes de la thermodynamique des proccessus irréversibles[114–119]. On peut espérer que ces dernières
tentatives seront étendues au cas d'un plus grand nombre de paramètres non mécaniques et en ne se limitant plus, malgré les difficultés de calcul, à la rhéologie d'un
milieu continu homogène.

Bien d'autres problèmes seraient à signaler qui seraient susceptibles de demander à la rhéologie fondamentale de nouveaux développements. C'est le cas, en particulier, de tous les problèmes qui concernent les actions aux interfaces sang-vaisseaux, et de ceux qui sont relatifs à la formation des caillots sanguins. Mais on a alors affaire à une situation très complexe, car aux problèmes de rhéologie soulevés se superposent des questions de physico-chimie et de biochimie qui sont loin d'être clarifiées.

REMARQUES SUR LES POSSIBILITÉS DE REPRÉSENTATION SYNTHÉTIQUE

L'énumération précédente nous montre que les problèmes posés à la rhéologie fondamentale par les problèmes partiels de l'hémorhéologie sont loin d'être résolus. Bien plus, on peut se demander si, lorsque ces problèmes seront résolus, il sera possible d'en déduire une solution utilisable du problème général. Il s'agit en effet de savoir, par exemple, comment, dans un système comprenant plusieurs types de microphases dont on connaît les comportements rhéologiques individuels, il est possible de préciser la contribution de chacun d'eux au comportement global du système hétérogène, et d'en déduire ce comportement global[120]. Dans le cas de phénomènes complexes, il n'est pas certain que l'on puisse procéder par une méthode de superposition, car il faudrait être sûr, par exemple, que les déformations relatives à certains processus demeurent petites par rapport aux autres pendant toute l'évolution du système[121]. Il faut d'ailleurs, d'une façon générale, être très prudent dans l'utilisation du principe de superposition[122] dans les systèmes à très nombreux paramètres, et ne pas perdre de vue que les relations de proportionnalité entre les variations des diverses grandeurs qui interviennent dans la représentation des phénomènes physiques ne sont généralement valables que tant que ces variations restent petites. Or, dans des systèmes aussi complexes que le sang, des variations qui sont petites par rapport à certains des éléments constitutifs peuvent être grandes par rapport à d'autres, du fait de la diversité des échelles. Il en résulte que les écarts à la linéarité seront très fréquents.

D'autre part, dans un phénomène aussi complexe que la circulation sanguine, les divers processus partiels ne sont pas indépendants les uns des autres. Il y a des interactions réciproques. Chaque processus, comme chaque système constitutif, est perturbé par les autres, et les perturbe par une sorte de contre-réaction généralisée. L'une des tâches des rhéologues fondamentalistes devra donc être de dégager les lois de composition des comportements partiels dont l'additivité simple est presque toujours à exclure. Il est possible qu'une des voies dans lesquelles il faudra s'engager pour éviter des calculs inextricables sera la recherche de grandeurs équivalentes ou fictives permettant de remplacer, dans la représentation d'un comportement général, un ou plusieurs systèmes ou processus partiels par un seul paramètre supplémentaire convenablement choisi. Ce problème rejoint d'ailleurs celui de la recherche des invariants dans les systèmes de haute complexité.

Au lieu de cette recherche difficile d'une représentation symbolique satisfaisante parce qu'aisément maniable tout en gardant une signification physique, on pourrait également s'orienter, ne serait-ce que pour des applications pratiques, vers l'emploi de machines calculatrices permettant de ne plus être arrêté par la lourdeur des calculs. De même, il est probable que les méthodes de simulation analogique pourront rendre

de très importants services dans la solution pratique des problèmes de rhéologie fondamentale que pose l'hémorhéologie.

Mais, dans tous les cas, si l'on veut arriver à un développement fécond pour toutes
les branches de la rhéologie, il faudra s'efforcer de bâtir tout l'édifice à partir des caractéristiques moléculaires et structurales des systèmes étudiés. C'est à partir d'une
microrhéologie tenant compte de toutes les propriétés physiques de la matière que l'on
peut espérer élaborer une rhéologie générale qui permette vraiment de comprendre ce
qui se passe lorsque des déformations se produisent.

LES CONDITIONS D'UN APPORT VALABLE DES DONNÉES EXPÉRIMENTALES EN HÉMORHÉOLOGIE

Si l'on veut que l'hémorhéologie soit un stimulant efficace pour l'ensemble de la
rhéologie, il est indispensable que les faits expérimentaux soient établis avec rigueur,
aussi bien *in vivo* qu'*in vitro*. En effet, dans les travaux sur les milieux biologiques et
les êtres vivants, il arrive fréquemment que de nombreuses données expérimentales
soient difficilement utilisables dans les représentations théoriques[123]. Ceci tient
évidemment au fait que dans bien des cas le schéma utilisé est beaucoup trop rudimen-
taire pour pouvoir rendre compte de tous les aspects de la réalité physique. Cependant,
il n'est pas rare que ce soit la signification des données expérimentales qui doive
être incriminée. La validité des mesures est parfois contestable, ne serait-ce qu'à
cause de la difficulté qu'il y a, dans les systèmes très complexes, à dégager les critères
d'une expérimentation reproductible[124].

Il arrive parfois que les conditions auxquelles doivent satisfaire une grandeur pour
être mesurable, au sens physique du terme, soient perdues de vue, en particulier la
nécessité pour cette grandeur d'être stationnaire par rapport à l'ensemble de ses
voisines de même nature[125]. Il y a, de plus, des conditions auxquelles doivent
satisfaire les caractéristiques de l'appareil de mesure pour que les réponses de cet
appareil puissent être significatives en tant que mesures de la grandeur considérée.[126]
Il est souvent difficile de remplir avec certitude toutes ces conditions dans le cas de
systèmes à un grand nombre de paramètres.

Un des problèmes qui se posent à l'expérimentateur est précisément de détecter,
parmi la multitude des variables observables, celles qui sont effectivement des grandeurs
mesurables. Mais ce qui est le plus délicat est de sélectionner parmi celles-ci, les grandeurs qui sont susceptibles d'être prises comme paramètres indépendants en vue de
l'étude d'un phénomène donné. En effet, pour obtenir la reproductibilité et un déter-
minisme exact pour un phénomène quelconque, il est indispensable d'en repérer les
paramètres éventuellement cachés, et aussi d'éliminer tous les paramètres surabondants.
Ces derniers sont ceux dont l'influence sur le phénomène étudié est inférieure à la
sensibilité des appareils de mesure, et aussi certains paramètres dont l'influence est
mesurable mais qui ne sont pas indépendants des paramètres déjà retenus. Donc,
d'une part, le nombre de paramètres à prendre en considération pour l'étude d'un
phénomène donné dépend de la finesse de la technique expérimentale dont on dispose.
D'autre part, dans le groupe de paramètres vrais dont l'influence est détectable, le
choix de ceux qui seront gardés comme paramètres indépendants doit être fait de
façon telle que, compte tenu des appareils utilisés, ces paramètres satisfassent le mieux

possible aux critères de grandeurs mesurables, caractère d'extremum et fréquence de présence[125, 126].

La grandeur dont les relations avec les paramètres choisis constitue le phénomène étudié doit évidemment aussi satisfaire le mieux possible à ces mêmes critères, ce qui conditionne le choix de l'appareillage et de la technique expérimentale. En termes de méthodologie générale, cela revient à définir le mieux possible le système physique abstrait tangent au système expérimental considéré. Rappelons qu'un tel système tangent, pour un phénomène donné, est un système fictif comprenant le nombre de paramètres minimum compatible avec l'existence de ce phénomène[127, 128].

Il importe de préciser que les paramètres cachés signalés plus haut correspondent à des paramètres dont l'influence sur le phénomène étudié n'est pas évidente *a priori* et dont l'oubli du contrôle entraîne la non reproductibilité des observations et des expériences. Ils peuvent donc être différents des paramètres cachés introduits parfois en rhéologie classique[118] et qui sont presque toujours des paramètres de structure. D'une façon plus générale, ce sont des paramètres qui ne peuvent pas intervenir dans un échange d'énergie utilisable avec l'extérieur, et qui, par suite, ne sont pas contrôlables de l'extérieur du milieu soumis aux contraintes.

Un des buts des recherches expérimentales apparaît ainsi être la caractérisation la plus exacte possible de systèmes tangents suffisamment simples pour être d'utilisation théorique facile, mais choisis de façon telle que leur ensemble conduise à une représentation aussi fidèle que possible des comportements réels. C'est à partir de tels systèmes abstraits que l'on doit chercher à définir les invariants ou les grandeurs équivalentes dont nous avons indiqué plus haut l'utilité pour une représentation globale des phénomènes de la circulation sanguine. En effet, les grandeurs équivalentes qui permettent, pour ainsi dire, de résumer le comportement d'un système partiel, peuvent intervenir comme paramètres extérieurs pour la caractérisation du système abstrait tangent à un autre système expérimental partiel. C'est par ce moyen que s'exprime l'interaction entre les systèmes partiels, ou entre les phénomènes partiels, dont nous avons vu plus haut l'importance. Il est à noter, d'ailleurs, que ce n'est que par l'introduction de ce type de paramètre que l'on peut rendre légitime l'extrapolation au comportement *in vivo* de résultats obtenus *in vitro*. C'est en effet le seul procédé commode qui permette de tenir compte des différences d'environnement et des simplifications de comportement qu'entraîne l'expérimentation *in vitro*. Mais, en contre-partie, pour rendre utilisable cette expérimentation *in vitro,* il est nécessaire d'en multiplier les paramètres extérieurs de façon à réaliser, au moins sommairement, une simulation des influences de l'environnement réel *in vivo*.

On peut donc espérer obtenir une représentation qui, tout en demeurant relativement simple et d'un maniement assez facile, fournisse une description satisfaisante de l'ensemble des faits. On voit que la réalisation d'un tel programme exige une large coopération entre scientifiques s'occupant de la science générale des écoulements et des déformations, du point de vue de la mécanique du continu aussi bien que de celui des mécanismes moléculaires, et scientifiques se consacrant à l'étude de la circulation sanguine, des propriétés du sang et de celles des vaisseaux sanguins. Il est aisé d'entrevoir à quel point cette collaboration serait fructueuse et quels progrès en résulteraient aussi bien pour la rhéologie fondamentale que pour l'hémorhéologie.

BIBLIOGRAPHIE

[1] GLASSTONE, S., LAIDLER, K. J. et EYRING, H. *The Theory of Rate Process*, McGraw-Hill, New York, 1941, pp. 447–516.

[2] POWELL, X. et EYRING, H. *Adv. Colloid Sci.* **1**, 183, 1942.

[3] TELANG, M. S. *J. Chem. Phys.* **17**, 536, 1949.

[4] KUBAT, J. *Kolloid Z.* **139**, 60, 1954.

[5] MULLER, F. H. *Proc. 2nd Int. Cong. Rheol.*, Butterworths, London, 1954, p. 38.

[6] WEYMANN, H. *Kolloid Z.* **138**, 41, 1954.

[7] PALIT, S. R. *Indian J. Phys.* **29**, 65, 1955.

[8] REE, T. et EYRING, H. *J. Appl. Phys.* **26**, 793, 800, 1955.

[9] BARBU, E. et JOLY, M. *J. Chim. Phys.* **53**, 951, 1956.

[10] JOLY, M. *Kolloid Z.* **145**, 65, 1956.

[11] MARON, S. H. et PIERCE, P. E. *J. Colloid Sci.* **11**, 80, 1956.

[12] MARON, S. H. et SISKO, A. W. *J. Colloid Sci.* **12**, 99, 1957.

[13] HOLZMÜLLER, W. *Kolloid Z.* **155**, 110, 1957.

[14] MOONEY, M. *Trans. Soc. Rheol.* **1**, 63, 1957.

[15] DAHLGREN, S. E. *J. Colloid Sci.* **13**, 151, 1958.

[16] DAHLGREN, S. E. *Kolloid Z.* **163**, 138, 1959.

[17] HOLZMÜLLER, W. *Kolloid Z.* **203**, 7, 1965.

[18] MACK, C. *J. Polymer Sci.* **13**, 279, 1954.

[19] BOURGOIN, D. *Rheologica Acta* **1**, 141, 1958.

[20] JOLY, M. *Discuss. Faraday Soc.* **25**, 150, 1958.

[21] JOLY, M. *Rheologica Acta* **1**, 180, 1958.

[22] BOURGOIN, D. *Materialprüf.* **1**, 391, 1959.

[23] BOURGOIN, D. *Cah. Groupe Fr. Etudes Rheol.* **4**, 33, 1959.

[24] JOLY, M. *J. Chim. Phys.* **59**, 249, 1962.

[25] BOURGOIN, D. *J. Chim. Phys.* **60**, 902, 911, 923, 1963.

[26] JOLY, M. *Biorheology* **2**, 75, 1964.

[27] BOURGOIN, D. *Proc. 4th Int. Cong. Rheol.*, LEE, E. H. (Editor), Interscience Publ. John Wiley, New York, 1965, part 3, p. 307.

[28] JOLY, M. In *Symposium on Biorheology*, COPLEY, A. L. (Editor), *Proc. 4th Int. Cong. Rheol.*, Interscience Publ. John Wiley, New York, 1965, part 4, p. 45.

[29] SCOTT BLAIR, G. W. In *Symposium on Biorheology*, COPLEY, A. L. (Editor), *Proc. 4th Int. Cong. Rheol.*, Interscience Publ. John Wiley, New York, 1965, part 4, p. 35.

[30] THOMAS, H. W. *Biorheology* **1**, 41, 1962.

[31] WATANABE, T., OKA, S. et YAMAMOTO, M. *Biorheology* **1**, 193, 1963.

[32] RUBINOW, S. I. *Biorheology* **2**, 117, 1964.

[33] GOLDSMITH, H. L. et MASON, S. G. *Biorheology* **3**, 33, 1965.

[34] OKA, S. In *Symposium on Biorheology*, COPLEY, A. L. (Editor), *Proc. 4th Int. Cong. Rheol.*, Interscience Publ. John Wiley, New York, 1965, part 4, p. 89.

[35] WHITMORE, R. L. In *Symposium on Biorheology*, COPLEY, A. L. (Editor), *Proc. 4th Int. Cong. Rheol.*, Interscience Publ. John Wiley, New York, 1965, part 4, p. 69.

[36] COPLEY, A. L. In *Symposium on Biorheology*, COPLEY, A. L. (Editor), *Proc. 4th Int. Cong. Rheol.*, Interscience Publ. John Wiley, New York, 1965, part 4, p. 3.

[37] JOLY, M. *Trans. Faraday Soc.* **48**, 279, 1952.

[38] JOLY, M. *Biorheology* **4**, 11, 1965.

[39] BRÅNEMARK, P-I. et LINDSTRÖM, J. *Biorheology* **1**, 139, 1963.

[40] BRÅNEMARK, P-I. In *Symposium on Biorheology*, COPLEY, A. L. (Editor), *Proc. 4th Int. Cong. Rheol.*, Interscience Publ. John Wiley, New York, 1965, part 4, p. 459.

[41] DINTENFASS, L. *Angiology* **13**, 333, 1962.

[42] RICHARDSON, E. G. *J. Colloid Sci.* **8**, 367, 1953.

[43] TAYLOR, G. *Proc. 2nd Int. Cong. Rheol.*, Butterworths, London, 1954, p. 1.

[44] SILBERBERG, A. et KUHN, W. *J. Polymer Sci.* **13**, 21, 1954.

[45] BARTOK, W. et MASON, S. G. *J. Colloid Sci.* **13**, 293, 1958; **14**, 13, 1959.

[46] FORGACS, O. L. et MASON, S. G. *J. Colloid Sci.* **14**, 457, 1959.

[47] RUMSCHEIDT, F. D. et MASON, S. G. *J. Colloid Sci.* **16**, 210, 238, 1961.

[48] TITCHEN, R. S. Thèse, Paris, 1952.

[49] VAN DEN BERG, H. J. Thèse, Leiden, 1953.

[50] DERVICHIAN, D. G., JOLY, M. et TITCHEN, R. S. *Kolloid Z.* **136**, 6, 1954.

[51] BOURGOIN, D. Thèse, Paris, 1963.

[52] HELLER, W. Résultats non publiés.

[53] MONRO, P. A. G. *Biorheology* **1**, 239, 1963.

[54] CHARM, S., McCOMIS, W. et KURLAND, G. In *Symposium on Biorheology*, COPLEY, A. L. (Editor), *Proc. 4th Int. Cong. Rheol.*, Interscience Publ. John Wiley, New York, 1965, part 4, p. 335.

[55] JACOBS, H. R. *Biorheology* 1, 129, 233, 1963.

[56] WEYMANN, H. D. *Proc. 4th Int. Cong. Rheol.*, LEE, E. H. (Editor), Interscience Publ. John Wiley, New York, 1965, part 7, 3, p. 573.

[57] CASSON, N. In *Rheology of Disperse Systems*, MILL, C. C. (Editor), Pergamon Press, 1959, chap. 5.

[58] REINER, M. et SCOTT BLAIR, G. W. *Nature* 184, 354, 1959.

[59] SCOTT BLAIR, G. W. *Nature* 186, 708, 1960.

[60] COKELET, G. R., MERRILL, E. W., GILLILAND, E. R., SHIN, H., BRITTEN, A. et WELLS, R. E. *Trans. Soc. Rheology* 7, 303, 1963.

[61] MERRILL, E. W., MARGETTS, W. G., COKELET, G. R. et GILLILAND, E. R. In *Symposium on Biorheology*, COPLEY, A. L. (Editor), *Proc. 4th Int. Cong. Rheol.*, Interscience Publ. John Wiley, New York, 1965, part 4, p. 135.

[62] SEGRÉ, G. In *Symposium on Biorheology*, COPLEY, A. L. (Editor), *Proc. 4th Int. Cong. Rheol.*, Interscience Publ. John Wiley, New York, 1965, part 4, p. 103.

[63] JOLY, M. *J. Chim. Phys.* 56, 897, 1959.

[64] ROBINSON, J. V. *J. Phys. Coll. Chem.* 53, 1042, 1949.

[65] RICHARDSON, E. G. *J. Colloid Sci.* 5, 404, 1950.

[66] EVESON, G. F., WARD, S. G. et WHITMORE, R. L. *Discuss. Faraday Soc.* 11, 11, 1951.

[67] MARON, S. H., MADOW, B. P. et KRIEGER, I. M. *J. Colloid Sci.* 6, 584, 1951.

[68] WILLIAMS, P. S. *Discuss. Faraday Soc.* 11, 47, 1951.

[69] GEUZE, E. C. W. A. et TSONG-KIE, T. *Proc. 2nd Int. Cong. Rheol.*, Butterworths, London, 1954, p. 247.

[70] DE VRIES, A. J. et VAN DEN TEMPEL, M. *Proc. 2nd Int. Cong. Rheol.*, Butterworths, London, 1954, p. 291.

[71] VON DER WAARDEN, M. *J. Colloid Sci.* 9, 215, 1954.

[72] PACKTER, A. *Kolloid Z.* 149, 109, 1956.

[73] HOFFMAN, R. D. et MYERS, R. R. *Proc. 4th Int. Cong. Rheol.*, LEE, E. H. (Editor), Interscience Publ. John Wiley, New York, 1965, part 2, p. 693.

[74] LANDEL, R. I., MOSER, B. G. et BAUMAN, A. J. *Proc. 4th Int. Cong. Rheol.*, LEE, E. H. (Editor), Interscience Publ. John Wiley, New York, 1965, part 2, p. 663.

[75] SHERMAN, P. *Proc. 4th Int. Cong. Rheol.*, LEE, E. H. (Editor), Interscience Publ. John Wiley, New York, part 3, p. 605.

[76] BOMBLED, J. P. *Cah. Groupe Fr. Rheol.* 1, 35, 1955.

[77] MOONEY, M. *J. Colloid Sci.* 6, 162, 1951.

[78] OLDROYD, J. G. *Proc. Roy. Soc. A* 218, 122, 1953.

[79] SIMHA, R. *J. Appl. Phys.* 23, 1020, 1952.

[80] WOODBURY, G. W. et PRAGER, S. *Proc. 4th Int. Cong. Rheol.*, LEE, E. H. (Editor), Interscience Publ. John Wiley, New York, 1965, part 2, p. 712.

[81] COPLEY, A. L. et STAPLE, P. H. *Biorheology* 1, 3, 1962.

[82] FRENCH, J. R., GROOM, A. C., ROWLANDS, S. et THOMAS, H. W., *J. Physiol.* 166, 5 P, 1963.

[83] BUGLIARELLO, G., KAPUR, C. et HSIAO, G. In *Symposium on Biorheology*, COPLEY, A. L. (Editor), *Proc. 4th Int. Cong. Rheol.*, Interscience Publ. John Wiley, New York, 1965, part 4, p. 351.

[84] ROWLANDS, S., GROOM, A. C. et THOMAS, H. W. In *Symposium on Biorheology*, COPLEY, A. L. (Editor), *Proc. 4th Int. Cong. Rheol.*, Interscience Publ. John Wiley, New York, 1965, part 4, p. 371.

[85] THOMAS, H. W., FRENCH, R. J., GROOM, A. C. et ROWLANDS, S. In *Symposium on Biorheology*, COPLEY, A. L. (Editor), *Proc. 4th Int. Cong. Rheol.*, Interscience Publ. John Wiley, New York, 1965, part 4, p. 381.

[86] THOMAS, H. W. *Biorheology* 3, 36, 1965.

[87] SILBERBERG, A. et KUHN, W. *Nature* 170, 450, 1952.

[88] SCHULTZ-GRUNOW, F. *Rheologica Acta* 1, 289, 1958.

[89] KOYAMA, R. *J. Phys. Soc. Japan* 13, 1167, 1958.

[90] SONG, C., CHARM, S. et KURLAND, G. In *Symposium on Biorheology*, COPLEY, A. L. (Editor), *Proc. 4th Int. Cong. Rheol.*, Interscience Publ. John Wiley, New York, 1965, part 4, p. 255.

[91] WEISS, G. H. *Biorheology* 2, 153, 1964.

[92] FREY-WYSSLING, A. In *Deformation and Flow in Biological Systems*, FREY-WYSSLING, A. (Editor), North-Holland Publ. Co., 1952, p. 322.

[93] HERMANS, J. J. In *Deformation and Flow in Biological Systems*, FREY-WYSSLING, A. (Editor), North-Holland Publ. Co., 1952, p. 344.

[94] FOX, E. A. et SAIBEL, E. In *Symposium on Biorheology*, COPLEY, A. L. (Editor), *Proc. 4th Int. Cong. Rheol.*, Interscience Publ. John Wiley, New York, 1965, part 4, p. 125.

[95] ERICKSEN, J. L. *Quart. Appl. Math.* 14, 318, 1956.

[96] GREEN, A. E. et RIVLIN, R. S. *Quart. Appl. Math.* 14, 299, 1956.

[97] LANGLOIS, W. E. et RIVLIN, R. S. *Rend. Mat.* **22**, 169, 1963.

[98] PIPKIN, A. C. *Proc. 4th Int. Cong. Rheol.*, LEE, E. H. and COPLEY, A. L. (Editors), Interscience Publ. John Wiley, New York, 1965, part 1, p. 213.

[99] PALMER, A. A. In *Symposium on Biorheology*, COPLEY, A. L. (Editor), *Proc. 4th Int. Cong. Rheol.*, Interscience Publ. John Wiley, New York, 1965, part 4, p. 245.

[100] WITTE, S. In *Symposium on Biorheology*, COPLEY, A. L. (Editor), *Proc. 4th Int. Cong. Rheol.*, Interscience Publ. John Wiley, New York, part 4, 1965, p. 451.

[101] WOMERSLEY, J. R. *J. Physiol.* **127**, 553, 1955.

[102] TAYLOR, M. G. *Phys. Med. Biol.* **3**, 273, 1959.

[103] McCOMIS, W., CHARM, S. et KURLAND, G. In *Symposium on Biorheology*, COPLEY, A. L. (Editor), *Proc. 4th Int. Cong. Rheol.*, Interscience Publ. John Wiley, New York, 1965, part 4, p. 231.

[104] MEISNER, J. E. et RUSHMER, R. F. *Circulation Res.* **12**, 455, 1963.

[105] WAYLAND, H. *J. Appl. Phys.* **26**, 1197, 1955.

[106] McDONALD, D. A. In *Symposium on Biorheology*, COPLEY, A. L. (Editor), *Proc. 4th Int. Cong. Rheol.*, Interscience Publ. John Wiley, New York, 1965, part 4, p. 205.

[107] LANGLOIS, W. E. *Quart. Appl. Math.* **21**, 61, 1963.

[108] CRIMINALE, W. O., ERICKSEN, J. L. et FILBY, G. L. *Arch. Ratl. Mech. Anal.* **1**, 410, 1958.

[109] GIESEKUS, H. *Rheologica Acta* **1**, 404, 1961; **2**, 50, 1962; **3**, 59, 1963.

[110] GIESEKUS, H. *Proc. 4th Int. Cong. Rheol.*, LEE, E. H. and COPLEY, A. L. (Editors), Interscience Publ. John Wiley, New York, 1965, part 1, p. 249.

[111] CHANDRASEKHAR, S. *Am. Math. Monthly* **61**, 32, 1954.

[112] CHANDRASEKHAR, S. *Mathematika* **1**, 5, 1954.

[113] NARASIMHAN, M. N. L. *Proc. 4th Int. Cong. Rheol.*, LEE, E. H. and COPLEY, A. L. (Editors), Interscience Publ. John Wiley, New York, 1965, part 1, p. 345.

[114] COLEMAN, B. D. et NOLL, W. *Arch. Ratl. Mech. Anal.* **13**, 167, 1963.

[115] COLEMAN, B. D. et MIZEL, V. J. *Arch. Ratl. Mech. Anal.* **13**, 245, 1963.

[116] COLEMAN, B. D. et MIZEL, V. J. *Proc. 4th Int. Cong. Rheol.*, LEE, E. H. (Editor), Interscience Publ. John Wiley, New York, 1965, part 3, p. 34.

[117] ROBINET, J. C. et BUVET, R. *Cah. Groupe Fr. Rheol.* (sous-presse).

[118] MANDEL, J. *Cah. Groupe Fr. Rheol.* (sous-presse).

[119] BRUN, L. *Cah. Groupe Fr. Rheol.* (sous-presse).

[120] DINTENFASS, L. *Proc. 4th Int. Cong. Rheol.*, LEE, E. H. (Editor), Interscience Publ. John Wiley, New York, 1965, part 3, p. 621.

[121] LIANIS, G. *Proc. 4th Int. Cong. Rheol.*, LEE, E. H. (Editor), Interscience Publ. John Wiley, New York, 1965, part 2, p. 109.

[122] PERSOZ, B. *Cah. Groupe Fr. Etudes Rheol.* **2**, 18, 1957.

[123] WEISSENBERG, K. In *Symposium on Biorheology*, COPLEY, A. L. (Editor), *Proc. 4th Int. Cong. Rheol.*, Interscience Publ. John Wiley, New York, 1965, part 4, p. 19.

[124] KOVACS, A. J. *Cah. Groupe Fr. Etudes Rheol.* **1**, 11, 1956.

[125] RENAUD, P., JOLY, M. et DERVICHIAN, D. *C. R.* **238**, 1389, 1954.

[126] RENAUD, P., JOLY, M. et DERVICHIAN, D. *C. R.* **240**, 2384, 1955.

[127] RENAUD, P., JOLY, M. et DERVICHIAN, D. *C. R.* **245**, 2213, 1957.

[128] RENAUD, P. *C. R.* **251**, 1465, 1960.

DISCUSSION

BURTON *(Canada)*:

The capillary vessels of the terminal vascular bed are often smaller than the red cells in diameter, and here we have what we call "bolus flow". Has this ever been tackled in classical rheology at all? It seems to me that it is so completely different that I wonder whether it would be useful to try to develop an equation which even included capillary flow.

JOLY *(France)*:

Certainly; but, I think, there is not yet a good theoretical approach for this problem. In a small capillary, the diameter of which is smaller than the mean size of the flowing particles, when they are at rest in the equilibrium state, the situation is perhaps not very different from what occurs in the extrusion of synthetic polymers. In polymer rheology, nevertheless, there is a difference in that the molecules of the polymer are still smaller than the inner diameter of the extruder. But there is perhaps a possibility of reconciling the two methods of theoretical approach.

BURTON:

Then would you feel that we should not try to get one magnificent equation for every case in hemorheology? Will we not have to have a separate set of equations for such bolus flow, rather than one equation which would take in Poiseuille flow as well as bolus flow?

JOLY:

I think that in the present state it is necessary to have a set of equations. But, perhaps, a new development of the superposition theory, and a new extension of the Boltzman principle can allow us to obtain some general equation. However, I am afraid that a complete general equation would be of very difficult use in practice.

THEORETICAL APPROACH TO THE EFFECT OF WALL SURFACE CONDITION IN HEMORHEOLOGY

SYOTEN OKA*

Department of Physics, Tokyo Metropolitan University
Setagaya-ku, Tokyo, Japan

1. INTRODUCTION

In a number of publications COPLEY[1], COPLEY and SCOTT BLAIR[2, 3], and COPLEY et al.[4] reported on findings of apparent viscosity of blood, plasma and serum in contact with glass and fibrin surfaces. The apparent viscosities always showed a decrease when the blood systems were in contact with fibrin as compared with glass and other surfaces. This phenomenon may be called "Copley–Scott Blair phenomenon". Substances foreign to blood, such as silicone, perspex (PMMA), lusteroid and paraffin had various effects on apparent viscosity, but always showed higher values for apparent viscosity than did fibrin surfaces.

The fibrin surface was selected because it has been postulated by Copley that the endo-endothelial lining of all blood vessels is covered by a film of fibrin which is constantly being formed and maintained, and also controlled by fibrinolytic processes in the more or less immobile layers next to the vessel wall. Physiologically, the proposed endo-endothelial fibrin film might constitute a major factor in aiding circulation by increasing the velocity of blood flow.

It has long been known that the cell-free marginal zone of plasma is formed not only in arteries, veins and capillaries in various species of the living animal, but also in artificial capillaries due to the axial accumulation of red blood cells. The thickness of the plasmatic zone increases with increased velocity of blood flow. It has been pointed out by COPLEY[1] that the marginal zone may well exist when plasma alone flows through a living blood capillary, for example, in plasma skimming.

The formation of the plasmatic zone means that Poiseuille's fourth-power radius law fails to hold[5]. SCHOFIELD and SCOTT BLAIR[6] introduced the term "sigma phenomenon" to describe all deviations from the fourth-power radius law. The flow of blood in capillaries of various sizes shows a considerable fall in apparent viscosity in the narrow tubes. The sigma phenomenon is closely related to the presence of the plasmatic zone[7, 8].

It has long been known that blood does not obey Newton's law of viscosity, that is, blood is a non-Newtonian fluid. SCOTT BLAIR[9] and COPLEY et al.[4] have shown that an equation proposed by Casson for varnishes and later applied by STEINER[10] to molten chocolate also applies to bovine, rabbit and human blood, on both glass and fibrin surfaces.

2. SLIPPAGE AT THE WALL

It is generally assumed in fluid mechanics that there is no slip at the wall in a flow of fluid through a tube. However, if there is a slip at the wall, the volume of flow Q per unit time will certainly increase, and consequently the apparent viscosity will decrease, as compared with the case where there is no slip at the wall.

HELMHOLTZ et al.[11] took into consideration the effect of a slip at a wall for a Newtonian fluid and obtained the generalized Poiseuille equation

$$Q = \frac{\pi R^4}{8\eta} \frac{P}{L}\left(1 + 4\frac{\lambda}{R}\right), \tag{1}$$

where R is the radius, P is the pressure difference along the length L and η is the coefficient of viscosity. λ is a constant which depends on the nature of the fluid and the wall surface and was called Gleitungskoeffizient. In a flow of water through a glass capillary, λ is zero because water wets glass. It is certain that no slip occurs, at any rate, in the case of substances which are wetted by the liquid[12]. WARBURG[13] showed that λ is also zero for mercury on glass notwithstanding that mercury does not wet glass.

TAMMANN et al.[14] measured the coefficient of viscosity of mercury in glass, steel, nickel and copper capillaries and found that these substances had various effects on the coefficient of viscosity. The coefficient of viscosity of mercury in a copper capillary was three times greater than that in a glass capillary. They attributed this effect to the fact that mercury wets copper wall.

However, it seems that there is no relation between the wettability of wall surfaces and the decrease of the apparent viscosity of blood. COPLEY et al.[15] have detected no appreciable difference between the wetting of glass and fibrin surfaces by blood, plasma or serum.

TRAUBE et al.[16] coated a glass surface with a layer of fatty acid by treating a glass capillary with a solution of fatty acid in ether. They found that the volume of flow of water in this capillary increased as compared with that in a clean glass capillary. A similar result was obtained when glass was coated with a layer of octyl alcohol. They attributed this effect to a certain lubricating action of the oriented film of fatty acid or octyl alcohol on a glass surface.

In the case of various suspensions of fibrous materials, the slippage phenomenon at a wall surface has long been recognized by several authors[6, 17–23]. Such suspensions display flow characteristics such as yield stresses, aggregation of particles and wall effects. Apparent slippage at a wall surface is likely with any suspension which has a yield stress. The suspension is necessarily discontinuous at a wall surface, and if the frictional forces between the material and the wall surface are less than those which bind it together, there will be a slippage of the body of the material. The existence of plug flow necessitates wall slip. MORRISON et al.[24] reported results of direct visual measurement of slip velocity with a coaxial cylinder viscometer for glycerol suspensions of cellulose powder with yield stresses.

Several investigations have been reported on the slippage of polymer melts at the wall of extruders. TORDELLA[25] has shown a possibility for slippage of a certain copolymer by means of photoelasticity photographs. BENHOW et al.[26] have shown the existence of the slippage of polyethylene by photographs. ISHIMARU *et al.*[27, 28] have found that the slippage velocity of polyethylene melt depends linearly upon the shear stress at the wall.

3. SLIPPAGE AND APPARENT VISCOSITY

We shall consider the effect of slippage on the apparent viscosity of time-independent non-Newtonian fluids. Fluids whose flow properties are independent of time may be described by a rheological equation of the form

$$\dot{\gamma} = f(\tau). \tag{2}$$

This equation implies that the rate of shear $\dot{\gamma}$ at any point in the fluid is a function of the shear stress at that point. MOONEY[20] derived an expression for the volume of flow of such a non-Newtonian fluid through a circular tube of radius R and length L

$$Q = \frac{\pi R^3}{\tau_R^3} \int_0^{\tau_R} \tau^2 f(\tau) d\tau + \pi R^2 v(R), \tag{3}$$

where

$$\tau_R = \frac{P}{2L} R \tag{4}$$

is the shear stress at the wall and $v(R)$ is the slip velocity at the wall. The apparent viscosity η_a is defined by

$$Q = \frac{\pi R^4}{8\eta_a} \frac{P}{L} \tag{5}$$

The slip velocity $v(R)$ is a function of τ_R, that is,

$$v(R) = s(\tau_R) \tag{6}$$

Equation (2) can be written

$$\frac{Q}{\pi R^3 \tau_R} = \phi(\tau_R) + \frac{\zeta(\tau_R)}{R}, \tag{7}$$

where

$$\phi(\tau_R) = \frac{1}{\tau_R^4} \int_0^{\tau_R} \tau^2 f(\tau) d\tau \tag{8}$$

and

$$\zeta(\tau_R) = \frac{s(\tau_R)}{\tau_R} \tag{9}$$

$\zeta(\tau_R)$ has been called by OLDROYD[29] the effective slip coefficient. It is the effective velocity of slip per unit shear stress at the wall.

$\zeta(\tau_R)$ can be evaluated from pipe flow experiments[30]. For a range of pipes of different radius, R, plot $Q/\pi R^5 \tau_R$ against τ_R. If there is a slip at the wall, the curve will be distinct for each value of R. Then from these curves at a selected value of τ_R determine $Q/\pi R^3 \tau_R$ as a function of $1/R$. When plotted, these points should give a straight line of slope $\zeta(\tau_R)$. By repeating this at different values of τ_R, $\zeta(\tau_R)$ can be evaluated as a function of τ_R. TOMS[31] has applied this technique to polymer solutions.

A Newtonian fluid is specified by the flow curve

$$f(\tau) = \frac{1}{\eta} \cdot \tau, \tag{10}$$

where η is the coefficient of viscosity. Substituting the above relation into eq. (7) we get

$$Q = \frac{\pi R^4}{8\eta} \frac{P}{L}\left(1 + 4\frac{\eta\zeta}{R}\right) \tag{11}$$

This is the Helmholtz–Piotrowski equation with

$$\lambda = \eta\zeta \tag{12}$$

From eqs. (5) and (11) we have

$$\frac{1}{\eta_a} = \frac{1}{\eta} + 4\frac{\zeta}{R} \tag{13}$$

It is clear that the slip increases the apparent fluidity.

Next we shall consider a non-Newtonian fluid obeying CASSON's equation[32]

$$\tau^{1/2} = k_0 + k_1 f(\tau)^{1/2}, \tag{14}$$

k_0 and k_1 being constants. Equation (14) can be rewritten

$$\begin{aligned} f(\tau) &= \frac{1}{\eta}(\tau^{1/2} - f^{1/2})^2 \quad &\tau > f \\ &= 0 &\tau < f \end{aligned} \right\} \tag{15}$$

two constants f and η being introduced instead of k_0 and k_1. f is the yield stress and η is a quantity having the dimensions of the coefficient of viscosity. Substituting eq. (15) into eq. (3) we get[33]

$$Q = \frac{\pi R^4}{8\eta} \frac{P}{L} F(\xi) + \pi R^2 v(R), \tag{16}$$

where

$$F(\xi) = 1 - \frac{16}{7}\xi^{1/2} + \frac{4}{3}\xi - \frac{1}{21}\xi^4 \tag{17}$$

$$\xi = \frac{p}{P}, \quad f = \frac{p}{2L}R \tag{18}$$

p is equal to the pressure when the shear stress at the wall becomes equal to the yield value f. When P is less than p, that is, $\xi > 1$, no flow occurs. From eq. (18) we have

$$\xi = \frac{2fL}{PR}. \tag{19}$$

From eqs. (16) and (5) we get

$$\frac{1}{\eta_a} = \frac{1}{\eta}F(\xi) + 4\frac{\zeta}{R} \tag{20}$$

The graph of $F(\xi)$ is shown in Fig. 1.

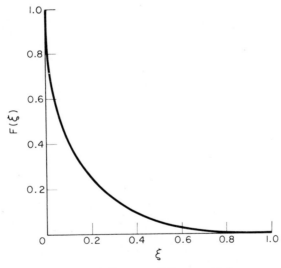

FIG. 1. PLOT OF $f(\xi)$ AGAINST ξ.

It has been suggested that the decrease of the apparent viscosity of blood in contact with fibrin may be caused by the slip at the wall. In order to clarify this point it will be necessary to evaluate $\zeta(\tau_R)$ from capillary flow experiments. The slip at the wall may be supported by the fact that blood is a suspension which has a yield stress.

On the other hand, there is certain experimental evidence against the slip at the wall. COPLEY and STAPLE[34] have observed that there appears to be a layer along the wall of the vessel which is more or less immobile.

According to HENNIKER[35], the surface zone of a liquid is not merely a mono-molecular layer with unaltered liquid immediately underneath it, but it is a region in which orientation extends to many molecular length. In this immediate region of solid surfaces there are local increase in viscosity.

4. PLASMATIC ZONE AND WALL SURFACE EFFECT

The existence of a plasmatic zone will result in an increase of the apparent viscosity of blood since the apparent viscosity of the plasmatic zone is less than that of the central core. Thus the plasmatic zone may be regarded as a kind of a lubricant. THOMAS[7] presented an improved analysis in terms of a simple model, consisting of a clear annulus of the suspending phase surrounding a core of the suspension.

In the following we will treat theoretically the influence of the plasmatic zone upon the apparent viscosity of blood flowing through a capillary. Following assumptions are made: (i) the thickness of the plasmatic zonc is uniform; (ii) the plasmatic zone consists of a Newtonian liquid with a coefficient of viscosity η_p; (iii) the central core obeys Casson's equation; (iv) there is no slip at the wall.

Then we have from eq. (3)

$$Q = Q_c + Q_p, \tag{21}$$

with

$$Q_c = \frac{\pi R^3}{\tau_R^3} \int_0^{\tau_{R-\delta}} \tau^2 f_c(\tau) \, d\tau \tag{22}$$

$$\left.\begin{array}{ll} f_c(\tau) = \dfrac{1}{\eta} (\tau^{1/2} - f^{1/2})^2 & \tau > f \\[2mm] \qquad\;\; = 0 & \tau < f \end{array}\right\} \tag{23}$$

$$Q_p = \frac{\pi R^3}{\tau_{R^3}} \int_{\tau_{R-\delta}}^{\tau_R} \tau^2 f_p(\tau) \, d\tau \tag{24}$$

and

$$f_p(\tau) = \frac{1}{\eta_p} \tau \tag{25}$$

where

$$\tau_R = \frac{P}{2L} R, \quad \tau_{R-\delta} = \frac{P}{2L} (R - \delta) \tag{26}$$

Neglect of $(\delta/R)^2$ and higher order terms yields

$$Q_c = \frac{\pi R^4}{8\eta} \frac{P}{L} F(\xi) - \frac{\pi R^4}{2\eta} \frac{P}{L} \frac{\delta}{R} (1 - \xi^{1/2})^2 \tag{27}$$

and

$$Q_p = \frac{\pi R^4}{2\eta_p} \frac{P}{L} \frac{\delta}{R} \tag{28}$$

Thus we have

$$Q = \frac{\pi R^4}{8\eta} \frac{P}{L} F(\xi) + \frac{\pi R^4}{2} \frac{P}{L} \frac{\delta}{R} \left[\frac{1}{\eta_p} - \frac{1}{\eta} (1-\xi^{1/2})^2 \right], \tag{29}$$

$F(\xi)$ being defined by eq. (17). Consequently, the apparent viscosity η_a is given by

$$\frac{1}{\eta_a} = \frac{1}{\eta} F(\xi) + 4 \frac{\delta}{R} \left[\frac{1}{\eta_p} - \frac{1}{\eta} (1-\xi^{1/2})^2 \right] \tag{30}$$

The second term in the right-hand side of eq. (30) represents the influence of the plasmatic zone upon the apparent viscosity of blood flowing through a capillary. It corresponds to the sigma phenomenon, showing the decrease of the apparent viscosity η_a with decrease in the radius R. The ratio of the second term to the first term becomes

$$\sigma = 4 \frac{\delta}{R} \left[\frac{\eta}{\eta_p} - (1-\xi^{1/2})^2 \right] \frac{1}{F(\xi)} \tag{31}$$

By taking $\delta/R = 1/20$ and $\eta/\eta_p = 3/1\cdot7 = 1\cdot76$, we can see that the effect of the plasmatic zone on the apparent viscosity is not negligible, because $\sigma = 0\cdot35$ even when $\xi = 0$.

The decrease of the apparent viscosity of blood in contact with fibrin suggests that δ is larger in fibrin-coated capillaries than in glass capillaries. This suggestion is supported by the finding of COPLEY and SCOTT BLAIR et al.[4] that blood on fibrin surfaces exhibited the sigma phenomenon, that is, anomalies with changes in capillary dimension, more markedly than on glass surfaces.

The red cells are covered by a film of proteins such as lipoprotein and they are negatively charged. Plasma proteins such as serum albumin, globulin and fibrinogen are negatively charged, too. It is plausible that the fibrin films on glass bear a negative charge, because the isoelectric point of fibrin s is 5·6 and fibrin i differs only slightly from fibrin s in amino acid composition[36]. The increase of the thickness δ of the plasmatic zone in fibrin-coated capillaries may be caused by the electrostatic repulsion between red cells and the fibrin. The fibrin will exert a repulsive force on the red cells and push them towards the tube axis. This results, of course, in an increase in δ. Silicone, perspex, lusteroid and paraffin will exert little influence upon δ because these substances are not polyelectrolytes.

The membranes of the endothelial cells of all blood vessels contain certain proteins. If the proteins are negatively charged, then it will aid circulation by increasing the thickness δ of the plasmatic zone and consequently decreasing the apparent viscosity of blood even if the endothelial cells are not covered by a film of fibrin. Thus it seems that the characteristics of the blood flow in living vessels as compared with glass capillaries lie in the electrostatic or electrokinetic forces upon red cells due to either the fibrin film or the proteins of the membranes of the endothelial cells. So it is anticipated that the apparent viscosities will always show a decrease when blood is in contact with substances which are negatively charged. If the endo-endothelial lining of all blood vessels is covered by a film of substances such as fibrin, it will aid circulation by decreasing the apparent viscosity of blood.

The decrease of the apparent viscosity of blood, plasma and serum in contact with fibrin suggests that the marginal zone peculiar to serum would be responsible for the effect. The small thickness δ_s of the marginal zone may be markedly influenced by the negative charge on the fibrin film.

REFERENCES

[1] COPLEY, A. L. *Nature* **181**, 551, 1958.

[2] COPLEY, A. L. and SCOTT BLAIR, G. W. *Rheol. Acta* **1**, 170, 1958.

[3] COPLEY, A. L. and SCOTT BLAIR, G. W. *Rheol. Acta* **1**, 665, 1961.

[4] COPLEY, A. L., SCOTT BLAIR, G. W., GLOVER, F. A. and THORLEY, R. S. *Kolloid-Z.* **168**, 101, 1960.

[5] SCOTT BLAIR, G. W. *Rheol. Acta* **1**, 123, 1958.

[6] SCHOFIELD, R. K. and SCOTT BLAIR, G. W. *J. Phys. Chem.* **34**, 248, 1930.

[7] THOMAS, H. W. *Biorheol.* **1**, 41, 1962.

[8] WATANABE, T., OKA, S. and YAMAMOTO, M. *Biorheol.* **1**, 193, 1963.

[9] SCOTT BLAIR, G. W. *Nature* **183**, 613, 1959.

[10] STEINER, E. H. *Intern. Chocolate Rev.* **13**, No. 7, 1958.

[11] HELMHOLTZ, H. VON and PIOTROWSKI, *Sitzungsber. der k. Adad. in Wien*, **40**, 1860.

[12] WHETHAM, W. C. D. *Phil. Trans. Roy. Soc. (London)* A **181**, 559, 1890.

[13] WARBURG, E. G. *Pogg. Ann.* **140**, 367, 1870.

[14] TAMMANN, G. and HINÜBER, *Z. anorg. Chem.* **167**, 230, 1928.

[15] COPLEY, A. L., GLOVER, F. A. and SCOTT BLAIR, G. W. *Biorheol.* **2**, 29, 1964.

[16] TRAUBE, J. and WHANG, S. H. *Z. phys. Chem.* **138**, 102, 1928.

[17] BUCKINGHAM, E. *Proc. Am. Soc. Testing Materials* **21**, 1154, 1921.

[18] DAILY, J. W. and BUGLIARELLO, G. *Ind. Eng. Chem.* **51**, 887, 1959.

[19] HAMM, G. G. H. and VAN ROSSEM, A. *Proc. Int. Rheol. Congress*, North Holland Publ. Co., Amsterdam, 1949, vol. II, p. 210.

[20] MOONEY, M. *J. Rheol.* **2**, 337, 1931.

[21] SCHOFIELD, R. K. and SCOTT BLAIR, G. W. *J. Phys. Chem.* **35**, 1212, 1931.

[22] SCOTT BLAIR, G. W. *J. Phys. Chem.* **34**, 1505, 1930.

[23] SCOTT BLAIR, G. W. and CROWTHER, E. M. *J. Phys. Chem.* **33**, 321, 1929.

[24] MORRISON, S. R. and HARPER, J. C. *Ind. Eng. Chem. Fundamentals* **4**, 176, 1965.

[25] TORDELLA, J. P. Prepaper presented at the Regional Technical Conference of SPE at Newark, N.J., 1962.

[26] BENHOW, J. J. and LAMB, P. *SPE Trans.* **3**, 7, 1963.

[27] ISHIMARU, Y., UI, J. and MORI, Y. *J. Soc. Materials Sci. Japan* **13**, 376, 1964.

[28] UI, J., ISHIMARU, Y., SAITO, S. and MORI, Y. *Chem. High Polymers (Kobunshi Kagaku)* **21**, 385, 1964.

[29] OLDROYD, J. G. *J. Colloid Sci.* **4**, 333, 1949.

[30] WILKINSON, W. L. *Non-Newtonian Fluids*, Pergamon Press, London, 1960, p. 129.

[31] TOMS, B. A. *J. Colloid Sci.* **4**, 511, 1949.

[32] CASSON, N. *Rheology of Disperse Systems*, MILL, C. C. (Editor) Pergamon Press, London, 1959, p. 84.

[33] OKA, S. In *Symposium on Biorheology*, COPLEY, A. L. (Editor), *Proc. 4th Int. Cong. Rheol.*, Interscience Publ. John Wiley, New York, 1965, part 4, p. 89.

[34] COPLEY, A. L. and STAPLE, P. H. *Biorheol.* **1**, 3, 1962.

[35] HENNIKER, J. C. *Rev. Mod. Phys.* **21**, 322, 1949.

[36] SCHERAGA, H. A. and LASKOWSKI, M. Jr. *Advances in Protein Chemistry* **12**, 1, 1957.

DISCUSSION

WHITMORE (*England*):

I would like to congratulate Professor Oka on a very interesting paper. One question I would like to ask him is how he thinks the theory would be affected if all the red cells were removed and you simply flowed the plasma down the tube. As I understand the experiments of Professor Copley and Dr. Scott Blair, they still obtain a change in viscosity when all the red cells are removed. In fact from what I remember, the effect was proportionally larger in that case than when the red cells were present. I wonder if Professor Oka could comment on this and also give some indication of the sort of interactions between the plasma and the fibrinogen wall which might give this effect even when the red cells were absent.

OKA (*Japan*):
I know little about the experiments on plasma. If the effect is large with plasma in contact with fibrin surface, slippage at the wall will be responsible for the effect, though the molecular mechanism of slippage is not yet clear.

BURTON (*Canada*):
Does the inclusion include the proteins?

OKA:
In the case of plasma and serum it will be difficult to consider a marginal zone which is responsible for the wall surface effect.

BURTON:
Is there any theory which would suggest that, when you have such small particles, the axial accumulating force would be enough to leave a zone free of protein molecules? I thought the theory of these forces would show that if the particles are very small, it would be a negligible force.

TAYLOR (*Australia*):
I think the question of scale comes in here. The size is involved. The effect on relative viscosity is roughly proportional, as I remember, to four times the ratio of the thickness of this layer to the radius of the tube. Now I think people (Professor Burton and Dr. Haynes) have found results which indicated that for red cell suspensions the layer delta was approximately 4 or 5 microns or something of that order and stayed more or less constant in all sizes of tubes.

BURTON:
I must add that it is extremely variable in different hematocrits.

TAYLOR:
Yes, and it would also get a bit thicker with higher rate of shear and so on, but within the range of, let us say, 5 or 10 microns, something like that. Now, consider the electrostatic forces arising from particles in an ionized solution. I remember once trying to work out the repulsive forces between red cells in suspension, and the effective radius of the forces was only a few Ångstroms because of the very highly ionized nature of the medium. I imagine that if one could do these experiments in media of different ionic concentration, one ought to expect different effects. Have you got any ideas about that, Professor Oka? The effects of the ionic concentration of the electrolytes will greatly diminish these repulsive forces or reduce them to a layer of perhaps a few Ångstroms which should be unmeasurably small. What do you think about that?

OKA:
I have not yet estimated quantitatively the repulsive forces between red cells and the fibrin surface. If the repulsive forces diminish rapidly with the distance from the surface, then the decrease of apparent viscosity of blood in contact with fibrin surface will be attributed to a slippage at the wall surface.

SILBERBERG (*Israel*):
I just wondered whether you had considered the possibility of explaining this effect by the viscoelasticity of the suspension itself; coupled with a decrease in the diameter of the capillary as a result of the layer which has been put on it. If you consider the equation for the shear at the wall, in a given viscometer under a given pressure gradient you find that the product of rate of shear at the wall D and the apparent viscosity η is proportional to the radius R of the tube. If the radius of the tube decreases, a constant pressure gradient the product ηD will decrease and the question arises whether the decrease of this product of rate of shear and apparent viscosity does in fact correspond to an increase of the rate of shear. Now this is a question of the rheological equation of the fluid, and depends on whether the logarithmic derivative of the viscosity with respect to the logarithm of the rate of shear $d\ln\eta/d\ln D$ is less than minus one. As this can easily be the case, the effect which was observed would result in principle. I am not sure as to whether the magnitude of the effect would come out right, but its sign would be correct.

OKA:

I have not yet considered the possibility of explaining the effect as being due to the viscoelasticity of blood. It seems, however, that blood shows viscoelasticity only under limited conditions.

RIVLIN (*U.S.A.*):

It seems to me that an experiment involving flow of a multicomponent system, such as that of blood in a capillary, is a rather complicated one to analyse. In such an experiment wall effects may well be masked by other effects, e.g. migration of the components due to variation of shear rate.

I would suggest that wall effects might better be studied (if this has not already been done) in a Couette apparatus in which the clearance is relatively small, so that the rate of shear is reasonably constant throughout the fluid. The effect of coating the walls with fibrin might well be investigated in this way.

BURTON:

Has anyone shown the effect of fibrin on the wall in a Couette apparatus?

OKA:

As far as I know, no one has ever shown the effect of fibrin on the wall in a Couette apparatus. I think, however, that the same effect will be found in a Couette apparatus with small clearance. It will not be difficult to calculate the effect of the width of the plasmatic zone δ upon the apparent viscosity of blood in a Couette apparatus.

BURTON:

I do just want to register some question about the validity of the mathematics, of which Professor Oka is not any more guilty than most of us. The point is this. Should one have any right to use integrals in a problem where the increments are not differentials? If there is a finite size of the red cell and therefore of the possible laminae, one should use a "sigma", (sum) of a set of terms, from n equals one to n equals the diameter of the tube divided by the minimum size of the laminae. The curious fact, that Haynes showed is that for normal hematocrit, one can explain the Fåhraeus–Lindquist effect and get a very good fit of that curve of size of tube simply on this basis, without calling upon axial accumulation, or plasmatic zones at all! However, when one does the same calculation for blood at other hematocrits, it becomes implausible. This fundamental question of the mathematics remains, when we are dealing with a situation where, perhaps, there are only five red cells across a tube. In such a case we really have no right to integrate instead of using a quantal summation. (I realize that Dr. Scott Blair's name "sigma phenomenon" has nothing to do with what I am talking about.) This is in a sense another kind of "sigma phenomenon", in that you ought to use as summation (sigma), and not an integral. I do not know whether anyone would like to comment on this difficulty that underlies all these theories where integration is done.

SCOTT BLAIR (*England*):

I am very much interested, Professor Burton, in what you have said because this is an idea which came to me when we first, Schofield and I, independently of Professor Fåhraeus, discovered the sigma phenomenon in 1930. Between 1930 and 1940, I struggled with the best way to do this summation, but my mathematics is extremely weak. By 1940, I had with me a young physicist who unfortunately died very soon afterwards. He was a great loss to physics. He was an extremely able man, Johnson Dix, and he worked this out for me for pastes of clay and soils which show sigma phenomena, using the summation method. We found that the results gave us a very good quantitative agreement with the experimental sigma phenomenon which Schofield and I had previously found with clays and soils. I think that this summation idea is in certain cases an extremely important factor because it is not justified to use an integration in certain cases such as the one that Professor Burton has outlined, where you cannot have narrow stream lines. But I think also that one should not go to the other extreme of trying to explain all sigma phenomena in these terms.

BURTON:

Perhaps I could just add that Dr. Haynes published a paper in which he compared the two theories. And as long as you work at normal hematocrit, the summation theory is extremely plausible, the size of the laminae required for the explanation being about the size of a red cell. However, when you go to lower hematocrits, or very much higher hematocrits, the summation theory becomes implausible. Similarly the theory of the plasma zone "delta", which is plausible at normal hematocrits, becomes implausible, in the opposite direction, at low hematocrits and, in the opposite direction, at high hematocrits. So perhaps the answer lies in the combination of the two theories. This is a fundamental question of the validity of the mathematics, I am sorry to hold up the meeting with a discussion of this; but I personally feel that it is very important.

GOLDSMITH (*Canada*):

Is not the idea of a stepwise summation instead of integration rather inadequate when dealing with a concentrated suspension flowing through a tube? Surely, one has to consider the particle interactions with each other and the wall, which are probably more important. While there is no question of not having laminar flow, the particle paths are not straight along the tube due to multi-body collision processes which have been observed in transparent suspensions (KARNIS, GOLDSMITH and MASON, *J. Colloid Sci.* **22**, 1966). In addition there is a hydrodynamic interaction with the wall which, as has been shown, has the same effect as having a clear plasmatic zone.

THE ADSORPTION OF SOLVATED MACROMOLECULES AND ITS RELATION TO THE VISCOSITY AND STABILITY OF DISPERSIONS

F. R. Eirich*

Department of Chemistry, Polytechnic Institute of Brooklyn, Brooklyn, New York, New York, U.S.A.

THE viscosity of blood is largely determined by the volume concentration and by the shape of its formed elements. Moreover, at a given concentration the state of dispersion of the formed elements has a decisive influence on the overall viscosity such that, the better its degree of dispersion, the lower the viscosity of a dispersed system. Consequently, blood circulation requires the least energy when the red cells are, and remain, single.

A high degree of dispersion of the erythrocytes and other cells, as is true for all colloidal systems, depends on surface charges and solvation. These derive not only from the chemical and physical structure of the cell membrane and its interaction with the water and the salts of the serum, but depend also on the adsorption of any and all other blood constituents in the plasma on the formed elements. Most adsorbates will either assist dispersion or be detrimental. The adsorbates which act as dispersing or stabilizing agents are those which increase the negative charge or the solvation or add protective adsorbed cushions to the red cell surfaces. All adsorbed elements which act in the opposite way may be considered as flocculants, agglutination or destabilizing agents. Prominent among the latter are many non-physiological substances in the blood and in particular denatured proteins, fibrinogen in various stages of fibrin formation, heparin binding substances, metal cations and other cationic materials, and many water soluble polymers above a certain molecular weight. In the following I wish to present some results of recent work[1] on the mechanism of adsorption of polymers, and also on the solvation of the peptide bond[2], which throw some light on the mechanisms of stabiling and destabilizing adsorption processes which presumably occur on the red cells.

At first, I wish to refer schematically to certain general, but essential, features of adsorption isotherms. As long as adsorption is restricted to monolayers it can be conveniently approximated by Langmuir isotherms which can be characterized by an affinity constant and a capacity factor (maximum amount absorbable), as shown in Fig. 1[3]. Interestingly, the adsorption of macromolecules on dispersed elements like red cells leads unexpectedly to isotherms very closely akin to the Langmuir type, but with a somewhat lower capacity. This has been interpreted elsewhere, and I think correctly, as a sign of mutual repulsion of the macromolecules within the adsorbed monolayer. The adsorption of macromolecules is most sensitive to their state in solution, in such a way that the less soluble the macromolecules are in the medium, the greater the amounts adsorbed on formed elements and, incidentally, also on the walls of the blood vessels.

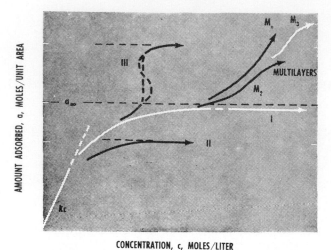

CONCENTRATION, c, MOLES/LITER

FIG. 1. VARIOUS KINDS OF ADSORPTION ISOTHERMS. MONOLAYERS EXHIBIT AN INITIAL STRAIGHT LINE WITH SLOPE EQUAL TO THE AFFINITY CONSTANT, k, AND A SATURATION CAPACITY (COMPLETE MONOLAYER) OF a_∞. MULTILAYERS ARE INDICATED BY A SUBSCRIPT; CONCENTRATION, c, REPRESENTS EQUILIBRIUM CONCENTRATION OF SUPERNATANT. I—LANGMUIR TYPE, WHERE $a = (a_\infty kc)/(1+kc)$. II—INTRALAYER REPULSION. III—INTRALAYER CONDENSATION. POLYMERS FOLLOW A TYPE II ISOTHERM.

Concerning the affinity of potential adsorbates to the red cell surface, in view of the latter's negative charge any cationic materials will be adsorbed at least to the point of neutralization and will be pulled strongly on to the particle surface. In other words, the affinity for cations is very high. Negatively charged macromolecules are adsorbed only if there is an appreciable difference between their average electrokinetic potential and that of the red cell; thus, their affinity will be small or zero. The affinity of neutral macromolecules for the red cell will be determined by such factors as polarity and dielectric constant, short and long range Van der Waals' forces, energetics of relative solvation of the red cells and of the macromolecules, displacement of other adsorbed materials including water and, very important, by the independent solubility of the macromolecules in the intercellular plasma. In view of this complexity, the quantities adsorbed (the capacities) as well as the affinities of adsorbates to the red cell surfaces are almost impossible to predict; on the other hand, they can be experimentally determined by addition of any agent in question to concentrated or diluted blood, allowing for equilibration and then measuring the concentration of additive per surface area of red cells, in the supernatant fluid. In fact, all the so-called agglutination or sedimentation reactions of blood are manifestations of such adsorption processes, but unfortunately the equilibrium concentration of the additive in the supernatant is usually not determined for lack of a clear concept of what is involved in the reaction.

Relative affinity and capacity of adsorbed macromolecules are of such importance for red cell stability because of the interaction of the adsorbed macromolecule with the surrounding fluid. If the affinity is very high, the macromolecules are pulled into the surface, coat the latter completely, and lose largely their own charge or solvation, thus begin to aggregate or condense with themselves within the adsorbed layer and also with other like layers on other cells. Such macromolecules act as a bridge, or cement, between the red cells and bring about their agglutination. If, on the other hand, the affinity is small, the macromolecules will be loosely held, repel one another in the interface and also when colliding with other likewise coated red cells. Adsorption of this kind leads to stabilization. This will be particularly true if the layer of adsorbed macromolecules has a certain thickness and if the latter are adsorbed in amounts sufficient to cover the red cell surface more or less completely. Since there will be always macromolecules of one kind or another which adhere to the red cells, be it native or pathological plasma proteins or those present from infused material, the study of the structure of adsorbed macromolecular monolayers as a function of their nature and of the solvent is important for all aspects of red cell stability.

Our technique of establishing the adsorption isotherms[1] was the conventional one of allowing the dispersed phase (glass, TiO_2, $CaCO_3$, carbon, latex) to come into equilibrium with the solution of the macromolecules and measuring the amounts adsorbed by the changes in concentration of the supernatant liquid. Two new techniques were designed to measure the hydrodynamic thicknesses of the adsorbed layers. The first consisted of allowing a sintered porous glass disk to equilibrate with polymer solution, and measuring the change in flow resistance before and after adsorption. Assuming validity of Poiseuille's law and determining the average pore radius, an average change in capillary radius can be calculated which is equal to the thickness of the adsorbed layer of macromolecules. Secondly, we measured the viscosity of a stable colloidal suspension, then allowed adsorption to take place and measured the viscosity again. The increase found is due to the increase in volume of the dispersed phase as a consequence of adsorption coating; again an average increase in particle radius can be calculated which is assumed to be the thickness of the adsorbed layer. Figures 2 and 3 show the process and the calculations schematically.

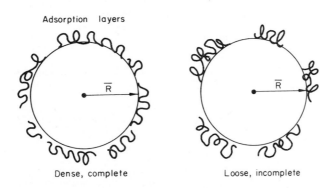

FIG. 2. CHANGES IN HYDRODYNAMIC DIMENSIONS DUE TO ADSORPTION. FOR CAPILLARY FLOW, POISEUILLE'S LAW APPLIES—I.E., $Q = \pi p (r - \Delta r)^4 / 8 \eta l$. FOR THE COATED PARTICLES, EINSTEIN'S LAW HOLDS—I.E., $\eta = \eta_0 (1 + 2.5\phi + 14\phi^2 + \ldots)$ AND $\phi = n/V \times 4\pi/3 (d/2 + \Delta r)^3$. Q = FLOW RATE; p = PRESSURE; η = COEFFICIENT OF VISCOSITY; ϕ = DISPERSED VOLUME; n/N = NUMBER OF PARTICLES PER UNIT OF VOLUME OF DISPERSION; d = PARTICLE DIAMETER.

It was found, as reported elsewhere[1], that for macromolecular weights in the customary range from a few ten thousandths to a million, the thicknesses of the adsorbed layers amounted from a hundred to a thousand Ångstroms and were proportional approximately to the square root of the molecular weight, and directly to the intrinsic viscosity. This result agrees very well with an earlier theory of polymer adsorption worked out in cooperation with FRISCH and SIMHA[4]. It was found further that the thicknesses varied with solvent power and temperature, also as expected

Particle Mean Diameters

d_1	Arithmetic mean	$\dfrac{\Sigma n_i d_i}{\Sigma n_i}$
d_2	Surface mean	$\dfrac{\Sigma n_i d_i^2}{\Sigma n_i d_i}$
d_3	Volume-surface mean	$\dfrac{\Sigma n_i d_i^3}{\Sigma n_i d_i^2}$ or $\dfrac{6}{\rho A_{\mathrm{sp}}}$
d_v	Volume mean	$\left(\dfrac{\Sigma n_i d_i^3}{\Sigma n_i}\right)^{1/3}$ or $(d_1 \cdot d_2 \cdot d_3)^{1/3}$

Pore Size Averages

$\lvert r \rvert$	$\dfrac{2V_{\mathrm{pore}}}{S}$	$\dfrac{\Sigma n_i r_i^2}{\Sigma n_i r_i}$
$\lvert r^2 \rvert$	$\dfrac{\vartheta C}{\pi N}$	$\dfrac{\Sigma n_i r_i^2}{\Sigma n_i}$
$\lvert r^4 \rvert \equiv \lvert r \rvert_i^4$	$\left(\dfrac{1}{N}\Sigma r_i^4\right)^{1/4}$	$\dfrac{\Sigma n_i r_i^4}{\Sigma n_i}$

V_{pore} = pore volume; S = pore surface; $\Sigma n_i = N$; $\vartheta = V_{\mathrm{pore}}/V_{\mathrm{total}}$; $C = R^2\pi$; R = disc radius; A_{sp} = specific surface area.

FIG. 3. METHODS OF AVERAGING.

from the theory, and this is true for adsorption from non-aqueous as well as from aqueous and salt containing solutions.

Combining the thickness data with those of the amounts adsorbed, which are equivalent to a few monolayers of monomeric units, one is led to the conclusion that the macromolecules are adsorbed in conformations not very different from random coils In particular it was found that varying the nature of the surfaces and macromolecules,

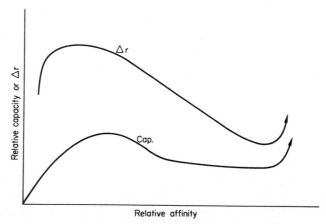

FIG. 4. SCHEMATIC REPRESENTATION OF THE COURSE OF ADSORPTION CAPACITY AND OF ADSORBED LAYER THICKNESS AS FUNCTION OF AFFINITY IN POLYMER ADSORPTION FROM SOLUTION.

and thus the forces acting between adsorbent and adsorbate, amounts and thicknesses for more or less neutral surfaces and macromolecules went through a complicated function as shown in Fig. 4. The correlation may not hold for the adsorption of poly-electrolytic macromolecules and for charged surfaces for which we have not succeeded yet measuring the adsorbed thicknesses with accuracy. It appears, though, as if similar but more extreme conditions prevailed, in that the polyelectrolytes may be drawn more completely onto the surfaces at the one end of the interaction spectrum, or be readily floated off by pH changes at the other end[3, 5]. Again, the solubility of the poly-electrolytic macromolecule plays a large role. Changing the solubility, e.g. by varying the ratio of charged to uncharged (or hydrophobic) units within the chain molecules, one finds, Fig. 5, a linear reciprocal relation between amounts adsorbed and the ratio

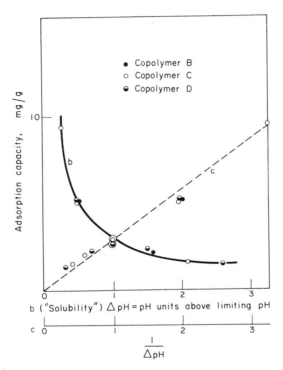

FIG. 5. ADSORPTION OF CROTONIC ACID–VINYLACETATE COPOLYMERS ON ANATASE VS. ΔpH.

of excess charged groups (over the minimum number of charged groups necessary to bring about solubility) to hydrophobic groups[6]. Close to the solubility limit, the amounts of polyelectrolytes adsorbed increase rapidly to the point where the adsorption process changes into one of induction of precipitation.

It is finally important that electrolytic and non-electrolytic macromolecules can be displaced, or can interchange, at the surface with low molecular weight adsorbates and also with other more readily adsorbable macromolecules[7]. Polymers show notorious hysteresis of desorptions on account of the necessary simultaneity of detachment from multiple adsorption sites[8]. In the presence of displacing agents, though, of low or high molecular weight, attachment sites freed by the first adsorbate can be occupied in stages by the displacing one, so that adsorption exchange can occur with practical speeds (say be noticeable in 15 min). These observations offer a mechanism for the understanding of how loosely adsorbed native plasma proteins which form a cushion around the red cells many Ångstroms thick can be displaced rapidly by partly or wholly denatured globulins, a process which must lead to red cell instability and agglutination.

The degree of instability would, of course, depend on the amounts adsorbed and the amounts displaced. In a corresponding model study[1c] it was found that depending on the auto-solvation or colloid stability of the uncoated dispersed units, various percentages of their surface had to be coated by either protective or agglutinating macromolecules to lead to either dispersoid stability or instability. Figure 6 shows schematically the relation between viscosity of the dispersion (viscosity to be at a stable

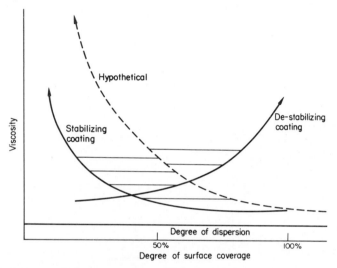

FIG. 6. VISCOSITY VS. DEGREE OF DISPERSION. (THE TIE-LINES SHOW HOW A GIVEN SURFACE COVERAGE DETERMINES THE DEGREE OF DISPERSION.)

minimum for fully dispersed particles, becoming non-Newtonian and rising eventually to a maximum or infinity for insufficient surface coating or adsorption of poorly soluble macromolecules) and relative coverage.

Macromolecules introduced as blood plasma extenders also participate in the adsorption equilibrium and may displace physiological or pathological adsorbates. Since the latter are destabilizing, the extender molecules act beneficially; for the same reasons they are a source of disturbance in healthy blood and lead, e.g. to rouleaux formation. There is an important effect of molecular weight. Normal, stable, serum proteins fall within narrow molecular weight ranges; they consist of folded chains so that the adsorbed layers stay within rather close limits of thicknesses. High molecular extender molecules have close to random coiled chains which can open further with very little extra energy. The result is multiple adsorption of large extender chains on several cells, or so-called "bridging", which creates flow units which raise blood viscosity markedly. Last, but not least, extender molecules will adsorb not only on red cells but also on other formed elements like platelets, and participate in a direct association equilibrium with large serum protein molecules. Thus they are likely to interfere with the stability of whole blood on every level, including also the coagulation process. It follows that, to be fully satisfactory, extender molecules will have to obey rather stringent functional requirements so as not to displace normal adsorbates from blood elements and veins, but do so with destabilizing agents. Some medium-low molecular weight dextrans seem to approach some of these needs but, as the papers and discussion of this conference show, their suitability is by no means fully established. Possibly, still smaller macromolecules carrying a few charges due to attached sulfate groups, with a mild heparin-like action, would leave the most desirable properties.

Going a step further back and carrying out a study of the solvation process of polypeptides themselves, we have been engaged[2] in determining the amount and locus of binding of water to the peptide group. Summarizing very briefly, we found, again on model compounds, that the peptide group is capable of forming definite compounds with water at low temperatures, as demonstrated by phase diagrams. These compounds may be expected to persist to some extent at body temperature and are modified by the nature of the substituents on the nitrogen or on the acid carbon. Two water molecules seem to be bound to the carbonyl group and one to the NH group and even to a doubly substituted nitrogen, although less strongly so. The water structure around the hydrophobic portions, in accordance with our results from heat capacity, enthalpy, entropy, IR, and NMR studies, seems to be less compatible with the often advocated iceberg structure and more like that of a thin layer of a clathrate water cage. One can visualize, just as changes of the balance between solvation and clathrate structure lead to more hydrophobic bonding between the protein chains, this type of bonding may occur also with hydrophobic portions of the red cell surfaces and thus to strong adsorption of more hydrophobic macromolecules and displacement of more soluble ones. We may see in this mechanism the molecular basis for the stronger affinity of partly denatured serum proteins.

Summing up, we have uncovered by way of model studies an adsorption mechanism which is likely to be responsible for changes in the dispersion stability, and thus of the viscosity, of whole blood: the fully dispersed red cells are stabilized by surface charges from dissociable groups of their partly lipoproteinic, partly carbohydrate sulfate, surfaces and are further protected by adsorption of serum albumins. If the surface structure is disturbed by adsorption of less negative low molecular weight compounds or, in particular, by displacement of the native albumin by less soluble macromolecules such as partly denatured globulins, the protection is being impaired and agglutination occurs. This process will affect not only red cells, but other formed elements, to interfere with their function, and lead to attachment of formed elements to the walls of the blood vessels.

REFERENCES

[1a] ROWLAND, F. Thesis, Polytechnic Institute, Brooklyn, New York, 1963.
[1b] ROWLAND, F. and EIRICH, F. R. *J. Polymer Sci.* A1 **4**, 2033, 1966.
[1c] ROWLAND, F., BULAS, R., ROTHSTEIN, F. and EIRICH, F. R. *Ind. Eng. Chem.* **57**, 46, 1965.
[2] ASSERSSON, P. Thesis, Polytechnic Institute, Brooklyn, N.Y., 1966.
[3] EIRICH, F. R. *Consiglio Naz. Richerche, Rome*, 1963.
[4] SIMHA, R., FRISCH, H. and EIRICH, F. R. *J. Phys. Chem.* **57**, 584, 1953; FRISCH, H. and SIMHA, R. *J. Chem. Phys.* **27**, 702, 1957.
[5] LOPATIN, G. and EIRICH, F. R. *Proc. 2nd Int. Cong. Surface Activity*, 1960.
[6] SCHMIDT, W. and EIRICH, F. R. *J. Phys. Chem.* **66**, 1907, 1962.
[7] THIES, C. Polymer Preprints, ACS, Fall, 1966.
[8] KORAL, J., ULLMAN, R. and EIRICH, F. R. *J. Phys. Chem.* **62**, 541, 1958.

DISCUSSION

GREGERSEN (U.S.A.):

What is the role of changes in dielectric constants of plasma that are produced by the hydrophobic and hydrophilic reactions that you have described?

EIRICH (U.S.A.):

The question is clear. Unfortunately, I do not think that a clear answer can be given. The role of the dielectric constant over small dimensions is very complex and has not been settled yet. One assumes ordinarily the bulk dielectric constant of water or of the corresponding solutions to be operative; but we know that the bulk dielectric constant loses its meaning over small distances. At close quarters, electric capacities and forces depend on the local polarizibilities which must be expected to change with the nature of the interfaces and of the adsorbed layers. However, I believe that the structural changes of interfaces and electric double layers through adsorptive and desorptive processes are the primary factors and that dielectric changes are the consequences rather than the causes.

GREGERSEN:

I happen to have seen a paper recently by William Pollock on the effect of various substances on the dielectric constant.

EIRICH:

I am aware of this. In this case, though, materials were added to the blood stream which are not normally there and which could change the bulk dielectric constant. Even so, I cannot believe that there could be any marked changes without killing the organism. If effects due to any such additions were seen, it must be that the infused materials again became adsorbed at critical surface areas and altered the local polarities. As a result, there are likely to be changes in hydration and further some salting-in or salting-out effects.

LONG (U.S.A.):

Do you have any feeling for how the adsorption of the polymers such as polyvinylpyrrolidone affects the viscoelastic property of the proteins?

EIRICH:

Ordinary molecules of serum proteins are relatively small and so are the plasma expander molecules. Since PVP is soluble in all proportions, neutral particles covered by it are protected and therefore mobile relative to neighboring particles. Thus, unless, e.g. the polyvinylpyrrolidone had molecular weights of over about 200,000, it would not affect the blood rheology when present in ordinary concentrations. Development of viscoelastic properties depends on particle to particle contact. If the pyrrolidone were to "bridge" red cells or protein molecules because of high molecular weight or concentration or because of poor cell or protein stability then, of course, the viscoelastic behavior would be changed, and the flow become more non-Newtonian. Moreover, particles like red cells which are large and depend for their stability on a negative net charge may be slightly destabilized because PVP adsorbs strongly on negative surfaces, displaces some other adsorbates and some adsorbed water, and thus leads to rouleau formation which, however, is hardly enough to produce noticeable viscoelasticity. The situation is different for dextran which has a much lower solubility, but lesser affinity to negative surfaces. It does not tend to create any more rouleau formation than PVP, but it presents a larger danger of bridging by small amounts of high molecular weight molecules.

WHITMORE (England):

Could Professor Eirich tell us what diameter capillary tubes he needs in order to obtain the viscosity changes which are required in order to calculate the thickness of the layer?

EIRICH:

The capillary tubes are of the order of $\frac{1}{2}$ micron. We use fritted glass discs to get sufficient numbers. These discs were very well characterized for length of capillaries and distribution of their radii by the mercury intrusion method and also by gas flow, so that we have a good description of this capillary system. Of course, these do not consist by any means of bundles of equal, straight, and parallel capillaries as the theory assumes; but from all we can see, this does not seem to be of great consequence. The main reason is that we rely in these "sinter glass disc viscometers" on relative measurements in the same way as for measurements in ordinary wide capillaries. For organic solvents we find no differences between viscosities of given solutions by these two methods. However, differences in viscosities of solutions by the two methods do occur whenever either the capillary walls or the particles carry electrical charges. Referring to the earlier discussions by Oka, Mason, and others on the free plasma layer along the wall during suspensoid flow, I think that in these cases charge interactions between wall and particles have also to be considered and will contribute to concentrating the particles in the tube centers and to creating a layer of high lubricity. In addition, there is yet another charged particle effect similar to that observed in sedimentation and diffusion. This arises in our opinion from a distortion of the electric double layer when charged particles enter capillary tubes of diameters not much larger than that of those of polyelectrolyte chains plus their ionic atmosphere. This polarization will lead to an electrophoretic entrance retardation of polymer, but subsequently to an electrophoretic flow acceleration of the solution. We believe we have seen evidence of these phenomena, among other things by way of viscosity differences when measured in narrow and wide capillaries. I repeat, however, that for uncharged polymers, in media of high dielectric constants or at high salt concentrations, the viscosities derived from sintered discs are exactly those calculated for regular Poiseuille capillaries.

THE DYNAMICS OF BLOOD FLOW IN CAPILLARIES

R. L. WHITMORE* †

Department of Mining Engineering
University of Nottingham
Nottingham, England

INTRODUCTION

Various theories have been developed to explain the flow behaviour of blood in vessels greater than about 40 microns in diameter in terms of idealized systems. Much less attention has been paid to model systems which are comparable with flow conditions in the capillaries, terminal arterioles and venules of living tissue where the cells follow each other down the vessels in single file either separately or in groups, although some experiments have been reported[1–4]. This aspect is considered in the present paper.

THEORY

Most theories of flow of stable two-phase systems in narrow tubes are based on the assumption that the positions which the elements of the dispersed phase can take up are restricted by mechanical[5, 6, 7] or hydrodynamic[8] interaction with the wall so that there is a fall in concentration of the dispersed phase near the wall. The result can be represented as a two-phase core, containing an increased concentration of the dispersed phase, surrounded by an annulus consisting completely or predominantly of continuous phase. Probably the most complete treatment of this model is due to THOMAS[9] who showed that the mean volume concentration of dispersed phase $\bar{c}$ in a tube of diameter a is related to the mean volume concentration in the feed c_0 by the equation

$$\frac{\bar{c}}{c_0} = \left(\frac{x}{a}\right)^2 + \frac{\left[1 - \left(\frac{x}{a}\right)^2\right]^2}{2\left[1 - \left(\frac{x}{a}\right)^2\right] + \left(\frac{x}{a}\right)^2 \frac{1}{\eta_{rc}}} \tag{1}$$

where x = diameter of the core

η_{rc} = viscosity of the core, relative to the continuous phase.

This may be termed the shearing-core model (Fig. 1).

Observation shows that in a living capillary the red cells, which constitute the bulk of the dispersed phase, tend to follow each other in a single axial file with their discoidal surfaces predominantly[10] (but not universally[11]) perpendicular to the vessel axis. As the flow rate rises, deformation is observed, the cells often becoming thimble-shaped and their effective diameter decreasing[12].

A reasonable model, therefore, consists of an axial core containing a train of cells

†Present address: Department of Mining and Metallurgical Engineering, University of Queensland, St. Lucia, Brisbane, Australia.

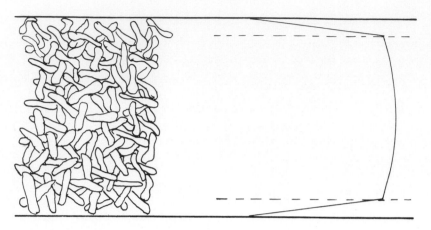

FIG. 1. SHEARING-CORE FLOW.

interspersed with plasma, surrounded by a sleeve of plasma in which the main shearing takes place (Fig. 2).

Then, from eq. (1), by assuming Newtonian behaviour for the plasma, $\eta_{rc} = \infty$ and x = effective diameter of a single cell, d,

$$\frac{\bar{c}}{c_0} = \frac{1 + \left(\dfrac{d}{a}\right)^2}{2} \tag{2}$$

And it can easily be shown from continuity considerations that the concentration of cells in the core, c, is given by

$$c = \bar{c}\left(\frac{a}{d}\right)^2 = \frac{c_0}{2}\left[1 + \left(\frac{a}{d}\right)^2\right] \tag{3}$$

When the blood is at rest d is equal to the diameter of a blood cell but it is difficult to assign a particular value when flow commences because the flexibility of the cell and the rate of shear to which it is exposed determine the extent of its deformation.

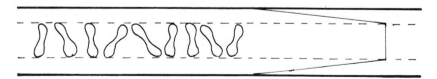

FIG. 2. AXIAL-TRAIN FLOW.

Assuming that d decreases with increasing flow rate there will be a corresponding rise in core concentration, c (from eq. (3)) and fall in mean tube concentration $\bar{c}$ (from eq. (2)) with flow rate. The limiting value of $\bar{c}$ is obtained when $c = 1$ and, from eq. (3),

$$\frac{d}{a} = \sqrt{\frac{c_0}{2 - c_0}}$$

Thus eq. (2) is only applicable for $\dfrac{d}{a} \geqslant \sqrt{\dfrac{c_0}{2-c_0}}$ and once this value is reached a further increase in velocity will not alter $\bar{c}$. It is probable that the core concentration c only approaches unity when the feed concentration c_0 is high. In general it is more likely that when $\dfrac{d}{a} \simeq \dfrac{1}{2}$ reorientation and redistribution of the cells commences, leading to the development of the conventional shearing two-phase core.

In Fig. 3 the results of the axial-train theory are shown for the flow of undeformed red cells 8 microns in diameter at a feed haematocrit of 40% down tubes of greater diameter than 8 microns. If cell deformation leads to a decrease in the effective cell diameter d, the concentration c will rise (eq. (3)) and the mean concentration $\bar{c}$ will fall (eq. (2)). Limiting values are included in Fig. 3. The results of applying Thomas's shearing-core theory are also shown, using the results of RAND et al.[13] at 212 sec^{-1} to calculate η_{rc} and assuming that the effective width of the annulus is equal to the cell radius. For a feed haematocrit of 40% the axial-train theory can only apply to vessels less than 16 microns in diameter at which value the core consists entirely of red cells, the mean concentration in the tube then being 25%. As mentioned above, it is

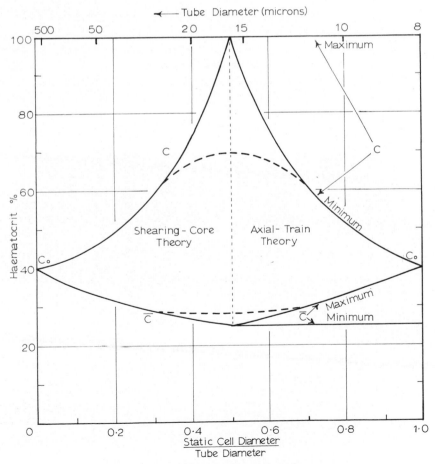

FIG. 3. CONCENTRATION CHANGES IN NARROW TUBES.

improbable that this situation would ever be reached in practice but that a smooth transition from an axial train of cells to a shearing core would be anticipated as the vessel diameter increased. Setting an arbitrary limit to cell concentration in the axial train at 70% the effect of tube diameter on cell concentration is shown tentatively in Fig. 3 by the chain line.

VELOCITY EFFECTS

The mean velocity of red cells v_c relative to that of the transporting plasma, v_p, when flowing down a tube is given by[14]

$$\frac{v_c}{v_p} = \left(\frac{1 - \bar{c}}{\bar{c}}\right)\left(\frac{c_o}{1 - c_o}\right) \tag{4}$$

Substituting for $\bar{c}$ from eq. (2), in the axial-train region

$$\frac{v_c}{v_p} = \frac{2\left[1 + \left(\frac{d}{a}\right)^2\right]^{-1} - c_0}{1 - c_0} \tag{5}$$

When the cells possess the same diameter as the tube, $d = a$ and, from eq. (5), cells and plasma travel at the same velocity. As the tube diameter increases, $\bar{c}$ falls and (from eq. (4)) the velocity of the cells relative to the plasma rises. It is clear that the velocity difference is a maximum when $\bar{c}$ is a minimum and, from Fig. 3, this should be in a vessel some 12–16 microns in diameter in the case of normal human blood flowing at low velocity. From eq. (4) the mean velocity of the cells would then be about 1·6–1·8 times that of the plasma.

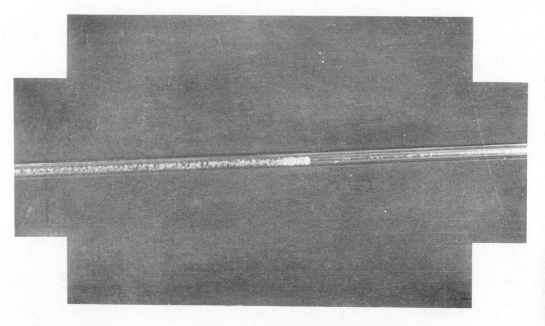

FIG. 4. HYPERCONCENTRATION OF SPHERES IN A TUBE.

One consequence of this result is that if a body flows down a tube which fits it closely and the suspending fluid contains particles about $\frac{1}{5}$ to $\frac{4}{5}$ of the tube diameter, the velocity of the small particles, relative to the fluid will be greater than that of the large body. Unless the particles are able to slip past the large body they will concentrate behind it. Figure 4 illustrates this effect for a 1·8 mm neutral-density sphere being carried down a tube 1·9 mm in diameter by a 5% suspension of neutral-density spheres 0·35–0·42 mm in diameter. It has been suggested as a possible mechanism for the hyper-concentration of red cells behind emboli in blood vessels of appropriate diameter[15].

VISCOSITY CHANGES

Assuming that the plasma is Newtonian it can easily be shown that at sufficiently high shear rates for Newtonian behaviour of blood to be assumed, the shearing-core theory leads to[5, 9, 14]

$$\left(\frac{x}{a}\right)^4 = \frac{1 - \dfrac{1}{\eta_{rm}}}{1 - \dfrac{1}{\eta_{rc}}}$$

where η_{rm} = measured viscosity of suspension of cells, relative to the plasma.
In a capillary tube where axial-train conditions prevail, $\eta_{rc} = \infty$ and

$$\eta_{rm} = \frac{1}{1 - \left(\dfrac{d}{a}\right)^4} \tag{6}$$

It will be observed that η_{rm} does not depend upon the volume concentration of the feed c_0 except in so far as eq. (6) is only applicable if $c < 1$ or,

$$\frac{d}{a} \geqslant \sqrt{\frac{c_0}{2 - c_0}} \tag{7}$$

From eqs. (6) and (7) the minimum possible value of η_{rm} at any concentration c_0 is given by

$$\eta_{rm(\min)} = \frac{(2 - c_0)^2}{4(1 - c_0)} \tag{8}$$

In Table 1, values for $\eta_{rm(\min)}$ calculated from eq. (8) are compared with the experimental values given by RAND et al.[13] for bulk blood measured at a shear rate 2 12 sec^{-1} and a temperature of 37°C. The big differences are notable.

When $d = a$, the train of cells completely fills the tube and, from eq. (6), $\eta_{rm} = \infty$. Under these conditions the present theory is clearly inapplicable because no assumptions are made regarding the drag exerted by the walls of a tube on the surface of a red cell moving in contact with it.

TABLE 1. RELATIVE VISCOSITY OF BLOOD

Haematocrit %	Axial-train theory	Bulk blood Rand *et al.*[13]
	Minimum value	Measured value
0	1·000	1·00
20	1·012	1·78
40	1·067	2·72
60	1·225	4·64
80	1·800	—

APPLICATIONS OF THE AXIAL-TRAIN THEORY

PROTHERO and BURTON[3] made measurements of the viscosity of human blood diluted with ACD when flowing through micropipette orifices averaging about 11 microns in diameter. The flow conditions were such that the axial-train theory should apply. PROTHERO *et al.*[3] found that in the haematocrit range 0–50%, the mean measured viscosity of the blood, relative to the suspending fluid was always less than 1·11, although there was some scatter in the results. The axial-train theory predicts, from eq. (8), that the minimum possible viscosity at 50% haematocrit should be 1·125 and values at other haematocrits are given in Table 1. These are in line with the values found by PROTHERO *et al.*[3] bearing in mind that their experiments were made at high flow rates (the Reynolds numbers were some 500 times greater than in living capillaries) so that the absence of a velocity dependence in the measured viscosity would be anticipated on the assumption that the cells were in most cases drawn into a continuous core by the large shearing forces present.

The theory also helps to explain MONRO's observations[16] that in the arterioles of a rabbit, which were some 12 microns in diameter, the cells travelled in groups rather than individually. Red cells in a blood sample are seldom identical in size. In the case of human beings some 5% differ from the mean value by more than 1 micron[17], and there are, no doubt, individual variations in flexibility. In a narrow vessel, large or rigid cells will fill a greater proportion of the cross-section than small flexible cells and from eq. (5) will attempt to travel slightly slower than average cells. The small cells will try to travel slightly faster than average cells so that in vessels of certain diameters the train of cells should break up into smaller groups each headed by a large or rigid cell, or tailed by a small or flexible cell, giving the phenomenon observed by Monro.

An explanation is also possible of a phenomenon sometimes associated with the observed difference in velocity between red cells and plasma when passing through living circulatory beds. The puzzling feature is not that the mean velocity of the cells exceeds that of the plasma but that, in some cases, the whole of the cell clearance curve is displaced relative to the plasma clearance curve so that it appears as if some of the red cells have swum ahead of the plasma with which they started. A model to explain this required the cells to be constrained in a core while plasma exchanged freely between the core and a surrounding plasma annulus[18]. It is difficult to contrive a mechanism which allows this behaviour in the case of ordinary shearing-core flow. Under axial-train conditions, however, bolus flow develops between the red cells[3, 4] as shown in Fig. 5. Conditions are then ideal for the exchange of plasma between the

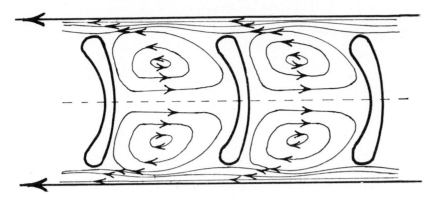

Fig. 5. Bolus flow. Flow lines are shown relative to the red cells.

slower-moving plasma elements in the annulus and that contained in the axial train, the red cells remaining in the axial train. It is interesting to note that when blood was flowed through tubes of 200 microns diameter both clearance curves commenced at the same instant[19]. In this case the ratio of red cell to tube radius was $<0{\cdot}1$ and axial-train flow could not possibly have occurred, shearing-core behaviour taking its place.

CONCLUSIONS

In tubes less than about two cell-diameters in diameter a satisfactory model of the flow behaviour of blood cells may be given by the axial-train theory. It leads to the conclusion that the haematocrit and viscosity of blood do not fall continually with decreasing vessel diameter but reach a minimum in tubes of approximately 12–25 microns diameter. The theory explains, reasonably satisfactorily, a variety of observations and measurements of blood flow which have been made in narrow tubes and capillaries.

ACKNOWLEDGMENTS

Grateful acknowledgement is made to the Nuffield Foundation for the financial support of research, of which the work described above forms part.

REFERENCES

[1] MULLER, A. *Arch. f. Kriesl.* **4**, 105, 1939.
[2] MULLER, A. *Helv. Phys. et Pharm. Acta*, **6**, 181, 1948.
[3] PROTHERO, J. and BURTON, A. C. *Biophys. J.* **2**, 199, 1962.
[4] GOLDSMITH, H. L. and MASON, S. G. *J. Colloid Sci.* **18**, 237, 1963.
[5] VAND, V. *J. Phys. Coll. Chem.* **52**, 277, 1948.
[6] MAUDE, A. D. and WHITMORE, R. L. *Brit. J. Appl. Phys.* **7**, 98, 1956.
[7] WHITMORE, R. L. In *Rheology of Disperse Systems*, MILL, C. C. (Editor), Pergamon Press, London, 1960, p. 49.
[8] SEGRÉ, G. and SILBERBERG, A. *J. Fluid Mech.* **14**, 136, 1962.
[9] THOMAS, H. W. *Biorheology* **1**, 41, 1962.
[10] MERRILL, E. W. and WELLS, R. E. *Appl. Mech. Rev.* **14**, 663, 1961.
[11] BRÅNEMARK, P-I., In *Symposium on Biorheology*, COPLEY, A. L. (Editor), *Proc. 4th Int. Cong. Rheol.*, Interscience Publ. John Wiley, New York, 1965, part 4, p. 459.
[12] BRÅNEMARK, P-I. and LINDSTRÖM, J. *Biorheology*, **1**, 139, 1963.

[13] Rand, P. W., Lacombe, E., Hunt, H. E. and Austin, W. H. *J. Appl. Physiol.* **19**, 117, 1964.

[14] Maude, A. D. and Whitmore, R. L. *J. Appl. Physiol.* **12**, 105, 1958.

[15] Whitmore, R. L. *Nature*, **209**, 298, 1966.

[16] Monro, P. A. G. *Biorheology*, **1**, 239, 1963.

[17] Britton, C. J. C. In *Disorders of the Blood*, J. & A. Churchill Ltd., London, 1963, 9th edn., p. 62.

[18] Whitmore, R. L. In *Flow Properties of Blood and Other Biological Systems*, Copley, A. L. and Stainsby, G. (Editors), Pergamon Press, Oxford, New York, 1960, p. 63.

[19] Thomas, H. W., French, R. J., Groom, A. C. and Rowlands, S. In *Symposium on Biorheology*, Copley, A. L. (Editor), *Proc. 4th Int. Cong. Rheol.*, Interscience Publ. John Wiley, New York, 1965, part 4, p. 381.

DISCUSSION

Joly (*France*):

I would like to ask Dr. Whitmore if there are any experimental data, *in vivo* or *in vitro*, showing that the blood cells move perpendicular to the direction of the capillary.

Whitmore (*England*):

I would say yes. Many of the cine films that have been taken do in fact indicate this tendency. It is not universal and you can see cells move in other orientations, particularly when the vessel is around twice the diameter of the cell. But when the cell fits fairly snugly into the vessel you do seem to get, on the whole, a tendency towards this type of orientation. I hope that some of the films we shall see later in the week will show more of this effect.

Bugliarello (*U.S.A.*):

I would like to ask Dr. Whitmore to clarify whether he has assumed an infinite viscosity in the core corresponding to the cells spanning the central portion of the tube.

Whitmore:

Yes, that is true.

Bugliarello:

Now if the cells are spaced, how close is this assumption to reality?

Whitmore:

Well, obviously, the assumption breaks down if you are getting extensive bolus flow. In fact, what we really require now is some work on bolus flow in order to include it in the general picture. But in the simplified model we assume that the core moves as a solid unit.

Bugliarello:

Thank you.

Goldsmith (*Canada*):

There is an important difference between the case of a liquid bubble or a deformable red cell flowing through a tube about the same size as the particle, and that of suspended rigid discs having diameters slightly less than that of the tube. With the bubble or the red cell there is deformation and the red cells orient themselves broadside on. However, rigid discs continue to rotate in the tube and neighbouring particles are unable to approach very closely whereas the erythrocytes or the bubbles can be touching each other. These observations may be of importance in trying to explain this phenomenon.

Whitmore:

Yes. Thank you for these comments. I think that one problem is that in all model systems if you use bubbles, you do not get the same condition at the interface as with a membrane such as you have in red cells. If you work with rigid particles, once again it is extremely unlikely that their behavior would be similar to that of the extremely flexible red cell, as, of course, Dr. Goldsmith's cine films show.

Charm (*U.S.A.*):

I tried to determine where you consider the continuity in your consideration of mean concentration of the core. I could not determine where it enters in your equation.

WHITMORE:

I considered continuity requirements of the plasma and the cells in calculating the concentration in the core. There is nothing particularly new about this, I followed the method which Thomas used.

MASON (*Canada*):

You stated it is well known that in a given sample of blood there is a range of flexibilities of the red cells. This is very important from a hemorheological point of view and I would be interested to know what experimental evidence you had in mind in making this assertion.

WHITMORE:

Well, that is a very good question. I have no experimental evidence at all, but the hematologists, as you know, tell us that the characteristics of the red cells change with age when, on the whole, they tend to shrink and get less flexible. I have no proof of this and I would be very glad for confirmation. How these measurements are made, I do not know. But this is what appears to be generally accepted in the hematology textbooks.

MASON:

This is perhaps a reasonable speculation to make but is it known for certain?

WHITMORE:

I am sure that there must be people here who are far more competent than I to answer your question. I hope sometime during the week, particularly when we come around to talking about red cells that this point will be answered. I assure you, Dr. Mason that your intense interest in this is no less than my own. I, too, would like to know how much evidence there is of the varying flexibility of the red cells.

BURTON (*Canada*):

There are some published data in answer to Dr. Mason's question about change of flexibility. We think that flexibility is largely a matter of shape, and there is an analysis of individual red cells by Rand and myself in the *Journal of Cellular and Comparative Physiology*. It gives the range of shapes, and from this by calculation one can deduce what size pore they could go through; because the red cell membrane cannot stand being stretched without hemolysis, but is easily bent. Therefore, the range of flexibility I would consider, is not due to changes in the membrane flexibility, but to changes in the deformability of the whole cell because of shape changes. I have recently given a review of this at the Microcirculatory Conference (in press) which deals with this point. The data were on a hundred individual cells in a sample of blood showing the range of shape, and the range of deformability calculated from the shape-factors.

SILBERBERG (*Israel*):

I also would like just to amplify this, referring to the work of Dr. Danon at the Weizmann Institute and the group of Katchalsky and others associated with them. They have demonstrated that the swelling of red cells can be controlled by changing the environment, either drastically or gradually, and that, depending on what conditions are chosen, you can allow the hemolysis to occur under conditions where no rupture of the red cell can take place over a much wider range of osmotic conditions than was normally suspected. Now this idea was used by Danon to differentiate between red cells which were by other devices also shown to be differentiated by age, and what he calls fragility of the red cell is very much reduced for young cells and then becomes more and more marked as the age of the cell goes up. And he has actually devised an instrument where cell populations can be studied by studying the rate at which hemolysis occurs under controlled osmotic conditions. Now, of course, this is not evidence of the, let us say, flexibility of the wall, but rather of its ability to distend under stresses. These two things must, however, be related and I think you would agree that it is true that the younger cells are more flexible.

BURTON:

I might add to that comment. I agree completely, but I would attribute this lack of flexibility with age to the well known change in shape with age, rather than to a change in the membrane stiffness, which may, of course, also occur.

ROWLANDS (*England*):

I would just like to mention a speculation which perhaps will be more relevant later on in the week, but it is slightly relevant to what Dr. Whitmore has been saying. A year ago, I had to give a review lecture. When I was looking at the properties of flowing blood in small blood vessels, several lines of evidence pointed to the possibility that in capillary flow water might be passing through the red cell. These lines of evidence come from Professor Burton's and Prothero's work on very narrow capillaries; from the classical work which,

I am afraid, most people have forgotten; that of Whittaker and Winton, on the hind limb of the dog, beautiful work done in 1933; from some work which Dr. Sirs will be describing later on in the week on the rate of exchange of gases across red cell membrane and from the work of Solomon on the rate of exchange of tritiated water across the red cell membrane and from well outside science, from the stability of a spinnaker of a sailing yacht. In light breezes, it is essential for the stability of the spinnaker, that is the sail you use when the wind is behind, for the fabric of the spinnaker to be penetrable to the air stream. Taking all these things together, in the course of this lecture, I put forward what is still only a speculation: that in the capillary, water is in fact passing under the shear gradient across the red cell membrane. Dr. Charm has of course got a very nice theory of the deformability of the red cell into the form of what I call a thimble. I think we ought to be careful not to call it a paraboloid shape at this stage, and perhaps when Dr. Charm gives his paper and when these other points have been raised, we might consider this possibility again.

WHITMORE:

Yes, I would like just to make one comment. There are many possibilities one can look at qualitatively but, I think, we can only really start to differentiate between them when we put in some figures and get something quantitative, even if it is only to see whether we have the right order of magnitude for these various effects. I suspect that in the case of a number of these effects an indication of the order of magnitude might help in deciding whether it is significant or not.

SIRS (*England*):

There are certainly differences between individuals in the flexibility of their red cells in disease and under normal conditions. (This work is not published, but it will come out, I hope, in about 9 months.) What interested me was that you said that there were differences between flexibilities in an individual. Now this I find very surprising. I have looked at this in gross detail, and I do not think this is normally the case. When the cell gets to this sort of condition in the normal individual, it is removed from the circulation. A lot of the work on older cells are artefacts because they have not been separated out correctly. There is some work by Prankerd on separation of the older cells, after adding serum albumin to make the solutions more dense, which I think is the only correct way of separating these cells, and in these circumstances, he suggests that what alters is the lipoprotein. The lipoids come out of the cell to make it more dense. Now as regards Professor Burton's point about some flexibility changes involving shrinkage, the interesting point which I will bring up later is: this is the case when it does not occur. His own data in fact confirm this. One other point of general interest, I'd like to make, is about this problem of the layer by the wall of the capillary being relatively stagnant (or laminar). On the relative dimensions put on the drawings and illustrated today, I find this rather incomprehensible. It is not compatible with normal physiological processes. You would not, across such a layer, get sufficient transport of oxygen to keep you alive. I looked at this problem with respect to the red cell. For a long time I thought it was possible that the resistance of the red cell membrane was due to such a water layer. Recent information suggests that this is not possible. If there is no stagnant layer round a cell which is moving with the stream it is difficult to visualize any such layer of significant dimension on the capillary wall. The other aspect that is not being taken into account is that these capillary walls are permeable. The water goes across them very easily, and I find it difficult to understand how you could get a stagnant layer adjacent to a system which will transport water through it quickly.

WHITMORE:

I hope I never mentioned the word "stagnant layer" in the whole of my paper. I am not postulating a relatively stagnant, partly stagnant, or completely stagnant layer in my theory. I am assuming that the fluid shears as a Newtonian fluid between the edge of the cell and the wall of the vessel.

SIRS:

What is worrying me is that the cell seems to be so very far away from this wall. If you have such a separation you must have relatively good mixing, an interchange of the fluid with its surroundings, as Professor Burton has more or less pointed out with his bolus flow, to get the oxygen exchange reasonably efficient. This is the essence of the problem.

WHITMORE:

I do not think this theory is incompatible with bolus flow. Of course, the extent to which it is going to be important will depend upon the spacing of the cells. If you get many of them together you will have a smaller number of boluses and this will alter the exchange, but this is a field which has not been explored yet so far as I know.

EIRICH (*U.S.A.*):

I think the best answer to the question of exchange has already been given by Dr. Whitmore, when he showed the turbulence between the cells. This would make for a very rapid exchange between the layers at the wall and the center of the tube, so that the bolus form or the orientation perpendicular to the stream lines should not delay any exchange. However, it is surprising that so many of the cells take up this position perpendicular to the stream lines. Going back to the older hydrodynamic investigations, Eisenschitz and Jeffery proposed that dispersed particles should take up positions of either maximum or minimum dissipation. It seems that here the particles take up positions of maximum dissipation and the question is "Why?". I hope that theoreticians interested in particle orientation and motion like Drs. Silberberg, Mason, Oka and others will investigate this point. If the flow resistance of the particles were indeed so large, it might be possible that they, with the counter ions may become transported by plug flow which might pull the red cells ahead of their accompanying serum layer, as you have described. As long as the position of the particles is that of maximum dissipation, there should be no separation between particles and surrounding plasma. When by changes in capillary dimensions the central position is established, one could well see the red cells going ahead of the serum. This is a possibility that one should keep in mind.

WHITMORE:

Thank you. In reply I would just say that all I did was to accept the usual evidence gleaned from many, many films and see where it took me so far as a simple hydrodynamic theory was concerned. But, of course, we must start and consider the stability of the cell and the exchange problems and so on. All these have got to be dealt with and we are only scratching the surface at present.

CONSIDERATIONS OF CERTAIN HEMORHEOLOGICAL PHENOMENA FROM THE STANDPOINT OF SURFACE CHEMISTRY

BUN-ICHI TAMAMUSHI*

Tokyo Joshi Daigaku, Tokyo, Japan

ABSTRACT†

Copley and his collaborators have found in their hemorheological studies that the flow characteristics of blood through glass capillaries, such as the viscosity–shear rate relation, the viscosity–capillary radius relation (sigma effect), or the wall adherence, show remarkable variations according to the condition if the glass wall is previously coated with fibrin or other substances, or not.

For these experimental facts, many considerations and discussions have already been made from various points of view. Nevertheless, it appears to the author of this paper that there are certain surface chemical aspects to be taken into account for understanding the observed phenomena, because the material system under investigation is a microheterogeneous system involving the interfaces of capillary wall/plasma (or serum) solution/cell particle and those of cell particle/plasma solution/cell particle. The interaction of cell particle with capillary wall or that of cell particles with each other, which is considered to control the flow characteristics of blood through capillaries, should be a function of surface forces acting through these interfaces, and, moreover, surface forces can take various forms according to the nature of adsorption or solvation layers at the interfaces.

On the basis of these general considerations, this paper tries to present an idea for understanding "slipping effect" as well as "sigma effect" in hemorheological phenomena. The role of Derjaguin's "disjoining forces" and that of "bimolecular adsorption mechanism" developed by the author is discussed in relation to rheological and surface chemical phenomena observed in simpler material systems.

†Author intends to submit complete paper to the journal *Biorheology*. (Editor.)

THERMODYNAMIC AND MODEL TREATMENT OF ACTIVE ION TRANSPORT IN ERYTHROCYTES

R. BLUMENTHAL,[1] B. Z. GINZBURG[2] and A. KATCHALSKY[1]

Polymer Department, Weizmann Institute of Science,[1] Rehovoth, Israel and Hebrew University,[2] Jerusalem, Israel

1. INTRODUCTION

The mechanical properties of red blood cells are determined mainly by the structure of erythrocyte membranes[1]. Thus the visco-elastic behavior of the membranes may be attributed to a macromolecular network supporting the cellular cover. It is, however, recognized that the cell membrane is not only a mechanical wall separating the cell from its surroundings but an organelle — a cellular organ — performing numerous physiological functions. Within its narrow confines of about 100 Å, the membrane encompasses an enzymatic system which carries out a complex metabolic process. The chemical process is coupled to the flows which pass the membrane, regulates their magnitude and determines their direction.

A direct proof that the processes are membrane bound is given by the fact that erythrocyte ghosts, obtained in careful hemolysis, can reproduce successfully both the mechanical and metabolic-diffusional behavior of the intact cell. The ghost retains most of the visco-elastic properties of the red blood cells and in addition it shows the remarkable pumping capacity for cations.

One of the most striking properties of erythrocyte membranes is their capacity to selectively accumulate potassium ions in the cell with a concomitant expulsion of sodium. When erythrocytes are cooled to 0°C the concentrations of sodium and potassium within and outside the cell equalize. If the temperature is raised to 37°C however, a sodium outflow and potassium inflow will set in until the attainment of a steady distribution of cations between the inner (i) and outer (o) solutions, characterized by an ion exchange or selectivity coefficient

$$\Gamma = \frac{c_K^i/c_{Na}^i}{c_K^o/c_{Na}^o} \cong 220.$$

This value is larger by two orders of magnitude than the selectivity coefficients found in technical ion exchange and requires an investment of an energy of at least $RT\ln\Gamma = 3.24$ kcal for every mole of ion exchanged. As shown by numerous workers[2–4], the source of this energy is an intracellular hydrolysis of adenosine triphosphate (ATP) to adenosine diphosphate (ADP) and inorganic phosphate (P_i). The intriguing aspect of

91

this process is the direct coupling within the cellular membrane of the ATPase activity with the ionic flows.

The objectives of this report are the thermodynamic analysis of active ion exchange and a detailed interpretation of the coupling process in terms of a lattice model. We shall make use of the phenomenological approach of non-equilibrium thermodynamics, which provides a convenient framework for the determination of the pertinent flows and forces in the red blood cell membrane.

In the subsequent analysis of the lattice model we may visualize the mechanism of the coupling process and may obtain explicit expressions for the coefficient relating flows and forces.

2. THE THERMODYNAMIC FORMALISM[5]

The thermodynamic analysis of any non-equilibrium process may be carried out in two steps. First, the irreversible processes proceeding in the system are combined in a dissipation function Φ, which represents the decrease in free energy at constant temperature per unit time due to irreversibility. For systems to which Gibbs equation can be applied locally at all points, the form of the dissipation function is:

$$\Phi = \sum_i J_i X_i \tag{1}$$

where the J_i's are the flows in the system and the X_i's are the generalized driving forces (e.g. gradients of chemical potential). The choice of the flows is to a certain extent arbitrary but for any flow J_i, the dimensions of the conjugate force is given by eq. (1).

Second, for sufficiently slow irreversible processes, linear phenomenological equations may be written which relate each flow to all forces or each force to all flows:

$$J_i = \Sigma L_{ik} X_k \quad \text{or} \quad X_i = \Sigma R_{ik} J_k \tag{2}$$

in which the L_{ii} and R_{ii} are straight phenomenological coefficients and the L_{ik} and R_{ik} are coupling coefficients relating non conjugated forces and flows.

As shown by Onsager[6] the matrix of the coefficients L_{ik} and R_{ik} is symmetrical so that

$$L_{ik} = L_{ki} \quad \text{and} \quad R_{ik} = R_{ki} \tag{3}$$

According to an observation of Curie[7] spatial symmetries within the system make some of the R_{ik}'s vanish. Thus in an isotropic space no coupling is possible between a scalar flow such as the flow of a chemical process—and a vectorial flow such as the directed flow of a permeating substance. The anisotropy of biological membranes on the other hand, permits the coupling of chemical with diffusional processes and justifies the analysis of active transport in terms of this formalism.[8]

For the study of active ionic fluxes across red blood cell membranes we shall consider the flows of sodium J_{Na}, potassium J_K, and an anion J_{An}, and the flow of a chemical reaction, which provides the driving energy of the exchange, J_r. The conjugated driving forces for the ionic flows are the differences of electrochemical potentials across the membrane

$$\Delta\tilde{\mu}_{Na} = \tilde{\mu}_{Na}^i - \tilde{\mu}_{Na}^o, \quad \Delta\tilde{\mu}_K = \tilde{\mu}_K^i - \tilde{\mu}_K^o \quad \text{and} \quad \Delta\tilde{\mu}_{An} = \tilde{\mu}_{An}^i - \tilde{\mu}_{An}^o \tag{4}$$

The metabolic process of ATP hydrolysis is driven by its affinity A

$$A = \mu_{ATP} + \mu_{H_2O} - \mu_{ADP} - \mu_{Pi} \tag{5}$$

With these flows and forces we may write for the dissipation function and the phenomenological equations under conditions of constant flows across the membrane:

$$\Phi = J_{Na}\Delta\tilde{\mu}_{Na} + J_K\Delta\tilde{\mu}_K + J_{An}\Delta\tilde{\mu}_{An} + J_r A \tag{6}$$

and

$$\Delta\tilde{\mu}_{Na} = R_{Na}J_{Na} + R_{NaK}J_K + R_{NaAn}J_{An} + R_{Nar}J_r$$

$$\Delta\tilde{\mu}_K = R_{KNa}J_{Na} + R_K J_K + R_{KAn}J_{An} + R_{Kr}J_r$$

$$\Delta\tilde{\mu}_{An} = R_{AnNa}J_{Na} + R_{AnK}J_K + R_{An}J_{An} + R_{Anr}J_r \tag{7}$$

$$A = R_{rNa}J_{Na} + R_{rK}J_K + R_{rAn}J_{An} + R_r J_r$$

The consensus of opinion is that the anion flow is passive and not coupled with the chemical process, so that $R_{Anr} = 0$. In resting erythrocytes all ionic flows vanish (i.e. $J_{Na} = J_K = J_{An} = 0$) and the phenomenological equations reduce to the simple form

$$\Delta\tilde{\mu}_{Na} = R_{Nar}J_r; \quad \Delta\tilde{\mu}_K = R_{Kr}J_r; \quad \Delta\tilde{\mu}_{An} = 0 \quad \text{and} \quad A = R_r J_r \tag{8}$$

Equations (8) may be combined to form expressions which do not contain the electrical potential. Thus

$$\Delta\tilde{\mu}_K + \Delta\tilde{\mu}_{An} = \Delta\mu_{KAn} = R_{Kr}J_r$$

$$\Delta\tilde{\mu}_{Na} + \Delta\tilde{\mu}_{An} = \Delta\mu_{NaAn} = R_{Nar}J_r \tag{9}$$

and

$$\Delta\tilde{\mu}_{Na} - \Delta\tilde{\mu}_K = \Delta\mu_{ex} = (R_{Nar} - R_{Kr})J_r$$

where the electroneutral differences in chemical potential may be written for ideal solutions as:

$$\Delta\mu_{NaAn} = RT\ln\frac{c_{Na}^i c_{An}^i}{c_{Na}^o c_{An}^o}$$

$$\Delta\mu_{KAn} = RT\ln\frac{c_K^i c_{An}^i}{c_K^o c_{An}^o} \tag{11}$$

and

$$\Delta\mu_{ex} = -RT\ln\frac{c_K^i/c_{Na}^i}{c_K^o/c_{Na}^o} = -RT\ln\Gamma$$

By determining the concentration ratios which appear in eqs. (11), Toor et al.[9] have demonstrated that for the normal human erythrocyte under physiological conditions

$$\Delta\mu_{NaAn} = -\Delta\mu_{KAn} = 1.62 \text{ kcal.}$$

where the anion is either Cl^- or HCO_3^-. Insertion of this equality into eqs. (9) shows that

$$R_{Nar} = -R_{Kr} \tag{12}$$

i.e. that the exchange of cations is a fully coupled process. Under the conditions defined above the dissipation function in eq. (6) reduces to

$$\Phi = J_{Na}\Delta\mu_{ex} + J_r A \tag{13}$$

This dissipation function permits a series of interesting predictions from the corresponding phenomenological equations

$$\Delta\mu_{ex} = R_{Na}J_{Na} + R_{Nar}J_r$$
$$A = R_{rNa}J_{Na} + R_r J_r \tag{14}$$

If we assume the Onsager reciprocity relation to hold for this case $R_{Nar} = R_{rNa}$. In the special case of the resting cell considered above, when $J_{Na} = 0$

$$-\left(\frac{\Delta\mu_{ex}}{A}\right)_{J_{Na}=0} = \frac{R_{Nar}}{R_r} \tag{15}$$

But since $\Delta\mu_{ex} = -RT\ln\Gamma$

$$-RT\ln\Gamma = \frac{R_{Nar}}{R_r}A \tag{16}$$

Thus the maintenance of a significantly unequal distribution of cations under conditions of negligible flow requires that the coupling coefficient R_{Nar} is non-vanishing. Further, upon cooling the erythrocytes to 0°C, it is possible to stop active transport and make $\Delta\mu_{ex} = 0$. If the cells are then heated to room temperature, a pumping out of sodium sets in. The flow of Na^+ under these conditions is given by:

$$\left(\frac{J_{Na}}{J_r}\right)_{\Delta\mu_{ex}=0} = \frac{R_{Nar}}{R_{Na}} \tag{17}$$

In other experiments the intracellular concentrations of ATP, ADP or P_i could be regulated so as to make $A = 0$, under which conditions eq. (14) reduces to:

$$(J_r/J_{Na})_{A=0} = -\frac{R_{rNa}}{R_r} \tag{18}$$

This relation predicts a flow of chemical reaction driven exclusively by means of the flow of sodium.

As a consequence of the Onsager relations ($R_{Nar} = R_{rNa}$) moreover, the absolute ratio of the flow of the transport-driven ATPase reaction to the driving flow is predicted to be equal to the ratio of a chemically maintained ion exchange force to the chemical driving force

$$(J_r/J_{Na})_{A=0} = -(\Delta\mu_{ex}/A)_{J_{Na}=0} \tag{19}$$

Equation (19) is a typical cross relation of non-equilibrium thermodynamics, which has the advantage that it is valid regardless of the values of the phenomenological coefficients.

3. MODEL REPRESENTATION OF ACTIVE ION EXCHANGE

Thermodynamics is a useful tool for the correlation of phenomena but cannot provide explicit expressions for the interpretation of the coefficients governing the relations. Thus, the coefficients R_{ik} are taken by thermodynamics for granted; and the interesting coupling coefficients R_{Nar} and R_{Kr} which correlate active ion exchange with chemical reaction have only formal significance. To endow the coefficients with physical contents, recourse to models has to be taken.

The model to be used here is based on the work of numerous investigators[2, 3, 4] who demonstrated that the hydrolytic breakdown of ATP is activated by the transported cation. Moreover POST et al.[2] and DUNHAM and GLYNN[3] showed that both Na^+ and K^+ are required for ATPase activity, and it is only when both are added simultaneously that ATP breakdown reaches its maximal values. WHITTAM[10] has adduced evidence that the process is anisotropic and that the sites of the reaction for Na^+ and K^+ are spatially separated. By introducing ATP and/or potassium directly into ghosts of red blood cells he could show that external sodium and ATP are not needed for the ATPase activity and it is only the intracellular Na^+ and ATP which favor the process. Similar experiments proved that K^+ must be present in the external medium to allow the conclusion of the process.

Recently GLYNN[11] obtained evidence from isotopic exchange rates of sodium transport which may be interpreted as though the Na is bound to a carrier which shuttles back and forth in the membrane. It is believed that the carrier either adsorbs or is phosphorylated by ATP and the form containing phosphorus or ATP has a selective binding affinity for sodium. On the other hand, the free carrier molecules combine preferentially with potassium and facilitate its transport into the cell.

On the basis of these considerations, the following model is constructed. Similar models were proposed by SKOU[12], POST[2], SOLOMON[13] and analysed kinetically by ROSENBERG and WILBRANDT[14].

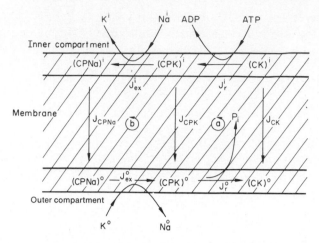

FIG. 1. SCHEMATIC REPRESENTATION OF CARRIER MEDIATED, ACTIVE, EXCHANGE OF Na^+——K^+. J_r^i IS THE RATE OF THE CHEMICAL PROCESS WHICH TRANSFORMS THE FREE CARRIER (CK^i) INTO A PHOSPHORYLATED CARRIER (CPK^i) ($CK^i + ATP \rightarrow CPK^i + ADP$). J_r^o REPRESENTS THE RATE OF DEPHOSPHORYLATION WHICH REGENERATES THE FREE CARRIER ($CPK^o \rightarrow CK^o + P_i$). J_{ex}^i IS THE RATE OF EXCHANGE OF POTASSIUM BY SODIUM ON THE INNER SIDE OF THE MEMBRANE ($CPK^i + Na^i \rightarrow CPNa^i + K^i$). J_{ex}^o REPRESENTS THE RATE OF SODIUM LIBERATION TO THE OUTER SOLUTION THROUGH EXCHANGE WITH EXTERNAL POTASSIUM ($CPNa^o + K^o \rightarrow CPK^o + Na^o$). J_{CK}, J_{CPK} AND J_{CPNa} ARE THE RATES OF FLOW OF THE DIFFERENT CARRIER FORMS ACROSS THE MEMBRANE.

The significance of the symbols used in the scheme is the following:

A potassium loaded carrier moves from the external concentration CK^o to the inner side of the cell membrane, where its concentration is CK^i. CK^i combines with intracellular ATP to give the phosphorylated form CPK^i, which readily exchanges the cation for sodium to give $CPNa^i$. The sodium is transported as CPNa to the outer side where its concentration is $CPNa^o$. Here it exchanges ions with the external potassium to give CPK^o and undergoes a dephosphorylation to CK^o.

The chemical processes involved in the model are those of phosphorylation (J_r^i) and dephosphorylation (J_r^o) and of intracellular and external ion exchange (J_{ex}^i and J_{ex}^o respectively). Since it is assumed that the transport of cations is exclusively carrier mediated, the diffusional transport is represented by the flows of the various forms of carrier: J_{CK}, J_{CPK} and J_{CPNa}.

We may readily assign to each of the chemical and diffusional flows the conjugate forces, represented in Table 1:

TABLE 1

Chemical flows and forces eq. (20)		Diffusional flows and forces eq. (21)	
J_r^i	$A_r^i = \mu_{CK}^i + \mu_{ATP} - \mu_{ADP} - \mu_{CPK}^i$		
		J_{CK}	$\Delta\mu_{CK} = \mu_{CK}^i - \mu_{CK}^o$
J_r^o	$A_r^o = \mu_{CPK}^o - \mu_{Pi} - \mu_{CK}^o$		
		J_{CPK}	$\Delta\mu_{CPK} = \mu_{CPK}^i - \mu_{CPK}^o$
J_{ex}^i	$A_{ex}^i = \mu_{CPK}^i + \tilde{\mu}_{Na}^i - \mu_{CPNa}^i - \tilde{\mu}_K^i$		
		J_{CPNa}	$\Delta\mu_{CPNa} = \mu_{CPNa}^i - \mu_{CPNa}^o$
J_{ex}^o	$A_{ex}^o = \mu_{CPNa}^o + \tilde{\mu}_K^o - \mu_{CPK}^o - \tilde{\mu}_{Na}^o$		

As seen above the net ATPase reaction consumes one mole of water. Since the activity of the water in the membrane is considered to be constant, the chemical potential of water may be incorporated into the standard chemical potential of the inorganic phosphate. Moreover we assume instantaneous equilibrium of inorganic phosphate between the membrane phase, where its chemical potential is μ_{Pi}^m, and the inner solution.

4. THERMODYNAMIC CONSIDERATION OF THE MODEL FOR ACTIVE ION EXCHANGE

We are now able to write the detailed dissipation function for all the processes accounted for in the model. This dissipation function is a *microscopic* function since it treats all the *molecular* ingredients of the active transport.

$$\Phi = J_r^i A_r^i + J_{ex}^i A_{ex}^i + J_{CK}\Delta\mu_{CK} + J_{CPK}\Delta\mu_{CPK} + J_{CPNa}\Delta\mu_{CPNa} + J_{ex}^o A_{ex}^o + J_r^o A_r^o \qquad (22)$$

To proceed further with our analysis it is advantageous to consider a stationary process in which the concentrations of the carrier forms do not change with time. In this case,

$$\frac{dCK^i}{dt} = -J_{CK} - J_r^i = 0 \quad \text{and} \quad \frac{dCK^o}{dt} = J_r^o + J_{CK} = 0$$

so that

$$J_r = J_r^i = J_r^o = -J_{CK} \qquad (23)$$

$$\frac{dCPNa^i}{dt} = J_{ex}^i - J_{CPNa} = 0 \quad \text{and} \quad \frac{dCPNa^o}{dt} = J_{CPNa} - J_{ex}^o = 0$$

so that

$$J_{ex}^i = J_{ex}^o = J_{CPNa} \qquad (24)$$

and

$$\frac{dCPK^i}{dt} = J_r^i - J_{CPK} - J_{ex}^i = 0$$

which gives on the basis of eqs. (23) and (24)

$$J_{CPNa} + J_{CPK} + J_{CK} = 0 \qquad (25)$$

Equation (23) shows that in a steady state the rate of phosphorylation in the cell must equal the rate of dephosphorylation on the outer side of the membrane. Equation (24) proves that the stationary rate of sodium–potassium exchange is equal both outside and inside the cell; while eq. (25) is a trivial expression for the fact that carrier transport takes place only within the membrane and that there is no accumulation of carrier on either side.

It is worth noting that the external flow of sodium J_{Na} is equal to the rate of sodium liberation in the external ion exchange (J_{ex}^o), so that

$$J_{Na} = J_{ex}^o = J_{CPNa} \qquad (26)$$

Inserting (23), (24), (25) and (26) into the dissipation function (22) will lead to the following expression

$$\Phi = J_r^i(A_r^i + A_r^o - \Delta\mu_{CK} + \Delta\mu_{CPK}) + J_{Na}(A_{ex}^i + A_{ex}^o + \Delta\mu_{CPNa} - \Delta\mu_{CPK}) \qquad (27)$$

With the aid of the expressions for the forces, eqs. (20) and (21), we readily obtain

$$A_r^i + A_r^o - \Delta\mu_{CK} + \Delta\mu_{CPK} = \mu_{ATP} - \mu_{ADP} - \mu_{Pi} = A \qquad (28)$$

where A is the affinity of the overall hydrolysis of ATP, independent of the intermittent steps. And similarly:

$$A_{ex}^i + A_{ex}^o + \Delta\mu_{CPNa} - \Delta\mu_{CPK} = (\tilde{\mu}_{Na}^i - \tilde{\mu}_{Na}^o) - (\tilde{\mu}_K^i - \tilde{\mu}_K^o)$$
$$= \Delta\tilde{\mu}_{Na} - \Delta\tilde{\mu}_K = \Delta\mu_{ex} \qquad (29)$$

Equation (18) is thus equivalent to:

$$\Phi = J_{Na}\Delta\mu_{ex} + J_r A \qquad (30)$$

But this is identical with eq. (13) under the conditions found experimentally, i.e. when $\Delta\tilde{\mu}_{An} = 0$, and $J_K = -J_{Na}$.

The identity of eqs. (30) and (13) shows that the *microscopic* dissipation function for any model reduces to the *macroscopic* function, if the model is correctly constructed.

5. LATTICE REPRESENTATION AND EVALUATION OF PHENOMENOLOGICAL COEFFICIENTS

The lattice treatment is well known from statistical mechanics of liquid and solid mixtures[15]. Recently the treatment was applied to a quantitative evaluation of transport through membranes. HECKMANN[16] analysed single file diffusion while HILL and KEDEM[17] discussed a larger number of cases including carrier-mediated passive and active transport. In the classic treatment of membrane transport, thermodynamic equilibrium is assumed at both surfaces of the membrane, while the irreversible processes within the membrane are interpreted in terms of the frictional interactions between the permeating species and the membrane matrix. According to the lattice model, the membrane is described as a thin layer and the transition of permeating species from one side to the other is described as a single event ("jump"). The latter approach is more appropriate to biological membranes which are in fact thin and are subject to important surface interactions with the permeating species. It permits the resolution of the complex processes of transport and chemical reactions into elementary steps, which may be described by simple relations among the known parameters of the system (e.g. adsorption-desorption rates, rates of transition, rates of ATP hydrolysis).

The aim of this section is to apply a lattice model to active ion exchange in the erythrocyte membrane and to calculate the straight and coupling coefficients according to the thermodynamic treatment.

In the present treatment the membrane is represented by two layers of sites which may be occupied by different forms of the carrier molecules. Each pair of corresponding sites in the inner and outer layers defines a "state" of the carrier system. The rate coefficient governing transition of the carrier from one side to another is denoted by ω; ω_p denoting the phosphorylated and ω_C the non-phosphorylated carrier.

The interaction of the carrier molecules with reactants in the adjacent solutions is characterized by the coefficients α. Thus the interaction with ATP, ADP, Na$^+$ and K$^+$ is represented by α_T, α_D, α_{Na}^i or α_{Na}^o and α_K^i or α_K^o, respectively. In an explicit form, the α's are product of the rate constant for the carrier-reactant combination and the concentration of the reactant. The α's of the ionic component comprise in addition an electrical term given by $\exp{(z_i\epsilon\psi/kT)}$ where ψ is the local electric potential, z_i the valence of the ion and ϵ the charge of a proton.

The lattice representation of the model is given in Fig. 2a.

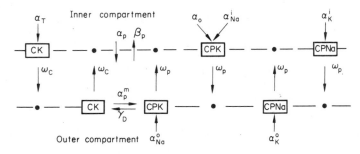

FIG. 2A. LATTICE FORMULATION OF CARRIER-MEDIATED ACTIVE ION EXCHANGE. EACH OF THE SIX CONSIDERED STATES OF THE CARRIER (E.G. CPNa PHOSPHORYLATED CARRIER-SODIUM COMPLEX, ON THE INNER SIDE) IS REPRESENTED AS A PAIR OF LATTICE POINTS ON OPPOSITE SIDES OF THE MEMBRANE. INTERACTIONS OF THE IONS OR CHEMICAL REACTANTS FROM THE SOLUTIONS WITH CARRIER MOLECULES ARE INDICATED BY ARROWS TO APPROPRIATE LATTICE POINTS. DIRECT ADSORPTION AND DESORPTION OF PHOSPHATE FROM THE UNIFORM INTRAMEMBRANE POOL AT CONCENTRATION P_i^m ARE INDICATED BY ARROWS TO THE MEMBRANE BETWEEN THE LATTICE ARRAY. THE COEFFICIENTS α_{Na}, α_K AND α_p ARE PRODUCTS OF THE ABSOLUTE ACTIVITIES IN THE MEDIA AND THE ADSORPTION RATE CONSTANTS OF SODIUM, POTASSIUM AND PHOSPHATE, RESPECTIVELY. α_T AND α_D ARE PRODUCTS OF ABSOLUTE ACTIVITIES AND REACTION RATE CONSTANTS OF ATP AND ADP. β_p AND γ_D ARE CONCENTRATION-INDEPENDENT RATE CONSTANTS FOR DESORPTION OF P_i FROM THE INNER SIDE AND THE CARRIER DEPHOSPHORYLATION REACTION ON THE OUTER SIDE. THE COEFFICIENT α_p^m OF THE PHOSPHORYLATION OF CK^o IS A PRODUCT OF A RATE CONSTANT AND P_i^m. ω_C AND ω_p ARE THE MOBILITIES OF CARRIER AND PHOSPHORYLATED CARRIER MOLECULES IN THE MEMBRANE.

The model takes into account the adsorption of phosphorus to the membrane only from the inner solution (α_p) and its liberation by dephosphorylation of CPK^o characterized by the rate constant γ_D. The steady state of inorganic phosphate concentration in the membrane is maintained by rephosphorylation of the carrier CK^o (represented by α_p^m) and by desorption into the interior of the cell (given by the coefficient β_p). The small leak of inorganic phosphate from the cells into external solution is neglected in this treatment. As shown in Appendix I, the phosphate coefficients are interrelated by $\alpha_p^m\beta_p/\alpha_p = \gamma_p$, where γ_p is the rate constant for the backreaction of dephosphorylation.

For calculational purposes, it is advantageous to redraw Fig. 2A in the form of a cyclic diagram as shown in Fig. 2B. The cyclic diagrams were introduced by

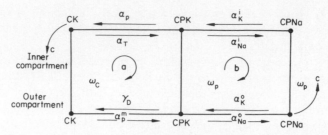

FIG. 2B. CYCLIC ANALYSIS OF PRECEDING LATTICE DIAGRAM IN TERMS OF CHEMICAL CYCLE a, ION EXCHANGE CYCLE b AND COUPLING CYCLE c.

CHRISTIANSEN[18] and BAK[19] into the study of chemical kinetics. HILL[20] developed a powerful method for the explicit evaluation of the relations between flows and forces using the cyclic diagrams as an essential tool in the calculation. It will be observed that our model comprises three cycles—the chemical cycle—a—in which the phosphorylation and dephosphorylation steps take place; a transport cycle—b—in which the ion exchange takes place; and an overall cycle—c—which provides the coupling between cycles a and b. In the general theory it is possible to assign flows to the cycles; then the two calculated flows, J_{Na} and J_r, are given by the expressions

$$J_{Na} = J_b + J_c \quad \text{and} \quad J_r = J_a + J_c \tag{31}$$

We shall here forego the rather sophisticated general treatment (cf. Appendix II) and follow a simpler approach which arises directly from eqs. (23) and (24) of the previous section.

While the thermodynamic treatment used, say, the expression $dCK^i/dt = -J_{CK} - J_r^i$ (eq. 23) without specifying what is comprised in J_{CK} or J_r^i, the lattice representation allows one to write explicitly

$$J_{CK} = \omega_C(CK^i - CK^o) \tag{32}$$

and

$$J_r^i = \alpha_T CK^i - \alpha_D CPK^i \tag{33}$$

so that

$$\frac{dCK^i}{dt} = -\alpha_T CK^i + \alpha_D CPK^i + \omega_C(CK^o - CK^i) \tag{34}$$

and another five similar equations for the other forms of the carriers. For the rates of phosphorylated carrier movement we may write

$$J_{CPK} = \omega_p(CPK^i - CPK^o)$$

and

$$J_{CPNa} = \omega_p(CPNa^i - CPNa^o) \tag{35}$$

Since there exist a constant number of carriers in the membrane the conservation of its total amount C is given by:

$$(CK + CPK + CPNa)^i + (CK + CPK + CPNa)^o = C \tag{36}$$

For the case of stationary flows each of the eqs. (34) equals zero, which is entirely equivalent to the assumption made in eqs. (23) and (24).

Despite the simplification introduced by stationarity, the simultaneous solution of eqs. (34) leads to bulky expressions which are difficult to grasp physically. It suffices to mention that the denominator of Hill's formulae (cf. Appendix II) for the present case is a 6×6 determinant containing all the concentrations and rate constants. To obtain more lucid expressions, we will assume a mechanism, in which the transition rates of carriers through the membrane are rate limiting, so that the concentrations of carrier forms and reactants can be evaluated from the equilibrium conditions for chemical reaction and ion exchange.

The assumption of equilibrium concentrations does not imply the vanishing of the chemical flows. By eqs. (23) and (24) the effective chemical reaction rates are limited to the rates of transport across the membrane. Since the intrinsic chemical rate constants are assumed to be large, however, slight deviations from equilibrium concentration will suffice to give the observed flows. Hence the overall concentrations may be evaluated from equilibrium conditions.†

The equilibrium conditions for phosphorylation and dephosphorylation are:

$$\alpha_T CK^i - \alpha_D CPK^i \simeq 0 \tag{37}$$

$$\alpha_p^m CK^o - \gamma_D CPK^o \simeq 0 \tag{38}$$

and the corresponding expressions for ion exchange equilibria are:

$$\alpha_{Na}^i CPK^i - \alpha_K^i CPNa^i \simeq 0 \tag{39}$$

$$\alpha_{Na}^o CPK^o - \alpha_K^o CPNa^o \simeq 0 \tag{40}$$

A further useful equation may be obtained by inserting eqs. (32) and (35) into (25):

$$\omega_C(CK^i - CK^o) + \omega_p(CPK^i - CPK^o) + \omega_p(CPNa^i - CPNa^o) = 0 \tag{41}$$

The set of eqs. (36)–(41) suffices to evaluate the concentrations of carrier forms and the relation between flows and forces for active ion exchange. Before writing down the explicit equations it is useful to open up the α's and to express them in terms of concentrations and conventional rate constants. This is best carried out by considering ratios (r) of the α's.

The ionic ratios for the outer and inner sides are defined as

$$r_i = \frac{\alpha_K^i}{\alpha_{Na}^i} = K_e \frac{c_K^i}{c_{Na}^i} \quad \text{and} \quad r_o = \frac{\alpha_K^o}{\alpha_{Na}^o} = K_e \frac{c_K^o}{c_{Na}^o} \tag{42}$$

†Analogous assumptions have generally been applied in enzyme kinetics, as well as Rosenberg and Wilbrandt's general calculations of carrier kinetics[14].

where K_e is the equilibrium constant for ion exchange, assumed to be equal on both sides of the membrane; the c's are the concentrations of the ions in the bulk phases.

To get a clearer grasp of eq. (34) let us consider the ratio of r_i to r_0. By the definition of the selectivity coefficient Γ

$$\Gamma = \frac{c_K^i/c_{Na}^i}{c_K^o/c_{Na}^o} = \frac{r_i}{r_o} \tag{43}$$

As pointed out above Γ is related to the driving force of ion exchange $\Delta\mu_{ex}$ by eq. (11)

$$\Delta\mu_{ex} = -RT\ln\Gamma \quad \text{or} \quad \Gamma = \exp\left(-\Delta\mu_{ex}/RT\right) \tag{44}$$

Now $\Delta\mu_{ex}$ may be regarded as the affinity of the overall exchange reaction. Close to equilibrium all affinities go to zero so that in our case we may linearize the exponential term in eq. (44) $\Gamma \simeq 1 - \Delta\mu_{ex}/RT$ and hence

$$\frac{\Delta\mu_{ex}}{RT} \simeq (1-\Gamma) = 1 - r_i/r_o \tag{45}$$

In a similar manner we may define the ratios of phosphorylation and dephosphorylation:

$$r_T = \frac{\alpha_T}{\alpha_D} = K_T\frac{c_{ATP}}{c_{ADP}} \tag{46}$$

where K_T is the equilibrium constant for the formation of the ATP-carrier complex or for the formation of a phosphorylated intermediate. And

$$r_p = \frac{\alpha_p^m}{\gamma_D} = \frac{\gamma_p}{\gamma_D}\frac{\alpha_p}{\beta_p} = \frac{K_N}{K_D'}c_p = \frac{c_p}{K_D} \tag{47}$$

where K_D' is the equilibrium constant for the dephosphorylation reaction in the lipid medium, K_N is the Nernst distribution coefficient for the inorganic phosphate between aqueous and membrane medium, while c_p is the concentration of inorganic phosphate inside the cell. K_D is the equilibrium constant for dephosphorylation of the carrier, if this process were to occur in the aqueous medium. It is related to the equilibrium constant for dephosphorylation in the membrane by $K_D = K_D'/K_N$. Here again the ratio of r_T to r_p has a clear macroscopic meaning:

$$\frac{r_T}{r_p} = \frac{c_{ATP}K}{c_{ADP}c_p} = \exp\left(A/RT\right) \tag{48}$$

where $K_D K_T = K$ is the equilibrium constant for the overall ATP hydrolysis, for which the macroscopic affinity A (cf. eq. 28) is given by $A = RT\ln(c_{ATP}K/c_{ADP}c_p)$. Very close to equilibrium we may linearize the exponential term in (48): $r_T/r_p \simeq 1 + A/RT$, so that

$$A \simeq RT\left(\frac{r_T}{r_p} - 1\right). \tag{49}$$

We may obtain the expressions for J_{Na} and J_r from $J_r = \omega_C(CK^o - CK^i)$ and $J_{Na} = \omega_p(CPNa^i - CPNa^o)$, where CK^i, CK^o, $CPNa^i$ and $CPNa^o$ were evaluated from the solution of the set of eqs. (36)–(41)

$$J_r = \frac{\omega_p r_p r_o}{D} C\left\{(r_i + 1)\left(\frac{r_T}{r_p} - 1\right) + \left(1 - \frac{r_i}{r_o}\right)\right\} \tag{50}$$

$$J_{Na} = -J_K = J_{ex} = \frac{\omega_p r_p r_o}{D} C\left\{\left(\frac{r_T}{r_p} - 1\right) + \left(1 + \frac{\omega_p}{\omega_c} r_T\right)\left(1 - \frac{r_i}{r_o}\right)\right\} \tag{51}$$

where the determinant D is given by

$$D = (r_i + r_T r_i + r_T)\left(r_o + \frac{\omega_p}{\omega_C} r_p r_o + \frac{\omega_p}{\omega_C} r_p\right)$$

$$+ (r_o + r_p r_o + r_o)\left(r_i + \frac{\omega_p}{\omega_C} r_T r_i + \frac{\omega_p}{\omega_C} r_T\right) \tag{52}$$

Inserting the affinities from eqs. (45) and (49) into (50) and (51) we obtain the thermodynamic form

$$J_r = \frac{\omega_p r_p r_o C (r_i + 1)}{RTD} A + \frac{\omega_p r_p r_o C}{RTD} \Delta\mu_{ex} = L_{11} A + L_{12} \Delta\mu_{ex}$$

$$\tag{53}$$

$$J_{ex} = \frac{\omega_p r_p r_o C}{RTD} A + \frac{\omega_p r_p r_o C}{RTD}\left(1 + \frac{\omega_p}{\omega_C} r_T\right)\Delta\mu_{ex} = L_{21} A + L_{22} \Delta\mu_{ex}$$

It is immediately seen that the matrix of the coefficients is symmetrical or that the Onsager theorem is obeyed and $L_{12} = L_{21}$. Moreover, we obtain the required expressions for the phenomenological coefficients

$$L_{11} = \frac{\omega_p r_p r_o}{RTD}(1 + r_i) C$$

$$L_{12} = L_{21} = \frac{\omega_p r_p r_o}{RTD} C \quad \text{and} \quad L_{22} = \frac{\omega_p r_p r_o}{RTD}\left(1 + \frac{\omega_p}{\omega_C} r_T\right) C \tag{54}$$

and

$$L_{11} : L_{12} : L_{22} = (1 + r_i) : 1 : \left(1 + \frac{\omega_p}{\omega_C} r_T\right) \tag{55}$$

As expected, the coefficients are not constants but functions of the concentrations, represented by the r's. Further the L_{ij}'s, which are generalized conductances, depend linearly on the mobility of the active carrier in the membrane (ω_p) and on the total carrier concentration C.

The preceding derivations illustrate how the imposition of the five stationarity conditions (eqs. 23 and 24) reduce the general 7×7 matrix of phenomenological coefficients, corresponding to the microscopic dissipation function in eq. (22), to a 2×2 matrix, in which the coupling relationships among the remaining flows and forces are immediately apparent.

By the second law of thermodynamics the dissipation function Φ is positive definite. This leads to the condition that $L_{11}L_{22} - L_{12}^2 > 0$. In our case

$$L_{11}L_{22} - L_{12}^2 = \left(\frac{\omega_p r_p r_o}{RTD} C\right)^2 \left(r_i + r_T \frac{\omega_p}{\omega_C} + r_i r_T \frac{\omega_p}{\omega_C}\right) > 0$$

as required.

6. COMPARISON WITH EXPERIMENTAL BEHAVIOUR

6.1. The model used in this paper is based on numerous experimental premises, as mentioned in section 4. It is therefore expected that upon closer inspection eqs. (50) and (51) will reproduce the underlying assumptions. Moreover, if the model is useful it should predict additional findings and should correlate experimental results in different fields. We shall indicate how the expressions derived in this paper may be used — leaving a more detailed analysis of available data to another publication.

Equations (50) and (51) are appreciably simplified if we assume that the mobilities of the phosphorylated and free carrier are equal or $\omega_p = \omega_C = \omega$. In this case the determinant in eq. (52) becomes:

$$D = 2(r_o + r_o r_p + r_p)(r_i + r_i r_T + r_T) = 2r_p r_T \left[1 + r_o\left(1 + \frac{1}{r_p}\right)\right]\left[1 + r_i\left(1 + \frac{1}{r_T}\right)\right]$$

It is useful to denote the terms $(1 + 1/r_p)$ and $(1 + 1/r_T)$, which do not depend on ion concentration, by new symbols ρ_p and ρ_T, respectively.

Thus

$$D = 2r_p r_T (1 + r_o \rho_p)(1 + r_i \rho_T) \tag{56}$$

Inserting ρ_p, ρ_T and D into (50) and (51), we obtain the following simple expressions for the rate of chemical reaction and the outward flow of sodium ions:

$$J_r = \frac{\omega C}{2}\left[\frac{1 + r_i}{1 - r_i \rho_T} - \frac{1 + r_o}{1 + r_o \rho_p}\right] \tag{57}$$

$$J_{Na} = \frac{\omega C}{2}\left[\frac{1}{1 + r_i \rho_T} - \frac{1}{1 + r_o \rho_p}\right] \tag{58}$$

The new expressions closely resemble those obtained kinetically by ROSENBERG and WILBRANDT[14] for active transport of non-electrolytes. The similarity lies in the isolation of the coefficient ωC from the concentration-dependent part in the square brackets; and in the clean separation of the "inner term" (containing r_i and ρ_T) from the "outer term" (containing r_o and ρ_p).

The partial differentials of J_r and J_{Na} to c_{Na}^i and c_K^o in eqs. (57) and (58) at constant concentrations of all other species have a positive value. This agrees with the observation that J_r and J_{Na} increase with increasing inner sodium and outer potassium. Moreover, we obtain the following expression for the partial differential of J_r to c_{Na}^o:

$$(\partial J_r / \partial c_{Na}^o)_{\substack{c\text{'s of all} \\ \text{other species}}} = -\frac{\omega C r_o}{2 r_p c_{Na}^o (1 + \rho_p r_o)^2} \tag{59}$$

This is in agreement with WHITTAM's observation[21] that J_r decreases with outer sodium and that the decrease becomes negligible at high external potassium: $\lim_{r_o \to \infty} (\partial J_r / \partial c_{Na}^o) = 0$.

6.2. As pointed out in the thermodynamic analysis, a case of special interest is the steady state with $J_{Na} = 0$. In this case we see from eq. (58) that

$$\left(\frac{r_i}{r_o} \right)_{st} = \Gamma^{st} = \frac{\rho_p}{\rho_T} \tag{60}$$

Since the stationary value of Γ is about 220, ρ_p is by two orders of magnitude larger than ρ_T, or $r_p \ll r_T$. The stationary rate of ATP breakdown is readily obtained by inserting (60) into (57):

$$(J_r)_{J_{Na}=0} = \frac{\omega C}{2} \frac{r_o(\Gamma^{st} - 1)}{1 + r_o \rho_p} \tag{61}$$

The measurements on the rate of chemical reaction at $J_{Na} = 0$ provide therefore an additional relation for the evaluation of the parameters of the model.

6.3. Numerous experiments were carried out on the dependence of ion exchange flow on the ionic concentration. The technique of the measurement has been adequately covered by several articles and by a recent monograph[10] and need not be considered herc. We shall show only that eqs. (57) and (58) predict closely the general trend of the experimental findings.

Let us write the explicit values of r_i and r_o and insert them into (50):

$$J_{Na} = \frac{\omega C}{2} \left[\frac{c_{Na}^i}{c_{Na}^i + K_e \rho_T c_K^i} - \frac{c_{Na}^o}{c_{Na}^o + K_e \rho_p c_K^o} \right] \tag{62}$$

Now let us denote the ionic concentrations at the stationary state ($J_{Na} = 0$) by $\bar{c}$. If we now keep all concentrations constant and change only the concentration of inner sodium to $c_{Na}^i - \bar{c}_{Na}^i + \Delta c_{Na}^i$, the flow of sodium will become

$$J_{Na} = \frac{\omega C K_e \rho_p \bar{c}_K^o}{2(\bar{c}_{Na}^o + K_e \rho_p \bar{c}_K^o)} \frac{\Delta c_{Na}^i}{(\bar{c}_{Na}^i + K_e \rho_T \bar{c}_K^i) + \Delta c_{Na}^i} = \frac{\alpha \Delta c_{Na}^i}{\beta + \Delta c_{Na}^i} \tag{63}$$

where

$$\alpha = \frac{\omega C K_e \rho_p \bar{c}_K^o}{2(\bar{c}_{Na}^o + K_e \rho_p \bar{c}_K^o)} \quad \text{and} \quad \beta = (\bar{c}_{Na}^i + K_e \rho_T \bar{c}_K^i)$$

Equation (63) shows that for small deviations from the stationary state, J_{Na} increases linearly with Δc_{Na}^i or $(J_{Na})_{\Delta c_{Na}^i \ll \beta} = \frac{\alpha}{\beta} \Delta c_{Na}^i$, and that it reaches a stationary value for large deviations $(J_{Na})_{\Delta c_{Na}^i \gg \beta = \alpha}$.

A similar behavior is expected for the dependence of J_{Na} on the external concentration of potassium:

$$J_{Na} = \frac{\omega C \bar{c}_{Na}^i}{2(\bar{c}_{Na}^i + K_e \rho_T \bar{c}_K^i)} \frac{\Delta c_K^o}{(\bar{c}_K^o + \bar{c}_{Na}^o / K_e \rho_p) + \Delta c_K^o} = \frac{\alpha' \Delta c_K^o}{\beta' + \Delta c_K^o} \tag{64}$$

There are indications that both eqs. (63) and (64) describe adequately the data reported in the literature (cf. ref. 10).

6.4. Finally we would like to consider the earlier experiments on the ATPase activity of fragmented erythrocyte membranes. In this case there is evidently no overall macroscopic flow of cations, although directed flow is expected through every membrane fragment. From the point of view of our model the particular feature of these experiments is that $\Delta\mu = 0$ or $r_i = r_o = r$ for all ionic compositions, so that

$$J_r = \frac{\omega C r (1+r)(\rho_p - \rho_T)}{2(1+r\rho_T)(1+r\rho_p)} \tag{65}$$

The rate of chemical reaction was studied by POST[2] for different compositions of sodium and potassium, keeping the total ion concentration at a constant level. Denoting the ion fraction of potassium by $x_K = c_K/(c_K + c_{Na})$ and of sodium $x_{Na} = 1 - x_K$, eq. (65) may be rewritten as

$$J_r = \frac{\omega C K_e (\rho_p - \rho_T)}{2} \cdot \frac{x_K [1 - x_K (1 - K_e)]}{[1 - x_K (1 - K_e \rho_T)][1 - x_K (1 - K_e \rho_p)]} \tag{66}$$

Equation (66) predicts that J_r increases from zero to a flat maximum region when the potassium concentration rises from zero to an intermediate value. When x_K approaches unity (i.e. the sodium concentration goes to zero), the rate of chemical reaction decreases and reaches a lowest value (practically zero for $K_e \ll 1$) at $x_K = 1$. In Fig. 3 the ATPase activity is plotted against the fraction of potassium ions for chosen values of K_e, ρ_p and ρ_T. WHITTAM and BLOND[22] obtained a similar curve for the sensitivity of ATPase activity to the combined presence of sodium and potassium ions in brain and in kidney. Our calculated curves show a similar asymmetry towards the potassium ion— J_r increases faster with x_K than with x_{Na}. From the experimental data it may then be possible to calculate ω, C, K_e, ρ_p and ρ_T.

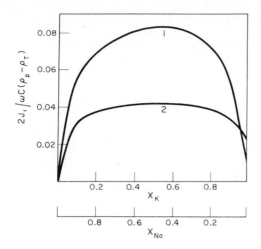

FIG. 3. THE ATPase ACTIVITY IN HOMOGENATED ERYTHROCYTE MEMBRANES PLOTTED AGAINST THE FRACTION OF POTASSIUM AND SODIUM IONS, CALCULATED FROM EQ.(66). $X_K = c_K/(c_K + c_{Na})$, $X_{Na} = c_{Na}/(c_{Na} + c_K)$. IN CURVES $1: K_e = 0.01$, $\rho_T = 10$ AND $\rho_p = 1000$; IN CURVE $2: K_e = 0.05$, $\rho_T = 2$ AND $\rho_p = 440$.

7. CONCLUDING REMARKS

We pointed out in the introduction that the erythrocyte membrane has a tough visco-elastic structure. It is difficult to envisage transport based on free diffusion which would act as an efficient carrier through such a membrane. The alternative approach would be that the carrier function is performed by macromolecules which undergo conformational changes. As is well known protein fibers are capable of contracting and expanding appreciably through chemical interaction. The mechanical forces developed in this contractile process are sufficient to overcome the resistance of the membrane and to carry the adsorbed ions through the surface network. Our working hypothesis is therefore that the free carrier molecules are contracted polymeric chains, selectively combining with potassium ions. Upon interaction with ATP they uncoil, through electrostatic repulsion, and expand towards the outer surface of the membrane. More-over, since phosphorylated macromolecules in an organic lipoid medium may have a preferential binding capacity for sodium ions, the expanding macromolecules will carry effectively sodium from the cell to the outer medium.

It is possible to estimate the number of contraction-relaxation cycles performed by the carrier molecules per second. The results of the work in different laboratories indicate that the total number of active sites involved in cation transport is 10^3–10^4 per erythrocyte. The flow of sodium at room temperature is of the order of magnitude 10^{-13} moles/cm²sec. Multiplying this number with the area of the membrane (1.5×10^{-6} cm²) and with Avogadro's number we obtain 10^5 ions/sec. These ions have to be carried upon the active sites, which therefore must perform $10^5/10^4$ to $10^5/10^3$, or 10 to a 100 cycles per second.

Recent studies on mechanochemical systems carried out in this laboratory [23] indicate that this rate of periodic performance can be readily obtained even on macroscopic systems. There exists, therefore, the possibility that micro mechano-chemical contractility underlies the operation of the ionic pumps in erythrocyte membranes.

APPENDIX I

The conditions of stationarity for inorganic phosphate on the inner (P_i^i) and outer (P_i^o) side of the membrane are

$$\frac{dP_i^i}{dt} = 0 = \alpha_p - \beta_p P_i^i + \omega_i(P_i^o - P_i^i) \tag{1'}$$

$$\frac{dP_i^o}{dt} = 0 = -\alpha_p^m CK^o + \gamma_D CPK^o + \omega_i(P_i^o - P_i^i) \tag{2'}$$

where ω_i denotes the mobility of the inorganic phosphate in the membrane.

From eq. (1')

$$P_i^i = \frac{\omega_i P_i^o + \alpha_p}{\omega_i + \beta_p} \tag{3'}$$

By inserting this expression into (2') we obtain

$$-\alpha_p^m CK^o + \gamma_D CPK^o + \frac{\omega_i}{\omega_i + \beta_p}(\alpha_p - \beta_p P_i^o) = 0 \tag{4'}$$

But close to equilibrium

$$-\alpha_p^m CK^o + \gamma_D CPK^o \simeq 0 \tag{5'}$$

Combining (4') and (5') yields

$$P_i^o = \frac{\alpha_p}{\beta_p} \tag{6'}$$

which upon insertion into (3') gives

$$P_i^i = \frac{\alpha_p}{\beta_p} = P_i^o \tag{7'}$$

The phosphate concentration is therefore the same throughout the membrane. It might be noted that by definition $\alpha_p^m = \gamma_D P_i$, or with eq. (7')

$$\alpha_p^m = \gamma_D \frac{\alpha_p}{\beta_p} \tag{8'}$$

APPENDIX II

The basic calculation problem is the evaluation of the partial flows (cf. Fig. 2B) by a topological method developed for flow graphs in electrical networks[24] and for composite chemical processes[18, 19]. The dominant term in the solution for each cycle is the difference of the products of α's in opposite directions. By a proper combination of the α's thermodynamic forces can be obtained to give in our case (cf. eq. (31))

$$J_r = J_a + J_c = c\left\{\left(1+\frac{a}{c}\right)\left(\frac{r_T}{r_p}-1\right)+\left(1-\frac{r_i}{r_o}\right)\right\} \tag{1''}$$

$$J_{Na} = J_b + J_c = c\left\{\left(\frac{r_T}{r_p}-1\right)+\left(1+\frac{b}{c}\right)\left(1-\frac{r_i}{r_o}\right)\right\} \tag{2''}$$

The coefficient

$$c = \omega_p r_p r_o / \Sigma \tag{3''}$$

where Σ is a more elaborate term than the determinant D (eq. (52)). It is obtained topologically by considering all partial diagrams leading to the cycles involved in the process. Close to equilibrium Σ reduces to the determinant D.

It is clear that (1'') and (2'') obey Onsager's symmetry theorem, though the forces are more general than the quasi-equilibrium thermodynamic affinities.

The explicit value of the terms a/c and b/c of eqs. (1'') and (2'') is

$$\frac{a}{c} = r_i + \omega_p\left(\frac{r_i}{\alpha_K^o}+\frac{1}{\alpha_{Na}^i}\right) \tag{4''}$$

$$\frac{b}{c} = \frac{\omega_p}{\omega_c}r_T + \omega_p\left(\frac{r_T}{\alpha_p^m}+\frac{1}{\alpha_D}\right) \tag{5''}$$

For a rapid chemical process in which active transport depends primarily on the transition through the membrane $\omega_p \ll \alpha_K^o$ or α_p^m or α_{Na}^i or α_D. In this case the general equations (1'') and (2'') reduce to eqs. (50) and (51) of the text.

ACKNOWLEDGMENT

This investigation was supported in part by the Public Health Service research grant No. GM–09432–04.

REFERENCES

[1] Rand, R. P. and Burton, A. C. *Biophys. J.* **4**, 175, 1964; Katchalsky, A., Kedem, O., Klibansky, C. and DeVries, A. In *Flow Properties of Blood and Other Biological Systems*, Copley, A. L. and Stainsby, G. (Editors), Pergamon Press, London, New York, 1960, p. 155.
[2] Post, R. L., Meritt, C. R., Kinsolving, C. R. and Albright, C. D. *J. Biol. Chem.* **235**, 1796, 1960.
[3] Dunham, E. T. and Glynn, I. M. *Physiol.* **156**, 274, 1961; Glynn, I. M. *Progr. in Biophys. & Biophys. Chem.* **8**, 292, 1957.
[4] Skou, J. C. *Biochem. Biophys. Acta* **23**, 394, 1957; **42**, 6, 1960.
[5] Katchalsky, A. and Curran, P. *Non Equilibrium Thermodynamics in Biophysics*, Harvard Univ. Press, Cambridge, Mass., 1965, p. 209.
[6] Onsager, L. *Phys. Rev.* **37**, 405, 1931; **38**, 2265, 1931.
[7] Curie, P. *Oeuvres*, Gauthier-Villars, Paris, 1908, p. 129; cf. also ref. 20, chap. VI, p. 57.

[8] KEDEM, O. In *Membrane Transport and Metabolism*, (Editors), KLEINZELLER, A. and KOTYK, A. Academic Press, N.Y. 1961, p. 81.
[9] TOOR, M. *et al.* Private communication.
[10] WHITTAM, R. *Transport and Diffusion in Red Blood Cells*, Arnold, London, 1964.
[11] GARRAHAN, P. J. and GLYNN, I. M. *Nature* **211**, 1414, 1966.
[12] SKOU, J. C. *Physiol. Rev.* **45**, 596, 1965.
[13] SOLOMON, A. K. *Biophys. J.* **2**, 79, 1962.
[14] ROSENBERG, T. and WILBRANDT, W. *J. Theoret. Biol.* **5**, 288, 1963.
[15] HILL, T. L. *Statistical Mechanics,* McGraw-Hill, New York, 1956.
[16] HECKMAN, K. *Z. phys . Chem.* N.F. **46**, 1, 1965.
[17] HILL, T. L. and KEDEM, O. *J. Theoret. Biol.* **10**, 339, 1966.
[18] CHRISTIANSEN, J. A. *Advances in Catalysis* **5**, 311, 1953.
[19] BAK, T. A. *Contributions to the Theory of Chemical Kinetics*, Benjamin, N.Y. 1963, p. 37.
[20] HILL, T. L. *J. Theoret. Biol.* **10**, 442, 1966.
[21] WHITTAM, R. and AGER, M. E. *Biochem. J.* **93**, 337, 1964.
[22] WHITTAM, R. and BLOND, D. M. *Biochem. J.* **92**, 150, 1964.
[23] KATCHALSKY, A., OPLATKA, A, and LITAN, A. *The Dynamics of Macromolecular Systems in Molecular Architecture in Cell Physiology*, HAYASHI, T. and SZENT-GYORGY, A. G. (Editors), Prentice Hall, N.J., 1966, p. 3; STEINBERG, I. Z., OPLATKA, A. and KATCHALSKY, A. *Nature* **210**, 5036. Cf. also GOLDACRE, R. J. *Intern. Rev. Cytol.* **1**, 135, 1952.
[24] MASON, S. J. *Proc. IRE* **41**, 1144, 1953; **44**, 920, 1956.

NOTE TO DISCUSSION

In Professor Katchalsky's absence Professor A. Silberberg read a text by A. Katchalsky which differed from the text of the final contribution. Since the discussion remarks have only bearing on the text read by Professor Silberberg, they had, therefore, to be deleted. (Editor.)

HEMORHEOLOGICAL THEORY II

11 July, p.m.

Chairmen: SYOTEN OKA, Japan
RAYMOND L. WHITMORE, England

WAVE ATTENUATION IN VISCO-ELASTIC ARTERIES

Donald A. McDonald* † and Urs Gessner

Department of Physiology and Biophysics, University of Alabama Medical Center, Birmingham,
and Dept. of Biomedical Engineering, Johns Hopkins University, Baltimore, U.S.A.

A satisfactory description of the properties of the arterial wall in rheological terms would be a most helpful contribution to the experimental study and interpretation of the dynamics of the arterial system. Womersley (1957) explored in great detail the hydrodynamics of the system in terms of elastic tubes filled with viscous liquid. This showed that the essential factors determining the characteristics of wave-propagation, the phase velocity and the attenuation were dependent both on the bore of the tube and the wave frequency in addition to the elastic modulus of the wall and the fluid viscosity. The fact that the viscosity of blood is non-Newtonian is well-known but it has been convincingly demonstrated by Taylor (1959a) that at the rates of shear found in the larger arteries the deviation from Newtonian behavior is extremely small. Both wave velocity and attenuation were quantitated by Womersley in an extensive tabulation of the numerical values of the appropriate mathematical functions in terms of a non-dimensional parameter $-\alpha$.

$$\alpha = R(\omega/v)^{1/2} \tag{1}$$

Various modifications of the model were investigated to make it physiologically realistic and the most successful one imposed a severe longitudinal constraint on the wall while allowing it to move freely in a radial direction. This is usually known as the "tethered" tube model and is mathematically very tractable in terms of oscillatory pressure–flow relations. Where reference is made below to Womersley values for phase velocity and attenuation in tubes with perfectly elastic walls it is to his values for this model. It is further assumed that the Poisson's ratio (σ) of the wall is 0.5 — it is almost certainly very close to this value — and that the wall is isotropic. This latter is a somewhat coarse approximation but its effect is minimized by the assumption of longitudinal constraint.

It was quite clear, however — even when Womersley was doing his analysis — that the arterial wall is far from being a perfect elastic body. Its elastic strain is not only determined by the stress but also by the rate of stress. Thus the wave-propagation velocity will be frequency-dependent from this cause alone and the wall-properties will introduce an attenuation additional to that due to the viscous drag of the liquid. This type of wall-property had been analysed by King (1947) by treating it as an elastomer but without taking into account the fluid viscosity. Womersley did a general analysis, in the months before his premature death, by treating the wall essentially in

---

†The experimental work by D. A. McDonald was performed while he was at Research Institute, University of Pennsylvania, Presbyterian Hospital Medical Center, Philadelphia.

terms of a simple visco-elastic model. Though possibly less sophisticated than the elastomer approach it had the great advantage that it could be coherently linked with the hydrodynamic behavior of the fluid. Although, as we shall see, it is not possible to give a satisfyingly realistic meaning to the mathematical parameters introduced by considering a model with a single spring and viscous dashpot in parallel, neverthe-less they provide a useful way of describing the quantitative effect on wave propaga-tion due to the rheological properties of the wall. In general the result is to increase the wave-velocity above that predicted from the measurement of the elastic modulus of the wall, under static conditions, and to increase the attenuation above that due to the viscous drag of the fluid. This latter result is somewhat ironic, for Womersley, in an early section of his 1957 monograph, expressed concern that the attenuation he had computed was too high to allow for the pressure-wave-propagation that was observed. Thus in the femoral artery of the dog the wave at the pulse-frequency would be atten-uated by 5–6% for each 10 cm of travel due to the blood viscosity alone. The experi-mental work reported here is mainly concerned with estimating the damping of a wave propagated along arteries, with only secondary attention being paid to the effects on wave-velocity. This is in part due to the fact that the expected effects on wave-velocity due to visco-elastic properties have been shown by TAYLOR (1959b) to be relatively small, and also because it is a topic that has received much more attention than that of attenuation.

EXPERIMENTAL APPROACHES

The obvious method of measuring attenuation in a simply propagated wave is to measure the pressure of a simple harmonic wave at two points a known distance apart. If the propagation constant is γ and the pressure at first point is P_0 then the pressure $P_{(x)}$ at a distance x cm is given by

$$P_{(x)} = P_0 e^{-\gamma x} \tag{2}$$

The propagation constant γ is complex so we write

$$\gamma = a + ib \tag{3}$$

then

$$a = \frac{1}{x} \ln \left| \frac{P_0}{P_{(x)}} \right| \tag{4}$$

and

$$b = \frac{1}{x}(\phi_0 - \phi_x) \tag{5}$$

where ϕ_0 and ϕ_x are the phase angles at points (0) and (x).

The phase velocity c_1 is given by

$$c_1 = \omega/b \tag{6}$$

In the arterial system when attempts were made to apply this procedure by subjecting the pressure wave to harmonic analysis it was found that the size of each frequency component shows a net increase over the length of the tree. This was shown to be mainly due to wave-reflection from the arteriolar terminations (MCDONALD and TAYLOR, 1959; MCDONALD, 1960). TAYLOR (1965) subsequently showed that the progressive increase in elastic modulus in arteries as they get further from the heart will also cause an amplification of the traveling wave. Indirect measurements by using phase velocity measurements are also very difficult because the presence of reflected waves only allows an apparent phase velocity to be measured the value of which is largely determined by reflection conditions.

To avoid this problem the first work on the visco-elastic properties of arterial wall was done on isolated segments. Hardung in 1952 initiated a series of papers on strips cut from arteries and introduced the nomenclature in eqs. (7)–(9) given below. LAWTON (1955) also used strips but analysed the results in terms of King's elastomer approach. BERGEL (1961) used whole segments of artery which were held at their *in vivo* length. A sinusoidal pressure from a pump was then imposed internally and the radial strain measured photo-electrically. The dynamic elastic modulus E' was then analysed, as Hardung had done, into real and imaginary parts thus

$$E' = E_{dyn} + i\eta\omega \tag{7}$$

where

$$E_{dyn} = E' \cos \phi \tag{8}$$

and

$$\eta\omega = E' \sin \phi \tag{9}$$

where ϕ was the phase angle between the pressure change (ΔP) and the radius change (ΔR_{outer}); ω is the angular frequency and η a term representing the viscous element.

Using Womersley's formulation (eqs. (17)–(25) p. 121) he then calculated the phase velocity and transmission, over a standard distance of 10 cm, expected in an artery filled with blood. His mean results for the thoracic and abdominal aorta and the carotid and femoral arteries of the dog are shown in Fig. 1. In subsequent figures our results are compared with his as they are the only previously published values for the variation of phase velocity and wave transmission of which we are aware.

The method we have used in entire arteries was first proposed by TAYLOR (1959c) and developed by one of us (U.G.) from a simpler analysis by Gessner and Bergel in 1966. In the presence of reflected waves pressures have to be measured simultaneously at three equidistant points along an artery, i.e. the interval P_1 to P_2 and P_2 to P_3 is x. No major branch should originate between P_1 and P_3. The propagation constant (eqs. (2) and (3)) is γ for any frequency component. This constant is assumed to be the same in both directions. Let there be a centrifugal, or forward traveling, wave P_f and a reflected wave P_r such that

$$P_2 = P_f + P_r \tag{10}$$

Then we can write

$$P_1 = P_f e^{+\gamma x} + P_r e^{-\gamma x} \tag{11}$$

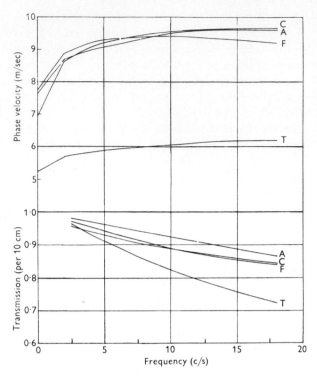

FIG. 1. THE PHASE VELOCITY AND TRANSMISSION OVER 10 CM IN FOUR DIFFERENT ARTERIES CALCULATED FROM THEIR DYNAMIC ELASTIC BEHAVIOR (FROM BERGEL, D. H., *J. Physiol.* **156**, 458, 1960).

and

$$P_3 = P_f e^{-\gamma x} + P_r e^{+\gamma x} \tag{12}$$

Thus it is easy to see

$$\frac{P_1 + P_3}{2P_2} = \cosh \gamma x \tag{13}$$

or

$$\gamma = \frac{1}{x} \cosh^{-1}\left\{\frac{(P_1 + P_3)}{(2P_2)}\right\} \tag{14}$$

As all P values are complex let us write

$$\left\{\frac{(P_1 + P_3)}{(2P_2)}\right\} = Q e^{i\phi} \tag{15}$$

as $\gamma = a + ib$ (eq. (3)) then it can be shown that

$$\frac{a}{b} = \frac{\cosh^{-1}}{\cos^{-1}}\left[Q^2 \pm (1 - 2Q^2 \cos 2\phi + Q^4)^{1/2}\right] \tag{16}$$

As in experimental work it is usually impossible to make the two intervals exactly equal, a method of estimation for two slightly differing intervals has been derived by GESSNER and FREDERICK (1965) using an iterative process on a digital computer.

We have applied this analytical method both *in vivo* and in whole excised vessels extended to their *in vivo* length in a bath of Krebs solution at body temperature. The dog thoracic aorta was initially studied; *in vivo* measurements from a catheter-tip manometer in the thoracic aorta (MCDONALD and ATTINGER, 1966) showed a large scatter and were abandoned. In the perfused aorta cannulas were inserted in inter-costal branches and all remaining branches ligated. The proximal end was attached to a sinusoidal pump and the distal end connected by a long soft rubber tube to a reser-voir under a pressure equal to an average mean arterial value. As the thoracic aorta along its length has an appreciable geometrical taper and also some elastic non-uniformity (MCDONALD, 1966) it was decided to use the common carotid artery. The effects of "tapering" in arteries are discussed below. Nearly 20 cm of this vessel can be utilized; the bore is constant and the wave-velocity throughout its length also appears to be constant (MCDONALD, 1966). As this vessel has no side-branches specially designed needles, angled so that they measure a lateral pressure while clamped to the inner side of the wall (MCDONALD and ATTINGER, 1966), were inserted at three points.

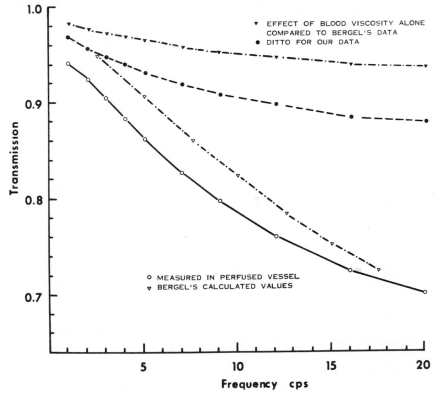

FIG. 2. THE TRANSMISSION OVER 10 CM OF THE PERFUSED THORACIC AORTA (SMOOTHED) — SOLID LINE COM-PARED TO THE VALUES FROM BERGEL IN FIG. 1 (BROKEN LINE). THE UPPER TWO LINES GIVE THE CORRES-PONDING VALUES FROM THE WOMERSLEY EQUATIONS INCORPORATING A PERFECT ELASTIC WALL. TWO CURVES ARE NECESSARY BECAUSE THE WAVE-VELOCITY IN OUR DATA WAS MUCH LOWER THAN IN BERGEL'S EXPERIMENTS AND HENCE 10 CM WAS A LARGER FRACTION OF THE WAVE LENGTH.

Careful matching of the frequency responses of the three manometer systems was made before insertion (f_0, 90–120 c/s; damping $< 10\%$ of critical). Excised carotids were also used; in both vessels perfusion was done initially with Krebs solution and repeated with the substitution of blood.

The mean values of the transmission over 10 cm in the thoracic aorta are shown in Fig. 2. The values obtained are compared to those of BERGEL (1961) from Fig. 1. It is seen that very similar values were obtained; strict comparison should be made with caution, however, because the phase velocity we measured in the excised vessel averaged 3.2 m/sec whereas Bergel's calculated value about 6 m/sec. This is indicated with the corresponding Womersley cases for the two differing wave-velocities. The attenuation due to the wall is seen to be greater than that due to the viscosity of the blood and the disparity increases markedly with frequency. It must also be pointed out that our measurements are over the whole thoracic aorta (*c.* 15 cm) and are "average" values because of the geometrical taper and elastic non-uniformity noted above. Bergel's measurements were made in the middle of a much shorter segment.

In Fig. 3 similar results are plotted for the common carotid artery in which the results from one perfused vessel and two sets of values measured in two different dogs *in vivo* are shown. The transmission loss over 10 cm is considerably larger in our values than in those of Bergel; the values for the perfused vessel lie on virtually the

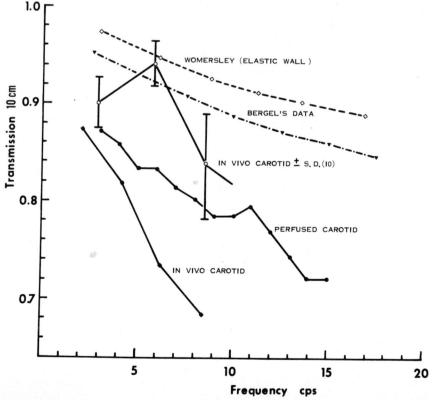

FIG. 3. TRANSMISSION OVER 10 CM IN THE COMMON CAROTID OF THE DOG. OUR DATA FROM ONE PERFUSED CAROTID AND TWO *in vivo* EXPERIMENTS ARE SHOWN—SOLID LINES. THESE ARE COMPARED TO THOSE FROM BERGEL (FIG. 1) AND THE CORRESPONDING WOMERSLEY VALUES.

same line as for the thoracic aorta. Again it can be seen how much higher the transmission loss is than that for the Womersley model with no wall-viscosity.

In Fig. 4 the transmission per wave length is plotted together with values for the phase velocity in terms of the value of α (eq. (1)). The rise of phase velocity at low values of α is shown markedly in our *in vivo* measurements and to a lesser degree in Bergel's excised specimens but is not shown in our excised vessel. The transmission per wave length in the arteries is seen to be dramatically lower than the Womersley values (marked $\exp -2\pi\, Y/X$). For theoretical analysis this is an easier form of display; the values for transmission over 10 cm in Figs. 2 and 3 are more easy to apply in the actual anatomical lengths found in the body.

The results show a very large variation between different experiments and clearly a considerably greater number of measurements will have to be made before any standard values can be determined. The method is sensitive to small errors in pressure measurement, especially at low frequencies. Measurement errors, however, will almost certainly cause errors in evaluating both real and imaginary parts of the propagation

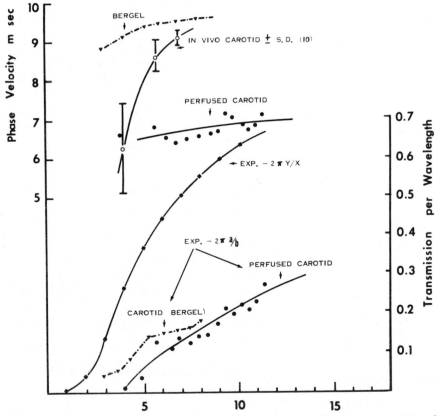

FIG. 4. PHASE VELOCITY (UPPER THREE CURVES WITH ORDINATE ON LEFT) PLOTTED AGAINST α (EQ. (1)). DATA FROM ONE CAROTID PERFUSED WITH BLOOD AND ONE *in vivo* ARE SHOWN—SOLID LINES, AND COMPARED TO BERGEL'S MEAN VALUES—BROKEN LINE. THE LOWER THREE CURVES (ORDINATE ON RIGHT) SHOW THE TRANSMISSION PER WAVE LENGTH (EXP $-2\pi\ a/b$) IN THE SAME PERFUSED CAROTID AND THE VALUES CALCULATED FROM BERGEL'S DATA. THE CURVE MARKED EXP $-2\pi\ Y/X$ IS THE CORRESPONDING WOMERSLEY CURVE ASSUMING NO VISCOSITY IN THE WALL.

constant; while the derived phase velocity remained at a consistent value we have assumed the attenuation is also reasonably accurate. Nevertheless the variation with frequency in each individual experiment is usually consistent. If we assume that the viscous element in the wall is primarily the smooth muscle we may conclude that considerable changes in attenuation can be caused by variations in the contractile state of the muscle. This was also suggested in one experiment when administration of the drug Aramine, which causes sustained contraction of vascular smooth muscle, resulted in a marked increase in attenuation. In a second dog the change was not significant although the rise in mean blood pressure was comparable in the two animals.

Some interesting observations pertinent to this discussion were drawn, from an earlier experiment using quite a different technique, regarding the influence of the non-homogeneities of the system on measurements made over large distances along the vascular tree. In this case the pressure wave was traveling from the periphery towards the heart. In a dog the circulation was maintained by a cardiac by-pass pump as used in cardiac surgery. Venous blood was pumped from the right ventricle through an oxygenator into the left femoral artery and the ascending aorta was clamped so that the mean arterial pressure was maintained at a steady level apart from slight slow oscillations due to the uneven action of the roller pump. A sinusoidal pump was attached to a cannula that was inserted in the right iliac artery as close to the termination of the aorta as possible pointing toward the heart. Pressure was measured through a needle (as described above) in the arch of the aorta and through a cannula in the left renal artery. (The distance between them was 35 cm.) The main object was to study the reflection of centripetal waves in the region of the heart. No evidence of reflection of such waves was found but the evidence of this was not considered conclusive because, with the largest stroke volume available, it was found that the pressure wave was very small by the time it reached the arch of the aorta and further experiments were postponed until a larger pump could be built. In comparing the results we must note that the elastic non-uniformity is greater because some abdominal aorta was included and that the branches in the region between the renal artery and the root of the aorta were open and hence there was a greater variation in the total geometrical cross-section. The attenuation calculated over 10 cm was larger than that measured in the thoracic aorta (Fig. 2) but this is to be expected from the effects of the non-uniform elastic effects analysed by Taylor (1965). As the wave-velocity increases with distance from the heart an increase in amplitude of the wave will be caused and this will reduce the attenuation due to viscous effects seen in a centrifugal wave. Conversely a centripetal wave will show an increased attenuation.

It, therefore, seems interesting to compare the retrograde attenuation in this experiment with the attenuation measured in the thoracic aorta where the propagation constant is assumed equal in both directions. In two runs (between 4–12 c/s and 3–10 c/s respectively) the arithmetical difference in the transmission per 10 cm was 0.188 ± 0.0255 S.D. (8) and 0.244 ± 0.0165 S.D. (15). In a third run between 11 and 20 c/s the difference was larger, 0.340 ± 0.016 S.D. (10). Thus the transmission over 10 cm at 3 and 10 c/s, from Fig. 2, were 0.91 and 0.79. The corresponding values in the second run using a retrograde wave were 0.71 and 0.52. The ratios of the two transmissions were also calculated and the corresponding values for the three runs were 1.314 ± 0.138, 1.415 ± 0.071 and 1.878 ± 0.121. Apart from the marked discrepancy between the third run at higher frequencies and the first two (for which no explanation is advanced) the ratio figures showed a progressive increase with frequency which shows here as a larger standard deviation. The average phase velocity between the two measuring points in the by-pass pump experiment was 3.15 m/sec and so was very close to that in the perfused aorta (3.2 m/sec). This would not have caused the discrepancy. The increase in the attenuation in the retrograde wave is reasonably consistent with values for the non-uniform elastic effect predicted from wave-velocity measurements made over 5 cm intervals along the aorta (MCDONALD, 1966).

THEORETICAL CONSIDERATIONS

As noted above, HARDUNG (1952) and BERGEL (1961) treated the wall as a simple spring and parallel dashpot model set out in eq. (7) as

$$E' = E_{dyn} + i\eta\omega$$

WOMERSLEY (1957) used a mathematical formulation, from analogy with an analysis of MORGAN and KIELY (1954), in which the terms for the elastic modulus, E, and the Poisson's ratio, σ, in the wave equation were replaced by complex terms such that

$$E_c = E(1 + i\omega\Delta E) \tag{17}$$

$$\sigma_c = \sigma(1 + i\omega\Delta\sigma) \tag{18}$$

The result of this substitution was explored in detail by TAYLOR (1959b) and showed that in place of the original Womersley equation

$$c_0/c = (X - iY) \tag{19}$$

we write

$$c_0/c = (X - iY)[1 - i\omega(\tfrac{1}{2}\Delta E + \tfrac{1}{3}\Delta\sigma)] \tag{20}$$

Here c is the complex wave velocity in an elastic tube filled with a viscous fluid and c_0 is the corresponding real value with an ideal fluid; X and Y are terms dependent on the parameter a (eq. (1)) and tabulated by Womersley. To simplify subsequent equations the substition was made for the last term in brackets in eq. (20)

$$W = (\tfrac{1}{2}\Delta E + \tfrac{1}{3}\Delta\sigma) \tag{21}$$

In the original Womersley model the phase velocity c_1 was given by

$$c_1/c_0 = 1/X \tag{22}$$

with a visco-elastic wall this becomes

$$c_1/c_0 = 1 / \left[X\left(1 - \frac{Y}{X}\omega W\right) \right] \tag{23}$$

TAYLOR (1959b) showed that in a visco-elastic (rubber) tube the values derived from eq. (23) approximate very closely to those in the 'tethered' tube model of Womersley.

The attenuation in the original Womersley equations was expressed as the transmission per wave length which was given by

$$\exp - 2\pi Y/X \tag{24}$$

and in the visco-elastic tube this becomes

$$\exp\left\{\left(-2\pi\frac{Y}{X}\right)\left(1+\frac{X}{Y}\omega W\right)\left(1-\frac{Y}{X}\omega W\right)^{-1}\right\} \tag{25}$$

In terms of the nomenclature of the measured propagation constant (eq. (3)) the transmission is given by

$$\exp - 2\pi a/b \tag{26}$$

From the measured values of a and b and the tabulated values of X and Y the value of ωW can be calculated from

$$\omega W = \frac{(a/b \cdot X/Y - 1)}{(a/b + X/Y)} \tag{27}$$

The values for ωW found in one of our experiments is shown in Fig. 4 and the corresponding value of W in Fig. 5.

The equivalence of the Womersley approach to the visco-elastic wall and that used by Hardung and Bergel may be outlined in the following way. The elastic modulus, E, of a cylindrical tube which is maintained at a constant length is given by Bergel (1961)

$$E = \frac{\Delta P}{\Delta A} \times \frac{2(1-2)a^2A}{A^2 - a^2} \tag{28}$$

where A is the external radius and a is the internal radius.

If a viscous element is introduced into this model there will be a phase shift between ΔP and ΔA. Hence we can write

$$\frac{\Delta P}{\Delta A} = \frac{\Delta P}{\Delta A}e^{i\phi} = \frac{E_c}{(1-\sigma_c^2)} \cdot \frac{(A^2 - a^2)}{2a^2A} \tag{29}$$

by introducing Hardung's complex elastic modulus

$$E' = E_c = E_{dyn}(1 + i\eta\omega/E_{dyn}) = E_{dyn}(1 + i\omega\Delta E)$$

and a corresponding complex σ_c (see eq. (18)) one finds

$$\left|\frac{\Delta P}{\Delta A}\right|e^{i\phi} = \frac{A^2 - a^2}{2a^2A} \cdot \frac{E_{dyn}}{1 - \sigma_{dyn}^2}[1 + i(\Delta E + \tfrac{2}{3}\Delta\sigma)] \tag{30}$$

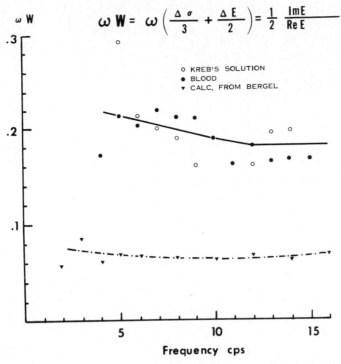

FIG. 5. THE TERM ωW (EQ. (22)) PLOTTED FOR DATA IN ONE PERFUSED CAROTID AND THE VALUES DERIVED
FROM BERGEL'S DATA.

when $\sigma = 0.5$ we find

$$\tan \phi = \omega(\Delta E + \tfrac{2}{3}\Delta\sigma) = 2\omega W \qquad (31)$$

(where W is defined in eq. (22))

or

$$\omega W = \tfrac{1}{2}\tan\phi \qquad (32)$$

The values of the term ωW calculated in this way from Bergel's data are compared to ours derived from eq. (27) in Fig. 5; they are shown again as W in Fig. 6. It can be seen that these latter values are rather less than half those derived in our experiments. It is interesting to compare these values with that estimated by TAYLOR (1959b) for the rubber tube. He estimated $W \approx 3 \times 10^{-4}$; the smallest value from our data is approximately 1×10^{-2} and from Bergel's data 4×10^{-3}. The frequency effect is close to an inverse relation as shown by the relative constancy of ωW. In Bergel's original data the term $\eta\omega$ likewise only increases slightly with frequency and, as he pointed out, this indicates that the simple model is not a realistic one. In other words the term η cannot be regarded as the viscosity of any particular element. Whether anything is to be gained by attempting to analyse a more complex array of components in series and parallel is a matter of opinion. It would seem to be doubtful while measurement of the total attenuation is not made more precisely than it has been thus far.

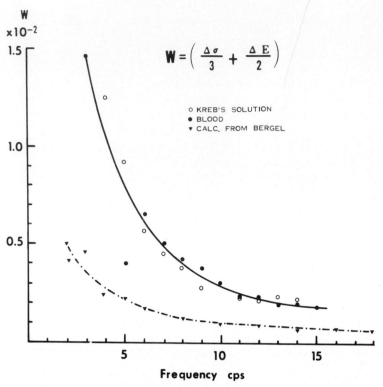

FIG. 6. THE VALUES OF W (EQ. (22)) CORRESPONDING TO VALUES OF ωW IN FIG. 5.

CONCLUSIONS

In summary, we can make the following observations. It would appear then that the relatively large attenuations reported here are, in all probability, average values for the wave propagation in the thoracic aorta. Differences between Bergel's results, the values from the three-point method and those obtained by the retrograde method are not so large that they cannot be explained in terms of existing models such as that of Taylor (1965), when applied to the aorta. In the case of the carotid which should be simpler because the geometry and elastic properties appear to be very nearly uniform the differences between our results and Bergel's is, in fact, greater. We find about the same transmission loss per unit length in the carotid as in the thoracic aorta; Bergel reported it as much smaller in the carotid (Fig. 1). The loss due to the viscosity of the blood increases in narrower tubes. The attenuation found experimentally (Figs. 2, 3, and 4) is much higher than that predicted from the viscous drag so that the effect of the viscosity of the wall is greater than that of the viscosity of the blood. The wall factor is not physically dependent on vessel calibre. The physiological interpretation assumes that the muscle component of the wall contributes most of the viscous element. There is more muscle in the carotid than in the thoracic aorta (BERGEL, 1961). One would, therefore, expect the wall factor as well as the viscous drag factor to be greater in the carotid. This is offset in regard to transmission per unit length, in comparison with the aorta, in that the wave-velocity is higher but we suggest that the range of values we obtain is more likely in the living animal than those of Bergel. Further observations with better control of the physiological state of the vascular smooth muscle than we have attained are clearly necessary.

Over a distance of 10 cm we find at 3 c/s a loss in transmission of approximately 5–10% in the thoracic aorta and of 10–16% in the carotid artery (our values) or 5% (Bergel). At 15 c/s the corresponding values are 25–27% (aorta) and 28% (ours) or 14% (Bergel) in the carotid. This marked increase with frequency accounts for the rapid damping of such features of the aortic pulse as the notch due to the closing of the aortic valves. The fact that studies of the lower frequency components of the arterial pulse behave as though the centrifugal wave were not attenuated (MCDONALD and ATTINGER, 1966) so that the features of the arterial tree such as the elastic non-uniformity and the geometrical form are of great importance. Some aspects of this are discussed but the widespread implications this has for a full description of the dynamics of the arterial tree cannot adequately be considered here.

REFERENCES

BERGEL, D. H. *J. Physiol.* **156**, 458, 1961.

GESSNER, U. and FREDERICK, D. H. Methods of determining the distensibility of blood vessels. *I.E.E.E. Trans. Bio-med. eng.*, **BME-13**, 2, 1965.

HARDUNG, V. *Helv. Physiol. acta*, **10**, 482, 1952.

KING, A. L. *J. Appl. Physiol.* **18**, 595, 1947.

LAWTON, R. W. *Circ. Research*, **3**, 403, 1955.

MCDONALD, D. A. *Blood Flow in Arteries*. Edward Arnold, London, 1960.

MCDONALD, D. A. Submitted to *Amer. J. Physiol.*, 1966.

MCDONALD, D. A. and ATTINGER, E. O. Submitted to *Circ. Research*, 1966.

MCDONALD, D. A. and TAYLOR, M. G. *Progress in Biophysics*, Pergamon Press, London, **9**, 107, 1959.

MORGAN, G. W. and KIELY, J. P. *J. Acoust. Soc. Amer.* **26**, 323, 1954.

TAYLOR, M. G. *Phys. Med. Biol.* **3**, 273, 1959(a).

TAYLOR, M. G. *Phys. Med. Biol.* **4**, 63, 1959(b).

TAYLOR, M. G. Ph.D. Thesis, Univ. of London, 1959(c).

TAYLOR, M. G. *Phys. Med. Biol.* **10**, 539, 1965.

WOMERSLEY, J. R. The mathematical analysis of the arterial circulation in a state of oscillatory motion. Wright Air Development Center, Tech. Rep. WADC TR56–614, Office of Technical Services, Dept. of Commerce, No. PB 151356, 1957.

AN EXAMPLE OF PRESSURE-PULSE PEAKING
IN A FLUID-FILLED TUBE†

A. C. L. BARNARD

IBM Scientific Center, Houston, Texas

IN HIS book, McDonald has listed the changes in the traveling pressure-wave in the arterial system: (a) the amplitude of the wave increases progressively as the wave passes away from the heart—the so-called "peaking" of the pulse, (b) the front of the wave becomes steeper[1]. The velocity pulse changes in the reverse way. I would like to report briefly a hydrodynamic calculation which reproduces these effects. The calculation was made by Drs. W. A. Hunt, W. P. Timlake, E. Varley, and myself at the IBM Scientific Center in Houston, Texas.

The Navier–Stokes equations for a cylindrically symmetric system, together with the continuity equation, were the starting point of the calculation. The equations were non-dimensionalized and some terms were seen to be small, if typical axial velocities are much greater than typical radial velocities. These small terms were neglected. However, several non-linear terms remained. The equations were integrated over the radial coordinate in order to work in terms of the total flow U, which is the quantity normally measured experimentally. Two equations were obtained in which the independent variables were time and axial distance. However, there were three dependent variables, U, cross-sectional area A and pressure P. In view of the results of PATEL, GREENFIELD and FRY[2], the required third equation was taken to be a linear pressure–area relationship. Two parameters depending on the velocity profile appeared in the equations. The profile is unknown, but the parameters may be estimated from rigid tube profiles. The following results have been found to be rather insensitive to these parameters.

The resulting system of equations is non-linear, but is quasi-linear and hyperbolic so that it may be solved numerically for cases of interest. Since one of the features of the arterial system is that the arteries become stiffer away from the heart, one interesting case is that of a non-tapering stiffening tube of infinite length. In the calculation for this case, the pressure pulse, radius and compliance, at the proximal end were as measured by LAWTON[3] in the abdominal aorta of a dog. The compliance was taken to decrease by a factor of 5, over a length of 40 cm[2].

The first figure has a graph of the tube properties in the lower part. In the upper parts the leading edges of the pressure and velocity pulses are shown at stations down the

---

†*Note of the Editor:* Dr. Barnard requested from the Conference Chairman permission to present a brief communication as part of the discussion of Professor McDonald's communication. This was granted. His contribution has therefore been placed after Professor McDonald's contribution and these two communications are discussed together with those by Dr. Seymour and by Dr. Taylor.

tube. It can be seen that in the stiffening section the front of the pressure pulse becomes more steep and the velocity pulse less steep. The second figure shows the complete pulses at the various stations, the zero cm pressure pulse being the input to the calculation and all other curves being results of the calculation. It can be seen that the pressure pulse becomes higher and narrower, whereas the velocity pulse becomes

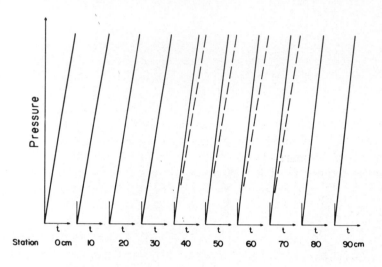

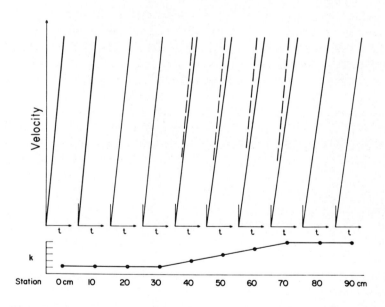

lower and wider as the disturbance travels down the tube. These results are emphasized in the third figure, where the pulses at 0 and 70 cm are superimposed. It is interesting to note that the leading-edge behavior occurs in the stiffening section, but the changes in the peak values occur upstream of the stiffening section. The latter effects are therefore due to modification of the pulse by partial reflection of itself from the stiffening

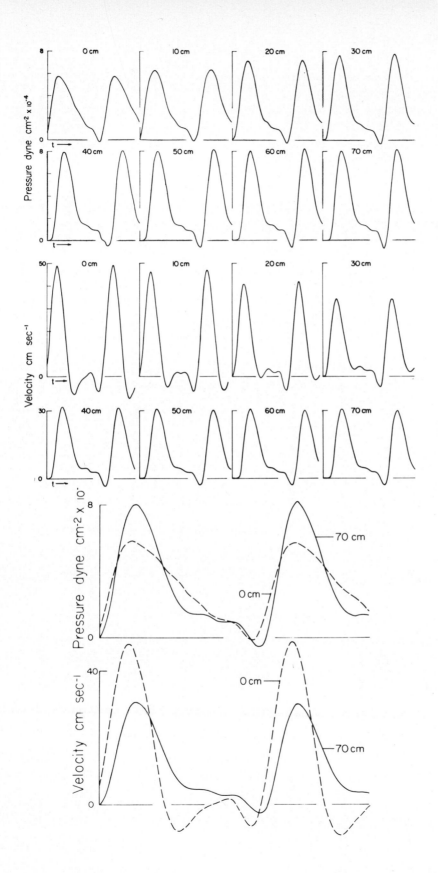

section of the infinitely long tube. Such reflection effects are automatically included in this type of calculation.

The system considered here, a non-branching, non-tapering, infinitely long tube with a stiffening section, is obviously not intended to be a realistic model of the arterial system. However, it may be significant that this simple system reproduces several of the effects noted in the arterial system.

A more complete account of this work has been submitted for publication elsewhere. The calculations were made at the Common Research Computer Facility of the Texas Medical Center in Houston. The Facility is supported by grants from the National Institutes of Health and other sources.

REFERENCES

[1] McDONALD, D. A. *Blood Flow in Arteries*, Edward Arnold, London, 1960, p. 258.
[2] PATEL, D. J., GREENFIELD, J. C., JR., and FRY, D. L. In *Pulsatile Blood Flow*, ATTINGER, E. O. (Editor), McGraw-Hill, New York, 1964.
[3] LAWTON, R. W. Quoted by WOMERSLEY, J. R., WADC Report TR56–614, 1957, p. 52.

HIGH FREQUENCY, PULSATILE FLOW IN A TAPERING, VISCO-ELASTIC TUBE OF VARYING STIFFNESS

BRIAN R. SEYMOUR* and ERIC VARLEY

Department of Theoretical Mechanics,
The University of Nottingham,
Nottingham, England

1. INTRODUCTION

One of the interesting problems in the study of the circulation is to determine conditions which produce a peaking of the maximum pressure and a decrease in the maximum flow in a pulse as it propagates from the proximal to the peripheral part of the arterial system. In this paper we determine the influence of the visco-elastic properties, the taper, and the variation in stiffness of the wall on this phenomenon. All these effects define a characteristic time scale. We consider high frequency pulses for which the time scale introduced by the variations in the flow variables is small compared with these time scales and also with that defined by the viscosity of the fluid. We restrict attention to the larger arteries and, since we are only interested in mean flows, to the mainstream. The boundary layer will be studied in a future paper.

In section 2 the problem is formulated and the basic equations of pulsatile flow are derived. Arguments are given to show that the pressure, which is continuous across the tube, can be taken as a functional in time of the change in tube area. In section 3 an asymptotic expansion valid for large frequency, ω, of the pulse is derived, and the first term calculated. This is used to discuss the influence of tapering, variation in stiffness, and the visco-elastic properties of the tube on the pressure peaking. The wall equation used can model the possibility of the walls being actively contractile.

2. BASIC EQUATIONS OF PULSATILE FLOW

Here we derive the basic equations describing the pulsatile axi-symmetric flow of an incompressible fluid down a flexible circular tube of variable cross-sectional area. The equations governing the flow are the continuity and momentum equations, which relate the velocity components $(\bar{u}, \bar{v})$ of flow in the $(\bar{z}, \bar{r})$ directions, to the deviatoric stress tensor $\bar{\tau}$, and the pressure $\bar{p}$ by

$$\frac{\partial \bar{u}}{\partial \bar{z}} + \frac{1}{\bar{r}} \frac{\partial}{\partial \bar{r}} (\bar{r}\bar{v}) = 0, \tag{2.1}$$

$$\frac{\partial \bar{\tau}_{rz}}{\partial \bar{r}} + \frac{\partial \bar{\tau}_{zz}}{\partial \bar{z}} + \frac{\bar{\tau}_{rz}}{\bar{r}} = \frac{\partial \bar{p}}{\partial \bar{z}} + \rho \left(\frac{\partial \bar{u}}{\partial \bar{t}} + \frac{\bar{u} \partial \bar{u}}{\partial \bar{z}} + \frac{\bar{v} \partial \bar{u}}{\partial \bar{r}} \right), \tag{2.2}$$

131

and

$$\frac{\partial \bar{\tau}_{rr}}{\partial \bar{r}} + \frac{\partial \bar{\tau}_{rz}}{\partial \bar{z}} + \frac{\bar{\tau}_{rr} - \bar{\tau}_{\theta\theta}}{\bar{r}} = \frac{\partial \bar{p}}{\partial \bar{r}} + \rho \left(\frac{\partial \bar{v}}{\partial t} + \frac{\bar{u}\partial \bar{v}}{\partial \bar{z}} + \frac{\bar{v}\partial \bar{v}}{\partial \bar{r}} \right).$$ (2.3)

Blood is a suspension of particles, but since we are only interested in mean flows in the larger arteries, where the maximum dimensions of a particle are very small compared with the tube diameter, we take the fluid to be Newtonian with the usual equation of state

$$\bar{\tau} = \mu \bar{e}$$ (2.4)

where μ is the viscosity and $\bar{e}$ is the rate of strain tensor, with components:

$$\bar{e}_{rr} = \frac{\partial \bar{v}}{\partial \bar{r}}, \quad \bar{e}_{\theta\theta} = \frac{\bar{v}}{\bar{r}}, \quad \bar{e}_{zz} = \frac{\partial \bar{u}}{\partial \bar{z}},$$

$$\bar{e}_{rz} = \frac{\partial \bar{v}}{\partial \bar{z}} + \frac{\partial \bar{u}}{\partial \bar{r}}, \quad \bar{e}_{r\theta} = \bar{e}_{z\theta} = 0.$$ (2.5)

We treat the flow as laminar, for, although conditions for turbulence may exist during cardiac systole it seems unlikely that fully developed turbulence is ever attained (HESS, 1917; RALSTON, TAYLOR and ELLIOTT, 1947). It has also been suggested (MITCHELL and SCHWARTZ, 1965) that turbulence is only likely to develop after acute bends or branching, and consequently laminar flow is expected in arteries which are straight continuations of their parent trunk.

Our aim is to determine the pulsatile flow in the region $\bar{z} > 0$ in terms of conditions at some station $\bar{z} = 0$, where u_0, v_0 and r_0 are the mean axial and radial velocities and mean radius over one cycle. We consider regions of flow for which the mean radial velocity is small compared with the mean axial velocity, but since the flow is pulsatile, the rate at which any dependent variable changes in the radial direction is necessarily large compared with the rate of change in the axial direction. Without this latter condition the dependent variables would vary independently of position down the tube. The flow would then be defined as oscillatory rather than pulsatile. Motivated by these physical considerations and the continuity equation we define

$$\epsilon = \frac{v_0}{u_0} << 1$$ (2.6)

and take as non-dimensional dependent variables

$$u = \frac{\bar{u}}{u_0}, \quad v = \frac{v}{v_0}, \quad p = \frac{p}{\rho u_0^2}, \quad \bar{\tau} = \frac{\bar{\tau}}{\rho u_0^2},$$ (2.7)

and as non-dimensional independent variables

$$r = \frac{\bar{r}}{r_0}, \quad z = \frac{\epsilon \bar{z}}{r_0}, \quad \text{and} \quad t = \frac{\bar{t}v_0}{r_0}.$$ (2.8)

We define the Reynolds number

$$\beta = \frac{\rho r_0 v_0}{\mu} \tag{2.9}$$

and consider regions of flow where β^{-1} and the derivatives occurring in eqs. (2.1)–(2.3) remain bounded in the limit as $\epsilon \to 0$. In terms of the variables (2.7), the limiting forms of (2.1)–(2.3), after using (2.4) and (2.5) become,

$$\frac{\partial u}{\partial z} + \frac{1}{r}\frac{\partial}{\partial r}(rv) = 0 \tag{2.10}$$

$$\frac{1}{r}\frac{\partial}{\partial r}(\beta^{-1}r\frac{\partial u}{\partial r}) = \frac{\partial p}{\partial z} + \frac{\partial u}{\partial t} + u\frac{\partial u}{\partial z} + v\frac{\partial u}{\partial r}, \tag{2.11}$$

and

$$0 = \frac{\partial p}{\partial r}. \tag{2.12}$$

(2.10)–(2.12) are the basic equations of pulsatile flow; for non-Newtonian behaviour β depends on $\partial u/\partial r$.

A pulse is regarded as a high frequency pulse with respect to the fluid if the time scale introduced by the variation of u at $z = 0$ is small compared with the time scale $\rho r_0^2/\mu$. There is experimental evidence (VON DESCHWANDEN et al., 1956; SPENCER and DENISON, 1963) and some theoretical evidence (HALE et al., 1955), to suggest that for high frequency pulsatile flow in the larger arteries the velocity profile is virtually flat over most of the tube. In a future paper (SEYMOUR and VARLEY, to be published) we discuss in detail this high frequency limit of (2.10)–(2.12). Here, where we are basically interested in mean flows, we consider regions of flow where

$$\frac{\partial u}{\partial r} = 0 \tag{2.13}$$

and replace the two boundary conditions, on the axial and radial velocities at the wall, by the one condition that the wall is a stream surface. We assume there is no separation of the boundary layer and take the radial velocity at the wall, $r = R(z,t)$, to be

$$v = \frac{\partial R}{\partial t} + u\frac{\partial R}{\partial z}, \tag{2.14}$$

where $u(z,t)$ is the mainstream axial velocity. From (2.10) and (2.13), together with the condition that $v = 0$ when $r = 0$, we obtain

$$v = \frac{-r}{2}\frac{\partial u}{\partial z}, \tag{2.15}$$

which when inserted in (2.14) gives

$$\frac{\partial A}{\partial t} + \frac{\partial}{\partial z}(uA) = 0, \tag{2.16}$$

where $A(z,t)$ is the (non-dimensionalized) area of the tube. Equation (2.11), with (2.13), reduces to

$$\frac{\partial u}{\partial t}+\frac{\partial}{\partial z}(p+\tfrac{1}{2}u^2)=0 \qquad (2.17)$$

which, together with (2.16), form two equations for the three unknowns $p(z,t)$, $u(z,t)$, $A(z,t)$. This system of equations is completed by the "wall equation", which we now consider in detail.

The "wall equation" must provide another relation between p, u and A. Most authors attempt to obtain this relation by postulating the rheological properties of the tube wall and also the boundary conditions on its outer surface, then solve the difficult problem of the interaction between its deformation and the fluid flow. Although the system is in fact highly non-linear and visco-elastic the approximations used to solve this interaction problem produce, in general, a linear relation between p and A!

The determination of an equation of state for the wall material is only necessary if the behaviour of this material in varying situations is required. If longitudinal movement of the wall and diffusion across its inner boundary are neglected then, since in the limit $\epsilon \to 0$ the ratios of shear forces on the wall to pressure force and of curvature in the z-direction to $1/r_0$ are vanishingly small, we have a material of unknown rheological properties whose outer boundary is subject to unknown conditions but whose inner boundary is subject to normal tractions producing changes in cross-sectional area of the tube. Rather than postulate the rheological properties of the material composing the wall and conditions at its outer boundary and then trying to solve the difficult interaction problem, we postulate the most general form of the relation between the variation of p and A at the wall which is compatible with experiment. This relation is characteristic of the wall material in this particular configuration when its inner boundary is subject to a normal traction. Since the properties of the wall and conditions at its outer boundary change, this relation can vary with z. If for example we assume the wall is composed of an elastic material which is tethered on the outside, and if the inertia of the wall is neglected, then the pressure is found to be a function of the current area. If wall inertia is considered the pressure is not determined by the current area but depends, in a known way, on the area at previous times; that is, the pressure is a functional in time of the area. This hysteresis, which could also be predicted by taking into account visco-elastic properties of the wall, has been studied by REMMINGTON (1955), and BERGEL (1961). To allow for all of these effects we take the pressure to be a general functional in time of

$$\bar{\lambda}(\bar{z},\bar{t}) = \frac{A(\bar{z},\bar{t})}{A_0(\bar{z})}-1, \qquad (2.18)$$

the fractional increase in area of the original area $A_0(\bar{z})$ when there is no flow and the pressure is zero.

Results of GREEN and RIVLIN (1957) show that this functional can be expanded as a sum of multiple integrals. Here, since max $|\bar{\lambda}(\bar{z},\bar{t})| \ll 1$ (see McDONALD, 1960), we restrict our attention to the second order theory for which

$$\bar{p}(\bar{z},\bar{t}) = \int_{\eta=0}^{\eta=\bar{t}} \bar{K}(\bar{t},\eta;\bar{z})\, d\bar{\lambda}(\eta,\bar{z}) \tag{2.19}$$

where

$$\bar{K}(\bar{t},\eta;\bar{z}) = \bar{K}_1(\bar{t}-\eta;\bar{z}) + \int_{\eta_1=0}^{\eta_1=\bar{t}} \bar{K}_2(\bar{t}-\eta,\bar{t}-\eta_1;\bar{z})\, d\bar{\lambda}(\eta_1,\bar{z}). \tag{2.20}$$

Contrary to (2.10)–(2.12) the variables are now in dimensional form. In (2.19) and (2.20) the kernel functions can depend on $\bar{z}$. These kernel functions could be determined in practice by dynamic and static experiments similar to those performed by BERGEL (1961), and by wave propagation experiments.

This functional relationship can also include the phenomena of the walls being actively contractile, when the characteristic time defined by the time variation of K_1 is negative. This is discussed in section 3.

3. FIRST ORDER SOLUTION

Our aim is to describe the mode of propagation of a "high frequency" pulse moving into the initially steady state region $\bar{z} > 0$ in terms of the variation of $\bar{\lambda}$ as the pulse passes the point $\bar{z} = 0$. To make the term "high frequency" precise we suppose that the variation of $\bar{\lambda}$ at $\bar{z} = 0$ introduces two characteristic constants: a measure of amplitude

$$\epsilon(\bar{t}_1) = \max_{0 \leq \bar{t} \leq \bar{t}_1} |\bar{\lambda}(0,\bar{t})|, \tag{3.1}$$

which is non-dimensional, and a characteristic time scale $\bar{t}_0$, so that

$$\bar{\lambda}(0,\bar{t}) = \epsilon F\left(\frac{\bar{t}}{\bar{t}_0}\right), \tag{3.2}$$

where F is a non-dimensional function of the non-dimensional time measure $\bar{t}/\bar{t}_0$. We work with variables which are non-dimensionalized by characteristic constants defined by the material of the wall, and which are normalized by the amplitude ϵ. We define

$$K_1 = \frac{\bar{K}_1}{\bar{K}_1(0;0)}, \quad K_2 = \frac{\bar{K}_2}{\bar{K}_2(0,0;0)}, \quad \lambda = \frac{\bar{\lambda}}{\epsilon}, \quad p = \frac{\bar{p}}{\epsilon \bar{K}_1(0;0)} \tag{3.3}$$

and

$$u = \frac{\bar{u}}{\epsilon C_0},$$

where

$$C_0 = \sqrt{\frac{\bar{K}_1(0;0)}{\rho}} \tag{3.4}$$

is the speed of the front leaving $\bar{z} = 0$ at $\bar{t} = 0$ (VARLEY, 1965). As the non-dimensional time and distance measures we take

$$t = \frac{\bar{t}}{\bar{\tau}_0} \quad \text{and} \quad z = \frac{\bar{z}}{C_0\bar{\tau}_0}, \tag{3.5}$$

where

$$\bar{\tau}_0 = -\frac{2\bar{K}_1(0;0)}{\dfrac{\partial \bar{K}_1}{\partial \bar{t}}(0;0)} \tag{3.6}$$

is a characteristic relaxation time defined by the material of the wall. In terms of these non-dimensional variables eqs. (2.16), (2.17), (2.19) and (2.20) become

$$\frac{\partial}{\partial t}(A_0\lambda) + \frac{\partial}{\partial z}[uA_0(1 + \epsilon\lambda)] = 0, \tag{3.7}$$

$$\frac{\partial u}{\partial t} + \frac{\partial}{\partial z}(p + \tfrac{1}{2}\epsilon u^2) = 0, \tag{3.8}$$

and

$$p = \int\limits_{\mu=0}^{\mu=t} K(t,\mu;z)\,d\lambda(\mu,z) \tag{3.9}$$

where

$$K(t,\mu;z) = K_1(t-\mu;z) + \epsilon\frac{\bar{K}_2(0,0;0)}{\bar{K}_1(0;0)}\int\limits_{\mu_1=0}^{\mu_1=t} K_2(t-\mu,t-\mu_1;z)\,d\lambda(\mu_1,z)\cdot \tag{3.10}$$

Here, for convenience, we choose initial conditions that

when $\qquad\qquad t = 0, \quad \lambda = u = p = 0, \quad \text{all } z > 0, \tag{3.11}$

while at $\qquad\qquad z = 0, \quad \lambda = F(\omega t) \quad \text{for} \quad 0 \leqslant t \leqslant t_1, \tag{3.12}$

where the non-dimensional frequency

$$\omega = \frac{\bar{\tau}_0}{\bar{t}_0}. \tag{3.13}$$

In this paper we construct the first order term of a formal asymptotic expansion satisfying (3.7)–(3.12) in the limit as $\omega \to \infty$, but

$$a = \frac{\bar{K}_2(0,0;0)}{\bar{K}_1(0;0)}\epsilon\omega$$

remains finite, but not necessarily small. Higher order terms, which in particular determine the form of the hysteresis, are given by Seymour and Varley.

Here we consider three properties of the tube which modify the pulse. They are:

1. Viscoelastic property, or the time rate of change of stiffness, $\partial K_1 / \partial t \neq 0$.
2. Axial inhomogeneity of the wall, or the space rate of change of stiffness, $\partial K_1 / \partial z \neq 0$.
3. Tube taper, or the space variation of the initial cross-sectional area, $\partial A_0 / \partial z \neq 0$.

We treat the pulse as "high frequency" with respect to all three effects. By this we mean that the incremental time rates of change of the flow variables are large compared with $|(1/\bar{K}_1)(\partial \bar{K}_1 / \partial \bar{t})|$, the incremental time rate of change of $\bar{K}_1$, and the incremental space rates of change of the flow variables are large compared with the incremental space rates of change of $\bar{K}_1$ and A_0.

We compare the mode of propagation of a high frequency pulse in the above general visco-elastic system with the simplest situation when K_1, K_2 and A_0 are constants. It might be thought that in the high frequency limit the simple situation, obtained by replacing K_1, K_2 and A_0 by local constant values, would approximate the visco-elastic system; however the results of VARLEY and ROGERS (1967) show this is not the case. Here we briefly follow part of the analysis of Varley and Rogers since we are only concerned with the first order solution. In a future paper we present the analysis for the general situation in more detail.

In the simplest situation, when K_1, K_2 and A_0 are constant, a pulse entering an initially uniform region is necessarily a simple wave, so that there exists a one parameter family of propagating surfaces, $\alpha(z,t) = $ constant, called *wavelets*, each of which carries a constant value of p, u and λ. The wavelets are characteristic surfaces of the governing equations for the flow. If $t = T(z,\alpha)$ denotes the time of arrival at the station z of the wavelet "α" which left $z = 0$ at $t = \alpha/\omega$, when $\lambda = F(\alpha)$, then

$$T = V(\alpha)z + \frac{\alpha}{\omega} \qquad (3.14)$$

where $V(\alpha)$,

$$p = P(\alpha), \quad u = U(\alpha), \quad \text{and} \quad \lambda = \Lambda(\alpha) \equiv F(\alpha) \qquad (3.15)$$

satisfy the ordinary differential relations

$$VU' - \Lambda' = 0 \qquad (3.16)$$

and

$$VP' - U' = 0 \qquad (3.17)$$

where

$$P = \Lambda\left(1 + \frac{a}{\omega}\Lambda\right). \qquad (3.18)$$

As $\omega \to \infty$, and (α, z) remains fixed,

$$P(\alpha) \to U(\alpha) \to \Lambda(\alpha) = F(\alpha). \tag{3.19}$$

The pulse may distort, but its amplitude is constant.

As for the simple wave, the propagation of a high frequency pulse in the more general visco-elastic system is most conveniently described if instead of (z,t) we take (z,α) as the independent variables, where $\alpha(z,t) = $ constant is the characteristic wavelet which left $z = 0$, in a direction $z > 0$, at time $t = \alpha/\omega$. Then in terms of

$$t = T(z,\alpha;\omega), \quad p = P(z,\alpha;\omega), \quad u = U(z,\alpha;\omega), \quad \text{and} \quad \lambda = \Lambda(z,\alpha;\omega) \tag{3.20}$$

conditions (3.7) and (3.8) become

$$\left[\epsilon U \frac{\partial T}{\partial z} - 1\right] A_0 \frac{\partial \Lambda}{\partial \alpha} + \frac{\partial T}{\partial z}(1 + \epsilon\Lambda) A_0 \frac{\partial U}{\partial \alpha} = \frac{\partial T}{\partial \alpha} \frac{\partial}{\partial z}(A_0 U[1 + \epsilon\Lambda]) \tag{3.21}$$

and

$$\frac{\partial T}{\partial z}\frac{\partial P}{\partial \alpha} + \left[\epsilon U \frac{T}{z} - 1\right]\frac{\partial U}{\partial \alpha} = \frac{\partial T}{\partial \alpha}\frac{\partial}{\partial z}[P + \tfrac{1}{2}\epsilon U^2]. \tag{3.22}$$

If (3.9) is differentiated at constant z we also obtain

$$\frac{\partial P}{\partial \alpha} - E\frac{\partial \Lambda}{\partial \alpha} = \frac{\partial T}{\partial \alpha}S, \tag{3.23}$$

where

$$E = K_1(0;z) + \frac{2a}{\omega}\int_0^t K_2(0, t - \mu;z)\, d\lambda(\mu,z), \tag{3.24}$$

and

$$S = \int_0^t K^{(1)}(t,\mu;z)\, d\lambda(\mu,z), \tag{3.25}$$

where

$$K^{(1)}(t,\mu;z) = \frac{\partial K_1}{\partial t}(t - \mu;z) + \frac{a}{\omega}\int_{\mu_1=0}^{\mu_1=t} \frac{\partial K_2}{\partial t}(t - \mu, t - \mu_1;z)\, d\lambda(\mu_1,z). \tag{3.26}$$

The condition that the wavelets are characteristic surfaces for the system (3.21)–(3.23) (COURANT and FRIEDRICHS, 1948) implies that

$$\left(\frac{\partial T}{\partial z}\right)^2 [E(1 + \epsilon\Lambda) - \epsilon^2 U^2] + 2\epsilon U \frac{\partial T}{\partial z} - 1 = 0 \tag{3.27}$$

and that

$$A_0(1+\epsilon\Lambda)\frac{\partial T}{\partial z}\frac{\partial}{\partial z}(P+\tfrac{1}{2}\epsilon U^2)+\left(1-\epsilon U\frac{\partial T}{\partial z}\right)\frac{\partial}{\partial z}(A_0 U[1+\epsilon\Lambda])-A_0(1+\epsilon\Lambda)\left(\frac{\partial T}{\partial z}\right)^2 S=0.$$
(3.28)

Conditions (3.21), (3.23), (3.27) and (3.28) with E and S given by (3.24)–(3.26), provide a complete set of equations for the dependent variables (3.20). These are to be solved subject to the imposed conditions at $z=0$ which imply that

$$\Lambda(0,\alpha;\omega)=F(\alpha),\quad\text{and}\quad T(0,\alpha:\omega)=\frac{\alpha}{\omega}\ ,$$
(3.29)

while the condition that the front $\alpha=0$ is moving into a uniform region implies that

$$\Lambda(z,0;\omega)=P(z,0;\omega)=U(z,0;\omega)=0\quad\text{for}\quad z>0.$$
(3.30)

Equations (3.21), (3.23), (3.27) and (3.28) can be satisfied by a formal asymptotic expansion

$$\omega\left(T-\int_0^z\frac{ds}{c(s)}\right)=\sum_{n=0}^N\omega^{-n}T_n(z,\alpha),\quad P=\sum_{n=0}^N\omega^{-n}P_n(z,\alpha),$$
(3.31)

$$U=\sum_{n=0}^N\omega^{-n}U_n(z,\alpha),\quad\text{and}\quad\Lambda=\sum_{n=0}^N\omega^{-n}\Lambda_n(z,\alpha),$$

where $c^2=K_1(0;z)$. When (3.31) is inserted in (3.21) and (3.23), and (3.30) is used, these imply that

$$P_0=cU_0=c^2\Lambda_0.$$
(3.32)

(3.32) together with (3.28) implies that

$$\frac{\partial\Lambda_0}{\partial z}+\frac{3}{4}\frac{\Lambda_0}{K_1}\frac{\partial K_1}{\partial z}+\frac{\Lambda_0}{2A_0}\frac{\partial A_0}{\partial z}-\frac{\Lambda_0}{2K_1^{3/2}}\frac{\partial K_1}{\partial t}=0\ ,$$
(3.33)

where in (3.33) and from now on, $K_1=K_1(0,z)$.
(3.33) integrates to give

$$\Lambda_0=F(\alpha)A_0^{-1/2}K_1^{-3/4}\exp\left(-\int_0^z\frac{ds}{c(s)\tau(s)}\right),$$
(3.34)

where

$$\tau(s)=-\frac{2K_1(0;s)}{\dfrac{\partial K_1(0;s)}{\partial t}}.$$

(3.32) and (3.34) imply that

$$P_0 = F(\alpha)\left(\frac{K_1}{A_0^2}\right)^{1/4} \exp\left(-\int_0^z \frac{ds}{c(s)\tau(s)}\right), \tag{3.35}$$

$$U_0 = F(\alpha)(K_1 A_0^2)^{-1/4} \exp\left(-\int_0^z \frac{ds}{c(s)\tau(s)}\right), \tag{3.36}$$

and the volume flow $V_0 = A U_0$ is given by

$$V_0 = F(\alpha)\left(\frac{A_0^2}{K_1}\right)^{1/4} \exp\left(-\int_0^z \frac{ds}{c(s)\tau(s)}\right). \tag{3.37}$$

Conditions (3.27) and (3.30) then imply that

$$\operatorname*{Lt}_{\omega\to\infty} \omega\left(T - \int_0^z \frac{ds}{c(s)}\right) = \alpha - F(\alpha)\int_0^z \left\{\left(\frac{3}{2}b + a\frac{K_2}{K_1}\right)A_0^{-1/2} K_1^{-5/4} \exp\left(-\int_0^s \frac{dy}{c\tau}\right)\right\}ds \tag{3.38}$$

where $b = \epsilon\omega$.

The variation of the dependent variables with time at constant z is given implicitly by relations (3.34)–(3.38). We note here that many authors do not distinguish between velocity and volume flow, but simply call both "flow". However, it can be seen from (3.36) and (3.37) that they are affected differently by a varying initial tube area.

It is known that the peak value of the pressure pulse increases as the pulse propagates from the proximal to the peripheral part of the arterial system, whereas the peak value of the "flow" pulse decreases. (3.35)–(3.37) clearly distinguish conditions which could produce these variations in the peak values of the pulse. These conditions, that the pressure peak increases, but the velocity and volume flow peaks decrease, are equivalent to the inequalities:

$$\frac{1}{2\bar{K}_1}\frac{\partial \bar{K}_1}{\partial \bar{z}} - \frac{1}{A_0}\frac{\partial A_0}{\partial \bar{z}} + \frac{\rho^{1/2}}{\bar{K}_1^{3/2}}\frac{\partial \bar{K}_1}{\partial \bar{t}} > 0, \tag{3.39}$$

$$\frac{1}{2\bar{K}_1}\frac{\partial \bar{K}_1}{\partial \bar{z}} + \frac{1}{A_0}\frac{\partial A_0}{\partial \bar{z}} - \frac{\rho^{1/2}}{\bar{K}_1^{3/2}}\frac{\partial \bar{K}_1}{\partial \bar{t}} > 0, \tag{3.40}$$

and

$$\frac{1}{2\bar{K}_1}\frac{\partial \bar{K}_1}{\partial \bar{z}} - \frac{1}{A_0}\frac{\partial A_0}{\partial \bar{z}} - \frac{\rho^{1/2}}{\bar{K}_1^{3/2}}\frac{\partial \bar{K}_1}{\partial \bar{t}} > 0. \tag{3.41}$$

(3.39) and (3.40) together imply

$$\frac{\partial \bar{K}_1}{\partial \bar{z}} > 0, \tag{3.42}$$

(3.39) and (3.41) imply

$$\frac{1}{2\bar{K}_1}\frac{\partial \bar{K}_1}{\partial \bar{z}} > \frac{1}{A_0}\frac{\partial A_0}{\partial \bar{z}} \tag{3.43}$$

and (3.40) and (3.41) imply

$$\frac{\partial \bar{K}_1}{\partial \bar{z}} > \frac{2\rho^{1/2}}{\bar{K}_1^{1/2}}\frac{\partial \bar{K}_1}{\partial \bar{t}} \ . \tag{3.44}$$

To cover the ambiguity in the use of the term "flow" we consider three cases. In order that the pressure peak increases but velocity peak decreases (3.39) and (3.40), and therefore (3.42) must hold; i.e. the wall stiffness must increase with z. This is consistent with known results that the peripheral arteries are stiffer than the proximal arteries (GREENFIELD and PATEL, 1962). For the pressure peak to increase but the volume flow peak to decrease (putting no restriction on the velocity flow), (3.39) and (3.41), and therefore (3.43) must hold. If the tube does not taper, then (3.43) reduces to (3.42) and the stiffness is again required to increase with $\bar{z}$. If we require both velocity and volume flow peaks to decrease while the pressure peak increases (3.39)–(3.41) and therefore (3.42)–(3.44) must all hold. We note that all three cases can be satisfied by an elastic non-tapering tube whose stiffness increases with $\bar{z}$.

The above inequalities do not exclude the possibility of

$$\frac{\partial \bar{K}_1}{\partial \bar{t}}(0,\bar{z}) > 0,$$

when the characteristic time τ, defined by the wall equation (2.19) is negative. This, as mentioned earlier, is equivalent to the statement that the muscle in the arterial wall is actively contractile. MCDONALD (1960) pointed out that the concept of the "peripheral heart" was abandoned by the early 1920s, and thought there was insufficient evidence to revive it. MITCHELL and SCHWARTZ (1965), however, suggest reasons why there is nothing inherently impossible about the concept that muscular arteries may be contracting rhythmically with each heart beat. We cannot attempt to answer this question, but simply state that our model can allow for this behaviour.

ACKNOWLEDGMENT

One of the authors (B.R.S.) wishes to thank the Science Research Council for the award of a research grant.

REFERENCES

BERGEL, D.H. *J. Physiol.* **156**, 445, 1961.
COURANT, R. and FRIEDRICHS, K. O. *Supersonic Flow and Shock Waves.* Interscience Publ., John Wiley, New York, 1948.
VON DESCHWANDEN, P., MÜLLER, A. and LASZT, L. *Abstr. Comm. XX Internat. Physiol. Congr.* Bruxelles, 930, 1956.
EVANS, R. L. *J. Theoret. Biol.* **3**, 392, 1962.
EVANS, R. L., BERNSTEIN, E. F., JOHNSON, E. and RELLER, C. *Amer. J. Physiol.* **202**, 619, 1962.
GREEN, A. E. and RIVLIN, R. *Arch. Rational Mech. Anal.*, 1957.
GREENFIELD and PATEL, *Circ. Res.* **10**, 778, 1962.
HALE, J. F., MCDONALD, D. A. and WOMERSLEY, J. R. *J. Physiol.* **128**, 629, 1955.
HESS, W. R. *Pflüg. Arch. ges. Physiol.* **168**, 439, 1917.
VON KRIES, J. Studien zur Pulslehre. *Akad. Verlagsbuch. von J. C. B. Mohr,* Freiburg i. B., 1892.
LAMBERT, J. W. *J. Franklin Inst.* **266**, 83, 1958.

McDONALD, D. A. *Blood Flow in Arteries*. Edward Arnold, London, 1960.

MITCHELL, J. R. A. and SCHWARTZ, C. J. *Arterial Disease*. Blackwell, Oxford, 1965, p. 61.

RALSTON, J. H., TAYLOR, A. N. and ELLIOTT, H. W. *Amer. J. Physiol.* **159**, 52, 1947.

REMMINGTON, J. W. *Amer. J. Physiol.* **180**, 83, 1955.

SEYMOUR, B. R. and VARLEY, E. (to be published).

SPENCER, M. P. and DENISON, A. B. In *Handbook of Physiology*, *Section 2*, *Circulation*, vol. II, HAMILTON, W. F. and DOW, P. (Editors), Amer. Physiol. Soc., Washington, D.C. 1963, p. 839.

VARLEY, E. *Arch. Rational Mech. Anal.* **19**, 215, 1965.

VARLEY, E. and ROGERS, T. G. (to be published).

THE INFLUENCE OF THE VISCOUS PROPERTIES OF BLOOD AND THE ARTERIAL WALL UPON THE INPUT IMPEDANCE OF THE ARTERIAL SYSTEM

M. G. TAYLOR*

Department of Physiology, University of Sydney, Sydney, Australia

THE material upon which this communication was based has been published in detail elsewhere (TAYLOR, 1966a, b) and therefore will not be recapitulated. However, the opportunity will be taken to outline some of the general conclusions which can be drawn from the calculations which have been made. There are two main aspects of circulatory physiology to which a study of vascular impedance is particularly relevant. First, the pressure–flow relations at the root of the aorta determine the stroke work of the heart; and secondly, the concept of vascular impedance is united with the analysis and description of pressure and flow in all parts of the arterial system. The physical analysis of the system can thus be used to determine, describe and explain many of the pressure–flow relations and transformations of pulsatile wave-patterns which are found in different regions.

Considering first the relations between arterial impedance and the work of the heart, we can conveniently divide the latter into two parts:

(i) A "steady" or *dc* term, which arises from the energy dissipated in driving the mean flow through the total peripheral resistance; this depends only on the dimensions of the vascular system and on the viscosity of the blood.

(ii) A "pulsatile" or oscillatory term, which arises from the energy dissipated by the oscillatory flow of blood, mainly in the arteries and small vessels; this depends not only on the viscosity of the blood, but also on the visco-elastic and architectural properties of the vascular system.

While in any given situation the "steady" term may be fixed, the "pulsatile" term will vary with the heart rate, according to the frequency characteristics of the input impedance which the vascular system presents at the root of the aorta. From this point of view, it is obviously desirable that the impedance should be as small as possible and further, that it should be as constant as possible over the working range of frequencies of the oscillatory components of flow. If the impedance were to have large maxima and minima in this range of frequencies, it would mean that the pulsatile component of external cardiac work would be subjected to corresponding fluctuations, and the system would operate less efficiently at some frequencies than at others. It has been found experimentally that the modulus of the input impedance of the arterial system, measured in the ascending aorta of the dog, decreases very rapidly over the range 0–4 c/s, passes through a minimum and then remains almost constant. It thus appears to possess the desirable features outlined above, and calculations have been carried out on a model system to explore the manner in which the properties of the arteries bring this about.

The model is of a set of randomly-bifurcating elastic tubes; there are seven orders of branching, and allowance has been made for the following factors:

(a) variation in wave-velocity, increasing in the peripheral segments;

(b) reflections from the terminations which, because of the random nature of the branching, are distributed at random distances from the origin;

(c) variation in cross-sectional area at branching;

(d) oscillatory motion of a viscous fluid in the tubes;

(e) the presence of a visco-elastic wall.

As far as the input impedance of a model of the major arteries is concerned, the steep fall and subsequent stabilization can be accounted for almost entirely by the presence of factors (a) and (b). The presence of viscosity, either in the wall or in the fluid, had relatively little effect on the general form of the impedance. When present, it did, naturally, lead to a more stable value for the impedance and removed some of the fluctuations at higher frequencies. A comparison was made of a system having only fluid viscosity with one having only wall-viscosity, taking realistic values for these. It was found that although the effects were relatively slight, the influence of wall-viscosity was the greater. A similar calculation, made for a model of a "peripheral" vascular bed, showed that, as one would expect, the effects of fluid viscosity became more significant where vessels of smaller diameter were involved.

As regards transmission, a similar situation was encountered. The major features of wave transmission in the arterial tree appear to depend upon the interacting effects of

(a) non-uniform arterial elasticity, leading to peripheral "amplification";

(b) reflected waves, leading to maxima and minima at "resonant frequencies"; (because of viscous damping and the interference of reflected components from the many scattered terminations, these effects are usually only appreciable at low frequencies);

(c) variation in cross-sectional area at branching; in general this is an expansion, and leads to a fall in wave amplitude;

(d) viscous damping arising from the properties of blood and of the arterial wall, which leads to attenuation of travelling waves.

Again, it was found that in the larger arteries the main cause of attenuation was the wall-viscosity. Fluid viscosity had much less influence on wave transmission than did quite small amounts of wall-viscosity. The values chosen were in the physiological range, with blood viscosity 0.04 poise, and the phase angle of the dynamic elastic constant of the wall $\theta_0 = 6°-12°$. In the vessels of a smaller model vascular bed, corresponding to the distribution of, for example, the femoral artery, the fluid viscosity became as important a cause of attentuation as the wall-viscosity.

Calculations, which have not yet been published, have also been made for still smaller vessels, of radius less than 0.3 mm. Here it was found that the damping was dominated by the fluid viscosity. There is, however, some uncertainty in the calculations, because no figures are available for the dynamic elastic constants of vessels of this size; the figure of $\theta_0 = 12°$ is, however, unlikely to be far wrong. An additional complication in this "arterial-arteriolar" model was that the vessels were small enough for the anomalous viscosity of blood to play a rôle, and the influence of the marginal zone was taken into account in the computations.

In summary, then, one may say that the major influence of the viscosity of blood upon the input impedance of the arterial system is exercised by way of the total peripheral resistance, which determines the "steady" component of the external work of the heart. The frequency-dependence of the input impedance, upon which the "pulsatile" component of cardiac work depends, is almost entirely governed by other factors, though the presence of blood viscosity leads to some stabilization at the higher frequencies. The viscous properties of the arterial wall do not affect the peripheral resistance, and therefore are without influence upon the "steady" component; they have some stabilizing effect upon the input impedance at the higher frequencies. Both blood viscosity and the viscosity of the arterial wall lead to attenuation of travelling waves; from the present computations it appears that in the major arteries the wall-viscosity is the more important, but that in the smaller vessels the influence of blood viscosity is as large or larger.

ACKNOWLEDGMENT

The National Heart Foundation of Australia supported the work upon which this communication was based.

REFERENCES

TAYLOR, M. G. *Biophys. J.* **6**, 29, 1966(a).
TAYLOR, M. G. *Biophys. J.* **6**, 697, 1966(b).

DISCUSSION

TAYLOR (*Australia*):

The effect of the elastic non-uniformity certainly is very striking. It does lead to these changes in pulse wave shape, it also leads to somewhat similar changes in the input impedance, but it won't explain the whole thing, not on its own. I did somewhat similar calculations, not with a non-linear program, just with a straight linear program with a stiffening tube and got somewhat similar results.

SEYMOUR (*England*):

Unfortunately we are a little behind Dr. Barnard in producing our graphs of the changes in the pressure and flow pulses. We have done some computation but this is not yet completed. In this we use the second order solution of our asymptotic series, and one can follow the effects of changes in stiffness, initial area and visco-elasticity on the pulse shape analytically, without reverting to solving the partial differential equations numerically. We hope our results will be published shortly.

One comment I would like to make on Dr. Barnard's observations: he mentioned that the initial "peaking" of the pressure pulse was due to a reflection. I think it was Lambert in a paper in 1958 who did some calculations using the characteristics showing this to be impossible. I do not know whether Dr. Barnard has seen this paper or has any comment on it?

BURTON (*Canada*):

I want to ask a question that is always bothering a lot of physiologists. I have my physiologist's hat on now. When we have these talks, they have been very popular for the last five or ten years, talking about Fourier analysis, frequency dependence, and so on. They are using theoretical models with a constant frequency, and, as every physiologist knows, the heart frequency changes from beat to beat in a quite remarkable way in many people. I am always bothered, having tried the experiments in a bathtub of getting standing waves. If it is not done strictly to the same frequency, you just get chaos, and I am wondering if someone has made a mathematical investigation of how strictly constant a frequency has to be that all this analysis is valid.

McDONALD (*U.S.A.*):

Dr. Burton's remarks are true of resonance or the formation of standing waves in the ordinary physical sense, but the interaction of a centrifugal wave with reflection coming only from the termination is much simpler. In any case, the normal heart beats at least as regularly, I should think, as Dr. Burton stirs his bath.

TAYLOR:

I think, I am in the happy position of being able to answer that one, with references. We have done this, Dr. Burton. It has been reported recently in *Circulation Research* and not only we, of course, but others have shown that, fortunately, the system is sufficiently linear to get away with the method of Fourier series analysis. In other words, you plot out the behavior of the system frequency by frequency from the harmonics of one pulse or train of pulses, then change the heart rate and plot out frequency by frequency for the harmonics of another train of pulses at a different rate, the points fall always on top of each other. I am also in the happy position of being able to say that we have recently done spectral analysis of this with a purely random system and it agrees very well, too. Fortunately, the non-linearities which do exist are so small that you cannot normally detect them. We have recently come up against this in analysis of pressure/diameter relations by Fourier analysis, and there is enough non-linearity in the normal pressure/radius relations of an artery to knock it around. We get the most bizarre phase relationships unless we take account of the non-linearity of the elastic constants. But with all respect, I think that Fourier analysis is a perfectly valid technique in the linear system and, even if the heart rate is wandering a little bit, you can move from one pulse to another and get repeatable results no matter what the frequencies are.

EIRICH (*U.S.A.*):

I wonder whether the following is a legitimate comment. As the heart sends its pressure pulse down the arteries, the latter expand and ease the work of the heart because the widening of the channels permits some radial flow which reduces the required pressure for pulse propagation. But after the passing of the pulse, the arteries must return to their original dimension, presumably due to a contraction of the muscles in the arterial wall. In ordinary visco-elastic systems, there is a hysteresis loop with a steeper slope on the upstroke and lower modulus on the reverse stroke. And it seems to me that in the arterial circle the modulus should be higher for the reverse stroke which does not seem to have been taken into account in any of these calculations.

SEYMOUR:

Well, I just repeat what I said earlier that our system can in fact include this but I am not a physiologist, I cannot say if it can happen or not.

TAYLOR:

On the question whether it happens or not, I think, it probably does not happen. The speed with which smooth muscles can contract is too slow for these responses. There does not seem to be much difference in the behavior of the elastic properties of an arterial system as regards these pulsatile events whether it is alive in the sense of the smooth muscle still being active or dead. There may be changes in viscosity. Some people have reported changes in the effective viscosity of the wall depending on the degree of contraction of the smooth muscle, changes so to speak in the mean level of the dynamic elastic constants. However, the story that the contraction of the smooth muscle actively propels blood, is something quite different. Hess, in 1918, wrote a long, furious article on this and described it as a "Luftschloss", and, I think, this is probably a fairly good description of it still. The speed of reaction of the smooth muscles is not fast enough to allow to do this, I think.

BURTON:

I agree completely with Professor Taylor on this. I do not think that the active contractions of the arterial system play any part in the circulation. It is a puzzling thing to physiologists or those who are interested in vasomotion and smooth muscle of vascular trees that there is much smooth muscle in the arteries. It plainly cannot be playing a physiological part in changing the resistance; if an artery halved its diameter, it would not really add very much to the total resistance. I think the answer has come from some histologists who are suggesting that the cellular elements in the arteries, which have mainly elastic tissue, are there not for a contractal function but to produce the fibers for repair, collagen and elastin. Otherwise, we are faced with the fact that, in the smooth muscle of the femoral artery, for example, it only seems to cause pathology and emergencies for the surgeon when it goes into spasm. It is very difficult to see how smooth muscle in arteries is playing a physiological rôle.

WIEDERHIELM (*U.S.A.*):

It appears that the contractile state of the vascular smooth muscle has a profound effect on the viscous characteristics of the vessel walls. I was wondering if perhaps the differences in the data of Bergel and McDonald may be related to such differences in contractile state. Secondly, I was also wondering whether Dr. Taylor had considered this factor in his model.

TAYLOR:

Well, it could indeed. The values of up to 12 degrees, which I chose for the phase angle of the elastic modulus, were the highest Bergel found. In some experiments we have recently done on the pressure/ diameter relations of arteries *in vivo* the phase angle is again about 0.1 to 0.12 radians. This is for carefully prepared vessels *in vivo*; it is a little surprising. I cannot explain the results. Dr. McDonald did mention in his paper that they gave a drug which caused a profound contraction of the smooth muscle and this produced a still greater degree of damping. So this probably is the explanation of the differences, although I find it a little hard to reconcile with the values that we have got, even down to quite small vessels like the saphenous artery in the dog which has a pulsatile excursion. I boast a little that the instrument of my colleague, Mr. Gow, measures pulsatile excursions of 8 microns quite faithfully and the phase angle there, I think, is only about 0.12 radian, which is quite small.

WIEDERHIELM:

I also would like to add a comment about the contractile capabilities of the vascular smooth muscle. In general, innervated segments of the blood vessels show sluggish dimension changes. However, in spontaneously contracting vascular smooth muscle, for example in bat wing venules, it is not uncommon to see contraction rates of 60 per minute. So whether smooth muscle contraction plays an important rôle in the arteries or not, the capability for rapid contraction still is there.

VARLEY (*England*):

I would like to stress that the permittable factors which Mr. Seymour calls frequency is not the usual frequency that you find when you do Fourier analysis. Mr. Seymour's pulse was quite arbitrary. It had an arbitrary shape in time, his frequency was the maximum rate at which the area was changing over some mean area. He assumed that it was large as compared with the visco-elastic properties of the tube. But in that part, the pulse could have been quite an arbitrary shape. This is a highly non-linear system. One cannot do a Fourier analysis; in fact, it is impossible to do so. As regards the non-linearity, of course, one does not notice non-linearity if one measures the wrong thing. If one is interested in calculating the pressure from the area, it is quite true to say that there is a linear relationship. But, if one is interested in calculating the rate at which pressure is changing in time, or the rate at which the area is changing with respect to time, then this is highly non-linear. One notes no linearity in things which are very sensitive to non-linearity, the pressure/area relationship is not sensitive to non-linearity. The time-rate of change of pressure and the time rate of change of area are sensitive to non-linearity. And the results that Dr. Barnard showed seem to agree with what would happen, that the acceleration of a pulse does in fact change in time as it goes along the vascular system.

HYDRODYNAMIC ASPECTS OF THE CIRCULATORY SYSTEM

S. I. RUBINOW*

Biomathematics Division,
Graduate School of Medical Sciences, Cornell University,
and Sloan-Kettering Institute, New York, N.Y.

and

JOSEPH B. KELLER*

Courant Institute of Mathematical Sciences,
New York University, New York, N.Y.

1. INTRODUCTION

Ever since the development of hydrodynamics and the theory of elasticity, theoreticians have attempted to apply these theories to the circulatory system. Most applications have concerned the flow of blood in a single artery. The blood has usually been assumed to be an inviscid, incompressible or slightly compressible fluid, although recently it has been treated as a viscous fluid. The artery has usually been treated as a thin elastic tube. The blood flow and corresponding motion of the artery wall have generally been assumed to be of small amplitude, so that the governing equations could be linearized. Then the motion could be analysed into time harmonic waves of fixed frequency and wave length. The main result of all these considerations is a relation between frequency and wave length, called the dispersion equation. From this relation the phase velocity, group velocity and attenuation rate, if any, of the wave can be found as functions of frequency and of the properties of the fluid and the tube wall.

The complete dispersion equation just referred to has not been investigated, so that only incomplete results for velocity and attenuation have been obtained. Usually only one mode of propagation has been examined, whereas there are infinitely many. Generally only the limit of long wave lengths has been studied, which fails to reveal the full behavior of the waves. In particular this limit may not account for the difference in behavior between a wave having the fundamental pulse frequency and its harmonics.

The obvious next step after studying the flow in a single tube is to apply the results to flow in a network of tubes, which may represent a portion of the arterial system. There have been practically no investigations of this kind.

We see that the state of analysis of the hydromechanical theory of blood flow in the circulatory system is quite incomplete. Therefore we have undertaken an intensive theoretical investigation aimed at extending this theory. Our study begins with flow in a single tube, then it considers the phenomena which occur at the junction of two or more tubes, and finally it deals with flow in a network of tubes. Here we shall present some of our results concerning the single tube and the junction problem, as well as some of their experimental implications.

2. MODEL OF THE CIRCULATORY SYSTEM

The arterio-venous part of the circulatory system is considered to be a network of elastic tubes containing a viscous compressible fluid. The tube walls are assumed to consist of an elastic or visco-elastic material which has uniform properties. The fluid velocity, pressure variations and density variations, as well as the displacements in the walls, are assumed to be small enough to be governed by linear equations of motion. In dimensionless terms this means that the Reynolds and Mach numbers of the flow, and the maximum strain in the walls, are small. Thus the flow of the fluid and the motion of the tube walls which accompanies it, are assumed to be small perturbations upon a state of rest. In addition, it is assumed that the arterio-venous system is imbedded in viscera which have a known reaction to any motion of the tubes. This reaction is represented by an impedance boundary condition on the outer surfaces of the tubes.

The objective of the study is to determine the fluid velocity and pressure and the tube motion throughout the network, due to a prescribed pressure pulse or a prescribed input velocity at the end of one of the tubes of the network. We have in mind that the prescribed pulse is produced by the heart at the entrance to the aorta. We suppose that the applied pressure is periodic in time. Then Fourier analysis shows that it consists of a number of components of different frequencies, all of which are integral multiples (harmonics) of the fundamental frequency, which is that of the applied pressure. Because of the linearity of the equations of motion, we can analyse separately the motion due to each harmonic component and then superpose them to obtain the resultant motion.

3. FLOW IN A SINGLE TUBE

To analyse the flow in a single tube, we assume that the tube is a long hollow right circular cylinder of finite thickness. Then we need the following parameters to describe the system: the coefficients of viscosity, the equilibrium density, and the sound velocity of the fluid; the density, radius, thickness, elastic modulus, and Poisson ratio of the tube; four impedance coefficients which represent the reaction of the viscera to the longitudinal and radial motions of the outer boundary of the tube. By introducing dimensionless variables we see that only certain dimensionless combinations of these parameters appear in the theory. This reduces the number of parameters and simplifies the analysis somewhat.

The solution of the equations of motion shows that in a single tube each harmonic component of the motion is characterized by certain complex numbers called amplitudes and propagation constants. The propagation constants are the roots of a transcendental equation called the dispersion equation. This equation has infinitely many roots. It follows that there are an infinite number of propagation constants for a given harmonic frequency component. With each propagation constant, there is a set of profiles for the fluid pressure, fluid velocity, and tube wall displacement. Such a set of profiles determines a mode and each mode has an amplitude. Thus there is an infinite set of modes. The amplitudes are determined by the strengths and phases of the modes in the applied pressure pulse. These amplitudes in turn determine the motions associated with the modes throughout the tube.

The propagation constants are generally complex numbers. If a propagation constant is essentially real, we call the mode associated with it a propagating mode. If the propagation constant is essentially imaginary, we say the mode associated with it is non-propagating. Non-propagating modes are disturbances which decay rapidly with distance along the tube, while propagating modes do not decay or decay only slightly. The propagating modes carry the energy of the wave motion. Each mode has a finite velocity of propagation, called its phase velocity, which is determined by the ratio of the angular frequency to the real part of the propagation constant of the mode. Each mode also has an attenuation coefficient, determined by the imaginary part of the propagation constant, which determines how rapidly the mode decays along the tube.

We have analysed the dispersion relation to determine all the roots and to see how they depend on the non-dimensional parameters of the problem. The mathematical difficulties reside in the analysis of this equation, and not in solving the differential equations of motion, which is perfectly straightforward for the circular cylindrical tube.

Some of the results of this analysis are contained in the figures. The results shown in the figures are for the simplified case in which the tube is very thin, the fluid is inviscid, and the effect of the viscera is negligible. Only for such simplified cases can analytical results be readily obtained. The curves in the figures are drawn schematically on the basis of analytic results. In the general case, the curves are drawn on the basis of computer calculations.

In Fig. 1 we have plotted the phase velocity c as a function of the frequency for every propagating mode in the case when the tube wall mass is small compared to the fluid mass. Thus the non-dimensional parameter m, which is one-half the ratio of tube

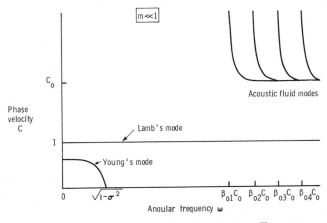

FIG. 1. PHASE VELOCITY c AS A FUNCTION OF ANGULAR FREQUENCY ω. THE UNIT OF FREQUENCY IS $\omega_0 = [E/\rho_1 a^2(1-\sigma^2)]^{1/2}$ AND THE UNIT OF VELOCITY IS $a\omega_0$. THE CONDITION $m \ll 1$ MEANS THAT THE TUBE WALL MASS IS SMALL COMPARED TO THE FLUID MASS. THE VALUE OF c FOR YOUNG'S MODE WHEN ω IS ZERO IS GIVEN BY THE EXPRESSION $c = [m(1-\sigma^2)/2]^{1/2}$. c_0 IS THE VELOCITY OF SOUND IN THE FLUID AND $\beta_{01}, \beta_{02} \ldots$ ARE NUMERICAL CONSTANTS.

mass to fluid mass per unit length of tube, is small, i.e. $m \ll 1$. The frequency is measured in units of $\omega_0 = [E/\rho_1 a^2 (1-\sigma^2)]^{1/2}$. This is the resonance frequency for radial oscillations of the tube. For a typical human aorta with Young's modulus $E \sim 10^6$ dynes/cm², Poisson ratio $\sigma \sim \frac{1}{2}$, tube density $\rho_1 \sim 1$ gm/cm³, and tube radius $a \sim 1$ cm, this frequency is about 200 c/s.

The following features should be noted. At low frequencies only two modes are propagating and the rest are non-propagating. Most of the studies in the past have been confined to the low frequency behavior of one of the two propagating modes. We shall call it the Young mode because the phase velocity at zero frequency was first given by YOUNG[1]. We see that this mode has a cut-off at the frequency $\omega = [1 - \sigma^2]^{1/2}$ above which it no longer propagates. The second propagating mode we shall call Lamb's mode, because its phase velocity was first investigated by LAMB[2].

It may be seen that the phase velocity of this mode remains relatively constant for all frequencies. Assuming $m = 0.1$ and $\sigma = \frac{1}{2}$, this phase velocity is about five times as large as that of the Young mode. The Lamb mode has not received sufficient attention by blood flow investigators. This is probably because most experimenters placed their sensing equipment in the interior of the fluid to measure the pressure. The profile of this mode indicates that for it the tube displacements are relatively more important than the pressure variations. This is borne out by VAN CITTERS'[3] observations of pulse wave transmission in elastic tubes. He seems to be the only investigator to have identified one of his measured velocities with the velocity of Lamb's mode. He placed his sensing apparatus directly on the wall of the tube.

It has been stated that the clinical significance of the measurement of the pulse wave velocity is that it yields an elastic constant of the artery wall from which the state of health of the artery can be inferred. We should like to emphasize that it is not necessary to catheterize an artery to make the pressure measurements necessary for determining the velocity. The same information can be inferred from measurements of the artery wall motion made external to the artery. The motion could be excited by impact and would be associated with Lamb's mode.

At rather high frequencies, we note in Fig. 1 the appearance of the fluid acoustic modes. In the units used in the figure, the velocity of sound in the fluid c_0 is about 100 if the fluid is blood. The quantities $\beta_{01}, \beta_{02}, \ldots$ are certain numerical constants. Asymptotically for very high frequency, the velocity of all these modes is c_0. As the frequency

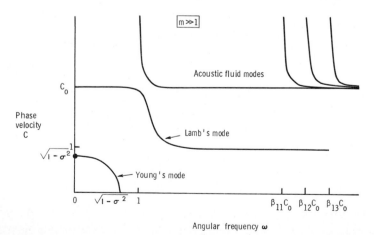

FIG. 2. THE SAME QUANTITIES AS FOR FIG. 1 ARE PLOTTED FOR THE CASE $m \geqslant 1$. THE TUBE WALL IS VERY MASSIVE COMPARED TO THE FLUID. THE QUANTITIES $\beta_{11}, \beta_{12} \ldots$ ARE NUMERICAL CONSTANTS. NOTE PARTICULARLY, IN CONTRAST WITH FIG. 1, THE VALUES OF c FOR YOUNG'S MODE AND LAMB'S MODE AT LOW FREQUENCIES, AND THE APPEARANCE OF c FOR THE FIRST ACOUSTIC FLUID MODE AT $\omega = 1$.

increases, new modes become propagating at almost regular intervals on the frequency axis. If the fluid were incompressible, these modes would be absent.

In Fig. 2 a similar plot has been made for the case when the tube wall is very massive compared to the fluid, i.e. $m \gg 1$. In this case, the tube behaves like an almost rigid pipe. The velocity of the Young mode no longer depends on the thickness of the wall or the density of the fluid, but depends only on the elastic modulus and density of the tube. The frequency cut-off is independent of m. The velocity of Lamb's mode becomes equal to the speed of sound at low frequencies and decreases to the value 1 at high frequencies. The values of ω at which the acoustic fluid modes become propagating are all reduced somewhat from the values that obtain in the case $m \ll 1$.

In Fig. 3 we have plotted the absolute value of the ratio of radial to longitudinal displacements of the tube, as a function of frequency, for the case $m \ll 1$. Only the ratios for the propagating modes have been shown. From such a plot we may see at a

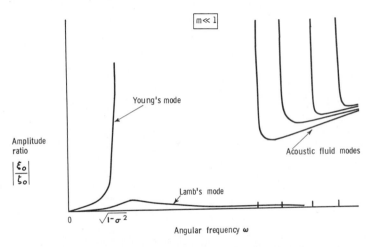

FIG. 3. THE AMPLITUDE RATIO $|\xi_0/\zeta_0|$ AS A FUNCTION OF ANGULAR FREQUENCY FOR THE CASE $m \ll 1$. $|\xi_0|$ IS THE MAXIMUM AMPLITUDE OF RADIAL DISPLACEMENT OF THE TUBE, AND $|\zeta_0|$ IS THE MAXIMUM AMPLITUDE OF LONGITUDINAL DISPLACEMENT OF THE TUBE. NOTE THE RADIAL RESONANCE OF YOUNG'S MODE AT $\omega = [1 - \sigma^2]^{1/2}$ AND THE RADIAL RESONANCES OF THE ACOUSTIC FLUID MODES AT HIGH FREQUENCIES.

glance whether a given mode is predominantly radial or longitudinal at a given frequency. Thus, we see that the Young mode can be characterized as longitudinal at low frequencies and as radial or transverse in the neighborhood of $\omega = [1 - \sigma^2]^{1/2}$. Lamb's mode is essentially a longitudinal oscillation at all frequencies. The acoustic fluid modes are neither longitudinal nor transverse, except at the frequencies just above those at which they become propagating, when they exhibit a striking radial resonance.

4. DISCUSSION

We have described some of the features of a hydrodynamic theory of the arterio-venous system. Because of the mathematical similarity between the model and a system of interconnected wave guides which convey electromagnetic energy, we may call it a wave-guide theory of the arterio-venous system. Such a theory can be simplified by giving up the details of the variation of pressure, velocity, etc. with radius at a given cross-section of a vessel. In that way, the wave-guide theory can be reduced to a multi-transmission line theory. Some characteristics of the single tube system that are worthy of emphasis are its multi-modality, its stop and pass-band frequency intervals for each mode, and its dispersive nature, i.e. its frequency-dependent phase velocities.

The mammalian heart beat is small compared to the artery wall resonance frequency ω_0. Even when several harmonics are considered, the arterio-venous system is a low frequency system. Therefore it can be viewed as a dual transmission line system: one line for the Young mode and the other for the Lamb mode.

What is the practical significance of the infinitely many modes which do not propagate at low frequencies? They play an essential role at junctions of branches and at stenoses of single vessels. At each such place, these modes are excited. This excitation is associated with a redistribution of energy among the propagating modes on the two sides of a junction or stenosis.

The theory might account for some physiological observations of blood flow for which there appear to be no adequate theoretical explanations. One of these is the change in shape of the pressure as it travels down the aorta. A related observation is the change in shape of the pulse wave as it passes from the aorta to the femoral artery.

Another puzzling observation is the post-stenotic dilation[4]. The analysis of the amplitude ratio we have presented (see Fig. 3) would tend to suggest that the Young mode and the acoustic fluid modes, because they are accompanied by radial resonances, tend to stretch the vessel outwardly, and thus weaken it. Thus the chain of events would seem to be as follows. Stenosis produces excitation of the Young mode near the radial resonance frequency, and the acoustic fluid modes. The resulting radial resonances lead to fatigue of the vessel which is followed by dilation.

There are numerous other phenomena to which the theory should be applicable.

ACKNOWLEDGMENTS

This work has been supported in part by the Office of Naval Research under Contract No. Nonr-401 (57) and the National Science Foundation under Grant No. NSF–GP 3668.

REFERENCES

[1] YOUNG, THOMAS. *Phil. Trans. Roy. Soc.*, Part I, 176, 1808.
[2] LAMB, H. *Manchester Lit. and Phil. Soc. Memoirs and Proc.* **42**, No. 9, 1898.
[3] VAN CITTERS, R. L. *Circ. Res.* **8**, 1145, 1960.
[4] See, for example, ROACH, M. R. *Circ. Res.* **13**, 537, 1963.

DISCUSSION

VARLEY (*England*):

What kind of freedom have you got in putting your initial condition on the shape of your pulse? As I understand it, you just looked for a traveling wave which is going in the z-direction: $\exp[ik(z-ct)]$ with a coefficient which is just a function of r.

RUBINOW (*U.S.A.*):

Yes, that is right. The coefficient is a function of r.

VARLEY:

What are these functions, are they Bessel functions?

RUBINOW:

Yes, they are Bessel functions.

VARLEY:

I must say, I was greatly relieved at the end of the paper to be reassured that these things did not really happen in the circulation. I remember once trying to calculate the radial resonances. We got some curious results at one stage, which I could not explain, and thought there might be radial rhythms involved. We calculated this and it turned out to be, I think, 200 or 300 cycles, something like that for a piece of dog's aorta, which is, of course, very well outside the range of the normal pulse rate.

RUBINOW:

That is the right order magnitude for the frequency at which the radial resonance occurs. For the aorta with an elastic constant of the order of ten to the sixth (in cgs units) and a radius of one centimeter, the order of magnitude of the resonance frequency is 150 or 200 c/s. Presumably, in the pulse under ordinary circumstances, you would not see it; but if you had a stenosis or a junction or some obstruction, then I think it could very easily get excited.

TAYLOR (*Australia*):

Well, yes. On the question of junctions, this is of course a difficult one. The sort of calculations that I have done and most people do is to just zero frequency.

RUBINOW:

Yes, that is, using the zero frequency result.

TAYLOR:

Yes, but then various people have tried in effect to determine experimentally the impedance of a junction. Hardung has tried that in Switzerland and Gessner tried it in Baltimore. And as it turns out, as I understand their results, there is only a small discrepancy between what you get as the impedance you calculate by just joining the two together, and the impedance you actually measure when they are in fact joined together. Fortunately, the effects of the actual architecture, and the hydrodynamics of the junction appear to be small and, therefore, are not going to disturb us very much. Have you any comments at all?

RUBINOW:

No, we have not looked at that problem as yet.

TAYLOR:

I think it will turn out to be small, at least, I hope so.

RUBINOW:

Well, that would simplify matters.

VISCOMETRIC FLOWS OF NON-NEWTONIAN FLUIDS

R. S. RIVLIN*

Center for the Application of Mathematics,
Lehigh University, Bethlehem, Pennsylvania, U.S.A.

1. INTRODUCTION

In this paper a simple analysis of certain viscometric flows of incompressible, iso-tropic, non-Newtonian fluids is given. None of the results is new, nor do they in any significant sense provide generalizations of the original calculations[1, 2]. The latter were based on the assumption of a constitutive equation valid for a much wider class of flows than the viscometric flows and the results obtained can therefore be related to many types of flow other than viscometric. This is not the case for the procedure used in the present paper. It has, however, the merit of far greater simplicity and draws only on the most elementary concepts of continuum mechanics. It may easily be applied to other viscometric flows, such as helical flow in a cylindrical annular region, not discussed here.

The procedure adopted in the present paper, like that of COLEMAN and NOLL[3, 4, 5], employs a constitutive equation which is, in effect, limited to viscometric flows. How-ever, the procedure of Coleman and Noll is much more elaborate than that adopted here, even as recapitulated in recent books[6, 7].

In the present paper, we start our discussion by considering the rectilinear shear of an isotropic fluid. It follows directly from the isotropy of the fluid that the shearing stress must be an odd function of the velocity-gradient, while the normal stress com-ponents must be even functions of the velocity-gradient. Since the normal stress com-ponents in an incompressible fluid are undetermined to the extent of an arbitrary hydrostatic pressure, it follows that the stress in the fluid (i.e. the normal and shear components) is characterized by three functions of the velocity-gradient. For each of the viscometric flows considered — Couette flow, torsional flow between discs and between cones, and Poiseuille flow — each element of fluid is subjected to a recti-linear shear of constant magnitude, the plane of the shear and the fluid element under-going the same superposed rigid motion. The stress at each point of the fluid is therefore determined from the equations of motion for rectilinear flow by substitution of the appropriate velocity gradient.

Application of Newton's second law to an appropriate body of the fluid enables us, in each case, to obtain ordinary differential equations for the velocity and pressure distributions in the fluid. These can be solved in each case, subject to suitable boundary conditions, to provide a complete analysis of the viscometric flow considered. Such an analysis is carried out in detail in the case of Couette flow, but is merely indicated briefly in the other cases considered.

Finally, in section 7, the problem of flow of a non-Newtonian fluid in a straight tube of non-circular cross-section is briefly discussed.

2. RECTILINEAR SHEAR

We consider a mass of fluid to be subjected to a rectilinear shearing motion, the velocity of each particle of the fluid being parallel to the x-axis of a rectangular Cartesian coordinate system (x,y,z) and proportional to its distance from the xz-plane. Thus, a particle of the fluid at x,y,z has velocity κy, say, parallel to the x-axis, where κ is a constant. The velocity-gradient throughout the fluid is then κ.

Let us consider the forces exerted by the surrounding fluid on the rectangular element of fluid $ABCDA'B'C'D'$, centered at P, shown in Fig. 1. Let $\mathbf{F}_y$ be the vector force exerted across $ABCD$, measured per unit area of $ABCD$. This force must, of course,

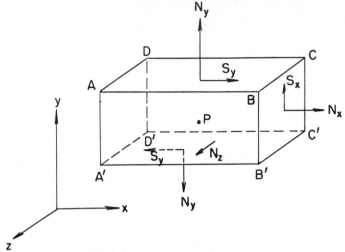

FIG. 1. FORCES ON $ADD'A'$ AND $DCC'D'$ NOT SHOWN.

depend on κ only, since this is the only parameter defining the motion in the fluid (apart from a uniform translational velocity which cannot alter the force). If the fluid is isotropic in its state of rest, then this force cannot have any component parallel to the z-axis. Its component parallel to the x-axis, which we denote by S_y and describe as the *shearing component*, must be an odd function of κ, since reversal of the velocity at each point of the fluid must change the sign of S_y. Thus,

$$S_y = \kappa f(\kappa^2), \tag{2.1}$$

where $f(\kappa^2)$ is some function of κ^2. The component N_y in the y-direction of the force $\mathbf{F}_y$, which we call the *normal component*, must of course be an even function of κ and we therefore write

$$N_y = f_y(\kappa^3). \tag{2.2}$$

The force on $A'B'C'D'$ is, of course, equal and opposite to that on $ABCD$.

In a similar manner, we see that the vector force $\mathbf{F}_x$ on $BCC'B'$, measured per unit area of this surface, can have no component in the z-direction and we denote the component in the y-direction (the shearing component) by S_x and that in the x-direction (the normal component) by N_x. As before it is evident that isotropy implies that S_x is an odd function of κ and N_x is an even function of κ. The force on $ADD'A'$ is, of course, equal and opposite to that on $BCC'B'$.

It is easily seen by taking moments about an axis through P parallel to the z-direction that

$$S_x = S_y. \tag{2.3}$$

The vector force $\mathbf{F}_z$ on $AA'B'B$ must, for an isotropic fluid, be perpendicular to this element and it must, furthermore, be an even function of κ. We denote this force by N_z. The force on $DD'C'C$ is equal and opposite to that on $AA'B'B$.

Collecting the results so far obtained, we have

$$S_x = S_y = S(\text{say}) = \kappa f(\kappa^2),$$
$$N_x = f_x(\kappa^2), \quad N_y = f_y(\kappa^2), \quad N_z = f_z(\kappa^2). \tag{2.4}$$

If the fluid is incompressible, then the forces acting on the faces of $ABCDA'B'C'D'$ are not uniquely determined by the velocity-gradient, but, for specified velocity-gradient, may be changed by an arbitrary hydrostatic pressure p, say. Equations (2.4) must then be modified to

$$S_x = S_y = S = \kappa f(\kappa^2);$$
$$N_x = f_x(\kappa^2) - p, \quad N_y = f_y(\kappa^2) - p, \quad N_z = -p. \tag{2.5}$$

These are the basic equations on which the remainder of the paper is based.

3. COUETTE FLOW

The fluid is contained in the annular region between two coaxial cylinders, as shown in Fig. 2. One of the cylinders, say the outer, is rotated with angular velocity Ω, while the other remains stationary. We ask ourselves the following question: What forces must be exerted on the fluid by the cylindrical walls and over the free surface of the

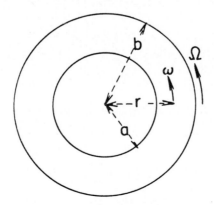

FIG. 2.

fluid in order that each particle of the fluid move in a horizontal circular path about the axis of rotation?

Let us suppose that particles located at radius r move with angular velocity ω, i.e. with speed $r\omega$. The angular velocity ω varies, of course, from zero at the wall of the inner cylinder to Ω at that of the outer cylinder. The radial gradient of the speed of the particles of the fluid is $d(r\omega)/dr$. Now,

$$\frac{d(r\omega)}{dr} = r\frac{d\omega}{dr} + \omega. \tag{3.1}$$

The second term on the right-hand side of (3.1) is due to the "rigid" angular velocity of the fluid element at radius r about the axis, and the first term is due to the shearing motion in the fluid. Thus, apart from its rigid motion, each element of the fluid undergoes a shearing motion with velocity-gradient $r\,d\omega/dr$, the plane of shear being horizontal. The forces on the element are given completely, apart from an arbitrary hydrostatic pressure p, by the formulae (2.5) with κ replaced by $r\,d\omega/dr$. Then, from the fact that the forces, including centrifugal forces, acting on each element of the material are in equilibrium, we can calculate the forces which must be exerted on the fluid by the walls and the forces which must be exerted on the free surface. We can also calculate the manner in which ω varies throughout the fluid.

Consider an annular region of the fluid between radii r and $r+dr$, as shown in horizontal cross-section in Fig. 3. The angular velocities at these radii are ω and $\omega+d\omega$

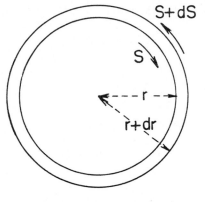

Fig. 3.

respectively. The forces on the surface at radius r, per unit length in the vertical direction, have tangential components S, say, per unit area and normal components N, say, while those on the surface at radius $r+dr$ have corresponding components $S+dS$ and $N+dN$, say. The fact that the resultant moment on this cylindrical annulus is zero means that

$$(r+dr)^2(S+dS) - r^2S = 0; \tag{3.2}$$

i.e., with the neglect of terms in the differentials dr and dS of higher degree than the first,

$$2S\,dr + r\,dS = 0. \tag{3.3}$$

This yields immediately

$$S = A/r^2, \tag{3.4}$$

where A is constant.

Now S is, of course, given by (2.5), with κ replaced by $r\,d\omega/dr$. We then have

$$r\frac{d\omega}{dr}f\left[\left(r\frac{d\omega}{dr}\right)^2\right] = \frac{A}{r^2}. \tag{3.5}$$

If f is a known function, this provides us with an equation for determining the manner in which the velocity-gradient $r\,d\omega/dr$ varies throughout the fluid. From this, the manner in which ω varies can be determined by integration. In carrying out this integration we introduce another integration constant B, say. Both A and B must be determined from the boundary conditions that $\omega = \Omega$ on the outer cylinder and $\omega = 0$ on the inner cylinder.

We now consider the balance of forces in the radial direction. In order to do so, we consider half of the cylindrical annulus of Fig. 3 (see Fig. 4). The force on the cylindrical

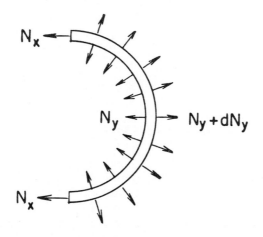

FIG. 4.

surfaces of this in the radial outward and inward directions are $N_y + dN_y$ and N_y respectively, per unit area. The forces on the "cut" ends are N_x per unit area. N_x and N_y are, of course, given by (2.5), with κ replaced by $r\,d\omega/dr$. In addition a centrifugal force $-r\omega^2$ per unit mass acts on the cylinder. Balance of forces in the horizontal direction in Fig. 3 then gives

$$2[(r+dr)(N_y + dN_y) - rN_y] - 2N_x dr = -2\rho r^2\omega^2 dr, \tag{3.6}$$

where ρ is the density of the fluid. The first term in (3.6) is the resultant of the radial forces on the surfaces of radii $r + dr$ and r in Fig. 4. The term $-2N_x dr$ is the resultant of the forces on the "cut" surfaces of the half-cylinder and the term on the right-hand side is the resultant of the centrifugal forces. Equation (3.6) leads to

$$\frac{dN_y}{dr} + \frac{N_y - N_x}{r} = -\rho r \omega^2, \tag{3.7}$$

again with the neglect of terms of higher degree than the first in the differentials. Introducing (2.5) into (3.7), we obtain

$$\frac{dp}{dr} = \frac{df_y}{dr} + \frac{f_y - f_x}{r} + \rho r \omega^2. \tag{3.8}$$

Whence

$$p = f_y + \int^r \frac{f_y - f_x}{r} dr + \int^r \rho r \omega^2 dr. \tag{3.9}$$

Introducing this expression for p into (2.5); we obtain

$$N_x = f_x - f_y - \int^r \frac{f_y - f_x}{r} dr - \int^r \rho r \omega^2 dr,$$

$$N_y = - \int^r \frac{f_y - f_x}{r} dr - \int^r \rho r \omega^2 dr,$$

$$\tag{3.10}$$

$$N_z = -f_y - \int^r \frac{f_y - f_x}{r} dr - \int^r \rho r \omega^2 dr,$$

$$S = r \frac{d\omega}{dr} f.$$

We recall that f, f_x and f_y are even functions of $r\, d\omega/dr$. We note that $-p$, N_x, N_y, and N_z are undetermined to the extent of a common arbitrary constant, reflecting the incompressibility of the fluid.

   Now suppose that the radii of the inner and outer cylinders are a and b respectively. The force exerted on the fluid by the outer cylinder is $N_y|_{r=b}$ per unit area directed radially outwards and that exerted by the inner cylinder is $N_y|_{r=a}$ per unit area directed radially inwards. The difference π in these forces $N_y|_{r=b}^{r=a}$ is given by

$$\pi = N_y|_{r=b}^{r=a} = - \int_b^a \frac{f_y - f_x}{r} dr - \int_b^a \rho r \omega^2 dr. \tag{3.11}$$

   If manometric tubes are introduced into the inner and outer cylindrical walls, as shown in Fig. 5, the fluid will therefore rise to different heights in the tubes. The fluid in the inner tube will stand at a height $-\pi/\rho$ above that in the outer.

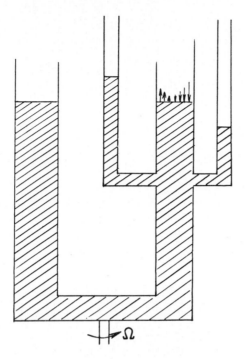

FIG. 5. VERTICAL CROSS-SECTION.

The forces which must be exerted on the free surface of the liquid in order to maintain the state of flow considered is N_z per unit area. This is given by the third of equations (3.10) and, of course, varies with radial distance. In practical experimental arrangements it is not possible to apply these forces, the free surface generally being left force-free. We may then expect a distortion of the free surface together with a circulatory flow near the surface in vertical planes, and that is the type of behavior which is usually observed.

4. TORSIONAL FLOW BETWEEN PARALLEL DISCS

We now consider a cylindrical mass of fluid contained between two rigid discs a distance h apart, as shown in Fig. 6. The upper disc is held stationary and the lower disc is rotated with angular velocity Ω. We ask what forces must be applied to the liquid by the discs in order that each particle of the liquid, in the plane at a distance z below the upper disc, move with angular velocity $\Omega z/h$ about the axis of rotation; i.e. the angular velocity of a particle is proportional to its distance below the fixed disc. We note that the speed with which a particle in this plane, at a radial distance r from the axis of rotation, moves is $\Omega zr/h$. Thus, each element of the fluid undergoes a shearing motion with velocity-gradient $\Omega r/h$, the plane of shear being vertical and the shearing motion being in the circumferential direction.

We can then use eqs. (2.5) to calculate the stress associated with the assumed motion by replacing κ by $\Omega r/h$. Then, proceeding in a manner somewhat similar to that employed in discussing Couette flow, we find that if the curved surface of the cylindrical mass of

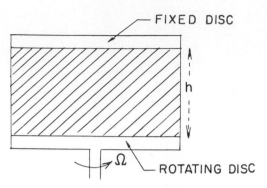

FIG. 6. VERTICAL CROSS-SECTION.

fluid is force-free, the forces which must be applied to the fluid by the upper disc are tangential forces Θ per unit area and normal forces N per unit area, given by

$$\Theta = \frac{\Omega r}{h} f\left(\frac{\Omega^2 r^2}{h^2}\right),$$

and   (4.1)

$$N = f_y\left(\frac{\Omega^2 r^2}{h^2}\right) + \int_a^r \frac{1}{r} f_x\left(\frac{\Omega^2 r^2}{h^2}\right) dr,$$

where a is the radius of the cylindrical mass. Those which are applied by the lower disc are equal and opposite at corresponding radii. Unlike the case of Couette flow, however, it is also necessary to apply forces distributed through the volume of the fluid. These just balance the centrifugal forces and are given by $r(\Omega z/h)^2$ per unit mass, directed radially inwards. In practice it is not possible to apply these forces and consequently, superposed on the assumed flow, we may expect a flow which is qualitatively of the type one might expect from a distribution of body forces $r(\Omega z/h)^2$ per unit mass, directed radially outwards. This will, of course, take place in vertical planes through the axis of rotation and will be circulatory in character.

In deriving the result given by eqs. (4.1), it is assumed that the curved surface of the cylindrical mass of fluid is force-free. If it is not, but is rather subjected to a uniform thrust P per unit area, then the shearing force Θ is unaltered, but the normal force N given by (4.1) is altered to $N - P$. In the usual experimental arrangement, due to GARNER, NISSAN and WOOD[8], the fluid is contained between the disc-like bases of two cups, as shown in vertical cross-section in Fig. 7. Manometric tubes are introduced into the base of the inner (stationary) cup and when the outer cup is set in motion the fluid rises in the tubes to a height depending on its radial position. The edge conditions in this arrangement defy calculation leaving P, the normal thrust on an imaginary cylindrical surface in the fluid corresponding to the broken line in Fig. 7, an undetermined quantity in the experiment. Thus, only the differences in the heights of rise of the fluid in the tubes can be interpreted in terms of the second of the formulae (4.1).

In this experimental arrangement, the secondary flow in vertical cross-sections through the axis of rotation can be minimized by decreasing h and Ω proportionately,

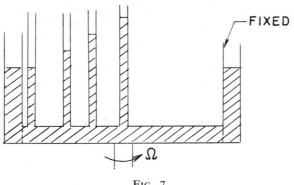

FIG. 7.

so that the rate of shear and normal force N at given r are unchanged. The centrifugal forces are, however, decreased and in addition the secondary flow resulting from them takes place in a narrower "channel" and hence more slowly.

5. TORSIONAL FLOW BETWEEN CONES

We now consider the liquid to be contained in the region between two coaxial cones, one of which is stationary, while the other—say the outer one—rotates about the common axis with angular velocity Ω, as shown, in vertical cross-section through the common axis of the cones, in Fig. 8. This is, of course, the configuration used in

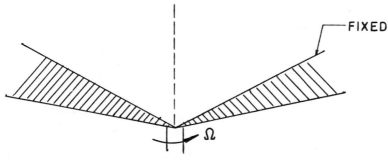

FIG. 8.

the Weissenberg rheogoniometer[9]. We ask what forces must be applied to the liquid in order that each particle shall move in a horizontal circle, with an angular velocity ω which depends on the polar angle θ only. We see that the speed of a particle at radial distance r from the apex of the cones and polar angle θ is $r\omega \sin \theta$. The gradient of this speed at constant r is $d(\omega \sin \theta)/d\theta$. Now,

$$\frac{d}{d\theta}(\omega \sin \theta) = \sin \theta \frac{d\omega}{d\theta} + \omega \cos \theta. \qquad (5.1)$$

The second term on the right-hand side of (5.1) represents the gradient due to the "rigid" angular velocity ω of a fluid element about the vertical direction. The first term is due to the shearing motion in the fluid. Thus, apart from its rigid motion, each element of the fluid undergoes a shearing motion with velocity-gradient $\sin \theta \, d\omega/d\theta$, the plane of shear being perpendicular to the radial direction. The forces on this element, i.e. the stress in the fluid, can then be obtained from eqs. (2.5) by replacing κ by $\sin \theta \, d\omega/d\theta$. Then, proceeding in a manner rather similar to that employed in discussing Couette flow, we find that the angular velocity distribution in the fluid must satisfy the equation

$$(\sin \theta)^3 \frac{d\omega}{d\theta} f\left[\left(\sin \theta \frac{d\omega}{d\theta}\right)^2\right] = A, \tag{5.2}$$

where A is an integration constant. This result is obtained by considering the moment about the common axis of the cones of the forces acting on the toroid bounded by the coordinate surfaces r, $r + dr$, θ and $\theta + d\theta$ and noting that only the shearing forces on the surfaces θ and $\theta + d\theta$ have non-zero moment. If f is a known function of its argument, eq. (5.2) can be solved. This introduces a second integration constant which, together with A, can be determined by imposing the boundary conditions that $\omega = 0$ on the inner cone and Ω on the outer one.

Next, the balance of forces (including inertial forces) in the r and θ directions on an element of the toroid bounded by the coordinate planes ϕ and $\phi + d\phi$ is considered. We find that, in general, such a balance cannot be obtained unless body forces are applied. We therefore consider that body forces with components F_r and F_θ per unit mass in the r and θ directions respectively are applied. Then, identifying the normal components of stress per unit area in the r, θ and ϕ directions with N_z, N_y and N_x respectively, given by eqs. (2.5), the balance of force equations yield

$$\rho F_r = \frac{\partial p}{\partial r} + \frac{1}{r}(f_x + f_y) - \rho r(\omega \sin \theta)^2$$

and   (5.3)

$$\rho r F_\theta = \frac{\partial p}{\partial \theta} - \frac{\partial f_y}{\partial \theta} - (f_y - f_x) \cot \theta - \rho r^2 (\omega \sin \theta)^2 \cot \theta.$$

We emphasize that the assumed flow field cannot, in general, be maintained unless body forces are applied. This is evidenced by the fact that if we take $F_r = F_\theta = 0$ in eqs. (5.3), then the pair of differential equations resulting cannot, in general, be integrated to yield an expression for p.

However, if we take $F_r = 0$, then the first of eqs. (5.3) can be integrated to yield

$$p = -(f_x + f_y) \log r - \frac{1}{2}\rho r^2 (\omega \sin \theta)^2 + F(\theta), \tag{5.4}$$

where $F(\theta)$ is an arbitrary function of θ. From (5.4) and (2.5), we see that N_y, which is the stress component in the θ-direction, is given by

$$N_y = f_y - F(\theta) + (f_x + f_y) \log r + \frac{1}{2}\rho r^2 (\omega \sin \theta)^2. \tag{5.5}$$

Since θ is constant on each of the cones containing the fluid, we see that, with the neglect of the inertial forces given by the last term in (5.5), the normal force exerted on the fluid by each of the conical boundaries varies logarithmically with r, an effect which has been observed (see, for example, ref. 7 and references given there). The fact that, in practice, the body force F_θ is not applied, will, of course, lead to secondary flow in axial planes. Further qualitative discussion of this problem was given in ref. 2.

6. POISEUILLE FLOW IN A CIRCULAR TUBE

We now consider the flow of the fluid along a uniform tube of circular cross-section under a constant pressure head. Each particle of the fluid is assumed to flow in a straight line with a velocity v which depends on its radial distance r from the axis of the tube. At each point the fluid is undergoing rectilinear shear with velocity-gradient dv/dr, the plane of shear being the plane through the point containing the axis of the tube. Making the substitution dv/dr for κ in eqs. (2.5) and using a procedure rather similar to that employed in the previous problems, we find that the velocity distribution is determined by the equation

$$\frac{dv}{dr} f\left[\left(\frac{dv}{dr}\right)^2\right] = \frac{1}{2}Pr,$$

(6.1)

where P is the pressure head per unit length, together with the boundary condition that $v = 0$ at the wall of the tube. The force in the longitudinal direction of decreasing pressure head exerted over a cross-section perpendicular to the length of the tube is

$$-f_x + f_y + \int^r \frac{1}{r} f_y dr + Pz,$$

(6.2)

where z is the distance of the cross-section from the zero pressure head end of the tube. The force exerted on the fluid by the wall of the tube, in a radially outwards direction, is

$$-\int^a \frac{1}{r} f_y dr - Pz,$$

(6.3)

where a is the radius of the tube. We note that this force is constant over the perimeter of a cross-section of the tube.

7. FLOW IN A NON-CIRCULAR TUBE

Finally, in order to illustrate the fact that, when we depart from the simple viscometric flows, the normal stress which is associated with simple shear of a non-Newtonian fluid can give rise to rather surprising flow effects, we shall consider briefly the flow of a non-Newtonian fluid in a straight tube of non-circular cross-section. To be explicit, we shall take the cross-section of the tube to be elliptical.

If we consider the flow of a Newtonian fluid down such a tube, under a pressure gradient which is uniform over the cross-section, we can readily calculate the distribution of velocity over the cross-section of the tube. This is done by assuming that each particle of the fluid flows in a straight line parallel to the length of the tube with a velocity which is zero at the wall. From the calculated velocity distribution, we can then determine the normal forces which must be exerted on the fluid by the wall of the tube and, as in the case of a circular tube, they are found to be constant around the boundary of a cross-section.

If the same assumption is made in the case of a non-Newtonian fluid, that each particle of the fluid flows in a straight line, it was found by ERICKSEN[10] that the set of differential equations which govern the problem are, in general, incompatible and therefore do not have a solution. This implies that the assumption of rectilinear flow must be incorrect. It follows[11, 12] that superposed on this rectilinear flow, there must be a transverse flow of the fluid in cross-sectional planes and this was calculated[11, 12] for sufficiently slow flows for which the departure from Newtonian behavior is small. It was found, in this case, that there is a circulatory flow in each of the quadrants of the elliptical cross-section, so that each particle of the fluid moves down the tube in a helical path.

It was also found[13] that the normal force exerted by the wall of the tube varied around the boundary of a cross-section.

ACKNOWLEDGMENT

This paper was prepared with the support of Office of Naval Research, U.S. Navy, Contract Nonr 562(40) with Brown University.

REFERENCES

[1] RIVLIN, R. S. *J. Rational Mech. Anal.* **5**, 179, 1956.
[2] RIVLIN, R. S. Report to Naval Research Laboratory, 1955.*
[3] COLEMAN, B. D. and NOLL, W. *Arch. Rational Mech. Anal.* **3**, 289, 1959.
[4] COLEMAN, B. D. and NOLL, W. *J. Applied Phys.* **30**, 158, 1959.
[5] COLEMAN, B. D. and NOLL, W. *Ann. N.Y. Acad. Sci.* **89**, 672, 1961.
[6] TRUESDELL, C. and NOLL, W. *The Non-linear Field Theories of Mechanics*, Encyclopedia of Physics, FLÜGGE, S. (Editor), vol. III/3, Springer, New York, 1965.
[7] COLEMAN, B. D., MARKOVITZ, H. and NOLL, W. *Viscometric Flows of Non-Newtonian Fluids*, Springer, New York, 1966.
[8] GARNER, F. H., NISSAN, A. H. and WOOD, G. F. *Phil. Trans.* A, **243**, 37, 1950.
[9] WEISSENBERG, K. *Proc. Int. Cong. Rheol.* **2**, 114, 1948.
[10] ERICKSEN, J. L. *Q. Applied Math.* **14**, 318, 1956.
[11] GREEN, A. E. and RIVLIN, R. S. *Q. Applied Math.* **14**, 299, 1956.
[12] LANGLOIS, W. E. and RIVLIN, R. S. *Rend. di Mathematica* **22**, 169, 1963.
[13] PIPKIN, A. C. and RIVLIN, R. S. *ZAMP* **14**, 738, 1963.

*Although never published, this report was circulated to various workers in the field and some of the results in it are contained in a paper by H. Markovitz and R. B. Williamson, *Trans. Soc. Rheol.* **1**, 25, 1957; see also Ref. 7.

DISCUSSION

CHARM (*U.S.A.*):
Dr. Rivlin, could you give a comment on the relative energy losses or energy requirement for pushing a fluid through an elliptical cross-section as compared with a cylindrical cross-section?

RIVLIN (*U.S.A.*):
Certainly. What kind of fluid?

CHARM:
A Newtonian fluid!

RIVLIN:
No instability, just ordinary laminar flow?

CHARM:
Just something like water.

RIVLIN:
You can look up the formula. It is in any book on viscometry or hydrodynamics.

CHARM:
Are there eddies that might be introduced in an elliptical cross-section?

RIVLIN:
Yes, for a non-Newtonian fluid.

CHARM:
This would occur only in a non-Newtonian fluid?

RIVLIN:
Yes! This is a specific feature that arises from the normal stress effect. It is one of the normal stress effects due to the fact that N_x, N_y and N_z if you remember my terminology, are not zero. For Newtonian fluids they are zero (or at any rate all equal); and then all these fancy effects do not come in at all.

EIRICH (*U.S.A.*):
Dr. Rivlin, in order to get a more direct connection between your excellent theoretical exposition and some of the problems discussed here, could you enlarge on the effects of normal stresses during sudden changes in the diameters of the capillaries or in connection with the capillary elasticity? What would the contribution of the elastic or normal stresses be to the overall resistance?

RIVLIN:
Yes, I think I can, but the answer is not very satisfactory. I think, however, that one can talk in a general kind of way on what happens. There are two further problems, which we have studied theoretically, but which I did not discuss because of shortage of time. These were both looked at by Langlois and myself about ten years ago and not in fact published. They are discussed in an *ONR* report of ours. The first one is flow in a convergent channel formed by two infinite planes, inclined at an angle to each other. The solution to the problem of the flow of a Newtonian fluid in such a channel is classical. Each particle flows in a straight line towards the apex of the channel. For visco-elastic fluids this is no longer true and the particles of the fluid move towards the apex of the channel in paths which are bent — at any rate according to my calculations. The second problem is that of convergent-flow in a cone. Again, the solution of the problem for a Newtonian fluid (in this case with the neglect of inertia terms) is classical. The particles of the fluid again move in straight lines towards the apex of the cone. For a non-Newtonian fluid this is no longer the case. Again, the paths are bent. I should say that in both of these calculations, for the convergent channel and convergent cone, the calculations were carried out for a slightly visco-elastic fluid and we have also found, as is rather evident, that similar results apply for slow flow of a general visco-elastic fluid. For fast flow the situation becomes more complicated, no doubt. I would like to point out that when one considers a non-Newtonian fluid flowing in a convergent channel or cone (and these remarks apply particularly to the latter case) we may expect, in addition to the normal stress effects, very marked effects arising from the fact that the rate of shear in a particle of the fluid is changing rapidly as it moves towards the apex. If the fluid is visco-elastic this could result in the stress at a point being much higher than one would expect from the actual value of the rate of shear at the point. I think this is a very important consideration which is not always appreciated, in the design of dies and in other problems concerning extrusion.

BURTON (*Canada*):

I'd like to return to this curious secondary flow you just say can happen in a non-Newtonian fluid in a tube of ellipsoidal cross-section. As a physiologist I wonder whether you think that it conceivably might be worth looking for in blood flowing in veins, which are nearly always ellipsoidal in life. It is conceivable that if there is this pattern of secondary flow, there obviously might be differences in deposition of lipids and so on, along certain lines along the vein. Would it be worth looking for this?

RIVLIN:

In any case, I doubt whether anyone has ruler straight arteries.

BURTON:

No, I am talking about veins. The arteries are cylindrical.

RIVLIN:

They are not straight anyway. And you get all sorts of effects like those that arise in a curved pipe. Even if it is straight, you get all sorts of complications, too. My answer to your question is, frankly, "No!" I feel that when one is looking for new effects of this kind, it is advisable to look for them first in situations where they are most easy to observe, unencumbered by other complicating effects. I am not satisfied that, in the case of the effect under discussion, this has yet been adequately done. Some years ago, Dr. Kearsley, of the Bureau of Standards, told me that, following our prediction, he had observed this effect, but he has not published any findings to date, as far as I am aware. I should point out that is is not an easy effect to observe. The flow in each of the four quadrants of the elliptical tube will be similar. Along the walls the velocity of the fluid is zero and the transverse velocity must evidently be zero at the center of the elliptical cross-section and at a point rather centrally located in each quadrant. This leaves a rather inaccessible region in the tube in which to look for the non-zero transverse velocity. Of course, it would be much easier to look for the variation of normal pressures around the elliptical boundary of the cross-section.

BURTON:

Well, this was my thought that the pressure variation has some relation to the helical flow.

RIVLIN:

They are not necessarily associated.

BURTON:

But the pressure variation on the walls is obtained in the case of a non-Newtonian fluid and not in the case of a Newtonian fluid.

RIVLIN:

Yes!

BURTON:

It seems to me that looking in the veins might be worth while because pathologists are always looking at them; and the normal pressures and circulations at the wall, we know, will determine deposition and so on.

RIVLIN:

I would not inhibit anybody from looking anywhere. My only point is that it is easiest to look in other places first. Then when you have the situation straightened out in less complicated contexts, you can go to more complicated ones.

TAYLOR (*Australia*):

Speaking as another physiologist, McDonald, of course, has looked at this, with filming of dye streams and so forth in the venous system. From his films, I would not say there was any evidence of it all. There was a very loose sort of spiraling of the entire stream that one could occasionally see. But stream lines, coming in from branches and so on, remain fairly intact for considerable distances before they diffuse.

MASON (*Canada*):

Is this effect reversible?

RIVLIN:

No! It is a square law effect, you see. It depends on the even power of forward velocity, if you like to look at it that way, or forward force. I understand that the way in which Kearsley observed the effect was the following. He allowed a solution of high-polymer to flow through a non-circular but straight glass tube. Injecting a small amount of dye at a point at one end, he was able to observe a helical structure in the flow,

of long pitch. The only doubt that remains is the possibility of some irregularity in the system being responsible for the helical flow. One has to be careful that one is not mistaking a bogus effect for a genuine one.
In a vein, even if one observed a helical structure in the flow, one could not be sure that it represented the
effect under consideration.

GELIN (*Sweden*):
   Can these streams in the four quadrants, you have drawn there, mix?

RIVLIN:
   Not according to my calculation. But, of course, the question is what happens in practice?

GELIN:
   Now I am back to what I think is very important from a practical point of view. Angiograms on the venous
side will only take up contrast in about a quarter of the lumen of the major vein when a small vein joins a
larger vein. So they will really not become a mixture of the injected contrast. As for example from the
splenic vein to the portal vein. They may never mix.

RIVLIN:
   The only trouble with that is the difference between your venous system and a perfectly straight elliptical
pipe. Now, you see, people do not have perfectly elliptical straight veins. This is what bothers me. The
moment you have a vein that is bent or anything like that, all sorts of new effects arise. Just realize that for
the last hundred years, many eminent hydrodynamicists, have worked on this problem, the plumbing problem.
You have a bend in a pipe. The problem is what happens when the water flowing in the pipe reaches the
elbow? In fact, rather complicated things happen and they are not at all easy to calculate. I am very pleased
about what you are saying, simply because you take me seriously, — more seriously than I take myself. I
feel that in giving this talk, I was not being modest when I said it was substantially irrelevant to blood flow.
I was being quite serious. I think it has nothing whatsoever to do with the major problems of hemorheology.
In my opinion, it does however have the following relevance. If people use apparatus for making viscometric
measurements, they should be aware of the pathology of the equipment they are using. That is all. Frankly,
I did not mean to be taken quite as seriously as I have been.

HEMORHEOLOGICAL TECHNIQUES

12 July, a.m.

Chairmen: FREDERICK R. EIRICH, U.S.A.
ALEX SILBERBERG, Israel

OUTFLOW VISCOMETRY USING A CHRONIC EXTERNAL ARTERIO-VENOUS SHUNT

W. G. FRASHER,*[1] H. WAYLAND[2] and S. SOBIN[1]

Los Angeles County Heart Association
Cardiovascular Research Laboratory
of Loma Linda University
School of Medicine[1]
Los Angeles, California
and
Laboratory of Microhydrodynamics and
Rheology
California Institute of Technology[2]
Pasadena, California, U.S.A.

THE physiologic significance of any characterization of the physical properties of blood depends on the extent to which the sampling process alters the test substance. *A priori* shed blood is not *in vivo* blood and particularly so when it has been rendered incoagulable.

In order to close the loop between the living organism and various methods of measuring physical properties of blood *ex vivo* a method has been devised which permits viscometric measurements in artificial tubes sampling from a free flowing stream of "native" blood. It is the purpose of this communication to describe the characteristics of this preparation and to report some experimental results from its use.

METHOD

Animal preparation. Twenty-one dogs have been surgically prepared with artificial external arterio-venous shunts in a modification of a method used by SCRIBNER *et al.*[1] in humans. The shunt originates in a stainless steel cannula accepting all flow into the left common carotid artery. The cannula is shaped to minimize flow disturbance. The fitting leads to a section of silicone rubber tubing fixed in the deep tissues of the neck and exiting from the skin in the dorsal one-third of the neck behind the Atlas. A Teflon† slip joint in the midline couples to an identical length of tubing which enters the skin on the opposite side, is fixed in deep tissues, and terminates in an identical stainless steel cannula discharging into the external jugular vein.

Manufacture of the components and surgical implantation are relatively simple procedures. After-care of the animal is demanding and infection at the skin exit sites an omnipresent hazard. Our current experience is that after allowing two weeks of healing one may anticipate useful periods of a minimum of two weeks, on up to a present maximum of five months.

†TM DuPont for fluorocarbon resins.

Hematologic findings and flow in the shunt. The following observations have been made on blood taken directly into a syringe from the carotid limb of the shunt: (1) Clotting times (Lee-White 3 tube) are normal; (2) clot retraction is normal; (3) platelet morphology and numbers and erythrocyte morphology are normal on stained smears; (4) hematocrits are normal; (5) erythrocyte counts by electronic counter are normal.

Simultaneous cardiac output determination by dye dilution and measurements of flow in the shunt by electromagnetic flowmeter in ten instances in seven animals show the following results: (1) Shunt flow is between 15 and 25% of the cardiac output; (2) mean shunt flow is 440 cc/min (range 280–670); (3) mean velocity is 83 cm/sec (range 53–126); (4) average peak instantaneous velocity during the cycle is 93 cm/sec (range 58–139); (5) reduced average velocity at the wall, $\bar{U}$ (see below), at peak values averages 246 sec^{-1} with a maximum in the set of 365. If we accept a viscosity of 4 cP as a reasonable value for blood under these conditions, the Reynolds number for maximum peak velocity is 1189.

Viscometric apparatus. The apparatus has been previously described[2] and is briefly summarized here. The measurement assembly is of silicone resin cast in a Tee shape such that the cross arm is identical in bore (3.4 mm) and continuous with the same tubing used in the shunt. The fine bore measurement tube branches from the cross arm with a junction precisely defined as the locus of intersection of two right circular cylinders whose axes are coplanar and perpendicular. Measurement tubes are: (1) 85 μ diam., 1.24–1.27 cm long; (2) 185 μ diam., 2.65–2.85 cm long; (3) 185 μ diam., 4.17–4.37 cm long. Provision is made to record upstream pressure opposite the measurement tube.

The outflow end of the measurement tube couples rigidly into a saline filled chamber with a vertical standpipe graduated in microliters. Chamber pressure is recorded at the level of the measurement tube and a separate drain is provided to remove excess fluid. In use, a continuous record at constant paper velocity registers upstream and chamber pressure. An observer signals the rising level of the meniscus in the standpipe at predetermined volume increments. The level of the meniscus is bled to the fiducial zero and the process repeated at will.

Calibration. The system is calibrated against an input of acid-citrate-dextrose at a constant driving pressure. Viscosity of the calibration fluid is independently determined in an Ostwald viscometer at the temperature measured at the time of calibration.

Experimental procedure. With the animal restrained but unanesthetized, the shunt fitting is uncoupled and control blood samples taken from the carotid tube. The tubes are immediately coupled to the measurement assembly and flow instituted (Fig. 1).

Theory and computations. In the current set of experiments, instrumentation permitted accurate evaluation only of an average upstream pressure while the actual head fluctuated continuously around the mean to an average value of ±10–25% of the mean value at rates of about 1.5 c/s. Additionally, the upstream source is pulsatile flow of unknown velocity profile. Until analysis of these features has been completed we have elected not to attempt any complex shear stress–shear rate analysis. Rather, we have used the Poiseuille model and computed an apparent viscosity (η_a). The meaning of this value is simply that at the observed average difference in pressure and the observed flow rate the proportionality constant η_a is that which would exist if blood were a Newtonian fluid. Although the model is imperfect, it permits assessment of changes imposed by different test conditions. Additionally the model may be a relatively good approximation at the experimental flow velocities[3].

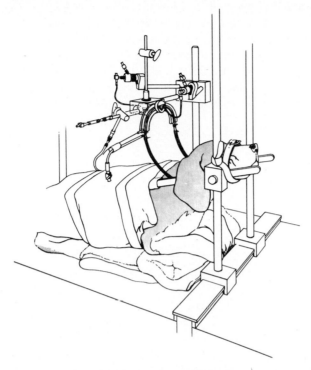

FIG. 1. DIAGRAM OF APPARATUS IN USE. FOR DESCRIPTION, SEE TEXT.

The reduced average pressure values (upstream and downstream) are differenced to give a net driving pressure (ΔP) over the interval between volume signals. Time of flow is read directly between volume marks (Δt). Let the measured volume be (q). Then:
For the calibration fluid:

$$(\Delta P \Delta t / q) \text{ cal} = (\eta_c / k) \text{ cal}$$

where η_c = viscosity of calibrating fluid and k = geometric factor;
and for blood:

$$(\Delta P \Delta t / q) \text{ blood} = (\eta_b / k) \text{ blood}$$

where η_b = experimental viscosity of blood; then:

$$(\eta_b / k)\,(\eta_c / k) = \eta_b / \eta_c = \eta_r$$

where η_r = relative viscosity of blood.
Let the independently determined viscosity of the calibrating fluid at the measured temperature be η_0, then

$$\eta_r \cdot \eta_0 = \eta_a$$

$\eta_a =$ the apparent viscosity of blood at the experimental temperature (although the exact temperature is not known).

There is insufficient independent evidence to make a reliable judgment respecting the error of the method. In principle, using the Newtonian calibrating fluid the expectation would be complete coincidence of independent runs (except for possible thermal change). The mean deviation of calibration results is, therefore, some measure of the observational error. In twenty-one determinations this deviation is 1.6%. To this must be added a gage error of perhaps 1% and a reading error of about the same magnitude. We have estimated an overall accuracy of ±5% in evaluating the meaning of deviations from average values.

RESULTS

Figure 2 shows an example of results obtainable in blood flowing without anti-coagulant. The upper two traces show the net driving pressure and a reduced average velocity whose physical meaning is diameters of flow per second. $\bar{U} = v/D = 4Q/\pi D^3$

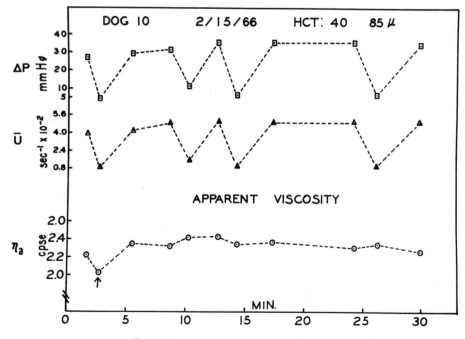

FIG. 2. VISCOSITY EXPERIMENT IN "NATIVE BLOOD".

It is an index to, but not a measure of, wall shear rate. The consistency of results despite widely varying pressure difference is apparent.

Figure 3 shows an unacceptable result. The increase in apparent viscosity while driving pressure increases obviously relates to a steadily decreasing flow velocity, $\bar{U}$, occasioned by obstruction of the measurement tube.

The primary difficulty in these as in other capillary tube measurements in blood is the obstruction or partial obstruction of the tube by white clot presumably triggered by platelet adherence at points of disturbed flow profiles[4].

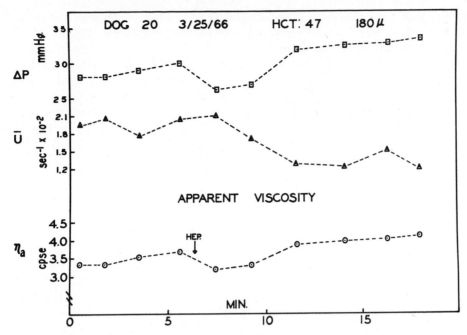

FIG. 3. UNACCEPTABLE EXPERIMENTAL RESULTS. INCREASED DRIVING PRESSURE AND VISCOSITY ACCOM-
PANIED BY FALLING $\bar{U}$ INDICATES OBSTRUCTION OF MEASUREMENT TUBE.

In the first studies with these flow sections white clot frequently plugged the outflow
tube and appeared on the interior mostly at the couplings, but also with some random
accretions. Empirically we can prevent this accumulation by soaking the sections in a
solution of 130 mg sodium heparin per cc for 12–18 hr before use and flushing with two
10 cc aliquots of acid-citrate-dextrose prior to connection. Samples taken from the
venous side of the section at one and five minutes show no significant alteration in
clotting time.

Chronic shunt tubes removed from animals at termination are free of visible accretions. No structural deposit can be seen on the tube with a light microscope, but the
surface stains with T-1824 dye resistant to saline flushing in contrast to fresh washed
tubing.

We have conjectured that a "curing" process occurs with blood perfusion involving
the deposition of plasma proteins or fractions of proteins. This film subsequently either
protects against the triggering of clotting mechanisms or at least prevents the adhesion
of the products to the tube at existing flow velocities. Sufficient heparin apparently
adheres to the flow assemblies to provide the same protection in pretreated tubes.

The results of a total of some thirty experimental procedures will be published elsewhere. The balance of this report concerns initial findings in a unique use of the
preparation which illustrates the complex nature of rheologic properties in the living
animal.

The special relationship of fibrinogen to the shear stress–shear rate behavior of blood,
particularly at low shear rates, and its necessity for the demonstration of yield stress have
been developed by workers in the laboratory of Professor Merrill at the Massachusetts
Institute of Technology[5, 6]. Investigators concerned with the clinical entity of

afibrinogenemia have devised a method to reduce the content of circulating fibrinogen effectively to zero by the slow infusion of thromboplastin[7]. We have followed this procedure in two of our shunt animals.

The first such study is shown in Fig. 4. Injected thromboplastin was made from dog brain by the method of BRAMBEL[8]. Fibrinogen levels were determined by the method of WARE[9]. The quantity of thromboplastin infused was insufficient to reduce the fibrinogen to the desired level. Note, however, that there is a definite relationship

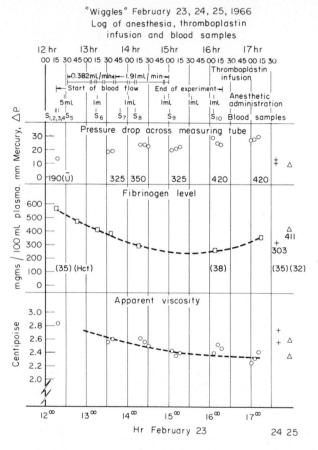

FIG. 4. INITIAL AFIBRINOGENEMIA STUDY (SEE TEXT).

between the reduction in fibrinogen level and the reduction in apparent viscosity. The fall in apparent viscosity is even more dramatic than the chart suggests. Note that the animal hemoconcentrated during the study so that the hematocrit went from 35 to 38. This change would increase the apparent viscosity under other conditions.

Determinations of apparent viscosity on the second and third days were inconclusive due to an enhanced tendency for clotting in the small tube. However, the early values charted are probably reliable and suggest that the viscosity is still reduced from the original control. Again, the reduction in hematocrit must be considered, but from other hematocrit data the persistent low level is a larger change than would be expected due to concentration change alone.

The second study, Fig. 5, resulted in reduction of fibrinogen essentially to zero. In this instance we demonstrated that induction of anesthesia had no effect on the measured viscosity. Again, there is a direct relationship between the reduction in fibrinogen and

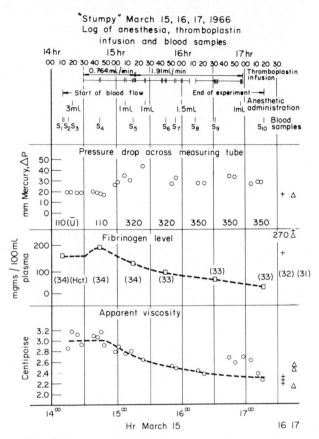

FIG. 5. SECOND AFIBRINOGENEMIA STUDY (SEE TEXT).

the reduction in apparent viscosity. Note also that the viscosity remains at a lower level on the second and third days. Here the value is certainly not explainable solely from hematocrit.

DISCUSSION

The primary interest in fibrinogen as a determinant of rheologic behavior has been directed at the low shear rate region. The current studies suggest that levels of fibrinogen may also have significant bearing on the high shear rate characteristics of blood in tube flow. From sketchy evidence available in the literature, we have postulated[2] that the shear rates in our measurement tubes approximate shear rates found in living vessels of comparable diameter.

Manifestly something other than fibrinogen content affects the measured viscosity on the second and third days. The work of ADELSON et al.[10], using radioactive tagged platelets and fibrinogen reveals two distinct processes following thromboplastin infusion. Platelet counts drop abruptly preceding the fall in fibrinogen. With small quantities of thromboplastin it can be shown that tagged platelets and fibrinogen reappear in circulating blood indicating sequestration but not destruction. With larger quantities of thromboplastin, while fibrinogen levels are restored in 24 hr, radioactivity does not reappear in circulating blood. This indicates destruction of both platelets and fibrinogen. The bulk of the circulating fibrinogen then is either newly produced or released from untagged pools.

On the second and third days of these studies, we observed failure of clot retraction after 24 hr. Thus, we conclude that our animals also had persistently diminished platelets.

It is difficult to relate platelet reduction to the lowered viscosity. If platelets exist as a sparse concentration of small discrete particles, they should have no effect on the flow properties of blood. None of the mechanisms resulting from disintegration of platelets should affect the measured viscosity except by adhering and plugging the tubes. This, in fact, seemed to occur, but before obstruction supervened the measured viscosity was reduced. Thus, it seems unlikely that platelet alterations explain the result.

A more attractive conjecture arises from the possible change in the nature of the fibrinogen. Natural fibrinogen probably consists of more than one form[11]. The circulating distribution of possible forms is not known. It is conceivable that the freshly generated fibrinogen on the second and third days is physically different to the extent that the rheologic nature of the total suspension is different. It is obviously of interest to extend observations of blood with freshly formed fibrinogen into the low shear rate regimen.

SUMMARY

Chronic external artificial carotid-jugular shunts in dogs have been used to measure apparent viscosity of blood in 85 and 185 μ silicone resin tubes. The geometry of the system requires input to the measurement tube normal to pulsatile flow through the shunt at an average velocity of 83 cm/sec at cycling rates of about 1.5 c/s generated by the animal's cardiovascular system. Initial studies in the preparation with thromboplastin induced afibrinogenemia show: (1) reduction in apparent viscosity at high shear rates paralleling reduction in fibrinogen; (2) persistent reduction in viscosity despite restoration of fibrinogen content on the second and third experimental days.

ACKNOWLEDGMENTS

This work was supported by United States Public Health Service Grants HE 08977, HE 08976, HE 07325. One of us (W.G.F.) is a Career Development Awardee, U.S. Public Health Service, National Institutes of Health, Bethesda, Maryland.

REFERENCES

[1] SCRIBNER, B., CAMER, J., BURI, R. and QUINTON, W. Trans. Amer. Soc. Artificial Internal Organs 6, 88, 1960.
[2] FRASHER, W., WAYLAND, H. and MEISELMAN, H. 4th European Conference on Microcirculation, Cambridge, England, 1966, HARDERS, H. (Editor), Bibl. Anat., S. Karger, Basel (in press).

[3] MERRILL, E., BENIS, A., GILLILAND, E., SHERWOOD, T. and SALZMAN, E. *J. Appl. Physiol.* **20**, 954, 1965.
[4] DOWNIE, H., MURPHY, E., ROWSELL, H., and MUSTARD, J. *Circ. Res.* **12**, 441, 1963.
[5] MERRILL, E., COKELET, G., BRITTEN, A. and WELLS, R. *Circ. Res.* **13**, 48, 1963.
[6] MERRILL, E., GILLILAND, E., LEE, T. and SALZMAN, E. *Circ. Res.* **20**, 437, 1966.
[7] RATNOFF, O. and CONLEY, C. *Bull. Johns Hopkins Hosp.* **88**, 414, 1951.
[8] BRAMBEL, C. *Arch. Surg.* **50**, 137, 1945.
[9] COCHRAN, B., WHITNEY, E. and WARE, A. *Pharm. Acta* **33**, 719, 1958.
[10] ADELSON, E., RHEINGOLD, J. and PARKER, O. *Blood* **15**, 596, 1960.
[11] FINLAYSON, J. and MOSESSON, M. *Biochem.* **2**, 42, 1963.

DISCUSSION

COPLEY (*U.S.A.*):

I found the presentation a beautiful one, and I congratulate Drs. Frasher, Wayland and Sobin. There are two phenomena you mentioned which appear to be of special interest. One, that you found a coating on the tube. This duplicates an experiment which goes back actually to Lister. He reported this a hundred and three years ago at the Royal Society in London. Lister found that if he placed, as a prosthesis, a caoutchouc or rubber tube, between two blood vessels, the carotid artery and the jugular vein, in sheep, the wall of the tube is coated by a thin layer of coagulated blood and that the blood contained in the prosthetic tube remains fluid, although it is coagulable. We repeated this experiment not in sheep but in dogs, and found the same phenomenon*. If the blood from the prosthetic tube was then placed on a dish, it coagulated promptly. Thus, fibrin acts as an antithrombotic agent which again is similar to the anticoagulant action of fibrin which we observed. The other phenomenon, which you mentioned, if I understood you correctly, is, if you used heparin at the outlet of your tube, you find after some time a clot. I would suppose that this is either a platelet agglutinate or is associated with platelet agglutination. In work we reported some twenty years ago, platelets in heparinized blood both *in vivo* as well as *in vitro* agglutinated. Another possibility would be that fibrinogen-fibrin complexes have formed in the heparinized blood. These in turn could cause clumping of red cells, a subject which will be treated in my presentation. Still another possibility may be due to precipitation or change in phase of proteins localized at the outlet of the tube. I think these possibilities might account for the clotting you observed. I wish to ask one question: What kind of method did you use for fibrinogen determinations?

FRASHER (*U.S.A.*):

We used the method of Ware which is a modification of Quick's old method.

COPLEY:

I should like to say something, in general, about fibrinogen determinations. We have no method for such determinations thus far which can, in all situations, such as fibrinolysis, account for only the amount of fibrinogen present in the sample. Ratnoff's method appears to be the most suitable one needing several modifications which we also developed and employed. We all need to make reliable fibrinogen determinations; and I hope that a good standard procedure can be developed which is so very important.

BARNHART (*U.S.A.*):

I was very interested in your suggestion that split products of fibrinolysis might account for some of your results. From our experience on induced microthrombosis, the resulting fibrinolytic products were cleared from the circulation in about 3½ hr. Even with large amounts of circulating split products I doubt they would remain in the circulation for 24 hr. I wonder if platelet release from the bone marrow might not provide platelets that have to develop their sticky quality with aging in the circulation. Perhaps a relative lack of platelet stickiness could be a factor in your described decrease in viscosity at 24 hr.

FRASHER:

I'd be delighted if somebody could suggest to me what influence platelets can have on the viscosity of blood. If they circulate as a dispersed concentration of very small particles, I would expect that they would have no effect at all. If, on the other hand, they are triggered so that they enter into the ordinary mechanisms for the clotting process, I would expect to see clotting in the tube, which we did see. But other than this, I would not expect to see any substantial effect on the apparent viscosity as we measure it. Now if this conjecture is in

*Copley, A. L., *Proc. 9th Congress Internat. Soc. Hematol.* Mexico City 1962. Universidad Nacional Autonoma de Mexico, Mexico City, 1964, vol. 2, p. 367.

error currently, I'd be delighted to hear it; but it is very difficult for me to account for our results of a lowered apparent viscosity on the basis of any of the normal mechanisms of platelet activity, unless they do something to the coating of red blood cells or the lining of tubes that I do not appreciate currently.

PHIBBS (*U.S.A.*):

In essence you have produced accelerated intravascular coagulation in these dogs and it is possible that they developed some of the sequelae of this process during the course of the experiment. Was there evidence of renal failure or a hemolytic anemia, and what was the general condition of the animals?

FRASHER:

Immediately upon the completion of anesthesia, they go again into the acoustic mode. They are in excellent condition; there is no evidence of renal abnormality at all. One cannot appeal to the general condition of the animal. It remains good! The animal is apparently healthy by all the measures we can make, within 12–14 hr after we finished the initial phase of the experiment.

TAYLOR (*Australia*):

I am interested in the hematocrit. It seems to me that the hematocrits are rather low for dogs. They normally are over 50%. Certainly, in greyhounds, I am told you can get hematocrits up to 60%. I am not quite sure what kind of beast that was you had on the slide there, but is this the normal value of the hematocrit about 35–40%?

FRASHER:

That without question is a beagle.

TAYLOR:

Just in relation to that: where did you measure the hematocrit effect? Because I am sure Dr. Palmer who is sitting here might be wondering just what is coming out of that tube because it is a slow flow from the marginal zone. I wonder if you have reduced hematocrit in your sampling tube.

FRASHER:

I am just delighted that you ask that question. Our system seems to set up the defined conditions for plasma skimming, and therefore the outflow hematocrits from our small measurements tubes, sampling from the margin of a high velocity stream ought to be reduced; but they are not as nearly as we can measure. Now these two slides are very preliminary. Although it seems like a simple matter, it is not in fact simple accurately to measure the hematocrit at the outflow end of the tube if you consider that one of our prime purposes is always to work at the outflow end against an osmotically balanced solution so that we do not have surface tension effects. So we have to discharge into a volume of fluid and then determine the hematocrit from the dilution. As far as we have gotten really successfully are the experiments which I show you on these two slides.

85 μ Con – 10 min			185 μ Con – 3 min			85 μ Con – 10 min			185 μ Con – 3 min		
42.5	43.3	42.5	42.0	43.5	40.1	42.0	43.1	41.9	43.0	43.5	42.7
42.5	43.3	42.5	42.0	43.5	40.1	42.0	43.1	41.9	43.0	43.5	42.7
42.5	43.3	42.5	42.0	43.5	43.4	42.0	43.1	41.9	43.0	43.5	42.7
42.5	43.3	42.5	42.0	43.5	41.2	42.0	43.1	41.9	43.0	43.5	42.7

Control hematocrits are all blood sampled directly from the carotid into the shunt, simply permitted to flow into a syringe. These are the hematocrits measured in an 85 mμ tube with flow over 10 min time. We do not really indicate any substantial reduction in hematocrit. These are the same outflow samples, just two sets of determinations. Here the same dog in an 185 μ tube; the control values and two independent determinations of the outflow values. This is the same experiment in another animal. The 85 μ tube, with control values and two independent determinations of outflow; the 185 μ tube control and two independent determinations of the outflow. So we do not have any evidence certainly that there is a reduction in the hematocrit; and the presumption is strongly that the hematocrit does not change under these circumstances. We suspect this may have something to do with the fact that the driving upstream pressure is pulsatile and may therefore materially influence the entrance of red blood cells into our small outflow tube. We cannot prove this yet.

PALMER (*Australia*):

Could I ask if you noticed any difference in the measured apparent viscosity using the larger and the smaller tube, the 85 and 185 micron tubes? Is there any evidence of the Fåhraeus–Lindquist effect?

FRASHER:

No! You saw the best demonstration which was, I think, the scattered points on the semilog plot of non-anticoagulated treated blood. If you look closely, there are symbols indicating the different size tubes; and the scatter among the different symbols is as wide as the scatter value.

SILBERBERG (*Israel*):

Did you compare the viscosities that you measured with viscosities determined by some *extra vivum* device?

FRASHER:

Not yet. This obviously is our purpose. But we have not done so as yet.

CHARM (*U.S.A.*):

What was the precision? It looked like it was about plus or minus 10%.

FRASHER:

Well, there is no good independent method by which we can determine our precision. We have estimated plus or minus 5%, but I give you plus or minus 10%. Do you mean that first slide? That was much closer. You perhaps did not appreciate the fact that the scale was expanded on the absolute viscosity values; but those values that I showed you on my first slide really all fell within about plus or minus $1\frac{1}{2}$%, or less. I have forgotten the exact figure. This is not true of all the experiments, though. This was a good one. For the accuracy of our method, we have pulled a figure of plus or minus 5% out of the air because as yet we do not have any independent method to verify our guess. At least the consistency runs within these limits.

TUBE VISCOMETRY OF BLOOD
AT LOW SHEAR RATES

HENRY R. JACOBS*

Department of Medicine, Northwestern University, Evanston, Illinois, U.S.A.

BLOOD viscometry in imitation of the events in the microcirculation will require very low shear rates and very low stresses. The problem is one of instrumentation, and of instrumental error.

Meniscal resistance, which is the reluctance of a capillary meniscus of blood to move is an important instrumental complication that introduces the possibility of error.

In 1946 Jacobs placed a section of blood in a fine glass tube and expected it to move when the tube was tilted from the horizontal. That it did not move until considerable tilt was reached indicated the presence of an adventitious friction, which is doubtless absent in the circulation of the body, but probably present in most viscometers.

It was necessary to find out if meniscal resistance could be ignored. If it were constant in all blood specimens, a standard correction might suffice and simple viscometers, like the tilted capillary tube, might be employed.

A "single meniscus apparatus" was described in 1962 that allowed the advancing and receding menisci to be observed separately. A horizontal capillary was attached to a large vertical chamber. The sample filled the capillary to half its length and the vertical chamber to a level that just balanced the capillarity of the meniscus in the capillary. The capillary meniscus was thus freed to respond in either direction to external force. It responded promptly in both directions to very small forces with water in a clean capillary, and with many organic liquids. Forward and backward movements generated identical linear rate–pressure plots arising from the origin. Aqueous solutions of salts and sugars behaved the same. There was no elastic recoil.

On the other hand, aqueous solutions of surface active agents showed pronounced resistance to motion; they also showed a maximum at $\frac{1}{4}$ to $\frac{1}{2}$ gram per liter. No accurate measure of capillarity was possible because the meniscus was sticky.

To secure flow lines an artifice had to be adopted. The hydrostatic pressure was adjusted so that the forward and backward speeds were the same at one driving pressure; then two more pressures were employed without balancing again. The results contain a mixture of two meniscal resistances, advancing and receding, in unknown proportions. From this study meniscal resistance of serum and plasma was estimated to reach about 20 dynes per centimeter of meniscus periphery. In a capillary 0.001 cm wide, this resistance amounts to 80,000 dynes per centimeter of capillary cross-section, roughly equivalent to the pressure from a vertical water column 80 cm high.

The two menisci are not identical. The receding meniscus seems more reluctant to move with blood and serum; but the advancing one shows more resistance with saline suspensions of washed red cells, deproteinized serum filtrates, and with water on intentionally soiled walls.

Elastic recoil is also different. When a meniscus is pushed steadily in one direction and released, it recoils instantly in the return direction if the return is an advancing meniscus. Often there is no recoil if the return is a receding meniscus.

The asymmetrical effect is marked in plasma. Plasma will not move in the single meniscus apparatus at 25 mm (water) pressure in the direction of the receding meniscus, but the advancing meniscus moves well at this pressure.

The high resistance and erratic performance of an advancing meniscus of water in a capillary intentionally soiled with castor oil or cigarette smoke was corrected instantly when water was replaced with dioctyl sodium sulfosuccinate (DSS) solution (10 grams per liter).

BUBBLES

To learn how much free wall a meniscus must have to develop its full resistance, a study of bubble length was made in a fine capillary. Organic liquids and water in a clean tube are insensitive to bubble length; their rate–pressure plots are linear and reach the origin.

Liquids with true meniscal resistance are very sensitive to bubble length. DSS, at $\frac{1}{2}$ gram per liter, will flow almost like water with a very short (0.5 mm) bubble, but it quickly develops resistance at slightly greater lengths, such as 1.0 mm. Meniscal resistance then grows rapidly with bubble length until the bubbles are 10–12 mm long, and more slowly until they are 20 mm long. Still longer bubbles shorten the liquid column so much that rates increase significantly again. Intercepts calculated from two-point flow lines increase rapidly as bubbles grow from 1 to 10 mm, then more slowly. (These results represent *two* menisci, one advancing and one receding.)

An experiment reversing the conditions supports the results from bubbles. A section of liquid in a capillary has a meniscus at each end, but they are separated by liquid instead of air and they have unlimited free wall to develop their resistance fully. Their intercepts are of the same order as those from long bubbles.

MENISCAL RESISTANCE IN SERUM, PLASMA AND RED CELL SUSPENSIONS

To learn whether meniscal resistance varies with blood samples, a survey of plasma and serum was made of normal and ill persons, using a modified "single meniscus apparatus". Meniscal resistance varies from person to person; hence, no standard correction for it is possible.

Red cell suspensions were also studied in the single meniscus apparatus. A curve relating log time to hematocrit value is convex to the concentration axis; its upper limb becomes vertical at 80% cells.

CHARACTERIZATION OF THE ACTIVE SUBSTANCE IN BLOOD

Serum standing in contact with its clot for six days in the ice box or at room temperature is unchanged in meniscal resistance. Serum dilutions in saline remain unchanged too.

Dilution of serum with saline increases the slope of the flow line until, at 1 : 16, the slope is the same as that of water and stays there with further dilution. The intercept (from two-point flow lines) remained unchanged from that of serum alone until 1 : 512, the highest dilution available for study. Dilutions higher than 1 : 512 showed:

(a) Erratic meniscal motion, especially in the advancing meniscus.
(b) Progressive slowing over the measured course.
(c) Soiling of the wall by liquid left behind by the receding meniscus, often forming diaphragms of liquid across the lumen of the capillary.
(d) Excessive elastic recoil, particularly in the direction of the advancing meniscus.
(e) Fragmentation of the advancing meniscus, with formation of fine froth.
(f) These complications persisted to high dilutions, often up to 1 : 131 072.

Deproteinizing serum or plasma with acid and heat produced a clear filtrate with very high meniscal resistance, in the advancing direction. The receding meniscus moved smoothly. Addition of alcohol removed all meniscal resistance.

Estimation of cholesterol in the filtrate showed it to be undiminished. Its presence and the effect of alcohol, together with wall soiling suggesting a hydrophobic substance, nominates a cholesterol-like material.

A VISCOMETER THAT ELIMINATES MENISCAL RESISTANCE

Since meniscal resistance cannot be ignored nor precisely corrected for, an instrument was designed that nearly eliminated meniscal resistance from measurement. Two basic principles were observed. First, the menisci of the sample should be as immobile as possible, and second, the means employed to indicate movement of the sample should be a separate device, although attached.

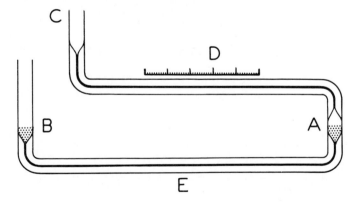

Fig. 1. The viscometer. Capillaries D and E are 0.25 mm in diameter. Lower capillary is 190 mm long. The lower capillary contains the sample, filling the entire capillary and the flared ends to the levels shown by the dotted areas. Air pressure applied to B or C drives the sample and indicator (in the upper capillary) back and forth.

The first principle, keeping menisci immobile, was satisfied by expanding the ends of the capillary and attaching them to larger (3–4 mm diameter) tubes which would contain the (now large) menisci. Considerable movement of the sample through the capillary could occur with insignificant motion of the menisci.

The second principle, a separate indicating device, was satisfied by placing a section of appropriate liquid in a capillary of the same diameter as that containing the sample and attached to it, yet separating sample from indicator by an air link.

The choice of liquid to serve as indicator was an important one. An aqueous liquid was mandatory, but water itself was not satisfactory because of its extreme sensitivity to wall soil. One per cent dioctyl sodium sulfosuccinate (DSS) in water proved excellent. It is immune to wall soil, owing to its detergent power; its meniscal resistance is very small and constant; and its tendency to froth is not troublesome. It has one small defect: it shows progressive slowing when it moves slowly at constant pressure along a fine capillary. This is learned by timing both the advancing and the retreating menisci on the same run over a measured course. For example, the advancing meniscus of a 40 mm section in a capillary 0.25 mm wide required 7.6 sec to travel 3 cm when driven by 10 mm (water) pressure, but the retreating meniscus took 8.0 sec. The difference vanished at 20 mm pressure.

Water and plasma and all liquids with large meniscal resistances trace linear flow lines arising from the origin. Correction for resistance from the flow indicator increased the slope of the flow lines slightly but did not affect the intercept, which remained zero.

Figure 2 shows what meniscal resistance can do. The full length experiment has plasma filling the capillary and the end tubes to their widest part, assuring nearly immobile menisci. The flow line is linear and reaches the origin; meniscal resistance

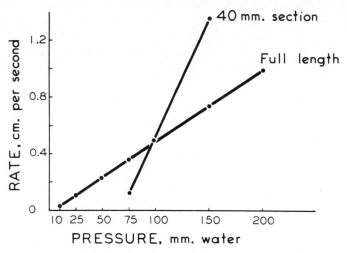

FIG. 2. PLASMA, WHICH HAS CONSIDERABLE MENISCAL RESISTANCE, SHOWS NONE IN THE FULL-LENGTH EXPERIMENT, BUT A GREAT DEAL IN THE SECTION EXPERIMENT.

has virtually been eliminated. The "section" experiment has a 40 mm section of plasma in the lower capillary; the section has two fine and highly mobile menisci that exhibit considerable resistance. The flow line is very steep; when extended it intersects the pressure abscissa near 67 mm. The section of plasma moved well under 75 mm (water) pressure, but not at all under 50 mm. An intercept of 67 mm for two menisci in motion is equivalent to approximately 20 dynes per centimeter of meniscus periphery.

In the standard full-length experiment, serum and plasma are much alike. Plasma is often only slightly more viscous than serum in normal subjects. In acute inflammatory disease, plasma is considerably more viscous than serum. In macroglobulinemia, as expected, both serum and plasma are more viscous than normal, with only little difference between them.

Suspensions of red cells in all vehicles show evidence of settling within the viscometer. Viscosity rises steadily with time. But when a fresh portion of the original suspension is employed late in the day to replace the original portion that had grown more viscous, the viscosity returns nearly to the earliest values of the day, only to start to rise again with time.

Suspensions in serum (homologous) often show "work-softening" early in the day: repeated measurements at constant pressure give steadily falling values for the viscosity early in the day, which is precisely the opposite of what happens with suspensions in plasma.

Figure 3 gives a collection of experiments with red cell suspensions. All show increasing viscosity with time, most of it reversible by stirring, indicating that settling is the cause.

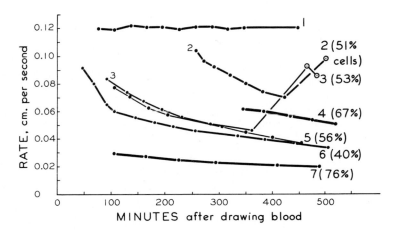

FIG. 3. SETTLING OF RED CELL SUSPENSIONS. 1. PLASMA ALONE AT 25 MM PRESSURE. 2. RED CELLS WASHED FOUR TIMES, SUSPENDED IN SALINE, SHOWING THE RETURN TO ORIGINAL VALUES WHEN A FRESH PORTION IS USED. 3. RED CELLS SETTLED IN PLASMA, ALSO SHOWING RETURN TO NEARLY ORIGINAL VALUES WHEN A FRESH PORTION IS USED. 4. RED CELLS SPUN DOWN FROM BLOOD DILUTED 1:33 WITH SALINE. 5. RED CELLS SETTLED IN PLASMA. 6. WHOLE BLOOD, MIXED WITH EDTA, AS DRAWN. 7. RED CELLS SPUN DOWN IN PLASMA.

SUMMARY

Meniscal resistance in viscometry of blood at low shear cannot be ignored. It is significantly large and varies from specimen to specimen. The material in blood responsible for meniscal resistance has been partially characterized. A viscometer that effectively eliminated meniscal resistance from measurement has been described. An aqueous liquid suitable for use as a flow indicator in fine tubes has been described. The problem of settling of cells within the viscometer was discussed. Settling occurs in all suspensions of red cells studied. It is less rapid as cell content rises, but even at 80% cells, settling is perceptible. No cure was offered.

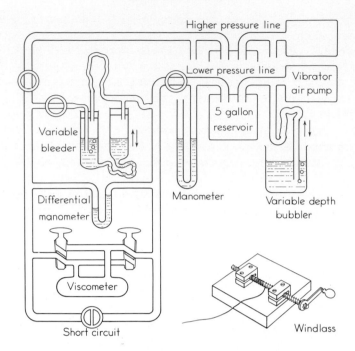

FIG. 4. AUXILIARY APPARATUS TO PROVIDE PRECISELY REGULATED AIR PRESSURES. A VARIABLE BLEEDER BY-PASS BETWEEN THE HIGHER AND LOWER PRESSURE LINES HELPS MAINTAIN A CONSTANT DIFFERENTIAL PRESSURE. A VOLTAGE REGULATOR SUPPLYING THE HOME AQUARIUM VIBRATOR AIR PUMPS IS ESSENTIAL.

ACKNOWLEDGMENT

This work was supported by U.S. Public Health Service Grant No. He-O5446.

DISCUSSION

SCOTT BLAIR (*England*):

This paper interested me very much, indeed, because it follows a line very similar to those of the experiments that were done by Professor Copley and myself when he was in London and followed up later by Mr. Glover and myself in Reading. The resistance offered to a meniscus moving along a tube, depends on two separate physical properties. One is the angle of contact between the liquid and the tube, which is very difficult to measure experimentally. The other is the surface tension. Surface tensions, of course, depend on how they are measured; but in general, if dynamic methods are used, a fair reproducibility can be obtained. I would like to ask Dr. Jacobs whether he determined by some other dynamic method the surface tension of these liquids through which it would be possible to get some approximate calculation at least of the angle of contact. And my second point is just to point out the historical point of interest. It was during the last century when a French worker studied (JAMIN, J. C. R. Acad. Sci. 50, 172, 1860) the flow of a large number of bubbles of liquid, water and other liquids, along tubes of this kind and measured resistances when large numbers of bubbles were caused to flow.

MEISELMAN (*U.S.A.*):

Are you able to extrapolate your pressure–flow data for the meniscal resistance down to some intercept on the pressure curve? If so, it is tempting to use this in some type of a Laplace equation, to measure the pressure drop across an interface and thus an interfacial tension. One needs here, of course, the contact angle. Can you calculate with this pressure drop anything which looks at all like a surface tension? Obviously it has to be at a given surface area; but can you obtain anything which looks like a reasonable estimate for the surface tensions of your liquids?

JACOBS (*U.S.A.*):

We have not studied surface tension effects in this work for one reason: surface active agents that lower surface tension with increasing concentration in a regular fashion exhibit meniscal resistance that rises to a maximum and falls again toward zero through a range of concentration in which surface tension is falling steadily. Maxima in meniscal resistance cannot therefore be related to surface tension in an easily comprehensible way. So with due apologies to Drs. Scott Blair and Meiselman, I suspect there is something more complicated going on in meniscal resistance than an exhibition of surface tension effects. My interest in meniscal resistance was certainly sharpened by the paper by the Frenchman mentioned by Dr. Scott Blair. In 1860 Jamin wondered how sap could rise 250 feet and higher in trees, so he studied a row of bubbles in a long open glass tube. He found that they would resist considerable force. But in 1930 Smith and Crane repeated the experiment with clean water in a clean tube and found no resistance at all. Recently Calderwood and others in England reported that glass tubes thoroughly cleaned soon became soiled again from smoke and petroleum residues in air. A meniscus of water in a fine glass tube propelled by a small force almost certainly will exhibit the effects of meniscal resistance unless extraordinary precautions are taken.

EIRICH (*U.S.A.*):

Did you find any relation between your maxima and critical micelle concentration? If so, a possible mode of interaction could be deduced.

JACOBS:

Micelle formation was probably absent in solutions of simple surface active agents we used, like hexyl resorcinol and dioctyl sodium sulfosuccinate. These solutions showed maxima in meniscal resistance in the presumed absence of micelle formation, hence that was not considered.

INSTRUMENTATION FOR THE STUDY OF *EX VIVO* BLOOD FLOW

K. WEISSENBERG*

The Royal Institution, London, England

ABSTRACT†

An instrument, termed Rheogoniometer, originally designed for a comprehensive testing of the flow properties of technological materials has been adapted to the testing of *ex vivo* flow of blood and of other biological material. A special study was made by Mr. T. Hutchinson and B. O. Shorthouse of fresh cell-free sheep plasma under conditions of steady shear rates, oscillatory shears, and combinations of both. It was found that the flow properties were strongly dependent on the particular conditions of flow with the shear moduli of viscosity and elasticity varying over several orders of magnitude. Of particular interest were the changes in the shear moduli observed in pulsative flow which was simulated in a flow produced by a combination of steady and oscillatory motions.

References to publications and details of both the original and the adapted Rheogoniometer can be obtained by application to the manufacturers Messrs. Sangamo Controls Ltd., North Bersted, Bognor Regis, Sussex, England.

†Author intends to submit complete paper to the journal *Biorheology*. (Editor.)

VISCOSITY OF BLOOD AT HIGH HAEMATOCRITS MEASURED IN MICROCAPILLARY (PARALLEL-PLATE) VISCOMETERS OF $r = 3-30$ MICRONS

L. DINTENFASS*

Department of Medicine, University of Sydney, Sydney, Australia

INTRODUCTION

As my interests are in the rheology of fluids, in general, and rheology of blood in cardiovascular diseases, in particular, extension of studies to regions of microcapillary flow should not be surprising. It is, in effect, a logical step in my investigation because (a) the rheology of blood is of greatest importance in small vessels, (b) any increase in blood viscosity or internal viscosity of blood cells will affect mainly microcapillary circulation, and (c) the so-called plugging of capillaries can be considered not as a nuisance but as an important rheological phenomenon.

Although flow of blood in capillaries, both *in vitro* and *in vivo*, is studied widely, very little information is available on flow of high haematocrit blood in very narrow capillaries, below a radius of 50 microns.

In order to carry on the work in capillaries of radii 3–30 microns, while at the same time retaining manageable flow times, capillary viscometers of the U-tube type have been constructed, in which the usual cylindrical capillary has been replaced by a slit formed by two parallel plates.

As one of the aspects of great interest to me is the internal viscosity of the red cell, and as this is not masked by aggregation of the red cells if high haematocrits are employed, the bulk of the work was carried out between 80 and 99% of red cells. A physiological justification for such haematocrits lies in the known elevation of haematocrits up to 80% in polycythaemia and in some diseases of new-born[1,2], as also, and perhaps even more important, our recent knowledge that redistribution of haematocrits takes place in the circulation due to plasma skimming, and local haematocrits of up to the nineties are quite feasible[3, 4,5].

On the basis of preliminary results obtained it will be possible to show that (i) viscosity of blood flowing through microcapillary channels is greatly affected by blood pH, (ii) Fåhraeus–Lindquist phenomenon is pronounced at very high haematocrits, and (iii) a reversal of Fåhraeus–Lindquist phenomenon appears to take place in capillaries of radii of the same size, or smaller, than the size of the red cell. It is intended to suggest that rheology of single cells (that is, the internal viscosity of blood cells) might form a contributary parameter of flow in microcapillaries.

EXPERIMENTAL METHODS

Microcapillary Viscometers

The capillaries were formed by rectangular plates made of Pyrex glass, $\frac{3}{4}$ to 1-inch thick, polished to the optical flatness, tolerance being few wavelengths of light only. Plates and viscometer are illustrated by Figs. 1a and 1b. Plates were separated by means of thin polythene strips greased with silicone grease, and clamped together by means of 2-inch "cramps". Channels of 2 mm bore run near the top and near the bottom of the plates. These channels deliver and collect blood. Polythene tubing of 2 mm bore is connected by means of plastic joints and sealed to glass channels with silicone grease

Fig. 1a. A photograph of a parallel-plate microcapillary viscometer of half-gap of 6.7 microns. Glass plates are supported by Meccano framework and clamped together by means of "cramps".

using a clamping device. Two 1-ml pipettes are connected to each of the polythene tubes. These pipettes can be moved up and down and are used to regulate the pressure drop. The capillaries of gap larger than 30 microns are formed by glass plates of dimensions 18×18 cm or 9×6 cm, while the 13·5 and 6·7 microns gap capillaries are formed by plates $11·5 \times 4·2$ cm. The length of capillary is 7 cm for the former, and 2 cm for the latter.

Material

Blood samples were obtained either from people or from giant Queensland toads. Blood samples from humans were obtained by venepuncture and collected in plastic bags containing acid-citrate-dextrose. Usually, viscometric tests were carried out within few hours of blood collection; on occasions, blood was tested on the following day. Adjustments of pH were made using isotonic bicarbonate or isotonic solution of sodium hydroxide. Packed cells were prepared by centrifugation. Haematocrit determinations were made by means of a microhaematocrit centrifuge, and were always made after the pH of the blood was stabilized. Care was taken in checking if platelet aggregates were present in the blood; if present, the blood was discarded. Platelets

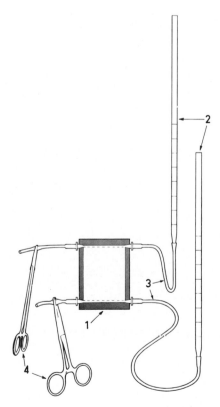

Fig. 1b. A diagrammatic representation of a parallel-plate microcapillary viscometer of half-gaps 15 to 25 microns. 1, glass plate; 2, pipettes; 3, polythene tubing leading from pipettes to 2 mm bore channels in the glass plate; 4, arterial clips used to clamp polythene tubing joined to the left part of the glass plate.

were removed partially by syphoning off the buffy coat; filtration of blood on glass wool was not found to be satisfactory.

Blood from toads was obtained by insertion of a needle into the aorta of the toad after the thorax was opened. Toads were warmed up before the incision was made to facilitate blood flow. Blood was anticoagulated with heparin and EDTA. (The surgery on toads was carried out by Mr. R. Lee of the Kanematsu Institute, Sydney Hospital.) Haematocrits and pH were tested the same way as for human blood; packed cells were prepared by centrifugation.

Viscosity Determination

The capillary viscometer was filled up with saline and the flow times of saline was always tested before blood was used. Blood, or packed cells, were taken into a 20 ml syringe fitted with a long plastic tube which could be inserted into the pipette and which reached to the bottom end of the pipette. Opening the clamp (arterial clip) on the left end of the channel (Figs. 1a and 1b) permitted pressure-filling of the top channel of viscometer. The parallel-plate microcapillary viscometer was situated vertically with a strong but diffused light source behind it; this permitted visual observation of the filling and the flow in the viscometer. Room temperature was accepted as the temperature of tests in this preliminary series. Temperature varied from 20° to 26°C, and the relevant temperatures are included in the data presented. The flow of 0·1 ml of blood was timed by means of a stop watch; the usual flow times were in the range from 30 sec to 4 hr. All viscosity data are given as relative to the viscosity of water. The nominal maximum rates of shear are calculated from equation $D = 0·75\ Q/wR^2$, where D is the rate of shear in sec^{-1}, Q is the volume flow in ml/sec, w is the half-width of the capillary in cm, and R is the radius or half-gap of capillary, in cm.

RESULTS AND DISCUSSION

A study of viscosity of blood in microcapillaries presented, at first, considerable difficulties due to clogging of the capillaries by aggregates of platelets or platelets and white cells. This effect, which was evident even in capillaries of 200 microns bore, was overcome either by separating platelets and white cells (removing buffy coat) from blood by aspiration or filtration, or—and most conveniently—by employing techniques of venepuncture using siliconized equipment in which platelet aggregation did not take place. The latter method was subject to chance, and only some blood samples were suitable for examination. Being aware from our earlier work (DINTENFASS and BURNARD[6]) that blood pH affects viscosity of blood, especially at high haematocrits, the first series of experiments was intended to supply information on this matter. The data obtained on blood of haematocrits 80, 93, 94·5, and 97%, using capillaries of radii 16·5, 24·0, and 25·5 microns, are illustrated by Figs. 2 and 3. A decrease of pH from 7·4 to 6·9 causes an elevation of viscosity by a factor of two, while a decrease of blood pH to 6·0 might result in 30-fold viscosity increase. As haematocrits were defined and adjusted after pH was stabilized, this effect cannot be attributed to an increase in haematocrit due to swelling of cells or due to the less dense packing of cells. It appears that rigidity of red cells is increased by lowering blood pH. This increase in rigidity is actually mild if compared with increases observed previously to be due either to reduced S–S haemoglobin or due to treatment of red cells with formaline (DINTENFASS

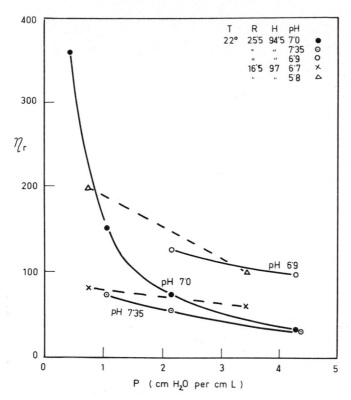

FIG. 2. RELATIVE VISCOSITY OF HUMAN BLOOD PLOTTED AS A FUNCTION OF THE PRESSURE GRADIENT.
H, HAEMATOCRIT; R, RADIUS IN MICRONS; T, TEMPERATURE. PLEASE OBSERVE THE EFFECT OF BLOOD
pH ON THE VISCOSITY OF PACKED RED CELLS.

[7]). The present observation on pH–viscosity relationship in blood confirms our earlier data and is also in agreement with observations by TEITEL (and NICOLAU[8]) that a decrease in pH results in an increase in filtration time of blood.

When blood, at any pH, was compared in smaller and larger capillaries, Fåhraeus–Lindquist phenomenon was clearly evident both at low and at high haematocrits. The order of viscosity decrease, corresponding to a decrease of radius (half-gap) from 25 to 6·7 microns, was 20 to 30% for haematocrits 40 to 86%; an amazingly large, about 30-fold, decrease in viscosity was observed in toads' blood of 98·5% haematocrits (Fig. 4).

Fåhraeus–Lindquist phenomenon is usually explained (HAYNES,[9] SCOTT BLAIR [10]) by the marginal zone of plasma, acting as a lubricant, by the axial concentration of red cells, or by unsheared lamina. Although these explanations sound most plausible for blood at low and medium haematocrits, it is rather difficult to understand the presence of a marginal plasmatic zone or the meaning of axial concentration of red cells in systems containing about 95–98% of red cells.

We already know that while the nature of internal viscosity or rigidity and deformability of the red cell is of relatively low importance at low haematocrits, it becomes of

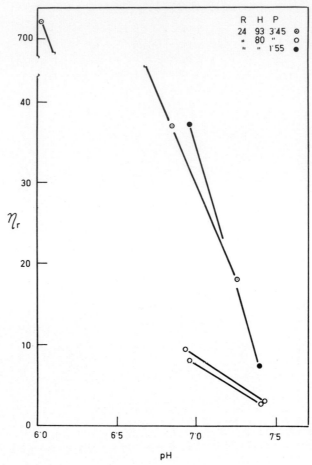

FIG. 3. EFFECT OF BLOOD pH ON THE RELATIVE VISCOSITY OF BLOOD AT 93 AND 80% HAEMATOCRIT. H, HAEMATOCRIT, %; R, RADIUS OF THE CAPILLARY, IN MICRONS; P, PRESSURE GRADIENT, IN CM OF H_2O PER CM LENGTH OF CAPILLARY; η_r, RELATIVE VISCOSITY.

very great importance at high haematocrits (DINTENFASS[11]) (Fig. 5). Suspensions of rigid particles reach infinite viscosity at volume concentrations of about 60%.

The pressure-flow diagram for packed red cells in microcapillary flow indicates clearly that packed red cells are non-Newtonian (Fig. 6a). This fits well with earlier data obtained by means of rotational viscometers (Fig. 6a), and confirms thixotropy or shear-thinning of packed red cells. As we cannot ascribe the mode of flow, in systems of packed red cells, to the aggregation of red cells, we must attribute it to the internal thixotropy of red cells and/or to complex intra- or inter-membrane movements. The term "internal viscosity" should include the physics of both the actual cell interior and the cell membrane.

It appears to me that Fåhraeus–Lindquist phenomenon in blood of high haematocrits includes, at least to some degree, the effect of the internal viscosity of the red cell. A question could be asked if there exists any mechanism which will permit blood viscosity

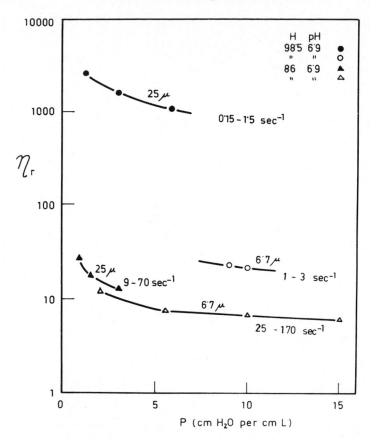

FIG. 4. FÅHRAEUS–LINDQUIST PHENOMENON IN BLOOD OF HAEMATOCRITS 86 AND 98·5%. RELATIVE VISCOSITY, η_r, OF BLOOD IS PLOTTED AGAINST THE PRESSURE GRADIENT, P EXPRESSED IN CM OF H_2O PER CM LENGTH OF CAPILLARY. RADII OF CAPILLARIES ARE INDICATED. THE RATES OF SHEAR ARE ALSO INDICATED IN THE FIGURE. H, HAEMATOCRIT, %.

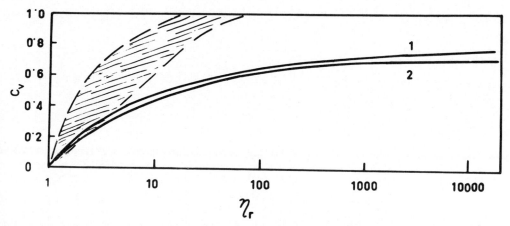

FIG. 5. RELATIVE VISCOSITY OF SUSPENSIONS AS A FUNCTION OF THE VOLUME CONCENTRATIONS OF THE SUSPENDED PARTICLES. CURVES 1 AND 2 CORRESPOND TO SUSPENSIONS OF RIGID PARTICLES. THE SHADED AREA CORRESPONDS TO DATA ON BLOOD GIVEN BY VARIOUS INVESTIGATORS. FIGURE AFTER DINTENFASS[11].

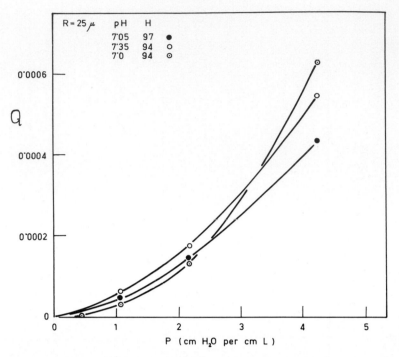

FIG. 6a. PRESSURE-VOLUME CURVES FOR PACKED HUMAN RED CELLS. VOLUME, Q, IN ML/SEC IS PLOTTED AGAINST PRESSURE GRADIENT, P, IN CM OF H_2O PER CM LENGTH OF CAPILLARY. THE HALF-WIDTH OF THE CAPILLARY WAS 42 MM, THE HALF-GAP (RADIUS, R) WAS 25 MICRONS. H, HAEMATOCRIT.

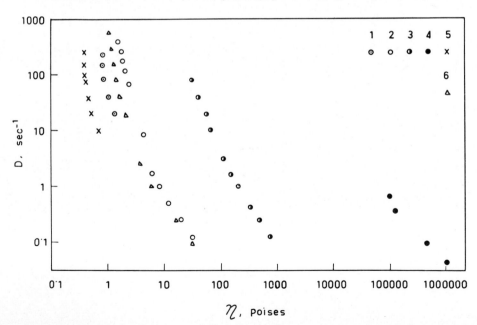

FIG. 6b. VISCOSITY-RATE OF SHEAR DATA OBTAINED BY ROTATIONAL VISCOMETERS (DINTENFASS[7]). THE PACKED RED CELLS OF HAEMATOCRIT 98%: 1, NORMAL CELLS; 2, SAME CELLS SWOLLEN IN HYPOTONIC SALINE; 3, SAME CELLS CRENATED; 4, CELLS TREATED WITH FORMALINE; 5 AND 6, NORMALS CELLS FROM DIFFERENT DONORS. D, RATE OF SHEAR, IN SEC^{-1}; η, VISCOSITY IN POISES.

in small vessels to be lower than in larger vessels, at equal nominal maximum shear rates. A possible answer is that in small vessels the internal viscosity of red cell never corresponds to zero rate of shear. Although, theoretically, a zero rate of shear zone lies along the axis of the vessel, due to rapid movements of the cell which occupies an appreciable part of the lumen, the various parts of a single cell are exposed to different velocity gradients. Either the memory of stress (thixotropic recovery time, relaxation

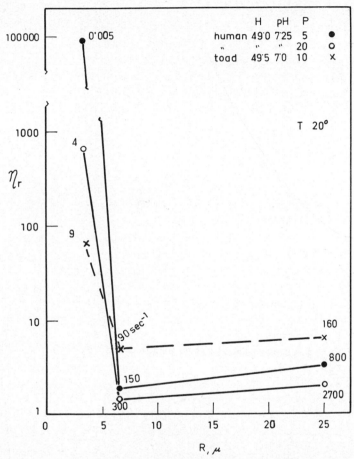

Fig. 7. Relative viscosity of human and toads' blood in capillaries of different radii. H, haematocrit; P, pressure gradient, in cm H_2O per cm of capillary length. Numbers inserted in different parts of the figure illustrate the rates of shear in sec^{-1}. Capillary radius (half-gap) is given in microns. Temperature, T, is 20°C.

time) or the internal circulation (or internal mixing) would keep the internal viscosity, and thus the suspension viscosity, less than that calculated from the theoretical velocity gradient profile.

That the internal viscosity must play a rôle is evident from Fig. 7, in which the relative viscosity of human and toads' blood is plotted against the capillary radius. It appears that a reversal of Fåhraeus–Lindquist phenomenon takes place at radii below 6 microns, at pressure gradients from 5 to 20 cm H_2O per cm length of capillary.

HAYNES[9] has suggested that a reversal of Fåhraeus–Lindquist phenomenon could be anticipated at very low near-zero pressure gradients. In the present experiment, however, the pressure gradient is not near-zero.

It must be noted that PROTHERO and BURTON[12] found red cells to flow through millipore capillaries of 3 microns bore at 4 to 20 cm H_2O pressure drop; however, as the length of millipore filter capillaries was 150 microns, the pressure gradients employed by them ranged from 270 to 1300 cm H_2O per cm length of capillary, and are thus not comparable to my values.

It is not yet clearly known how the flow in parallel-plate capillaries correlates with the flow in cylindrical glass capillaries. Using methods of HAYNES and BURTON[13] I calculated slopes of linear segments of pressure-flow curves of few series of experiments. When these slopes were compared with the data of HAYNES and BURTON (Ref. 13, p. 946, Fig. 6), it was evident that the slope corresponding to a parallel-plate capillary of half-gap 25 microns approximates the slope of cylindrical capillary of 57 microns radius.

CONCLUSIONS

Fåhraeus–Lindquist phenomenon was found to be valid in capillaries down to radius of 6 microns, for blood up to 99% haematocrit. The viscosity of blood is less in smaller capillaries, although in each capillary the viscosity is also a function of pressure gradient and shear rate. In general, lower viscosities correspond to higher rates of shear and, vice versa, higher viscosities correspond to lower rates of shear. The viscosity of blood, at any pressure gradient or in any particular capillary, depends on blood pH, a decrease in blood pH causing an elevation of blood viscosity.

The rôle of the internal viscosity of red cell in Fåhraeus–Lindquist phenomenon is not yet clear. While it is not implied that Fåhraeus–Lindquist phenomenon is due to the internal viscosity of the red cells, it is suggested that the internal viscosity (or specifically, the internal thixotropy) of red cell might be a contributing factor.

A reversal of Fåhraeus–Lindquist phenomenon appears to take place in capillaries of radii below 6 microns, both for human and toads' cells, although the volume of the toad red cell is about 11-fold larger than that of the human cell.

This phenomenon, as well as the effect of blood pH, are interpreted as due to internal rheology of single red cells.

An interaction of the Fåhraeus–Lindquist phenomenon and the phenomena due to the rheology of single cells results in a curve with a minimum, when the blood viscosity is plotted against the capillary radius. If this curve is followed in the direction of the decreasing radii, the first section of the curve corresponds, at low and medium haematocrits to the Fåhraeus–Lindquist phenomenon caused by axial flow or plasmatic zone, etc., and at high haematocrits to Fåhraeus–Lindquist phenomenon influenced — at least in part — by the internal thixotropy of the red cell. At very small radii a reversal of Fåhraeus–Lindquist phenomenon will take place.

Clogging of capillaries by platelet aggregates may take place in cylindrical capillaries of up to 200 microns radii, and this effect should not be confused with a proper reversal of Fåhraeus–Lindquist phenomenon. Clogging ability of platelets and white cells is due to their high internal viscosity and rigidity (DINTENFASS[14]).

ACKNOWLEDGMENTS

I am greatly indebted to Dr. A. A. Palmer, of Sydney Hospital, for his friendly help and advice. Support for this study was given by the National Heart Foundation of Australia. The parallel-plate microcapillary viscometers were constructed from funds supplied by the Medical Research Fund of Sydney Hospital.

Valuable technical assistance was given by Mr. R. Lee of Kanematsu Institute, Sydney Hospital, who performed surgery on giant toads.

REFERENCES

[1] BURNARD, E. D. and GRAUAUG, A. L. *Pediatrics* **28**, 545, 1961.
[2] DANKS, D. M. and STEVENS, L. H. *Lancet* **2**, 499, 1964.
[3] MCHEDLISHVILI, G. I. *Capillary Circulation*, Georgia Acad. Press, Tbilisi, 1958.
[4] PALMER, A. A. *Quart. J. Exp. Physiol.* **44**, 149, 1959.
[5] PALMER, A. A. *Amer. J. Physiol.* **209**, 1115, 1965.
[6] DINTENFASS, L. and BURNARD, E. *Med. J. Australia* **1**, 1072, 1966.
[7] DINTENFASS, L. *J. Lab. & Clin. Med.* **64**, 594, 1964.
[8] TEITEL, P. and NICOLAU, C. T. In *Proceedings of Symposium of Molecular Biology and Pathology*, C. T. NICOLAU (Editor), Bucharest, 1964, p. 59.
[9] HAYNES, R. H. *Amer. J. Physiol.* **198**, 1193, 1960.
[10] SCOTT BLAIR, G. W. *Rheol. Acta* **1**, 123, 1958.
[11] DINTENFASS, L. *Angiology* **8**, 333, 1962.
[12] PROTHERO, J. W. and BURTON, A. C. *Biophys. J.* **2**, 213, 1962.
[13] HAYNES, R. H. and BURTON, A. C. *Amer. J. Physiol.* **197**, 943, 1959.
[14] DINTENFASS, L. *Experimental and Molecular Pathology* **4**, 597, 1965.

DISCUSSION

WHITMORE (*England*):

Just two comments I think one might make on this paper. The first is that when one reaches haematocrits of around 90%, one wonders exactly what it is that is being measured and whether in fact one can genuinely look upon the result as a viscosity. I think from this point of view, it would be very interesting if somebody could test high concentrations of packed blood cells in an instrument like a rheogoniometer and see if they can detect any normal forces. As the cells move over one another in shear a normal force of the type described by Bagnold for rigid particles might develop, but it is difficult to detect with ordinary blood. We have tried this, but if any normal force was present it was inside the sensitivity of the instrument. But I think that with packed cells the normal force might be appreciably larger. If we found one, I think we should have to look again at the whole question of whether in fact it is a genuine viscosity we are measuring with packed cells. The second point I would like to make refers to Dr. Dintenfass's discovery of a minimum viscosity in blood flowing in a slit, when the width is 7 or 8 microns. I was very interested in this because it is, of course, just the effect which one would expect from a change-over from the equivalent of shearing-core to axial train flow, on a two-dimensional model. It is the first experimental evidence I have seen of the effect and it is very interesting from that point of view.

PALMER (*Australia*):

Dr. Dintenfass stressed that this was a preliminary investigation and obviously it would be desirable to test a great many more radii in the region where this sudden change occurs, and this he has not yet done. I think he believes that the effects being measured are a combination of the internal viscosity of the red cell, the properties of the red cell membrane itself, its mechanical properties and the actual frictional forces between the individual red cells; of course there is still some plasma left, even in the most concentrated suspension.

DINTENFASS (*Australia*) (written communication):

Dr. Palmer explained my point of view perfectly. I would like to add that the use of the concept of viscosity as it is done today, concerns only the first coefficient of viscosity, the shear coefficient. It is very likely that the second coefficient of viscosity is quite relevant in such pressure-controlled system as blood circulation. It is also most likely that, while normal stress is negligible in suspensions of red cells or in normal anti-coagulated blood, it might be, perhaps, quite large either under some specific metabolic conditions or in some pathological states. Thus, I would not exclude that normal stress might be of importance. A point I would like to make is that a determination of the first coefficient of viscosity only, as we do, is in principle an approximation of a particular system's rheology. Dr. Whitmore is very right in bringing this philosophical point into discussion, as it allows us to obtain a proper perspective on experimental rheology.

BURTON (*Canada*):

I found this a fascinating paper; and I think Dr. Dintenfass is to be congratulated on looking at packed cells even though people would say: well, what has that got to do with the physiological problem? But the point I wanted to make is that how important it would be to use a technique such as Dr. Phibbs described to see just what shape these cells were in the packed bottom of a haematocrit tube. I think the method would work beautifully. The tightest possible packing of cells of a normal biconcave shape, is only 58%, and it is quite obvious that in the bottom of the centrifuge tube packed cells must be some sort of polyhedra. Do you think that you, Dr. Dintenfass, should do this with quick freezing technique and freeze substitutioning sections? I think it would enormously help our understanding of what is happening if we had these pictures.

PALMER:

Yes, I shall ask Dr. Dintenfass about this.

DINTENFASS (written communication):

The shape of the red cells after centrifugation, as also their degree of packing, will depend on the internal fluidity of the cells. The red cells of normal haemoglobin and at normal pH will allow the tightest configuration possible. On the other hand, red cells containing abnormal haemoglobins (as for instance S–S haemoglobin, and especially in reduced state), or at very low blood pH, or treated with the crosslinking agents, will deform only slightly and will not pack tightly; the intercellular spaces will be quite appreciable and up to 40 per cent of the total volume. These are, in effect, the suspensions which show maximum viscosity. Professor Burton's suggestion on quick freezing technique is most relevant and it would be illuminating to apply it.

SCOTT BLAIR (*England*):

I had a very friendly discussion with Dr. Dintenfass when he passed through England once, on a point here on which he and I could not possibly agree. I think it is very confusing, this use of the word "thixotropy". I do not know on this particular occasion in which sense he is using the word. But I think he always uses it to mean what everybody else, since the days of GOODEVE (C.F.) and WHITFIELD (G.W.) (*Trans. Faraday Soc.* **34**, 511, 1938) calls "shear thinning". I think he simply means that as we increase the rate of shear, the viscosity falls. Professor Dintenfass says that it does not matter whether there is a time factor involved here, whether there is a notable hysteresis, because this is, as Reiner says about the mountains, just a question of time scale. If you could measure fast enough, you would find hysteresis even in cases which we would call shear thinning. But most rheologists use the word thixotropy to imply that, with the apparatus used, you can actually measure a time during which it takes the system to recover its original consistency; i.e. that the relationship between stress and shear rate is not monotonic. I think it is better to keep to the use of the term as defined by Freundlich and his pupils. He told me personally, just before his death, that he did not approve of its use to mean "shear thinning". I think we want to be very clear indeed when we talk about the thixotropy of a system of this sort, in which sense we are using the word.

PALMER:

I am sure that you have correctly stated Dr. Dintenfass's view. He believes, as you say, that there must be a finite time and therefore is no sharp distinction between shear thinning and thixotropy.

DINTENFASS (written communication):

I do not recognize a difference between thixotropy, false body, shear thinning, etc., in respect to suspensions which reduce their viscosity with increasing rates of shear till the moment when all the structural viscosity is broken down, such mechanically broken-down system approximating—at any further increase of the rate of shear—a Newtonian system. All such systems I call thixotropic, as in all such systems a finite time is required both for breakdown of the structural viscosity and for the recovery of the original viscosity. The recovery time, which I call "thixotropic recovery time", may be in order of days in the case of gel-paints, hours in the case of many industrial suspensions, and seconds and minutes in the case of human blood. Thixotropic recovery time depends not only on the intrinsic properties of the suspension or emulsion tested, but also on the levels of rates of shear between which this recovery is measured. That is, for instance, a sample of blood can be stirred up at the rate of shear of 100 sec^{-1} and the recovery followed at 10 sec^{-1}, and in such case very little will be observed. However, this blood sample can be stirred up at 100 sec^{-1} and its recovery followed at 0.1 or 1 sec^{-1}, and here most significant recovery times can be easily noted. In principle, a thixotropic recovery time between any two levels of shear rates is a sum of the thixotropic recovery times in all intermediate levels. Also, the duration of recovery time becomes longer the lower is the rate of shear used in following up (or scanning) of the recovery of the thixotropic system. As Dr. Scott Blair rightly said, quoting Professor Reiner, all is a question of time scale. I might add that in the case of blood, the thixotropic recovery time is of significant interest at low rates of shear, and low rates of shear are encountered throughout the entire blood circulation system. One point I would like to add: Although I describe blood as thixotropic, I still envisage a possibility that, under some conditions, influenced perhaps by the pathology of cells or pathology of tissue in which these cells flow, blood or red cells might show dilatant or thixotropic–dilatant behaviour. The term "dilatant" is used to describe a material in which viscosity increases as the rate of shear increases. Con.plex materials might show both thixotropy and dilatancy, either simultaneously or consecutively, depending on the rheological characteristics of the subphase.

ÉTUDE DE LA VISCOSITÉ DU SÉRUM SANGUIN, SEUL ET ASSOCIÉ À DE LA PÉNICILLINE, À L'AIDE D'UN DISPOSITIF DE MESURE DE LA VISCOSITÉ EN CONTINU

J. Zimmer,* H. Bergoend et A. Basset

Laboratoire de Recherches Cutanées et d'Allergie, Chaire de Clinique des Maladies Cutanées et Syphilitiques, Faculté de Médecine de Strasbourg, Strasbourg, France

Des problèmes d'allergie humorale nous ont amenés à pratiquer la viscosimétrie du sérum sanguin. Pasquet[1] a montré que la viscosité du sérum, provenant de personnes allergiques à l'aspirine, augmente après y avoir ajouté de l'acide acétyl-salicylique. Cette variation de la viscosité, il l'attribue à la formation du complexe antigène-anticorps de poids moléculaire nettement plus élevé que celui de chacun des éléments de la réaction. Rhéologiquement parlant, il est logique de penser que l'apparition de grosses molécules dans un milieu se traduise par une augmentation de la viscosité de celui-ci.

Mais avant d'entamer des travaux sur les réactions immunochimiques proprement dites, nous nous proposons d'étudier, dans ce travail, la viscosité de sérum humain normal seul et associé à de la pénicilline.

(A) MATÉRIEL

I. *Viscosimètre*

Comme les immunoglobulines anti-allergènes des malades sensibilisés ne représentent qu'une fraction minime des protéines responsables de la viscosité du sérum, il faut se servir d'un viscosimètre très sensible permettant de détecter de très faibles variations. Pasquet[1] a utilisé un matériel difficile à manier, auquel nous avons préféré un appareillage de conception plus récente, à la fois plus sensible, plus précis et plus facile à manipuler. Cet appareillage appelé par le constructeur:† "Ensemble pour la mesure de la viscosité" ou "Autoviscanalyseur", est basé sur le principe de Couette. Il en diffère cependant par les points suivants:

La cuve et le pendule ne sont pas cylindriques mais cylindroconiques comme le montre la fig. 1.

Le pendule en laiton argenté est plein; un canal de faible diamètre le traverse en son centre, parallèlement à son axe principale comme le montre la fig. 2; à sa partie supérieure est aménagé un réceptacle circulaire, qui communique avec le canal central comme le montre la fig. 3.

† Société Electrona, 13, rue Jean-Jaurès, à Strasbourg-Lingolsheim, 67 (France).

Fig. 1. Pendule et cuve vus de côté.

Fig. 2. Cuve vue d'en haut et pendule vu d'en bas; à noter: l'orifice du canal central.

Fig. 3. Pendule en place dans la cuve; à noter le bord supéro-interne chanfreiné de la cuve et le réceptacle circulaire à la partie supérieure du pendule.

Fig. 4. Vue de l'"ensemble pour la mesure de la viscosité"; a noter de gauche à droite: l'enregistreur, le viscosimètre, un bain-marie, la pompe proportionnante, l'échantillonneur et le thermostat.

La mesure de la viscosité n'est pas réalisée point par point mais en continu; le liquide à mesurer n'est pas placé dans la cuve avant chaque détermination, mais traverse continuellement l'entrefer avec un débit d'environ 2,5 ml par minute; il arrive par le canal au centre du pendule pour être prélevé sur le bord supéro-interne, chanfreiné de la cuve comme la montre la fig. 3 (ce prélèvement par aspiration en continu présente également l'avantage de supprimer la couche superficielle gênante, que les solutions de protéines ont tendance à former).

Les résultats sont inscrits de façon automatique et continu par un enregistreur électriques couplé au viscosimètre, comme le montre la fig. 4.

Le viscosimètre fonctionne comme appareil de zéro; le pendule est maintenu dans une position fixe par une contre-tension électrique proportionnelle à la viscosité.

L'entrefer présente les caractéristiques suivantes: rayon = 10 mm, épaisseur = 1 mm; cette dernière est la même au niveau du cylindre comme dans la partie conique.

La cuve est mobile et baigne dans un bain-marie. Elle tourne à raison de 66 tours à la minute.

II. *Appareils accessoires du viscosimètre*

(1) *La pompe d'amener du liquide.* Le rôle principal de la pompe est de maintenir un courant continu et constant de liquide à travers l'entrefer du dispositif viscosimétrique. Différents modèles peuvent être utilisés. Nous avons préféré nous servir de la pompe proportionnante "Technicon". Son jeu de tubes permet de prélever et de mélanger les réactifs de façon automatique, continue et reproductible.

(2) *Le distributeur d'échantillons.* Nous utilisons le distributeur d'échantillons "Sampler II Technicon". Il permet de prélever alternativement l'échantillon et le liquide témoin.

(3) *Le thermostat.* Le thermostat réglable est du type fermé, il maintient constante la température du bain-marie du dispositif viscosimétrique. Les mesures sont effectuées à 20°C.

(4) *Les bains-marie.* Le mélange réactionnel segmenté par des bulles d'air passe à

travers des bobines de délai, plongées dans deux bains-marie, l'un à 37,5°C et l'autre à 20°C.

(5) *L'enrégistreur*. L'enrégistreur (fig. 4) avcc décalage d'échelle permet de travailler avec la même sensibilité quelle que soit la viscosité du milieu étudié. 1 mm. sur le papier correspond à 6×10^{-3} centipoises.

(B) RÉACTIFS

I. *Les sérums humains*

Les sérums humains proviennent de personnes saines ou de malades hospitalisés ne présentant pas d'allergie à la pénicilline.

II. *La solution physiologique tamponnée à* pH 7,2 *de Meyer–Levine* (M–L)

La solution M–L a été choisie comme diluant des sérums et de la glycérine, comme solvant de la pénicilline et comme milieu témoin dont la viscosité sert de base à certaines mesures.

Composition de la solution M–L.   (1) *Solution mère*

Bicarbonate de soude	2,52 g
Acide 5,5′-diethylbarbiturique	4,60 g
5,5′-diethylbarbiturate de soude	3,00 g
Chlorure de sodium	83,80 g
Chlorure de magnésium	1,00 g
Chlorure de calcium à 2 molécules d'eau	0,20 g
Eau bidistillée q.s.p.	2.000,-ml

(2) *Solution diluée* (M–L)

Solution mère	1 vol.
Eau bidistillée	4 vol.
le pH de cette solution est ajustée entre	7,3 et 7,4

III. *Le sérum humain dilué au* $\frac{1}{3}$ *(dilution finale)*

Le sérum humain (1 vol.) est dilué par le jeu de tube à la sortie de la pompe par 2 vol. de M–L pur ou contenant de la pénicilline en solution.

IV. *Les solutions de pénicilline*

Différentes quantités de pénicilline-G sont dissoutes dans le M–L. La concentration en pénicilline de chacune de ces solutions est calculée en fonction du taux final dans le milieu réactionnel (1/10 à 1/1600 − P/V), en tenant compte du facteur de dilution qui est de $\frac{2}{3}$.

V. *La solution de glycérine à 5%*
Composition:

Glycérine	5,00 g
Phénol	0,10 g
Eau bidistillée q.s.p.	100 ml

(C) MÉTHODE

I. *Principe*

Cette méthode est basée sur le principe de mesure relative de la viscosité avec renouvellement automatique et continu du liquide dont la viscosité est déterminée et enrégistrée sur papier à l'aide d'un enregistreur potentiométrique électrique.

II. *Mode opératoire*

La pompe proportionnante prélève et mélange les réactifs à l'aide de 2 tubes, l'un d'un débit de 2,4 ml/min., relié en permanence à un récipient qui contient du M–L ou les solutions de pénicilline dans le M–L, l'autre de 1,2 ml/min. relié à l'échantillonneur. A l'aide de ce deuxième tube nous pouvons prélever alternativement soit du M–L, soit l'échantillon à étudier—position reculée (fig. 5) ou avancée (fig. 6) du bras de prélèvement. La colonne de liquide est segmentée avec de l'air à raison de 1,6 ml/min. et

FIG. 5. ECHANTILLONNEUR "SAMPLER II—TECHNICON" AVEC BRAS EN POSITION RECULÉE.

FIG. 6. ECHANTILLONNEUR "SAMPLER II—TECHNICON" AVEC BRAS EN POSITION AVANCÉE.

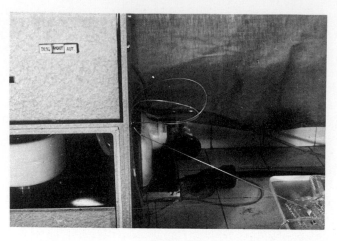

FIG. 7. TUBE CAPILLAIRE QUI AMÈNE LE LIQUIDE AU VISCOSIMÈTRE.

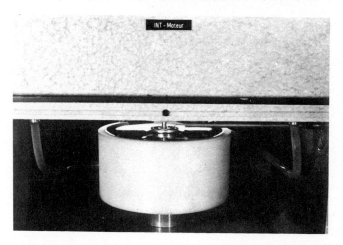

FIG. 8. LA CUVE ET LE PENDULE EN PLACE DANS LE BAIN-MARIE DU VISCOSIMÈTRE; À NOTER LE CAPILLAIRE
D'AMENER DU LIQUIDE.

propulsée à travers 2 bobines de mélange puis 2 bobines de délai, immergées dans 2
bains-marie, l'un à 37°C (6 min.) et l'autre à 20°C (2 min.). Après débullage, le liquide
est repris par la pompe à l'aide d'un tube de 2,5 ml/min et envoyé dans le viscosimètre
où il arrive par un capillaire (fig. 7) dans le réceptacle à la partie supérieure du pendule
(fig.: 3, 7 et 8). Par le canal central (fig. 2) il est dirigé vers le fond de la cuve. En
remontant, il traverse l'entrefer. Pendant ce temps la viscosité est mesurée et enregistrée. Arrivé au bord supéro-interne de la cuve il est éliminé par aspiration. La fig. 9
montre le diagramme des fluides de ce procédé. La durée totale de l'opération depuis le
prélèvement jusqu'à la mesure et l'enregistrement est de 9 min.

III. *Tracés viscosimétriques*

(1) *Tracé du type I: rectiligne-parallèle* (fig. 10.). Lorsque les deux tubes de
prélèvement envoient de la solution témoin, M–L, dans le viscosimètre—bras de
l'échantillonneur en position reculée (fig. 5)—on enregistre une ligne de base parallèle

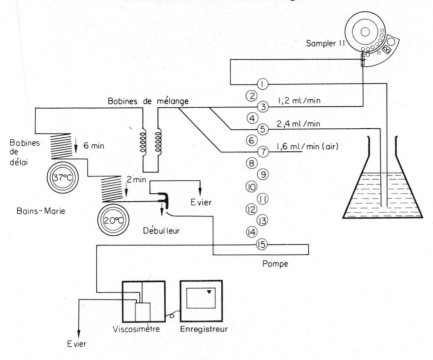

Sampler II

Bobines de mélange

1,2 ml/min

2,4 ml /min

1,6 ml/min (air)

Bobines de délai   6 min

37°C

Bains-Marie

2 min

20°C

Débulleur

Evier

Pompe

Viscosimètre   Enregistreur

Evier

FIG. 9. DIAGRAMME DES FLUIDES.

à l'axe de déplacement du papier. Après un certain temps on actionne manuellement l'échantillonneur, Son bras, relié au tube 1,2 ml/min. se met en position avancée (fig. 6) et aspire une solution de viscosité supérieure à celle du témoin. Le M–L continue à être prélevé par le tube 2,4 ml/min. L'échantillon dilué de 1 à 3 dans le M–L en cours de route, arrive au viscosimètre et remplace progressivement le liquide témoin. Au fur et à mesure que le nouveau milieu plus visqueux que le premier refoule celui-ci de l'entrefer, on enregistre une déviation du tracé viscosimétrique qui aboutit à une deuxivme ligne parallèle à la première, d'ordonnée différente. L'amplitude de la déviation traduit la différence de viscosité entre les deux milieux comme le montre la fig. 10.

Nous ne citons ce type de tracé, intéressant pour des travaux d'un autre ordre, que pour mémoire.

(2) *Tracé viscosimétrique du type II ou curviligne* (fig. 11). Pour obtenir un tracé viscosimétrique de ce type, l'échantillonneur est commandé automatiquement par une came. Cette dernière porte le profil 2–4, c'est à dire qu'elle met le bras de l'échantillonneur en position avancée (fig. 6) pendant 2 min. et en position reculée (fig. 5) pendant 4 min. et ainsi de suite. Appelons la position avancée "prélèvement" et la position reculée "lavage". Le liquide de lavage, dans notre cas le M–L, sert également de blanc.

Lorsque l'on démarre la mesure sur la position lavage, les deux tubes 1,2 et 2,4 ml/min. envoient du M–L dans le viscosimètre. On enregistre la ligne de base parallèle à l'axe de déplacement du papier. A l'instant 4 min. la came met le bras sur prélèvement. Le tube 1,2 ml/min. aspire, à la place du M–L, l'échantillon (solution de glycérine à 5%) de viscosité supérieure à celle du témoin. L'augmentation de la viscosité est

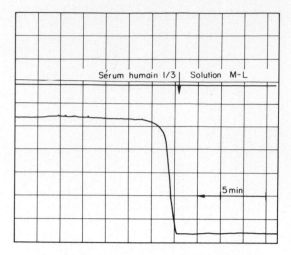

FIG. 10. TRACÉ VISCOSIMÉTRIQUE DU TYPE 1.

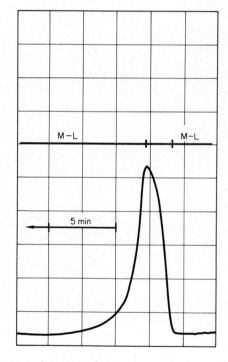

FIG. 11. TRACÉ VISCOSIMÉTRIQUE DU TYPE II (GLYCÉRINE).

enregistrée par une déviation du tracé comme le montre la fig. 11. Deux minutes plus tard, le bras est remis automatiquement sur lavage. Le tracé viscosimétrique retourne sur la ligne de base. Nous avons ainsi réalisé un tracé viscosimétrique curviligne (fig. 11), dont la hauteur du pic traduit la différence: viscosité de l'échantillon dilué au $\frac{1}{3}$ moins viscosité du témoin. La distance en hauteur entre deux traits du papier est égale à 10 mm.

Cette façon de procéder est de beaucoup plus économique tout en donnant des résultats parfaitement reproductibles comme le montre la fig. 12.

(D) RÉSULTATS ET DISCUSSION

I. *Le tracé viscosimétrique du sérum (type II)* (fig. 13)

Le tracé viscosimétrique du sérum est différent de celui de la gylcérine comme le montre la fig. 13. La branche descendante de la courbe, au lieu de retomber sans accident sur la ligne de base, accuse dans sa deuxième moitié une nouvelle remontée,

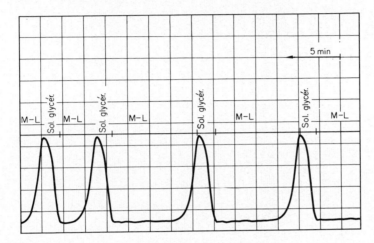

FIG. 12. ESSAI DE REPRODUCTIBILITÉ DE TRACÉS VISCOSIMÉTRIQUES DU TYPE II (GLYCÉRINE) AVEC ESPACE-MENT SIMPLE ET DOUBLE PAR INTERCALAGE D'UN ÉCHANTILLON M-L.

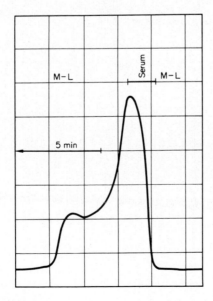

FIG. 13. TRACÉ VISCOSIMÉTRIQUE DU SÉRUM (TYPE II); À NOTER LE PIC SECONDAIRE DÛ À UN RETARD D'ÉVACUATION DES PROTÉINES.

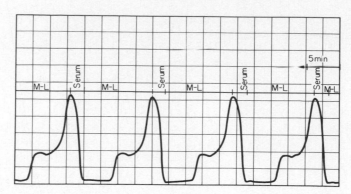

F𝗜𝗚. 14. E𝗌𝗌𝗔𝗜 𝗗𝗘 𝗥𝗘𝗣𝗥𝗢𝗗𝗨𝗖𝗧𝗜𝗕𝗜𝗟𝗜𝗧𝗘́ 𝗗𝗘 𝗧𝗥𝗔𝗖𝗘́𝗦 𝗩𝗜𝗦𝗖𝗢𝗦𝗜𝗠𝗘́𝗧𝗥𝗜𝗤𝗨𝗘𝗦 𝗗𝗨 𝗧𝗬𝗣𝗘 II 𝗗'𝗨𝗡 𝗠𝗘̂𝗠𝗘 𝗦𝗘́𝗥𝗨𝗠, 𝗧𝗢𝗨-
𝗝𝗢𝗨𝗥𝗦 𝗔𝗩𝗘𝗖 𝗘𝗦𝗣𝗔𝗖𝗘𝗠𝗘𝗡𝗧 𝗗𝗢𝗨𝗕𝗟𝗘 𝗣𝗔𝗥 𝗜𝗡𝗧𝗘𝗥𝗖𝗔𝗟𝗔𝗚𝗘 𝗗'𝗨𝗡 𝗘́𝗖𝗛𝗔𝗡𝗧𝗜𝗟𝗟𝗢𝗡 M–L 𝗣𝗢𝗨𝗥 𝗔𝗦𝗦𝗨𝗥𝗘𝗥 𝗨𝗡 𝗥𝗘𝗧𝗢𝗨𝗥
𝗖𝗢𝗠𝗣𝗟𝗘𝗧 𝗗𝗨 𝗧𝗥𝗔𝗖𝗘́ 𝗦𝗨𝗥 𝗟𝗔 𝗟𝗜𝗚𝗡𝗘 𝗗𝗘 𝗕𝗔𝗦𝗘.

moins importante que la première, pour ne retourner au zéro qu'avec un certain retard. Retard qui nous a obligé d'intercaler entre chaque échantillon de sérum un échantillon de M–L. Ceci nous donne le programme suivant: 4 min. de lavage, 2 min. de prélève-ment de sérum, 4 min. de lavage, 2 min. de prélèvement de M–L et encore 4 min. de lavage. On est obligé de doubler au moins le temps de lavage après le passage du sérum pour être sûr d'éliminer entièrement les protéines. Dans nos conditions de travail, le sérum présente un tracé viscosimétrique à 2 pics, un principal et un secon-daire. Ce dernier, plus faible que le premier, est probablement dû à une élimination tardive des protéines qui se sont accrochées aux parois du pendule et de la cuve et de ce fait se sont attardées dans le dispositif.

Ce tracé est parfaitement reproductible comme le montre la fig. 14.

II. *Modification de la viscosité du sérum humain et de son tracé viscosimétrique sous l'influence de la pénicilline*

La fig. 15 montre une série de tracés viscosimétriques d'un même sérum (dilution finale au $\frac{1}{3}$) avec M–L pur (tracé témoin) et 11 solutions de pénicilline dans M–L, titrant (dilutions finales dans le mélange P/V) 1/10, 1/20, 1/30, 1/40, 1/50, 1/60, 1/100, 1/200, 1/400, 1/800 et 1/1600.

Cette étude montre que l'addition de pénicilline au sérum provoque une modification de la viscosité de celui-ci et supprime le pic secondaire de son tracé viscosimétrique (type II). La variation de la viscosité tout en étant conditionnée par l'addition de l'antibiotique n'est pas proportionnelle à la concentration de celui-ci. Pour la dilution 1/1600 la viscosité est nettement inférieure à celle du témoin. Elle va décroissant jusqu'à la dilution 1/200, remonte au-delà et dépasse même la valeur témoin pour des fortes concentrations comme le montre le graphique de la fig. 16.

Le pic secondaire du tracé viscosimétrique du sérum déjà nettement abaissé pour la dilution 1/1600 diminue progressivement pour disparaître entièrement à 1/200; il ne réapparaît plus au-delà.

La dilution 1/200 est un point critique aussi bien pour la viscosité que pour le pic secondaire; il partage le champ expérimental en deux zones, l'une englobant les fortes dilutions et l'autre les faibles dilutions de l'antibiotique.

D'un côté, dans la zone des fortes dilutions, la plus proche de la réalité physiologique,

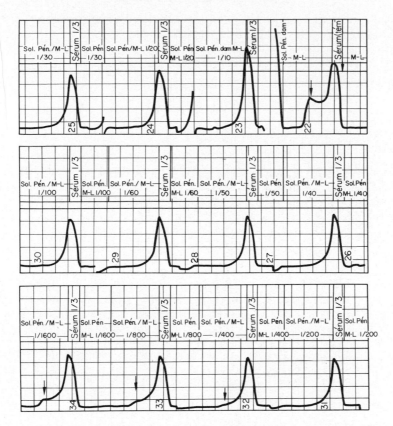

FIG. 15. Série de tracés viscosimétriques d'un même sérum (dilution finale au $\frac{1}{3}$) avec du M–L pur (tracé témoin en haut à droite) et 11 solutions de pénicilline dans M–L de droite à gauche et de haut en bas.

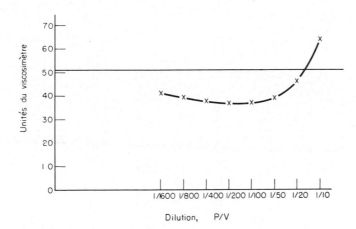

FIG. 16. Variation de la viscosité du sérum humain dilué au $\frac{1}{3}$ en fonction de la concentration finale en pénicilline; le trait plein parallèle à l'abscisse indique la valeur de la viscosité du témoin (sérum-M–L).

il est possible d'imaginer que des phénomènes d'interaction moléculaire, pénicilline-protéine, soient la cause de la dépression de la viscosité.

De l'autre côté, dans la zone des faibles dilutions par contre, il n'est pas exclu que des réactions de dénaturation des protéines sériques prennent le dessus ct provoquent cette augmentation assez brutale de la viscosité.

CONCLUSION

A l'aide de ce viscosimètre de conception récente et originale il nous a été possible d'étudier la viscosité du sérum sanguin sous forme de tracé viscosimétrique enregistré automatiquement en continu et caractérisé par un pic secondaire. Les protéines responsables de cet accident secondaire du tracé sont neutralisées par la pénicilline, laquelle à partir d'une concentration donnée empêche complètement l'apparition de celui-ci.

De plus, l'antibiotique, additionné au sérum à des concentrations variables, provoque une modification de la viscosité de celui-ci. Cette dernière tombe progressivement en-dessous de la valeur témoin pour des taux croissants de pénicilline, passe par un minimum, puis remonte assez rapidement et devient supérieure au témoin.

Il n'est pas exclu que des phénomènes d'interaction moléculaire, pénicilline-protéines, soient responsables de la partie la plus intéressante, de ces modifications.

BIBLIOGRAPHIE

[1] PASQUET, G. Thèse, Imprimerie Générale Lyonnaise, Lyon (France), 1960.

MODEL STUDIES

12 July, p.m.

Chairmen: M. JOLY, France
GEORGE W. SCOTT BLAIR, England

REGULATORY EFFECTS OF MACROMOLECULAR SURFACE LAYERS ON FLOW THROUGH TUBES

A. SILBERBERG*

Polymer Department, Weizmann Institute of Science, Rehovoth, Israel

IN MODELLING the flow of blood through the circulation it is customary to idealize the boundary conditions at the vessel–plasma and cell–plasma interface. Both tube walls and particles are assumed to be rigid and the transitions, wall–suspending medium and particle–suspending medium, are taken to be geometrically sharp. More sophisticated rheological properties have at times been assigned to the tube walls and particles, but the fiction of a sharp transition at the interface is still maintained in most analyses. There is, of course, no lack of awareness of the reality of the physiological situation, but the use of more appropriate boundary conditions always seemed to be associated with more difficulties than the corrections introduced thereby were believed to make worth while. In this attitude the effects of macromolecular surface layers, in particular, have been seriously underestimated.

The present discussion is thus concentrated on the effects encountered when macromolecules interact with the interface. This clearly represents the most serious source of departure from simple conditions (in the mechanical sense) in view of the size of the molecular units involved. While small molecules may profoundly affect the chemical and electrical properties of interfaces they will not normally present mechanical interferences. Moreover, macromolecules adsorb and interact more readily with surfaces, so that the presence of such layers may almost be taken for granted where interfaces are in contact with macromolecular solutions.

We shall discuss three aspects of this problem:
(a) Mechanical effects of macromolecular layers at interfaces in the presence of flow.
(b) Conditions of adsorption of macromolecules from solution.
(c) Macromolecular valve action due to a combination of mechanical and chemical influences.

MECHANICAL EFFECTS

It must be appreciated that the adsorption of flexible, i.e. open chain, macromolecules at interfaces leads in almost all cases to a loose association of the macromolecule with the surface. Many segments of the macromolecular chain are in contact with the surface, but many others are held in long, loosely coiled loops which penetrate far into the solvent medium. Even if the surface on which adsorption has occurred is perfectly smooth and rigid, the presence of the adsorbed layer introduces a region[1, 2] (as much as $0 \cdot 1 \, \mu$ thick) which is pervaded by macromolecular chains in fairly high concentration. If flow occurs past such an interface it begins to be slowed down at the extremes of this region and dies down to zero at the rigid support surface more gradually than would otherwise be the case. Effectively, the diameter of the flow tube has been reduced. In other words, when compared with a tube having clean walls, but in which the same flow pattern exists in the core, the comparison tube will have a diameter smaller than that of the original tube from rigid wall to rigid wall. This reduction measures an average thickness of the layer and is in fact one of the ways of determining it[1].

The question arises, however, if the layer is not in itself a function of the flow rate. Experimentally, no clear cut evidence exists but theoretically it seems likely that the layer will thicken as the flow rate is increased. With the flow pattern to be expected in these cases, a lift force tending to displace the macromolecules from the surface seems possible. Under rapid flow conditions the effective thickness of the film may increase to the point where the overall flow rate through narrow channels is being seriously affected. Films of this kind could act as self-regulatory devices on the flow.

In blood flow this could affect the situation in the narrow gaps between cells and the vessel wall in flow through the microcirculation. Effectively these gaps would then be much smaller than they seem. We could also state that the viscoelastic properties of the intervening medium are very different from those of plasma.

Films of macromolecules can moreover be expected on the cells themselves. As radial migration effects are sensitive functions of the particle radius[3, 4], a few percent change in this parameter could cause differentiation effects in wider vessels and control the size or presence of plasmolytic zones in these situations.

ADSORPTION OF MACROMOLECULES FROM SOLUTION

Macromolecules are highly surface active agents. A small tendency of a chain segment to adhere to the surface is multiplied enormously by the high recurrence of such active sites along the macromolecular chain. The removal, moreover, of a macromolecule even from dilute solution to the surface represents a rather small osmotic loss per segment. In most circumstances, therefore, a macromolecule has little to lose and much to gain by adhering to the surface[5]. Once at the surface, however, it finds it entropically much more favorable to adopt a conformation in which there is a high alternation of states along the chain: an alternation between states where the segments are in the surface, by virtue of the actual contact, and states where the segments are confined in free standing loops.

A curious situation now arises concerning the statistical mechanics of these two-dimensional adsorbed trains and the three-dimensional loops[6]. Whereas the partition function for the trains tends to infinity as the average train size increases, that for the loops tends to a limit as the average loop size becomes infinitely large. It is in the nature of the statistical mechanical solution of the problem that the product of the train and loop partition functions must be constant. Depending on conditions in the solvent phase, therefore, the relative contribution of the loops or trains in this product will predominate. If conditions are such that the contribution of the train partition function tends to increase, the loops will decrease and the trains will increase in length. This is the case of very strong adsorption but the limiting situation of zero loop size corresponding to an infinite train partition function is unattainable as it corresponds to an infinite interaction energy. When, on the other hand, solvent conditions favour the loops over the trains, desorption will occur at the point when the loops tend to infinity. At this point, however as we have seen, the loop partition function is of finite magnitude so that the train partition function which matches it in the product is finite as well and corresponds to a finite, attainable train size. In other words, there exists a well defined critical state of the system where the transition from adsorption to desorption occurs. It can be shown that the nature of the solvent plays a big role in determing the critical conditions and that solvation of the polymer considerably modifies the above picture. Long loops will arise when the macromolecule solvates well, while no long loops at all are possible when the solvent–solvent interaction is stronger than the polymer–solvent interaction[6].

It becomes clear, therefore, that the mechanical effects of adsorbed polymer layers, which depend mainly on average loop size, are controlled by the composition of the plasma phase as well as by the surface characteristics of cell and vessel wall. At points close to critical conditions, in particular, rather minor changes in solvent or surface conditions can profoundly affect the layer characteristics.

This becomes especially marked when the macromolecules are attached to the surface, at some selected points along the chain either permanently or at strongly adsorbing groups which occur interspersed with the standard more weakly adsorbing groups along the same chain. In such cases a small variation in solvent can push conditions beyond the critical point for the weakly interacting groups and the macromolecule, while still remaining attached to the surface at the few points of strong interaction, will suddenly have an overwhelming tendency to remove all intermediate sections away from the surface[6]. Very thick layers can be generated rather abruptly in these cases.

MACROMOLECULAR VALVE ACTION

The effect just described represents the basis of a medium controlled mechanical intervention on the macromolecular level. Under suitable circumstances variations in the thickness of the layer from effectively zero to $0 \cdot 1 \mu$ or more may be brought about by rather modest changes in the concentration or composition of the solvent phase. These changes, moreover, would be localized being representative of solvent conditions at the spot. Waves of alternately expanded and collapsed surface films can be envisaged along an interface.

Insofar as macromolecular surface films are shown to be influential in the flow of suspensions these medium-controlled effects would find themselves reflected in the overall flow characteristics. In even narrower vessels, however, such changes in effective diameter would be overwhelming. The possibility exists, therefore, that the passage of solution or solution components through the vessel wall (or other biological membrane of interest) is controlled by a medium-determined molecular valve action operating in pores of suitable size.

CONCLUSION

Ideas are developed about self-regulatory and medium-controlled macromolecular surface layers acting as flow determining devices in the microcirculation and in the pores of biological membranes. While on the physiological level these ideas are still speculatory, experimentation on model systems has recently been initiated with the intention of establishing the general feasibility of such effects.

ACKNOWLEDGMENT

This work is being supported by a grant No. G–65–45 from Life Insurance Medical Research Fund.

REFERENCES

[1] ÖHRN, O. E. *Arkiv. Kemi.* **12**, 397, 1958.
[2] ROWLAND, F. Ph.D. Thesis, Polytechnic Institute of Brooklyn, 1963.
[3] SEGRÉ, G. and SILBERBERG, A. *Bibl. Anat.* **4**, 83, 1964.
[4] SILBERBERG, A. *Biorheol.* **4**, 29, 1966.
[5] SILBERBERG, A. *J. Phys. Chem.* **66**, 1884, 1962.
[6] SILBERBERG, A. *J. Chem. Phys.* **46**, 1105, 1967.

DISCUSSION

WHITMORE (*England*):

To what extent do you think the size and shape of the molecules which you deal with in this way are related to the size and shape of the protein molecules which are found in plasma? Do you think that molecular weight range is comparable? I wondered if you could give any details on whether your primary results should be directly applicable to protein or how this could affect the results?

SILBERBERG (*Israel*):

It would not be applicable to very compact molecules, but I was thinking of denatured globulins, serum albumins or fibrinogen, particularly if some polymerization of fibrin has already occurred.

EIRICH (*U.S.A.*):

I was very glad to see the treatment and results of Dr. Silberberg's theory which agree very well with what we have found experimentally, although it is not the first theory to do so. What I was interested in particularly was the following problem: We have assumed that the distribution of segments above the particle surface follows some kind of barometric law. This, of course, is a crude model and certainly untrue because, after all, the lower segments are in direct interaction with the surface whereas the upper segments are not held to the surface at all, but are held only by covalent chains to the segments directly attached to the surfaces. In other words, there are two different kinds of forces holding segments in the vicinity of the surface and one has no right to assume a barometric distribution which is based on a continuous field. I do not know whether any theory has taken this into account, but we have some experimental indications that there are in fact two layers of segmental density, a dense one very close to the surface, say within about 30–50 Ångstroms which contains about 10 times as many segments as the farther layer whose loops dangle into the solution. My question then is whether Dr. Silberberg can take this into account in his present theory.

My second refers to his very interesting suggestion that some of the variability of blood viscosities is not so much due to aggregations but to the variable distance to which the segments may extend into the plasma. I think this is possible, but raise the question whether the variations occur within physiological limits and rapidly enough to make themselves felt over short periods?

In response to the preceding question of the Chairman: most normal serum proteins should become adsorbed in their native folded state; that is, the serum albumins and globulins should become attached in a more or less globular shape. Differences in distribution and stability should occur by virtue of the adsorption of long, extended, i.e. denatured, molecules. These denatured proteins would have a tendency to attach themselves more strongly to the surface because of their more accessible non-polar or hydrophobic groups and show relatively few dangling segments. It is questionable how far an adsorbed chain can change its conformation near the surface, or can denature there. Thus, one should try to derive information on the double distribution of non-polar, strongly, as well as weakly held segments and, secondly, see whether changeable segment distributions could assist the denaturation of serum proteins held to the surfaces of the formed elements.

SILBERBERG (*Israel*):

As to the first question: A double distribution of segments is in fact what we put into our model. It is because one has this two-fold range of concentrations that the interaction solvent–polymer which I discussed very briefly, plays such an important role. There is what I now call a second interface, formed between the first layer and the more diffuse parts of the adsorbed molecule. Here one gets additional interactions because schematically speaking it is as though two phases with different polymer concentration come into contact. On this model, therefore, very much higher concentrations of segments are found near the surface than in layers further away from it. I am delighted that Dr. Eirich's experiments confirm this prediction. The strict applicability of these considerations to actual blood-flow problems, is of course a very serious question from the point of view of this Conference and is hard to answer at this juncture. I have stressed in my talk the conditions under which these effects might obtain in the circulation. To be effective, layers would have to be thick, but it is possible to envisage thick layers even of albumins or globulins, particularly if their denaturation is partial. However, until the results of model experiments have been analysed, it would perhaps be best not to exaggerate the possible influence of these layers. On the other hand, on considerations of flow across biological membranes the mechanism of shape changes, which I suggested, might well be the important factor in controlling the amount of flow that is taking place. As far as rate is concerned, conformational changes of macromolecules already at the surface could be very rapid, within 10^{-3} sec say.

WAYLAND (*U.S.A.*):

Since the excellent pictures of Professor Bloch will not be shown tomorrow, I would like to raise a question with our present speaker and possibly Professor Eirich in this particular session. I think anyone who has seen a large number of high speed movies of blood flow, is quite aware that any plasmatic zone is at best a statistical thing. This means that you do not have a simple, clean, clear zone from which the red cells are removed but merely that they, on the average, have a lower density near the wall. Also of course, this is accentuated by wall exclusion, which becomes more important as the tubes get smaller and smaller. The question I want to pose is whether or not the possibility in a change in the frictional force between the erythrocytes and the wall might not be an important factor in explaining some of the differences that may be observed if we change the character of the tube wall, if indeed there are real differences. Rather than being due to a change in the width of the plasmatic zone through repulsion, could this effect be due to a change in the effective erythrocyte wall friction, since erythrocytes do move very close to the wall in any situation in the smaller vessels that I have ever seen.

SILBERBERG:

I have discussed how a diffuse macromolecular layer would change the boundary conditions in terms of hydrodynamics. In addition, however, it is possible to get interactions which might have a very temporary nature occurring at the vessel wall with some adsorbed proteins or even with some of the permanent components of the erythrocyte membrane or endothelial lining and these could very well delay the particle in a way, which might not necessarily be apparent to the eye. This could be just an entangling effect or a real secondary bond which is temporarily joined and impedes particle progress. Nevertheless I would still like to suggest an analysis in terms of purely hydrodynamic picture where the adsorbed layers influence the flow pattern near the wall and this in turn influences the rate at which particles pass along the wall.

WAYLAND:

What we measure as viscosity is essentially a dissipation of energy into heat, and certainly if you are moving these erythrocytes very, very close to the wall and this wall is not a simple structure, is it not conceivable that there could be a difference in the amount of dissipation depending upon the nature of the wall itself?

SILBERBERG:

Yes, I would agree to that. I think one may have the same sort of situation as in a concentrated polymer system, where the interactions range from hydrodynamic ones to actual aggregates of a temporary nature. Structures are continually being broken up and built up again as flow takes place. All these are dissipative processes.

ROWLANDS (*England*):

I have been most fascinated by these ideas that are entirely new to me and I have been wondering about the implications in the microcirculation. I thought that we might perhaps have an explanation of vasomotion which has always puzzled me for years: the fact that the very small capillaries do cyclically flow or that at least the flow of fluid in them does cyclically close and open. When, in fact, you look at electron microscope pictures of the capillary endothelium, as far as I remember, there is no sign of such a protein layer there which, you postulate, may be of the order of a micron thick. But it also occurred to me that the very curious structure in the renal tubules, called the brush border, which may have a function such as you were outlining in the discussion a few moments ago, and I am wondering if there are in effect any renal experts here who could contribute a little further to this discussion as to whether the brush border in the renal tubules might in fact be a protein layer of this sort which is very sensitive to changes in the pH or osmotic constituents of the fluid in the renal tubule and may help in the considerations of the absorption and reabsorption of substances from the renal tubules.

SILBERBERG:

    I do not believe that you could necessarily see such layers with ease in the electron microscope. The average amount of protein in the layer corresponds to a surface cover only a few Ångstroms thick if collapsed into a compact coating and might remain undetected in this form. Only a specially designed fixing process would permit the diffuse layer to maintain itself during the preparation of the material for the electron microscope. I do not know, of course, whether this was not perhaps done in the case of the electron micrographs which you have seen and whether the absence of such visual evidence must be regarded as conclusive.

ON THE USE OF MODELS IN FLUIDS RESEARCH

HUNTER ROUSE* and ENZO O. MACAGNO

Institute of Hydraulic Research,
The University of Iowa,
Iowa City, Iowa, U.S.A.

THOUGH crude dimensional and physical bases for the principles of similitude can be traced back to classical times, Galileo appears to have been the first actually to utilize principles of scale-model simulation, in his discussions of structural strength[1] — including, it is pertinent to note, the bone structure of living bodies. When the motion of a fluid was first modeled is more difficult to say[2], for any state of flow can correctly be regarded as the model of another, and even an empirical flow relationship is usable as a law of similarity. However, avowed models of water wheels were built and investigated by John Smeaton as early as 1759. Otto Lilienthal began his whirling-arm studies of miniature lifting vanes in 1866, and in the same period William Froude conducted his first towing-tank studies of model ships. Fargue, in 1875, initiated tests of river models, and a decade later Osborne Reynolds conducted laboratory experiments on estuarial tides.

Some of these investigations were based upon the most primitive principles of similitude, and others were quite sophisticated for their time. But only slowly did it come to be realized that the laws of similarity are simply one outcome of the Vaschy theorem of dimensional analysis (now commonly associated with the name of Buckingham). It is by this theorem that a series of dimensional variables completely describing a flow phenomenon can be organized into a set of non-dimensional groups of variables, generally fewer in number by the difference between the number of variables and the number of dimensional categories involved in their measurement (more specifically, the rank of the dimensional matrix in question[3]).

For example, if the flow boundaries are determined by the lengths $L_1, L_2, \ldots, L_n$; if the flow is described by the time t, the velocity V, and the differential pressure Δp or the shear τ; and if the fluid properties involved are the density ρ, the specific weight γ, the viscosity μ, the surface tension σ, and the elasticity E; then the Vaschy theorem will permit the variables to be arranged as follows:

$$\varphi\left(\frac{L_2}{L_1}, \cdots \frac{L_n}{L_1}, \frac{tV}{L_1}, \frac{V}{\sqrt{\Delta p/\rho}}, \frac{V}{\sqrt{L_1\gamma/\rho}}, \frac{\rho V L_1}{\mu}, \frac{V}{\sqrt{\sigma/\rho L_1}}, \frac{V}{\sqrt{E/\rho}}\right) = 0$$

The last five terms have come to be known as the Euler, Froude, Reynolds, Weber, and Mach numbers. Whereas the expression states in general that the several terms vary in an interdependent fashion, similitude-wise it indicates that a model will behave like its geometrically similar prototype (i.e. the Euler numbers will be the same) only if the Froude, Reynolds, Weber, and Mach numbers (or whichever of these are appropriate) are respectively equal in magnitude.

Lilienthal (and Smeaton, in effect) ignored all four of these parameters and considered the Euler number to depend on the geometry alone. Froude and Reynolds utilized the Froude criterion (attributable to Ferdinand Reech in 1831) for wave action, and eventually both also simulated surface resistance, though neither actually used the Reynolds number (first formulated by Lord Rayleigh in 1878[4]) as a resistance parameter. Froude was apparently the first to realize that both wave resistance and surface resistance could not be simulated simultaneously at model scale if the same fluid were used in model and prototype (note the appearance of L in the denominator of one and in the numerator of the other parameter), and he devised a method of simulating the first type of resistance and correcting for the second that is still followed today. By the turn of the century Fargue's and Reynolds' successors in river simulation had also encountered difficulties with surface resistance, though with regard to roughness rather than viscous action. Their solution—exaggeration of the vertical scale in comparison with the horizontal—would have sufficed for either effect, although the extent of the model distortion was somewhat arbitrary and hence required in turn another correction dictated by trial and error.

The fact that such models depend primarily on the Froude criterion for similarity has proved of extra use in connection with the simulation of flow with density stratification—whether due to thermal, saline, or sedimentary effects. In fact, replacement of specific weight in the Froude number by the differential specific weight $\Delta\gamma$ has the effect of reducing the gravitational term $g' = \Delta\gamma/\rho$ in such a manner as to simulate most of the usual free-surface phenomena at a density interface even as g' approaches zero. To be sure, as $\Delta\gamma/\rho$ becomes large, two densities (or a density gradient) and possibly also two viscosities (or a viscosity gradient) must be introduced. In these days of space flight, on the other hand, zero gravity can readily be approached for even the air–water combination, and modeling liquid flow under near-weightless circumstances is no longer a hypothetical condition. Of special interest physiologically is the fact that hydrostatic effects (indicated by what could be called the Archimedes number $p/\gamma h$ then disappear much as they do for conditions of neutral buoyancy—i.e. as $\Delta\gamma/\rho \to 0$.

Flows without a free surface or density interface would seem relatively simple to model were it not for the fact that fluid motion at small scale tends to be laminar and at large scale turbulent, and it is not often feasible to modify velocities and fluid properties sufficiently to yield the same order of Reynolds numbers at widely different scales. Often, to be sure, states of turbulence do not change rapidly with the Reynolds number, and the latter can be "distorted" considerably without serious effect. For extreme changes in linear scale, another type of approximation has suggested itself: to simulate the molar diffusion of a turbulent flow (say in the natural atmosphere or ocean) by the molecular diffusion of the laboratory fluid. In some respects this is satisfactory (indeed, many approximate analyses involve the assumption of a constant diffusion coefficient), but in general it is limited in its usefulness by the fact that the molar action varies with the state of motion and the molecular with the fluid temperature only.

The Weber criterion of similarity is perhaps the least used of any, probably because capillary phenomena are the most infrequently modeled. In fact, except for the formation of sprays, its importance to date has been rather negative in nature, for the action of surface tension makes it almost impossible to simulate many gravitational or viscous effects at reduced scale satisfactorily—for example, the entrainment of air by flowing water or the diffusion of liquid nappes in air: in fact, any mixture of gaseous and liquid media flowing simultaneously. On the other hand, modeling such visco-capillary effects as lubrication of the eye should be quite feasible.

The Mach number, of course, finds its greatest application in the transsonic, supersonic, and hypersonic flow of gases or the motion of boundaries at comparable velocities. Liquids sometimes actually attain the speed of sound nowadays, and the elastic waves of water hammer have been recognized for almost a century. It is significant to note that the name Cauchy, originally used instead of Mach for such effects in fluids, is now restricted to the elastic action of the boundary material alone. Both Mach and Cauchy numbers, for example, are important in the forced vibration of flow boundaries. In blood flow, on the other hand, it is the Cauchy number which is pertinent, for the elastic modulus of the blood is so great compared with that of the blood vessel that only the latter plays a role in its modeling. Simulation of boundary elasticity by fluid elasticity (the "Windkessel" method) is thus an artifice of limited rather than general usefulness.

The purely mechanical variables just discussed are commonly increased by both thermal and electrical variables, especially in present-day investigations of the ionized gases known as plasmas. In modeling the flow of body fluids, at least the last named complexity should remain irrelevant, whereas thermal and electrical effects may someday play a role. On the other hand, much can be learned by considering the flow pattern as a function of only the boundary geometry—for instance, in the study of eddy formation in the larger body passages. In its fundamental aspects, the pattern of such motion is independent of any characteristics beyond the geometric, for fluid viscosity and boundary elasticity often have merely a secondary influence at the most.

As a matter of fact, geometrically similar flows involving only one fluid property are perforce dynamically similar—i.e. the corresponding number is a constant; examples are pressure–velocity changes (the density), hydrostatics (specific weight), Couette or Poiseuille flow (the viscosity), and so on. Two fluid properties yield a number that varies with only one other number—problems of resistance, standing waves, capillary flow in soils—and similarity can readily be obtained by making the independent number the same in both model and prototype, through variation of the velocity scale (i.e. $s_v = v_m/v_p$) in accordance with the length and property scales. It is when three or more properties are involved that no amount of velocity variation will yield the desired result. The classic example of such a situation is the requirement already mentioned of satisfying both the Froude and the Reynolds criteria simultaneously, and the artifice of scale distortion has been shown to provide one means of approximate solution. However, elimination of the velocity scale between the two numbers will show that exact similarity is still possible if the remaining scales are related as follows[5]:

$$\frac{s_l(s_g)^{1/3}}{(s_\nu)^{2/3}} = 1$$

Evidently, operation in another gravitational environment could conceivably compensate for variation in one or the other remaining scale ratio. If, on the contrary, the same gravitational conditions prevail in the two systems, the length scale must vary with the $\frac{2}{3}$ power of the scale of kinematic viscosity ν.

Even if a liquid could be found that is an order of magnitude less viscous than water, the cost of supplying it in sufficient quantity for towing tanks or river models would surely be economically prohibitive. Biological models, on the other hand, are relatively limited in volume, even if enlarged considerably relative to their prototype; in fact, since the range of viscosities above that of water is far greater than that below, moderate enlargement of a biological model has much in its favor. The search for fluids with other desired properties is also more practicable, in particular since (contrary to the specific weight) all three properties would probably be independently variable. Consider, for example, the necessity of satisfying the Reynolds and Mach numbers together. Elimination of the velocity scale then yields

$$\frac{s_l s_c}{s_\nu} = 1$$

in which $c = \sqrt{E/\rho}$, the celerity of sound. Again it should be relatively easy to find fluids and materials satisfying the modeling requirements if the model is larger than the prototype, since s_c is likely to be very nearly unity. If, however, it is the Cauchy rather than the Mach number that is involved, as is more apt to be the case, the boundary rather than the fluid elasticity would be involved; the ratio of fluid and boundary densities, moreover, would have to be the same in model and prototype. Because of the latter requirement, a scale relationship of identical form would result,

$$\frac{s_l s_{c'}}{s_\nu} = 1$$

the scale of boundary sonic velocities $s_{c'}$ being subject to comparatively great variation.

Since most biological fluids and boundary materials are non-Newtonian and non-Hookean, respectively, their more sophisticated modeling will necessarily be two degrees higher in complexity than the sort just discussed. It goes without saying that the manner of departure from the Newtonian and the Hookean should be the same in model and prototype. Depending upon the manner of departure, the scale relationship is formulated accordingly. Some biological fluids[6] present the additional complication of being cell-laden, and when passing through very fine passages they involve somewhat the same problem as ship navigation through narrow canals. Basically, of course, the modeling procedure is straightforward, but such matters as those just introduced could well make perfect simulation extremely difficult.

A simulation process quite distinct from the foregoing use of scale models is found in the analog: a device that behaves in certain respects in a similar manner despite operation according to a different physical principle. Typical examples of flow analogs are the Hele Shaw method of showing patterns of irrotational motion, the Prandtl membrane analogy for stress distribution, the electrolytic tank, the electrical resistance circuit for representing conduit resistance, and complex networks thereof. The last named are essentially analog computers.

Also distinct are what have come to be called mathematical models: either simplifications of the equations of motion, or arbitrary formulations which — like the analogs — yield reasonable approximations to the actual occurrences. Whereas the latter process is often in frank recognition of the fact that the actual occurrence is not understood (for example, Prandtl's phenomenological approach to fluid turbulence), a model based on the equations of motion is limited in its simulation only by the mathematical ability of the investigator. In these days of analog and digital computers, the degree of similarity that is attained leaves little to be desired — except, to be sure, greater capacity for detail on the part of the computers. Exact solutions of complex states of unsteady, non-uniform irrotational flow are almost the rule, and two-property problems of various sorts have also given way to such attack. Of particular importance in this regard is the fact that the investigator is in no way limited by the practical choice of fluids having the required properties.

Two types of computer solution directly related to blood flow are under continuing investigation at the Iowa Institute of Hydraulic Research. One is the formation of eddies at abrupt changes in conduit section[7]. Although the ultimate goal of simulating turbulence generation by such means may never be realized, not only is the pattern of laminar flow as a function of the Reynolds number already at hand, but the detachment of eddy subdivisions due to velocity perturbations has also been reproduced. Though this has been accomplished only for Newtonian fluids, there is no reason why it cannot be extended to the non-Newtonian as well. To explore this possibility, the basic equation of motion for a deformable continuum

$$\rho \frac{\partial u}{\partial t} = -\frac{\partial p}{\partial x} + \frac{\partial \tau}{\partial y}$$

has been represented by a finite-difference equation and integrated numerically for different expressions of the shearing stress τ. In this manner the classical problem of flow establishment starting from rest under a constant pressure gradient has been solved at Iowa[8] for both dilatant and pseudo-plastic fluids–indeed, for practically any type of relation $\tau = f(\partial u/\partial y)$. The computational model has already been extended to annular pipes, of which the circular is a special case, and to variable pressure gradients, including pulsating. The computational model is well adapted to the introduction of a time-dependent relationship between stress and rate of deformation, and work is also under way in this direction. The latter stage is particularly significant in view of recent results that show a time-dependent behavior in the measurement of blood viscosity[9].

REFERENCES

[1] GALILEO, G. *Dialogues Concerning Two New Sciences*, translation by H. CREW and A. DE SALVIO, McMillan, New York, 1914.
[2] ROUSE, H. and INCE, S. *History of Hydraulics*, Dover Publications, New York, 1963.
[3] ROUSE, H. (Editor), *Advanced Mechanics of Fluids*, Interscience Publ. John Wiley, New York, 1959.
[4] STRUTT, J. W. (LORD RAYLEIGH) *Theory of Sound*, Macmillan, London, 1877–9.
[5] MACAGNO, E. O. *Ciencia y Técnica* **116**, No. 585, 1951.
[6] MERRILL, E. W. and WELLS, R. E. Jr. *Applied Mechanics Reviews* **14**, No. 9, 1961.
[7] MACAGNO, E. O. *La Houille Blanche*, No. 8, 1965.
[8] MACAGNO, E. O. *C.R. Acad. Sci. Paris* **262**, 1121–4, 1966.
[9] GREGERSEN, M. I. Studies on blood viscosity at low shear rates, Progress Report to U.S. Army Medical Research and Development Command, Columbia University College of Physicians and Surgeons, New York, 1965.

DISCUSSION

JOLY (*France*):
    I would like to know if your model is still valid in the case of large interacting forces between the kinetic units. I am thinking of the case of concentrated suspensions of very small particles when the interfacial forces and the interaction forces between these particles are very high.

ROUSE (*U.S.A.*):
    It is not in my experience that intermolecular forces can be modeled satisfactorily in the manner suggested by Dr. Joly.

WHITMORE (*England*):

I wonder, Professor Rouse, whether you have been involved in work on capsule flow. This, I believe, the Canadians have studied while trying to flow capsules down tubes. And this strikes me as being, to some extent, a model for cells flowing down tubes. The difference, I think, with the flow in narrow tubes is the extreme flexibility of the red cells and one of the problems is to include this in the model.

ROUSE:

Only what John S. McNown worked out for the resistance of spheres in cylindrical tubes, the spheres ranging from the diameter of the tube down to something that was of no consequence. It is my guess that it was done in a way that would not be a very great deal of help to you. He produced stability when the sphere was almost the size of the tube by tilting the tube. He had a rolling-ball viscometer—in fact, he used the viscometer for the one limit of such a condition. As far as the two-phased flow is concerned, we have worked to some degree with paper stock, but it has been largely qualitative rather than quantitative. The matter of sediment suspension is another one of the same sort. But these have their own particular problems, and I do not think they display the biological characteristics that you are particularly interested in.

SOME MODEL EXPERIMENTS IN HEMODYNAMICS. III

H. L. GOLDSMITH[*1] and S. G. MASON[*2]

University Medical Clinic, Montreal General Hospital[1] and Department of Chemistry, McGill University[2],
Montreal, Canada

INTRODUCTION

The work described below is part of a continuing investigation of the microscopic flow properties of suspensions of model rigid and deformable particles, previously reported in Parts I and II of this series (GOLDSMITH and MASON, 1962a, 1964) and recently extended to suspensions of human red blood cells (GOLDSMITH, 1966a). In these studies, the individual particle movements, their interactions with each other and the vessel wall in Couette or Poiseuille flow are observed directly through a microscope and recorded with a cine camera for subsequent frame by frame analysis. The purpose of the experiments is to establish the basic phenomena involved at the microrheological level and to relate these to the overall or macroscopic flow properties of the dispersions.

Beginning with steady flow of Newtonian liquids at very low Reynolds numbers, a study was made of the spin and rotation of single rigid spheres, rods and discs, and the deformation of liquid drops and flexible threads. These experiments were followed by observations of particle interactions and collisions in dilute suspensions (<5% by volume) as well as the effect of the vessel wall on the particle translational and rotational motions. Finally the behavior of spheres and cylinders in flowing concentrated suspensions (up to 45% by volume) was investigated.

Many of the phenomena observed in dilute and concentrated suspensions were analysed in terms of rigorous hydrodynamic theory (GOLDSMITH and MASON, 1967), and some of the results appeared to be significant in relation to the flow of blood in both large and small vessels. Recently, this relationship has been strengthened through observations made of the microscopic flow properties of single red cells and rouleaux (GOLDSMITH, 1966a), which, as described in the first part of this paper, resemble those of model rigid and deformable cylinders and linear aggregates.

The second part deals with an extension of the model particle studies to steady and oscillatory flow in circular tubes at higher Reynolds numbers where inertial effects become important. Of special significance to blood flow are the observed radial migrations of spheres and cylinders which in concentrated suspensions lead to the formation of a plasmatic layer free of particles near the wall and a consequent reduction in viscosity.

ROTATION AND DEFORMATION OF LINEAR AGGREGATES

1. *Model chains of spheres and discs* (ZIA *et al.*, 1966)

Chains of metal coated rigid spheres suspended in a dielectric liquid were made by applying an electric field so that the particles attracted each other and arranged themselves in linear arrays in the direction of the field (WINSLOW, 1949; ALLAN and MASON, 1962). Since the spheres were not necessarily in contact with each other, the aggregates could be regarded as thread-like particles with neither tensile strength nor stiffness. They were, however, found to rotate and remain straight in Couette flow after removing the electric field (Fig. 2).

The measurements were made in a concentric cylinder Couette apparatus illustrated in Fig. 1 using chains from 2 to 10 spheres suspended in viscous oils of 50 poise viscosity.

As predicted by theory based on the lubrication equations for spheres in close proximity (ZIA *et al.*, 1967), at low velocity gradients (<0.5 sec^{-1}) the aggregates rotated in a spherical elliptical orbit similar to that calculated by JEFFERY (1922) for a rigid prolate spheroid, i.e. the motion of the long axis of the chains was somewhat like that of a precessing top. The variation with time of the angle ϕ of the long axis with respect to the Y-axis of the Couette flow field (Fig. 3) was variable

$$\frac{d\phi}{dt} = \frac{G}{r_e^2+1}(r_e^2\cos^2\phi + \sin^2\phi),$$

(1)

FIG. 1. PHOTOGRAPH OF THE COUETTE DEVICE USED IN STUDYING THE ROTATION AND DEFORMATION OF LINEAR CHAINS. THE SUSPENDING OIL AND PARTICLES ARE CONTAINED IN THE ANNULUS BETWEEN TWO COUNTER-ROTATING CYLINDERS, THE OUTER ONE BEING INSULATED SO THAT AN ELECTRIC FIELD CAN BE APPLIED ACROSS THE CYLINDERS. PARTICLES ARE VIEWED DIRECTLY THROUGH A MICROSCOPE IN LIGHT TRANSMITTED FROM BELOW THROUGH THE GLASS BOTTOM OF THE ANNULUS ALONG AN AXIS PARALLEL TO THE PLANES OF SHEAR. ALSO SHOWN IN THE PHOTO ARE THE TWO ARMS OF A DEVICE FOR ATTACHING MICRO-BURETTES TO RELEASE PARTICLES INTO THE FLUID AT ACCURATELY KNOWN POSITIONS.

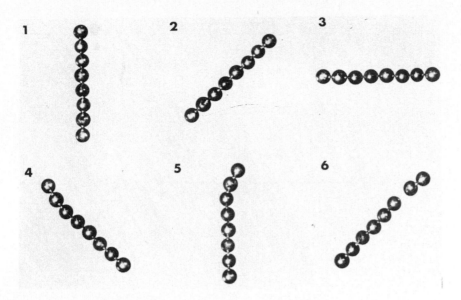

FIG. 2. THE ROTATION OF A CHAIN OF EIGHT METAL-COATED POLYSTYRENE SPHERES FORMED BY APPLYING AN ELECTRIC FIELD ACROSS THE ANNULUS OF THE COUETTE APPARATUS SHOWN IN FIG. 1. WITH THE ELECTRIC FIELD OFF AND THE SUSPENDING LIQUID MADE TO FLOW, THE CHAIN ROTATED CLOCKWISE AS A RIGID ROD AS SHOWN IN POSITIONS 1 TO 3. HOWEVER, UNDER COMPRESSION IN THE QUADRANT AT POSITION 4 BUCKLING OCCURRED WHICH FINALLY LED TO BREAK UP AND SEPARATION UNDER TENSION IN THE SUCCEEDING QUADRANT AT POSITION 6. (AFTER ZIA et al., 1966.)

being maximum when at right angles to the flow ($\phi = 0°$ and 180°) and minimum when in the direction of flow ($\phi = 90°$ and 270°). Here, G is the velocity gradient and r_e the axis ratio of the equivalent spheroid having the same period of rotation T as the chain of spheres

$$T = \frac{2\pi}{G}\left(r_e + \frac{1}{r_e}\right). \qquad (2)$$

Moreover, in accord with theory, the chain length was found to vary periodically between a minimum when oriented at right angles to the direction of flow and maximum when parallel to it.

At higher G's (>2 sec^{-1}) the chains buckled in the quadrant in which the spheres were subject to compressive stresses and generally broke into two in the same position in the chain in the succeeding quadrant where tensile forces were exerted on the particles (Figs. 2, 3).

When, however, a liquid immiscible with the suspending oil such as water was introduced so that a meniscus bridged the gaps between the spheres, the chain rotated without breaking since the interfacial tension provided strength (Fig. 4). The rotational orbits were then similar to those of flexible threads of fibers in shear flow (FORGACS and MASON, 1959a).

It was also possible to make stacks of tiny polystyrene discs by direct manipulation without the aid of an electric field. These rotated as rigid rods obeying (1) until a G was

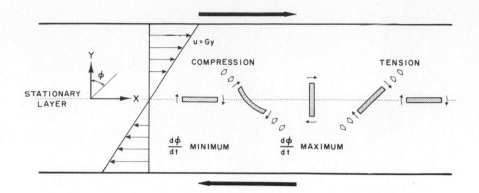

FIG. 3. DIAGRAM OF THE LAMINAR COUETTE FLOW OF A NEWTONIAN LIQUID BETWEEN TWO PARALLEL
PLATES MOVING IN OPPOSITE DIRECTIONS. A FLEXIBLE ROD IS SHOWN IN SUCCESSIVE POSITIONS AS IT
ROTATES WITH VARIABLE ANGULAR VELOCITY $d\phi/dt$ IN THE MEDIAN PLANE WITH ITS CENTER IN THE STA-
TIONARY LAYER, AND SPENDING MORE TIME ALIGNED WITH THE FLOW THAN AT RIGHT ANGLES TO IT.
UNDER THE ACTION OF THE VELOCITY GRADIENT THE FLUID EXERTS COMPRESSIVE STRESSES ON THE ROD IN
THE QUADRANT ($-90 < \phi < 0$) CAUSING IT TO BUCKLE AND TENSILE STRESSES IN THE SUCCEEDING QUAD-
RANT CAUSING IT TO STRAIGHTEN OUT AGAIN. EXPERIMENTALLY, COUETTE FLOW MAY BE REALIZED IN
THE ANNULUS BETWEEN COUNTER-ROTATING CYLINDERS AS IN THE DEVICE SHOWN IN FIG. 1. HERE, DUE TO
CURVATURE, THE VELOCITY GRADIENT IS NOT CONSTANT ACROSS THE ANNULUS BUT INCREASES IN GOING
FROM INNER TO OUTER CYLINDER. THE EFFECT IS MINIMIZED BY KEEPING THE ANNULUS WIDTH SMALL IN
COMPARISON TO ITS DISTANCE FROM THE CENTER OF ROTATION OF THE COUETTE.

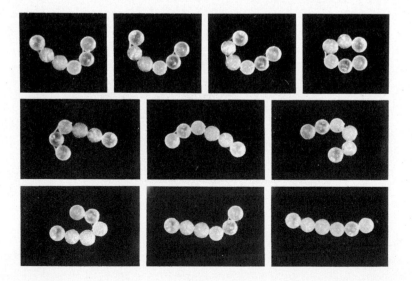

FIG. 4. A CHAIN OF POLYSTYRENE SPHERES, HELD TOGETHER BY THE INTERFACIAL TENSION OF A WATER
MENISCUS BRIDGING ADJACENT SPHERES, ROTATING AND BENDING (SEQUENCES RUN FROM LEFT TO RIGHT)
IN A PERIODIC ORBIT SIMILAR TO THAT OF THE SNAKE ORBIT OF A FIBER OR A ROULEAU OF RED CELLS SHOWN
IN FIG. 8. (AFTER ZIA et al., 1966.)

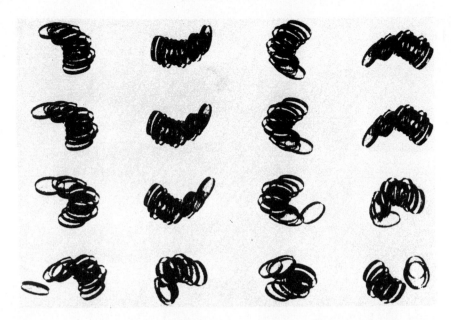

FIG. 5. A STACK OF ELEVEN POLYSTYRENE DISCS ROTATING CLOCKWISE IN COUETTE FLOW (SEQUENCES RUN FROM LEFT TO RIGHT) WITH G BEING PROGRESSIVELY INCREASED SO THAT THE DISCS SLID OVER EACH OTHER AND EVENTUALLY SEPARATED.

reached at which they bent and broke apart by sliding of the faces over one another (Fig. 5). As with spheres, the addition of a second liquid prevented break-up.

Unlike aggregates of rigid spheres, chains of liquid drops made by direct manipulation were found to separate while rotating—presumably due to internal circulation within the drops (Fig. 6a) but could be brought together again by reversing the flow. When a third liquid, immiscible with the drops and the suspending phase, bridged the gaps

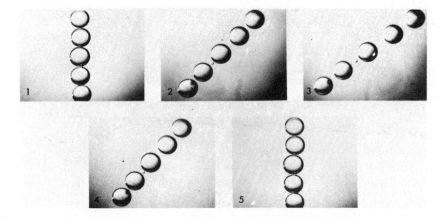

FIG. 6a. CHAIN OF FIVE LIQUID DROPS SEPARATING DURING ROTATION THROUGH 50°, BUT WHICH WERE BROUGHT BACK REVERSIBLY TO THEIR ORIGINAL POSITION.

between the spheres the chain bent, as observed with rigid sphere systems, but with the individual drops being deformed by the velocity gradient (Fig. 6b).

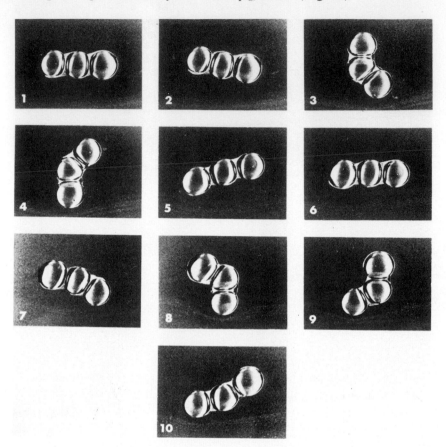

FIG. 6b. CHAIN OF THREE LIQUID DROPS HELD TOGETHER BY A SECOND IMMISCIBLE LIQUID PHASE WHICH BRIDGES THE DROPS (CF. THE CASE OF RIGID SPHERES SHOWN IN FIG. 4). THE CHAIN ROTATED IN COUETTE FLOW LIKE A FLEXIBLE THREAD WITH PERIODIC BENDING AND STRETCHING.

2. *Red cells and rouleaux* (GOLDSMITH, 1966a, b)

Dilute suspensions of human red blood cells were observed under a microscope when flowing through rigid polypropylene or glass tubes of diameter from 80 to 200 microns. The cell motions could be followed by mounting the tubes on a mechanically driven microscope stage and matching the speed of the stage to that of a particle in the tube (Fig. 7). At mean linear velocities $\bar{u}$ ranging from 1 to 4 tube diameters/second (i.e. at wall shear rates $G = 4\bar{u}/R$ from 8 to 32 sec^{-1}, R being the tube radius) both single cells and linear and branched aggregates or rouleaux were seen in suspensions of less than 2% hematocrit prepared from freshly drawn blood.

The rotation of single cells resembled those of rigid discs (GOLDSMITH and MASON, 1962b) with the angular velocity $d\phi/dt$ maximum at $\phi = 90°$, 270° when the axis of revolution was aligned with the flow (cell face at right angles to the flow, Fig. 8a). Small rouleaux of 4 cells having length approximately equal to diameter rotated with

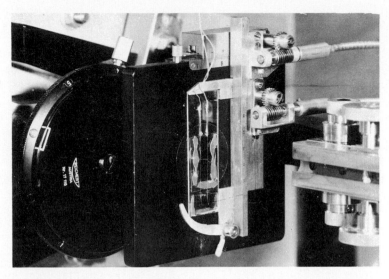

FIG. 7. CLOSE-UP VIEW OF THE VERTICAL TRAVELLING MICROSCOPE STAGE USED TO OBSERVE THE FLOW OF ERYTHROCYTES IN TUBES. THE GLASS SLIDE ON THE STAGE HAS TWO POLYPROPYLENE TUBES MOUNTED ON IT WHICH PASS THROUGH A FLAT CHAMBER FILLED WITH PLASMA TO AVOID OPTICAL DISTORTION. POLYTHENE CATHETER TUBING OF WIDE BORE CONNECTS THEIR UPPER ENDS TO AN INFUSION PUMP (NOT SHOWN). ON THE UPPER RIGHT ARE THE WORM AND GEAR WITH FLEXIBLE DRIVE SHAFTS CONNECTED TO A D.C. MOTOR WHICH ENABLE HORIZONTAL AND VERTICAL TRAVEL OF THE STAGE.

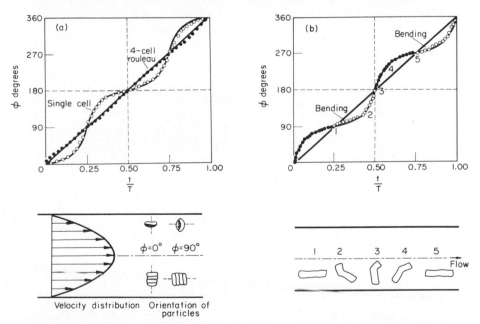

FIG. 8. ROTATIONS AND ORIENTATIONS OF SINGLE CELLS AND ROULEAUX IN POISEUILLE FLOW. (a) MEASURED VARIATION IN THE ϕ-ORIENTATION OF A SINGLE ERYTHROCYTE (OPEN CIRCLES) AND A FOUR-CELL ROULEAU (CLOSED CIRCLES) WITH FRACTION OF THE PERIOD OF ROTATION T. (b) VARIATION IN THE ϕ-ORIENTATION OF A FIFTEEN-CELL ROULEAU WITH TIME SHOWING, IN THE LOWER PART, BENDING OF THE PARTICLE WHICH BEGAN IN THE QUADRANT WHERE THE STRESSES ARE COMPRESSIVE. THE SOLID LINES DRAWN WERE CALCULATED FROM JEFFERY'S THEORY (1922) FOR OBLATE (a) AND PROLATE (b) SPHEROIDS RESPECTIVELY. (AFTER GOLDSMITH, 1966b.)

almost uniform angular velocity whereas longer aggregates behaved as rod-like particles, as was observed with chains of rigid spheres. Moreover, regular rouleaux of n particles in linear array rotated in spherical elliptical orbits (JEFFERY, 1922) for oblate spheroids ($n = 1, 2, 3$) or prolate spheroids ($n > 5$) as shown in Fig. 8.

Depending on the length of the rouleaux and the value of G, the aggregates bent while rotating in those quadrants of the orbit where compressive forces acted on the cells. In the succeeding quadrants the rouleaux tended to straighten out as illustrated by the tracings in Fig. 8b. Such "springy" orbits had previously been observed with flexible threads (FORGACS and MASON, 1959a) and wood pulp fibers (FORGACS and MASON, 1958). From an analysis of the stresses acting on the particle surface, the axial force of compression F acting on the central cross section of a rotating rod, diameter $2b$, can be shown to be

$$F = \pi\eta_0 G b^2 \sin 2\phi f(r_e), \tag{3}$$

where η_0 is the suspending phase viscosity and $f(r_e)$ a function of the equivalent axis ratio (GOLDSMITH and MASON, 1967). According to (3) the maximum positions of tension and compression occur when the particle axis of revolution is oriented at $+45°$ and $-45°$ respectively to the Y-axis of the field (Fig. 3). Moreover, for a given axis ratio there exists a critical value of $\eta_0 G$ at which buckling sets in and which can be shown to depend on the bending modulus of the material. The rouleaux were found to be extremely flexible, the bending modulus being only 10^{-7} that found for dacron or nylon flexible threads (FORGACS and MASON, 1959b).

As previously observed with long flexible threads and fibers, at a given value of $\eta_0 G$ an increase in the axis ratio increased the flexibility of the linear aggregates. Thus,

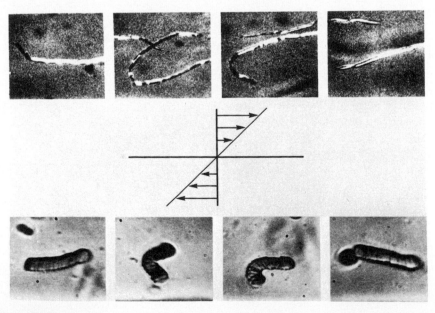

FIG. 9. COMPARISON OF THE SNAKE ORBIT EXECUTED BY A FLEXIBLE WOOD PULP FIBER SUSPENDED IN CORN SYRUP (VISCOSITY 90 POISE) IN THE UPPER PORTION WITH THAT OF A ROULEAU OF 24 HUMAN RED CELLS IN PLASMA (VISCOSITY 0.02 POISE) IN THE LOWER PART.

rouleaux of more than 20 cells (axis ratio > 5) were able to rotate in "snake orbits" (Fig. 9) in which the ends of the particles were capable of independent movement.

It has been shown in tube flow, both in the absence of inertial effects at effectively zero Reynolds numbers and in their presence at small values of the Reynolds number, that deformable drops and flexible fibers migrate towards the tube axis (GOLDSMITH and MASON, 1962b; KARNIS et al., 1966a) at rates which increase with their size, deformation and the velocity gradient. Similar results have now been obtained with suspensions of rouleaux of red cells.

OSCILLATORY AND PULSATILE FLOW OF MODEL SUSPENSIONS

A preliminary study of the microrheology of suspensions of rigid spheres in oscillatory flow through circular tubes was described in Part II of this series (GOLDSMITH and MASON, 1964). The work has since been extended to rigid cylindrical particles and deformable drops in oscillatory and pulsatile flow (steady flow superimposed on oscillatory flow).

The particle motions were observed in vertically mounted 1 cm radius tubes through a travelling microscope, as illustrated in Fig. 10. Suspension flow was controlled by a steady infusion pump in parallel with a reciprocating pump, the latter producing sinusoidal flow (TAKANO et al., 1967a).

1. *Translation, rotation and deformation of single particles* (TAKANO et al., 1967a)

In the absence of inertial effects, the displacement profile in the pulsatile flow of a Newtonian liquid is given by the superposition of the equations for oscillatory flow (SHIZGAL et al., 1965) and Poiseuille flow:

$$x(r, t) = -A(r) \cos [\omega t + \epsilon_0(\alpha, r)] + \frac{2Q}{\pi R^4} (R^2 - r^2). \tag{4}$$

$x(r,t)$ is the axial displacement at a radial distance r from the tube axis and time t, $A(r)$ the total amplitude of oscillation which is a function of the volume displacement per cycle and the dimensionless number $\alpha = R(\omega\rho/\eta_0)^{1/2}$, ω being the angular frequency and ρ and η_0 the respective density and viscosity of the suspending medium; $\epsilon_0(\alpha, r)$ is the phase angle and Q the steady volume flow rate.

Using tracer rigid spheres having radii $<0.03R$ it was possible to verify (4); with larger neutrally buoyant spheres of radii $= 0.1R$ the measured displacements Δx were still in agreement with (4) except near the wall where there was appreciable drop with $\Delta x_{meas} < \Delta x_{theory}$ as had previously been found in steady flow at all Reynolds numbers (GOLDSMITH and MASON, 1962b; KARNIS et al., 1966a).

The observed angular velocities, $d\phi/dt$, of small rigid spheres ($r_e = 1$), discs and rods were in good agreement with JEFFERY's theory (1922) for Couette flow when the oscillatory velocity gradient at a given radial distance was inserted into eq. (1). Exceptions were again found with particles close to the wall where the observed angular velocities were smaller than those predicted by theory.

As in steady flow, suspended liquid drops were deformed into ellipsoids under the action of the velocity gradient (Fig. 11). The theory for deformation in Couette flow

FIG. 10. VERTICAL TRAVELLING MICROSCOPE AND FLOW TUBE USED TO OBSERVE THE OSCILLATING AND PULSATILE FLOW OF SUSPENSIONS OF PARTICLES. THE PHOTOGRAPH SHOWS A PRECISION BORE GLASS TUBE WHICH PASSES THROUGH A SQUARE GLASS CELL FILLED WITH LIQUID OF THE SAME REFRACTIVE INDEX AS GLASS TO OBVIATE DISTORTION EFFECTS. THE MICROSCOPE AND CINE CAMERA ARE DRIVEN BY A CONTINUOUSLY VARIABLE D.C. MOTOR AND AT THE TWO ENDS OF THE FLOW TUBE ARE MOUNTED PRESSURE TRANSDUCERS ENABLING CONTINUOUS MONITORING OF THE FLUCTUATING PRESSURE GRADIENT. NOT SHOWN IN THE PHOTO ARE THE INFUSION AND RECIPROCATING PUMPS ARRANGED IN PARALLEL TO GIVE PULSATILE FLOW.

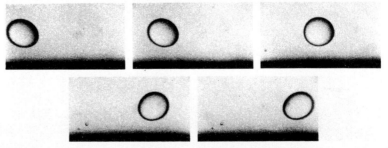

FIG. 11. PHOTOMICROGRAPHS OF THE OSCILLATING DEFORMATION OF POLYGLYCOL OIL DROPS IN SILICONE OIL ($\lambda = 10$) DURING ONE HALF CYCLE OF 0.7 SEC, $\alpha = 2.4$. THE DROPS WERE DISTORTED INTO ELLIPSOIDS HAVING THEIR LONG AXES ALIGNED WITH THE FLOW.

(TAYLOR, 1934), which has been found to hold for small drops in Poiseuille flow, may also be applied to oscillatory flow. For small deformations D defined by

$$D = \frac{L-B}{L+B},$$

L and B being the respective length and breadth of the ellipsoidal drop, TAYLOR (1934) showed that D is given by the ratio of viscous to interfacial tension forces:

$$D = \frac{Gb\eta_0}{\gamma} \frac{19\lambda+16}{16\lambda+16}, \tag{5}$$

b being the undistorted drop radius, γ the interfacial tension and λ the ratio of drop: suspending phase viscosity. Good agreement with theory in oscillatory flow was obtained in systems of low λ when the fluctuating value of G was substituted into (5) giving

$$D(r,t) = \frac{G^* b\eta_0}{\gamma} \frac{19\lambda+16}{16\lambda+16} \cos(\omega t - \delta_1), \tag{6}$$

G^* being the amplitude of the velocity gradient in oscillatory flow and δ_1 the phase lag between G and the pressure gradient.

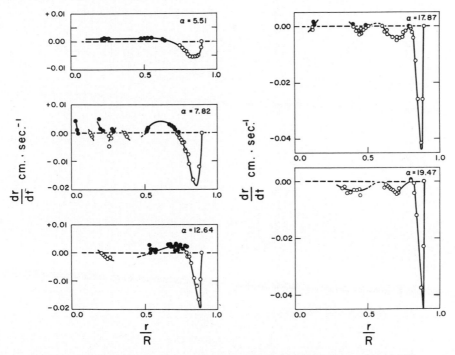

FIG. 12. PLOT OF THE RADIAL MIGRATION VELOCITIES OF RIGID SPHERES HAVING RADII $0.11R$ IN A SUSPENSION UNDERGOING OSCILLATORY FLOW AT INCREASING VALUES OF α. AT $\alpha < 6$ THERE WAS ONLY ONE EQUILIBRIUM POSITION (WHEN THE SOLID LINE CROSSES THE DASHED LINE); AT HIGHER α SEVERAL POSITIONS OF ZERO dr/dt WERE OBSERVED. (AFTER TAKANO et al., 1967b.)

In systems of $\lambda > 10$, however, the drop deformation lagged the velocity gradient and was smaller than predicted by (6). This was probably due to the dissipation of energy in extensional viscous flow within the drop.

2. *Radial migration* (TAKANO *et al.*, 1967b)

In many respects, the migration of rigid and deformable particles, observed over several cycles in oscillatory or pulsatile flow, paralled that in the tubular pinch effect found in steady flow (SEGRÉ and SILBERBERG, 1962; KARNIS *et al.*, 1966a) at comparable particle Reynolds numbers (a value of the particle Reynolds number in oscillatory flow may be calculated by using the root mean square particle linear flow velocity averaged over the cross sectional area). Thus, with *rigid* spheres, rods and discs, inward migration to an equilibrium position was observed with particles close to the wall of the tube, and outward migration with particles initially situated on the axial side of the equilibrium position. The rate of migration increased with increasing radial distance from the equilibrium position and with increasing particle size and Reynolds number. As in the case of the tubular pinch effect, the phenomena are presumed to be due to inertia.

However, in oscillatory and pulsatile flows, the radial distance of the equilibrium position changed with increasing α and this appeared to be associated with the cor-

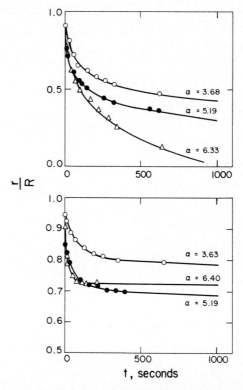

FIG. 13. THE INCREASE IN INWARD MIGRATION RATE OF FLUID DROPS IN SILICONE OIL WITH INCREASING α. IN THE UPPER GRAPH, WATER DROPS ($\lambda = 10^{-2}$) MIGRATED TO THE TUBE AXIS WHEREAS IN THE LOWER HALF POLYGLYCOL DROPS ($\lambda = 10$) REACHED ALMOST ZERO RADIAL VELOCITY WHEN STILL QUITE CLOSE TO THE TUBE WALL. (AFTER TAKANO *et al.*, 1967b.)

responding changes in velocity gradient profile across the tube. As illustrated in Fig. 12, when $\alpha > 6$ the existence of more than one equilibrium position was observed.

The effect of steady flow superimposed on sinusoidal flow at low α was to shift the equilibrium positions toward the tube axis; at high α there was no noticeable change in position.

Deformable liquid drops were always observed to migrate inwards with the radial velocities $-dr/dt$ increasing with increasing α and r (Fig. 13). In systems of low λ the drops migrated rapidly to the axis, but viscous drops ($\lambda > 10$), because of the lag between deformation and velocity gradient, migrated at very low radial velocities when still close to the wall (Fig. 13).

3. *Two-phase flow*

When suspensions of rigid spheres having volume concentrations from 5 to 30% were subjected to steady or oscillatory flow at values of Q or α at which inertial effects were pronounced, a particle-free zone developed at the wall (KARNIS *et al.*, 1966a;

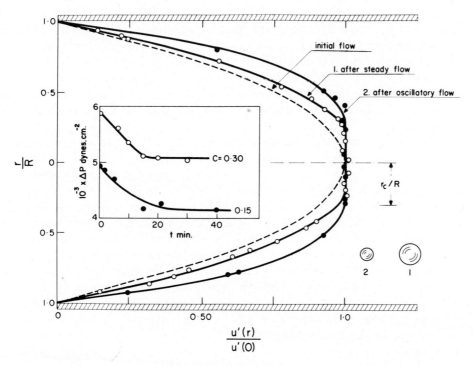

FIG. 14. THE EFFECT OF A PARTICLE-FREE ZONE ON THE PRESSURE GRADIENT AND VELOCITY PROFILE OF CONCENTRATED SUSPENSIONS OF RIGID SPHERES IN TUBES. SHOWN IS A PLOT OF THE RATIO OF THE MEASURED PARTICLE VELOCITY AT A RADIAL DISTANCE r TO THAT AT THE TUBE CENTER, AS A FUNCTION OF THE DIMENSIONLESS RADIAL DISTANCE FROM THE TUBE AXIS. THE DASHED LINE IS THE INITIAL PARABOLIC VELOCITY PROFILE; THE SOLID LINES ARE THE FINAL VELOCITY DISTRIBUTIONS AFTER INWARD MIGRATION OF SPHERES AT THE TUBE PERIPHERY, (1) WHEN THE SUSPENSION WAS SUBJECTED TO STEADY FLOW AT HIGH FLOW RATES, AND (2) WHEN SUBJECTED TO OSCILLATORY FLOW AT $\alpha = 5.1$. AS A RESULT OF THE TWO PHASE FLOW THERE IS PARTIAL PLUG FLOW OVER A RADIAL DISTANCE r_c IN THE TUBE CENTER AND THE PRESSURE GRADIENT (SHOWN INSET) DECREASES WITH TIME UNTIL EQUILIBRIUM IS REACHED. (AFTER KARNIS *et al.*, 1966a.)

SHIZGAL et al., 1965). At a given instant, the width of this zone was not constant along the tube length but fluctuated about a mean value which increased with time of flow until equilibrium was reached. At a given particle size, the mean equilibrium layer thickness decreased with increasing concentration but its rate of formation increased with increasing α (TAKANO and MASON, forthcoming publication).

As a result of the development of a two-phase flow with a concentrated core of rigid spheres surrounded by a layer of suspending fluid, there was a drop in the pressure gradient in both steady and oscillatory flow (Fig. 14). There was also a marked change in the velocity profile in steady flow with an area of partial plug flow in the central region of the tube where there were no particle rotations. Such velocity distributions had previously been observed at high concentrations in steady flow at very low Reynolds numbers (KARNIS et al., 1966b) but there, in the absence of particle migration, it was due to a wall effect. In the present case, the blunted velocity profile resulted from two-phase flow, i.e. having a central core of high viscosity surrounded by a sphere-free layer of low viscosity.

CONCLUDING REMARKS

Many aspects of the investigation into the microrheology of blood such as the interactions of cells and rouleaux in dilute and concentrated suspensions, and the flow behavior of white cells and platelets, remain to be studied. Of particular interest, however, and arising out of the present experiments are observations of the break-up of rouleaux (GOLDSMITH, 1966b) from which, with the aid of the underlying theory (equation (3)), it should be possible to measure the magnitude of the forces holding the cells together.

While there appears to be a sound theoretical basis for the phenomena observed in the related model experiments with rigid and flexible linear chains, no satisfactory explanation has yet been advanced to account for the two-way migration of rigid particles in steady or oscillatory flow through circular tubes. Calculations have been made of the sideways force due to inertia exerted on a spinning sphere moving through an unbounded fluid otherwise at rest (RUBINOW and KELLER, 1961) and on a sphere in an unbounded parabolic shear flow (SAFFMAN, 1965), and while able to predict qualitatively certain of the observed features of radial migration in Poiseuille flow, they cannot account for the two-way drift of neutrally buoyant particles. The experimental results (BRENNER, 1966) indicate that the presence of the walls is of fundamental importance, and as has been pointed out (SEGRÉ and SILBERBERG, 1962; BRENNER, 1966) no theory which does not explicitly consider inertial and wall effects may be expected to explain the observed migrations.

The importance of the tubular pinch effect and/or inward migration due to deformation of red cells in blood flow is not clear at present. The present studies indicate that rouleaux migrate axially and there is evidence both in vitro (BUGLIARELLO et al., 1965) and in vivo (PHIBBS, 1966) to show that a small particle-depleted zone does exist at the wall in vessels of 80 to 1000 microns diameter. The resulting two-phase flow may be expected to reduce the dissipation of energy in the flow. The possibility of an oscillatory flow superimposed on steady flow further decreasing the energy dissipation, by increasing the width of the marginal zone over that in steady flow (Fig. 14), is presently being investigated (TAKANO and MASON, forthcoming publication).

ACKNOWLEDGMENTS

The authors wish to thank the National Heart Institute of the United States Public Health Service for its support of the model particle studies (Grant HE-05911) and the Medical Research Council of Canada for supporting the investigation into the flow behavior of red blood cells (Grant MA-1835).

REFERENCES

ALLAN, R. S. and MASON, S. G. *Proc. Roy. Soc. (London)* **A 267**, 62, 1962.

BRENNER, H. In: *Advances in Chemical Engineering*, DREW, T. B. and HOOPES, J. W., JR. (Editors), vol. 6, Academic Press, New York, 1966.

BUGLIARELLO, G., KAPUR, C. and HSIAO, G. In: *Symposium on Biorheology*, COPLEY, A. L. (Editor), *Proc. 4th Int. Cong. Rheol.*, Interscience Publ. John Wiley, New York, 1965, part 4, p. 351.

FORGACS, O. L. and MASON, S. G. *TAPPI* **44**, 695, 1958.

FORGACS, O. L. and MASON, S. G. *J. Colloid Sci.* **14**, 473, 1959(a).

FORGACS, O. L. and MASON, S. G. *J. Colloid Sci.* **14**, 457, 1959(b).

GOLDSMITH, H. L. *4th Europ. Conf. Microcirculation*, HARDERS, H. (Editor), Cambridge, 1966, Karger, Basel/New York, *Bibl. Anat.* 1967, in press (1966a).

GOLDSMITH, H. L. *Science* **153**, 1406, 1966(b).

GOLDSMITH, H. L. and MASON, S. G. *2nd Europ. Conf. Microcirculation*, HARDERS, H. (Editor), Pavia, 1962, *Bibl. Anat.* **4**, 462, Karger, Basel/New York, 1964 (1962a).

GOLDSMITH, H. L. and MASON, S. G. *J. Colloid Sci.* **17**, 448, 1962(b).

GOLDSMITH, H. L. and MASON, S. G. *3rd Europ. Conf. Microcirculation* Jerusalem, 1964, HARDERS, H. (Editor), *Bibl. Anat.* **7**, 353, Karger, Basel/New York, 1965.

GOLDSMITH, H. L. and MASON, S. G. In: EIRICH, F. R. *Rheology: Theory and Applications*, vol. IV, Academic Press, New York, 1967.

JEFFERY, G. B. *Proc. Roy. Soc. (London)* **A 102**, 161, 1922.

KARNIS, A., GOLDSMITH, H. L. and MASON, S. G. *Can. J. Chem. Eng.* **44**, 181, 1966(a).

KARNIS, A., GOLDSMITH, H. L. and MASON, S. G. *J. Colloid Interface Sci.* **22**, 531, 1966(b).

PHIBBS, R. H. (1966) In: *Hemorheology. Proc. 1st Internat. Conf.* COPLEY, A. L. (Editor), Pergamon Press, Oxford, New York, 1967, p. 617.

RUBINOW, S. I. and KELLER, J. B. *J. Fluid Mech.* **11**, 447, 1961.

SAFFMAN, P. G. *J. Fluid Mech.* **22**, 385, 1965.

SEGRÉ, G. and SILBERBERG, A. *J. Fluid Mech.* **14**, 136, 1962.

SHIZGAL, B., GOLDSMITH, H. L. and MASON, S. G. *Can. J. Chem. Eng.* **43**, 97, 1965.

TAKANO, M., GOLDSMITH, H. L. and MASON, S. G. *J. Colloid Interface Sci.* **23**, 248, 1967(a).

TAKANO, M., GOLDSMITH, H. L. and MASON, S. G. (1967b) Forthcoming publication.

TAKANO, M. and MASON, S. G. Forthcoming publication.

TAYLOR, G. I. *Proc. Roy. Soc. (London)* **A 146**, 501, 1934.

WINSLOW, W. M. *J. Appl. Phys.* **20**, 1137, 1949.

ZIA, I. Y. Z., COX, R. G. and MASON, S. G. *Science* **153**, 1405, 1966.

ZIA, I. Y. Z., COX, R. G. and MASON, S. G. *Proc. Roy. Soc. (London)*. In press, 1967.

DISCUSSION

FÅHRAEUS (*Sweden*):

How was the blood taken? I find the degree of rouleaux formation which you showed quite abnormal.

GOLDSMITH (*Canada*):

The blood was taken from the vein of a healthy human subject and heparinized. A few minutes after the beginning of the flow experiments the rate of aggregation increased and this may well be due to the different environment and/or temperature.

RUBINOW (*U.S.A.*):

Would you say that the red blood cell or the rouleau behaved more like rigid spheres or like the liquid drops? That is, did they exhibit a tubular pinch effect or did they move all the way in toward the axis?

GOLDSMITH:

An investigation into the radial migration of red cells is presently under way and the evidence to date shows that both single cells and rouleaux migrate inwards. However, the results are incomplete.

RUBINOW:

They move all the way in towards the axis?

GOLDSMITH:

Yes, all the way inward. That is the evidence at present.

EHRLY (Germany):

I would like to ask you if you have investigated the flexibility of the rouleau in a system when surface active substances are added.

GOLDSMITH:

No, this is an initial investigation. There are obviously many other things to be done.

EHRLY:

I asked this because we found, that the addition of a surface active agent to an aggregated blood lowers the apparent viscosity of the blood. And maybe your investigation could give us some explanation of the viscosity-lowering mechanism.

GOLDSMITH:

In the initial stages of this investigation I have not yet studied the effect of surfactants.

LONG (U.S.A.):

I'd like to ask you if you have, in your studies so far, noticed any difference between the red cell and leucocyte, the red cell being fairly non-rigid, the leucocyte being more rigid.

GOLDSMITH:

In view of the work of Phibbs and Palmer, this is of great interest, but I am afraid I have not yet studied leucocytes.

MASON (Canada):

I'd like to address my question not to my colleague the speaker, but to the physiologists and biologists in the audience and others who care to answer. From the point of view of microrheological studies of blood and other dispersed systems, it is very important to know something about the particles. We have been wondering how much attention we should pay to rouleaux-like particles as compared with single cells? When asking this question of individual biologists, some reply that rouleaux and other aggregates are normal structures and others very categorically say that they are abnormal. It is not, of course, for people like Goldsmith and myself to say which is true, but we would like to have some guidance as to the importance of aggregation in blood.

BURTON (Canada):

I do not have an answer to Dr. Mason's question, but the point of view I would put is that I understand perfectly why it is sensible to start with individual particles and with low hematocrits. But when one looks and we'll see Dr. Phibbs' pictures of normal or nearly normal hematocrit it becomes rather academic whether you are talking about individual particles, red cells, or rouleaux because the cells are so tremendously crowded. As you know, you can make a simple geometrical calculation, which shows that there is no room for more than a 58% hematocrit, if the cells are the normal shape. This is the maximum packing one can have, and when a normal hematocrit is said to be 45–50, you realize how awfully crowded the circulation is. It becomes rather academic to me to say: "Are you dealing with rouleaux or individual particles?" This is a situation where the interaction between the particles is obviously a dominant factor in the problem. And it seems to me that hemorheology has just made a beginning on the forces that can act on small aggregates, and on individual particles which may cause axial accumulation and rotation. There is not room to do much rotation in blood of normal hematocrit. One cannot conceive of these beautifully interesting motions and rotations with a variable angular velocity happening, even at normal hematocrit. We all need to have the true picture of just how crowded the blood is in the circulation at normal hematocrit. I have described it as like a crowded cocktail party, and from one cocktail party the red cells have to proceed down very narrow alleys in the capillaries to the next party.

MASON:

I agree in part with what Dr. Burton has said: in fact, we recognized this crowding problem in a completely different context a good many years ago, in studying the flow behaviour of fiber suspensions. But just recently, we presented a paper which is now being published (KARNIS, GOLDSMITH and MASON, *J. Colloid Sci.* **22**, 531, 1966) and in which we have studied the microrheological behavior of concentrated suspensions of rigid spheres. We have gone to concentrations of 45% by volume and even higher, where there is continuous interaction between the particles. One can argue that it is unrealistic even to think of an isolated particle in such a system. But I can assure you that we have put a great deal of order into the extremely complicated phenomena that occurred there, and we have been able to do this because of our earlier studies with the single particles, with pairs of particles, with triplets, quadruplets and thus synthesizing the system.

SIRS (*England*):

I wonder if I could take up this question of hematocrit again. I think the figures Professor Burton is quoting apply to blood in large vessels. There is a subtle difference here between bulk blood and blood in the places where it is actually, so to speak, manipulated, which is in the capillaries. When the capillary size is about the same size as the red cell, it is then possible, quite easily, to get up to nearly 100% hematocrit and this is, I think, the place where we have got to make a decision about whether the cell is an individual or whether it is rouleau. Personally, I doubt very much whether rouleaux are *in vivo* a natural phenomena.

BURTON:

May I just add one comment to that, even though I think my general statement is still true in that, as I said, it is not possible to have more than 58% hematocrit without deforming the cells. In the capillary they have to be deformed, into cylinders. So my general statement, I think, is still true, if you emphasize and underline "without deformation" of the normal shape.

FÅHRAEUS:

One thing is certain, and that is, the degree of aggregation of the red corpuscle is the same in the venous system as in the glass tube, when you only keep the blood standing still. In my doctor's thesis in 1921, I have treated this on many pages, and it is incredible that this is in question. The aggregation tendency of the red cells is quite the same outside or inside the vessel. On the whole, for instance, there must be a rather special physiological reason why the horse already has a very, very strong aggregation of the red corpuscles normally. But what I had hoped to hear in this gathering is: what is the meaning of this aggregation, the rouleau formation, and why is this so very much higher in the horse than in people?

GELIN (*Sweden*):

I have admired the Mason contributions during the last six years very much. One thing which their method may permit, as Dr. Goldsmith pointed out is to measure the magnitude of the force needed to split aggregates of different kinds. As Professor Fåhraeus stressed here, some animals will have a tendency to rouleau formation, even in the normal state, as the horse. But they are loose; they will, I think, behave almost like your loose rouleaux here. There are other kinds of aggregates where the force keeping them together is much more rigid. The agglutinate, for example, cannot be split off just by movements; there is a tremendous force necessary to separate these aggregates. And I think, therefore, that the physiologic application of these studies is very important, even if they were made on extremely diluted blood. Back to Professor Burton's point here, it does not apply to normal physiology at all, of course. If we consider, however, the distribution of cells within different parts of the capillaries under a physiologic situation, the hematocrit is fairly low in the narrow capillary tube, but very much higher on the venular side or in the sinusoid. There, quite other shearing forces are acting than in the on-flow side. What it means, according to my experience with aggregation, is a tendency to stasis on the off-flow side, but favoring the flow rate of cells on the on-flow side.

COPLEY (*U.S.A.*):

I would just like to make a brief comment on Dr. Mason's question, whether rouleaux are pathological or not. I should think that, outside of their pathological role, rouleaux can be quite physiological. I would even think that they occur in all of us right now without their causing any damage and I hope, tomorrow, to show to some extent that the formation of large complexes of fibrinogen and fibrin helps the formation of such rouleaux. There are other aggregates, as Professor Gelin has pointed out; they look quite different from rouleaux and their significance in pathology or normal physiology is not quite clear to me. We might show some of these kinds of aggregates tomorrow, although I would not be able to explain why these non-rouleau aggregates also occur in normal human subjects. Now, I think the matter of rouleau formation or the physiological presence of rouleaux has been stressed all along by Professor Fåhraeus. I think this point, which he has made so very often, is to some extent borne out by some of the findings which we are going to present tomorrow.

SILBERBERG (*Israel*):

I wondered whether you observed a dependence of the ability of your discs and rods to stick to each other on their surface characteristics. Not so much in those cases where you added water purposely, but in those instances when they were apparently only in contact with silicone oil.

MASON:

We do not yet know the answer. We do not consider that any of these particles are in true contact with one another. They are very close together, but at the moment, we do not know how close they are. We will be interested to look into this problem because here we have a technique that offers a possibility of measuring adhesion forces; and calculation shows that the technique is capable of measuring extremely small forces of the order of 10^{-12} grams. We simply have not come to that yet.

LONG (*U.S.A.*):

Dr. Rosen and I in our laboratories have been interested in a phenomenon similar to that you have described. One of our most difficult problems has been the elimination of thermal currents. I did not see anything in the illustrations to suggest that you were able to insulate your various columns and apparatus from thermal currents. When we were able to eliminate thermal currents, the pattern of fall of a red cell in a plasma medium was quite different. Its characteristics settled down quite a bit.

MASON:

These experiments were done in very viscous media having fifty to a hundred poise viscosity. Thus, very small thermal disturbances would have little effect. However, I believe that we have eliminated even very small disturbances simply by thermostating the whole room to $\pm 0\cdot 2°C$.

LONG:

There are no thermal currents within the apparatus?

MASON:

First we tried to establish an environment in which thermal conditions were even from place to place within the area of the apparatus and no thermal gradients existed with very highly viscous media. We worked with systems in which the densities of the phases were very carefully matched. We had to develop a number of criteria, one of which is the reversibility of such phenomena. This is a very rigorous criterion for establishing an experimental series of conditions.

WAYLAND (*U.S.A.*):

All of these facts you mentioned are important; but if you are working in this area and you are breathing, you are setting up some enormous thermal currents as far as this apparatus is concerned; if you are just breathing, if you have people working in the laboratory breathing, and breathing in the direction of your tubes.

GOLDSMITH:

Well, I doubt very much that this would affect the viscous suspensions with which we worked.

SEGRÉ (*Italy*):

I want to ask Dr. Goldsmith if he thinks that the very sensitive methods he has developed for measuring forces between particles could be used also to study the force which is responsible for the formation of necklaces of particles in Poiseuille flow. In the necklaces I refer to, the particles are kept at an equilibrium, nontouching, position by hydrodynamic forces. Could the electric field method be used to change the equilibrium distance and eventually to cause the particles to collapse into a necklace of your type?

GOLDSMITH:

It might be possible to devise an experimental means of doing this. We have observed a phenomenon in Couette flow analogous to necklace formation in Poiseuille flow: the rotation of a doublet of rigid spheres which remain in each other's field of influence while rotating without actually coming very close together. By coating the spheres with metal and applying an electric field it should be possible to bring them together.

MODELING OF PRESSURE–FLOW RELATIONS IN ARTERIES AND VEINS

E. ATTINGER,* A. ANNÉ, T. MIKAMI and H. SUGAWARA

Research Institute, Presbyterian-University of Pennsylvania Medical Center and the Bioengineering Dept. of the Moore School of Electrical Engineering and Dept. of Physiology, School of Veterinary Medicine, University of Pennsylvania, Philadelphia, Pennsylvania, U.S.A.

IN ORDER to describe the dynamic behavior of the circulatory system quantitatively, it is necessary to know the transfer functions between instantaneous pressures and flows at the inputs and outputs of its different parts. These transfer functions are space-, time- and pressure-dependent and are determined by the physical properties of the blood, the vascular geometry and the viscoelastic properties of the vessel walls. Two types of models have been proposed for the analysis of pressure–flow and stress–strain relationships in the cardiovascular system.

In the first type, a lumped parameter model initially developed by O. FRANK[1], the space dependence of the variables is not considered but the nonlinear pressure–volume relations of the various vascular chambers are included. However, because an infinite wave velocity is implied, the deformations of the pressure and flow pulses which occur as these pulses travel toward the periphery can not be accounted for. Furthermore, the model is incapable of predicting the distribution of the cardiac output among the many parallel vascular beds, an important factor in the assessment of the function of the cardiovascular system under different physiological and pathological conditions. Because of the uncertainty associated with the clinical evaluation of arterial pressure–volume characteristics the further development of this model[2, 3] has not led to a satisfactory method for the routine determination of cardiac output in patients. On the other hand, it has been extremely useful for the study of the regulation of cardiac output[4–6].

The second type is represented by the distributed parameter model of a single vascular segment and was first proposed by WITZIG[7]. The parameters are time- and space-dependent, permitting the simulation of finite wave velocities as well as of the changes in the shape of the pressure and flow pulses occuring between two points of the system. These models are usually based on the linearized Navier–Stokes equations[8]. Satisfactory agreement has been obtained between experimental data and the results predicted by Womersley's theory in the case of uniform vascular segments[9, 10]. However, more recent data indicate that elastic and geometric non-uniformity, vessel wall viscosity and branching are important for a detailed description of the pressure–flow relations in blood vessels. By including these factors into models of the peripheral circulation it has been possible to obtain a realistic simulation of the behavior of the input impedance into various vascular beds[11–13]. Since the relative importance of these factors is discussed by M. Taylor elsewhere in this symposium, I will concentrate my remarks on the behavior of the cardiovascular system under various distending pressures in an attempt to apply Womersley's analysis to a non-linear system.

THEORY

Our model has been designed for the study of the control mechanisms which govern the distribution of the cardiac output between the different peripheral vascular beds. It represents therefore a compromise between the complexity associated with a distributed system, the data available for the determination of its parameters and manageable solutions in terms of control theory.

In its present form (Fig. 1) no control loops have yet been included, but the model is capable of simulating the mechanical behavior of the peripheral circulation of the anesthetized dog quantitatively. The cardiac output is distributed between 8 parallel vascular beds (head 2, gut 1, kidney 2, legs 2, pelvis 1). Each individual bed consists

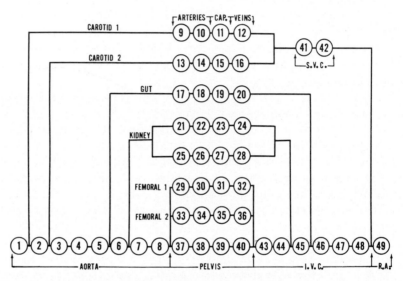

FIG. 1. DIAGRAM OF THE MODEL OF THE PERIPHERAL CIRCULATION, CONSISTING OF 8 PARALLEL VASCULAR, BEDS. EACH NUMBERED BLOCK REPRESENTS ONE VASCULAR SEGMENT AND CONTAINS A NUMBER OF FOUR-TERMINAL NETWORKS. EACH VASCULAR BED IS SUBDIVIDED INTO FOUR FUNCTIONAL UNITS: LARGE ARTERIES, SMALL ARTERIES, CAPILLARIES AND VEINS.

of four parts: the large arteries, the small arteries, the capillaries and the veins. The aorta is divided into 8 segments of 5 cm length each and the major artery of each vascular bed originates at the appropriate aortic segment. Similarly, the venous outflows from the individual beds merge with the vena cava flow at the appropriate sites. The inferior vena cava consists of 6 and the superior vena cava of 2 segments of 5 cm length each. (The dimensions of the subdivisions of the aorta and the venae cavae are based on measurements obtained from 8 dogs weighing between 18 and 25 kg.) The 2 venae cavae join at the right atrium where the model terminates. The distribution of the cardiac output was determined by simultaneous measurements of flows and pressures at various sites in 31 dogs (mean arterial pressure 100 to 150 cm H_2O) and is shown in Fig. 2[14]. About 30% of the ascending aorta flow is directed to the forepart of the body,

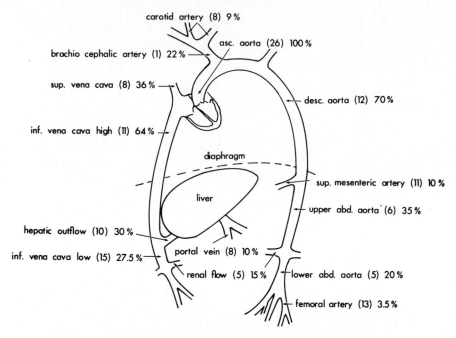

carotid artery (8) 9%

asc. aorta (26) 100%

brachio cephalic artery (1) 22%

sup. vena cava (8) 36%

desc. aorta (12) 70%

inf. vena cava high (11) 64%

diaphragm

sup. mesenteric artery (11) 10%

liver

upper abd. aorta (6) 35%

hepatic outflow (10) 30%

inf. vena cava low (15) 27.5%

portal vein (8) 10%

renal flow (5) 15%

lower abd. aorta (5) 20%

femoral artery (13) 3.5%

FIG. 2. FLOW DISTRIBUTION EXPRESSED AS PERCENTAGE OF ASCENDING AORTA FLOW: AVERAGE VALUES FROM 31 DOGS. THE NUMBERS IN PARENTHESIS INDICATE THE NUMBER OF DOGS IN WHICH THE FLOW MEASUREMENTS WERE CARRIED OUT (FROM REF. 14).

30% to the gastrointestinal system (hepatic outflow), 15% to the kidneys and 20% to the hindpart. Each of the 49 blocks shown in the diagram of the model consists of a number of four-terminal networks of the type shown in Fig. 3. Using a pressure-voltage and flow-current analogy the values for R, L, and C are calculated on the basis of hemodynamic parameters as shown at the bottom of the figure. It will be seen that the values of these parameters are determined primarily by the radius of the vascular segment ($R \sim 1/r^4$; $L \sim 1/r^2$; $C \sim r^3/Eh$) and therefore by its distending pressure. The impedance of the series branch in the four-terminal network shown on the left-hand side of Fig. 3 is:

$$Z_{lo} = R + j\omega L \tag{1}$$

Translated into hemodynamic terms, this becomes:

$$Z_{lo} = \frac{8\mu l}{\pi r^4} + j\omega \frac{\rho l}{\pi r^2} \tag{1a}$$

Neglecting any flow through the shunt resistance the impedance of the parallel branch is simply:

$$Z_{tr} = \frac{1}{j\omega C} \tag{2}$$

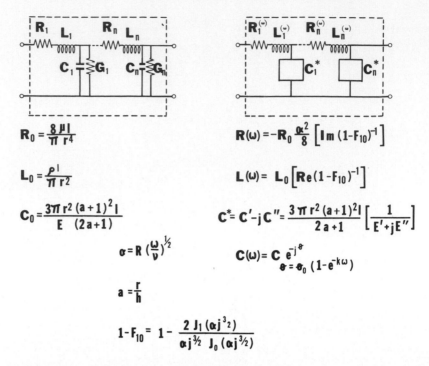

$$R_0 = \frac{8\mu l}{\pi r^4}$$

$$R(\omega) = -R_0 \frac{\alpha^2}{8}\left[Im\,(1-F_{10})^{-1}\right]$$

$$L_0 = \frac{\rho l}{\pi r^2}$$

$$L(\omega) = L_0\left[Re(1-F_{10})^{-1}\right]$$

$$C_0 = \frac{3\pi r^2(a+1)^2 l}{E\ (2a+1)}$$

$$C^* = C' - jC'' = \frac{3\pi r^2(a+1)^2 l}{2a+1}\left[\frac{1}{E'+jE''}\right]$$

$$\sigma = R\left(\frac{\omega}{\nu}\right)^{\frac{1}{2}}$$

$$C(\omega) = C\,e^{-j\delta}$$
$$\delta = \delta_0\,(1-e^{-k\omega})$$

$$a = \frac{r}{h}$$

$$1-F_{10} = 1 - \frac{2\,J_1(\alpha j^{3}{}_2)}{\alpha j^{\frac{3}{2}}\,J_0(\alpha j^{\frac{3}{2}})}$$

FIG. 3. TWO FOUR-TERMINAL NETWORKS USED AS BUILDING BLOCKS FOR THE MODEL OF THE PERIPHERAL VASCULAR BED. THE VALUES OF THE NETWORK PARAMETERS ARE CALCULATED ACCORDING TO THE EXPRESSIONS BELOW THE DIAGRAMS. ON THE LEFT THESE PARAMETERS ARE FREQUENCY INDEPENDENT, ON THE RIGHT FREQUENCY DEPENDENT. TWO POSSIBLE CHOICES FOR A FREQUENCY DEPENDENT COMPLIANCE ARE INDICATED BY: C^* AND $C(\omega)$.
FOR C^* THE PARAMETERS IN THE PARALLEL BRANCH ARE GIVEN BY:

$$C(\omega) = C' = K\frac{E'}{(E')^2 + (E'')^2}$$

$$G(\omega) = \omega C'' = \omega K\frac{E''}{(E')^2 + (E'')^2}$$

THE SECOND EXPRESSION FOR $C(\omega)$ IS THAT PROPOSED BY TAYLOR[12]. THE PRESSURE DEPENDENCE OF THE NETWORK PARAMETERS IS DISCUSSED IN THE TEXT.

or, in hydrodynamic terms:

$$Z_{\mathrm{tr}} = \frac{1}{j\omega}\frac{E(2a+1)}{3\pi r^2(a+1)^2 l} \tag{2a}$$

For a cylindrical tube the elastic modulus E_t of the wall material can be expressed as [15]:

$$E_t = (1-\sigma^2)\frac{\Delta P}{\Delta r}\frac{r^2}{h} \tag{3}$$

and the vascular compliance as [18]:

$$C = \frac{\Delta V}{\Delta P} = \frac{3\pi r^2(a+1)^2 l}{E(2a+1)} \tag{3a}$$

The symbols used in these and subsequent equations have the following meanings:

r = vessel radius
a = vessel radius/wall thickness
l = length of segment
μ = blood vessel viscosity
ρ = blood density
ω = angular frequency
E = elastic modulus of the wall material
ΔP = pressure difference
ΔV = change in volume
Δr = change in mean radius
σ = Poisson ratio
h = wall thickness

WOMERSLEY[8] has shown that for a sinusoidal pressure gradient $\partial p/\partial z = -Ae^{j\omega t}$, the instantaneous flow $(\dot{Q})$ in a uniform, distensible tube of infinite length can be expressed as:

$$\dot{Q} = \frac{\pi r^4}{\mu} \frac{A}{j^3 \alpha^2}(1 - F_{10})e^{j\omega t} \tag{4}$$

where:

$$\alpha^2 = \frac{r^2 \omega \rho}{\mu} \tag{5}$$

$$j = \sqrt{-1}$$

$$1 - F_{10} = 1 - \frac{2J_1(\alpha j^{3/2})}{\alpha j^{3/2} J_0(\alpha j^{3/2})}$$

J_0 and J_1 are Bessel functions of the first kind of zero and first order, respectively.

It will be seen that for pulsatile flow the pressure–flow relations depend markedly on the nondimensional parameter α. Because of the interaction of inertial and viscous forces, R_0 and L_0 of the equivalent network in Fig. 2 are frequency-dependent $R(\omega)$ and $L(\omega)$. The longitudinal impedance thus becomes:

$$Z_{l0} = \frac{j\omega \rho}{\pi r^2}(1 - F_{10})^{-1} = R(\omega) + j\omega L(\omega) \tag{6}$$

Since the vascular wall is viscoelastic its compliance C and the equivalent capacitance in the network must be complex (C^* or $C(\omega)$). The complex modulus of elasticity E^* shows an increase from its static value between 0 and 3 cps, and remains relatively constant at higher frequencies. This increase is least in the aorta. Similarly, the phase angle increases significantly in the low frequency range[16, 17]. On the right hand side of Fig. 2, two possible expressions for the complex compliance are shown.

Defining a complex elastic modulus:

$$E^* = E' + jE'' \tag{7}$$

$$C^* = C' - jC'' = \frac{3\pi r^2(a+1)^2}{2a+1} \frac{1}{E'+jE''} \tag{8}$$

$$= \frac{3\pi r^2(a+1)^2}{2a+1} \left[\frac{E'}{(E')^2+(E'')^2} - \frac{jE''}{(E')^2+(E'')^2} \right]$$

and the parameters of the parallel network branch:

$$C(\omega) = C' = \frac{3\pi r^2(a+1)^2}{2a+1} \frac{E'}{(E')^2+(E'')^2}$$

$$G(\omega) = \omega C'' = \omega \frac{3\pi r^2(a+1)^2}{2a+1} \frac{E''}{(E')^2+(E'')^2} \tag{9a}$$

C' represents the dynamic elastic component and $\omega C''$ the viscous retarding force.

The second expression for the frequency dependence of C was proposed by TAYLOR[12]. Taking into account the data obtained by HARDUNG[16] and BERGEL[17] he replaced C by $Ce^{-j\Theta}$. In this expression the magnitude remains constant, but the phase angle varies with frequency ω according to:

$$\Theta = \theta_0(1 - e^{-k\omega}) \quad \text{where } k \text{ is a constant.}$$

The design of the arterial side of the model is similar to that which NOORDERGRAAF developed for an analog computer[18]. However, our model includes the micro-circulation and the venous system, is programmed for a digital computer, and the calculations are based on network rather than transmission line theory. We have previously shown that by substituting 8 four-terminal networks for each of the 48 vascular segments of the model the results are practically identical to those obtained when each segment is represented by a uniform transmission line[19]. The frequency components of the pressure pulse in the ascending aorta and the right atrium are used as input and output voltages, respectively. The computer is given the necessary data to calculate the overall parameters of each of the 49 blocks for the desired distending pressure and told by how many four-terminal networks it has to represent 1 block. Using classical network theory it then proceeds to calculate the $ABCD$ parameters for each block, multiplies these parameters for 1 parallel bed, converts them into Y-parameters, adds those, reconverts into $ABCD$ parameters and so on, until the calculations for the whole model are carried out. In the final printout pressures, flows and impedances are available at the input and the output of each block, permitting an evaluation of the model in terms of experimental results.

RESULTS AND DISCUSSION

As discussed in detail elsewhere[9, 11, 12, 13] the transmission characteristics of the arterial tree are influenced significantly by branching, geometrical tapering and non-uniform elastic properties. In contrast, the behavior of the venous system appears to be determined primarily by its distending pressure. In order to evaluate the pressure dependence of the parameters R, L and C, defined by the equations in Fig. 3, the

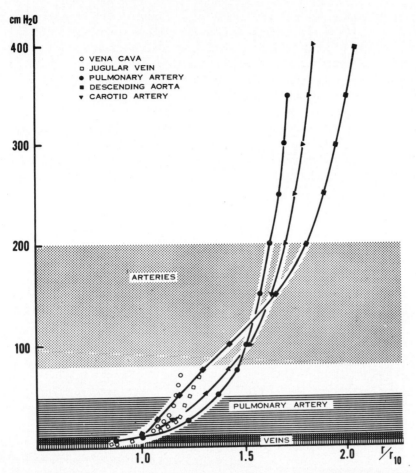

FIG. 4. RELATION BETWEEN RADIUS AND PRESSURE FOR DIFFERENT VESSELS. THE SHADED AREAS INDICATE
THE NORMAL RANGE OF OPERATING PRESSURES FOR ARTERIES, THE PULMONARY ARTERY AND THE LARGE
VEINS. THE VALUES FOR THE REFERENCE RADIUS AT A DISTENDING PRESSURE OF 10 CM H_2O ARE GIVEN IN
TABLE 1.

TABLE 1. RADIUS (r_{10}) AND WALL THICKNESS (h_{10}) FOR DIFFERENT VESSELS AT
A DISTENDING PRESSURE OF 10 CM H_2O.
(The number in parentheses indicates the number of vessels investigated)

	r_{10}(cm)	h_{10}(cm $\times 10^{-2}$)	h/r
Jugular vein (7)	0.323 ± 0.023	1.136 ± 0.107	0.035
Inferior vena cava (4)	0.73 ± 0.053	1.49 ± 0.12	0.021
Superior vena cava (3)	0.656 ± 0.051	1.20 ± 0.10	0.018
Portal vein (1)	0.568	1.26	0.022
Pulmonary artery (5)	0.551 ± 0.079	3.102 ± 0.64	0.056
Descending aorta (4)	0.444 ± 0.030	11.03 ± 0.71	0.25
Carotid artery (5)	0.126 ± 0.011	3.78 ± 0.43	0.30

pressure–volume characteristics of a number of canine vascular segments were
measured statically and dynamically as described previously[11]. Some of these data
are shown in Figs. 4–6.

In Fig. 4 the change in relative radius (r/r_{10}) is plotted against distending pressure. Since the determination of the radius at pressures of less than 2 cm is difficult (the vascular cross section becomes elliptic under these conditions) a pressure of 10 cm H_2O was chosen as the reference for a mathematical expression of the pressure-dependence of the radius. The average values (mean and S.E.M.) for radius (r_{10}) and wall thickness (h_{10}) at this pressure are listed in Table 1. For all vessel types the change in radius for a given pressure increase was considerably larger at low as compared to high distending pressures. Over the whole normal operating pressure range (indicated by the shaded areas in the figure) the relative radius changed by about 30% for the larger veins, by 50% for the pulmonary artery and by 25% for the large arteries. However, the change in radius associated with the pressure pulse is only in the order of 5%.

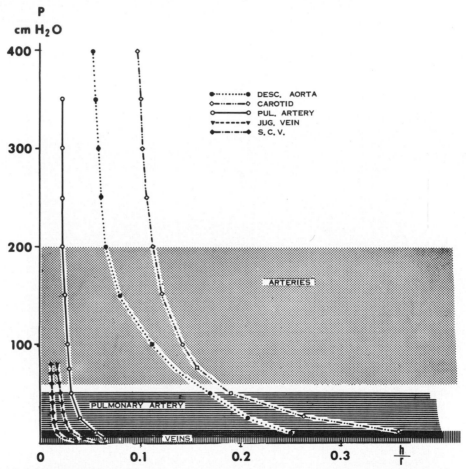

FIG. 5. RELATION BETWEEN PRESSURE AND RADIUS/WALL THICKNESS RATIO (h/r) FOR ARTERIES AND VEINS. NOTE THE LARGE CHANGES IN THIS RATIO FOR LOW DISTENDING PRESSURES. THE SHADED AREAS INDICATE THE NORMAL RANGE OF OPERATING PRESSURES FOR VARIOUS VESSEL TYPES.

Figure 5 illustrates the variations in the ratio wall thickness/radius over the same pressure ranges. The values for the wall thickness at the different pressures were calculated from the measurements obtained at the reference pressure and the changes in radius, when the vascular segment was distended keeping its length constant. Assuming isovolumetry of the wall material, the expression for the wall thickness at any pressure is:

$$h_t = -r + \left[r^2 + 2h_0\left(r_0 + \frac{h_0}{2}\right) \right]^{1/2} \tag{10a}$$

where the subscripts 0 indicate the reference conditions. For thin-walled tubes, this relation can be simplified to

$$h_a = \frac{h_0 r_0}{r} \tag{10b}$$

with an error of less than 10% for a ratio $h_0/r_0 < 0.2$. Because this condition does not hold for arteries (Table 1) we have used the exact expression (eq. (10a)) for our calculations. The changes in h/r are largest at low distending pressures and are therefore more important for the analysis of the venous than for that of the arterial system. In all the vessels studied the change was significant throughout the physiological pressure range. Figure 6 shows the pressure dependence of the elastic moduli (E_t, eq. (3)). It will be seen that for the vessels examined, the pressure dependence of the elastic modulus can be approximated by a straight line on a log–log plot. Above distending pressures of 10 cm H_2O the veins and pulmonary arteries appear to be stiffer than the arteries. While the exponential approximation of the pressure dependence of the elastic modulus can be used over the whole physiological pressure range, this is not the case for the vascular compliance ($\Delta V/\Delta P$). From eq. (3b) it will be seen that this parameter depends not only on the elastic modulus, but also on radius and wall thickness. As a result, a simple exponential relation between pressure and compliance is valid only over a limited pressure range (Table 3). In addition to the nonlinearities at large strains pressure–radius and pressure–volume curves are characterized by frequency-dependent hysteresis. For this reason complex expressions for the elastic modulus and compliance have been suggested (eqs. (7)–(9)).

It is of interest to evaluate to what extent these nonlinearities appear when the analysis of the cardiovascular system is based on linear methods. In Table 2 some results

TABLE 2. FOURIER ANALYSIS OF PRESSURE CHANGES (P IN CM H_2O) IN CAROTID ARTERY SUBJECTED TO SINUSOIDAL VOLUME CHANGES (V IN CM^3) AT DIFFERENT DISTENDING PRESSURES AND FREQUENCIES (C^* represents the dynamic compliance with modulus M and phase $\phi°$).

f(cps)	1 1 cps		2 1 cps		3 5 cps		4 5 cps		5 5 cps	
	V	P	V	P	V	P	V	P	V	P
Harmonic 0	0.6	75	0.6	160	0.6	160	0.6	160	0.6	250
1	0.16	65	0.16	120	0.16	120	0.045	20.0	0.045	25.0
2	0.0016	17.7	0.0007	38.9	0.001	37.4	0.0003	1.06	0.00006	2.1
3	0.002	5.8	0.0021	11.07	0.0002	10.5	0.0002	0	0.0003	0.7
4	0.0012	1.61	0.0007	2.7	0.0002	2.0	0.00007	0.08	0.00006	0.7
	M	$\phi°$	M	$\phi°$	M	$\phi°$	M	$\phi°$	M	$\phi°$
C^*_{dyn} (cm^3/cmH$_2$O)	0.0025	5.2	0.0013	4.8	0.0013	5.4	0.0023	7.5	0.0018	5.2

TABLE 3. PRESSURE DEPENDENCE OF RADIUS, RESISTANCE, INERTANCE AND
COMPLIANCE FOR VARIOUS VESSELS

		Pressure range cm H_2O
Jugular Vein	$\dfrac{r}{r_{10}} = 0.8645(P-1.0)^{0.137} - 0.168$	1 to 20
	$\dfrac{r}{r_{10}} = 0.256 \log P + 0.794$	20 to 70
	$R = 56P^{-0.900}$	1 to 20
	$L = 8.69P^{-0.442}$	1 to 20
	$C = 116P^{-0.942}$	3 to 20
Vena Cava	$\dfrac{r}{r_{10}} = 0.1973(P-1.9)^{0.2597} + 0.6605$	1 to 25
	$\dfrac{r}{r_{10}} = 0.22 \log P + 0.79$	15 to 70
	$R = 1.61P^{-0.686}$	1 to 20
	$L = 1.42P^{-0.301}$	1 to 30
	$C = 275P^{-0.875}$	1 to 25
Descending Aorta	$\dfrac{r}{r_{10}} = 0.0046P + 0.954$	0 to 150
	$\dfrac{r}{r_{10}} = 1.10 \log P - 0.75$	70 to 350
	$R = 111P^{-1.199}$	50 to 300
	$L = 9.9P^{-0.556}$	50 to 300
	$C = 846P^{-0.954}$	90 to 250
Carotid Artery	$\dfrac{r}{r_{10}} = 0.1775P^{0.3615} + 0.592$	0 to 100
	$\dfrac{r}{r_{10}} = 0.550 \log P + 0.425$	75 to 350
	$R = 170P^{-0.732}$	10 to 300
	$L = 45.5P^{-0.352}$	10 to 300
	$C = 848P^{-1.090}$	70 to 300

of an experiment are listed, where a carotid artery segment was subjected to sinusoidal volume variations at different frequencies and distending pressures. Both the volume changes and the resulting pressure oscillations were treated by Fourier analysis. The harmonic distortion of the sinusoidal volume change was less than 2%. At large strains (27% of the initial volume) there was a marked distortion of the pressure wave at any distending pressure and frequency as manifested by the appearance of higher harmonics. The magnitudes of the second, third and fourth harmonic were, respectively, 30, 10, and 2% of that of the first harmonic. At small strains (7.5% of the initial volume) the harmonic distortion of the resulting pressure signal was almost negligible (8% of second and 3% of third harmonic). The dynamic compliance exhibited a constant phase angle (about 5°) for all strains and frequencies. Its magnitude depended on distending pressure and amount of strain, but only little on frequency. These results confirm our previous findings[20] that the application of Fourier analysis to the cardiovascular system is justified as long as one deals only with the small strains associated with the arterial pressure pulse.

An additional complication in the analysis of the stress–strain relationships in the vasculature is represented by the stress relaxation exhibited by the vascular wall.

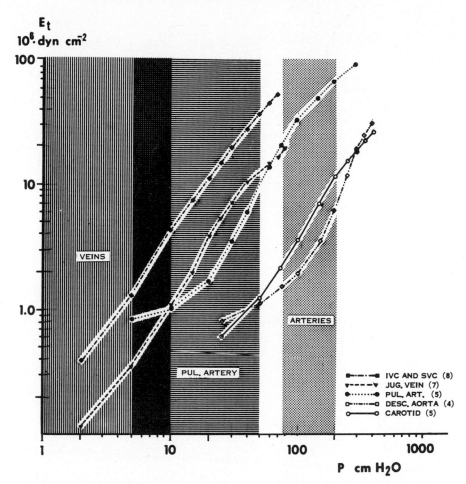

FIG. 6. PRESSURE DEPENDENCE OF THE ELASTIC MODULUS E_t FOR ARTERIES AND VEINS. THE PLOTTED CURVES REPRESENT THE AVERAGES FROM ALL EXPERIMENTS AND THE STANDARD ERRORS OF THE MEAN ARE LESS THAN 5% OF THE MEAN AT EACH DISTENDING PRESSURE. THE SHADED AREAS REPRESENT THE NORMAL RANGE OF OPERATING PRESSURES FOR VARIOUS VESSELS (COORDINATES ARE IN LOG SCALE).

Figure 7 shows the stress relaxation curves of a segment of jugular vein subjected to a series of volume changes in the form of step functions. There is an exponential decrease of pressure with time at constant volume. The analysis of these data reveals that in the general expression for such stress relaxation curves

$$P = P_0 e^{-\alpha t} + P_a, \tag{11}$$

all parameters vary as a function of sampling time. In the particular case illustrated these relations are as follows:

$$\frac{1}{\alpha} = 1.094 t^{1.018} \tag{12a}$$

$$P_{0x} = (1.0795 - 0.088 \log t) P_{08} \tag{12b}$$

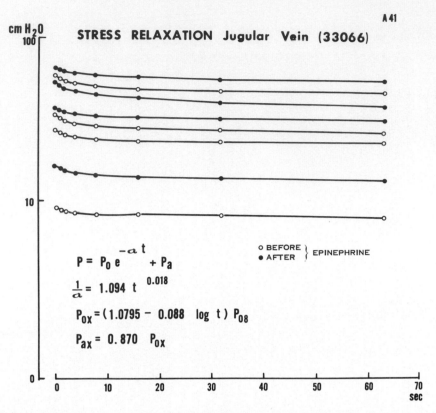

FIG. 7. STRESS RELAXATION IN THE JUGULAR VEIN. THE INDIVIDUAL CURVES ILLUSTRATE THE CHANGE IN STRESS (PRESSURE) WITH TIME AFTER A STEPWISE INCREASE IN VOLUME HAD BEEN PRODUCED. THE EQUATIONS AT THE BOTTOM DESCRIBE THREE TIME-DEPENDENT PARAMETERS OF THE STRESS RELAXATION EQUATION:

$$P = P_0 e^{-\alpha t} + P_a$$

WHERE $1/\alpha$ = TIME CONSTANT
     P_{0x} = INITIAL PRESSURE ASSOCIATED WITH SAMPLING POINT AT $t = x$ SEC
     P_{08} = INITIAL PRESSURE ASSOCIATED WITH SAMPLING POINT AT $t = 8$ SEC
     P_{ax} = ASYMPTOTIC PRESSURE ASSOCIATED WITH SAMPLING POINT AT $t = x$ SEC.

$$P_{ax} = 0.870 P_{0x} \tag{12c}$$

where

$$\frac{1}{\alpha} = \text{time constant}$$

$$P_{0x} = \text{initial pressure associated with sampling point at } t = x \text{ sec}$$

$$P_{08} = \text{initial pressure associated with sampling point at } t = 8 \text{ sec}$$

$$P_{ax} = \text{asymptotic pressure associated with sampling point at } t = x \text{ sec}$$

The expression for stress relaxation then becomes

$$P = (1.0795 - 0.088 \log t)(e^{-t^{-0.018}/1.094} + 0.870) P_{08} \tag{13}$$

This, of course, indicates that the viscoelastic behavior of the vascular wall is characterized by a spectrum of time constants and complicates the task of finding a simple expression for the complex viscoelastic moduli.

From the above data the pressure dependence of radius, resistance, inertance and compliance could be formulated. Two equations were necessary to express the radius as a function of pressure over the whole pressure range investigated. At low distending pressures a power function of P, at high pressures a log function of P represented the best approximations to the experimental data. The pressure dependence of the network parameters could be approximated well by

$$y = aP^{-b} \qquad\qquad (14)$$

where y represents either R, L or C and a and b are constants. The exact expressions are listed in Table 3 together with the pressure ranges over which they are valid (less than 10% difference between experimental and predicted data at any point). The coefficients b varied from 0.875 in the IVC to 1.09 in the carotid artery for compliance, from 0.3 in the IVC to 0.556 in the aorta for inertance and from 0.686 in the IVC to 1.2 in the aorta for resistance.

From the data listed in Tables 1 and 3, values for r_{10}, a and b were estimated for each segment of the model. Together with the distending pressure P they represent the input to the computer from which the parameters R, L, C and α for each segment and mean pressure are calculated. Because the stress–strain relations are linear for the stress range corresponding to the pressure pulse, linear network theory can then be applied at each mean pressure.

The curvilinear stress–strain relations of blood vessels and their effect on the pressure–flow relations have been well established and were reviewed in detail by WEZLER[2]. The coefficients in eq. (14) may vary in each vessel within wide limits depending upon its "vascular tone". a decreases and b increases progressively with vasoconstriction. For example, in perfusion experiments of dog hindlimbs, values for a ranging from 1.5 to 260,000 and for b from 0.26 to 1.35 over pressure ranges from 20 to 220 mm Hg were observed[21, 22]. This corresponds to flow rates varying from 0.000062 (virtual occlusion) to 8.7 cm³/min at a perfusion pressure of 10 mm Hg and from 1.29 to 125 cm³/min at a perfusion pressure of 200 mm Hg. These extreme changes are mediated at the level of the small vessels, where quantitative measurements are difficult to obtain. For any vascular bed the coefficients of eq. (14) represent the combination of values for each vessel in the bed and the weight of the individual contributions are not known[14]. The values reported in this paper refer to unconstricted vascular beds of anesthetized dogs.

Before discussing the results obtained with our model consisting of pressure-dependent parameters, I would like to briefly review the conclusions we arrived at on the basis of the previous version with pressure-independent parameters[9, 11].

(a) The microcirculation effectively prevents the transmission of the arterial pulse from the arterial to the venous system. The behavior of the aortic input impedance is not significantly influenced by changes in venous hemodynamics.

(b) The arterial input impedance decreases to a fraction of its d.c. value for the first harmonic and oscillates around the characteristic impedance at higher frequencies. These oscillations are minimal at the origin and the termination of the aorta, and most marked in the descending aorta. The phase angles of the impedance are negative at low frequencies, and (except for the mesenteric bed) become positive at higher frequencies. Oscillations of the input impedance expected from a uniform transmission line model can be significantly reduced by a number of factors, among which non-uniformity both with respect to geometry and elastic wall properties appears to be most important.

(c) The behavior of the aortic input impedance in this model is primarily determined by the parameters chosen for the networks representing the aorta and its larger branches.

(d) The wave velocity in the venous system is a fraction of that in the arterial system. Measurable pulsatile pressures are only present in the thoracic venae cavae, originate in the right atrium and are rapidly dampened out. However, pulsatile flow persists throughout the venae cavae.

(e) The frequency dependence of R, L and C had little effect on the behavior of the aortic input impedance but is important for the analysis of pressure–flow relations in the major aortic branches.

(f) The effects of convective acceleration in the thoracic and deceleration in the abdominal aorta, related to the particular geometry of that vessel, can be adequately simulated by dividing the aorta into eight uniform segments.

Turning now to the more recent results I will briefly discuss the effects of changes in distending pressure on impedance, transmission of the pressure pulse and wave velocity. The effects of changes in distending pressure on the pressure–flow relations are large in terms of the d.c. impedance but have relatively little influence on the frequency-dependent input impedance of the different vascular beds. In contrast, the behavior of the vascular impedance of the venous flow channels shows marked changes if the distending pressure falls below 5 cm H_2O.

Figure 8 illustrates the normalized input impedance of the femoral bed. For comparison, results obtained from simultaneous measurements of pressure and flow at a mean arterial pressure of 150 cm H_2O in seven dogs (mean and S.E.M.) are also indicated. The model data were obtained at arterial mean pressures of 100, 150 and 200 cm H_2O, respectively. There is excellent agreement between the experimental and the model data both with respect to magnitude and to phase. The changes with pressure in the frequency-dependent part of the input impedance are small. However, the phase angles remain negative at 100 cm H_2O while they cross over to positive values at 10 cps for 150 cm H_2O and 12 cps for 200 cm H_2O. These results agree well with data we obtained recently in animals where the mean pressure was altered by changing the blood volume[14].

In Fig. 9 the transmission of the first four harmonics of the pressure pulse along the aorta is shown for the same three distending pressures. At all three pressures the amplitude of the first harmonic increases monotonically toward the bifurcation. This pressure rise is steeper in the abdominal as compared to the thoracic aorta, and the increase is largest at 150 cm H_2O. For all the other harmonics the amplification of pressure with distance becomes larger as the distending pressure increases and minima and maxima move toward the thorax, indicating changes in the reflection pattern associated with the alteration in mean pressure. There is progressive damping of the higher harmonics as the pressure decreases (see fourth harmonic at 100 and 200 cm H_2O). This is in agreement with experimental data we obtained on the propagation of the venous pres-

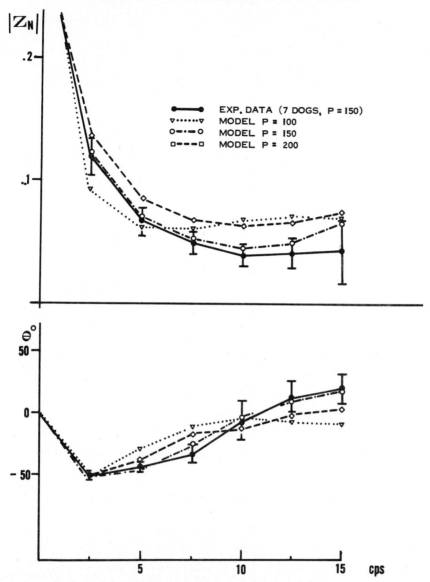

FIG. 8. INPUT IMPEDANCE OF THE FEMORAL ARTERY (NORMALIZED MAGNITUDE AND PHASE) OBTAINED FROM THE MODEL AT THREE DIFFERENT ARTERIAL MEAN PRESSURES: 100, 150 AND 200 CM H_2O. FOR COMPARISON THE AVERAGE VALUES (MEAN AND S.E.M.) OBTAINED FROM 7 DOGS AT A MEAN PRESSURE OF 150 CM H_2O ARE ALSO SHOWN.

sure pulses[11, 14]. Although venous flow is pulsatile throughout the venae cavae, the frequency components of the venous pressure pulse can only be recovered from the thoracic venae cavae at normal venous pressures.

Based on the data shown in Figs. 4–6 we have calculated the wave velocities for the vena cava as a function of pressure using the following three expressions:

$$C_A = \left[\left(\frac{Eh}{2\rho r}\right)\right]^{1/2} \quad \text{(Moens Korteweg)} \qquad (15)$$

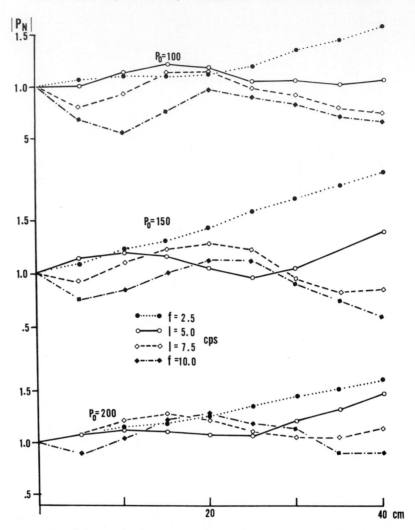

FIG. 9. TRANSMISSION OF THE PRESSURE PULSE ALONG THE AORTA IN THE MODEL AT THREE DIFFERENT ARTERIAL MEAN PRESSURES: 100, 150 AND 200 CM H₂O. THE FREQUENCY COMPONENTS OF 2.5, 5, 7.5 AND 10 CPS ARE SHOWN. THEIR MAGNITUDE (NORMALIZED WITH RESPECT TO MAGNITUDE AT THE ORIGIN OF THE AORTA) IS PLOTTED ON THE ORDINATE, DISTANCE ALONG THE AORTA ON THE ABSCISSA.

$$C_B = \left[\left(\frac{Eh}{2\rho r} \right) \left(\frac{2 - \gamma}{2 - (2\gamma - \gamma^2)(1 - \sigma - 2\sigma^2) - 2\sigma^2} \right) \right]^{1/2} \quad \text{(Bergel)} \quad (16)$$

$$C_C = \left[\left(\frac{Eh}{3\rho} \right) \left(\frac{2r + h}{(r + h)^2} \right) \left(1 - F_{10} \right) \right]^{1/2} \quad \text{(Womersley)} \quad (17)$$

where $\gamma = 1/a = h/r$, and the other symbols are as defined earlier.

Only in the last of these expressions (C_C) is the wave velocity frequency-dependent. (An additional frequency dependence could be introduced in all three equations by substituting the complex modulus of elasticity for E. Equations (15) and (16) differ only by the expression in the second brackets, which is determined by wall thickness, radius and the Poisson ratio. It will be seen (Fig. 10) that for $0 < \sigma < 0.5$ and $0 < h/r < 0.5 \rightarrow C_B \geqslant C_A$.

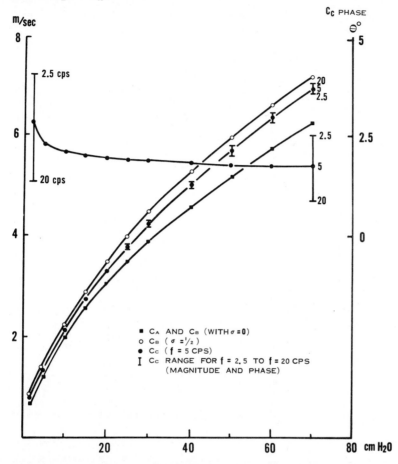

FIG. 10. PRESSURE DEPENDENCE OF THE WAVE VELOCITY IN THE VENA CAVA CALCULATED FROM THREE DIFFERENT EXPRESSIONS (SEE TEXT). ONLY C_C IS FREQUENCY-DEPENDENT, AND THEREFORE COMPLEX. THE CHANGE IN PHASE ANGLE IS SHOWN IN THE UPPER PART OF THE FIGURE. EXCEPT FOR THE JUGULAR VEIN AND THE CAROTID ARTERY THE PHASE ANGLE IS ALWAYS LESS THAN 5°.

However, the differences are small: for $\sigma = 0$, 2% ($\gamma = 0.1$) to 10% ($\gamma = 0.5$) and for $\sigma = 0.5$, 0($\gamma = 0.5$) to 12% ($\gamma = 0.1$). For C_C the wave velocity is complex. The modulus is somewhat lower than that of C_B and increases slightly with frequency. Except for the jugular vein (10°) and the carotid artery (20°) the phase angle is always less than 5° and decreases as pressure and frequency increase. This agrees with the increased damping at lower pressures implied in the data of the transmission of the pressure pulse (Fig. 9).

The pressure dependence of the wave velocity in different vessels is illustrated in Fig. 11. Below a distending pressure of 10 cm H_2O the wave velocity is less than 2 m/sec in all vessels. It rises most rapidly in the thin-walled vessels (venae cavae, jugular vein and pulmonary artery) and least in the aorta, where a significant increase occurs only when the distending pressure exceeds 150 cm H_2O.

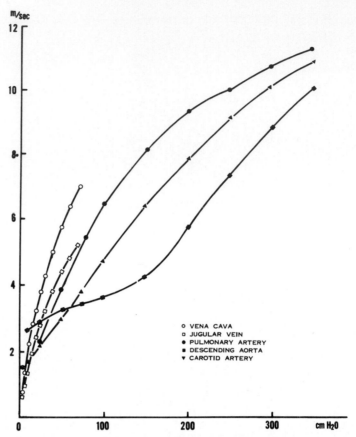

FIG. 11. WAVE VELOCITY (C_C IN FIG. 10) CALCULATED AS A FUNCTION OF PRESSURE FOR DIFFERENT VESSELS USING DATA FROM FIGS. 4 TO 6.

The wave velocities obtained at two different distending pressures in the aorta of the model are shown in Fig. 12. In the top panel the wave velocity (average for all frequencies) is plotted against distance along the aorta (mean and S.E.M.). At 100 cm H_2O the velocity ranges between 4 and 5.5 cm/sec throughout the aorta. At the higher pressure the pressure wave travels much faster and shows larger oscillations (5–10 m/sec) indicating again an alteration in the reflection pattern and a decrease in damping.

At the bottom of the figure the wave velocities in the thoracic and abdominal aorta are plotted against frequency. For 100 cm H_2O the velocities at the two sites are similar; however, at the higher pressure, the frequency patterns are quite different. The ratios of the average velocities at the two pressures are 1.85 in the thoracic and 1.63 in the abdominal aorta, remarkably close to the values one would predict from Figs. 10 and 11.

In our initial attempts at constructing an analog of the peripheral circulation we used a model consisting of six parallel vascular beds and only 21 four-terminal networks[23]. All the vascular beds originated at the peripheral end of the aorta and terminated at one point in the vena cava. With this earlier model it was possible to match the experimentally observed input impedance in the aorta over the physiological frequency range (0–20 cps), provided the Fourier components of the right atrial pressure were used as

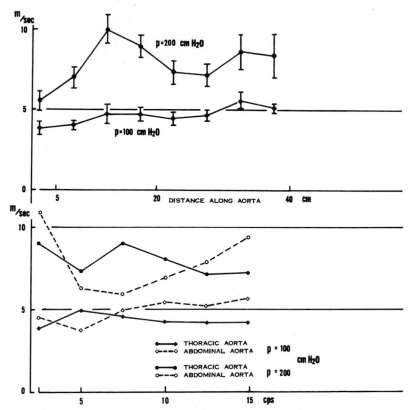

FIG. 12. WAVE VELOCITY IN THE AORTA, CALCULATED FROM THE MODEL. IN THE TOP OF THE FIGURE THE VALUES FOR THE FREQUENCIES 2.5, 5, 7.5, 10, 12.5 AND 16 CPS HAVE BEEN AVERAGED FOR EACH SEGMENT (MEAN AND S.E.M. ARE SHOWN) AND PLOTTED AGAINST DISTANCE ALONG THE AORTA FOR TWO MEAN PRESSURES (100 AND 200cm H_2O). IN THE BOTTOM OF THE FIGURE THE VALUES FOR THE FIRST 4 (THORACIC) AND SECOND 4 (ABDOMINAL) SEGMENTS HAVE BEEN AVERAGED AT EACH FREQUENCY AND PLOTTED AGAINST FREQUENCY FOR THE SAME TWO DISTENDING PRESSURES.

output generator voltage. However, only by applying right atrial pressures at the output could the increase of the aortic impedance with frequency, which occurred after the initial minimum at about 2 cps, be prevented. It soon became apparent that a larger number of networks and a more adequate geometrical representation were necessary if the physiological pressure–flow relations in the peripheral circulation were to be simulated. If one introduces geometrical and elastic tapering one can always obtain a "physiological" behavior of the input impedance into any vascular bed, provided a sufficient number of segments and branches are used. There are two reasons for this: By increasing the number of networks representing the total transfer function the overall effects of mismatched individual impedances are minimized and errors in the assumption of network and transmission line parameters tend to cancel out better. However, it becomes considerably more difficult to associate the network parameters with their specific physiological counterparts.

With the experimental data available at this time the parameters of only a few vascular segments can be evaluated objectively. For this reason we have limited the representation of each vascular bed to 4 segments. Since there is no unique solution for the synthesis of the complex networks required to simulate the peripheral circulation, the evaluation of the validity of such a model must be based on more than one type of comparison with experimental data. For instance, it is possible to obtain an excellent fit between experimental and model data for the frequency spectrum of a vascular impedance, while the transmission of the pressure pulse may be quite different in the two sets of data. Such discrepancies clearly restrict the usefulness of an analog. Our present model simulates the peripheral circulation well with respect to vascular impedances, pressure transmission and wave velocity. Its major advantage lies in the ease with which the different parameters can be changed as a function of the operating pressure and/or blood volume of the system. This permits the theoretical investigation of the contribution of various vascular beds and segments to vasomotor mechanisms.

SUMMARY

1. A distributed parameter model of the peripheral circulation has been programmed on a digital computer, using four-terminal network theory. The model contains 8 parallel vascular beds, each of which has been divided into four parts. The flow distribution between the different beds was determined experimentally.

2. The parameters of each four-terminal network are frequency dependent according to Womersley's theory.

3. The pressure dependences of radius, wall thickness, elastic modulus and vascular compliance were established experimentally for a number of vessels. These data were used to formulate the pressure dependence of the network parameters.

Although the stress–strain relations are markedly non-linear over the physiological pressure range, the validity of linear techniques for the analysis of the vascular system over the small strains associated with pulsatile pressure has been confirmed.

4. The effects of parameter distribution (number of networks per segment), branching, geometrical and elastic tapering are briefly discussed.

5. Data obtained from the model are in good agreement with experimental results.

6. In contrast to the venous system the arterial system is relatively insensitive to changes in arterial and venous distending pressures, as far as the frequency spectrum of the impedance is concerned. On the other hand, the transmission of the pressure pulse is markedly influenced by the distending pressures both in terms of wave velocity and damping.

7. Some of the problems in evaluating models in terms of the physiological system are pointed out.

ACKNOWLEDGMENT

This work was supported by NIH Grant H#–09694–01, –02, U.S. Public Health Service, Bethesda, Maryland.

REFERENCES

[1] FRANK, O. Z. Biol. **37**, 483, 1899.
[2] WEZLER, K. and SINN, W. Strömungsgesetz des Blutkreislaufs, Cantor Publishers, Aulendorf, 1953.
[3] COPE, F. W. Adv. Biol. Med. Phys. **10**, 277, 1965.
[4] GRODINS, F. S. Quart. Rev. Biol. **34**, 93, 1959.
[5] GUYTON, A. C. Circulatory Physiology: Cardiac Output and its Regulation, Saunders Co., Philadelphia, 1963.

[6] WARNER, H. R. *Fed. Proc.* **21**, 87, 1962.

[7] WITZIG, K. Üeber erzwungene Wellenbewegungen zaeher inkompressibler Fluessigkeiten in elastischen Rohren, Doctoral thesis, Univ. Bern, 1914.

[8] WOMERSLEY, J. R. The mathematical analysis of the arterial circulation in a state of oscillatory motion, Wright Air Development Center Tech. Report WADC–TR–614, 1958.

[9] ATTINGER, E. O., SUGAWARA, H., NAVARRO, A., RICCETTO, A. and MARTIN, R. *Circulation Res.* **19**, 230, 1966.

[10] GREENFIELD, J. C., Jr. and FRY, D. L. *Circulation Res.* **17**, 340, 1965.

[11] ATTINGER, E. O., ANNÉ, A., SUGAWARA, H. and MIKAMI, T. *Proc. 4th Ann. Symp. Biomath. Computer Sci.*, Houston, Texas, 1966 (in press).

[12] TAYLOR, M. G. *Biophysical J.* **6**, 29, 1966.

[13] WESTERHOF, N. and GESSNER, Y. *Proc. 18th ACEMB* **7**, 35, 1965.

[14] ATTINGER, E. O., SUGAWARA, H., MIKAMI, T., NAVARRO, A. and MARTIN, R. *Angiologica*, **4**, 1, 1967.

[15] BERGEL, D. H. *J. Physiol.* **156**, 445, 1961.

[16] HARDUNG, V. *Helv. Physiol. Acta* **11**, 194, 1953.

[17] BERGEL, D. H. *J. Physiol.* **156**, 458, 1961.

[18] NOORDERGRAAF, A., VERDOUW, P. D., VAN BRUMMELEN, A. G. W. and WIEGEL. In: *Pulsatile Blood Flow*, McGraw-Hill, New York, 1964, p. 373.

[19] ATTINGER, E. O., ANNÉ, A. and SUGAWARA, H. *Proc. 18th ACEMB* **7**, 81, 1965.

[20] ATTINGER, E. O., ANNÉ, A. and McDONALD, D. A. *Biophysical J.* **6**, 292, 1966.

[21] PAPPENHEIMER, J. R. and MAES, J. P. *Am. J. Physiol.* **137**, 187, 1942.

[22] GREEN, H. D., LEWIS, R. N., NICKERSON, N. D. and HELLER, A. L. *Am. J. Physiol.* **141**, 518, 1944.

[23] ATTINGER, E. O. and ANNÉ, A. *Ann. N.Y. Acad. Sci.* **128**, 810, 1966.

DISCUSSION

BARNARD (*U.S.A.*):

The lower two terminals are ground reference, are they not?

ATTINGER (*U.S.A.*):

They are connected together throughout the system. That's right.

BARNARD:

So that physiologically the lower two terminals correspond to reference pressure level outside the vasculature, whereas at the upper level, the extreme input would be at the left ventricle, and the extreme output at the right atrium.

ATTINGER:

That's right.

BARNARD:

In view of this: could you tell us what the physiological significance of the shunt resistance is? It seems that this would represent some blood which leaves the left ventricle but does not arrive at the right atrium.

ATTINGER:

Essentially it represents blood which is lost through the vascular walls and through arterial branches which have not been taken into account in the model. Of course, finally this lost fluid will return to the right atrium through the ground line (as in any transmission line).

BARNARD:

I do not see that it does.

WIEDERHIELM (*U.S.A.*):

I just had a question about the time course of stress relaxation. I noticed that the time scale extended to approximately 60 to 100 sec in your slides. Do you find any evidence for stress relaxation during more prolonged time periods?

ATTINGER:

Oh, yes, there are some. FEDER* from Chicago has shown these, too. But we have only gone to 60 sec on these plots because, afterwards, the representation becomes quite simple.

*Digest 6th Int. Conf. on Med. Electronics and Biol. Eng., Tokyo, 1965.

WIEDERHIELM:

I believe there is substantial evidence that the time course of stress potential recovery is different than that of stress relaxation. Has this been worked into the model?

ATTINGER:

No, we have not done this. We just got our data about two months ago. We have not yet included these more complex phenomena.

ROWLANDS (*England*):

I do not want in any way to appear to denigrate this most excellent work; and perhaps I misread the diagram or other people would have noticed it. I may have been mistaken, but you appear to have no hepatic circulation in your model.

ATTINGER:

That is right.

ROWLANDS:

The outflow from the superior vena cava appears to go into the distal end of the inferior vena cava.

ATTINGER:

No, it goes directly into the atrium. There are two venous outflows, each vena cava goes separately into the atrium. The reason for omitting the hepatic circulation is that if you want to include control loops into such a model, you have to draw a limit somewhere with respect to the degree of complexity you want to simulate. Arbitrarily we have lumped the whole gastrointestinal and hepatic systems into one for the purpose of this model.

BURTON (*Canada*):

The real problems of physiology are the influence of the sympathetic nervous system in changing the diameters and the tone and the elasticity of all these vessels and such things as Starling's law, which means that the output coming back to the heart has something to do with the input. Do you intend to include these factors? Fixed values which apply to only one state of the body, cannot lead you far, unless you go on to study a large number of different parameters. I am fully aware just how complicated this is, but without doing this, does this really tackle the physiological problem at all?

ATTINGER:

I am sorry if I have not made this clear. The parameters of the networks are expressed in terms of vessel radius, wall thickness and the elastic modulus of the vessel wall. All these values are pressure and frequency dependent. The pressure dependence can be expressed by exponential approximations as shown in the slides. The computer is given the reference vessel radius (r_{10}) as well as the exponent and coefficient of the exponential relation and then calculates radius, resistance, inductance and compliance for the desired distending pressure for each segment separately before proceeding with the calculation on the model *per se*. Depending on what input data he is given he can simulate vasomotion in all the beds or in only one.

BURTON:

Yes, but how can this be, when the physiological situation changes? Suppose you inject adrenalin: the skin vessels will constrict very strongly, the muscle vessels will dilate, the coronary vessels will slightly dilate; I could go on making it more and more complicated. Can you take care of this by an equation using a universal parameter expressing a change in all vessels in the same direction?

ATTINGER:

The parameters and their pressure dependence are different not only for each segment of the vascular bed but also change in a given segment with vascular tone. Wezler and Sinn in their review on bloodflow have given some values about the range of change of a and b in eq. (14). The perfusion experiments of the hindleg of dogs reported by Pappenheimer and by Green indicate that they may change by a factor of 10^5, depending on what data you take. At one extreme you have practically complete occlusion of the vascular bed, at the other the bed is fully dilated. In our model we can investigate this whole range, applying the changes to a single vascular segment or to any combination of segments or vascular beds.

BURTON:

And will you also not have to put eventually the very important feedback, as in the carotid sinus reflex? It would mean that every variable is dependent on every other.

ATTINGER:

That is right. But one has to begin somewhere.

LAMINAR FLOW REGIMES FOR RIGID-SPHERE SUSPENSIONS

Alvin H. Sacks* † and E. Glenn Tickner†

Vidya, Itek Corporation, Palo Alto, California, U.S.A.

INTRODUCTION

For many years now, workers in physiology have been aware that the flow of blood in the capillary beds and other vessels of the microcirculation bears little resemblance to the classical Poiseuille flow in which every fluid particle travels parallel to the cylindrical vessel wall. If one watches the blood cells moving in a small living vessel (such as those in the frog's web or the hamster's cheek pouch), he observes that in vessels where the red cell diameter varies from one-tenth to perhaps one-half of the vessel diameter the flow is unsteady and there may be large radial excursions of the red cell as it moves along the vessel. Under such conditions, one may well ask whether the blood is even behaving as a fluid. In any case, the flow gives the appearance of turbulence (and this term has been applied), although the Reynolds numbers are several orders of magnitude too low for turbulence to occur.

It seems apparent that the type of flow discussed above cannot be adequately described as either laminar or turbulent, and one might expect to find several different flow regimes even in the very low Reynolds number range for particle suspensions. These would presumably depend upon the ratio of particle size to tube diameter as well as upon the Reynolds number.

It is important to note that at these extremely low Reynolds numbers, if we consider a suspension of solid particles in a Newtonian fluid, the flow of the fluid will certainly be laminar. However, since particles placed in an initially Poiseuille flow will move at different velocities depending upon their radial location, it follows that one particle will begin to overtake another and if they pass in close proximity an interaction will take place. Hence, laminar flow of a fluid containing suspended particles does not imply rectilinear motion. In fact, local interactions may be expected to produce rather complex particle motions.

A number of experimental studies have been conducted to investigate particle motions and the nature of these interactions[1–9], and several theoretical studies have been made of their effect on the gross apparent viscosity of the two-phase fluid suspension. However, the emphasis has generally been placed on determining "viscosity laws" for particle suspensions, with the aim of predicting viscosity or skin friction as a function of particle concentration. The first significant theoretical work in this direction was that of Einstein[10], whose analysis was developed for low concentrations and did not account for particle interaction. More recently, theories have been advanced to account for particle interaction and hence to handle higher concentrations[11, 12]. *But in no instance is the flow said to be Reynolds-number dependent.*

†Present address: Palo Alto Medical Research Foundation, Palo Alto, Calif.

Experimental work on the flow of blood in small vessels has drawn attention to the question of radial migration of the cells. Both the experiments of M. TAYLOR[13] and A. A. PALMER[14] indicate a definite tendency of blood cells to leave the walls and migrate toward the axis of the vessel, leaving a cell-free plasma sheath near the vessel wall. This phenomenon has been studied both theoretically and experimentally by other investigators who obtained seemingly contradictory results. G. JEFFREY[15] developed a theory for the motion of rigid ellipsoids suspended in a liquid. His work indicated that particles would not migrate inwardly in pipe flow, but would only rotate. G. I. TAYLOR[16] considered the case of a suspension of liquid spheres in a base fluid and found that each suspended liquid particle in pipe flow experienced both radial and distortional forces. The former would cause an inward radial particle migration, while the latter could ultimately cause the particles to break up. For rigid spheres, however, Taylor's results agreed with that of Jeffrey—no radial migration. Consequently, particle migration was thought to be associated with flexibility of the particle. However, EIRICH, BUNZL, and MARGARETHE[17] observed a radial migration of rigid glass rods flowing through capillary tubes, which contradicts the above hypothesis.

A more extensive experimental study of particle motions was performed by GOLD-SMITH and MASON[6–8] who studied Poseuille flow with suspensions of rigid spheres, rods, and disks, as well as with liquid drops, at very low concentrations. For rigid particles, they found that Jeffrey's analysis checked their experimental results. For the fluid drops, these investigators observed a marked radial migration and change in particle shape as predicted by Taylor. However, at nearly the same time, SEGRÉ and SILBERBERG[4] also conducted a series of experiments with rigid spheres at very low particle concentration, and observed a contradictory phenomenon. These investigators found that the rigid spheres migrated to a radial position half way between the tube axis and the wall, thereby yielding a high particle concentration in an annulus at the half-way position. More recently, GOLDSMITH and MASON[9] confirmed this effect by rerunning their tests at higher Reynolds numbers. Meanwhile, RUBINOW and KELLER [18] performed a non-linear theoretical analysis which predicts an inward radial force on rigid spheres.

With this background in mind, a set of fundamental experiments has been devised to investigate the flow of viscous fluids with suspended rigid particles over a wide range of low Reynolds numbers. The experiments are similar to those of OSBORNE REYNOLDS[19], in that we should expect the possibility of more than one type of particle motion. The present study differs from that of Reynolds primarily in the high fluid viscosity and the presence of suspended particles. The primary purpose of these experiments is to study the behavior of particle suspensions in low Reynolds numbers flow and to attempt to determine the values of the governing nondimensional parameters and the possibility of various types of motion.

THEORETICAL CONSIDERATIONS AND PARAMETERS

The complexities of the physical problem under consideration, namely, the flow of whole blood through the flexible, semi-porous vessels of the microcirculation, are certainly such as to defy a straightforward mathematical formulation. Even the composition of the blood itself, with its high concentration of flexible red cells (erythrocytes) in the shape of biconcave disks and the larger, less numerous, white cells (leukocytes), makes the flow problem mathematically intractable. However, an engineering approach to some of the gross behavior of the microcirculation is offered by dimensional analysis. In order to apply this technique, we shall start with a simple, Newtonian fluid (representing blood plasma) which is flowing through a rigid tube under a constant pressure gradient. We can then proceed to consider the addition of rigid particles, then flexible particles, and so on, until we approach the real problem as closely as possible.

Consider first a Newtonian fluid of constant density ρ, and viscosity μ, to be flowing with a constant mean velocity V_m through a rigid cylindrical tube of diameter D, and length l. The pressure drop per unit length (dp/dx) must be a function of the above physical variables. That is,

$$\frac{dp}{dx} = f(\rho, \mu, V_m, D, l) \tag{1}$$

By employing dimensional analysis[20], we find that one can express this pressure drop in dimensionless form, C_f, as a function of two dimensionless groups; that is,

$$C_f = \frac{D^2(dp/dx)}{V_m\mu} = f_1[(\rho V_m D/\mu), (l/D)] \tag{2}$$

or

$$C_f = f_1[Re, (l/D)] \tag{3}$$

It can also be shown[21] that for very long tubes $(l/D > 100)$ and laminar flow $(Re < 2000)$, the above expression becomes

$$C_f = \frac{16}{Re} \tag{4}$$

This, then, is the particular form of eq. (3) for laminar flow in long pipes.

If this same Newtonian fluid contains rigid spherical particles of diameter d, density ρ, and volumetric concentration ϕ, then dimensional analysis yields the following functional relationship:

$$C_f = f_2(Re, l/D, d/D, \phi) \tag{5}$$

Hence, we may expect that the pressure-flow relationship for a suspension of rigid spheres in a Newtonian fluid will depend upon the particle concentration and the ratio of particle size to tube size, as well as on the Reynolds number and the tube length-diameter ratio.

By proceeding to add the necessary complexities to the mathematical model, one can progress through the vessels of the microcirculation using dimensional analysis to extract the functional relationships among the non-dimensional variables. The results of such an analysis are presented in Table 1 for rigid tubes, and in Table 2 for flexible tubes. It can be seen that the number of variables becomes quite staggering, despite the fact that Tables 1 and 2 do not include the effects of pulsatile flow or flexible particles of such general shapes as to represent blood cells. Further, such physiological variables

TABLE 1. DIMENSIONLESS PARAMETERS AFFECTING THE PRESSURE DROP ALONG RIGID TUBES FOR SUSPENSIONS OF SOLID AND FLEXIBLE PARTICLES IN A NEWTONIAN BASE LIQUID

Base Fluid Properties (ρ, μ)	Tube (D, l)	Fluid Velocity (V_m)	Spherical Particles (d, m)	Non-Spherical Particles (minimum dimension, a)	Tube Geometry (α, conical)	Solid Particles $\gamma_p \neq \gamma_f$ $(\Delta\gamma, g)$	Tube Inclination (θ)	Particles Dynamic Friction (f)	Flexible Particle (E)
$C_f = g(Re, l/D)$									
$C_f = g(Re, l/D, d/D, \phi)$									
$C_f = g(Re, l/D, d/D, \phi, a/d)$									
$C_f = g(Re, l/D, \phi, a/d, \alpha)$									
$C_f = g(Re, l/D, \phi, a/d, \alpha, Fr, \Delta\gamma/\gamma)$									
$C_f = g(Re, l/D, \phi, a/d, \alpha, Fr, \Delta\gamma/\gamma, \theta)$									
$C_f = g(Re, l/D, \phi, a/d, \alpha, Fr, \Delta\gamma/\gamma, \theta, f)$									
$C_f = g(Re, l/D, \phi, a/d, \alpha, Fr, \Delta\gamma/\gamma, \theta, f, Ca)$									

TABLE 2. DIMENSIONLESS PARAMETERS AFFECTING THE PRESSURE DROP ALONG FLEXIBLE TUBES FOR SUSPENSIONS OF SOLID AND FLEXIBLE PARTICLES IN A NEWTONIAN BASE LIQUID

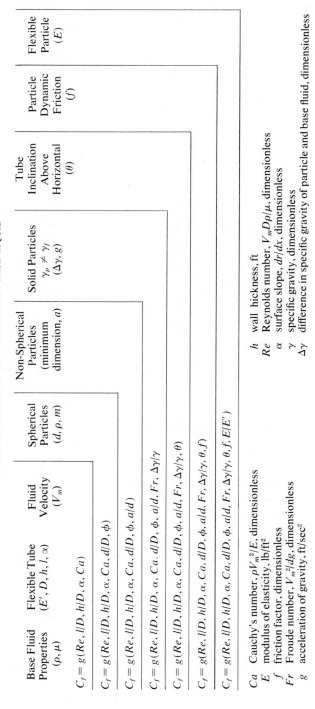

Base Fluid Properties (ρ, μ)	Flexible Tube (E', D, h, l, α)	Fluid Velocity (V_m)	Spherical Particles (d, ρ, m)	Non-Spherical Particles (minimum dimension, a)	Solid Particles $\gamma_p \neq \gamma_f$ $(\Delta\gamma, g)$	Tube Inclination Above Horizontal (θ)	Particle Dynamic Friction (f)	Flexible Particle (E)

$C_f = g(Re, l/D, h/D, \alpha, Ca)$

$C_f = g(Re, l/D, h/D, \alpha, Ca, d/D, \phi)$

$C_f = g(Re, l/D, h/D, \alpha, Ca, d/D, \phi, a/d)$

$C_f = g(Re, l/D, h/D, \alpha, Ca, d/D, \phi, a/d, Fr, \Delta\gamma/\gamma)$

$C_f = g(Re, l/D, h/D, \alpha, Ca, d/D, \phi, a/d, Fr, \Delta\gamma/\gamma, \theta)$

$C_f = g(Re, l/D, h/D, \alpha, Ca, d/D, \phi, a/d, Fr, \Delta\gamma/\gamma, \theta, f)$

$C_f = g(Re, l/D, h/D, \alpha, Ca, d/D, \phi, a/d, Fr, \Delta\gamma/\gamma, \theta, f, E/E')$

Ca Cauchy's number, $\rho V_m^2/E$, dimensionless
E modulus of elasticity, lb/ft^2
f friction factor, dimensionless
Fr Froude number, V_m^2/dg, dimensionless
g acceleration of gravity, ft/sec^2

h wall thickness, ft
Re Reynolds number, $V_m D\rho/\mu$, dimensionless
α surface slope, dr/dx, dimensionless
γ specific gravity, dimensionless
$\Delta\gamma$ difference in specific gravity of particle and base fluid, dimensionless

as vessel porosity, osmotic pressure, diffusion, electrical charges, and chemical reactions have not been considered.

Because of the vast complexities of the physiological problem, the present experimental study will be restricted to the flow of rigid, spherical particles having the same density as that of the suspending fluid and subjected to a steady pressure drop. This is the case described by eq. (5).

Having established the dimensionless parameters essential to the problem at hand, *we need not work at the inconveniently small scale of the living microcirculation.* Accordingly, we shall scale our experiments to a size which permits easy observation. It is, in fact, the lack of such scaling in simulated biological systems which we feel has rendered observations and measurements difficult in the past and has often led to inconclusive results.

Since the physical problem with which we are concerned here is the flow of whole blood in living vessels, it behooves us to investigate the physiological ranges of the non-dimensional variables brought out in the foregoing analysis. Therefore, from a

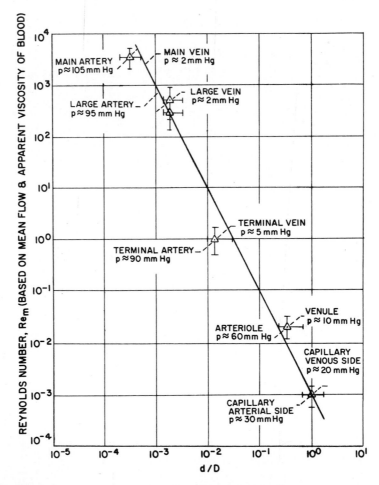

FIG. 1. VARIATION OF REYNOLDS NUMBER WITH CELL-TO-VESSEL DIAMETER RATIO THROUGHOUT THE VASCULAR TREE.

knowledge of the approximate mean size of the normal red cell (about 8.5μ) and a rough knowledge of the sizes of blood vessels and mean flow rates throughout the system[22], we have constructed a plot of mean flow Reynolds number versus ratio of cell size to vessel size from the capillary beds to the great vessels of the human body (see Fig. 1). The approximate nature of this plot cannot be overemphasized, in view of the uncertainties of measurement, the wide normal deviations from one individual to another, the pulsatile flow in the arterial side, and the constantly varying flow conditions in a given individual. However, it is instructive to note that both the Reynolds number and the diameter ratio vary by several orders of magnitude throughout the system and that, for the vessels of the microcirculation, the Reynolds numbers are those of creeping flow ($Re < 10$). The mean pressure levels are indicated on the plot, and it is noted that the red cell concentration is relatively constant throughout the system at about 44% by volume.

For the present experimental investigation, we shall attempt to bracket the ranges of the arterioles and venules, since it is in these vessels that the types of flow discussed herein are frequently seen under the microscope. Because we shall be dealing with rigid spheres in the present study, it will not be possible to match the high concentrations of whole blood at ratios of particle diameter to tube diameter approaching unity. For this reason, it would seem that simulating the flow in the capillaries might require the use of flexible particles. At any rate, the ranges of concentration and Reynolds number covered in the present experiments using rigid spheres are illustrated in the following chart.

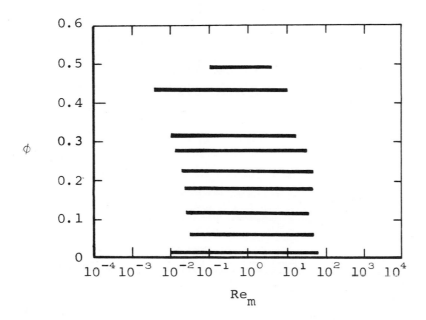

The ratios of particle diameter to tube diameter will vary from 0.2 to 0.9, and we shall be dealing only with long tubes ($l/D > 100$). Hence, we shall not be concerned with the variable l/D in the present tests, since it is expected that entrance effects will be negligible and the flow in all tubes will behave as though the tubes were infinitely long.

EXPERIMENTAL TESTS AND APPARATUS

The purpose of this study was to observe the various flow regimes of two-phase flow in long cylindrical tubes. To this end, experimental tests were performed whereby a base fluid with rigid spheres in neutral suspension would flow from a reservoir through three long horizontal tubes and discharge into the open air (see Fig. 2). The three tubes

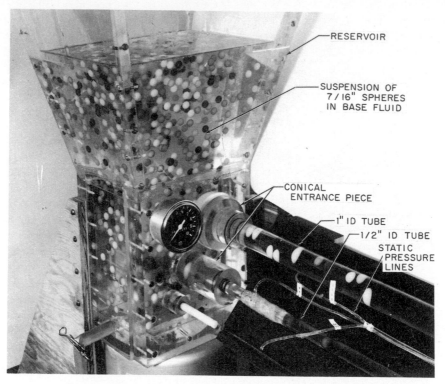

FIG. 2. CLOSEUP OF RESERVOIR SHOWING PARTICLE SUSPENSION.

provide three different particle-size-to-tube-size ratios for one fluid mixture. In order to permit visualization of the entire flow process, the reservoir, tubes, and connectors were all made to clear plexiglas, and the multicolored rigid spheres were suspended in clear oil. During the study, the particle size and concentration were varied for a range of flow rates in tubes of three different diameters.

The spheres† used throughout the tests were of two sizes, $\frac{7}{16}$ inch (0.4374 ± 0.0008 (s.d.)) and $\frac{3}{16}$ inch (0.1869 ± 0.0006 (s.d.)) in diameter. They were dyed in five different colors (red, blue, yellow, blue-green, and white) to assist in determining individual particle motions. The spheres were made of linear polyethylene with a specific gravity of 0.951, and 0.956, respectively. A clear Newtonian oil of the same specific gravity was obtained by combining castor oil and safflower oil, whose specific gravity completely bracket the spheres, even with the manufacturer's tolerances. Thus, the proper combination of the two oils will make the spheres neutrally buoyant. Later tests verified that the final combination of oils was in fact Newtonian.

†Supplied by Colonial Kolonite Co., 2232–30 W. Armitage Ave. Chicago, Illinois.

The flow was initiated in a 3-cubic-foot closed reservoir in the shape of a truncated, inverted rectangular pyramid (see Fig. 2). This shape was chosen to minimize the fluid volume in the reservoir (because of the high cost of the particles), yet obtain the maximum surface area of the fluid within the reservoir, in order to maintain the smallest possible change of fluid pressure head in the reservoir during each test. The static pressure at the tube entrance was then maintained at a constant level by pressurizing the space supplied by the fluid head plus a static gas pressure in the reservoir above the fluid. This regulated gas-pressurization system was capable of maintaining a constant pressure ($\pm 5\%$) for pressure levels anywhere from 0.1 psi (5 mm Hg) to 6.0 psi (300 mm Hg).

A polished conical entrance piece, with a 30° semi-vertex angle, provided the means of obtaining a smooth entrance flow to each tube. All of the sharp corners were smoothed.

The two-phase fluid suspension passed from the reservoir through the entrance adapter and along one, two, or three tubes in parallel. These three tubes, with inner diameters of 1, $\frac{1}{2}$, and $\frac{1}{4}$ inch, were made of clear extruded plexiglas. The tubes were assembled in 6-foot lengths, giving a maximum length of run of nearly 40 feet. Both ends of each 6-foot section were machined to guarantee a flush fit and were connected to one another by short sleeves with "o" ring seals to prevent leakage.

Since the three tubes were in parallel, one, two, or three tubes could be fed from the same reservoir simultaneously. Generally, the use of more than one tube was restricted to the lower flow rates, where the limited amount of fluid in the reservoir would not be depleted during a single test. Each tube was mounted in a grooved wooden board which kept the tubes parallel and horizontal throughout the tests.

A curved rubber weir was placed on the discharge end of each tube. The curved weir with its horizontal opening in the top provided the means for inhibiting atmospheric air from entering the discharge end of each tube, but did not introduce significant pressure loss. (This loss was checked by measuring the pressure in the tubes just upstream of the discharge end.)

Pressures and Temperatures

The static fluid pressure was measured by two strain-gauge-type differential pressure transducers with a range of $7\frac{1}{2}$ psi ($\pm 1\%$ full-scale accuracy), and the output signal from the transducers was recorded on an oscillograph. One of these transducers continually monitored the static fluid pressure within the reservoir to insure that steady-state had been achieved and was maintained. The other transducer was attached to a specially designed "Gatling gun" adapter which permitted the transducer to monitor the static pressure at any one of 7 positions along each of the three tubes, one at a time. The pressure at all 21 positions was recorded during each test by manual rotation of the adapter. The time required to cover all 21 positions was approximately 30 sec. This was considered to be sufficiently rapid, since only those runs for which the pressures remained steady were considered valid. By this technique, the single pressure transducer took the place of an entire manometer board (see Figs. 3 and 4).

In order to check whether thermal effects were significant in the present tests, two sensitive copper-constantan thermopiles were installed in the apparatus. One thermopile measured the difference in temperature between the reservoir fluid and the discharge fluid, and the other thermopile was used to measure the difference in room temperature just above the tubes at two different stations along the pipe (see Fig. 3). The resulting system measures temperature differences (ΔT) of $\pm 0.05°F$.

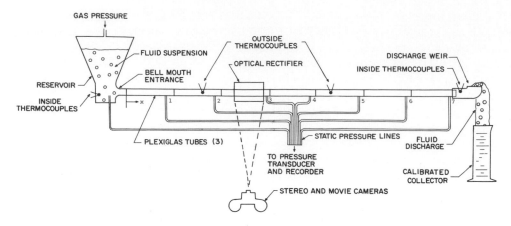

FIG. 3. SCHEMATIC OF EXPERIMENTAL SETUP.

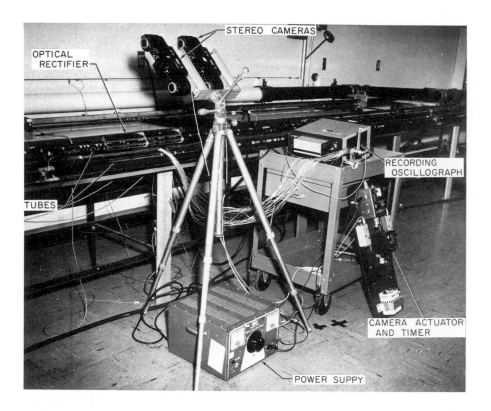

FIG. 4. STEREO-CAMERA ARRANGEMENT: (a) $d/D = \frac{3}{16}$.

All of the raw and reduced data of the present tests are published elsewhere† as Table 3. The temperature data are included in this table.

†Owing to its length, Table 3 has been deposited as Document No. 8984 with the ADI Auxiliary Publications Project, Photoduplication Service, Library of Congress, Washington 25, D.C. A copy may be secured by citing the Document No. and by remitting $2.50 for photoprints, or $1.75 for 35 mm microfilm.

Flow Rates and Particle Concentrations

The mean volume flow rate for each tube was determined by measuring the time required to fill a container of known volume for each run. The measured volume included both fluid and particles and was found to be accurate to within ±2% except at the very high flow rates where timing errors increased the errors to ±10%.

The average particle concentration by volume was determined by counting the total number of particles of known diameter collected in a container of known volume. For the tests involving the lower particle concentrations ($\phi < 10\%$), the concentrations were also determined by counting the number of particles remaining in the tubes at the end of each test. The accuracies for the concentrations of the larger and smaller spheres are considered to be ±4% and ±6%, respectively.

Since particle concentrations ϕ varied somewhat from run to run, the values presented in the figure legends were obtained by averaging all the concentrations for runs made with the same fluid mixture in the reservoir.

Particle and Fluid Motion

Visual studies of the particle motions were made by means of high-speed color motion pictures and color stereoscopic still pictures. The purpose of using color film was to simplify the tracking of the individual spheres which were manufactured in five different colors. The motion pictures were used to study gross properties such as flow regimes and gross particle migration, whereas the stereoscopic stills were taken to determine particle distribution and to analyse individual particle trajectories. Most pictures were taken through an optical rectifier consisting of a hollow flat-faced plastic cover matched to the cylindrical 1-inch tube and sealed with optical compound. This experimental arrangement is shown in Fig. 4.

The flow regimes and particle motions discussed in the ensuing paragraphs are based on visual observations and study of the movie films. The analysis of the stereoscopic still pictures is considered beyond the scope of the present paper.

In order to obtain a qualitative picture of the fluid velocity profile across the tube, colored dye was injected through rubber-capped ports by means of a hypodermic needle. The needle was first passed through the rubber cap to the far wall of the tube, and then dye was released continuously as the needle was withdrawn. This produced a streak of dye across the tube diameter which then followed the fluid motion.

DATA REDUCTION

Since the viscous behavior of a fluid mixture is characterized by the variation of wall shear stress with rate of strain, these quantities are of primary importance in the present study. The wall shear stress is determined by equating the pressure forces to the viscous forces on a cylindrical fluid element of length Δx and diameter D. Thus, we find in the limit as $\Delta x \to 0$[21]

$$\tau_w = (D/4)(dp/dx) \tag{6}$$

In the present tests, the pressure decreased linearly along the tube so that dp/dx was simply the slope of the pressure curve. All of these slopes are presented in Table 3 along with the computed shear stresses. These stresses are considered to be correct within

±1%, except for a few tests which were run at very low pressures. These latter cases are considered to be accurate within ±9%.

The volumetric flow rate Q, through a cylindrical pipe, is related to the shear stress τ by the equation[21]

$$\frac{8Q}{\pi D^3} = \frac{1}{\tau_w^3} \int_0^{\tau_w} \tau^2 \dot{\gamma} d\tau \tag{7}$$

where $\dot{\gamma}$ is the strain rate, which can be expressed as some function $f(\tau)$. It can be shown that *only* a Newtonian fluid exhibits a linear relationship between $(Q/\pi D^3)$ and τ_w. This was found to be the case for all the tests of the present study. For the case of a Newtonian fluid, eq. (7) reduces to

$$\frac{8Q}{\pi D^3} = \frac{\tau_w}{4\mu} \tag{8}$$

which yields a strain rate, $\dot{\gamma}$, of

$$\dot{\gamma} = \frac{32Q}{\pi D^3} \tag{9}$$

Hence, the strain rate is obtained directly from the volumetric flow rate. The computed strain rates are considered to be accurate within ±2%, except at the highest flow rates where additional errors enter owing to the short time required to fill the calibrated collector. For these few cases, the errors can be as high as ±12%.

DISCUSSION OF RESULTS

General Observations

When a simple Newtonian viscous fluid flows slowly through a cylindrical tube in response to a steady pressure gradient, the velocity profile is parabolic, and the velocity vanishes at the wall and reaches a maximum value on the tube axis. Hence, if a single particle of the same density is added to the fluid, so long as the particle size is very small compared with the tube size, the particle will move parallel to the tube wall at a velocity which depends upon its radial position in the tube. The presence of such a particle will not significantly alter the parabolic velocity profile in the tube. If additional small particles are added to the fluid, each in turn will travel at the local fluid velocity appropriate to its radial location in the tube. However, since any two particles at different radial positions will have different axial velocities, one must overtake the other, and if they pass in close proximity, each must be deflected by the presence of the other, thus producing a motion with both axial and radial components which are time-dependent. Such motions have been studied by GOLDSMITH and MASON[8]. As the concentration increases, the randomness of this motion will increase with the frequency of impacts or near-impacts, until the concentration becomes so large as to inhibit the relative particle motions within the tube and decrease the frequency of impacts. Thus, at very high concentrations, the velocity profile will become more steady and nearly uniform across the tube, eventually producing a plug-type flow.

So far we have considered only particles which are very small compared with the tube diameter. For larger particles, the presence of even a single particle must alter the fluid flow locally, since the velocity of the rigid particle must be made up of a translational and a rotational component. Hence, even a single large spherical particle without rotation would cause a local flattening of the velocity profile. If the particle size approaches the tube size, the velocity profile must be uniform across the tube at the location of the particle. The fluid velocities between particles will have a more complex pattern.

It seems clear from the above considerations that one may expect at least three different "flow regimes" for particle suspensions in laminar flow; that is, at low Reynolds numbers. The first is the classical Poiseuille flow which pertains to laminar flow of the suspending Newtonian fluid with no particles. This will apply as well to small concentrations of small particles. At the very high concentrations, we can again expect a steady flow but with nearly uniform velocity across the tube. But at intermediate concentrations, there must be a flow which is unsteady in time and involves radial motions as well as axial. Furthermore, the dimensional analysis discussed earlier indicates that Reynolds number may also be an important parameter.

In the present experiments, these and additional flow regimes were clearly observed and were, in fact, found to be Reynolds-number dependent. The first, or Poiseuille, regime was found to prevail for particle concentrations of about 1% or less with d/D less than $\frac{1}{2}$. There is, of course, a local flattening of the velocity profile at a particle, but in general the particles moved steadily parallel to the tube wall, the central particles moving faster, and the ones at the wall simply rolling on the wall. For particle diameters approaching the tube diameter ($d/D = 7/8$), the particles, in general, did not roll or touch the wall, but moved centrally at a constant speed.

For higher particle concentrations ($0.01 < \phi < 0.30$) the unsteady, irregular "tumbling" regime of frequent impacts and near impacts was observed, being particularly pronounced for $d/D = \frac{3}{8}$. For a smaller diameter ratio ($d/D = \frac{3}{16}$) at the same concentrations, the radial motions were less pronounced, and there appeared to be a relatively large central core of particles having fairly uniform velocity. The surrounding particles (fewer in number) simply rolled along the wall and appeared to act as ball bearings for the faster central core. This regime seemed to bear a strong resemblance to the living microcirculation. It was also observed that when the core passes a segment of the tube having no particles on the wall, the whole core displaces radially toward the empty wall and then back toward the axis of the tube. The entire motion therefore gave the impression of a large central core of particles following a snaking axial motion with the remaining particles either moving at a lower velocity or simply rolling along in contact with the wall.

Increasing the particle concentration ($\phi > 0.45$) appeared to eliminate all particle impacts and radial motion and produced a "plug-type" flow, although the central particles were still seen to be moving faster than those at the wall. At these concentrations, the rigid spheres were essentially packed together, each in contact with its neighbors.

So far, we have discussed only particle size and particle concentration. Actually, a major observation of the present tests was in the effect of Reynolds number. For the large particles ($d/D = \frac{3}{8}$), it was observed that, for a given concentration, increasing the Reynolds number beyond a certain "critical" value suddenly eliminated particle interactions and the spheres then moved parallel to the tube wall at a uniform speed. Hence, by increasing the Reynolds number (i.e. by increasing the pressure in the reservoir), one moves out of the unsteady "tumbling regime" and into a steady, uniform "streaking" regime. At this condition (i.e. in the streaking regime), it was further observed that no particles remained on the wall, and that an occasional particle near the axis of the tube would overtake all of the other particles, following a rather sinuous path along the tube axis. This would seem to indicate that the fluid velocity profile in the streaking regime has a maximum at the center, but that the particles migrate to a preferred radial position between the axis and the wall of the tube, and hence to a position of constant velocity. This observation is in complete agreement with the findings of Segré and Silberberg.

For the small particles ($d/D = \frac{3}{16}$), increasing the Reynolds number beyond the critical value produced a more subtle effect, because of the smaller radial motions produced by particle interaction. In this case, the central core remained more or less unchanged, but no particles remained on the wall. Thus, for moderate concentrations of the smaller particles at Reynolds numbers above the critical, we have a central "coring" with "plasma skimming" rather than the more perfectly ordered "streaking" in which the particles seek an intermediate radial position.

It seems clear that the existence of a transition Reynolds number must depend on d/D, since particles whose diameters are greater than half that of the tube can hardly pass one another, and for particles whose diameters approach that of the tube impacts can only occur in the axial direction. This latter case would correspond to the "plastic flow regime". By this, we mean a regime in which particles in close proximity and approaching the tube diameter move axially through the tube without rotation, yielding a velocity profile approximating that of a Bingham plastic. In the present experiments, transition was observed for $d/D = \frac{3}{16}, \frac{3}{8}$, and $\frac{7}{16}$, but not for $d/D = \frac{7}{8}$ or $\frac{3}{4}$.

Another general observation of the present tests for the larger particles, was the tendency of particles to group together under certain conditions. In particular, at particle concentrations somewhat below those of plug flow, it was observed that relatively steady separate plugs of particles would form, each plug separated from its neighbor by some discrete length in which unsteady tumbling is observed. These periodic plugs are reminiscent of the periodic turbulent plugs observed by Osborne Reynolds in his classical experiments with pure water. Even in the plastic flow regime, discrete groups of particles would form at regular intervals for the higher concentrations. The length of the steady plugs appeared to increase with increasing particle concentration, thus reducing the regions of unsteady tumbling flow.

It should be mentioned that the above types of flow were observed to occur over the entire length of the tube, indicating that entrance effects were unimportant and that l/D was not a significant parameter over the range tested.

Flow Regimes

In view of the foregoing observations and the findings of previous investigators regarding the various types of particle behavior in liquid suspensions, it seems worthwhile to attempt a crude classification of flow regimes which may be obtained in a suspension of rigid spheres in laminar flow. Recalling that the nondimensional parameters involved are those of eq. (5), and restricting ourselves to long pipes ($l/d > 100$), we have only three controlling parameters; namely, particle concentration ϕ, particle-to-tube diameter ratio d/D, and Reynolds number Re. Furthermore, we have found experimentaḷy that the Reynolds number can be divided into two ranges, those below a critical value, and those above. Therefore, the array of laminar flow regimes can be conveniently summarized in terms of d/D and particle concentration as shown below:

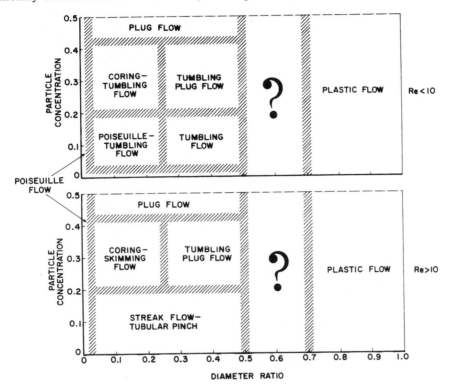

The boundaries shown in these charts are admittedly approximate and tentative as they are based on the limited data of the present experiments. The areas indicated by question marks have not been investigated. However, certain pertinent observations can be made. It can be seen, for example, that the effect of Reynolds number is restricted to an intermediate range of particle concentrations and particle-to-tube diameter ratios. That is, for sufficiently high concentrations we have steady plug flow, and for sufficiently large particle-to-tube diameter ratios we have steady plastic flow, regardless of Reynolds number. However, for particle concentrations between about 1 and 40% and diameter ratios between 0.05 and 0.5, we find that for Reynolds numbers below 10 we have various types of tumbling flow with strong particle interactions. At Reynolds numbers above 10, for the smaller diameter ratios, we may have either coring flow or streaking flow, depending upon the particle concentration. It should be noted that the streaking regime has previously been referred to by Segré and Silberberg as the "tubular pinch effect", and the coring regime here corresponds to the axial migration or "plasma skimming" noted by previous workers. In any case, the essential change which seems to occur as one passes from below to above the critical Reynolds number is that particles leave the tube wall. That is, at Reynolds numbers above 10, no particles remain on the wall. If the particle diameter and concentration are relatively low ($d/D < \frac{1}{2}$; $\phi < 0.20$), then all particles seek a single radial position nearly midway between the wall and the tube axis and travel at a uniform speed in the axial direction. For increasing concentrations of small particles, the additional particles tend to fill in the innermost positions near the axis, and we find a relatively solid core moving with nearly uniform velocity, and surrounded by a particle-free layer of clear liquid. This type of flow has often been referred to as "plasma skimming".

With regard to the physiological problem of blood flow in the human body, reference to Fig. 1 indicates that one may expect transition ($Re \approx 10$) to occur somewhere between the great vessels and the terminal veins or arteries. Further, because of the combinations of Reynolds number and vessel size as reflected in d/D on the figure, we should not expect to find the streaking flow regime (the "pinch effect") in the human circulatory system. Rather, as we move from the great vessels toward the capillary beds, we should expect to find first coring or plasma skimming, then tumbling plug flow in the arterioles and venules, and finally plastic flow in the capillaries. It seems doubtful that true steady plug flow would occur at physiological concentrations, because of the flexibility of the red cell.

Aside from the various flow regimes discussed above, the transition Reynolds number is believed to be related to two commonly observed features of the living circulatory system. First, the rather sudden drop in pressure as one moves from the large arteries and approaches the arterioles may well be associated with the increase in skin friction produced by transition from coring or plasma skimming to tumbling plug flow. Second, contact between the suspended red cells and the vessel wall can evidently occur only at Reynolds numbers below about 10. This restricts the wall contact to those parts of the circulatory system in which exchanges across the vessel wall are required for the life process. In the remainder of the system, the red cells are not in contact with the wall, and wall friction is therefore minimized for the efficient transport of blood.

Another facet of the present results is the intrinsic unsteady nature of the tumbling plug flow regime, for which the Reynolds numbers and vessel sizes correspond to the arterioles and venules. This would imply that one might expect unsteady flow on the venous side of the capillary beds even if the pressure drop is steady.

These observations are admittedly based on experiments which fall far short of simulating the flow of whole blood in living vessels. Nevertheless, they appear to be in reasonable agreement with the physiological facts.

Although the various flow regimes discussed above can only be adequately demonstrated by means of motion pictures, some schematic sketches have been prepared to illustrate more graphically the individual particle behavior for each regime. These sketches are shown in Fig. 5, for two different ratios of particle diameter to tube diameter, in which the time-averaged velocity profiles are indicated by the dashed lines. These were observed by the dye-injection technique.

For small particle to tube diameter ratios, the various types of flow are illustrated in Fig. 5(a). The particle concentration increases toward the right, and the Reynolds number increases towards the bottom of the page. At the very high concentrations, we have plug flow for all Reynolds numbers. It can be seen that increasing the particle concentration tends to produce a central core, with a consequent flattening of the velocity profile, while increasing the Reynolds number beyond the critical value produces a particle-free layer along the wall.

For intermediate particle-to-tube diameter ratios (Fig. 5(b)), we have a rather definite tumbling regime below the critical Reynolds number. Above the critical Reynolds number, we have the streaking regime, with particles seeking a preferred radial position. For higher concentrations, an occasional particle appears near the tube axis, snaking its way past the others at a higher velocity. Comparison with Fig. 5(a) shows that

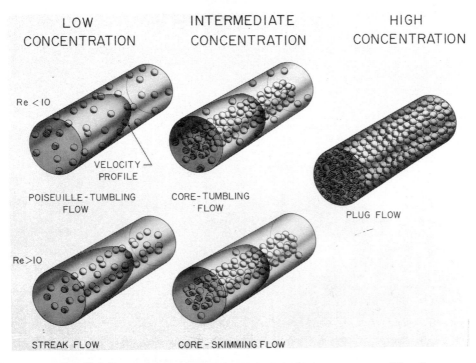

FIG. 5(a). LAMINAR FLOW REGIMES FOR RIGID-SPHERE SUSPENSIONS. $d/D = \frac{3}{16}$.

roughly the same phenomenon occurs for the smaller d/D, although the presence of more particles for a given concentration gives the appearance of a more definite central core. Consequently, for the smaller d/D, one would have to go to a much lower concentration to find the streak regime or "tubular pinch effect".

For the higher concentrations of intermediate-sized particles, the tumbling plug flow described previously is illustrated on Fig. 5(b), which shows particles or groups of particles leaving the leading end of one plug, exhibiting tumbling flow, and then attaching to the trailing end of the next. For still higher concentrations, we have simple plug flow.

For the various regimes with particles whose diameter approaches that of the tube, there is, of course, no tumbling and there appears to be no Reynolds number effect. At low concentrations, we have plastic flow, with particles remaining near the tube axis and apparently never touching the wall. As the concentration increases, we again find intermittent plug flow, with the particles forming discrete groups at even "wave lengths", and finally pure plug flow.

A limited series of additional tests were performed (data not included) using disks rather than spheres. The disks were made by simply pressing the spheres to approximately the same thickness-to-diameter ratio as red blood cells. In general, the resulting

FIG. 5(b). LAMINAR FLOW REGIMES FOR RIGID-SPHERE SUSPENSIONS. $d/D = \frac{3}{8}$.

data lead to the same conclusions, of which the most pertinent is that there exists a critical Reynolds number which separates two distinctly different types of laminar flow. In addition to the general gross behavior, which compares with that of the spherical particles, the disk data revealed two other flow characteristics which bear a marked similarity to the living system. These two observations are:

(1) A high degree of "flipping" (irregular tumbling) of individual particles, owing to the shear gradients in the tube, was observed when the Reynolds numbers (Re) were less than 10. For this case, the average rate of rotation seemed to be proportional to the strain rate. For Re greater than 10, the particles not only migrate to a favored radial position (halfway between the center and wall) but also seek a preferred orientation. In the case of the large disks ($d/D > \frac{1}{2}$), the disks cannot migrate to this position so they roll along the wall, independent of angular position, like a tire on a road.

(2) For very low shear rates and $Re < 10$, many of the disks were observed in a rouleaux formation which is reminiscent of the flow of whole blood. The maximum number of disks in any given rouleau was found to be four, and this number decreased with an increase in strain rate until only single unattached particles were observed.

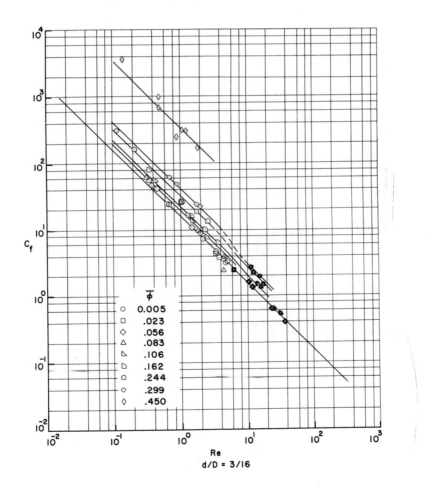

FIG. 6a. VARIATION OF FRICTION FACTOR WITH REYNOLDS NUMBER BASED ON BASE FLUID VISCOSITY.

Viscous Behavior of Suspensions

The quantitative experimental data of the present tests are presented in Fig. 6 in the form of skin-friction coefficient versus Reynolds number. It can be seen that in all cases, both the base fluids and the fluid suspensions are Newtonian, since the data all fall on 45° straight lines on a log-log plot. That is, the friction factor is inversely proportional to Reynolds number for all particle sizes and all concentrations. (Plots of shear stress against strain rate also reveal that the fluid is Newtonian.) However, it can be seen that at a Reynolds number of about 10 (based on tube diameter and viscosity of the suspending medium), there is a rather abrupt decrease in skin-friction coefficient. This change corresponds to the change from the "tumbling regime" into the "streaking regime" in which particle interactions do not occur.

In order to gain further insight into this phenomenon, it is instructive to plot the "relative viscosity" of the fluid suspension as a function of particle concentration. Such a plot is presented in Fig. 7, in which the suspension viscosity is obtained from stress, strain rate data using the customary definition ($\mu = \tau/\dot{\gamma}$) and the relative viscosity is the ratio of μ to the base fluid viscosity, μ_b. From Fig. 7, it can be seen that, for a given particle size and concentration, there are two possible values for relative viscosity. The higher value corresponds to the tumbling regime of particle interactions, while the lower value corresponds to the streaking regime with no particle interactions. Which curve applies depends upon the Reynolds number.

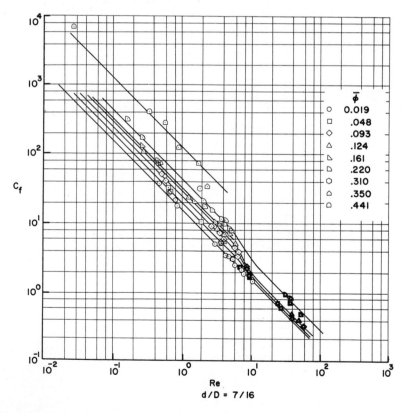

$$d/D = 7/16$$

Fig. 6b

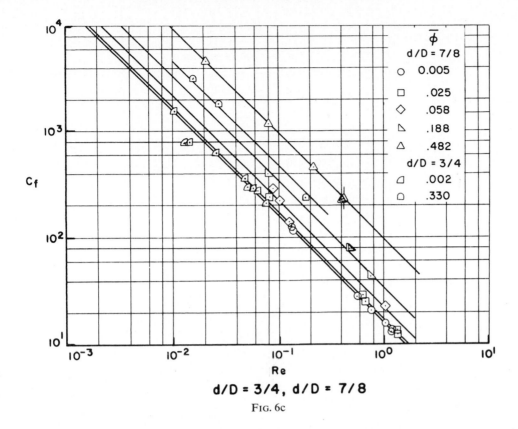

d/D = 3/4, d/D = 7/8

Fig. 6c

It is interesting to note that the lower viscosity curve of the streaking regime is predicted very well by the Einstein equation which is based upon the assumption of no particle interactions and is ordinarily thought to be restricted to very low particle concentrations. However, it can be seen that for Reynolds numbers above the critical value, good agreement is obtained with concentrations up to nearly 30%. On the other hand, for Reynolds numbers below the critical value, deviations from the Einstein equation occur as soon as the particle concentration exceeds a few percent.

There are several theories for predicting the higher viscosity curves associated with particle interaction, and two of these are shown on Fig. 7. It can be seen that the interaction theory of HAPPEL[11] predicts the viscous behavior very well for the higher d/D ratios, while that of SIMHA[12] predicts the behavior for the smaller particles. In both cases, the theories appear to work even at the highest concentrations tested. There are two cases for which neither of these theories makes a satisfactory prediction of relative viscosity. One is the case of Reynolds numbers above the critical value. In this case (the "streaking regime"), particle interactions do not occur, and the viscous behavior follows the prediction of Einstein's equation. The other exception is that of high concentrations of particles having a diameter approaching the tube diameter. In this case, we have something approaching the "plug flow" of a Bingham plastic in which a large central core moves with uniform velocity. The relative viscosity for this condition can be determined by arguing that the velocity profile of the suspension is that of a Bingham plastic in which the spheres are replaced by a cylinder of comparable

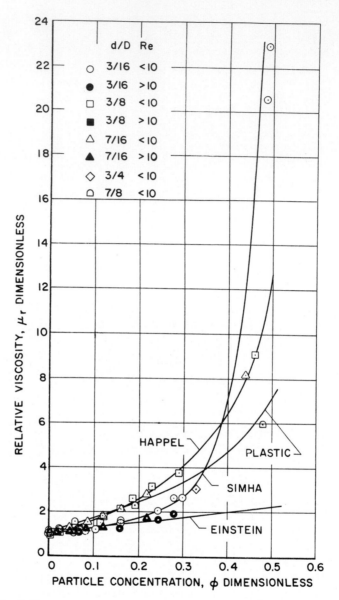

FIG. 7. VARIATION OF RELATIVE VISCOSITY WITH PARTICLE CONCENTRATION.

mass[21]. The resulting expression for relative viscosity for this "plastic flow regime," is found to be

$$\mu_r = \frac{1}{1 - \frac{4}{3}\phi^{1/2} + \frac{1}{3}\phi^2} \tag{10}$$

This result, along with the experimental data and other theories, is plotted in Fig. 7.

In as much as the theories of both Simha and Happel were developed to treat the same problem, the reason that each appears to work for a different range of d/D is not immediately apparent. Both theories are based on replacing the surrounding or neighboring particles by an artificial spherical shell at which certain assumptions are imposed with regard to the disturbance velocity produced by the neighboring particles. However, one important difference in the two theories lies in the method of determining the radius of the spherical boundary at which the assumed boundary conditions are imposed. In Happel's theory, this radius is selected by simply matching the ratio of solid volume to total volume with the actual particle concentration. In Simha's theory, however, a less direct relationship is derived from arguments regarding the "shielding" effect of the nearby particles on those farther away. This leads to a larger radius of the boundary, since the influence of neighboring particles is reduced. This of course leads to a lower predicted viscosity, as can be seen in Fig. 7. Both theories are mathematically restricted to vanishing ratios of particle diameter to tube diameter, since solid boundaries are not considered. The predictions seem to be quite good for all concentrations, one for small d/D, the other for larger d/D. The theory imposing the smaller artificial boundary (Happel) appears to work better for the larger d/D in which the tube wall plays a more important role and the shielding effect of neighboring particles becomes unimportant. However, neither theory actually accounts for the tube wall as such, and both theories fail for the largest ratio of d/D at high concentrations.

Returning now to the plot of skin-friction coefficient versus Reynolds number, it is interesting to reconstruct this plot using a Reynolds number based on the suspension viscosity rather than the base fluid viscosity. Figure 8 has therefore been constructed

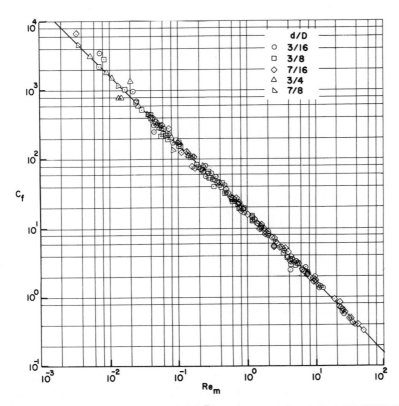

FIG. 8. VARIATION OF FRICTION FACTOR WITH REYNOLDS NUMBER BASED ON SUSPENSION VISCOSITY (SUMMARY OF ALL DATA).

by using the results of Fig. 7. It can be seen that all of the data of the present tests now fall on the straight line defined by $C_f = 16/Re_m$ which is the line describing laminar flow of a Newtonian fluid. We therefore conclude that all of the flow regimes discussed herein can properly be classified as laminar. Hence, the randomness and time-dependence of the tumbling flow regimes do not reflect turbulence but rather a combination of particle concentration and Reynolds number for which steady rectilinear flow cannot be maintained.

CONCLUSIONS

An experimental study has been made of the flow of rigid-sphere suspensions in cylindrical tubes at low Reynolds number. Measurements have been made of the pressure drop and flow rates over a range of particle concentration, ratio of particle size to tube size, and Reynolds number. In addition, visual observations were made of the particle motions and fluid velocities across the tube by means of motion pictures and dye injection. As a result of these studies, the following conclusions can be drawn:

1. The fluid suspensions investigated herein were in all cases Newtonian and the flow was found to be laminar.

2. For high particle concentrations and/or large particle-to-tube diameter ratios ($d/D > \frac{3}{4}$), the flow is steady and shows no dramatic change with Reynolds number.

3. For concentrations between about 2 and 40%, there is a marked difference in suspension behavior above and below a critical tube Reynolds number of about 10.

4. For concentrations between about 2 and 40%, steady flow cannot be maintained below a Reynolds number of about 10. Particle interactions are abundant, and contact with the vessel wall is common.

5. For Reynolds numbers below the critical value, the relative viscosity as a function of concentration agrees with the interaction theories of either Simha or Happel, depending on the ratio of d/D.

6. At Reynolds numbers above the critical value, the flow is generally steady and no particles are found on the vessel wall.

7. The flow at Reynolds numbers above the critical value is characterized by a decrease in relative viscosity to approximately that predicted by the non-interaction theory of Einstein.

8. For particle diameters approaching the tube diameter, the variation of relative viscosity with concentration agrees with that predicted for a Bingham plastic.

ACKNOWLEDGMENT

This work was supported by the Air Force Office of Scientific Research (Mechanics Division) under Contract No. AF 49 (638)–1491.

SUMMARY

An experimental study is made of the flow of density-matched rigid-sphere suspensions in rigid cylindrical tubes at low tube Reynolds numbers. It is found that a number of distinct types of flow exist within the laminar range whose character is determined by particle concentration, particle-to-tube diameter ratio, and Reynolds number. In particular, the phenomena of "plasma skimming", and "tubular pinch effect", and a random-type of unsteady "tumbling" flow are each observed for particular combinations of the above parameters.

It is found that except for very high concentrations, there is a dramatic change in flow regime at a tube Reynolds number of about 10. Below that value, particle interactions produce a complex, unsteady particle motion. Above that value, particle interactions virtually cease, and no particles remain on the vessel wall. This change in flow regime is accompanied by a sudden drop in relative viscosity to approximately that predicted by the noninteraction theory of Einstein. It is shown that the fluid suspension is in all cases Newtonian and the motion is laminar, even for those cases which give the appearance of turbulence.

REFERENCES

[1] EICHHORN, R. and SMALL, S. *J. Fluid Mech.* **20**, pt. 3, 513, 1964.

[2] MANLEY, R. and MASON, S. G. *J. Colloid Sci.* **7**, 354, 1952.

[3] BARTOK, W. and MASON, S. G. *J. Colloid Sci.* **12**, 243, 1957.

[4] SEGRÉ, G. and SILBERBERG, A. *J. Fluid Mech.* **14**, 115, 1962.

[5] OLIVER, D. R. *Nature* **194**, 1269, 1962.

[6] GOLDSMITH, H. L. and MASON, S. G. *J. Fluid Mech.* **12**, 88, 1961.

[7] GOLDSMITH, H. L. and MASON, S. G. *J. Colloid Sci.* **17**, 448, 1962.

[8] GOLDSMITH, H. L. and MASON, S. G. *3rd European Conference on Microcirculation*, Jerusalem, 1964, HARDERS, H. (Editor), *Bibl. Anat.* **7**, 353, Karger, Basel, New York, 1965.

[9] GOLDSMITH, H. L. and MASON, S. G. *2nd European Conference on Microcirculation*, Pavia, 1962, HARDERS, H. (Editor), *Bibl. Anat.* **4**, 462, Karger, Basel, New York, 1964.

[10] EINSTEIN, A. *Ann. Physik* **19**, 289, 1906 and **35**, 104, 1911.

[11] HAPPEL, J. *Low Reynolds Number Hydrodynamics*. Prentice-Hall Inc., Englewood Cliffs, N. J., 1965.

[12] SIMHA, R. *J. Appl. Phys.* **23**, 1020, 1952.

[13] TAYLOR, M. *Austral. J. Exp. Biol.* **33**, 1, 1955.

[14] PALMER, A. A. *Am. J. Physiol.* **209**, 1115, 1965.

[15] JEFFREY, G. B. *Proc. Royal Soc., Ser. A*, **102**, 161, 1923.

[16] TAYLOR, G. I. *Proc. Royal Soc., Ser. A*, **138**, 41, 1932.

[17] EIRICH, F., BUNZL, M. and MARGARETHE. *Koll. Zeitschr.* **75**, 20, 1936.

[18] RUBINOW, S. I. and KELLER, J. B. *J. Fluid Mech.* **11**, 447, 1961.

[19] REYNOLDS, O. *Philosoph. Trans. Royal Soc.* 1883.

[20] BRIDGMAN, P. W. *Dimensional Analysis*. Yale Univ. Press, New Haven, 1947.

[21] WILKINSON, W. L. *Non-Newtonian Fluids*. Pergamon Press, New York, 1960.

[22] McDONALD, D. A. *Blood Flow in Arteries*. Monographs of the Physiological Society, No. 7, Williams and Wilkins Co., Baltimore, 1960.

DISCUSSION

SEGRÉ (*Italy*):

I would like to suggest that your observation can be interpreted in terms of the tubular pinch effect, whose gradual development may be followed for a given Reynolds number, at different distances from the inlet, or alternatively, at a fixed position, for increasing *Re* values. It is really striking the visual difference between the flow of a well developed pinch of particles and the flow of a pinch which has not completely developed yet. I mean that the chaotic motion you observed can be simply the result of the different velocities of the particles which are at different radial positions, while the order you see above a certain Reynolds number may reflect the fact that the tubolar pinch effect has now completely developed so that all the particles, being at the same radial position, move exactly with the same velocity. They can no more overcome one the other, they simply move as a rigid configuration.

SACKS (*U.S.A.*):

Of course, I think that is exactly what is happening. The interesting question is why. We do not understand the reasons for this change at a critical Reynolds number. Certainly that is what is happening, and I'd like to mention that the distinction between this erratic tumbling motion and turbulence is clear from the reversibility of the motion as well as from the variation of skin friction with Reynolds numbers.

GELIN (*Sweden*):

I was very impressed by your dye mixture to the suspending medium here. At low Reynolds numbers you had the suspending medium to go faster than the suspended particles. Did you repeat that at faster flow rates?

SACKS:

I am afraid that our dye studies were not that systematic. We simply injected dye occasionally to see what was going on. So I do not know.

GELIN:

Because that is identical with what I think is going on in the postcapillary flow systems in venules and in sinusoids, but not in the larger veins.

SACKS:

I should have mentioned also that we ran up to ratios of 1 or almost 1, where there was a single particle in the vessel, but, of course, they were not flexible. So it does not represent very realistic cases. But they did not touch the vessel wall.

CHARM (*U.S.A.*):

We have just submitted a paper which is relevant to this with respect to the flow of red cells over a wide range of tube diameters and cell concentrations. We also used the Reynolds number which is based on a plasma viscosity and plotted this against a modified friction factor. We covered the range of Reynolds numbers that you covered here. We could not detect any such interruption in the plot. So I suggest that maybe the model that you have or the materials that you have may be different than red cells in flow. Perhaps we did detect some characteristic of deformability of the cell or something of this nature.

SACKS:

Now, that is possible. However, I wonder what this modification to the friction factor was that you are talking about.

CHARM:

We did not modify the stream friction factor. The modification dealt with cell concentration, volume fraction of the cells. There was a friction factor times some function of the cell concentration. This simply was a means of reducing all concentration to a single plot. It was a dimensionless group which includes the cell concentration.

SACKS:

We do not know whether this phenomenon will occur in blood, that is true.

GOLDSMITH (*Canada*):

Many of these experiments are very fascinating. But I think it is only fair to point out that some of the phenomena can be explained in terms of available theory. First, there is the observation that the dye travels faster than the particles: this is a wall effect which would be noticeable in your experiments in which the particles are very large, occupying from three-sixteenths to seven-sixteenths of the tube diameter. At all radial positions, the particles will lag the fluid velocity and hence the dye, which travels with the fluid velocity, will run in advance of the particles. Secondly, you say that the transition at Reynolds number 10 may be important in the physiological system, in larger vessels. You should, however, at the same time, take into account the particle size. The tube Reynolds number is probably the wrong quantity to use. The tubular pinch effect is basically related to what BRENNER (*J. Fluid Mech.* **4**, 195, 1958) and others define as the particle Reynolds number, which is a function of the slip of the particle, i.e. the difference between the particle velocity and the undisturbed fluid velocity at the center of rotation of the particle. In the larger vessels, the red cells occupy a very small fraction of the vessel diameter and the slip would be negligible. I wonder, therefore, whether the phenomena that you observe at Reynolds numbers above 10, which in themselves are most interesting, are relevant to flow in larger vessels *in vivo*.

SACKS:

No. Certainly, I think if you get to the large vessels where the ratio of cell diameter to tube diameter is vanishingly small, this is not applicable. However, this transition appears to occur in a range where it is applicable, namely, where the range is about what we covered in our tests. And I think it is applicable. Furthermore, I really disagree with the use of the particle Reynolds number. I do not see the significance of that as a variable, partly because of difficulties in measuring local velocities and partly because it does not reflect an overall effect on the flow regime whereas we get consistent results basing the Reynolds number on the tube diameter.

EIRICH (*U.S.A.*):

I wanted to make the same point; it would be very interesting to look at both Reynolds numbers, that for the particles themselves as well as for the flow in the tube. I think one will find that the Reynolds numbers of the particles have a definite influence on the overall critical number. Have you introduced the viscosity of the pure liquid, or of the suspension? This is another point to be clarified.

In this context I would like to mention that rapid changes in the stress-strain relationship at certain Reynolds numbers, or at certain stress limits, is well known in all systems of viscoelastic behaviour or where large concentrations of rigid particles are present. There the rate of shear becomes suddenly faster at critical stresses or, vice versa, the stress smaller at critical rates of shear. This is quite well know e.g. for the flow of polymeric melts or of highly concentrated solutions.

Finally, a point of personal clarification: could you, please, repeat the definition of the skin-friction factor?

SACKS:

The Reynolds number on this final plot was based on the apparent viscosity of the fluid suspension whereas we also plotted it against Reynolds number based on the base fluid viscosity. In that case, you do get the breaks at a Reynolds number of about the order of 10. Now the skin friction factor we used was the classical Fanning skin friction factor based on the mean flow velocity and the diameter of the tube. I do not know if that answered all your questions. I was not aware that this critical Reynolds number is well known in other fields.

MODEL STUDIES OF THE HYDRODYNAMIC CHARACTERISTICS OF AN ERYTHROCYTE. I. METHOD, APPARATUS AND PRELIMINARY RESULTS

G. Bugliarello,* H. J. Day, A. Brandt,
A. J. Eggenberger and G. C. C. Hsiao

Biotechnology Committee and Civil Engineering Department,
Carnegie Institute of Technology,
Pittsburgh, Pennsylvania, U.S.A.

INTRODUCTION

One of the basic problems in hemorheology remains the detailed determination of the kinematic and dynamic characteristics of the motion of individual erythrocytes, and of the flow in the plasma matrix. The determination of these characteristics is a necessary step toward: (a) the rational prediction of the bulk characteristics of the transport processes occurring in blood—not only the flow–resistance relationship, but also the transfer of heat and mass; (b) the gaining of greater insight into the role of external hydrodynamic processes on the physiology of the erythrocyte and the vessel wall.

Phenomena other than hydrodynamic ones of course can play a very significant role in the erythrocyte–plasma–boundary interactions. Today, however, the nature and role of the non-hydrodynamic components are far from clear. Thus an understanding of the hydrodynamic components of the interaction becomes important, in order to single out the contribution that these components can make to the overall phenomena.

The characteristics that should be determined for a variety of flow and boundary conditions, rheological fluid characteristics and erythrocyte shapes corresponding to physiological situations, include:
  (i) The forces and momenta exerted:
     (a) by the flow field on the erythrocyte,
     (b) (as a subclass of (a)) by the erythrocyte on neighboring ones,
     (c) by the erythrocyte on the boundaries.
 (ii) The velocity distribution in the fluid surrounding the erythrocyte.
(iii) The distribution of hydrodynamic stresses:
     (a) on the surface of the erythrocyte,
     (b) on the boundary of the vessel as an erythrocyte sweeps past it.

Clearly, determination of these characteristics with actual erythrocytes, *in vivo* or *in vitro*, does not appear to be possible at the present state of our technology, except perhaps for a few aspects, under extremely simplified conditions. Thus resort must be made either to mathematical or physical models.

Mathematical models have been able thus far to describe only very simplified situations, but are in the long range a very hopeful approach; in the measure they develop and are found reliable, they will lessen the need for physical models. Most, if not all physical models to date have been relatively small-scale models of erythrocytes — rigid spheres, gas bubbles, rigid or flexible discs — capable of simulating only the bulk characteristics of the erythrocyte — flow interaction.

Purpose of this paper is to describe an apparatus for large-scale model studies of the hydrodynamics of an erythrocyte, and also to present some sample results of a mathematical model of the flow field between vessel-spanning erythrocytes in the capillaries of the microcirculation.

LARGE-SCALE PHYSICAL MODELLING OF AN ERYTHROCYTE

A large-scale physical model of an erythrocyte makes it possible to obtain information in considerable detail; the model can be instrumented to measure pressure distributions, the flow field can be determined by suitable methods, forces can be measured with accuracy, etc.

These advantages are achieved, however, at a price. The first adverse element is cost. In order to reach the low Reynolds numbers characterizing the hydrodynamics of an erythrocyte, an extremely viscous fluid is required. Such a fluid should also be transparent, so as to allow visual observations. Generally, fluids satisfying both requirements are expensive and difficult to handle. Thus, it becomes necessary to compromise between cost and desirable fluid properties.

Other difficulties are the achievement of faithful models of an erythrocyte (in terms of shape, flexibility, etc.) and of its hydrodynamic environment. Since the structure and rheological properties of a red blood cell are today still largely conjectural, it is obviously impossible at present to specify the corresponding characteristics of the model. Even if these characteristics could be specified, the design of a physical model conforming to them is not a trivial task.

Exact simulation of the hydrodynamic environment is not easily achieved either. Neither a conventional hydrodynamic tunnel nor a towing tank can generate a flow pattern identical to that experienced by the erythrocyte in a vessel. Thus, a decision must be made as to the characteristics to be emphasized in the simulation — a decision, again, in which cost can be a decisive element. Clearly, a hydrodynamic tunnel is considerably more complex a device, for the same model scale, than a towing tank.

Although, as these considerations suggest, exact similarity is not easily achieved with a large-scale model, such a model offers at present the only feasible means of acquiring basic information that can provide reference data for the interpretation of *in vivo* or *in vitro* observations, and lead to more informed hypotheses for the formulation of realistic hemodynamic theories.

Hemodynamic Towing Tank

The physical modelling of the erythrocyte hydrodynamics is carried out in our laboratory in an *ad hoc* towing tank (henceforth called the hemodynamic towing tank). It may be noted parenthetically that a distinguished precedent in the use of a large-scale towed model of a microscopic biological flow phenomenon was G. I. TAYLOR's determination of the hydrodynamics characteristics of a large and very simplified mechanical model of a swimming spermatozoan, towed in glycerine[1].

The hemodynamic towing tank is shown in Fig. 1. The tank is parallelepipedal in shape, 2 ft 7 in. wide, 3 ft deep and 15 ft long. Transparent walls, supported by a rigid steel frame, permit visual observation.

In order to reproduce a variety of basic flow field situations, the erythrocyte models can be towed in a fluid otherwise at rest, or can be kept still in a flow field generated by two vertical counter-rotating walls, or can be subjected to a combination of these two conditions.

The towing carriage from which the models are suspended is mounted on precision bearings moving on precision circular rails, which are suspended in turn from a vibration-free mounting frame hanging rigidly from the ceiling of the laboratory and spanning the entire length of the tank. The carriage is towed by a steel wire wound around a pulley driven by a $\frac{1}{8}$ h.p., 3450 r.p.m. a.c. induction motor, through a Graham cone-drive speed reducer (input 3450 r.p.m.) and a Boston Gear constant-ratio speed reducer (speed ratio 10). A detailed view of the towing carriage and towing arm is shown in Fig. 2, and

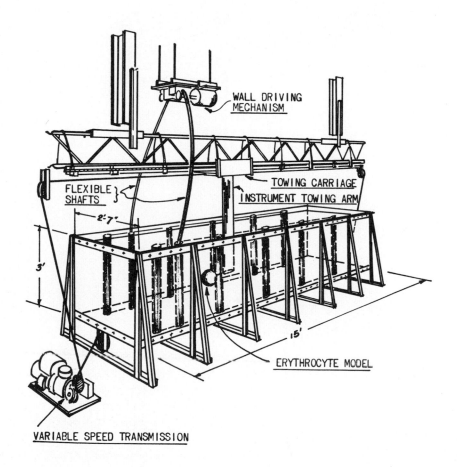

FIG. 1. HEMODYNAMIC TOWING TANK — ARTIST'S DRAWING.

the calibration of the towing carriage movement in Fig. 6a. The models are attached to the towing carriage by an instrumented towing arm whose vertical portion is shielded from drag forces by a hollow hydrofoil. To minimize the vibrations imparted by the towing carriage, the towing arm is also connected to a vibration damper consisting of two glycerine-filled baffled cylinders.

Each of the two counter-rotating walls generating the shear field across the tank consists of a wide endless plastic belt, wound around a system of vertical circular

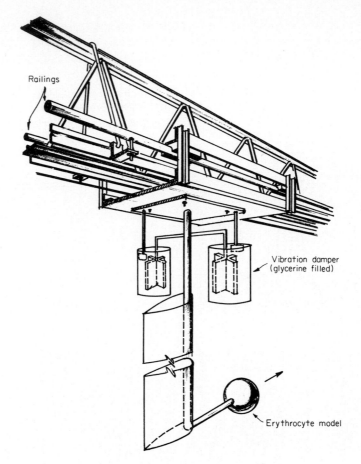

Railings

Vibration damper
(glycerine filled)

Erythrocyte model

FIG. 2. TOWING CARRIAGE AND TOWING ARM.

cylinders. The belt is driven by the cylinder at one of its extremities, which is connected to a flexible shaft. The shaft is driven by an electric motor through a variable speed transmission with one power outlet for each wall. This arrangement insures that both walls are driven at exactly the same velocity; the ratio of the velocities of the two walls can however be altered by a differential.

A schematic top view of the tank with the counter-rotating walls in place is shown in Fig. 3. The distance between the walls can be altered at will, and the walls themselves can be easily removed.

Figure 4 is a general view of the towing tank, showing also the two large tanks for the storage of the towing fluid (glycerine). The glycerine is pumped to and from the towing tank by a model L–288 Viking heavy duty pump, driven through a gear reducer by a 5 h.p. motor.

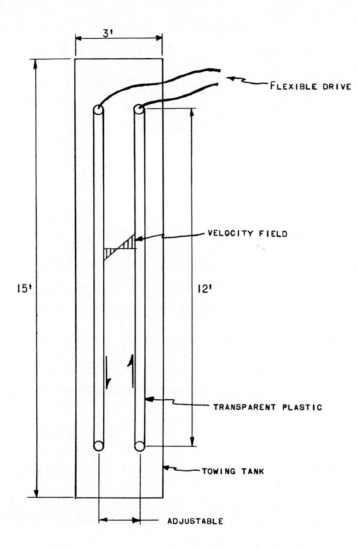

FIG. 3. HEMODYNAMIC TOWING TANK — SCHEMATIC TOP VIEW WITH COUNTER-ROTATING WALLS.

Towing Arm Instrumentation

At present, the towing arm is instrumented for the measurement of drag and yaw forces on the model. Subsequently, it will also be instrumented for the determination of moments about the axis of the model.

The forces on the model are measured by strain gages, mounted on the broad surfaces of relatively thin parallelepipedal sections of the otherwise circular towing arm.

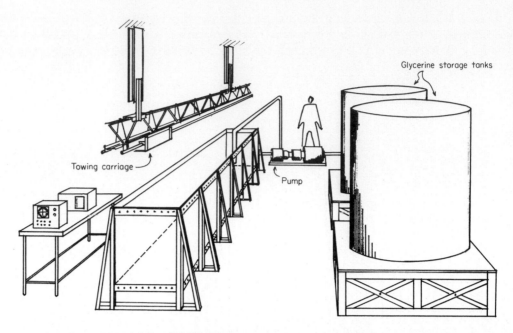

FIG. 4. HEMODYNAMIC TOWING TANK — ASSEMBLY.

Figure 5 shows the location of the gages and the arrangement for the measure of drag forces.

The gages for the measurement of the drag force are aligned parallel to the axis of the towing area, on surfaces which are normal to the flow direction. Those for the measure of the yaw forces are on surfaces also parallel to the axis of the towing arm, but rotated by 90° with respect to the previous ones, so as to be parallel to the flow direction. The high torsional stiffness of the parallelepipedal sections virtually eliminates torsional moments and reduces the measurement of the yaw forces to a measurement of bending forces in a direction normal to the flow.

Four gages are used for each type of measurement, in the temperature-compensating Wheatstone bridge shown at the bottom of Fig. 5: two active gages, with resistances $+E_A$ and $+E_B$, and two passive (unstrained) ones, with resistances $-E_A$ and $-E_B$. The passive gages are subject to the same changes in temperature as the active ones; thus any thermal effect is balanced out in the bridge and any unbalancing is due only to mechanical strain.

If M_A is the bending moment at A due to the drag force (acting in direction normal or to the axis of the towing arm), M_B the moment at B and X_{AB} the distance between A and B, the drag force is

$$F = \frac{M_A - M_B}{X_{AB}}$$

where M_A and M_B are of course proportional to the changes in resistance of the gages. The yaw force is measured in the same fashion.

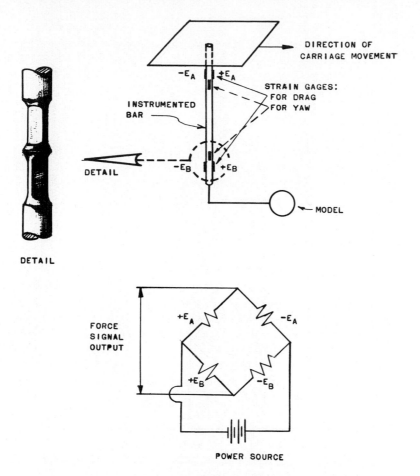

FIG. 5. INSTRUMENTATION OF HEMODYNAMIC TOWING CARRIAGE.

The strain gages are Budd Metal Film Type CX 141–B, having a gage factor of $2.02 \pm \frac{1}{2}\%$ and a resistance of 120 ± 0.2 ohm, mounted with a waterproof coating. The output from the gages is amplitude-modulated by an R–C coupled amplifier, demodulated and fed into an oscillograph recorder.

The towing arm has been calibrated statically, by known weights applied to the model by a system of pulleys. Sample calibration curves for drag at various recorder attenuation are shown in Fig. 6b.

Erythrocyte–Wall Interaction

In order to determine the hydrodynamic phenomena arising from the interaction of an erythrocyte with a boundary, the arrangement shown in Fig. 7 is used. The boundary is an instrumented movable plexiglass wall which can be placed at varying distances from the erythrocyte model. A small piezometer hole drilled in the wall is connected to the inlet of pressure chamber P_1 of a Sanborn 592–300 transducer-converter, which provides phase-sensitive demodulation and filtering of the transducer's a.c. output, and,

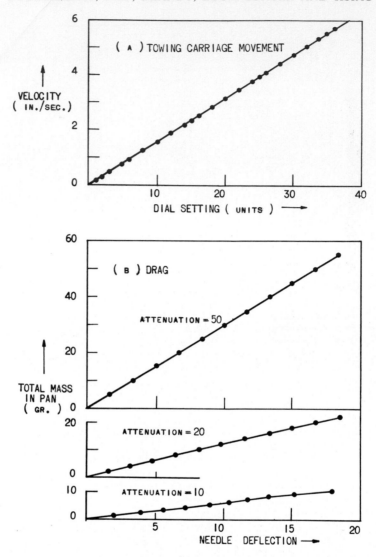

FIG. 6. HEMODYNAMICS TOWING TANK — SAMPLE CALIBRATION CURVES — (A) TOWING CARRIAGE MOVEMENT, (B) DRAG, AT VARIOUS ATTENUATIONS.

in turn, to an Autograph strip-chart recorder. The normal working linear range of the transducer and converter is from −40 to +40 mm Hg, and the sensitivity 5 mv d.c./mm Hg.

As shown schematically by Fig. 8, a sweep of the erythrocyte model past the piezometer hole yields a time distribution of the pressure exerted by the erythrocyte on the wall. By varying the vertical position of the erythrocyte with respect to the piezometer hole, a family of profiles is obtained, yielding by interpolation the complete wall pressure distribution surface. Simultaneously, the total hydrodynamic action exerted by the wall on the erythrocyte model can be measured by the towing arm instruments.

As also shown in Fig. 8, this experimental arrangement permits easy simulation of

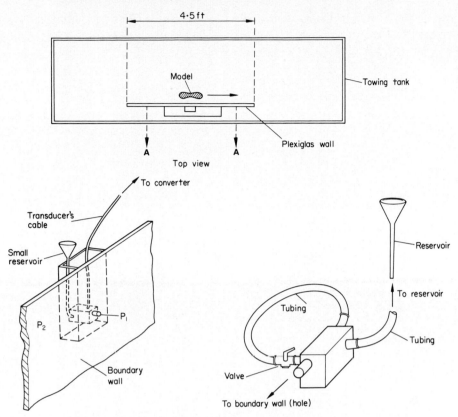

FIG. 7. ERYTHROCYTE–WALL INTERACTION EXPERIMENTS. MEASUREMENT OF WALL PRESSURES.

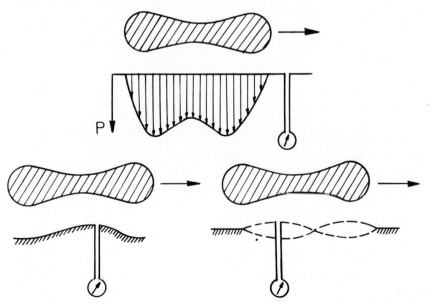

FIG. 8. ERYTHROCYTE–WALL INTERACTION EXPERIMENTS. SCHEMATIC EXAMPLES.

the interaction of the erythrocyte with a variety of physiological boundaries, by giving appropriate configurations and characteristics to the portion of the wall containing the piezometer hole.

Similarity Considerations; Testing Fluid

Let us consider, as shown schematically in Fig. 9a, an erythrocyte in a non-uniform shear field such as that characterizing flow in a vessel. Although we have evidence from our previous studies[2] of a tendency of the erythrocyte to align itself preferentially

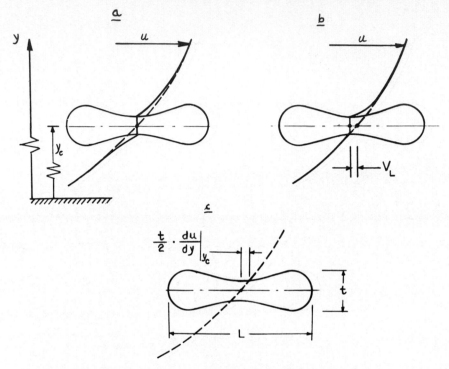

FIG. 9. FLOW RELATIVE TO AN ERYTHROCYTE.

(at least in the peripheral regions) in a direction parallel to the flow, the following considerations apply regardless of actual shape or orientation.

Since an erythrocyte can move as a whole only at one velocity, it will experience on either side shear stresses which are opposite in direction, and arise from the velocity difference between the velocity of the boundary of the erythrocyte and the original undisturbed velocity profile. If the erythrocyte is endowed with fluidity, it may develop an inside circulation, which will reduce the shear stresses at the boundary. The erythrocyte is furthermore likely to lag with respect to the velocity of the original undisturbed flow field (Fig. 9b). Other factors being equal, (flexibility, shape, etc.), the characteristics of the flow field around the erythrocyte, and hence the stresses on the erythrocyte, will be governed by the velocity difference across the erythrocyte (approximately equal to $t\dfrac{du}{dy}\bigg|_{y_c}$, where t is the thickness of the erythrocyte, u the undisturbed velocity at distance y from the boundary and y_c the value of y at the center of the erythrocyte), and by the velocity lag V_L. The thickness t varies of course along the erythrocyte; so may also vary the slope du/dy, particularly if the vessel is narrow, or not uniform in the axial direction, or if the flow is unsteady. In first approximation, it may however suffice to consider an average representative value for both.

By analogy to flow over a flat plate, if the plasma is assumed to be Newtonian, a Reynolds number for the erythrocyte in a shear field can then be defined as

$$\Re_E = \frac{\frac{t}{2} \frac{du}{dy}\Big|_{y_e} L}{\nu} \tag{2}$$

where L is the length of the erythrocyte and ν the viscosity of the plasma. If the plasma is non-Newtonian and can be represented by some simple rheological model, eq. (2) can be transformed into a generalized Reynolds number. The length of the erythrocyte varies, of course, in the direction normal to the drawing, so that L is, like t, an arbitrarily set linear dimension.

Since du/dy varies along the radius of the vessel, $\Re_E$ varies accordingly. As an orientative value, setting $du/dy = U/R = 2V/R$, where R is the radius of the vessel, U the maximum velocity (at the centerline of the vessel) and V the average velocity ($= U/2$ for Poiseuille flow), the erythrocyte Reynolds number becomes

$$\Re_E = \frac{VtL}{R\nu} \tag{3}$$

For an arteriole with $R = 20\,\mu$, assuming $L = 8\,\mu$, $t = 2\,\mu$, $V = 1$ cm/sec and $\nu = 1.2 \times 10^{-2}$ cm²/sec, eq. (3) gives $\Re_E = 1.7 \times 10^{-3}$ (while the corresponding tube Reynolds number $V = 2R/\nu$ based on $\nu \simeq 4 \times 10^{-3}$ cm²/sec is $\simeq 0.1$). For an artery with $R = 5$ mm and $V = 30$ cm/sec (corresponding to a tube Reynolds number of 750), $\Re_E$ is $\simeq 8 \times 10^{-4}$.

A Reynolds number for a towed model of the erythrocyte is defined as

$$\Re_T = \frac{U_T L_T}{\nu_T} \tag{4}$$

where U_T is the towing velocity, L_T a characteristic linear dimension of the model, homologous to L in eq. (3), and ν_T the kinematic viscosity of the fluid in the model.

Assuming $U_T \simeq 0.5$ cm/sec, $L_T = 10$ cm, and $\Re_T = 1 \times 10^{-3}$, equality of R_T and R_E would require a ν_T given by

$$\nu_T = \frac{U_T L_T}{\Re_E} \tag{5}$$

or $\nu_T = 5 \times 10^3$ cm²/sec, corresponding to a ratio ν_T/ν between the kinematic viscosities of the fluid in the model and that of plasma of approximately 4×10^5 — a value not practically attainable.

As long, however, as the kinematic viscosity in the model is sufficiently high to insure that inertial effects are not significant, $\Re_E$ and $\Re_T$ do not need to be identical. Following the example of G. I. TAYLOR[1], glycerine has thus been selected as a towing fluid—a choice not without shortcomings, but at present, the most convenient compromise between requirements and cost. With glycerine, the ratio v_T/v is of the order of 10^3; with transparent silicone oils it can increase by an order of magnitude, but so would the cost of the fluid, and the complexity of the fluid-handling system.

Erythrocyte Models

The initial experimental program in the hemodynamic towing tank is to determine the hydrodynamic characteristics of a series of idealized reference shapes and flow and boundary conditions. Subsequently, the program will be expanded to consider increasingly realistic models.

The reference shapes selected thus far are both rigid and flexible. Figure 10 shows two rigid ones. The flexible shapes present greater and not yet fully resolved difficulties, both in achieving a desired shape and in applying a distributed towing force to the model without limiting its freedom to adjust to the configuration determined by the hydrodynamic forces.

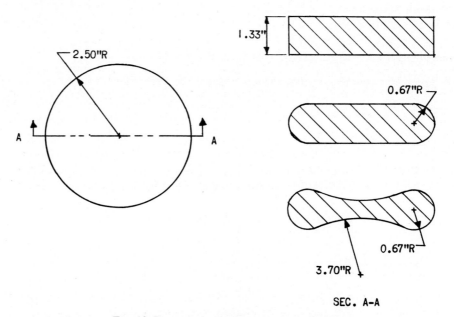

FIG. 10. REFERENCE MODELS OF ERYTHROCYTES.

Thus far the apparatus has been undergoing only calibration tests, and no results are yet available at R_t values of physiological significance. It may be worth noting, however, that some measurements at very high $\Re_T(\simeq 104)$, have shown the drag of the biconcave model to be almost double of that of the disc with faired edges.

MATHEMATICAL SIMULATION OF THE TRANSPORT PROCESSES IN THE CAPILLARIES

A physiologically very significant aspect of the erythrocyte–flow interaction occurs in the capillaries where the erythrocyte may span the entire cross-section of the vessel.

PROTHERO and BURTON have called attention to the convective currents which are set up in capillaries in the axial plasmatic gaps between erythrocytes, and have shown by a physical air-liquid model the significance of such a pattern in accelerating the exchange of gases and heat between the capillary and the environment[3]. Even with a physical model, however, detailed determination of the flow pattern in the gaps is extremely difficult; the difficulties are compounded in the determination of the diffusion pattern.

In order to study these phenomena, we have thus found it expedient to resort to mathematical simulation. From initially very simple models, we hope to proceed to increasingly realistic reproductions of the actual phenomena.

The aims of our approach are two-fold:

1. To determine the flow-pattern in the gaps, and from it the pressure distribution and energy dissipation
2. On the basis of this information, to determine the characteristics of the diffusion process in the gaps.

The flow pattern is determined by a numerical solution of the Navier–Stokes equations, omitting the inertia term; the characteristics of the diffusion process, by a random walk simulation[4].

Abbreviated accounts of preliminary results, obtained with very simple models have already been published[5, 6], and more extensive results will be given elsewhere[7]. Here, we will confine ourselves to presenting some sample and hitherto unpublished results for the flow pattern and to discuss briefly the potential of these mathematical models.

The insert in Fig. 11 shows a model consisting of two idealized erythrocytes (or

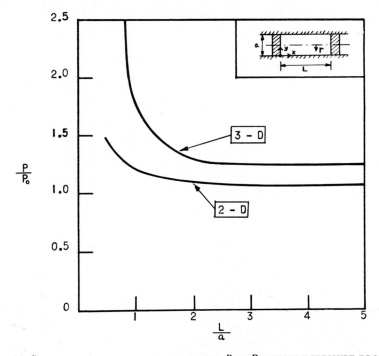

FIG. 11. SLUG FLOW—RATIO OF PRESSURE DROP P TO POISEUILLE PRESSURE DROP P_0.

groups of erythrocytes) spanning a vessel, and separated by a plasmatic gap of length
L. Either two-dimensional conditions (2–D), or three-dimensional ones (3–D) with
axial symmetry have been considered. Numerical solution of the Navier–Stokes
equations together with the continuity equation leads to the determination of the
velocity distributions in the gap. From these, the energy dissipation can be computed.
Figure 11 shows the ratio of the pressure drop P to the pressure drop P_0 of the corresponding Poiseuille flow, as a function of the gap dimensions, and of the dimensionality
of the field.

The absolute streamlines ψ (with respect to a fixed observer) and the relative streamlines ψ_R (with respect to an observer moving with the velocity of the erythrocytes) for
a gap of dimensions $L/a = 1.0$ are shown in Fig. 12. Since the pattern is symmetrical
with respect to the centerline, only the half of the flow field from the wall to the centerline
is plotted.

The circulation pattern indicated by the closed ψ_R curves is the phenomenon that,
as shown by Prothero and Burton, enhances the diffusion of gases and heat in the
plasmatic gaps. The quantitative information contained in curves such as those in
Fig. 12 makes it possible to compute the circulation times for each relative streamline,
and to use these data as input to the stochastic model of the diffusion process.

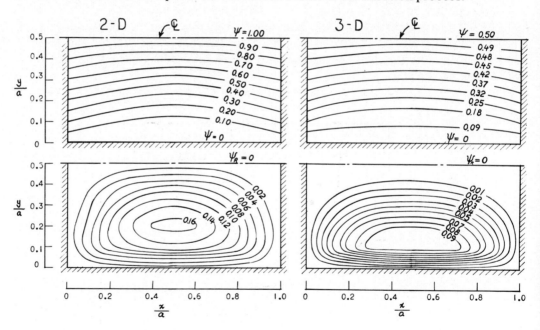

FIG. 12. SLUG FLOW — ABSOLUTE STREAMLINES ψ AND RELATIVE STREAMLINES ψ_R FOR $L/a = 1.0$.

Currently, the flow model is being extended to the case of erythrocytes with curved
boundaries, and also of axially symmetrical erythrocytes spanning only portions of
the cross-section. The stochastic diffusion model is similarly being extended to a
variety of boundary conditions.

Clearly, in the measure that the systematic model exploration of the features of the
transport processes in the plasmatic gaps develops, it will become increasingly possible,
in combination with pertinent *in vivo* observations stimulated by the models, to under-

stand in full the physiological significance of the flow in these vessels. As an example, suffice it here to point out that, from Fig. 11, a plasmatic gap with an average L/a value of about 2 would yield pressure drops not substantially higher than those for larger L/a ratios. This value of L/a is still sufficiently low as to insure a vigorous convection pattern. It would thus be interesting to determine whether indeed the *in vivo* situation is characterized by a meaningful average value of L/a, and whether such a value represents a compromise between energy dissipation and effectiveness of the mass and heat process.

ACKNOWLEDGMENTS

Research supported by grant HE 05557 of the National Institutes of Health, U.S. Public Health Service, and by a Bakhmeteff Fellowship in Fluid Mechanics to A. Brandt in 1963–4. The Dow Chemical Company and the Shell Oil Company have generously supplied the glycerine for the hemodynamic towing tank. A grant from the U.S. Office of Naval Research has enabled the first author to travel to Reykjavik to present this paper.

REFERENCES

[1] TAYLOR, G. I. *Proc. Royal Soc., London* A **209**, 447, 1951.
[2] BUGLIARELLO, G. and HAYDEN, J. W. *Trans. Soc. Rheol.* **7**, 209, 1963.
[3] PROTHERO, J. and BURTON, A. C. *Biophysical J.* **1**, 564, 1961.
[4] BUGLIARELLO, G. and JACKSON, E. D. III. *J. Eng. Mech. Division, ASCE*, **49**, Aug. 1964.
[5] BRANDT, A. and BUGLIARELLO, G. *Proc. 18th Annual Conf. Engrg. in Med. and Biol.*, Philadelphia, 1965, p. 159.
[6] BUGLIARELLO, G. and HOSKINS, J. W. *Proc. 19th Annual Conf. of Engrg. in Med. and Biol.*, San Francisco, 1966.
[7] BRANDT, A., BUGLIARELLO, G. and HSIAO, G. C. C. (paper in preparation).

DISCUSSION

CHARM (*U.S.A.*):

What would be the effect of introducing a flexibility in the cell of your mathematical model of the flow in the capillary?

BUGLIARELLO (*U.S.A.*):

Again, let me emphasize that this is just a beginning. Our plans are to proceed gradually with increasing complexity. The next step, which can be done rather easily, is to introduce as a variable the configuration of the rigid model, i.e. the shape. The subsequent step would be to try to match the boundary conditions from the outside and, rather than introducing flexibility, to introduce a circulation inside the cell. This is something a little bit more complicated, but it can be done. Finally, from here, we shall attempt to consider flexibility.

CHARM:

One of the other things that puzzled me was: how do you know in which direction your circulation takes place? I could not tell from your diagram whether it was clockwise or counter-clockwise.

BUGLIARELLO:

Let me show again what happens. The velocity profile is converted from being uniform — at the boundary of the erythrocyte — to having zero velocity at the wall — in the gap between erythrocytes. Thus, for continuity, the plasma in the gap between erythrocytes must be diverted from the peripheral region to the central portion of the vessel. This results in the circulation we have shown. If the main flow direction in our figure is from the left to the right, the circulation is clockwise; if it is from the right to the left, counter-clockwise.

BURTON (*Canada*):

I am delighted with your theoretical solution of this problem. Prothero, who discovered this experimentally, used bubbles of air interrupted by water, and experimentally produced a curve of the ratio of the actual resistance to flow to the Poiseuille flow. I think that your graph agrees very well with his.

BUGLIARELLO:

Very well indeed.

BURTON:

As a ratio of the distance between the boluses and the diameter.

BUGLIARELLO:

Very well, there is very good agreement.

BURTON:

Did you solve that problem rigorously? I know how difficult it is with corners.

BUGLIARELLO:

Yes, you have singular points at the corners. But this is a rigorous numerical solution of the Navier-Stokes equation, or rather of its first approximation, neglecting higher terms.

BURTON:

And would you agree that if you transfer this by modeling theory to the capillary that this curious circulation, circus movement, if you like, probably takes place at least 10 to 20 times in the length of a capillary?

BUGLIARELLO:

The rate of circulation varies with the longitudinal spacing between cells.

BURTON:

Well, this was assuming a hematocrit of half . . .

BUGLIARELLO:

Yes.

BURTON:

Also, do you have any results from your calculations of how much you expect that this would speed up equilibration of gases coming through the wall? Prothero did that approximately, and found a very startling effect, but I would be happier if someone else had also done it.

BUGLIARELLO:

We are doing this by analogue simulation technique. We have a technique worked out. We already have a considerable amount of results, but, unfortunately, I do not have them with me, because I felt that they may not have been of interest in the rheological sense. Generally, however, it appears that at low Reynolds numbers the circulation is only a weak contributor to the equilibration process, and that molecular diffusion plays a predominant role. Going back to these models, I may say one last thing: the model with straight rigid boundaries is not fully unrealistic, if one thinks in terms of rouleau formation. So if you have 5 erythrocytes, then a large gap, then 25 erythrocytes, as some of Monro's movies have sometimes shown, the model should be a fairly effective representation of reality.

MASON (*Canada*):

We have been interested recently to try to explain a phenomenon which I believe was first described by Professor Fåhraeus, namely the accumulation of particles behind an advancing air-suspension meniscus. We have solved this problem with the aid of a theory developed by SAVIC in Ottawa (BHATTACHARI and SAVIC, *Proc. 1965 Heat Transfer and Fluid Mechanics Inst.* CHARWAT, A. F. (Editor), Stanford University Press, 1965) which yields an analytical solution similar to the one that you presented here, but for somewhat different boundary conditions in that the advancing and receding boundaries are in viscous fluids. It is rather interesting that Savic developed this theory to explain the accumulation of certain structures in geological eruptions, that is, in the flow of lava through fissures in the earth. Here we have the calculations that connect geophysics with hemorheology.

SILBERBERG (*Israel*):

I wonder whether you have calculated the pressure distribution over the surface of the erythrocyte in these model calculations.

BUGLIARELLO:

This is something we are in the process of doing; it is quite easy to obtain. This type of calculation is what I meant when I mentioned the matching of the boundary conditions at the plasma–erythrocyte interface, as by these calculations we can in return deform the erythrocyte according to the pressure.

SILBERBERG:

Do you have any idea where the pressure . . . I mean, which way the pressure would run: with its high in the center or . . .?

BUGLIARELLO:

I really do not know at this stage.

SILBERBERG:

I just wondered if this could explain the deformation that is observed of the erythrocytes?

BUGLIARELLO:

This could explain something like that, perhaps, but without data I cannot give you a good answer. Thus far, our main interest in these studies has been not so much the details of the erythrocyte deformation as the study of the circulation in the plasmatic gaps. We are really trying to put on a quantitative basis what Dr. Burton has been doing. We are, thus, also trying to study the exchange between the walls and the capillaries. Now we have a stochastic simulation technique worked out, and it appears to be a very good technique as compared to the conventional solution of the diffusional equation because it is much simpler. We can for instance easily change the boundary condition, and consider unsteady processes. We hope to have results by the end of this summer.†

WAYLAND (*U.S.A.*):

This particular model has great merit in terms of the diffusion problem. But I would think from the pictures that I have seen, one would have to allow some fluid flow past the erythrocyte in order to explain the bullet shape and in fact, this appears to be what is really happening. It seems to me that the shear stresses on the wall there may indeed be more important than the hydrodynamic pressure. If you do not have large shear stresses at the rim, the ramhead at the center would tend to bulge the red cell in the opposite direction. One would have to sophisticate the model quite a bit in order to get any real explanation of the shape. But this is quite independent of the validity or the usefulness of the model in studying the diffusion problems.

BUGLIARELLO:

We are primarily interested in the diffusion problem, and in order to solve the diffusion problem, we have to have some reasonable velocity fields. When we have these first results, we then will consider different shapes. But this may take some doing.

† Note Added in Proof. An initial report of the work with this technique is given in G. BUGLIARELLO and J. W. HOSKINS, Stochastic simulation of corrective diffusion in the axial plasmatic gaps of capillaries, *Proc. 20th Annual Conf. of Eng. in Med. and Biol.,* San Francisco, Nov. 1966.

CELLULAR AND FIBRIN CLOTTING

13 July, a.m.

Chairmen: KENNETH M. BRINKHOUS, U.S.A.
SIGURDUR SAMUELSSON, Iceland

ASPECTS OF BLOOD FLOW AND PLATELET AGGLUTINATION

W. E. STEHBENS* †

Department of Experimental Pathology,
John Curtin School of Medical Research,
Australian National University,
Canberra, Australia

AREAS of intimal proliferation have been described in the aorta[1, 2] and about the orifices of the large distributing arteries[3–5]. In the cerebral arteries of foetuses and infants, intimal proliferation occurs as separate pads or cushions at specific anatomical sites, viz. face, dorsum, apex and lateral angles[5] (nomenclature introduced by STEHBENS[6]) rather than as a diffuse thickening about forks. The thickening at the face and dorsum of the fork is eventually continuous with that over the apex. Lateral angle pads are situated immediately beyond the site where the lateral wall begins to curve into the proximal side of the daughter branch. They occur frequently but not as commonly as facial and dorsal pads.

In other animals similar thickenings occur in the cerebral arterial forks[7–9] and also in extracranial vessels[10]. The relationship of these thickenings to the pathogenesis of atherosclerosis has yet to be determined. However there is evidence that they are implicated[5, 10, 11] because such pads are sites of predilection for lipid deposition in cholesterol-fed rabbits[10] and for spontaneous lipid deposition in sheep[11, 12].

Their anatomical localization about arterial forks strongly suggests that haemodynamic factors are involved in their pathogenesis and though frank turbulence might not occur at forks, disturbances of flow are conceivable at these sites. Platelet deposition *in vitro* can be induced by disturbances of flow[13, 14] and for this reason early platelet agglutination and sticking to endothelium were investigated by the rabbit ear chamber technique[15]. These same changes were investigated subsequently by electron microscopy[16].

In non-inflamed rabbit ear chambers, platelets did not usually adhere to the vessel wall and the presence of a platelet in the plasma zone was not necessarily an indication that it was about to stick to the endothelium. When platelets adhered they did so at very localized points of attachment or clung to endothelial spikes. On occasions other platelets adhered to those already attached and thereafter all were washed away only to be replaced by others in the stream.

In the ear chamber it was much more usual to see one or two platelets adhering to leucocytes which were rolling along the vessel wall. However, not all leucocyte sticking is associated with this phenomenon.

†Present address: Department of Pathology, Washington University School of Medicine and Jewish Hospital of Saint Louis, Saint Louis, Missouri, U.S.A.

Following very mild trauma an accentuation of this tendency of platelets to adhere to leucocytes resulted in the gradual build-up of platelets–leucocyte thrombi which shed embolic fragments — the so-called thrombo-embolism. This process can be widespread or localized to a single vessel. Its most striking feature is the extreme propensity which platelets exhibit for aggregation following the most mild trauma[15].

Occasionally small spherical refractile bodies consistently the same size as platelets rolled along the endothelium in much the same manner as leucocytes. Because of their size they were believed to be altered platelets. Non-deformed platelets never rolled along the endothelium.

Vascular forks and unions were examined for platelet sticking. At the apex of a fork, platelets like red cells, were held against the vessel wall but only momentarily and infrequently.

At vascular forks widening of the marginal plasma zone was observed at sites corresponding to the lateral angle pads in the forks of distributing arteries. When branches

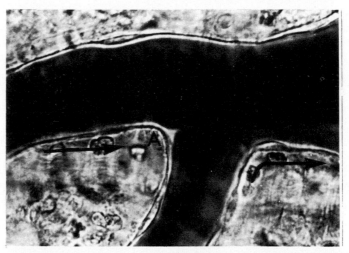

FIG. 1. JUNCTION OF TWO VENULES WITH A SMALL TRIANGULAR INCREASE IN MARGINAL PLASMA ZONE AT THE APEX (A). DIRECTION OF FLOW IS INDICATED BY THE ARROWS. ×640.

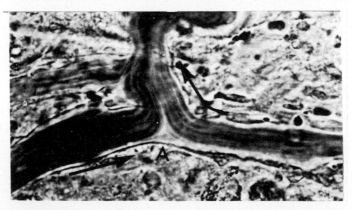

FIG. 2. TWO VESSELS JOINING AT A VERY WIDE ANGLE. LARGE TRIANGULAR INCREASE IN MARGINAL PLASMA ZONE AT APEX (A). DIRECTION OF FLOW IS INDICATED BY THE ARROWS. ×640.

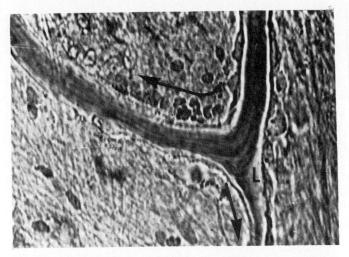

FIG. 3. VASCULAR FORK WITH WIDE LOCALIZED INCREASE IN THE MARGINAL PLASMA ZONE AT THE LATERAL ANGLE (L). ARROWS INDICATE DIRECTION OF FLOW. ×640.

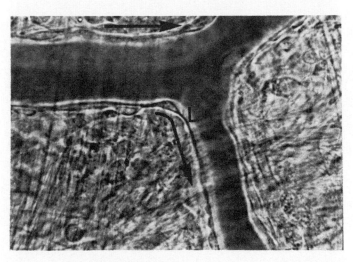

FIG. 4. VASCULAR FORK WITH INCREASE IN MARGINAL ZONE AT LATERAL ANGLE (L) AND CONTINUATION OF ASYMMETRICAL POSITION OF AXIAL STREAM DISTALLY INTO THE BRANCH. ×640.

joined to form a common stem, a triangular increase in the marginal plasma zone occurred and again corresponded to the site of the apical pads at arterial junctions of similar configuration. These increases in the width of the plasma zone (Figs. 1–4) resembled the areas of separation at which eddies could conceivably occur in larger vessels[17]. In the rabbit ear chamber however, no eddies were observed at such sites nor did they appear to be subjected to platelet adhesion.

Eddy currents were observed in vessels in the ear chamber at the junction of a fast with a slow or stagnant stream. They were also observed in front of or behind spurs which occasionally projected into the lumen. Whilst platelets were seen swirling in these eddies, they did not show any tendency to aggregate or to adhere to the vessel wall. Moreover, microthrombi were not observed in conjunction with eddies.

In our laboratory more severe change and a more extreme incidence of thrombi have been observed associated with trauma or consequent upon the intravenous injection of agents which induce platelets to aggregate. Predominantly the change was confined to an accentuation of thrombo-embolism though at times small aggregates of platelets adhered along localized areas of the vessel wall.

Therefore while widening of the marginal zone occurred in regions which correspond to the sites of some of the intimal pads, platelets displayed no proclivity to stick there.

During an electron microscopic investigation of the structure and function of the carotid body, it was found that in some vessels the mild trauma incidental to the surgical exposure of the relatively inaccessible carotid body had induced platelet aggregation[16]. The platelet changes appeared to be similar to the early thrombo-embolism observed in the rabbit ear chamber. The rich blood supply to the carotid body had facilitated their localization. In several vessels the unagglutinated platelets that were observed conformed to previous descriptions[18, 19].

It has been deduced from ear chamber observations that in early aggregation, no deformation in shape occurs and that the zones of contact between platelets are minimal. The platelets resemble pins sticking to a magnet. In what appears to be a later stage, a few platelets display modification of shape and larger areas of apposition. Pseudopodial projections were uncommon. Dendritic forms, degranulation and re-arrangement of granulomere location were not found and so it is presumed that the aggregation observed was the very earliest manifestation of intravascular thrombosis.

Small platelet aggregates were often embedded in amorphous material within the lumen. Hazy fibrillary or amorphous material surrounded other platelet aggregates, often being most dense in the interspace between platelets or between platelets and other formed elements of the blood. There is a distinct possibility that such deposits may be concerned with the adherence of platelets at this very early stage of aggregation. Simultaneously elongated and drumstick forms of the dense granules were observed and also round or oval forms with eccentric dense zones. In all, cross-

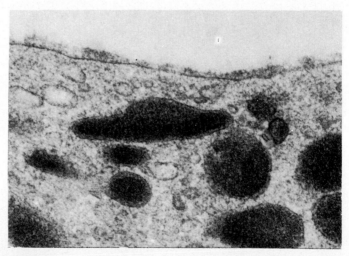

Fig. 5. Electron micrograph of portion of a platelet in early aggregation. Note the cross-striation in the elongated dense granule and the amorphous material on the platelet surface. ×60,000.

striation (Fig. 5) was at times observed, the periodicity being approximately 170 to 180 Å, which is less than that recorded for fibrin[20, 21]. Though the significance of this cross-striation is unknown, at present it cannot be regarded as fibrin because of the considerable difference in the periodicity. In larger aggregates, the platelets were more closely packed and alteration in shape was much more noticeable. Even in the largest aggregates distinct fibrin formation and degranulation were little in evidence.

In conclusion, it is stated that the variations in the plasma or marginal zone at forks or unions in small vessels of the ear chamber correspond in location to some intimal pads or cushions seen at vascular forks in human infants and other animals. No evidence was found to suggest that such sites were associated with any increased proclivity for eddy currents to occur or for platelets to aggregate or for thrombosis to form at least in the vessels of the ear chamber.

Platelet sticking to endothelium was not a prominent feature of early thrombo-embolism. Rather, platelets adhered to rolling leucocytes more frequently and with the further addition of platelets and leucocytes, larger aggregates formed.

Electron microscopy of such early thrombo-embolism revealed that:

1. The early changes *in vivo* were not associated with the bizarre shapes so frequently seen in *in vitro* studies.
2. Amorphous material of unknown significance was present about and between the platelets in early aggregation.
3. The dense zones and elongated forms of the dense granules exhibited cross-striation with a periodicity less than that of fibrin.
4. The application of platelets to one another or to the formed elements of the blood suggested that they were being pushed or pulled together to form the closely packed mosaic seen in large platelet masses. This transformation could however, be related to the remarkable propensity of platelets for spreading.

ACKNOWLEDGMENTS

My thanks are due to Dr. T. J. Biscoe and Dr. M. D. Silver who gave assistance. The National Heart Foundation of Australia provided financial support.

REFERENCES

[1] WILENS, S. L. *Am. J. Path.* **27**, 825, 1951.
[2] MOVAT, H. Z., MORE, R. H. and HAUST, M. D. *Am. J. Path.* **34**, 1023, 1958.
[3] DOCK, W. *J. Am. Med. Ass.* **131**, 875, 1946.
[4] MOON, H. D. and RINEHART, J. F. *Circulation* **6**, 481, 1952.
[5] STEHBENS, W. E. *Am. J. Path.* **36**, 289, 1960.
[6] STEHBENS, W. E. *J. Path. Bact.* **78**, 179, 1959.
[7] HASSLER, O. *Acta psychiat. et neurol. scandinav.* **11**, 4, part 2, 66, 1961.
[8] JENNINGS, M. A., FLOREY, H. W., STEHBENS, W. E. and FRENCH, J. E. *J. Path. Bact.* **81**, 49, 1961.
[9] STEHBENS, W. E. *J. Path. Bact.* **86**, 161, 1963.
[10] STEHBENS, W. E. *Am. J. Path.* **43**, 969, 1963.
[11] STEHBENS, W. E. *J. Atheroscler. Res.* **5**, 556, 1965.
[12] STEHBENS, W. E. *Nature, London* **203**, 1294, 1964.
[13] MURPHY, E. A., ROWSELL, H. C., DOWNIE, H. G., ROBINSON, G. A. and MUSTARD, J. F. *Canad. Med. Assoc. J.* **87**, 259, 1962.
[14] GEISSINGER, H. D., MUSTARD, J. F. and ROWSELL, H. C. *Canad. Med. Assoc. J.* **87**, 405, 1962.
[15] SILVER, M. D. and STEHBENS, W. E. *Quart. J. Exp. Physiol.* **50**, 241, 1965.
[16] STEHBENS, W. E. and BISCOE, T. J. *Am. J. Path.* **50**, 219, 1967.

[17] STEHBENS, W. E., D.Phil. Thesis, University of Oxford, 1960.
[18] DAVID-FERREIRA, J. F. *Inter. Rev. Cytol.* **17**, 99, 1964.
[19] HAYDON, G. B. and TAYLOR, D. A. *J. Cell. Biol.* **26**, 673, 1965.
[20] HAWN, C. V. Z. and PORTER, K. R. *J. Exp. Med.* **86**, 285, 1947.
[21] HALL, C. E. *J. Biol. Chem.* **179**, 857, 1949.

DISCUSSION

WHITMORE (*England*):

I would like to refer to the very excellent photographs in which Dr. Stehbens showed convergent flow between two venules into a larger vessel and particularly the way the two plasmatic zones joined together to give a streak-up of the center of the tube. In view of the fact that you have three-dimensional symmetry to allow for, it has always struck me as somewhat surprising that you can in fact get such nice, clear axial streaks immediately upstream of a junction. I wondered if he could indicate whether he would look upon this as a usual phenomenon or an unusual one. He just showed us one junction at which you could very clearly see the light streak of plasma up the middle of the collecting tube. Now if one watched that for a period of time, and if the ratio of flow from the two inlets varied, would this alter the picture? If you looked at a bigger area, would you expect to see that sort of flow at most of the junctions? Is it, in other words, a usual or an unusual phenomenon?

STEHBENS (*Australia*):

The small triangular increase in the marginal zone at a junction occurs very frequently. I think you would see it at most junctions. Not every junction will have the central marginal zone with a pale area running up the very center between two axial zones, but this is still quite common. It is readily seen if you look at a number of ear chambers and it has been observed in various animals. I think Thoma in the last century first described the clear marginal zone in between two axial streams. At times one can see as many as three axial zones in the one venule where three branches unite.

VOICE FROM THE AUDIENCE:

What is the frequency of this happening? Is it a fifty–fifty chance or what?

STEHBENS:

No, less than one in ten junctions, certainly. But it is not just a transitory phenomenon. When you see it, it will stay there for quite a long time.

BRINKHOUS (*U.S.A.*):

We have been studying with Dr. Rodman an *in vitro* model of platelet agglutination, including the changes that have been variously described as viscous metamorphosis, degranulation, etc. We, too, have been very much interested in what the first change is in the platelet. I suppose, it depends to some extent what is used as control or starting material, but, in general, we noted there was *first* or simultaneously with aggregation a central concentration or aggregation of organelles. It did seem that in many of your electron micrographs there was a peripheral zone clear of organelles present in the aggregated platelets.

STEHBENS:

The organelles very rarely enter the very periphery of the platelet and the peripheral zone of the platelet, the so-called hyalomere consists of plasma membrane, microtubules, cytoplasm and a few tubular invaginations from the actual plasma membrane.

BRINKHOUS:

It appears that many of the platelets have a relatively wide zone immediately beneath the plasma membrane that is clear of organelles, unrelated to tangential cutting. We have called this, stage I in the Rodman *in vitro* model and we can sharply disassociate this change from the stage of aggregation which we have called stage II, with stage I appearing first. I do not know whether this invariably occurs or not, but we would infer that many of the platelets which you have shown have gone from stage I through stage II in this series of changes.

STEHBENS:

Most of the material examined was of early aggregation and *in vivo* material, being less prone to artefact, is more reliable than *in vitro* material. A significant increase in the width of the hyalomere was not noted in this material and one must, of course, be sure not to be deceived by the plane of section. Central displacement of the granulomere originally described by light microscopy is different. In a small aggregate all of the chromomeres were allegedly aggregated around one central point and the platelet hyalomeres were arranged around the periphery like a rosette.

REES (*U.S.A.*):

I wonder if Dr. Stehbens could comment on the nature or the constancy of the electron-dense material shown in one electron micrograph apparently bridging a platelet aggregate. Was this evident frequently? Or did different sections provide further insights into the nature of this material?

STEHBENS:

It was quite common in the material that I examined. This amorphous material was present around at least three of the electron micrographs that I showed. Whether this is actually significant or not, I am not prepared to say at the moment, because the tissue was lightly perfused at the commencement of fixation.

THROMBODYNAMOGRAPHIC INVESTIGATIONS ON CLOT RETRACTION

M. E. LEROUX*

Centre Hospitalier Regional "Bretonneau", Tours, and Laboratoire d'Hématologie, Faculté de Médecine de Tours, Tours, Indre-et-Loire, France

ABSTRACT†

Clot retraction can be investigated with the thrombodynamograph (thrombelasto-graph) by simultaneously recording the structuration and evolution of the clots formed in the platelet rich and the homologous platelet free plasmas (PRP and PFP).

The graphic differences between retraction and fibrinolysis are described and a code of chronometric and dynamic values is proposed to express clot retraction. The thrombodynamographic aspects of hyporetractility and hyperretractility are reported in pathological and experimental conditions.

Clot retraction cannot be ascribed to a volumetric reduction of a mass of fibrin, which is not specific and depends on various parameters solely connected with conditions of observation. It should be approached in terms of mechanical forces, specifically linked to the thrombodynamic activity of the living active platelets, which structurize the clot and act as antagonist forces of syneresis, linked to the fibrin structures. The formation, structuration and evolution of the clots are controlled by the force resulting from these antagonist forces.

Retraction should be considered as the indicator of the normal or impaired structural and dynamic equilibrium of the clot and, hence, of its hemostatic ability.

DISCUSSION

SCOTT BLAIR (*England*):

Je suis certain que Monsieur le Docteur Leroux comprend parfaitement l'anglais, alors c'est mieux que je parle ma langue propre.

I think it is extremely interesting, the paper that Dr. Leroux has given, but one or two points I did want to ask him about: I have been doing very similar experiments with a very similar apparatus but there is one big difference which may account for differences in his findings and mine, perhaps. My experiments were done with cows' blood and his with human blood. And there are no doubt big differences which I had no time to introduce into my own paper. If the outer vessel of my apparatus is made of silicone glass, then we get what I have hitherto regarded as retraction. We get an irregular curve, not a very nice smooth curve such as are many of his. If, on the other hand, we make the whole apparatus of stainless steel, the inner and the outer cylinder, then we do not get that until after many hours. After some hours, after the addition of the coagulant, following the coagulation, we get a period during which there is no doubt a balance between coagulation and softening. We than get a very smooth softening curve which I shall talk about later, and I have assumed always, though not yet proved, that this is fibrinolysis. Perhaps I am wrong.

LEROUX (*France*):

I cannot answer Dr. Scott Blair, because I have not had any experience with ox plasma. You used ox plasma, did you not?

† The paper was not received at this publication's deadline and the author expressed the intention to submit it for publication to the journal *Biorheology*. (Editor.)

SCOTT BLAIR:
  Cows' blood.

LEROUX:
  I never tried that and I cannot say what would have happened there. As for fibrinolysis, in the presence of the Kunitz inhibitor, you obtain the same picture as that in normal human blood. This means that there is no fibrinolysis at all, because this inhibitor is a strong antiplasmin and certainly prevents every fibrinolysis.

HARTERT (*Germany*):
  If you take silicone glass you would nearly get the same form of thromboelastogram. You could also take teflon and several other materials. The main thing is that the surface is unwettable. Thus, you could also take gold or something like that, which has a low surface tension against water. Yet if it is wettable, platelets will go to that surface and if the fibrin strands have no direct contact with the surface, but are only conducted by the layer of platelets, the clot will loosen very soon. You cannot get real thromboelastograms if there is a loosening. And I may confirm my friend Leroux that this coming together of the two lines, if there are platelets in the clot, is dependent in some way on the platelet action, but an action, which is inside the clot and not on its surface. It is not loosening, but weakening of the normal clot, which brings about the decrease of amplitude after having reached a maximum amplitude. The more platelets there are, the more pronounced this action is. Perhaps it is some kind of overactive action on the fibrin fibers which are first isometrically tensioned, but afterwards this process goes in the reverse direction, and so we have the weakening of the clot. If you block fibrinolysis, you get the same pattern of the thromboelastogram, so this phenomenon cannot be fibrinolysis.

BEHAVIOUR OF PLATELETS IN CLOT RETRACTION.
A STUDY BY ELECTRON MICROSCOPE

H. HARTERT*

Department of Medicine, Städt. Krankenhaus, Kaiserslautern, and Faculty of Medicine,
University of Heidelberg, Heidelberg, Germany

CLOT retraction is a process which, under favourable conditions, can be observed in every normal blood clot *in vitro* as well as apparently in comparable clots *in vivo*. A clot poor in platelets will not retract. So the fibrin meshwork of the clot is unable to shrink with the absence of platelets. It is well known, on the other hand, that platelets in a milieu free of fibrinogen or fibrin may retract, probably by action of their pseudopodia as some authors believe (LÜSCHER, 1956). Yet it is also known that fibrinogen cannot be washed and cleaned totally away from the surface of the platelets. They even seem to contain fibrinogen in special vacuoles. So one may say retraction is impossible without platelets and probably also without fibrinogen. Both platelets and fibrin are indispensable for retraction of the clot.

A still not quite solved question is that of the interaction between platelets and fibrin in case of retraction. Another unsolved question is how the shrinking of the rather solid fibrin strands takes place.

As we could prove recently, clot retraction is by no means a process separate from blood clotting. On the contrary, the development of its activity is part of the clotting process itself. In our experiments it could be shown that retraction starts immediately with the development of fibrin strands if there are enough vital platelets. The great delay, which we usually observe between clotting and retraction, is due to mechanical impediments. They consist mainly of the adherence to the container wall and still more important of the viscous resistance of the serum to be squeezed out from the shrinking clot. This resistance increases with the size of the clot because of the longer distance the serum has to travel. It will also increase if the meshes of the clot become narrower by shrinking. A very thin layer of clotted plasma will very easily retract because of the short way the serum has to go in order to leave the clot. Yet there is also the condition that this clot should not adhere to any surface, which then would prevent retraction. A third condition is, that the clot should not be in contact with a fluid, for example paraffin oil which forces the clot to wrap itself with an impermeable layer of fibrin and lipoprotein molecules (BORN 1955, 1956), sealing off the meshwork against any loss of serum. In this case the serum can only retract, if the sealing layer has been torn by the inside pressure of the clot, caused by the tendency of the fibrin strands to shrink, so to speak, a contraction, which remains isometric as long as contraction is not allowed by mechanical obstacles. One can escape the wrapping layer, if the fluid which surrounds the clot is serum, or a protein-free electrolyte solution similar to that of blood. To measure the actual retracting force and its development in relation to time it was necessary to escape the previously mentioned obstacles. This was possible by the use of the retractograph (HARTERT, 1959), which has been described in detail elsewhere.

Further experiments with the retractograph suggested a theory of retraction, which I will mention briefly for basic understanding.

We know from the investigations of Gross and his colleagues as well as from Born, that platelets early in the clotting process release ATP, which indicates a high consumption of energy. Exactly coinciding in time is found the most pronounced increase in retraction activity. It can be assumed, that a simultaneous glycolytic process furnishes the energy causing retraction. At least the chemical nature of some integral part of retraction could be proven by the fact that retraction comes immediately to a standstill, if the retracting specimen is cooled from +37 to +4°C (Fig. 1). It still resumes the former activity if temperature rises again to 37°C. The curve continues with its development from where it was interrupted by cold. If on the other hand retraction is blocked by a mechanical brake in the retractograph it will very quickly recover almost like rubber to that point which corresponds with the curve of undisturbed retraction (Fig. 2). This

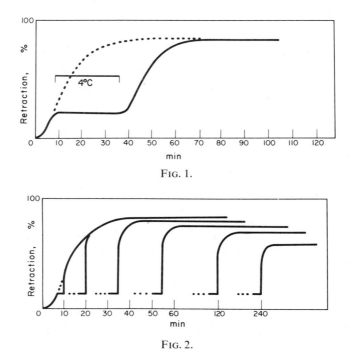

FIG. 1.

FIG. 2.

indicates that, undisturbed by mechanical blocking, the development of a retractive tension has continued. A still greater rubber-resembling quality of the platelet rich fibrin clot is shown by the same slide: the expanded clot after complete retraction always returns to its original position if the pull is released. Another slide (Fig. 3) shows a diagram made with the thrombelastograph (HARTERT, 1959), [which in France has been renamed thrombodynamograph, a word which has the advantage to sound "dynamically"]. According to Scott Blair the blood clot has the physical qualities of a Maxwell body, which means a combination of viscous and elastic qualities. As could be shown by this experiment (Fig. 3) the viscous part of the physical (mechanical) fibrin quality is greatest in the beginning of the fibrin development whereas elasticity seems to prevail more and more, if clotting and retraction come to an end. The stand still in this diagram was each time 3 min.

FIG. 3.

Some elastic quality as well as an increasing tension or isometric contraction, which tends to shorten each fibrin strand, seems to develop under the influence of platelets or more particularly of the ATP-induced glycolytic activity. In a very short period of time during fibrin development the tension of the clot seems to be wound up like the spring of a clock. It is a transformation of chemical into mechanical energy. The chemical energy is available only for a comparably short time. In this time it is active in accumulating mechanical energy, which may be released at any time and at any speed. It can again be compared to a clock, which can be started or stopped, the speed of which can be regulated and which will remain working until the spring has unwound. It is perhaps due to the viscous quality of fibrin that a clot tension which is not transformed into contraction in about four hours will weaken to half of its original strength and then decline asymptotically (Fig. 4).

These basic remarks regarding the *functional* aspects of clot retraction shall now be continued through the results of our *structural* investigations by electron microscope. The question is still unsolved, as to what kind of molecular or other change of platelets and/or of fibrin brings about the sometimes extreme shrinking of the clot (up to 95%). Some theories claim (LÜSCHER, 1956), that the pseudopodia to be observed in viscous metamorphosis on glass and other artificial surfaces may contract and so bring about

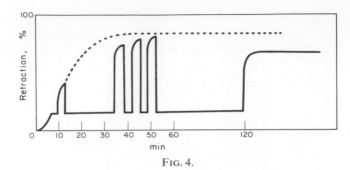

FIG. 4.

retraction by more or less passive folding of the fibrin fibres. Another group of investigators is convinced that side to side aggregation of the fibres is the clue (KUHNKE, 1958; KÖPPEL, 1962).

Our own opinion was, that by some molecular process the fibrin strands themselves reduce their length or bring about an isometric tension before actual contraction goes ahead.

To examine retraction in different phases by electron microscope it was necessary to find out a situation, where retraction proceeds without contact with solid surfaces. This, as mentioned before, was necessary to avoid disturbance of platelet evolution during clotting process. This evolution is strongly altered by surfaces and so would not reflect an uninfluenced correlation between platelets and fibrin. In the next figure (Fig. 5) may be seen the freely suspended clotting plasma between a specifically heavier

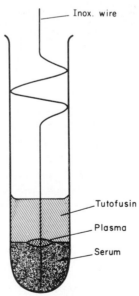

FIG. 5.

layer of serum and a lighter layer of Tutofusin solution. The recalcified but still fluid platelet-rich plasma was placed by a very thin pipette between the two layers. The specific weight of the plasma was between those of the two adjoining layers. It was

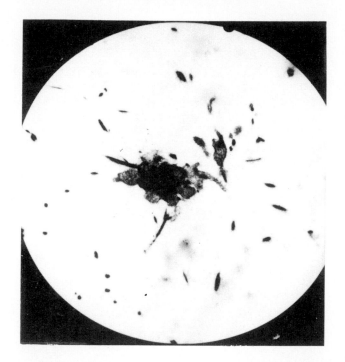

Fig. 6.

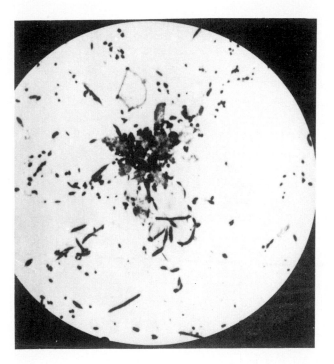

Fig. 7.

situated there like a very flat lens without contact with the walls of the container. Vertically through it went a thin wire of stainless steel for the practical handling of the clot. The glass container was placed in a water bath at 37°C.

5, 15 and 30 min after recalcification the retracting clot was fixed by osmium tetroxide (Caulfield solution) and subsequently imbedded in araldit. The specimens were then cut serially and the sections photographed in the electron microscope.

The three groups of electron microscopical photographs from sections of 5, 15 and 30 min old clots represented mainly platelets and fibrin fibres in different shapes and positions. The main difference at the first glance was the increase in number of fibrin strands inside and outside of the platelets and the change of the aspect of platelets which surprisingly did not show any pseudopodia (Figs. 6 and 7).

The statistical evaluation (NÜTZENADEL, 1966) of several parameters in these pictures is shown in the next table (Fig. 8). There was a significant increase of fibrin fibres inside the platelets (1) as well as outside the platelets (2). Also the number of the

MINUTES	5	5	15	30
Strands inside P.	79	79	101	330
Strands outside P.	94	94	106	440
Strands at edge of P.	52	49	56	105
Area of platelet	12·6	11·9	13·9	9·2
Circumference of P.	10·4	10·2	10·9	9·9

FIG. 8.

fibres in contact with the rim of the platelet increased statistically (3). The area of the platelets decreased statistically only in the the 30 min specimen (4), whereas the circumference remained about the same (5) This can be explained by its increasing irregularity by shrinking and folding of the surface layer.

For our problem it is important to notice, that the increase in the number of fibres outside the platelets after completion of clotting was highly significant. Compared with the 5 min value the increase of fibres in the group after 15 min was 1·1 and after 30 min 4·7 (Fig. 9). Also inside the platelet, which partially had dissolved after the fifteenth

Increase of Fibres

After	15 MIN	30 MIN
Inside P.	1·3	4·2
Outside P.	1·1	4·7

FIG. 9.

minute, the fibres in the same way increased in number. After 15 min its amount was 1·3 compared with the 5 min specimen. After 30 min it was increased to 4·2, which corresponds nicely with the increase outside the platelets.

From these photographs and figures it is impossible to say what really happens in retraction. Yet it is possible to differentiate some facts regarding clot retraction.

1. There was no evidence of molecular alterations of the fibrin strands in or near the platelets, which would have been made apparent by altered density or weak contours of the fibrin strands.
2. There was no evidence of pseudopodia or of an action of the platelets to be compared with that of pseudopodia.
3. There was no evidence of side by side aggregation of the fibrin fibres which could explain the decrease of volume in the clot.
4. The definite increase of fibrin fibres in the photographs only admits the explanation, that all fibres came closer together by the retraction process. If the number of fibres decreases four times, this would mean a decrease to one fourth of the area or, in three dimensions, the decrease in volume to one sixteenth of the original volume. These figures correspond well with the retraction in platelet-rich plasma clots to be observed otherwise.

Figure 10 shows schematically the frames of an electron microscope. On the left side above may be seen the field before retraction. The lower left shows the effect of retraction by side to side aggregation. In this case the number of fibres would remain the

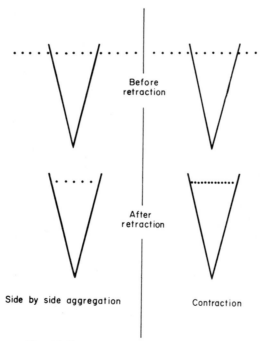

Before
retraction

After
retraction

Side by side aggregation

Contraction

FIG. 10. FLAMES OF ELECTRON MICROSCOPE.

same and the fibres would become thicker. On the upper right there is again the starting position of retraction. On the lower right there is the situation as we saw it in our experiments.

So it seems to be very probable that retraction goes on by shrinking of the whole clot without losing its structural inner proportions. This is a behaviour of the clot, which would demand a shortening or more precisely a contraction of each fibrin strand itself. It may well be, that thrombosthenin, an actomyosin resembling protein, discovered by BETTEX-GALLAND and LÜSCHER (1961), plays a part in the contraction of fibrin strands. Yet since the latitudinal stripes of the fibrin seem to be constant in their distance in every stage of fibrin development, this hypothesis had to include the idea, that contraction goes on by equal jerking movements. These jerking movements would then happen over the equidistant latitudinal stripes.

Further experiments have to explain whether this is really so and eventually how this is accomplished.

REFERENCES

BORN, G. V. R. *J. Physiol.* **133**, 61, 1955.

BORN, G. V. R. *Bioch. J.* **62**, 33, 1956.

BORN, G. V. R. Personal communication, 1956.

BETTEX-GALLAND, M. and LÜSCHER, E. F. *Proc. 8th Congr. Europ. Soc. Haematol.* Vienna, 1961, S. Karger, Basel, New York, 1962, No. 367.

HARTERT, H. *Proc. 4th Int. Congr. Biochem.*, Vienna, 1958, DEUTSCH, E. (Editor), Pergamon Press, London, 1959, vol. X, p. 239.

HARTERT, H. *Proc. 8th Congr. Europ. Soc. Haematol.* Vienna, 1961, S. Karger, Basel, New York, 1962, No. 368.

HARTERT, H. In *Symposium on Biorheology*, COPLEY, A. L. (Editor), *Proc. 4th Int. Cong. Rheol.*, Interscience Publ. John Wiley, New York, 1965, part 4, p. 571.

KÖPPEL, G. *Thrombos. Diathes. Haemorrh.*, Suppl. 2, 7, Friedrich-Karl Schattauer Verlag, Stuttgart, 1962.

KUHNKE, E. *Pflugers Arch.* **268**, 87, 1958.

LÜSCHER, E. F. *Vox sanguinis* **1**, 133, 1956.

LÜSCHER, E. F. *Proc. 4th Int. Congr. Biochem.*, Vienna, 1958, DEUTSCH, E. (Editor), Pergamon Press, London, 1959, vol. X, p. 75.

NÜTZENADEL, W. Elektronenoptische Untersuchungen zur Frage der Retraktion. Diss. Heidelberg (in press), 1966.

SCOTT BLAIR, G. W. In *Flow Properties of Blood and Other Biological Systems*, COPLEY, A. L. and STAINSBY, G. (Editors), Pergamon Press, Oxford, New York, 1960, p. 172.

WALLER, H. D., LÖHR, G. W., GRIGNANI, F. and GROSS, R. *Thrombos. Diathes. Haemorrh.* **3**, 520, 1959.

DISCUSSION

BURTON (*Canada*):

Since this is a question of special interest to me, I take the opportunity to ask it. Since the energy of retraction depends, you said, on glycolysis and ATP, could you tell me if it is affected by the oxygen tension? I have a special interest in this in another connection.

HARTERT (*Germany*):

I cannot answer this.

BURTON:

Is it being worked out how it depends quantitatively on substrate, enzyme concentrations, and so on?

HARTERT:

The limiting factor is the hexokinase reaction, as found by WALLER, LÖHR, GRIGNANI and GROSS (*Thromb. Diath. Haem.* **3**, 491, 1959).

BURTON:

It is a most interesting observation. I am afraid I was quite ignorant of this fact, until I learned it from your paper this morning.

EIRICH (*U.S.A.*):

Firstly, I would like to request a clarification of the apparently mixed use of the words contraction and retraction. I wonder whether they were used synonymously or whether any particular significance was attached to either. It seems to me that contraction signifies a volume change, and retraction a longitudinal change. Secondly, I would like to support Dr. Hartert's statement, namely, that syneresis must be, whatever the cause, a continuation of the clot formation process of desolvation, with water or serum being squeezed out and separated as the process of solidification continues. Thirdly, I thought it most significant that Dr. Hartert found a complete standstill whenever he lowered the temperature. Any ordinary chemical reaction would slow down exponentially, but could not come completely to a stop. Therefore, it seems that a phase transformation must be involved, i.e. that the contracting phase is changed into the glass state or crystallizes so that the reaction is completely stopped. I think this is very significant for what is going on. Finally, I would like to have some comments on the distance of the serrations which Dr. Hartert mentioned. Again, if one could learn more about how and why this distance does not change as I understand it, one could again infer a great deal concerning the actual mechanism.

HARTERT:

Thank you, Dr. Eirich, for your interesting comments. First I would answer that if I say contraction or retraction, it is nearly the same. It is only because the term retraction has been applied to this procedure by somebody, and really it is contraction. Retraction is perhaps only meant if one looks at the vessel because it may be that vessels are cleared by this retraction of the clot in moving from one part of the wall and going to the other where it sticks. The other two items were not questions but very interesting remarks. The distance of cross-striation is about 200–240 Å, it is nearly constant. But this has not been observed under too many different conditions. I am just going on to look at this. But nearly always, if fibrin has been observed, ultramicroscopically, you would have seen this at the same distance. Of course it seldom occurred that clots in the very early stage had been fixed so it may be that these distances are different because in my photographs you cannot see latitudinal stripes.

STEHBENS (*Australia*):

It is known that platelets are capable of phagocytosing particulate matter including fibrin, but from your electron micrographs it is not clear whether or not fibrin was within the platelet or within the platelet clump. Did you look at electron micrographs of higher resolution to ascertain the precise relationship of fibrin to the platelets?

LUCHINI (*U.S.A.*):

Bang and his co-workers have published beautiful electron micrographs of fibrin at very early stages of polymerization. An interesting observation that they have made is that these stripes, which appear only with phosphotungstic acid staining techniques and have a periodicity of 220 Å, are not always perpendicular to the axis of the fibril. In the case of a fibril, which does exhibit banding perpendicular to its long axis and which then bifurcates, the banding of the branch follows the original plane of banding parallel to the long axis of the original fibril and would not be parallel to the long axis of the branch. Whether this is an artefact of the specimen preparation or staining procedure, I do not know; however, according to Bang, this is quite constant and so not dependent on the technique.

COPLEY (*U.S.A.*):

I had not known, as Dr. Stehbens states, that platelets are capable of phagocytosis. However, we could show with different strains of tubercle bacilli (mycobacteria) that they adhere to and are clumped together with platelets within 1 min and as early as 10 sec after they are introduced into the circulation (COPLEY, A. L. and BALÉA, T., *Compt. rend. Soc. Biol.* **150**, 73, 1956; COPLEY, A. L., BALÉA, T. and CHRYSSOSTOMI-DOU, O., *Ann. Inst. Pasteur* **91**, 736, 1956; COPLEY, A. L., MAUPIN, B. and BALÉA, T., *Acta Tubercul. Scand.* **37**, 151, 1959). These embolizing platelet-mycobacterial conglutination clumps are carried in the circulation to different organs, where they obstruct parts of the microcirculation and produce microaneurysms and other changes in blood capillary vessels. In the lungs, these emboli, after erosion of affected capillaries, are then emptied in the acini or other surrounding tissues. Phagocytosis of these conglutinates by leucocytes begins only then when they become stationary and, thus, phagocytosis is a secondary process (COPLEY, A. L. and BALÉA, T., *Pathol. et Biol., Semaine des Hôpitaux* **8**, 1137, 1960). I believe, this faculty of the platelets to free the circulation from invading mycobacteria is not limited to these microorganisms, but may well include other bacteria and possibly also viruses. (COPLEY, A. L., *Proc. 8th Int. Congr. Hematol.*, Tokyo, 1960, Pan-Pacific Press, Tokyo, vol. 3, p. 1760, 1962), and probably, in general, other particulate matter. I think that this rôle of the platelets is not identical with phagocytosis. However, it needs to be established whether certain platelet enzymes, as possibly contained in their granules, have the capacity to kill microorganisms, as is the case in phagocytosis with polymorphonuclear leucocytes. I am making this comment, because I think that this rôle of the platelets as a rather instantaneous police force, so to speak, in the circulation will need to be studied, particularly since many problems in mammalian hemorheology may well be affected by this function of platelets. I would appreciate knowing if Professor Hartert and Dr. Stehbens have findings to support this thesis of the role of platelets.

STEHBENS:

The phagocytic properties of platelets was first described by TAIT (*Quart. J. Exper. Physiol.* **12**, 1, 1918). Subsequently in 1960, STEHBENS and FLOREY (*Quart. J. Exper. Physiol.* **45**, 252, 1960) confirmed these findings after the intravenous injection of suspensions of particulate matter. Since the advent of electron microscopy, DAVID-FERREIRA (*Inter. Rev. Cytol.* **17**, 99, 1964) SCHULZ and WEDELL (*Klin. Wochenschr.* **40**, 1114, 1962) and MOVAT, *et al.* (*J. Cell Biol.* **27**, 531, 1965) have confirmed the light microscopic studies. ERICHSON and CINTRON (*Proc. 4th European Conf. on Microcirculation*, 1966) produced evidence that platelets were able to phagocytose fibrin. At present what happens to the material engulfed is unknown, but I agree that study of this subject would be profitable. It is likely that the packing of platelets in viscous metamorphosis may well be akin to the property of phagocytosis and "spreading".

BASIC EQUATIONS FOR THE FLOW OF BLOOD THROUGH AN ARTIFICIAL CAPILLARY AND FOR FIBRIN POLYMERIZATION AND SOFTENING

G. W. Scott Blair*

Physics Department, National Institute for Research in Dairying, University of Reading, Shinfield, Berks., England

First I considered in general terms, what were the simplest and most intelligible principles implanted in our understanding by nature. Now I examined the chief ways in which invisibly small bodies might differ in size, shape and situation, and how their mutual collisions could give rise to sensible effects. Lastly, when I found just such effects as these in the bodies perceived by our senses, it appeared to me that these might well have come about in precisely the way supposed   (René Descartes).

BASIC EQUATIONS

Rheology is constructed from "basic equations". The most fundamental are those derived from the laws of Hooke: *ut tensio sic vis*; and of Newton: "the resistance which arises from the lack of slipperiness of the parts of a liquid, other things being equal, is proportional to the velocity with which the parts of the liquid are separated from one another" (translation taken from Reiner[1]).

The characteristics of basic equations are (i) that they express the simplest possible relation between the variables consistent with the qualitative properties of the systems studied; (ii) that they represent a simple model or process; and (iii) that they apply, within reasonable limits of accuracy to a fairly wide range of materials or conditions. *They do not apply to all materials or conditions*, hence Newton's caveat "other things being equal". Many real materials obey Hooke's law fairly accurately and many others are very closely Newtonian. When we come to deal with materials that are not Hookean or Newtonian, the simplest modifications are the relaxing (elastic) liquid and the damped (viscous) solid. The basic equation for relaxation is that of Maxwell[2]. Its model consists of a Hookean and a Newtonian element in series which gives the simplest possible model for relaxation. Many materials, including blood clots, under certain conditions[3], follow Maxwell's equation closely; but in his original paper, Maxwell was careful to point out that there were systems already well-known even in his day which would not do so. The basic equation for the viscous solid is equivalent to Lord Kelvin's model of a Hookean and a Newtonian element in parallel, which was independently proposed by Voigt. It was Kelvin who said "When you can measure what you are speaking about and express it in numbers, you know something about it; but when you cannot express it in numbers, your knowledge is of a meagre and unsatisfactory kind." Herein lies the whole purpose of the present paper.

Poiseuille and, independently, Hagen, established experimentally the basic equation for the streamline flow of a Newtonian liquid through a long narrow rigid impermeable

345

tube of even cross-section. (In future, such a tube will be referred to as an "artificial capillary".) Some years later, it was shown that this basic equation followed from Newton's law, with the addition only of a few fairly obvious boundary conditions, but Poiseuille and Hagen did not know this.

It is possible to construct a table[4] with the Hookean and Newtonian laws at the top, followed by those of Maxwell and Kelvin and including basic equations of increasing complexity for the less simple systems.

The purpose of the present paper is to suggest what are the basic equations in the sense defined above, for (a) the flow of full blood through an artificial capillary, (b) the *extra vivum** coagulation of full blood and (c) its eventual softening, presumably through fibrinolysis, when this occurs.

(a) *The Flow of Blood through a Single Artificial Capillary*

Some years ago, the writer examined not only his own data on the flow of cows' blood but published data from as many sources as possible for various species and found[5] that good straight lines were obtained when the square roots of shear stress (τ) and of shear rate (γ) were plotted against one another. Many later writers have verified the wide validity of this finding.

The equation represented by the plot may be written

$$\tau^{1/2} - \tau_0^{1/2} = A\dot{\gamma}^{1/2} \tag{1}$$

and was originally proposed by CASSON[6, 7] for suspensions in varnish.† Casson postulated a special structure for his suspensions in which "particles . . . combine to form clusters or floccules of definite cohesive strength". MERRILL *et al.*[8], working on human blood at very low shear rates, comment that "*Casson makes the assumption that the axial ratio of the rod-like aggregates is inversely proportional to the square root of the shear rate*" (my italics).

Human blood forms rouleaux and it is possible that there might exist a structure not altogether unlike that postulated by Casson, though the model cannot fit at all closely. But bovine blood obeys Casson's equation over quite a wide range of fairly high shear rates and does not form rouleaux.

The Casson equation gives a very convenient way of deriving parameters from flow curves of blood which may be plotted against tube radius, etc., but it cannot be the basic equation, since it does not represent a simple model or process to describe the qualitatively known behaviour of this material.

The qualitative facts are that blood is a suspension which must have some structure when at rest, since, when sheared, the apparent viscosity falls with increasing shear stress and rate. Although thixotropy has been observed in blood treated with heparin (COPLEY[9]), it is a fair approximation to say that in blood, the relation between τ and $\dot{\gamma}$ is monotonic, i.e. the structure very quickly re-establishes itself as soon as stress is removed and there is a measurable unique value for τ for each value of $\dot{\gamma}$. Blood also has a yield-value, probably literally in the sense that it will not flow at all at very low

---

*See Introductory Lecture.

†Casson very correctly places vertical lines around his strain-rate and stress symbols. This implies that he is concerned only with magnitudes and not with directions. This is implied in the present paper.

stresses and certainly in the sense that the Casson flow curve extrapolates to a finite positive value on the stress axis.

The writer has recently shown[10, 11] that, ignoring the yield-value for a moment, a very simple mechanism can be postulated which leads to a power relation between τ and $\dot{\gamma}$, for such suspensions. Summarizing very briefly, stress and shear-rate are assumed to have independent effects in breaking down the structure, or, more correctly, the stress breaks it down and the shearing prevents it reforming. If we assume that the rate at which the number of bonds increases with diminishing stress is inversely proportional to the stress; and the rate at which the number of bonds reforms with falling shear-rate is inversely proportional to shear-rate, we get two exponential equations which combine together to give a power equation. (For the complete argument, the original papers must be consulted.) Now if we subtract a term to allow for the yield-value stress τ_0, we get the equation:

$$\tau - \tau_0 = B\dot{\gamma}^N \tag{2}$$

which was empirically proposed by HERSCHEL AND BULKLEY for rubber-benzene sols in 1926[12]. As early as 1942, COPLEY, KRCHMA and WHITNEY had suggested the use of this equation for blood[13]. This, it is claimed, is the "basic equation" for the flow of blood through a single artificial capillary.

How does it transpire, then, that Casson's equation, which is entirely different holds so well? Unfortunately, Casson's equation holds "too well" for many materials which could hardly have a structure of the kind postulated by him. The writer has been able to find some twelve papers in which data are given for all sorts of materials, including blood, showing good straight lines when $\tau^{1/2}$ is plotted against $\dot{\gamma}^{1/2}$. With the exception of a few of those of MERRILL et al.[8] none of the published graphs ranges over more than $1\frac{1}{2}$ decades of stress.

Taking an imaginary series of shear-rates, and putting $A = 1$ (which simply alters the units in which stress is calculated) the writer[14] has worked out values of τ for a wide range of τ_0 — values in eq. (1) and plotted $\tau - \tau_0$ against $\dot{\gamma}$ on double logarithmic paper over some four decades. Except in the trivial case of the true fluid ($N = 1$, $\tau_0 = 0$) the graphs are, of course, curvilinear; but, over one decade these "theoretical" graphs cannot be distinguished visually from straight lines. Allowing for experimental errors, this range could be extended to at least $1\frac{1}{2}$ decades. To check this, several published graphs, including one of the writer's own on blood (Fig. 1) were plotted using both eqs. (1) and (2). Although eq. (2) is unsatisfactory in practice, being more difficult to use, because a curvilinear graph must be extrapolated to find τ_0, it is shown to hold at least as well as eq. (1). A statistical analysis is included in the original paper.

(b) Fibrinolysis

Although coagulation normally precedes fibrinolysis, the kinetics of the latter are simpler than those of the former and they will therefore be discussed in the reverse order.

Evidence for the proposed "basic equation" derives partly from the writer's own experiments, a brief description of which should therefore now be given.

The instrument used consists of two identical torsiometers, essentially similar to that described by BURNETT and SCOTT BLAIR[15] for studying coagulation of milk.

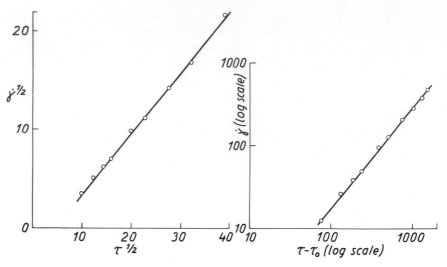

FIG. 1. COMPARISON OF CASSON AND HERSCHEL AND BULKLEY PLOTS FOR BLOOD. REPRODUCED BY KIND
PERMISSION OF THE PUBLISHERS OF *Rheologica Acta*.

The principle is very similar to that of the thrombelastograph except that there is
no damping mechanism, normally no time interval between the oscillations, the bob
oscillates instead of the container and the sample under test is much larger (50 ml).
Each oscillation of 15° takes the same time (about 40 sec), i.e. slower than the thrombelastograph during the course of the experiments. Normally, two tests are run simultaneously, one serving as control but it is difficult to get exact agreement between

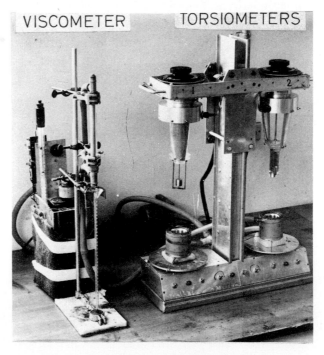

FIG. 2. PHOTOGRAPH OF THE DOUBLE TORSIOMETER.

duplicates with contact coagulation. A photograph of the torsiometers is shown in Fig. 2. The oscillating cylinder and container are made of stainless steel. Originally the container was of siliconed glass but with this surface there was sometimes retraction, which interfered with measurements of fibrin softening. It was assumed that the softening is due to fibrinolysis, in agreement with BUDTZ-OLSEN's view[16] that retraction and lysis are quite independent phenomena.

Blood samples (about 150 ml) are taken from the jugular vein of a cow, discarding the first portions, and transferred, in a siliconed glass tube within a thermos flask at 37°C to a nearby laboratory. The coagulant is then added, (normally bovine brain extract though contact coagulation is sometimes used); a small sample is placed in the top of the viscometer and two samples of 50 ml each are placed in the torsiometers, one of them being treated in various ways and the other serving as a control. Both torsiometers and the viscometer are surrounded by a waterbath at 37°C. A small quantity of kerosene is used to cover all blood surfaces which would otherwise be exposed to air. Citrate treatment and recalcification are not used.

The torques on the springs of the torsiometers are measured normally at the end of each swing, indicated by the lighting of a small bulb. What the torque really measured will be discussed later.

Unfortunately, no thrombelastograph was available but a splendid collection of thrombelastograms is to be found in the *Atlas de Thrombodynamographie* by MARCHAL et al.[17]. Hitherto, the diagnostic value of the diagrams has had to depend on quite arbitrary geometrical constructions. Thrombelastograms which appeared to be suitable were very greatly enlarged photographically and the widths of the diagrams (A') were measured at intervals along the time scale (see SCOTT BLAIR[18]).

Our own diagrams and the thrombelastograms consist essentially of three parts: an initial sigmoid region of coagulation (to be discussed later); a middle "mixed" region which will not be studied here and a third region, where it may be assumed that the influence of further coagulation is negligible and the falling value of A' when the curve was smooth is taken to indicate fibrinolysis, in the case of cows' blood, though this is not yet proved. This last region gives curves which suggest (from the thrombelastograms) that, with human blood, fibrinolysis continues asymptotically towards complete destruction of all rigidity; whereas our bovine samples give curves which are asymptotic to a level at which only about a third of the structure is destroyed. Whether, in the latter case, the enzyme attacks only a limited type of bond in the fibrin structure, or whether it is itself being destroyed during the course of fibrinolysis, cannot be decided on the evidence of existing data alone. There is little doubt that normal cows' blood shows fibrinolysis.*

The simplest possible equation to describe an enzymatic destruction of fibrin bonds, or a combination of such first-order reactions, would be:

$$\frac{-dA'}{dt} = \frac{A'}{t_f} \tag{3}$$

where t_f is the time taken for A' to fall to $1/e$th of its initial value.

If the equation holds, a plot of log A' vs. time should be linear, though the correct rate-constant cannot be determined so long as the start of the fibrinolytic process is confused with the later stages of coagulation, so that the theoretically "initial" value of $A'(A'_0)$ cannot be determined.

*Note added in proof: This is no longer believed.

Measurements from photo-enlarged printed thrombelastograms are not very accurate but Fig. 3a shows that the curves are as straight as might be expected. Since both the A' scale and the time scale are arbitrary, they are not shown on the graphs. Page and number references from the Atlas for the individual curves are given in the original paper. Some of the thrombelastograms were from recalcified citrated blood and some from native blood. Coagulants such as brain extract do not appear to have been used.

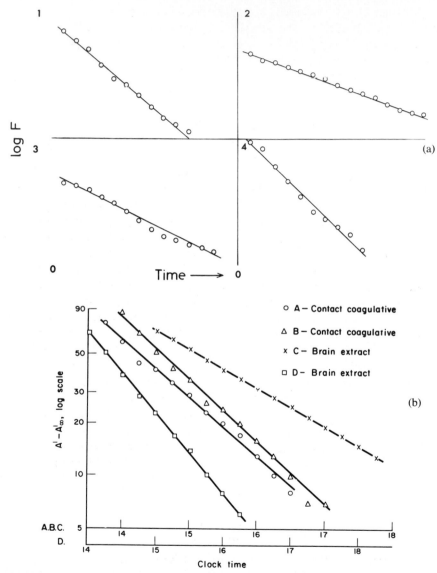

FIG. 3. (a) FIBRINOLYSIS FROM THROMBELASTOGRAMS (HUMAN BLOOD). (b) DITTO FOR COWS' BLOOD FROM TORSIOMETER.

Figure 3b shows a number of similar curves from our own experiments on bovine blood, subtracting an asymptotic value of A' before taking the logarithms. These are satisfactorily linear and it is therefore concluded that the "basic equation" for fibrinolysis is the very simple exponential, eq. (3), with an additional term in the case of cows' blood.

(c) *Coagulation*

Figure 4 shows complete curves from the torsiometer. It is evident that the first (coagulation) region is sigmoid. The third region only appears to be sigmoid because of

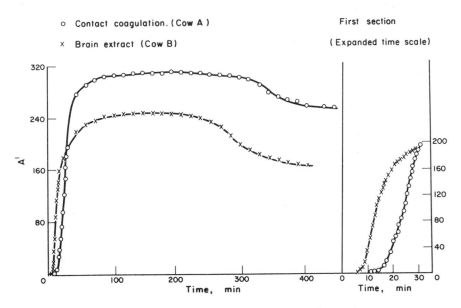

FIG. 4. COMPLETE TORSIOMETER CURVE (COWS' BLOOD).

the presence of the "mixed" region 2. It is evident that, when two long-chain molecules are linked at one point, the same pair is likely to link very soon at other points. The initial stages of coagulation thus involve an acceleration but, as the number of free linkage-points becomes increasingly limited, the process must eventually slow down; i.e. the curve must be sigmoid.

The simple first-order equation (3) may be rewritten:

$$\ln (A'_0/A') = t/t_f \qquad (3a)$$

In order to find the simplest possible modification of this equation that might describe coagulation, we will first write a generalized equation:

$$\ln (A'_0/A') \propto f(t) \qquad (3b)$$

To find the simplest value of $f(t)$ which might account for coagulation, we note that, whereas in fibrinolysis at zero time, A' is maximal and at infinite time it is minimal, for coagulation the reverse is the case: at zero time it is zero and at infinite time, maximal. The function of t chosen must therefore reverse these boundary conditions and must also provide a sigmoid type of curve. The simplest function which satisfies these conditions is the reciprocal, $1/t$.

Hence we write:

$$\ln (A'_\infty / A') \propto 1/t,$$

where A'_∞ is the final value of A' or, since the proportionality constant has the dimensions of time, t_c is, in fact, the time taken for A to reach $1/e$th of its final value A'_∞

$$A' = A'_\infty \, e^{-t_c/t} \tag{4}$$

This equation meets the above requirements and is the "basic equation" for coagulation. It is tested by plotting $\ln A'$ vs. $1/t$ and, although at the time not understood, it was found to hold so well for coagulating milk and, with the apparatus then available, reasonably well for blood, that it was published some years ago[19]. Special logarithmic-reciprocal graph paper is used for plotting these data.

Before discussing further its significance, some data must be given, since one of the requirements of a "basic equation" is that it should be "applicable to a fairly wide range of materials or conditions".

It proved difficult to test the equation with the enlarged thrombelastograms. Since we are plotting a reciprocal time against $\log A'$ it is essential to find the correct time zero. This is the moment at which polymerization of fibrin starts and neither the thrombelastograph nor the torsiometer is sufficiently sensitive to detect this accurately. In measuring the enlarged thrombelastograms, an attempt was made to determine this starting point from the beginnings of the slightest trace of widening of the base line. The results are, naturally, far from accurate but Fig. 5a shows that the curves are reasonably linear. As in Fig. 3a no units are given.

Using the torsiometer, a separate viscometric test was made on a small sample of blood flowing down a vertical stainless steel tube through a hypodermic needle used as a capillary, into a graduated vertical siliconed glass tube. The height of the rising column of initially liquid blood (surmounted by a spot of kerosene) was recorded every six seconds using a metronome. The readings, subtracted from the initial "head" were then plotted on semi-log paper against time. At such relatively high rates of shear, blood is almost Newtonian; moreover, the first effect of a coagulant is probably to reduce viscosity slightly and this would tend to cancel the slight rise due to the falling head. Figure 6 shows that it is possible to determine the starting time to about 1/10 min from the breakaway from the linear part of the curve. It is only when these independently determined time-zeros are used, that eq. (4) is found to hold. Data are shown in Fig. 5b. There is a danger in using a flow method to determine the start of fibrin polymerization since DINTENFASS and ROZENBERG[20] have shown that native blood starts to coagulate (by contact) sooner at higher than at lower rates of shear in a cone-cone viscometer. In the present work, this source of error became serious only when higher concentrations of brain extract were used, giving a very short coagulation time. Also since the error diminishes in importance as coagulation proceeds, no torsiometric data were used until five minutes had elapsed after the indicated start of polymerization. In many cases, of course, the torsiometer readings during these first few minutes were too small to be reliable in any case. Certain experiments were done without adding brain extract in order to avoid this source of error; but this has the disadvantage that the causative agent of coagulation is probably complex. There is contact with steel surfaces but the presence of traces of tissue juice cannot be altogether ruled out.

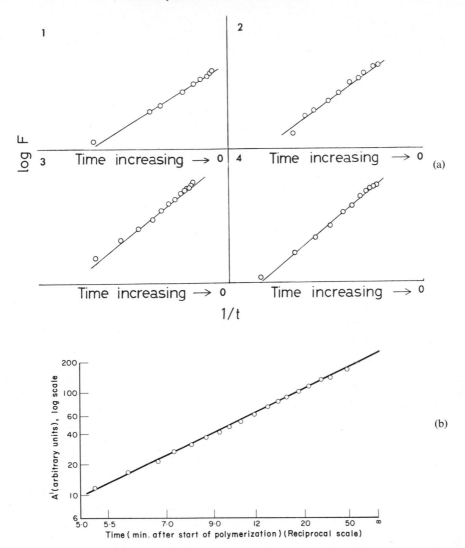

FIG. 5. (a) COAGULATION FROM THROMBELASTOGRAMS (HUMAN BLOOD). (b) COAGULATION FROM TORSIO-
METER (COWS' BLOOD).

Many curves like that shown in Fig. 5b have been obtained with bovine blood. Except occasionally at the start of the experiment, where the time errors are largest, very
good straight lines are obtained.

WHAT DOES THE TORSIOMETER MEASURE?

Equation (4) would appear to be isomorphic with the well-known "basic equation"
which relates viscosity (η) to absolute temperature (T) with fair accuracy for most
unassociated liquids.

$$\eta = A e^{Q/RT} \qquad (5)$$

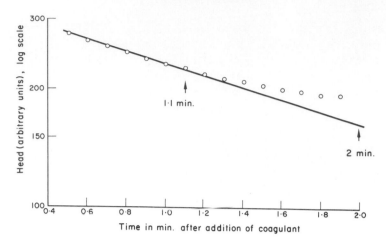

FIG. 6. "VISCOSITY" CURVE SHOWING FIRST TRACE OF POLYMERIZATION (COWS' BLOOD).

In gases, viscosity is caused by the molecules "getting in each other's way" and it increases with rising speed of movement, i.e. with temperature. In liquids, the molecules are more like a flock of birds, trying to fly in formation in spite of a gale, as HINSHELWOOD has put it[21]. As temperature falls, the kinetic energy of the molecules is reduced but the potential barriers are not much affected, hence viscosity rises. In coagulation (at constant temperature) the kinetic energy remains unchanged but the potential energy to be overcome progressively increases. It is therefore not surprising that similar equations, differing of course in sign and substituting time (i.e. extent of process of coagulation) for temperature, should prove to be basic. No doubt it should be possible to derive eq. (4) from probability considerations.

But a difficulty at once presents itself. Equation (5) is generally taken to apply only to liquids (including super-cooled liquids: glasses) but not to elastic systems, since the picture is of a process of diffusion in which the molecules exchange places by overcoming potential barriers between them. When a shearing force is applied, there is a greater tendency to move in one direction than in the reverse direction, hence flow. FERRY et al.[22] however, have successfully applied this equation to a purely elastic modulus of a fibrin gel prepared from thrombin and fibrinogen. The temperature dependence of rigidity would be a measure of the strength of junction points in the fibrin structure. The bonds break down as temperature increases.*

It is generally claimed that the thrombelastograph measures rigidity and not viscosity. In fact all such oscillatory methods measure a mixture of both, which may be described as a "complex modulus".

Torsiometers, including the thrombelastograph, do not record the viscosity of liquid blood, nor changes in that of the serum during the process of coagulation. But, in the course of their oscillatory motion, part of the energy is alternately stored and released and part dissipated as heat. The resistance associated with the latter part is called either "the imaginary part of the elastic modulus" or (when this is divided by the frequency) "the viscosity". It is in this sense, that torsiometers measure both elasticity and viscosity, i.e. the viscosity of the whole structure, not that of the continuous phase.

*The writer is indebted to Professor Ferry for a personal letter concerning this point. He describes the linear ln G : $1/T$ curves as "a purely empirical observation".

Unfortunately, neither the thrombelastograph nor the torsiometer has a sinusoidal motion but our experiments have proved that, in the case of the latter, this does not matter, since the complex modulus is almost entirely independent of the (very low) frequency. This has been tested by running two torsiometers on the same sample simultaneously at different speeds (see Fig. 7). There is also some indirect evidence that

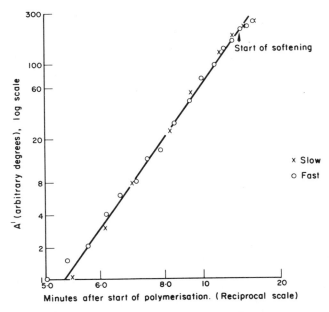

FIG. 7. TWO TORSIOMETER RUNS ON IDENTICAL COWS' BLOOD: FREQUENCIES AS 2 : 1.

the "real" (elastic) part of the measured complex modulus does represent by far the greater part of the whole. In general, one would expect a reduction of frequency to increase the proportion of the real to the imaginary part. It is unlikely, but not impossible, that this would happen without showing any change in the value of the complex modulus over the course of the coagulation if the two parts were of comparable magnitude, and most unlikely that the viscous part would preponderate at such low frequencies.

It is therefore correct to describe the measure of firmness A' as "a measure of the complex modulus". The term "complex viscosity" could equally well be used but might tend to be misleading. (An excellent elementary explanation of complex moduli is to be found in a paper by MARVIN[23].

By making a time-pause between the swings of the thrombelastograph the oscillation curve comes nearer to a sinusoidal form than does the sharply-peaked curve of the torsiometer. It therefore seems very likely that here also A' measures the complex modulus fairly closely and that the elastic part preponderates.

Since this is not (to our knowledge) fully proved, we have preferred to write A' for consistency throughout this paper; but it would probably be quite safe to write G^* (the usual symbol for the complex modulus) and to assume the equation $G^* = G' + iG''$ where G' is the real part and G'' the imaginary (i.e. viscous) part of the modulus.

DISCUSSION

Two points remain to be considered: it may be objected that it is well-known that all three of the processes discussed in this paper are extremely complex and that our "basic equations" are far too simple. There is the whole question of radial displacement of particles in flow in artificial tubes: even the end-stage of coagulation, fibrin polymerization, is a highly complex reaction, probably involving both hydrogen and sulphur linkages; and fibrinolysis is certainly not just a simple destruction of fibrin by the enzyme plasmin. But it must be remembered that most of these reactions are first-order and that a combination of first-order reactions is itself first-order. Moreover, the relative speeds of the reactions may differ greatly and if, as is the case, we can *in fact* get very simple equations to fit them, it would be absurd to complain! Moreover, as has been pointed out, basic equations are not expected to hold in all cases. They serve as a kind of scaffolding around which more complex terms may be introduced.

The second point is the significance of the time constants t_c and t_f. Unfortunately the latter is difficult to measure because of the confounding of coagulation and fibrinolysis in the middle region. The obvious methods for getting over the difficulty would be either to extrapolate the two equations or to determine t_f from the logarithmic curve using GUGGENHEIM's method[24]. With more accurate data this could be done with human blood but would be more difficult with cows' blood. Indeed the ratio t_c/t_f is less likely to prove interesting for normal cows' blood because of the relatively long period of time during which A' remains almost unchanged. There is presumably some fibrinolysis, since the coagulation equation no longer holds but there is also some further coagulation. It has proved impossible so far to determine the time at which "exponential" fibrinolysis, free from the influence of coagulation, really starts.

Since t_c is the time taken for the blood to reach $1/e$ th of its ultimate firmness and t_f, the time taken for fibrinolysis to reach $1/e$ th of completion, a high value of t_c and a low value of t_f, i.e. a high value of t_c/t_f, would imply a blood that remained liquid for a long time whereas a low value of this ratio would imply a blood that coagulated quickly and stayed coagulated for a long time. This number might have considerable clinical importance.

In general rheology, REINER[25] has pointed out that all materials flow if one waits long enough and that the decision as to whether to consider, say, a piece of glass as a solid or a liquid, depends simply on the ratio of relaxation time to observation time. He has called this ratio "the Deborah Number" from the quotation in the book of Judges: "The mountains flowed* before the Lord". "For God, one thousand years are like a day". Dare we suggest that t_c/t_f, if and when it can be accurately measured, should be called "The Pharoah Number"? Surely the first plague of Egypt was the biggest experiment in blood coagulation (and, presumably, fibrinolysis, since the rivers continued to flow with blood) in recorded history.

ADDENDUM

Since writing this paper, my attention has been drawn to two facts which would modify my wording. First, there is as yet no evidence for cows' blood that softening is due to fibrinolysis and there is definite evidence that, except in pathological cases, the

---

*"Flowed" is the correct translation, not "melted". Our Icelandic friends are used to mountains that flow and are very familiar with the latter text, which is quoted in their National Anthem.

softening shown in the thrombelastograms is not fibrinolysis. The phenomenological term "softening" should therefore be substituted for "fibrinolysis" throughout. Secondly, Hartert* has pointed out that the width of a thrombelastogram, which I have called A', is not itself a measure of the rigidity. If the material had an infinite rigidity, the recorded deflections would still be finite and would have a value which Hartert designates as 100. It is therefore necessary to plot, not $\log A'$, in Figs. 3a and 5a but $\log [(A'_\infty.A')/(A'_\infty - A')]$. The figure of 100 is, of course, not applicable to the data shown in the figures, but, from Hartert's paper, it is assumed that A'_∞ is about twice the maximum value of A'. Theoretical straight lines on the $\log A'$ plots, both for coagulation (plotting against $1/t$) and softening (plotting against t) were recalculated making this correction and, except for the highest points, the curves were found to be as nearly linear as those shown in the figures. This means that, although the wrong parameter was plotted, the conclusions are not incorrect.

It is hoped some day to recalculate a number of thrombelastograms for both equations, making the appropriate correction.

ACKNOWLEDGMENTS

My best thanks are due to Mr. B. Brown for bleeding the cows and to Mr. J. Burnett who did most of the experiments with cows' blood. I have consulted too many of my friends and colleagues about the subject of this paper to mention them all by name and I hope that a collective "thank you" will suffice.

The programme for work on coagulation of blood carried out in this laboratory is financed by Grant No. HE-05732 from the U.S. National Institutes of Health.

REFERENCES

[1] REINER, M. *Deformation, Strain and Flow*, H. K. Lewis, London, 1960, 2nd ed. p. 8.
[2] MAXWELL, J. C. *Phil. Mag.* **35**, 129, 1868.
[3] SCOTT BLAIR, G. W. and BURNETT, J. *Kolloid-Z.* **168**, 98, 1960.
[4] SCOTT BLAIR, G. W. *Proc. 4th Ann. Conf. on Adhesion and Adhesives*, 1966 (In process of publication).
[5] SCOTT BLAIR, G. W. *Nature* **183**, 613, 1959.
[6] CASSON, N. *Brit. Soc. Rheol. Bull.* No. 52, 5, 1957.
[7] CASSON, N. *Rheology of Disperse Systems.* MILL, C. C. (Editor), Pergamon Press, 1959 p. 84.
[8] MERRILL, E. W., MARGETTS, W. G., COKELET, G. R. and GILLILAND, E. R. in *Symposium on Biorheology*, COPLEY, A. L. (Editor), *Proc. 4th Int. Cong. Rheol.*, Interscience Publ. John Wiley, New York, 1965, part 4, p. 135.
[9] COPLEY, A. L. *Science* **94**, 543, 1941.
[10] SCOTT BLAIR, G. W. *Rheol. Acta* **4**, 53, 1965 (corrected p. 152).
[11] SCOTT BLAIR, G. W. *Cah. Groupe franç. Rheol.* **1**, (2) 75, 1966.
[12] HERSCHEL, W. H. and BULKLEY, R. *Kollold-Z.* **39**, 291, 1926.
[13] COPLEY, A. L., KRCHMA, L. C. and WHITNEY, M. E. *J. Gen. Physiol.* **26**, 49, 1942.
[14] SCOTT BLAIR, G. W. *Rheol. Acta,* 1966.
[15] BURNETT, J. and SCOTT BLAIR, G. W. *Dairy Inds.* **28**, 220, 1963.
[16] BUDTZ-OLSEN, O. E. *Clot Retraction*, Blackwell, Oxford, 1951.
[17] MARCHAL, G., LEROUX, M. E. and SAMAMA, M. *Atlas de Thrombodynamographie*. Service de Propagande Edition, Information, Paris 1962.

*HARTERT, H. *Flow Properties of Blood and Other Biological Systems.* COPLEY, A. L. and STAINSBY, G. (Editors), Pergamon Press, 1960, p. 188.

[18] Scott Blair, G. W. In process of publication 1966.
[19] Scott Blair, G. W. and Burnett, J. *Biorheol.* **1**, 183, 1963.
[20] Dintenfass, L. and Rozenberg, M. C. *J. Atheroscler.* **5**, 276, 1965.
[21] Hinshelwood, Sir C. N. *The Structure of Physical Chemistry*, Oxford Univ. Press, 1952.
[22] Ferry, J. D., Miller, M. and Shulman, S. *Arch. Biochem. Biophys.* **34**, 424, 1951.
[23] Marvin, R. S. *Ind. Engng. Chem.* **44**, 696, 1952.
[24] Guggenheim, E. A. *Phil. Mag.* (7th ser.), **2**, 538, 1926.
[25] Reiner, M. *Physics Today* **17**, 62, 1964.

DISCUSSION

CHARM (*U.S.A.*):

I think I would like vigorously to disagree with Dr. Scott Blair's analysis of the Casson and the Herschel and Bulkley equations. We have experimentally dealt in considerable detail with both of these. We have found that eq. (2) (Herschel–Bulkley) that you have on the board here, does not apply over wide ranges of shear stress and shear rate. As a matter of fact, in the *Proceedings of the Third European Congress on Microcirculation*, we published a paper in which we employed eq. (2) to compare tube flow measurements with viscometry measurements and we noticed that the deviation between these occurred because of attempting to extrapolate eq. (2) to high shear rate ranges. We have found that eq. (1), the Casson equation, will apply between 1 and 100,000 reciprocal seconds. We do find that you can make eq. (2) and eq. (1) agree over more than perhaps 2 decades. If one tries to extrapolate much beyond that, you find sharp deviations. Most of our work has been done with human blood. I do not know if there should be any difference with the type of blood, but at least with human blood, I feel quite safe in making this statement.

SCOTT BLAIR (*England*):

Thank you. This might seem to be a telling criticism of my suggestion that the Herschel and Bulkley equation is the basic equation for flow of blood. But I would just point out that, as I said before: I have never thought that the scaffolding I saw when I went through the streets of Reykjavik, was the final house! I have shown that, at least over say 1½ decades, it is impossible to distinguish the one equation from the other and this means that we could use either equation when we are doing experiments over a limited range. I think that it is better to use the Herschel and Bulkley equation—no, not *better* to use, because it is more difficult to use, but I think it is the more "basic equation" over such ranges because it can be derived, as I have explained all too briefly and very badly, I am afraid. I have tried to derive it from first principles, whereas the Casson equation appears to me to be entirely empirical, at least as applied to cows' blood. With regard to which equation fits better over many decades, the evidence is conflicting.*

BUGLIARELLO (*U.S.A.*):

I would like, too, to urge some caution in applying the Herschel–Bulkley equation because we have to be a little bit careful as to what we do mean by first principles. I think perhaps if we think in terms of first principles in continuum mechanics, we must first take into account the recent developments by Knowles, by Professor Rivlin, by Truesdell, Moll, Markovitz and others. These developments show really that basic equations are far more complicated than the type of two-dimensional equations you are considering. We may find data that fit the two-dimensional model, but when we try to extrapolate or to make use of these data to describe situations in a three-dimensional situation, we may very well find that these simply do not apply.

SCOTT BLAIR:

Yes, I think I would agree with this. But I think it is well perhaps to start with the scaffolding: scaffolding is perhaps not the right word, it should be the concrete blocks: concrete structures that are built up, around which the building is later constructed and that, where possible, we should use those constructions around which to build equations. I do not like the Casson equation except as a very useful, extremely useful, way of getting parameters for blood because it is so easy to use; whereas I say the Herschel–Bulkley equation seems to me to have some meaning. But I would like to say again: by "basic equation" I mean something like the equations that Hooke and Newton originally proposed which have had to be altered, transformed, added to, multiplied, changed in a hundred and one ways, I wanted to try and find just what are the foundations on which and from which the much more complex equations, which I agree must be found, could be based?

*See note added by G. W. Scott Blair to his paper on page 356. (Editor.)

HARTERT (*Germany*):

It may be of some importance for the establishment of equations that the thrombelastogram is a non-linear curve, 100 mm amplitude mean an elasticity modulus of ∞. The amplitude of normal native human blood is about 40 mm. The amplitude of a recalcified citrated plasma, slightly centrifuged before to get rid of the red cells but to maintain the much lighter platelets, will normally be about 50 mm. This amplitude was taken as a normal comparative value. It was put in linear correlation to the scale of amplitude by adjusting it to an "arbitrary elasticity modulus" ϵ of 100. The formula for the linear elasticity modulus, plotted against the amplitude in mm is $a \cdot 100/(100-a)$ (a = amplitude in mm). The amplitude of both the upper and lower curves of the thrombelastogram is not ideally symmetrical. So it is necessary to take both curves into account. The decrease of the thrombelastogram after having reached its maximum is dependent on the presence of platelets. Its magnitude in a wide range is proportional to the amount of platelets present. Inhibition of fibrinolysis by several agents does not inhibit the platelet-related decrease of the thrombelastogram which we called clot relaxation. Somehow this relaxation seems to be a reversal of the platelet-induced strengthening of the clot. In regard to plasma, this process seems to have a similar significance for the clotting of blood as it has been proposed with a more general view by Dr. Scott Blair.

PLATELET ALTERATIONS IN RESPONSE TO FIBRINOGEN SPLIT PRODUCTS

Marion I. Barnhart,* D. C. Cress, R. L. Henry and Jeanne M. Riddle

Wayne State University School of Medicine, Department of Physiology and Pharmacology
and Henry Ford Hospital, Department of Laboratories, Detroit, Michigan, U.S.A.

Platelet aggregation can be an event of value in hemostasis, but also may lead to thrombosis, embolization and infarction. Although many agents such as thrombin[1], thrombocyte agglutinating factor[2], adenosine diphosphate[3], collagen[4] and endotoxin[5] can aggregate platelets *in vitro*, the extent of their involvement *in vivo* has not been satisfactorily resolved. Two central constituents, adenosine diphosphate[6] and fibrinogen[7] appear essential for platelet aggregation to occur regardless of other stimuli.

Alterations in fibrinogen metabolism[8] and fibrinolysis[9] occur readily in response to a variety of stresses. It was of interest to us to study the influences of fibrinogen and fibrin degradation products *in vivo*. In the course of our work on infusion of fibrinogen split products resulting from plasmin digestion, we observed a spectacular drop in the circulating platelet count. These platelet aggregations could not be attributed to activation of blood clotting mechanisms because prothrombin concentration was not reduced to signal the release of thrombin. Such findings encouraged us to follow in detail the effect of fibrinogen split products (FSP) on platelet aggregation in both *in vitro* and *in vivo* systems.

In contrast to the experience of others [10–12], our group has found that certain fibrinogen split products (β_2 fibrinogen derivative D) can aggregate platelets and even alter their morphology as determined by electron microscopy. Perhaps the time is appropriate for re-evaluation of the significance of breakdown products of fibrin and of fibrinogen in the general circulation as well as locally. Certainly the increased platelet and leucocyte stickiness encountered after *in vivo* formation or infusion of FSP merits serious consideration of these proteolysis products as influential in promoting a block to blood flow. Such a hemostatic plug could be beneficial or harmful depending on the circumstances.

MATERIALS AND METHODS

Animal experimentation. Dogs and purified proteins of canine origin were used throughout the experimentation. Each dog served as his own control. Blood samples anticoagulated with sodium citrate (3.2%) and blood cell and platelet counts were performed before anesthetization with sodium pentobarbital and at intervals throughout the experiment which frequently went as long as 12 hr. Preinfusion samples were taken to determine the effects of surgical stress unrelated to FSP. Samples were also taken during and at intervals after infusion of FSP for 8–10 hr or until the dog expired.

Some dogs were monitored with the aid of the Physiograph (E. and M. Instrument Co., Texas) for heart function, blood pressure and respiration. Thus the extent of stress and the physiologic adaptations could be followed. Stress due to surgery or unexplained reasons was minimal in dogs 75, 76, 84 and 88.

Fibrinogen split products (FSP). Purified canine fibrinogen prepared according to BARNHART and FORMAN[13] was the starting material for proteolysis. Such fibrinogen was 95–98% clottable and homogeneous by immunoelectrophoresis against univalent antifibrinogen and multivalent antiplasma (Fig. 1). This fibrinogen was reacted with

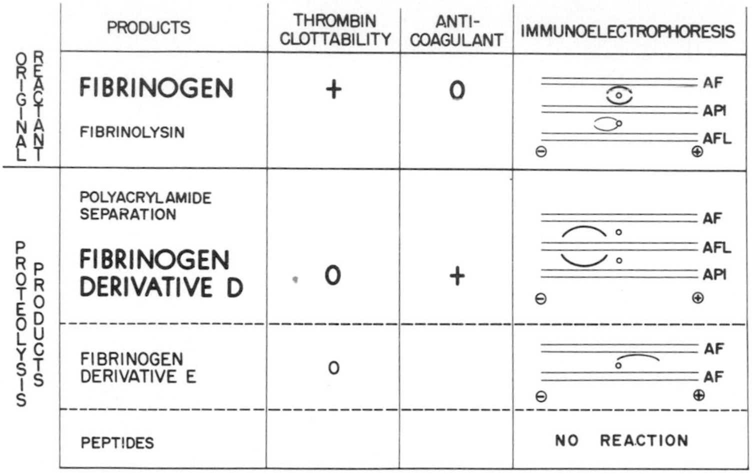

	PRODUCTS	THROMBIN CLOTTABILITY	ANTI-COAGULANT	IMMUNOELECTROPHORESIS
ORIGINAL REACTANT	**FIBRINOGEN** FIBRINOLYSIN	+	0	AF / API / AFL
PROTEOLYSIS PRODUCTS	POLYACRYLAMIDE SEPARATION **FIBRINOGEN DERIVATIVE D**	0	+	AF / AFL / API
	FIBRINOGEN DERIVATIVE E	0		AF / AF
	PEPTIDES			NO REACTION

FIG. 1. TABULATION OF PROPERTIES OF CANINE FIBRINOGEN AND THE PROTEOLYSIS PRODUCTS RESULTING FROM FIBRINOLYSIS.

Thrombolysin (Merck Sharp Dohme Division of Merck & Co., West Point, Pa). Proportions were 2000 MSD units of Thrombolysin per gram of purified fibrinogen. Digestion proceeded in phosphate buffer, pH 7.4, at 37°C for about 3 hr. Samples were taken at 30 min intervals to determine the developing anticoagulant power of the emerging proteolysis products. A modification of the antithrombin assay of FLETCHER, ALKJAERSIG and SHERRY[14] was used for this. The predigestion clotting time was about 21 sec when undiluted samples of the digest were added to a control normal plasma system. At the end of the digestion period, the anticoagulant power developed, prolonged the clotting time beyond 2 min when 1:10 dilutions of the lysate were added to the control normal plasma system.

The fibrinogen split products were separated from Thrombolysin and any undigested fibrinogen by gel filtration through Bio-Gel P 200 (Bio-Rad Laboratories, Richmond, California). The first void volume did not contain any protein and was discarded. The second and third void volumes were collected in 5 ml fractions. The contained FSP was evaluated by immunoelectrophoresis with univalent antifibrinogen for fibrinogen derivatives D and E[15]. The larger molecular weight proteins appeared first. Derivative D was the major breakdown product that resulted from the action of Thrombolysin. By immunoelectrophoresis derivative D was in the β_2 region and reacted with antifibrinogen only (Fig. 1). Derivative E was a minor breakdown product and on immunoelectrophoresis was located at the point of origin and extended into the α_2 region (Fig. 1). In most experiments, the FSP used contained a small amount of derivative E.

In dog 88 and the *in vivo* platelet experiments, essentially pure derivative D was used.

Quantitation of non-clottable fibrinogen products of proteolysis. An immunologic assay was applied to serum samples and the amount of fibrinogen-related molecules was determined by quantitative precipitin reaction with univalent antifibrinogen. With thrombin clottable fibrinogen removed, a measure was gained of the non-clottable fibrinogen molecules. Serial dilutions to 1/320 were prepared with physiologic saline and defibrinated plasma or other fluid samples to insure conditions of antibody excess or equivalence in the test. The precipitin was developed by adding 0.1 ml of one of the dilutions to 4.8 ml physiologic saline with antifibrinogen (0.1 ml) added finally. The mixture was incubated at 37°C for 1 hr and the turbidity resulting from the antigen–antibody complexes was measured by nephelometry in a Turner Spectrofluorometer. The readings were converted to fibrinogen equivalents by reference to a standard curve prepared by mixing purified fibrinogen with antifibrinogen. Results were expressed as milligrams of fibrinogen related molecules (FRM).

Platelet preparations for in vitro *aggregation.* Platelet rich plasma (PRP) was prepared from 20 ml samples of fresh dog blood anticoagulated with sodium citrate (3.2%) in physiologic saline. Blood cells were sedimented by centrifugation at 164 g yielding platelet-rich plasma. The platelets were concentrated by centrifuging at 2520 g for 10 min and the platelet button was resuspended in half the original plasma volume. Such platelets were functional for about 4 hr. Washed platelets were used in some studies. Whole blood was employed for some of the electron microscopy.

Electron microscopy. Platelets were studied as whole mount preparations collected on Formvar coated slides. Procedure followed that described by REBUCK and associates[16] except that sodium citrate was used rather than heparin. This change in anticoagulants did not change either the platelet morphology or magnitude of aggregation from that described as typical in the presence of heparin. The citrated plasma was then available for assay of various blood coagulation proteins.

Details of the platelet preparations follow. A hemorepellant 19 gauge needle (Fenwal) and siliconized 20 ml syringe was employed to collect 9 ml of whole blood. After detaching the needle, the blood was promptly delivered into a siliconized bottle containing 1 ml sodium citrate (3.2%). A Formvar coated slide was immediately introduced and the citrated blood flooded over the slide. With the bottle on its side, the preparation was incubated at 37°C. After 8 min, the Formvar slide with its adherent platelets was removed and thoroughly washed in Tyrode's solution at 37°C. Platelets were fixed for 15 min with buffered osmium tetroxide[17]. The Formvar film with the adherent platelets was transferred from the slide to grids for electron microscopy. An RCA-EMU-3H electron microscope operating at 50 KV was used to view and photograph the platelets. Platelets were classified according to morphologic type with 200 individual platelets counted for a differential. The number and quality of the platelet aggregates were determined for each 100 individual platelets.

RESULTS

Bovine as well as canine degradation products of fibrinogen infused into dogs effectively reduced circulating platelet counts[18]. Details of experiments with canine FSP illustrate the general experience and further avoid the possibility of foreign protein reactions. By immunoelectrophoresis, the β_2 fibrinogen derivative D was the predominant or only constituent of the FSP used in the experiments to follow (Fig. 2).

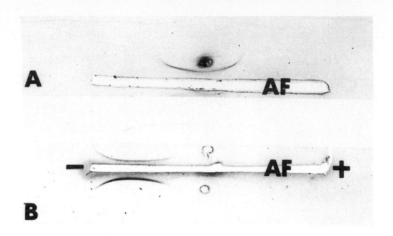

FIG. 2. IMMUNOELECTROPHORETIC PATTERNS OF FIBRINOGEN AND ITS PROTEOLYSIS PRODUCTS. A. PURIFIED CANINE FIBRINOGEN REMAINS AT THE POINT OF APPLICATION AND FORMS A SINGLE PRECIPITIN ARC WITH ANTIFIBRINOGEN (AF). B. THE PRECIPITIN ARC IN THE UPPER PORTION MARKS THE REACTION OF PURIFIED β_2 FIBRINOGEN D REACTING WITH ANTIFIBRINOGEN. THE LOWER PRECIPITIN ARCS (ONE IS VERY FAINT EXTENDING THROUGH THE β AND α REGIONS AND REPRESENTS THE MINOR CONSTITUENT FIBRINOGEN DERIVATIVE E) ALSO RESULTED FROM INTERACTION WITH ANTIFIBRINOGEN.

TABLE 1. CHANGES IN PLATELETS FOLLOWING INFUSION OF FSP

Dog	Dose mg/kg	Platelet counts per mm³						
		Actual		% change with hrs.				
		Pre	Post	$\frac{1}{12}$	1	$2\frac{1}{2}$–$3\frac{1}{2}$	$4\frac{1}{2}$	5
71	177	450,000	187,000	−58	−44	−34	−31	
72	228	455,000	125,000	−72	−56	−39	−10	
76	55	145,000	46,500	−68		−8	−21	
83	33	280,000	165,000	−41	−53	−38		−18
84	20	212,500	155,000	−27	−11	+16		+23

Platelet disappearance following FSP infusion. Following the infusion of FSP (20–228 mg/kg body wt), the peripheral platelet count declined sharply (Table 1). The immediate decrease averaged 54% in the 5 dogs. The response appeared dose dependent. With the smallest dose (20 mg/kg in dog 84) the platelet count regained normal limits (±15%) by 1 hr. In dog 76 (55 mg/kg) restoration of the preinfusion platelet count took 3 hr. In dog 72 (228 mg/kg) the time required was $4\frac{1}{2}$ hr. The platelet data obtained for dogs 71 and 83 were complicated by longer periods of surgical stress prior to infusion which may account for the slower restitution times.

The platelet disappearance might have its explanation in at least two different mechanisms. First, the possibility existed that FSP or an unrecognized stress effect had activated the blood coagulation system to release thrombin which had aggregated the platelets. Second, FSP, *per se,* might aggregate platelets with the larger aggregates filtered by the microcirculation to produce lower peripheral platelet counts.

There was little or no evidence that FSP activated prothrombin to produce defibrination. Prothrombin concentration, as determined by two-stage assay[19], was not significantly altered by the infusion of FSP (Table 2). Thus, platelet disappearance could not be related to thrombin evolution.

TABLE 2. EXTENT OF PROTHROMBIN ACTIVATION DURING EXPERIMENTATION

Dog	Drug infused	Prothrombin U/ml			
		Pre	Immediate post	Actual change units	% Change
71	Bov. FSP	106	90	16	−14
72	Bov. FSP	146	117	29	−19
75	Dog FSP	89	86	3	−.09
76	Dog FSP	116	127	13	+11
82	Hum. Alb.				
	Dog FSP	91	84	8	−.06
83	Dog FSP	92	100	15	+.08
84	Dog FSP	174	182	8	+.04
88	Dog FSP	169	166	3	−.09

Further evidence that defibrination had not occurred with FSP infusion was gained from the fibrinogen assays[20] on plasma collected during experimentation. In dog 72, the preinfusion level was 120 mg% and was found to be 128 mg% after FSP. Pre- and post-infusion values for dog 76 were 210 mg% and 197 mg% respectively. In dog 84, fibrinogen was 185 mg% before and 174 mg% after FSP.

The platelet disappearance seemed more related to the presence of altered fibrinogen (FSP) than to activation of the proteins concerned in coagulation. Data from dog 84 illustrated these points especially well (Fig. 3).

The second explanation offered for platelet disappearance, namely a direct effect of FSP, was considered. During the *in vivo* experiments with FSP, occasional platelet aggregates were observed in the platelet counting chamber although only single platelets were counted. It was clearly established that such aggregates were not elicited by faulty technique in the blood sampling. It became apparent that these aggregates appeared only after infusion of FSP. The aggregations were sufficiently impressive throughout the series to encourage *in vitro* studies of platelets and FSP. It seemed possible that FSP might directly affect the platelet surface to induce aggregation.

FSP aggregates platelets in vitro. Several different test systems were employed to determine if FSP had a direct effect on platelets. Aggregation of platelets was achieved with either washed platelets or platelet-rich plasma. Platelet counts were made on the test system (0.3 ml contained 0.1 ml platelets, 0.1 ml saline and 0.1 ml FSP with a concentration of 4.7 mg protein/ml) and compared with the control system containing only platelets and saline. A 43% reduction in platelet count occurred immediately and persisted for 15–30 min when FSP was present.

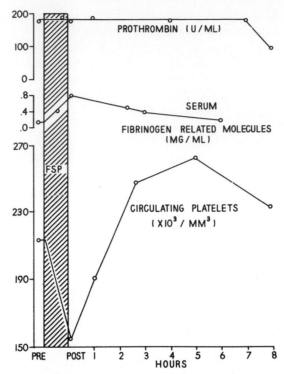

FIG. 3. DEMONSTRATION OF PLATELET DISAPPEARANCE WITHOUT PROTHROMBIN ACTIVATION AFTER INFUSION OF FSP (20 MG/KG BODY WT). NOTE THE IMMEDIATE RISE IN NON-CLOTTABLE FIBRINOGEN RELATED MOLECULES WHICH WERE RAPIDLY CLEARED FROM THE BLOOD. CORRECTION OF THROMBOCYTOPENIA WAS COMPLETE BY 2 HR POST INFUSION.

Observation of platelet aggregation with phase microscopy. Freshly prepared platelet-rich plasma was observed with the phase microscope before and during mixing with either FSP or ADP or a mixture of FSP and ADP. Concentrations of FSP and ADP were selected that were ineffectual in producing aggregates visible by phase. However, combination of these two ineffective reagents promptly aggregated the platelets (Fig. 4). Only a few single platelets could be found. Platelet fusion and viscous metamorphosis had probably not occurred as the aggregates could be partially dispersed by gentle agitation.

Observations of platelet morphology and aggregation with electron microscopy. To gain more insight into the platelet changes induced by FSP and ADP, whole mount preparations were studied with the electron microscope. Platelets in either platelet-rich plasma or whole blood aggregated readily when FSP was added to confirm and extend the observations with phase microscopy. Furthermore, the surface morphology and the alterations in response to FSP and ADP could be appreciated. These platelet changes were compatible with the concept of platelet activation.

The responses of platelets in whole blood systems to added FSP and comparison with responses to ADP and saline controls, emphasize the fact that β_2 fibrinogen derivative D alone can be a powerful aggregating agent for platelets (Fig. 5c). FSP (Fig. 2, center section) was added to whole blood to give final concentrations from 0.09 to 0.72 mg/ml. The number of platelet aggregates formed was concentration dependent.

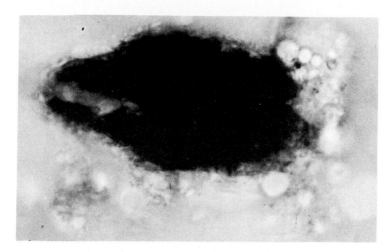

FIG. 4. PHASE PHOTOMICROGRAPH OF PLATELET AGGREGATE INDUCED BY FSP AND ADP ACTING ON PLATELET-RICH PLASMA *in vitro*. COPY ON PAN X FILM FROM KODACHROME X TRANSPARENCY, ORIGINAL EXPOSURE 8 SEC, BLUE DAYLIGHT FILTER, × 3780.

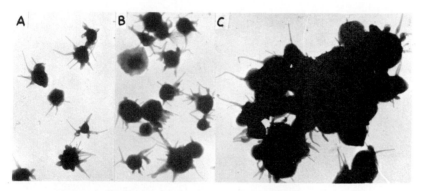

FIG. 5. ELECTRON MICROGRAPHS OF PLATELETS FROM CITRATED WHOLE BLOOD. COMPARISON OF EFFECTS OF β_2 FIBRINOGEN DERIVATIVE D (0.7 MG/ML PLATELETS) WITH THE CONTROL SITUATION AND AFTER ADP. A. EXAMPLE OF PLATELET MORPHOLOGY BEFORE FSP INFUSION. INDIVIDUAL DENDRITIC PLATELETS. THE RARE PLATELET AGGREGATES CONSISTED OF ONLY 2–3 PLATELETS. × 3970. B. PLATELETS PLUS ADP $(1 \times 10^{-5}$ MG/ML). DENDRITIC PLATELETS PREDOMINATE. THE NUMBER OF PLATELET AGGREGATES WAS INCREASED BUT THE AGGREGATES REMAINED SMALL. × 3970. C. PLATELETS PLUS FSP (0.7 MG/ML). PLATE-LET AGGREGATES WERE INCREASED IN NUMBER AND CONTAINED MANY PLATELETS. PLATELETS HAD SHORT AND FEW PSEUDOPODS IN COMPARISON TO THE CONTROL. × 4760.

With 0.72 mg FSP, 44 aggregates formed per 100 individual platelets counted. With 0.2 mg FSP, 30 smaller aggregates were found. With 0.09 mg FSP/ml only 13 small aggregates were counted per 100 single platelets. All of the aggregates were composed of dendritic type platelets which appeared loosely bound.

The β_2 fibrinogen derivative D obviously altered the morphology of even the individual platelets. Many appeared somewhat swollen and the number of dendrites were more stubby and reduced in number. For example, platelets in the control saline environment had 93% of the single platelets in the dendritic form (Fig. 5a). Of these, 93% had from 4–8 long pseudopods. In contrast, the platelets exposed to 0.2 mg FSP/ml had 81% in the dendritic form but only 60% had more than 4 dendrites and these were usually short and blunt.

When FSP was combined with ADP and platelet morphology examined an increase was observed in the number of spread forms. However, the aggregates produced remained largely dendritic and the actual number of aggregates found was 81. The aggregates were larger than with either FSP or ADP alone (Fig. 5b). Occasionally platelet clumps showed peripheral hyalomeric fusion and spreading. It would appear that for viscous metamorphosis to occur, an additional stimulus may be necessary.

In vivo *platelet aggregation during infusion of FSP*. One final experiment was undertaken in a dog infused with FSP in an attempt to identify the described platelet alterations in the circulating blood. A small dose of FSP (9 mg/kg body wt) was given to simulate the conditions of the *in vitro* platelet work with the electron microscope. The dog had an estimated plasma volume of 528 ml so that the FSP concentration should have been near 0.2 mg/ml plasma. By immunologic assay, 0.15 mg/ml serum was measured. The FSP was infused more rapidly than in previous dog experiments. Platelet counts and plasma samples for blood coagulation tests were taken before, during and at several intervals after the FSP was given. Concurrently whole blood samples were taken for electron microscopy of the circulating platelets.

By mid-infusion of the FSP, which was predominantly β_2 fibrinogen derivative D, the peripheral platelet count had fallen 85%. At this time, small platelet aggregates were visible in both the phase counting chamber and by electron miscroscopy (Fig. 6b).

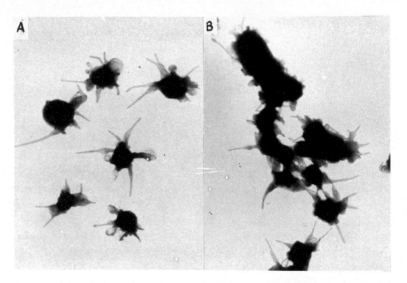

FIG. 6. ELECTRON MICROGRAPHS OF PLATELETS THAT WERE EXPOSED WITHIN THE CIRCULATION OF DOG 88 TO THE INFLUENCES OF FSP. A. CONTROL PLATELETS. × 6350. B. MID-INFUSION OF FSP. NOTE THE AGGREGATES. THESE VARIED IN SIZE. A RETURN TO THE CONTROL MORPHOLOGY OCCURRED BY $1\frac{1}{2}$ HR AFTER FSP. × 5950.

Neither prothrombin nor fibrinogen concentration changed significantly during the period when the platelet aggregates were visible. The changes in platelet morphology and the aggregation clearly related to FSP, *per se*.

The ultrastructure and extent of aggregation as elucidated by electron miscroscopy presented a similar pattern to the *in vitro* test systems (Fig. 7). The peak response for platelet aggregation came at mid-infusion (10 min). At this time 30 aggregates were found per 100 single platelets. It is remarkable that this value is the same value achieved with 0.2 mg FSP/ml with the *in vitro* system. Also similar was the observation of

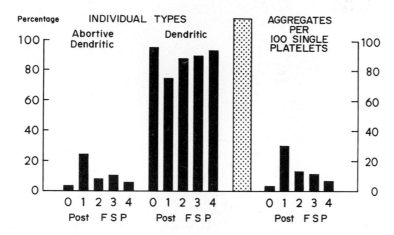

Fig. 7. Differential data collected on platelet alterations during *in vivo* infusion of FSP into dog 88. The numbers along the bottom of the graph represent samples before (0) and at intervals after FSP infusion. Note the appearance of abortive dendritic forms in the first sample taken at mid-infusion (10 min of FSP). The peak number of aggregates were found at this time also. The return to control morphology was rapidly achieved as the dose of FSP was 9 mg per kg body wt.

dendritic platelets with short blunt pseudopods. By $1\frac{1}{2}$ hr the platelet morphology had returned to the preinfusion state.

It seems most unlikely that the described changes and especially the platelet aggregations noted during infusion of FSP arose in the test system for electron microscopy. It was not possible at this time to examine circulating platelets in the microcirculation and permit FSP to influence the platelets while watching. A poor substitute was to examine carefully made peripheral blood smears for the presence of aggregates. The venipunctures were performed with siliconized equipment on an exposed femoral vein and the smear made immediately. Thus, contamination with thromboplastin was minimized. Unaware of the sequence of slides, counts were made on the number of platelet aggregates seen per 100 individual platelets. Only 6 small aggregates were found in the control smear. Immediately after FSP, 48 platelet aggregates were counted and those aggregates contained 10 or more platelets. By $1\frac{1}{2}$ hr after FSP only 10 small aggregates (2–3 platelets) were found per 100 single platelets. It seems reasonable that the smears provided worthwhile information on the existence of platelet aggregates in the circulation of a dog infused with FSP.

FSP and leucocyte stickiness. Neutrophils were also observed on the electron microscope grids prepared from the previously described *in vivo* experiment (Fig. 8). Ordinarily not many leucocytes or erythrocytes stick to the Formvar film. At mid-infusion of FSP, 50 neutrophils were counted per 100 single platelets. An occasional aggregate was seen with platelets and 1 or more neutrophils. The response was not visible in later samples.

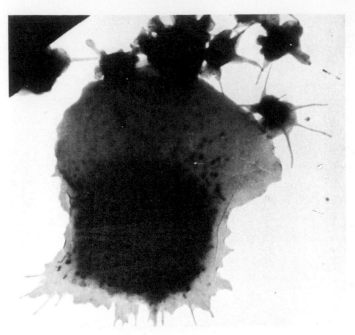

FIG. 8. ELECTRON MICROGRAPH OF LEUCOCYTE-PLATELET ADHESION SEEN AT MID-INFUSION OF FSP INTO
DOG 88. × 6340.

DISCUSSION

All of the data collected in this study direct attention to the ability of fibrinogen
split products to alter platelet morphology and also to aggregate platelets. The fibrinogen split product demonstrated as effective by itself was the β_2 fibrinogen derivativeD.
This degradation product of fibrinolysis was different from the ones tested by KOWALSKI
and associates[10], HIRSH, FLETCHER and SHERRY[11] and ZUCKER and JERUSHALMY
[12] in that it was canine, highly purified, non-clottable, and had immunoelectrophoretic
properties greatly different from fibrinogen and the proteolysis product D resulting
from a short digestion period. Furthermore, the quantities employed to elicit platelet
aggregation were relatively small and ranged from 0.09 to 0.7 mg/ml platelets in
contrast to the larger amounts of 2–8 mg/ml platelets used by the other groups.

Depletion of circulating platelet numbers consistently occurred with infusion of
purified FSP or when degradation products of *in vivo* fibrinolysin were present[21].
The coagulation system could not be implicated in the platelet decline. The disappearance of platelets under these circumstances probably resulted from the *in vivo* formed
platelet aggregates filtering out in the microcirculation. Platelet aggregates were
observed by phase microscopy, electron microscopy and in carefully prepared blood
smears taken during the elevation of non-clottable fibrinogen split products in the serum.
The possibility exists that small vessels were effectively plugged by the described
platelet aggregates to block blood flow. Such aggregation was transient because normal
platelet levels were achieved in the circulating blood ordinarily within 1–3 hr.

The bone marrow has little capacity to restore large deficits in the circulating pool
of platelets. CRADDOCK and associates[22] found 3–4 days were required for recovery

of platelet numbers in thrombocytopenic dogs. Studies in our laboratory on megakaryo-cyte development and potential in dogs indicated only 10% of the megakaryocyte population were recognizable as platelet formers and ready to release fully functional platelets to the circulation[23]. Such observations make it seem unlikely that the platelet recovery following platelet depletion, results from release of bone marrow reserves. More reasonable is the return of platelets from areas of temporary aggregation. From the *in vitro* study of platelets exposed to FSP, it was apparent that platelets were stuck together largely in the dendritic form and were rather easily dislodged from one another. Observations with the electron microscope further confirmed that fusion of the aggregated platelets had not occurred to create irreversible clumps of platelets.

Numerous agents acting alone or in combination can elicit platelet aggregation[3]. In searching for a unifying link for platelet aggregation MARCUS and ZUCKER[3] and HASLAM[6] have focused attention on ADP as essential for platelet aggregation even though other agents superficially appeared to be responsible. Also, there is good evidence that a fibrinogen-like atmosphere around the platelet is necessary for aggrega-tion. CROSS[7] found platelet aggregability by ADP was lost in the absence of fibrin-ogen and was restored by either plasma euglobulin[24] or plasma. GUGLER and LUSCHER[25] found that defective platelet responses in afibrinogenemia could be normalized by adding fibrinogen. Thus ADP and fibrinogen-like molecules appear to be basic requirements for platelet aggregation.

Our work with the β_2 fibrinogen proteolysis product D illustrates that a molecule related to fibrinogen can induce changes in platelet morphology and lead to aggregations. These effects may result on the basis of electrostatic attraction to the negatively charged platelets, or there may be cross-linking of surface oriented fibrinogen or fibrin with the proteolysis product. In either event, the electrical properties of the platelets may be sufficiently altered to encourage adhesion, cohesion and aggregation. It is also possible that the surface coating could become thick enough in the presence of larger amounts of FSP to block access of the platelet active agents. Also, a thick shell of FSP could perhaps stiffen the surface so that effective pseudopodia might be unable to develop and further platelet activation.

At present we do not understand the role of FSP in platelet function or to what extent the transient platelet aggregates may provide a temporary hemostatic plug or even block blood flow to contribute to anoxia and other sequelae of thrombosis. What is apparent is that non-clottable fibrinogen related molecules normally exist in small amounts (0.2 mg/ml) in the serum and plasma[21]. Doubling the serum content en-hanced platelet stickiness, altered the morphology and induced aggregates. An increase in non-clottable fibrinogen related molecules occurs *in vivo* in response to generalized fibrinolysis[21] accompanying thrombosis and during extracorporeal circulation[26]. SEEGERS, NIEFT and VANDENBELT[27] in 1945 reported that fibrin breakdown pro-ducts and fibrinogen breakdown products had similar chemical, functional and electro-phoretic properties. Thus with either fibrinogen or fibrin proteolysis, products like β_2 fibrinogen D may result and remain in the blood long enough to influence platelets and blood cells. These influences may be different at different times and in different loca-tions. However, enhanced platelet and cell stickiness and even small aggregations surely will affect the hemorheology of the blood.

SUMMARY

Fibrinogen split products of fibrinolysis, especially the β_2 fibrinogen derivative D, alter platelet morphology and temporarily aggregate platelets. Both *in vivo* and *in vitro* experiments provide the supporting data.

Observation of the ultrastructure of platelets exposed to FSP showed dendritic aggregates without evidence of viscous metamorphosis. However, pseudopodial formation was limited and the platelets appeared swollen when compared to preinfusion controls.

The platelet changes were concentration dependent with the largest aggregates achieved with 0.7 mg FSP/ml platelets. This concentration represents a three-fold increase over the non-clottable fibrinogen molecules measurable in serum by quantitative immunoprecipitin test.

It is suggested that fibrin and fibrinogen proteolysis products may play an important role in hemostasis and may be significant in thrombosis.

ACKNOWLEDGMENT

This work was aided by NIH research grant HE 03447 from the Public Health Service, Bethesda, Maryland, U.S.A.

REFERENCES

[1] RODMAN, N. F., Jr. and BRINKHOUS, K. M. *Fed. Proc.* **22**, 1356, 1963.
[2] MASON, R. G., LeRoy, C. and BRINKHOUS, K. M. *Henry Ford Hosp. Int. Symp. on Blood Platelets*, Detroit, 1960, JOHNSON, S. A., MONTO, R. W., REBUCK, J. W. and HORN, R. C. (Editors), Little, Brown and Co., Boston, 1961, p. 111.
[3] MARCUS, A. J. and ZUCKER, M. B. *The Physiology of Blood Platelets*. Grune and Stratton, New York, 1966.
[4] ZUCKER, M. B. and BORRELLI, J. *Proc. Soc. Exp. Biol. Med.* **109**, 779, 1962.
[5] REAM, V. J., DEYKIN, D., GUREWICH, V. and WESSLER, S. *Fed. Proc.* **23**, 459, 1964.
[6] HASLAM, R. J. In *14th Annual Symp. on Blood*, Detroit, 1966. *Thrombos. Diathes. Haemorrk.* **15**, 261, 1966.
[7] CROSS, M. J. *Thrombos. Diathes. Haemorrh.* **12**, 524, 1964.
[8] NEUHAUS, O. W., BALEGNO, H. F. and CHANDLER, A. M. *Am. J. Physiol.* (in press), 1966.
[9] VON KAULLA, K. N. *Chemistry of Thrombolysis: Human Fibrinolytic Enzymes*, Charles T. Thomas, Springfield, 1963.
[10] KOWALSKI, E., KOPÉC, M. and WEGRZYNOWICZ, Z. *Thrombos. Diathes. Haemorrh.* **10**, 406, 1964.
[11] HIRSH, J., FLETCHER, A. P. and SHERRY, S. *Am. J. Physiol.* **209**, 415, 1965.
[12] ZUCKER, M. B. and JERUSHALMY, Z. In *14th Annual Symp. on Blood,* Detroit, 1966. *Thrombos. Diathes. Haemorrh.* **15**, 631, 1966.
[13] BARNHART, M. I. and FORMAN, W. B. In *Blood Coagulation, Hemorrhage and Thrombosis.* TOCANTINS, L. M. and KAZAL, L. A. (Editors), Grune and Stratton, New York, 1964.
[14] FLETCHER, A. P., ALKJAERSIG, N. and SHERRY, S. *J. Clin. Invest.* **38**, 1096, 1959.
[15] NUSSENZWEIG, V. and SELIGMAN, M. *Rév. Hémat.* **15**, 452, 1960.
[16] REBUCK, J. W., RIDDLE, J. M., JOHNSON, S. A., MONTO, R. W. and STURROCK, R. M. *Henry Ford Hosp. Med. Bull.* **8**, 273, 1960.
[17] PALADE, G. E. *J. Exper. Med.* **95**, 285, 1952.
[18] BRECHER, G. and CRONKITE, E. P. *J. Appl. Physiol.* **3**, 365, 1950.
[19] WARE, A. G. and SEEGERS, W. H. *Am. J. Clin. Pathol.* **19**, 471, 1949.
[20] WARE, A. G., GUEST, M. M. and SEEGERS, W. H. *Arch. Biochem.* **13**, 231, 1947.
[21] BARNHART, M. I., CRESS, D. C., HENRY, R. L. and RIDDLE, J. M. *Thrombos. Diathes. Haemorrh.* **17**, 78, 1967.
[22] CRADDOCK, C. G. Jr., ADAMS, W. S., PERRY, S. and LAWRENCE, J. S. *J. Lab. Clin. Med.* **45**, 906, 1955.
[23] BARNHART, M. I. and WALSH, R. T. *Fed. Proc.* **25**, 552, 1966.

[24] BORN, G. V. R. and CROSS, M. J. *J. Physiol.* **170**, 397, 1964.
[25] GUGLER, E. and LUSCHER, E. F. *Thrombos. Diathes. Haemorrh.* **14**, 361, 1965.
[26] BARNHART, M. I. In *Blood Clotting Enzymology.* SEEGERS, W. H. (Editor), Academic Press, New York, 1967.
[27] SEEGERS, W. H., NIEFT, M. L. and VANDENBELT, J. M. *Arch. Biochem.* **7**, 15, 1945.

DISCUSSION

BRINKHOUS, (*U.S.A.*):

Is there any cation requirement for your FSP action on the platelets? Also, you mentioned that with ADP, the additional effects could be accounted for simply by addition. There was no suggestion of synergism. I was very interested as to how you determined this point, because, as you know, we have been very interested in the combination of fibrinogen and ADP in the agglutination or aggregation of platelets. In certain species, particularly the pig, platelets will not aggregate with fibrinogen in appropriate concentration and they will not aggregate with ADP. But if one adds both fibrinogen and ADP, you have some beautiful synergism, rapid aggregation occurs. It occurred to me that reanalysis of your data, looking for synergism, would be of interest.

BARNHART, (*U.S.A.*):

In answer to your question on cation requirements, all of our test systems had a plentiful supply except the washed preserved platelet system. Even here aggregation occurred with added FSP except it was not as spectacular as in the plasma or whole blood platelet systems. With respect to the ADP and FSP effects being additive or synergistic, the data can be interpreted either way. In one experiment with observation by phase microscopy, neither ADP nor FSP alone elicited visible aggregation. However, extensive aggregation occurred when these two ineffectual concentrations of ADP and FSP were together. In another experiment with the electron microscope, the results illustrated additive influences, when only the number of aggregates formed were considered. However, it was not established if these aggregates contained the same number of platelets.

PHIBBS, (*U.S.A.*):

The early adhesion of a platelet to a granulocyte, and your failure to see it later, was of interest. This is probably a non-specific process. I wonder, if it is worth looking at the granulocytes in such a preparation later on to see if phagocytosis of these altered platelets by the granulocytes has occurred. This is important in terms of what happens to these changed platelets once they are in the circulation. Are they removed by plugging capillaries or are they cleared by phagocytosis — which might be less injurious to the microcirculation.

BARNHART:

We were excited, too, in finding leucocytes and platelets adherent to one another. Also erythrocytes became more sticky. The larger aggregates unquestionably are filtered out in the microcirculation to account for the prompt drop in circulating platelets. The bone marrow reserves appear inadequate to restore the described decrease in platelet count as only 10% of the megakaryocytes are present as adult platelet formers. The fact that platelets reappear within 1–3 hr, in our best experiments, is good evidence that platelets are returning from sites of sequestration. Either the force of blood flow, local fibrinolysis or leucocyte activity are likely factors in the separation and restitution of the peripheral platelets. Of course, persistence of such platelet aggregates in the microcirculation can be an advantage or disadvantage depending on the circumstances.

SILBERBERG, (*Israel*):

I may have missed it in your presentation, but I wonder whether you have any molecular information about these FSP preparations. And what are the molecular shape, weight, and so on?

BARNHART:

As a physiologist I am most interested in function, but I recognize the value of associated physicochemical work on these altered fibrinogen molecules. We have very little information except on the homogeneity of the FSP. It is likely that the D molecule has molecular weight near 100,000.

HARTERT, (*Germany*):

I would like to ask Dr. Barnhart if she thinks that the pseudopods are only arising in contact with foreign surfaces or if they are really essential in the evolution of platelets.

BARNHART:

I wish I really knew the answer. The fact that our test system for electron microscopy was incubated for 8 min was perhaps time enough for some *in vitro* changes, even though anticoagulated. It seems to me the observed pseudopods and spreading illustrate degrees of activation. I have no idea whether these changes occurred in the circulation or as response to contact with the Formvar. We need to know how circulating platelets look at high magnification.

ON THE RÔLE OF FIBRINOGEN–FIBRIN COMPLEXES IN FLOW PROPERTIES AND SUSPENSION-STABILITY OF BLOOD SYSTEMS

A. L. Copley,* B. W. Luchini and E. W. Whelan

Hemorrhage and Thrombosis Research Laboratories, Veterans Administration Hospital,
East Orange, New Jersey and Department of Pharmacology, New York Medical College,
New York, New York, U.S.A.

The rôle of fibrinogen in the formation of red cell aggregates has long been known and was particularly emphasized in the work of Fåhraeus[1]. This phenomenon has become of particular interest in any consideration of the flow properties of whole blood. The term fibrinogen denotes a soluble plasma protein which, upon the action of the enzyme thrombin, is converted to fibrin monomers. This initial fibrin formation leads either to polymerization terminating in a coagulum or, in a collateral pathway, to one of the fibrin monomers which will form a soluble high molecular weight complex with fibrinogen not leading to a coagulum.

We have established that fibrinogen–fibrin complexes affect both the suspension stability and the flow properties of red cell suspensions in plasma or in systems containing purified fibrinogen. There is yet no clear, unambiguous relationship between red cell clumping and changes in the flow properties and suspension-stability of whole blood systems containing fibrinogen–fibrin complexes.

This presentation is confined to the alterations in suspension-stability and flow properties of red cell–plasma systems resulting from fibrinogen–fibrin complex formation. A more comprehensive study will be submitted for publication.

BACKGROUND

Fibrinogen, purified from human plasma, is an elongated molecule with a molecular weight of 340,000. In recent years evidence has accumulated that even the most highly purified fibrinogen preparations may contain more than one clottable component by chromatographic analysis[2, 3]. Figure 1 illustrates a gel permeation chromatogram of a fibrinogen preparation having a clottability of about 95%. The column contains a permeable polyacrylamide gel, Bio-Gel P-200, which excludes protein with a molecular weight of 10^6 or larger. The first peak (Fig. 1, peak I), eluted at the void volume, contains fibrinogen–fibrin complexes. Fibrinogen is shown to be eluted as a second peak (Fig. 1, peak II).

The conversion of fibrinogen to fibrin by thrombin[4], a β-globulin, has been shown to involve several steps, as shown in Fig. 2a. The first enzymatic step (Fig. 2a, step I) is the formation of a partially activated fibrin monomer through hydrolysis of the fibrinogen–fibrinopeptide A bond, releasing fibrinopeptide A into the clot liquor. In

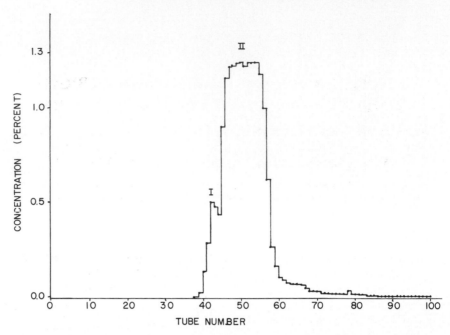

FIG. 1. GEL-PERMEATION CHROMATOGRAM. SAMPLE FIBRINOGEN (92% CLOTTABLE), 5 × 100 CM COLUMN, BIO-RAD P-200 GEL, FLOW RATE 240 ML/HR. PEAK I, FIBRINOGEN–FIBRIN COMPLEX. PEAK II, FIBRINOGEN.

the usual coagulation pathway, where there is sufficient thrombin activity present, this first monomer is rapidly, fully activated by thrombin in a second enzymatic step involving the hydrolysis of the fibrinogen–fibrinopeptide B bond (Fig. 2a, step II). It is this last monomer which, when fully polymerized, forms a coagulum or clot (Fig. 2a, steps III and IV). If, however, the concentration of thrombin is low enough or if competitive inhibitors interfere with the action of thrombin on fibrinogen, or if a thrombin-like enzyme derived from the venom of the Brazilian snake Bothrops jararaca

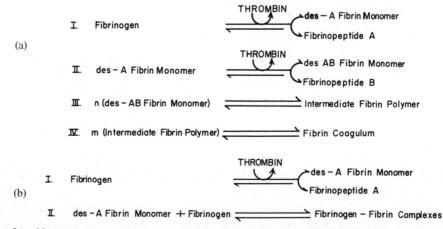

FIG. 2. a. NORMAL PATHWAY OF FIBRIN FORMATION, THROMBIN CONCENTRATION $> 10^{-2}$ UNITS PER ML. A COAGULUM IS FORMED. b. ALTERNATE PATHWAY OF FIBRIN FORMATION, THROMBIN CONCENTRATION $< 10^{-2}$ UNITS PER ML. THE FIBRINOGEN–FIBRIN COMPLEX IS FORMED.

is present, the second enzymatic step, involving the hydrolysis of the fibrinopeptide B bond, does not predominate. Instead, the partially activated fibrin monomer will form dissociable complexes with fibrinogen (Fig. 2b, step II). Under these conditions no clot or coagulum will form.

COPLEY and LUCHINI[5] reported in 1964 on the purification and physico-chemical characterization of these fibrinogen–fibrin complexes. In 1965, LUCHINI and COPLEY[6] presented a preliminary report of our continuing studies on the kinetic basis of fibrino-peptide release and fibrin monomer production. These kinetic studies have provided evidence regarding the enzymatic permissibility for the formation of fibrinogen–fibrin complexes as a physiological occurrence.

The cold precipitable protein, found by THOMAS et al.[7] in the blood of endotoxin-treated rabbits and later characterized by SHAINOFF et al.[8], appears to be similar or identical to the fibrinogen–fibrin complexes described by us[5]. In purified fibrinogen solution, direct formation of fibrinogen–fibrin complexes by thrombin may be readily demonstrated. The optimum concentration of thrombin in purified fibrinogen systems is in the order of 10^{-3} NIH units per ml, although fibrinogen–fibrin complex formation can occur with thrombin concentration of 10^{-4} to 10^{-3} NIH units per ml.

A different approach must be used in plasma systems, because of the variable amounts of thrombin inhibitors present. An excess of heparin in the presence of a plasma protein, the so-called anti-thrombin III[9], will largely, but not completely, inactivate thrombin (Fig. 3). Of interest in this connection is the work of HEINRICH et al.[10] who demonstrated the formation of a cryoglobulin in heparinized plasma, to which thrombin is added. In this situation nearly optimum amounts of thrombin are available for the production of fibrinogen–fibrin complexes.

Heparin + Plasma Cofactor + Thrombin ⇌ Inactive Thrombin Complex

Approximately 0.05% of the thrombin activity in this Inactive Thrombin Complex is available to act on Fibrinogen.

FIG. 3. MECHANISM OF INHIBITION OF THROMBIN BY HEPARIN–ANTITHROMBIN II COFACTOR.

EXPERIMENTAL

Viscosity measurements were made by the use of the Wells–Brookfield LVT cone and plate viscometer. Because of the lack of sensitivity and accuracy at low shear rates and because of possible variable interface effects, only measurements at shear rates of 5.75 sec^{-1} and above are included in the data presented. Two factors are used to correct for non-linearity of instrument response and for minor variations of hemato-crit. The first correction factor is subtracted from each set of averaged torsion measure-ments, made with experimental samples and their controls. This correction compen-sates for the non-linearity of the viscometer to standard viscosity oils. The correction factors used are illustrated in Fig. 4. A second correction of viscosity is made, wherever the tested sample of blood differs in hematocrit from its control by more than 0.25%. The second correction factor assumes proportionality between the viscosities of each tested sample of blood and its control. The derivation of this correction factor is shown in eqs. (1) and (2):

$$\frac{V_c V_t}{V_s} = V_t^*,\tag{1}$$

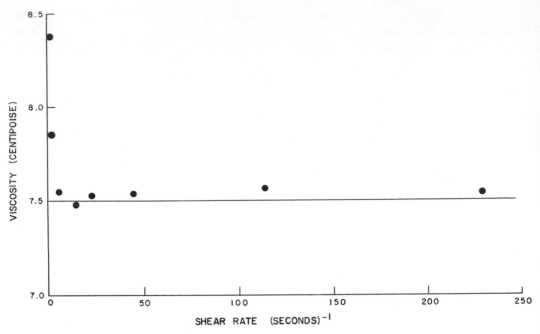

FIG. 4. MEASUREMENT ERROR OF WELLS–BROOKFIELD LVT CONE AND PLATE VISCOMETER. VISCOSITY OF STANDARD OIL AT $37.0°$C, 7.5 CP. THE MEASURED MEAN ERROR ($N \geqslant 7$) IS USED AS A CORRECTION FACTOR TO BE SUBTRACTED FROM ALL EXPERIMENTAL DETERMINATIONS OF VISCOSITY.

where $V_c =$ viscosity of standard curve at hematocrit of control, $V_t =$ viscosity of tested blood, $V_s =$ viscosity of standard curve at hematocrit of V_t, $V_t^* =$ corrected viscosity of tested blood. Therefore

$$(\log V_c) + (\log V_t) - (\log V_s) = \log V_t^*. \tag{2}$$

A divider is used to measure the distance of V_t above or below the standard curve, shown in Fig. 5b, for the shear rate concerned, at the hematocrit of the test sample. This distance, keeping the same sign, is measured off at the hematocrit value of the control and the corrected viscosity V_t^* is noted. Shear stresses are then calculated from viscosity according to

$$\frac{V\dot{\gamma}}{100} = \tau \tag{3}$$

where $V =$ viscosity (centipoise), $\dot{\gamma} =$ shear rate (sec^{-1}), $\tau =$ shear stress (dyne cm^{-2}).

Blood was obtained from apparently healthy donors, extreme care being taken to avoid contamination with procoagulant containing tissue fluids. The tourniquet was loosely applied to the upper arm, as to permit continuous outflow and not to occlude the arterial supply to the forearm. In this way, 500 ml of blood were secured in about 10 min, without the aid of vacuum. Venipuncture was accomplished with a sharp 37 mm long, 18 gauge needle. The puncture of the vein and the placing of the needle about 1 cm into it must be done, on the first attempt, without any difficulties. Otherwise, another vein, preferably the antecubital vein of the other arm, must be used for a new

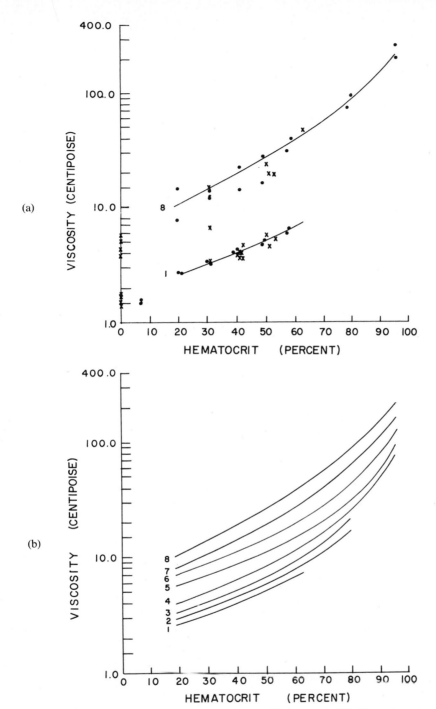

FIG. 5. a. VISCOSITY AS A FUNCTION OF HEMATOCRIT. UPPER LINE (8)1.15 SEC^{-1}, LOWER LINE (1)230 SEC^{-1}. THE RED CELL SUSPENSIONS ARE HANDLED UNDER CONDITIONS IDENTICAL TO THOSE OF CONTROL SAMPLES DURING EXPERIMENTAL RUNS. VALUES OBTAINED (·) DURING EMPERIMENTS DESIGNED TO ESTAB-LISH THESE CURVES; CONTROL VALUES OBTAINED (×) DURING ACTUAL EXPERIMENTS ON FIBRINOGEN−FIBRIN COMPLEX PRODUCTION. b. VARIATION OF VISCOSITY DEPENDENT UPON HEMATOCRIT. HANDLING OF SAMPLES AS DESCRIBED ABOVE. SHEAR RATES: (8) 1.15 SEC^{-1}; (7) 2.30 SEC^{-1}; (6) 5.75 SEC^{-1}; (5) 11.5 SEC^{-1}; (4) 23.0 SEC^{-1}; (3) 46.0 SEC^{-1}; (2) 115 SEC^{-1}; (1) 230 SEC^{-1}.

attempt. The needle must then be carefully anchored by supporting its hub on a small gauze pad and fixing both securely to the skin. The reason for this precaution is to avoid any possible laceration or injury of the vein by the needle, thus preventing the release of procoagulant tissue fluids. The first 20 ml of blood are not used for the preparation of plasma.

The blood was collected directly into polycarbonate centrifuge tubes, containing the anticoagulant used. Heparinized plasma (Liquaemin sodium, Organon) is used in blood systems in which fibrinogen–fibrin complexes are to be generated. We can confirm the work of HEINRICH et al.[10] who found 24 units of heparin added per ml whole blood in the presence of thrombin to constitute the optimum concentration of heparin for the formation of what they thought to be cryoglobulin. This unitage of heparin in the presence of thrombin we found to form fibrinogen–fibrin complexes. Oxalate plasma was prepared by adding 1 vol. 0.1 M sodium oxalate to 9 vol. whole blood. The oxalate plasma is used for thrombin assay. The anticoagulants were mixed with the blood by slow inversions as to exclude any bubble formation or foaming.

Blood was also collected directly into glass bottles, containing 4 mm glass beads, which subsequently were shaken for 30 min by hand to defibrinate the blood without hemolysis. The defibrinated blood was filtered through a bed of Dacron wool and the red cells were separated from the serum by centrifugation.

Hematocrits were measured in heparinized capillary tubes and corrections were made for trapped plasma according to CHIEN et al.[11]. Sedimentation velocities or rates were determined employing Westergren tubes. In the same systems containing fibrinogen–fibrin complexes and in the corresponding controls, 1:200 dilutions were made in the respective plasma phase. The number and size of rouleau clumps and the number of free erythrocytes were determined.

Bovine thrombin (Topical Thrombin, Parke-Davis) was dissolved in the serum obtained from the defibrinated blood. This stock thrombin was diluted with serum so that 0.2 ml thrombin-serum would clot 0.2 ml oxalate plasma from the same donor in 15 to 25 sec. Non-hemolyzed, autologous serum from the defibrinated blood of the same blood withdrawal was used to dissolve the lyophilized thrombin. This procedure was adopted for two reasons: firstly, as a rapid, reproducible means to avoid changes in mean corpuscular red cell volume and, secondly, to control in the blood system the amounts of antithrombins present.

The test mixture for the generation of fibrinogen–fibrin complexes was made by slowly adding 1 part of the above thrombin–serum mixture to 9 parts of the heparinized plasma. The control sample to this serum–thrombin–plasma mixture consists of 1 part serum plus 9 parts of plasma. Under the stated conditions, fibrinogen–fibrin complexes will form rapidly and will be stable for a number of hours. Occasionally, there was a plasma-serum control which will also contain fibrinogen–fibrin complexes. This is thought to be an artefact which probably resulted from faulty collection of blood.

Results

The viscosity of blood systems, in which fibrinogen–fibrin complexes were generated, was consistently increased as compared with its control. When these data are plotted according to CASSON's equation[12, 13, 14], the resulting line appears to be straight and may be extrapolated to the shear stress intercept. Figure 6 shows Casson's plot at about 30, 40, 50 and 60% hematocrit of samples containing fibrinogen–fibrin complexes and

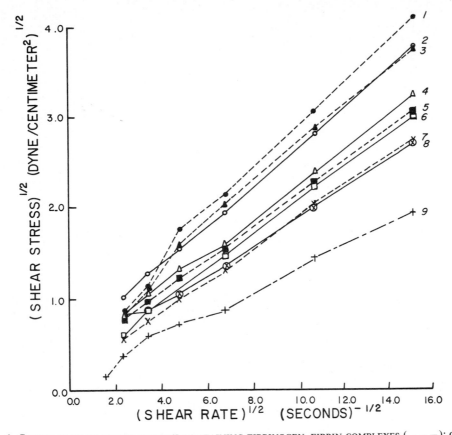

FIG. 6. CASSON PLOT OF BLOOD SYSTEMS CONTAINING FIBRINOGEN–FIBRIN COMPLEXES $(-\,-\,-)$; CONTROL BLOOD SYSTEM (———) AND THE PLASMA PHASE $(+\,-\,\cdot-\,+)$. HEMATOCRIT VALUES ARE: $(1, \bullet$ AND $2, \bigcirc)$ 58.5; $(3, \blacktriangle$ AND $4, \triangle)$ 51.25; $(5, \blacksquare$ AND $6, \square)$ 41.25; $(7, \times$ AND $8, \otimes)$ 31.0.

their corresponding controls. At each hematocrit, the shear stress is higher for the sample of blood containing fibrinogen–fibrin complexes. From Fig. 7 it can be seen that plasma behaves as a Newtonian fluid.

For sedimentation rates, each sample is tested at 3 or more dilutions using the plasma phase as the diluent. Figure 8 illustrates 1 hr sedimentation rates for blood systems containing fibrinogen–fibrin complexes and their control. As can be noted, there is a consistent marked increase in sedimentation rates at hematocrit values of less than 40. Experiments done, where the sedimentation rate has been calculated from sedimentation times taken at predetermined intervals, show an increasing rate of sedimentation, which reaches a maximum and then falls off. For systems containing fibrinogen–fibrin complexes, both the maximum sedimentation rate attained and the initial sedimentation rate are increased as compared to controls. It is not yet clear whether consistently increased rouleau formation accompanies increases in sedimentation rate, in viscosity and in extrapolated yield shear stress, all of which are found where fibrinogen–fibrin complexes are present.

The method we used for determining red cell clumping by dilution is not adequate, because of probable disaggregation of red cell clumps originally present in the un-

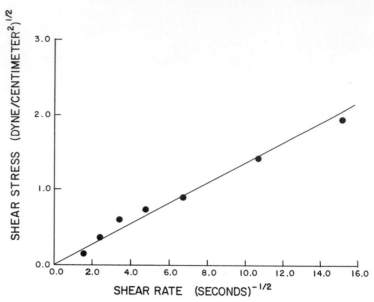

FIG. 7. CASSON PLOT OF PLASMA PHASE SHOWN IN FIG. 6. (•) EXPERIMENTALLY DERIVED VALUES; LINE DERIVED ACCORDING TO LEAST SQUARE FIT OF DATA.

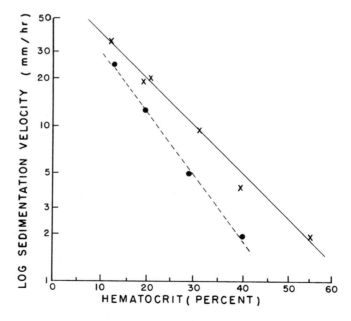

FIG. 8. SEDIMENTATION VELOCITY OF BLOOD SYSTEM CONTAINING FIBRINOGEN–FIBRIN COMPLEXES (×) AND PAIRED CONTROL BLOOD SYSTEMS (•). MEASUREMENTS ARE FOR 0 TO 1 HR SEDIMENTATION IN WESTERGREN TUBES, 2.5 MM IN DIAMETER, 200 MM IN LENGTH.

diluted blood systems. However, it should be noted that, by using this method, only rouleau clumps are consistently associated with viscosity and sedimentation changes, as shown in Fig. 9a. Occasionally, a second type of clump, which may be called a "conglomerate red cell clump", shown in Fig. 9b, may be seen. This conglomerate

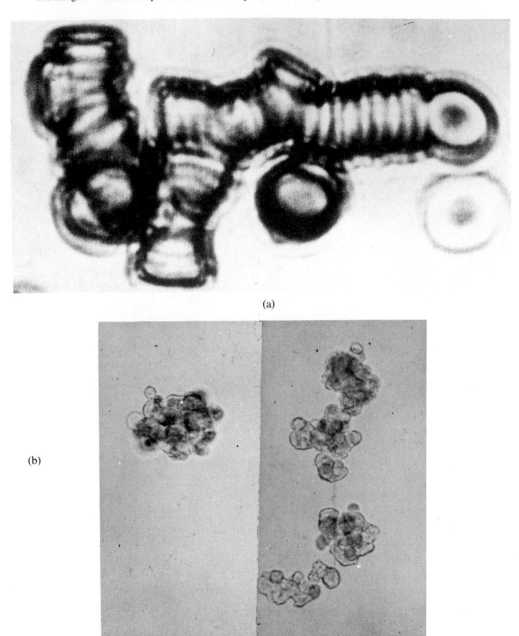

(a)

(b)

FIG. 9. a. TYPICAL ROULEAU CLUMP. b. CONGLOMERATE RED CELL CLUMPS.

type of clump did not occur consistently within any given experiment, nor was it found in the blood of all apparently healthy donors.

Fibrinogen–fibrin complexes have also been generated in isotonic fibrinogen–red cell systems in the absence of thrombin inhibitors by the addition of minute amounts of thrombin in the range of 0.001 to 0.003 NIH units per ml. These experiments are technically more difficult to perform because of the difficulty in avoiding changes in the mean corpuscular volume of the erythrocyte. However, the changes are of approximately the same magnitude as are found in the serum–thrombin–plasma systems. These experiments will be reported elsewhere.

DISCUSSION

"Suspension-stability of the blood" is the term which FÅHRAEUS[1] introduced in his monograph in 1921 and which he defined as "the agglutination and sinking speed of the red corpuscles". Since "agglutination" is considered by one of us (15, 16) as a term denoting the irreversibility of the clumping of cellular elements, the term "aggregation", which is meant to denote a reversible process, is to be preferred, particularly since in rouleau formation of red cells this appears to be the case. However, in those instances in which both reversible and irreversible clumping occur, the non-committal term "clumping" should be used for both red cell aggregation and agglutination[16].

We have given a detailed description of the procedures of securing the blood, because in our experience, any deviation from strict adherence to them will affect the results. As can be seen from Fig. 5a, the viscosity values of the controls from eight experiments agree well with values obtained in the calibration for the standard curves (Figs. 5a, 5b). Occasionally, the control and test samples did not exhibit significant differences in viscosity. In these instances, the control samples were found to have increased viscosity values probably due to handling of the blood, resulting in the activation of thrombin. The amounts of thrombin needed for the production of fibrinogen–fibrin complexes range from 10^{-5} to 10^{-7} of the potential thrombin contained in plasma. It is, therefore, evident that any minute activation of prothrombin to thrombin due to handling or to procoagulant containing tissue fluids will result in the generation of fibrinogen–fibrin complexes.

The simple vertically positioned viscometer of KAWAI, FUKADA and associates[17] was employed for measurements of apparent viscosity. Professor Fukada was so kind to make this instrument available to us. However, from preliminary observations secured with this instrument, as well as with the frame viscometer[14], the shear rates were too high for studying the flow properties of the usually rather loose red cell aggregates. These rouleau clumps might become dissociated into smaller clumps and single red cells with shearing forces within the ranges of operation of these viscometers. Another serious objection to the use of these capillary viscometers relates to phase separation in blood systems with a high sedimentation rate. As can be noted in Fig. 5b, at the hematocrit value of 50, an increase of hematocrit of 1% will result in a viscosity increase of 5 to 8%. Because of this fact, even small changes in hematocrit due to uneven sampling techniques or to phase separation in a horizontal capillary may result in erroneous viscosity values. These objections have been met in our use of the Wells–Brookfield viscometer as follows. The blood samples are mixed continuously on a mechanical rotator at 1 r.p.m. for at least 15 min before they are pipetted into the viscometer cup. The other objection would apply to the possibility of phase separation during the 40 min required for a complete set of measurements. To avoid this phase separation, we made use of the highest speed to mix the specimen under test between each change in shear rate.

Because of the limitations of the Wells–Brookfield instrument, it is not clear whether shear stresses at shear rates lower than 5.75 sec^{-1} continue to obey Casson's equation.

Therefore, no conclusions can be drawn from our data as to the presence of a yield value, other than that which is found by extrapolation.

MERRILL *et al.*[18] found that fibrinogen was largely responsible for the non-Newtonian behavior of blood. The authors state: "Even though a high concentration of β-globulin did not produce a yield value in the absence of fibrinogen, a significant increase occurred in the viscosity and in the yield shear stress for the sample of red blood cells suspended in a β-globulin fraction in the presence of fibrinogen." With reference to this work of MERRILL *et al.*, it should be noted that the β-globulin fraction of plasma, fraction III, is a source and starting material used in the purification of prothrombin. Furthermore, this β-globulin fraction does contain small, but variable amounts of thrombin. In this light, the studies of MERRILL *et al.*[18] and of other investigators need to be re-examined as to possible presence of fibrinogen–fibrin complexes.

We do not yet know exactly what concentration of fibrinogen–fibrin complexes is necessary for the viscosity and sedimentation rate changes. One reason for this uncertainty is the difficulty in preparing fibrinogen which is completely free of complexes which, thus far, we did not overcome. The Schlieren diagram (Fig. 10a) represents the

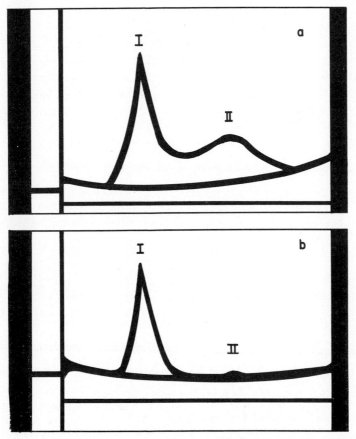

FIG. 10. ANALYTICAL ULTRACENTRIFUGAL ANALYSIS OF FIBRINOGEN (PEAK I) AND FIBRINOGEN–FIBRIN COMPLEXES (PEAK II). a. PARTIALLY PURIFIED FIBRINOGEN–FIBRIN COMPLEXES. b. HIGHLY PURIFIED FIBRINOGEN (FIG. 1, PEAK II).

sedimentation of a mixture of fibrinogen and fibrinogen–fibrin complexes. Peak I is the fibrinogen, peak II is the fibrinogen–fibrin complex. The lower Schlieren diagram (Fig. 10b) represents the fibrinogen used in the experiment. There remains a trace of material which sediments at the same position as the fibrinogen–fibrin complex, shown in peak II. COPLEY and LUCHINI[5] reported earlier the purification of fibrinogen–fibrin complexes to a purity of 97 to 98%. However, complexes of this purity had to be dissolved in a high ionic strength buffer containing sodium bromide which is incompatible with red cell suspensions. We succeeded only recently in preparing stable, fibrinogen–fibrin complex enriched fractions in isotonic saline solution.

In situations where increased formation of thrombin occurs in the circulation, marked alterations in flow properties of blood may result leading to pathological disturbances, e.g. different forms of shock, including endotoxin shock, and hypovolemic shock, different forms of trauma including burns, certain thrombotic states, cryoglobulinemia, intoxications (among others, alcohol), and various conditions due to inflammatory processes. Although, as yet no clear-cut relationship between fibrinogen–fibrin complexes and increases in rouleau formation has been established, our experiments are suggestive of such a relationship.

CONCLUSIONS

It can be expected that fibrinogen–fibrin complexes are physiologically present, since thrombin in minute amounts is constantly being formed or activated in the circulation. In blood systems consisting of red cells suspended in plasma-serum or in fibrinogen solutions, where fibrinogen–fibrin complexes have been generated, there is an increase in the extrapolated yield shear stress and an increased viscosity, accompanied by a decreased suspension-stability.

ACKNOWLEDGMENTS

This work was aided in part by the Office of Naval Research, United States Department of the Navy under contract Nonr 2754(03) with New York Medical College.
Our thanks are due to Miss Hester Caldwell, Miss Vernell Ferrell, Mr. Richard Hanig and Miss Mary Kunde for their technical assistance.

REFERENCES

[1] FÅHRAEUS, R. The Suspension-Stability of the Blood, P. A. Norstedt and Soner, Stockholm, 1921 (Acta Med. Scand. supplement 55).
[2] BERN, W. and KORSAN-BENGTSEN, K. Thromb. Diath. Haem. 9, 151, 1963.
[3] FINLAYSON, J. S. and MOSESSON, M. W. Biochemistry 2, 42, 1963.
[4] LASKOWSKI, M., JR., RAKOWITZ, D. H. and SCHERAGA, H. A. J. Am. Chem. Soc. 74, 280, 1952.
[5] COPLEY, A. L. and LUCHINI, B. W. Life Sciences 3, 1293, 1964.
[6] LUCHINI, B. W. and COPLEY, A. L. Federation Proc. 24, 386, 1965.
[7] THOMAS, L. R., SMITH, T. and VON KORFF, R. Proc. Soc. Exp. Biol. Med. 86, 813, 1954.
[8] SHAINOFF, J. R. and PAGE, I. R. J. Exp. Med. 116, 687, 1962.
[9] SEEGERS, W. H. Prothrombin. Harvard University Press, Cambridge, Massachusetts, 1962, p. 309.
[10] HEINRICH, R. A., VORDER HEIDE, E. C. and CLIMI, A. R. W. Am. J. Physiol. 204, 419, 1963.
[11] CHIEN, S., DELLENBACK, R. J., USAMI, S. and GREGERSEN, M. I. Proc. Soc. Exp. Biol. Med. 91, 1155, 1965.

[12] CASSON, N. In *Rheology of Disperse Systems*, MILL, C. C. (Editor), Pergamon Press, London, New York, 1959, p. 84.
[13] SCOTT BLAIR, G. W. *Nature* **183**, 613, 1959.
[14] COPLEY, A. L., SCOTT BLAIR, G. W., GLOVER, F. A. and THORLEY, R. S. *Kolloid-Ztschr.* **168**, 101, 1960.
[15] COPLEY, A. L. *J. Colloid Sci.* **7**, 323, 1952.
[16] COPLEY, A. L. *Rheol. Acta* **1**, 663, 1961.
[17] KAWAI, H., FUKADA, E., IBE, T. and SHONO, H. In *Symposium on Biorheology*, COPLEY, A. L. (Editor), *Proc. 4th Internat. Congr. Rheol.*, Interscience Publ. John Wiley, New York, 1965, part 4, p. 281.
[18] MERRILL, E. W., MARGETTS, W. G., COKELET, G. R., BRITTEN, A., SALZMAN, E. W., PENNELL, R. B. and MELIN, M. In *Symposium on Biorheology*, COPLEY, A. L. (Editor), *Proc. 4th Int. Congr. Rheol.*, Interscience Publ. John Wiley, New York, 1965, part 4, p. 610.

DISCUSSION

LEE (*U.S.A.*):

I was very much intrigued by Dr. Copley's paper. I just wanted to bring to the attention of the group that there has been considerable evidence accumulating over the past six years that, in many states of disease, complex macromolecular systems of divers sorts are present in the protein capsular material which is present on aggregated cells. For example, in 1961 we reported, in a study of prolonged pump oxygenator perfusion, protein material extractable from such aggregates, consisting of denatured high molecular weight globulins, both alpha 3 and beta globulins. Thompson and his group, in the last year, reported such aggregates to yield protein capsules consisting of complexes of both fibrinogen and globulins, when the aggregation is induced by the administration of a relatively medium molecular weight hydroxyethyl starch. In addition, in the thermal burned patient or animal, extractable capsular material can be obtained from aggregated cells which again seems to have several species of protein material present. At least, this can be demonstrated by qualitative electrophoresis. This is going to be a very important area for further study, that is, to identify precisely and concisely the nature of the macromolecular complex which comprises the capsule or surface gel of erythrocytes in disease conditions causing impairment of tissue perfusion or under which intravascular aggregation may occur.

SILBERBERG (*Israel*):

I thought this is an extremely interesting contribution and I wonder whether you have any information about the quantitative effects of this fibrinogen–fibrin complex. I mean, can you in any way relate it to the amount of rouleau formation in a red cell suspension?

COPLEY (*U.S.A.*):

We had hoped to do this. We thought to establish a kind of an index for the degree of rouleau formation, but, thus far, we did not succeed to secure a definite relationship. We are still working on this particular problem.

SILBERBERG:

I have another question. Do you know, this complex, is it a one to one complex of fibrinogen and one fibrin molecule or is it unspecified as yet?

COPLEY:

We do not know yet whether it is just a one to one complex of fibrinogen–fibrin molecules or not. This still has not been determined. Perhaps my associate, Mr. Luchini, can answer this question in more detail.

LUCHINI (*U.S.A.*):

I think part of the answer is that complex formation is temperature dependent. At 37°C the complex seems to be smaller than at 20°C. At 20°C, by light scattering measurements, the molecular weight is in the order of 5,000,000. We have not yet determined molecular weight or the shape factors accurately. There does seem to be a difference in the amounts of fibrin and fibrinogen in the complex at a given temperature and under the same ionic and pH conditions. The exact relationship or ratio we do not know, we have not determined yet.

BRINKHOUS (*U.S.A.*):

I understand, Dr. Copley, that you have had fibrinogen preparations with different amounts of the fibrin complex in them. Is there a great deal of difference in the effect with preparations with different complex concentration?

COPLEY:

We have not done nearly as many concentration studies as we had hoped to before this presentation, but from the evidence which we do have now, there is an increase in viscosity in our blood systems which depends upon the concentration of fibrinogen–fibrin complexes.

SWANK (*U.S.A.*):

I would like partially to answer a question which Dr. Copley himself asked. He had two slides showing aggregates, one of rouleau formation and the other of an irregular type of aggregation. Following large fat meals in hamsters, we have observed this irregular, very tight aggregation in the cheek pouch, in the living circulation after these large butterfat meals. Rouleau formation could also be seen. We have also seen the irregular type of aggregation *in vitro* in preparations of blood drawn from an animal that had been given large fat meals. The subjects were dogs, rabbits and humans. In addition, there is also the rouleau formation. The type of irregular clumping occurs and it is very marked when you inject the high molecular weight dextran into animals. It is also produced *in vitro* with very high molecular weight dextran.

COPLEY:

Thank you very much, Dr. Swank. I should like to mention at this point that in some of our apparently healthy blood donors, who had a meal before we took the blood, there might have been such an indication, but we cannot be sure of such an influence on the irregular non-rouleau type of red cell clump. We did not study the influence of fatty or other meals on red cell clumping. Regarding your comment on high molecular dextran, I recall observing irregular red cell clumps when I employed high molecular weight dextran in studies in 1948. At that time, when dextran was first studied in patients in the United States, I was among the first investigators to use it in America. We were entrusted to make an evaluation of dextran. We used a preparation called macrose, produced by a Swedish firm, and found that the patients which I studied went into shock following infusion of this preparation. This prompted me to abandon the clinical investigation. I found that the blood in these patients showed highly irregular non-rouleau clumps of red cells and the sedimentation rate was markedly increased. Similar findings of such irregular clumps I found in rabbits which were infused with this dextran preparation, which must have been a highly irregular molecule.

EHRLY (*Germany*):

In respect to the slides showing two types of aggregated erythrocytes, I would say that we have seen the non-rouleau type *in vitro* and *in vivo* only in a few cases with human blood. Such clumping of red cells is seen in antigen–antibody reactions involving cold agglutination. I would like to ask Professor Copley whether such agglutination could not have led to the non-rouleau type of aggregates, when photographed at room temperature.

COPLEY:

I would not know whether cold agglutination and cryoglobulin play a role in the formation of non-rouleau aggregates. We have not studied this question. These aggregates are not dispersed by gentle heating. It is of interest that the fibrinogen–fibrin complexes behave like cryoglobulins in being precipitated at low temperatures and dispersed at higher or physiological temperatures.

HARTERT (*Germany*):

The formation of fibrin aggregates has also to be taken into consideration, if heparin is added to maintain the fluidity of plasma. Govaerts described this phenomenon many years ago. As first published by me in 1950, very small amounts of heparin *in vitro*, as well as *in vivo*, will appreciably shorten the clotting time in the thromboelastograph. A graph, in which the concentration of heparin is plotted against clotting time, shows an ascending line for the clotting time, if the heparin concentration is increased. With still relatively small amounts of heparin, this line crosses the normal range of clotting time and goes on then to increasingly prolonged values. I wonder, if these heparin-fibrinogen aggregates would be responsible for the shortening of the clotting time.

COPLEY:

First of all, the complexes with which we are dealing do not contain heparin and do not require heparin for their formation. The interesting observations made first by Govaerts and then by you, Professor Hartert, with very small amounts of heparin are well known to us. In our work we used from 3 to 50 units per ml plasma. The optimum concentration of heparin is 24 units per ml for the production of fibrinogen–fibrin complexes. This concentration of heparin exceeds by far that needed to initiate acceleration of coagulation as shown in a shortened coagulation time. It might very well be that the platelet agglutination which we found many years ago to be brought about by heparin augments further the shortening in clotting time.

PHASE SEPARATION

13 July, p.m.

Chairmen: Jørn Ditzel, Denmark
Roy L. Swank, U.S.A.

SOME ASPECTS OF PLASMA SKIMMING

A. A. PALMER*

Research Department, Kanematsu Memorial Institute, Sydney Hospital, Sydney, Australia

STUDIES of human blood flowing through branching slit-like glass channels of minor axis 30 and 35 μ (PALMER, 1965) have shown that there is a progressive increase in haematocrit from near the wall to the axial plane such that the laminar haematocrit is a linear function of the fraction of flow between the wall and the plane considered. It was pointed out that the progressive axial increase in haematocrit might only apply to a restricted range of minor axis dimensions and studies with larger and smaller channels were needed. The present paper deals principally with studies using channels of smaller minor axis in the region of 12 μ and compares the results with earlier studies. A few observations using a slit of 112 μ are included.

METHODS AND MATERIALS

The method was similar to that previously described with some modifications noted below. Briefly, blood, constantly mixed with a magnetic stirrer, was made to flow vertically downwards from a reservoir through a slit-like channel of rectangular cross-section which divided into branches. The effluent from the branches was collected, measured and analysed for red cell content. Pressure gradient and relative flow rates from the branches were controlled and measured. The reservoir and branching channels were kept at 37°C in a water bath.

In the present experiments a channel with five branches instead of three was used since the extra branches gave information about the shape of the haematocrit profile without the necessity of repeating the experiment at different flow ratios.

The channels, Fig. 1, were made from polished glass prisms with inclined surfaces at the lower end, together enclosing an angle of 90° into which four chisel-shaped $22\frac{1}{2}°$ wedges were fitted to make five symmetrical branches. The prisms and wedges were separated at the edges by narrow strips of platinum or Monel metal foil. Three channels were made using respectively foil of 12, 25 or 100 μ thickness. The three channels were identical in other dimensions as they were built in succession from the same glass parts: length of channel above branches, 1·13 cm; major transverse dimension of parent slit and of branches, 3·32 cm; length of branch slits, 1·3 cm. The glass wedges were made first and the inclined faces on the large prisms were then ground and polished to fit them exactly. The glass parts were made by Francis Lord Ltd. of Sydney. Expoxy resin, Araldite, was used to seal the edges of the channels and to attach Monel metal connections to the outlets and a glass reservoir to the inlet. It was found necessary to surround the channel with a rigid clamp to prevent changes in the small dimension of the slit. The parts of the clamp which fitted along the faces parallel with the channel were made with glass plates so that the blood flow could be observed

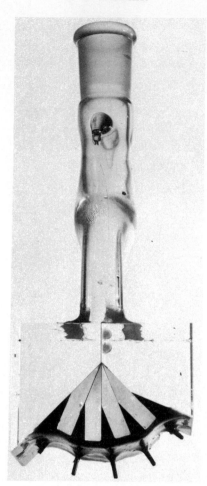

FIG. 1. FIVE-BRANCH CAPILLARY SLIT BUILT FROM GLASS PRISMS WITH METAL FOIL SPACERS. RESERVOIR IS PLACED IMMEDIATELY ABOVE THE PARENT SLIT; OUTLET TUBES ARE VISIBLE BELOW.

with a dissecting microscope through a transparent water bath during an experiment. This was necessary to exclude the presence of bubbles, obstructing particles or cellular aggregates and to determine that the streamlines were parallel with the channel.

Chisel-shaped wedges were used because they were more easily ground and polished to a fine unchipped edge than symmetrical wedges. However, the edge was not less than 25 μ thick and it was necessary to arrange the openings of the branches around a quadrant of a circle below the end of the parent channel. Foil 25 μ thick was used in the branches of the 12 and 25 μ slits; the radius of the quadrant was then about 200 μ; it was of the order of 1 mm in the 112 μ channel when 100 μ foil was used. Thus the blood stream diverged before entering the branches but there is good reason to believe from previous experiments that this does not significantly change the cell distribution. The wedges were set in place under a dissecting microscope with the help of a metal jig.

The dimensions of the slits were checked by timing the rate of flow of distilled water at known temperature and pressure, making due allowance for resistance in the branches and outlet tubes. These estimates agreed within 10% with optical measurements.

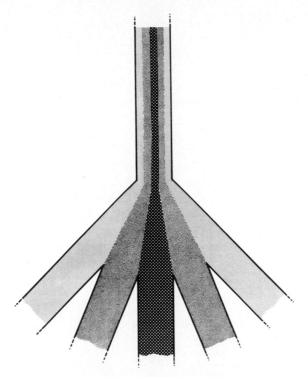

FIG. 2. DIAGRAM (NOT TO SCALE) OF THE PRESUMPTIVE FLOW PATTERN IN THE 5-BRANCH CHANNEL WHEN FLOW FROM THE BRANCHES IS SYMMETRICAL. CENTRAL, PERIPHERAL AND INTERMEDIATE ZONES FROM THE PARENT CHANNEL ENTER THE CORRESPONDING BRANCHES.

The human blood was freshly drawn through a siliconed needle into a sterile plastic transfusion bag containing disodium citrate, 2·2 g and dextrose 1·8 g in 75 ml of distilled water. When volumes of blood less than 250 ml were to be withdrawn half the anticoagulant mixture was first removed except in some experiments where blood–anticoagulant mixture at pH 5·7 was tested when additional citric acid was added. It was found that the above procedure, using a siliconed needle, almost always gave specimens of blood which remained free from platelet or leucocyte aggregates for at least 8 hrs and subsequent addition of heparin or membrane filtration such as were used in earlier experiments became unnecessary.

RESULTS

Figure 3 is a graphical representation of the results of an experiment with the 5-branch channel of slit minor axis 25 μ. Each column represents the data from one branch, for convenience labelled A, B, C, D and E, where A and E denote the peripheral branches and C the central branch. The heights of the columns are proportional to the haematocrit of the sample from the branch and the widths of the columns are proportional to the fraction of the total flow carried by the branch. Column C may be considered as consisting of two parts, one from each side of the axial plane, and if these are regarded as separate columns then the centre points of the tops of the three columns on each side of the axial plane fall almost exactly on a straight line. This line, which will be referred to for convenience as the *haematocrit-flow profile*, also passes through the point of intersection of the horizontal line representing the inflow haematocrit and the vertical line which bisects the flow of one half of the channel. This must occur if the line is straight throughout and intersects the *y*-axis (line representing the wall) at a positive haematocrit value or zero. The straight haematocrit-flow profiles derived from this and other similar experiments with the 5-branch slit agree closely with the straight haematocrit-flow profiles given by previous experiments with asymmetrical 3-branch slits (PALMER, 1965) and comparison of the results shows that the slope of the haematocrit-flow profiles was greatest in the 25 μ slit and least in the 35 μ slit; the mean values for K, half the gradient, being 18·4% for the 25 μ slit, 16·0% for the 30 μ slit, and 13·3% for the 35 μ slit with inflowing blood haematocrits in the vicinity of 37%. These values for K can be seen to be approximately inversely proportional to the minor axes of the slits and the same relationship is valid for most of the results in Fig. 8 which are considered below.

Before the experiment of Fig. 3 the flow of distilled water through the channel was tested and the rate of flow from each branch was approximately equal within 3% except for the flow from branch D which was 10% lower; thus in this experiment, but not in

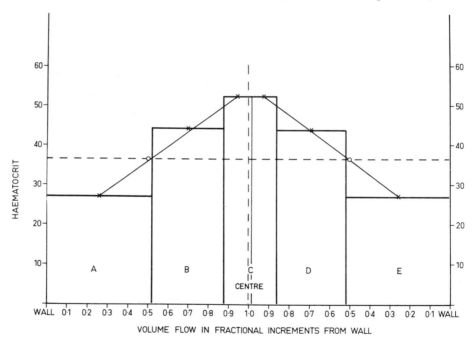

FIG. 3. GRAPHICAL REPRESENTATION OF THE RESULTS OF AN EXPERIMENT WITH THE 5-BRANCH CHANNEL OF SLIT MINOR AXIS 25 μ. EACH COLUMN REPRESENTS THE DATA FROM ONE BRANCH LABELLED A, B, C, D AND E, WHERE A AND E DENOTE THE PERIPHERAL BRANCHES AND C THE CENTRAL BRANCH. THE HEIGHT OF THE COLUMN IS PROPORTIONAL TO THE HAEMATOCRIT OF THE SAMPLE FROM THE BRANCH AND THE WIDTH OF THE COLUMN, PROPORTIONAL TO THE FRACTION OF FLOW CARRIED BY THE BRANCH.

those discussed later, the widths of the columns are very nearly proportional to the apparent relative fluidity ($1/\eta$) of the blood in the corresponding branch and outlet tube. This is shown in Fig. 4 which illustrates the progressive decrease in fluidity from wall to axis.

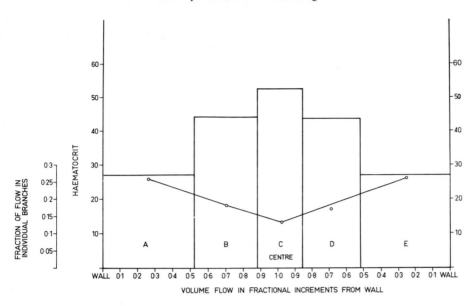

FIG. 4. In this diagram the heights of the open circles correspond to the fraction of total flow taken by individual branches, and since this had been made approximately equal for water, the height is roughly proportional to the relative fluidity of the blood from the branch.

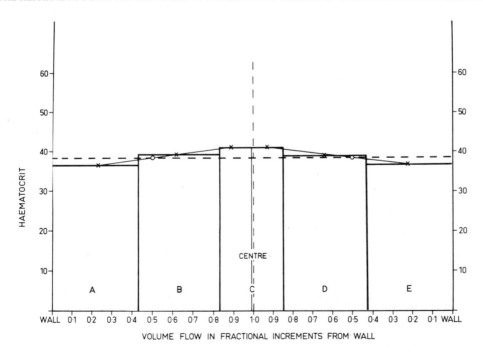

FIG. 5. Graphical representation of the results of an experiment with the 5-branch channel of slit minor axis 112 μ. Each column represents the data from one branch labelled A, B, C, D and E, where A and E denote the peripheral branches and C the central branch. The height of the column is proportional to the haematocrit of the sample from the branch and the width of the column, proportional to the fraction of flow carried by the branch.

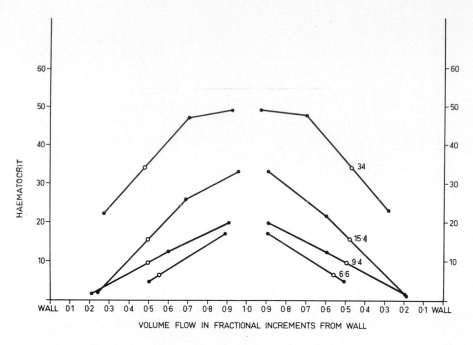

Fig. 6. Haematocrit-flow profiles from experiments using the 5-branch channel of minor axis 12 μ with various inflow haematocrits.

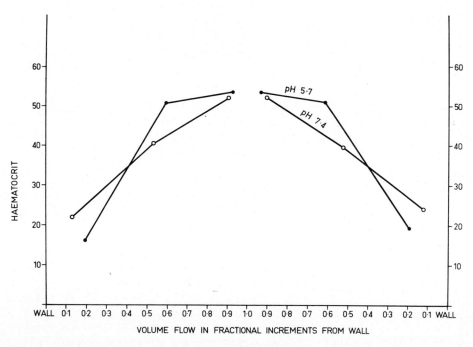

Fig. 7. Haematocrit-flow profiles from experiments using the 5-branch channel of minor axis 12 μ with inflow haematocrit approximately 38·5% at pH 5·7 and pH 7·4.

Figure 5 is a graph of an experiment with a channel of 112 μ slit width. The gradient is much less than with the 25 μ slit but there is a similar linear relationship.

Figure 6 shows haematocrit-flow profiles from experiments with a 5-branch slit of minor axis 12 μ, for inflow haematocrits in the vicinity of 7, 9, 16 and 38%. The profiles are linear only in the region of 9% becoming notably curved and flattened towards the axis at 38%. At inflow haematocrits below about 7% virtually complete plasma skimming occurred in the most peripheral branches with the relative flow rates used in these experiments.

It was noticed that the haematocrit-flow profile in the 12 μ slit was much less flattened near the axis with some specimens of blood in the vicinity of 38% haematocrit than with others and it was found that this was related to the pH. Figure 7 shows that the axial flattening of the haematocrit-flow profile is very pronounced at pH 5·7 but the profile tends towards a straight line at pH 7·4. Specimens with intermediate values of pH, 6·6 and 7·3 gave lines which fell in between.

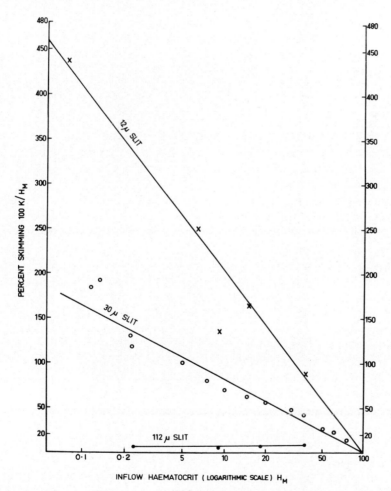

Fig. 8. Comparison of plasma skimming over a range of inflow haematocrits in channels of slit minor axes respectively 12, 30 and 112 μ. The inflow haematocrit, H_M, is plotted on a logarithmic scale.

A comparison of plasma skimming over a range of inflow haematocrits in the three channels of slit minor axes respectively, 12, 30 and 112 μ is shown in Fig. 8. The value plotted on the vertical axis as a measure of plasma skimming with the 3-branch system, was the difference, K, between the haematocrits of the central and peripheral branches, expressed as a percentage of the inflow haematocrit H_M. K is also half the slope of the haematocrit-flow profile. When the profile was curved there was no strictly comparable value but the difference between the mean haematocrit of the central three branches and the mean haematocrit of the peripheral branches was used as a reasonable compromise. This comparison between results from the 3-branch and 5-branch channels is considered permissible as it has been shown from the results of Fig. 3 that the different geometry of the channels did not significantly alter the results at haematocrit 36%.

With the logarithm of inflow haematocrit, H_M, plotted along the horizontal axis the points from the 12 and 30 μ channels each form a series scattered about a straight line passing through zero at 100% haematocrit. There is a progressive increase in percentage skimming with decreasing inflow haematocrit in the ranges studied. With the 112 μ slit, however, preliminary studies indicate that there is no progressive increase below haematocrit 40%. The percentage skimming is roughly inversely proportional to the slit width at most haematocrit values for the 12 and 35 μ channels but this relationship only holds at 40% haematocrit for the 112 μ channel.

DISCUSSION

The close agreement between the haematocrit-flow profiles derived from results with the symmetrical 5-branch slit of 25 μ minor axis and those derived from the earlier results with the asymmetrical 3-branch slits of 30 and 35 μ lends support to the validity of the principles involved.

The progressive decrease in fluidity from wall to axis shown in Fig. 4 is a consequence of the haematocrit gradient. The fluidity (reciprocal viscosity) is almost inversely proportional to the haematocrit in the range of haematocrits encountered in this experiment (MAUDE and WHITMORE, 1953). These results emphasize the importance of axial drift in the mechanism of the Fåhraeus–Lindqvist phenomenon; but the formula commonly used to relate the phenomenon to axial drift assumes a cell-free peripheral zone and an axial core of constant haematocrit and will require modification if the present finding of a progressive axial haematocrit gradient applies also to tubes of circular cross-section.

The problem of transforming the haematocrit-flow profile to a spacial haematocrit profile has been discussed in a previous paper (PALMER, 1965). A knowledge of the velocity profile is required and except at low haematocrits the velocity profile will depart significantly from the parabolic form because of the increasing viscosity towards the axis. It may be possible to compute the velocity profile using the present haematocrit data to calculate the zone viscosity but that is complicated by the influence of shear rate on viscosity at low rates of shear and by the possible influence of unsheared laminae when the channel diameter approaches the dimensions of the cells.

The curvature of the haematocrit-flow profile at higher inflow haematocrits, observed in the 12 μ slit but not in the larger slits may be related to the observation of BUGLIARELLO and HAYDEN (1963) that, other factors being equal, the velocity profiles were generally considerably blunter in smaller tubes at higher haematocrits. A similar phenomenon is to be expected in slits. Blunting of the velocity profile implies reduced shear rate and shear gradient in the blunt region, with, for a given flow, increased shear rate (slope of the velocity profile) in the peripheral zone and increased shear gradient (curvature of the velocity gradient) in the zone at the edge of the blunt region. If, as seems probable, axial drift is a function of the *shear gradient* whereas the dispersion of cells, tending to oppose axial drift, is a function of *shear rate*, a blunt velocity profile might be expected to lead to the kind of blunt but steep-sided haematocrit profile noted at higher inflow haematocrits in the 12 μ slit.

An explanation for the accentuation of the flattening of the haematocrit-flow profile with change of the reaction of the blood from pH 7·4 to pH 5·7, shown in Fig. 7, may perhaps be found in the observation of DINTENFASS and BURNARD (1966) that there is a pronounced increase in the internal viscosity of human red cells with reduction of pH. This increase in the internal viscosity of the cells is likely to be reflected in the viscosity of the blood at high haematocrits such as prevail at the centre of the stream in these experiments, with consequent increased flattening of the haematocrit-flow profile as suggested above. Alternatively, or perhaps additionally, the effect of pH may be mediated through the change in cell volume which it causes; since the effect is only evident in the narrowest slits it presumably depends on the ratio of cell diameter to channel diameter and an increase in cell size may be equivalent to a reduction in channel diameter. It is notable that the haematocrit-flow gradient in the peripheral region is steeper at lower pH; this also could be attributed to increased cell size and to increased central viscosity leading to increased shear gradient in a zone at the edge of the region of central high viscosity.

SUMMARY

1. The distribution of red cells in citrated human blood flowing through slit-like glass channels of minor axis about 25 μ was deduced from the measured haematocrits of the effluent blood from five symmetrical branches. The results agreed with the results of earlier experiments in which three branches were used and the proportion of blood flowing from the axial branch was successively varied. Both methods indicate a progressive increase in haematocrit from near the wall to the axial plane such that laminar haematocrit is a linear function of the fraction of flow between the wall and the plane considered. This plot has been termed the haematocrit-flow profile.

2. With a slit of minor axis 12 μ the haematocrit-flow profile was linear with inflowing blood haematocrit, H_M, in the vicinity of 10%; it became progressively curved and flattened near the axial plane as the haematocrit was increased towards 40%.

3. Changing the pH of the blood of H_M 38% over the range pH 5·7 to pH 7·4 progressively reduced the curvature of the haematocrit-flow profile in the 12 μ slit.

4. Virtually complete plasma skimming occurred in the peripheral branches of the slit of minor axis 12 μ with H_M less than 7% when the proportion of flow in each peripheral branch was reduced to about 10% of the total.

5. As H_M was reduced from 40 to 1%, in either the 12 or the 30 μ slit percentage skimming rose roughly in inverse proportion to log H_M. However, preliminary results with a slit of minor axis 112 μ in the range H_M 40% to 2% showed relatively constant percentage skimming.

6. With the three slit widths studied, at H_M 40%, skimming was approximately inversely proportional to the minor axis of the slit.

ACKNOWLEDGMENTS

This research was supported, in part, by The National Heart Foundation of Australia.
I wish to thank Mrs. Therese Innis for valuable technical assistance.

REFERENCES

DINTENFASS, L. and BURNARD, E. D. *Med. J. Aust.* **1**, 1072, 1966.
MAUDE, A. D. and WHITMORE, R. L. *J. Appl. Physiol.* **12**, 105, 1958.
PALMER, A. A. *Am. J. Physiol.* **200**, 1115, 1965.
BUGLIARELLO, G. and HAYDEN, J. W. *Trans. Soc. Rheol.* **7**, 209, 1963.

DISCUSSION

BUGLIARELLO (*U.S.A.*):

I believe we should all be grateful for the type of work Dr. Palmer is doing because the problem of the flow of blood through bifurcations is probably one of the very significant ones, particularly in the microcirculation. I would like, however, to call attention to the essential differences between the two-dimensional type of situation that he is investigating and the three-dimensional situation. We have been doing work on models, on three-dimensional models and we reported these results in *Science*, in 1964, and at the Jerusalem Microcirculation Conference. And I wonder whether I could take a moment and make a drawing on the blackboard to show some of the essential differences. If you have a tube with a branch, then the fluid layer which has deflected into the branch, cannot be determined by looking at the tube only in profile. You have to look at the cross-section of the tube and consider the isovels, or contour lines of equal velocity, upstream of the bifurcation. The fluid layers that are deflected into the branch are the layers which have a lower momentum; they are the layers which can be deflected more easily. However, the portion of the fluid that will be deflected into the branch will not, in general, be symmetrical with respect to the axis of the branch. This region is going to be influenced by the diameter of the branch, by the isovel configuration, by the flow rate in the two branches, and by the hematocrit, which in turn will affect the distribution of the velocities. The experimental results we have obtained with a model suspension of neutrally buoyant spherical particles, are consistent with this interpretation of the phenomenon.

MEISELMAN (*U.S.A.*):

I am curious to know what you mean when you say, "blood" is flowing down the tube. I do not want to get into the nebulous field "is blood blood?" when it is outside the body, but I am curious to know how you drew it into the ACD solution; do we assume that it is the normal per cent dilution that normally is used in the blood bank? What I am really driving at is how you got your 5·7 pH when normally ACD treated blood is about 6·8 or 6·9. How did you dilute this blood?

PALMER (*Australia*):

In that instance, we added some further citric acid. The other changes were made by altering the proportion of ACD in the blood.

GELIN (*Sweden*):

I am curious about the three-dimensional view on this. Will that hold also for two branches going out at the same distance?

BUGLIARELLO:

Yes, it will. The configuration of the flow going into the branches will be determined really by the momentum of the flow that is upstream of the branches, and so the division of this flow in different branches will be affected.

GELIN:

Then they are affected this way?

BUGLIARELLO:

It will depend on the relative flow to the two branches. In other words, if one branch has a greater amount of flow than the other, then the surface of separation will eat more into one side than the other, of the upstream flow region. We must always keep in mind the three-dimensionality of the phenomenon, which makes the upstream separation surface a curved one, rather than plane.

GELIN:

When I studied plasma skimming in capillary models, with right angle branches and three outlets, I found that hematocrit did not really influence the separation too much at all, but slowing down of the flow was very essential, as aggregation was extremely essential for separation.

BUGLIARELLO:

We plotted diagrams of this effect, the ratio of the concentration between the side branch and the upstream branch versus the upstream concentration. When dealing with a high concentration of the other 40%, the effect will be less pronounced than when dealing with the concentration of the order of 20% or so. At a certain moment, when hematocrit becomes sufficiently high upstream, the effect of hematocrit is not bound to be very large.

PALMER:

We have done some experiments in which we did use circular tubes, not very narrow ones and we had a branch which originated from a complete encircling gap; we were hoping in that way to get successive lamellae.

BUGLIARELLO:

Yes, I imagine that would be a very interesting experiment to perform.

PALMER:

I only have preliminary results with that apparatus. They are consistent with the results in the slit.

WIEDERHIELM (U.S.A.):

In order to evaluate the applicability of these model studies to the living system, the geometry of course becomes an exceedingly important factor. I was particularly interested in the length of the channels that Dr. Palmer used.

PALMER:

The early ones were about 3 cm long, but I progressively reduced the length, and we found that the results were exactly the same. As far as we went, I presume an equilibrium distribution is developed; in the later experiments, the channel was 1 cm long before the branches.

WIEDERHIELM:

In the microcirculation you rarely find unbranched blood vessels of this length. This is why I am wondering if you would expect to find this degree of radial drift of red cells in the blood vessels in the body.

PALMER:

That is a good point.

BURTON (Canada):

I would like to draw the attention of those who have not seen it, to a quite remarkable paper by Moffat and Forman in the Journal of Physiology, where they made studies of living blood vessels which had small cylindrical side vessels. At a certain time, in the uterine artery, the side branches have "arterial cushions" so that the orifice of the side artery enters from near the middle of the stream. They found quite remarkable differences in hematocrit in the side branches. I would agree, I think, that the actual profile of the entrance to the side arteries may make an enormous difference to this problem. I wonder if anybody used this sort of ramp, these arterial cushions up to the orifice of the side branches, in a model, and found the results that Moffat did.

PALMER:

No, I have not done that. In the first model, you remember that one of the branches which had the lower hematocrit, was in fact, a continuation of the main channel. In other words, the angle branching makes no difference at all. I am not saying that the configuration around this region might not make a difference. It well might. It is very hard, actually, to control that precisely when you are down to about 12 microns.

Segré (*Italy*):

I would like to ask Dr. Palmer if he has found any correlation between the velocity of flow and the amount of plasma skimming.

Palmer:

Yes, this is a rather complex relationship. We do not have time to go into it properly here. It depends on the sedimentation rate of the blood and the dimension of the channel. If one uses normal blood, then there is very little change over a wide range of velocity. Skimming actually tends to increase a little, down towards the low region and perhaps to increase a little in the high region. With high sedimentation rate blood, however, there might be a very striking increase at low velocities which I imagine is due to the persistence of rouleaux with larger effective particle size. Now this applies only to the larger channels. When you go down to 12 microns, the sedimentation rate makes hardly any difference, presumably because rouleaux are broken up in the very fine channels.

ON THE CHARACTERISTICS OF THE
MARGINAL PLASMA LAYER

S. E. Charm* and S. Brown

Department of Physiology, Tufts University School of Medicine, Boston, Massachusetts

and

G. S. Kurland

Departments of Medicine, Harvard Medical School and Beth Israel Hospital, Boston, Massachusetts, U.S.A.

INTRODUCTION

Many observations made since Poiseuille's time suggest that a marginal layer at the wall develops in blood flow. Fåhraeus and Lindquist[1] explained the decrease in the apparent viscosity of blood in small capillary tubes on the basis that the marginal plasma layer results in a decreased hematocrit and hence, viscosity within the tube. Vejlens[2] suggested the application of dimensional analysis as a means of cataloging the behavior of the marginal layer.

Taylor[3] observed that the marginal gap increased with flow rate and pressure to an asymptotic value. Bayliss[4] using a light intensity measurement confirmed Taylor's conclusion.

Scott Blair[5] in a review of current knowledge, speculated that there are probably many mechanisms responsible for the marginal layer, but had no doubt of a hydrodynamic tendency for larger suspended particles to move towards the center of a capillary tube.

Charm and Kurland[6], by comparing the viscometry of blood as measured in a cone and plate viscometer with that determined in a small capillary tube, attempted to calculate the marginal layer width.

Thomas[7], analysing Kumin's data for oxblood, calculated the characteristics of the marginal layer, and found that it increased with pressure. Watanabe, Oka and Yamamoto[8] suggested that the thickness of the cell-free zone is independent of the radius of the tube indicating that a hydrodynamic wall effect is more important than the thermodynamic accumulating tendency. Bugliarello, Kapur, and Hsiao[9], using photography, claimed to confirm Thomas's results in vertical tubes, but not in horizontal tubes. The last three references are particularly important since they have presented peripheral layer widths quantitatively.

Charm et al.[10] derived an expression for a Casson fluid in laminar flow with a marginal layer at the wall. Using this equation, marginal gaps were calculated for tube diameters between 70 and 300 μ, and cell concentrations varying from $\phi = 0.05$ to $\phi = 0.5$. It was found that the marginal layer increased to a point and then remained constant with increasing velocity. In the following study, the preliminary results presented by Charm et al.[10] are expanded to permit a more accurate examination of the effect of cell concentration, velocity and tube diameter on the marginal layer width.

REASONS FOR GAP FORMATION

There have been a number of attempts to explain the hydrodynamic force which causes the gap formation, SAFFMAN[11], RUBINOW and KELLER[12], GOLDSMITH and MASON[13] and GOLDSMITH and MASON[14]. Most of these analyses consider a "Magnus effect", as origin of the force causing the radial migration of cells. SEGRÉ and SILBERBERG[15] made the remarkable observation that under certain conditions, particles collect in an annulus at a distance of about $\frac{2}{3}$ of the radius from the center. Thus, they point out that a hydrodynamic force also acts to move particles toward the wall.

CALCULATION OF THE MARGINAL LAYER

Elsewhere[10], an equation has been derived for blood flow that expresses a general relationship between pressure drop, the velocity of blood, and the marginal layer width, see eq. (1).

$$\bar{V} = \frac{P}{\mu L}\left(\frac{R_c}{R_w}\right)^2 (R_c)^2 \left[[1 - \alpha\phi']\left(\frac{1}{8} - \frac{1}{2}\left(\frac{R_p}{R_c}\right)^2 + \frac{1}{4}\left(\frac{R_p}{R_c}\right)^4\right) - \frac{4}{3}(1 - \alpha\phi')\left[\frac{R_p}{R_c}\right]^{1/2} \right]$$

$$\left[\frac{3}{14} - \left(\frac{R_p}{R_c}\right)\frac{1}{R_c^2} - \frac{2}{7}\left(\frac{R_p}{R_c}\right)^{7/2}\right] + \left(\frac{R_p}{R_c}\right)(1 - \alpha\phi')\left[\frac{1}{6} - \frac{1}{2}\left(\frac{R_p}{R_c}\right)^2 + \frac{1}{3}\left(\frac{R_p}{R_c}\right)^3\right]$$

$$+ \frac{1}{4}\left(\frac{1}{2}\left(\frac{R_w}{R_c}\right)^2 - \left(\frac{R_w}{R_c}\right)^2 + \frac{1}{2}\right) + (1 - \alpha\phi')\left(\frac{R_p}{R_c}\right)^2\left[\frac{1}{4}\left(1 - \left(\frac{R_p}{R_c}\right)^2\right)\right.$$

$$\left.\left. - \frac{2}{3}\left(\frac{R_p}{R_c}\right)^{1/2}\left(1 - \left(\frac{R_p}{R_c}\right)^2\right) + \frac{1}{2}\left(\frac{R_p}{R_c}\right)\left(1 - \frac{R_p}{R_c}\right) + \frac{1}{4}\left(\frac{R_p}{R_c}\right)^2\left[\left(\frac{R_w}{R_c}\right)^2 - 1\right]\right]\right] \quad (1)$$

It is assumed the blood viscometry may be expressed by Casson's equation, see eq. (2). The flow model for which eq. (1) is derived is based on laminar flow, with a cell-free layer at the wall. Next to the cell-free layer, proceeding to the center, is an annulus of sheared cell agglomerates often in the form of individual cells. Proceeding further

$$\sqrt{\tau} = K\sqrt{\gamma} + \sqrt{C} \quad (2)$$

toward the center and next to the annulus of sheared cells is a plug of unsheared cells. When the shear stress in the tube exceeds the yield stress of the blood, the plug is sheared.

Under those conditions where a marginal layer does not exist, those terms including it are simply dropped from eq. (1). The term $(R_p/R_c)^2$ in eq. (1) will usually be negligible compared to R_p/R_c. Thus, dropping $(R_p/R_c)^2$ from eq. (1) and expressing the equation in a dimensionless form, eq. (1) becomes eq. (3).

$$\frac{32\mu}{D\bar{V}\rho} = \frac{PD}{\bar{V}^2\rho L}\left[1 - \left(1 - \frac{2\delta}{D}\right)^4 + \left(1 - \frac{2\delta}{D}\right)^4(1 - \alpha\phi')\right] + \frac{C_1}{\bar{V}^2\rho}\left[\frac{16}{3}\left(1 - \frac{2\delta}{D}\right)^3(1 - \alpha\phi')\right.$$

$$\left. - \frac{32}{7}\left(1 - \frac{2\delta}{D}\right)^3(1 - \alpha\phi')\left[\frac{PD}{C_1 L}\left(1 - \frac{2\delta}{D}\right)\right]^{1/2}\right] \quad (3)$$

EXPERIMENTAL

Fresh human blood drawn in ACD buffer was divided into suspensions with cell volume fractions varying from 0.05 to 0.44. The pressure–velocity relationships of the blood were measured in tube diameters ranging from 70 to 2000 μ at 37°C. The apparatus is described in detail elsewhere[6]. The viscometry of the blood was carried out in Brookfield cone and plate viscometers between shear rates of 1 and 1500 sec^{-1}. A high speed digital computer was employed to determine the blood yield stress, and Casson viscosity from the viscometry data, and to calculate the gap width from eq. (3).

RESULTS

The gap width, δ, is plotted as a function of the dimensionless group

$$\frac{\text{yield stress}}{(\text{velocity})^2(\text{density})} \quad \text{or} \quad \frac{C}{\bar{V}^2\rho},$$

for several tube diameters and hematocrits. It appears from Fig. 1a and Fig. 1b that the δ/D approaches an asymptotic value when $C/\bar{V}^2\rho$ is less than 0.001. At greater values of $C/\bar{V}^2\rho$, the δ/D generally decreases with increasing values of $C/\bar{V}^2\rho$. This occurs in suspensions with a variety of yield stresses and in various tube diameters. However, data in the region where $C/\bar{V}^2\rho$ is greater than 5×10^{-4} are still relatively

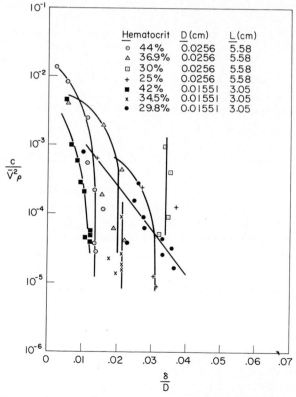

Hematocrit	D (cm)	L (cm)
o 44%	0.0256	5.58
△ 36.9%	0.0256	5.58
□ 30%	0.0256	5.58
+ 25%	0.0256	5.58
■ 42%	0.01551	3.05
x 34.5%	0.01551	3.05
• 29.8%	0.01551	3.05

FIG. 1a. δ/D VS. $C/\bar{V}^2\rho$ FOR VARIOUS TUBES AND HEMATOCRITS.

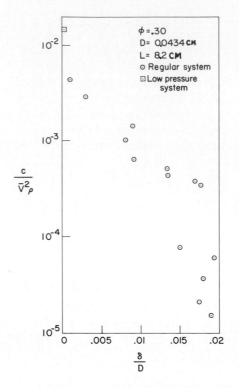

FIG. 1b. δ/D vs. $C/\bar{V}^2\rho$ for wide range of flow rate. The lowest velocity was determined in a flow system employing a pressure transducer capable of measuring a head of 0.5 mm H_2O.

meager, and further study is required to substantiate the critical conditions governing where the asymptotic gap widths are achieved. One run covering a particularly wide range of low flow conditions as well as high flow is plotted in Fig. 1b. The asymptotic values of δ/D are plotted in Fig. 2, as a function of hematocrit and tube diameter. It is observed that asymptotic δ/D or $(\delta/D)_a$ increases with decreasing diameter. When the cell volume fraction ϕ is below 0.20, the $(\delta/D)_a$ for tube diameter between 155 and 2000 μ appear to fall on the same line. When ϕ is greater than 0.2, the curves deviate from each other. The $(\delta/D)_a$ for the 71 μ diameter tube fall on a line separate from the others at the lower hematocrits, but which approaches the other lines at high hematocrits. In general, at values of greater than 0.3, the δ/D drops sharply. Each of the points in Fig. 2 has been determined from at least five different pressures. The calculated gap widths were checked in certain dilute suspensions against photomicrographs of the gap and were found to agree within experimental error. Even in very dilute suspensions, it may be observed that the cells concentrate in a central core, see Fig. 3.

However, in concentrated suspensions, cells bounce from the tube wall and the marginal layer is of a statistical nature rather than as it appears in Fig. 3. The gap widths in a 155 μ diameter tube for cells washed in Hanks solution (albuminated Ringers) are shown in Table 1. In this case, the yield stress is nearly zero. Over the range of pressures studied, the gap width ranged from 5.35 to 6.20 μ. The difference is not significant (see error analysis).

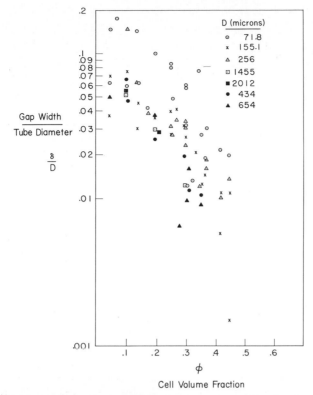

FIG. 2. ASYMPTOTIC VALUES OF δ/D VS. ϕ FOR VARIOUS TUBE DIAMETERS.

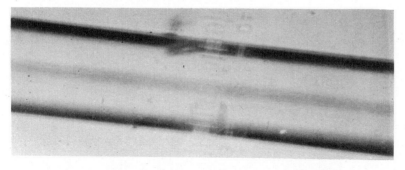

FIG. 3. WIDE MARGINAL LAYER IN A DILUTE SUSPENSION.

DISCUSSION OF RESULTS

A number of our observations do not agree with some of the conclusions of BUGLIARELLO[9] and THOMAS[7]. BUGLIARELLO *et al.*[9] employed photographic measurement of the marginal layer using high speed photography. He found that in vertical tubes 40–83 μ in diameter, the gap remained constant at low shear rates and increased with velocity at higher shear rates. This is not confirmed by Figs. 1a and 1b. It is not clear how reproducible the results were. In horizontal tubes, the results were inconclusive. Bugliarello also concluded that the trend of the gap became different at

TABLE 1. GAP WIDTHS FOR CELLS WASHED IN HANKS SOLUTION

Sample	δ	(Diameter) Hanks soln. μ	K^2 (poises)	C dynes cm²	D (cm)	$P \times 10^{-4}$ dynes cm²	$\bar{V}$ cm sec	δ	δ_{AVE}	$\dfrac{\delta_{AVE}}{D}$
Cournoyer 18 May 66	0.248	0.0074	0.0135	0.0069	0.1551	35.00	76.7	6.20	5.94	0.0383
						32.27	70.56	6.10		
						12.13	26.53	6.20		
						6.67	14.24	5.35		
						5.33	11.51	5.85		

lower hematocrits, e.g. ϕ less than 0.28. This is not confirmed by Fig. 2. THOMAS[7], analysing KUMIN's data[16] for oxblood concluded that the gap width varied with shear stress at the higher shear stresses which is not in agreement with our observation. Kumin's data are not ideally suited to this type of analysis since different samples were employed for each of the tube diameters studied. It was then essentially necessary to assume that the viscometry of all these samples were the same in order to make the calculation suggested by Thomas.

An attempt to fit Kumin's data into our analysis failed because of this. However, HERSHEY and CHO[17], employing an analysis similar to Thomas's, noted that the calculated gap approaches an asymptotic value at higher shear rates much as we observed.

BENIS[18] has reported that the cells washed in albuminated Ringers solution do not develop a marginal layer. However, it may be seen from Table 1 that a marginal layer has been calculated for cells washed in albuminated Ringers solution. The yield stress for this suspension is zero when determined with a Weissenberg Rheogoniometer with couvette cylinder attachment. When determined with a cone and plate viscometer, the yield stress is 0.0069 dynes/cm², which is essentially zero. The value of $C/V^2\rho$ in this case is less than 0.001. Since the yield stress is zero, $C/\bar{V}^2\rho$ is also zero. It is interesting to note that $(\delta/D)_a$ for this suspension falls on the same point in Fig. 2 as $(\delta/D)_a$ for cells suspended in plasma. However, for cells in plasma, the yield stress is greater than for cells in Hanks solution, and the cells in plasma indicate a smaller gap width at the same low velocities than cells in Hanks solution. This would be expected if the yield stress truly influenced the gap width in the low-flow regions.

This suggests that the yield stress affects not the asymptotic gap width, but the velocity at which the asymptotic gap width is achieved. However, our low-flow data is still meager and further study is required to substantiate this.

ERROR ANALYSIS

From a partial differentiation of eq. (3), it is possible to obtain an expression for the change in gap width with respect to a change in velocity, see eq. (4). Now if dV/V is the

$$\frac{dV}{V}\left[\frac{1-\alpha\phi\left(1-\dfrac{2\delta}{D}\right)^4}{\left(1-\dfrac{2\delta}{D}\right)^3}\right]\frac{D}{\delta} = \alpha\phi' 8\frac{d\delta}{\delta} \tag{4}$$

fractional error in measuring velocity, then $d\delta/\delta$ is fractional error associated with the calculated gap width due to the error in measuring velocity. Consider the following case:

$$D = 100 \; \mu$$
$$\alpha = 2$$
$$\delta/D = 0.03$$
$$\phi' = 0.3$$
$$dV/V = 0.01 \text{ or a } 1\% \text{ error in measured velocity}$$
Then $\qquad\qquad dV/V = 0.044 \text{ or } 4.4\% \text{ error in } \delta.$

However, at higher hematocrits in larger tubes where δ/D is much smaller and D/δ is much larger than in this example, the error in δ may be much greater. For example, in a $1500 \, \mu$ tube at high hematocrits, the theoretical error may be as high as 20%.

CONCLUSIONS

Our results indicate that:

1. The gap increases with velocity and finally reaches an asymptotic value, see Fig. 1.

2. The gap attains the asymptotic value when the dimensionless group $C/\overline{V}^2\rho$ is less than 5×10^{-4}, see Fig. 1.

3. The gap width may be calculated using eq. (3).

4. The δ/D noted in Fig. 2 may be employed with eq. (3) for calculating pressure-velocity characteristics of red cell suspensions.

5. In very dilute suspensions, the cells appear to concentrate in central core, see Fig. 3.

6. The SEGRÉ–SILBERBERG effect[15] does not appear to apply under the conditions tested, see Fig. 3, but more detailed examination may be required to observe this.

7. The marginal gap is calculable in all tube diameters between 71 and $2000 \, \mu$ and is most prominent in dilute suspensions.

ACKNOWLEDGMENT

This work was supported by Public Health Service Grant # HE 08783–02.

REFERENCES

[1] FÅHRAEUS, R. and LINDQUIST, T. *Am. J. Physiol.* **96**, 3, 1931.
[2] VEJLENS, G. *Acta Path. Microbiol. Scand.* Suppl 33, 1938.
[3] TAYLOR, M. *Aust. J. Exp. Biol. Med. Sci.* **33**, 1, 1955.
[4] BAYLISS, L. E. *J. Physiol.* **149**, 593, 1959.
[5] SCOTT BLAIR, G. *Rheologica Acta* **1**, 123, 1958.
[6] CHARM, S. and KURLAND, G. S. *Am. J. Physiol.* **203**, 417, 1962.
[7] THOMAS, H. W. *Biorheology* **1**, 41, 1962.
[8] WATANABE, T., OKA, S. and YAMAMOTO, M. *Biorheology* **1**, 193, 1963.
[9] BUGLIARELLO, G., KAPUR, C. and HSIAO, G. In *Symposium on Biorheology*, COPLEY, A. L. (Editor), *Proc. 4th Int. Cong. Rheol.*, Interscience Publ. John Wiley, New York, 1965, part 4, p. 351.

[10] CHARM, S. E., KURLAND, G. S. and BROWN, S. Submitted to *Biorheology*.
[11] SAFFMAN, P. G. *J. Fluid Mech.* **1**, 540, 1956.
[12] RUBINOW, S. I. and KELLER, J. B. *J. Fluid Mech.* **11**, 447, 1961.
[13] GOLDSMITH, H. L. and MASON, S. G. *J. Colloid Science* **17**, 448, 1962.
[14] GOLDSMITH, H. L. and MASON, S. G. *Biorheology* **3**, 33, 1965.
[15] SEGRÉ, G. and SILBERBERG, A. *J. Fluid Mech.* **14**, 136, 1962.
[16] KÜMIN, K. Inaugural Dissertation, Doctor der Medizin der Universität Bern. Physiologisches Institut der Universität Freiburg, Schweiz.
[17] HERSHEY, D. and CHO, S. Unpublished communication presented at American Institute of Chemical Engineers Meeting, Philadelphia, Pa., Dec., 1965.
[18] BENIS, A. M. The flow of human blood through models of the microcirculation. Sc.D. thesis, Department of Chemical Engineering, Massachusetts Institute of Technology, Cambridge, Massachusetts, 1964.

SYMBOLS

C = yield stress of blood
C_1 = yield stress of central core
D = tube diameter
K = Casson viscosity
L = length
P = pressure drop
R_c = radius of the cell core
R_p = radius of plug in central cell core
R_w = radius of tube
T = absolute temperature
$\bar{V}$ = mass average velocity
α = constant which is a function of temperature and cell concentration

$$= 0.07 e^{\left(2.49\phi + \frac{1107}{T} e^{-1.65\phi}\right)}$$

δ = gap width
γ = shear rate
μ = plasma viscosity
ϕ = cell volume fraction in reservoir
ϕ' = cell volume fraction in central core $= \phi \dfrac{Q_{total}}{Q_{core}}$
τ = shear stress
$\dfrac{d\delta}{\delta}$ = fractional error in gap width
$\dfrac{dV}{V}$ = fractional error in velocity
$\left(\dfrac{\delta}{D}\right)_a$ = Asymptote value of $\dfrac{\text{gap}}{\text{diameter}}$
Q_{total} = Total flow rate

DISCUSSION

BUGLIARELLO (*U.S.A.*):
   I still continue to be a little bit confused by the approach Dr. Charm follows in determining the marginal layer, because it appears to me that he is assuming a model that predicts a marginal layer and then determines the characteristics of the marginal layer according to this model. Certain values for the marginal layer are

obtained on the basis of this analysis, but still we do not really have an experimental confirmation that there is a marginal layer having these characteristics. A second point I would like to make is that the marginal layer is not a clearly defined zone, a clear boundary; it is rather, a statistical concept, as we have found in our measurements, when we observed that the marginal layer had a standard deviation of approximately the same magnitude as the layer. May I say one third thing: I think it is, however, plausible to expect that when the velocity increases beyond a certain value, the dimensions of the marginal layer at a certain moment may decrease. For instance, Bagnold, as mentioned by Whitmore in his paper at the last Biorheology Conference, has shown that there is the possibility of dispersive pressures. And certainly this would be a phenomenon that could explain these results. Thank you.

CHARM (*U.S.A.*):

You might consider a correction factor to bring our experimental data into line with the equation which we derived. This is the way we perhaps looked at it originally. The fact is that the correction factors always fall within reasonable values for the widths of marginal layers. You never get a correction factor that is greater than the diameter of the tube, or that is impossible to be a marginal layer. I think this is important. Secondly, as I mentioned, we did measure and check in certain cases the gap width that we calculated against photographs. I think this is an experimental check, that the existence of this layer is indeed the way we think it is. True enough, the photograph we showed is a time average over perhaps a hundredth of a second. What this simply means is, from the pressure velocity point of view, that this behaves as if it were indeed an average gap width. Our main interest in doing this was to determine energy losses. This means that the flow behaves as if there were an average marginal layer of this type, even though a statistical layer may actually exist in some cases.

PALMER (*Australia*):

I agree with Professor Bugliarello that the marginal layer is just a statistical one, and probably there is a gradual transition from the peripheral plasma layer to the concentrated zone at the center; that is at least what our experience seems to show. I should also like to ask whether Dr. Charm has taken into account other factors which might be important as the shear rate increases. Apart from the width of the marginal zone, there will be increased orientation of the red cells in the central parts and, furthermore, there will be increasing deformation of the cells. I think that there are other factors which have to be considered in addition to the actual distribution of the cells as you increase the flow rate.

CHARM:

These considerations, if they are in fact considerations, are accounted for in the experimental shear stress–shear rate measurements. If these phenomena in fact exist, I think they would make themselves evident.

GOLDSMITH (*Canada*):

Surely this matter could be settled if measurements of pressure were combined with good cine-photography which, *in vitro*, is not too difficult, using small thin walled tubes. Even though one cannot look into a blood suspension of 40% hematocrit, in tubes of diameter greater than 80 microns, at least it is possible to look at the wall, and by taking high speed movies, to get some indication of the existence of a particle-depleted zone.

CHARM:

As you note, it is quite difficult to look at tubes that are much greater than a hundred microns in diameter.

WHITMORE (*England*):

Could I just ask one point for clarification? It is: what is the minimum diameter of vessel to which you found the theory applied? A comment I would like to make is that the trouble with most of the models which we are using is that we assume two continuous phases, whereas, in fact, the inner one is a particle fluid mass and (particularly when the tube gets small) you must decide where you are going to take the edge of the model of your inner core to be. Should you take the center of the particle or the outer edge of the particle? If your outer layer of fluid works out to be 4 microns wide, for example, and your red cell is about 8 microns diameter wide and you assume the core to pass through the center of the particle, which you generally have to do, then, of course, any plasma layer which you get from viscosity measurements will be, as Dr. Bugliarello showed, purely statistical and not necessarily entirely visible.

CHARM:

The only comment I would make again is that from a pressure-velocity point of view, the flow does behave as if it has an average marginal layer of this type of width, even though the actual marginal layer is irregular or statistical. The minimum diameter studied was 71.8μ.

Thomas (*U.S.A.*):

My name has been mentioned already, so I presume that I have to say something. First of all, I would like to point out the danger of attributing a greater significance to the two zone model for blood flow in tubes, than was originally intended. In my own paper (*Biorheology* **1**, 41, 1962), for instance, I attempted to set down the equations for conservation of momentum and mass that must be met in such a situation. These equations, it is clear, can be completely solved if the concentration profile can be expressed as a function with one disposable parameter. The simplest function is the two zone model, assuming a core at constant concentration at the axis, surrounded by a hypothetical clear layer of supernatant fluid at the wall. (In fact, there is a good deal of circumstantial evidence in favour of this model.) If one has available a comprehensive set of data of "apparent" viscosity one can determine the value of the wall layer δ and its variation with parameters such as concentration, flow rate and tube bore. Similarly, if one has a sufficiently comprehensive set of data of the "dynamic" concentration, one may achieve the same end. But without additional direct evidence of the true concentration profile, the computed value of δ is no more than a characteristic of the net radial migration of red cells within the tube. There need not strictly be an observable clear marginal layer at the wall. In fact, the calculated values for δ are so small, of the order of a few microns, that in all probability red cells still remain in contact with the wall. Given enough data one could correlate measurements of "apparent" viscosity, of "dynamic" concentration, and of differences in mean velocities of red cells and their suspending phase, by making use of the two phase model. I would be worried if the correlation failed. Even fundamental laws of physics would be challenged. Secondly, I would like to comment on the apparent difference in results for computed δ between Dr. Charm and myself. I have had the advantage of seeing Dr. Charm's paper before today, and of discussing it with him. The difference between us is not great, and really concerns the behaviour in δ as the shear rate approaches the two limits of 0 and ∞. I have used the averaged data of Kumin, but Dr. Charm points out that this might be unsatisfactory since for single samples the results of Kumin are inconsistent, and are not even amenable to analysis. Dr. Charm has plotted his results in an entirely different manner to myself, he uses a logarithmic plot which stretches out the extreme results to $+\infty$ and $-\infty$. I used a reciprocal plot, so that the extrapolation to infinite shear stress was at a finite abscissa, with small values of shear stress still being at infinity. This difference in method of plotting is perhaps exaggerating any difference between us.

Rowlands (*England*):

I am sure Dr. Charm is aware of this and probably many others, but I think it is worth restating that the width of this marginal layer, if such there be, is almost certainly an important function of hematocrit because the formation of the marginal layer is being opposed by what Thomas has called the shear-induced particle diffusion, which I called microturbulence at the Brown University Meeting (and got shot down by the rheologists because to them it had a different meaning), but the irregular motion of the red cells, causes them to diffuse out of the central core. The other thing I would like to say is that we, of course, as many of you know, had a different approach to this problem by means of measuring the difference in circulation times of red cells and of the suspending phase, both in animals and in 200 micron nylon tubes. And we have obtained a little bit of supporting data. Both Dr. Charm and Dr. Palmer have mentioned the rather unexpected lack of dependence upon velocity in the formation of the marginal zone. For what it is worth, we, in our nylon tubes, did try to look for a difference in the difference in circulation times when we varied the velocity through the tubes and could not find any consistent change with velocity. Looking back at our animal experiments, we did in fact find that the greatest difference in circulation times we got in our animal experiments, was in an animal with a very low cardiac output and a long circulation time, indicating a low flow.

PLASMA EXPANDERS

13 July, p.m.

Chairmen: Jørn Ditzel, Denmark
Roy L. Swank, U.S.A.

HEMORHEOLOGIC EFFECTS OF THE DEXTRANS ON ERYTHROCYTE AGGREGATION: HEMODILUTION VERSUS DISAGGREGATION

ROE WELLS*

Departments of Medicine, Harvard Medical School and Peter Bent Brigham Hospital, Boston, Mass., U.S.A.

THE hemorheologic effects of the dextrans have been extensively explored. Little question remains as to their ability to function as an emergency fluid for the correction of acute blood loss or hypovolemia. They exhibit a powerful oncotic effect of attracting isovolumes of extravascular fluid into the vascular space. Accordingly, dilution of the cellular elements and proteins is consequence of their administration. The bulk of contemporary studies on dextrans have focused upon the question as to whether they also reverse, protect against, or influence erythrocyte aggregation or blood sludging. The first dextrans used in laboratory study were of high molecular weight and caused profound cellular aggregation of the blood. When dextran of lower molecular weight was produced, at levels approximating albumin, this aggregation process did not occur. It was logical, therefore, to determine if even lower molecular weight dextrans might reverse or prevent erythrocyte aggregation. It was observed that cell aggregation created by administration of high molecular weight dextrans (150,000+) was reversed by low molecular weight dextrans (40,000) (Dextran 40). Administration of Dextran 40 to animals in which injury or equivalent stress had created impaired microvascular flow also showed improved flow, and reversal of stasis and aggregation. These and related observations were quite logically presented as evidence that Dextran 40 had a disaggregating effect upon cellular aggregates[1]. Later, studies of tagged dextran revealed it to be incorporated in the red cell envelope[2] and in addition, erythrocytes in dextran solutions had more pronounced electronegativity than controls[3]; supporting the concept that dextran improved the suspension stability of blood and indirectly supporting the disaggregation concept. But the question as to whether dextran improves the fluidity of blood by disaggregation of aggregated cells or their attracting forces or by the simple mechanism of hemodilution remains to be established. Cell aggregates, changed from a concentrated suspension to one of lesser volume concentration, will show dispersion of the aggregated systems. The examination of this question is best carried out *ex vivum* in order precisely to separate the effects of dilution versus intercellular actions. However, a major compromise must be faced; namely, dextran is a relatively viscous solution (10% Rheomacrodex in saline is 3.40 cP at 37°C) and cannot, in absence of a semi-permeable membrane, attract any water into the test system. As long as this problem is recognized, the *ex vivum* results can be more accurately interpreted.

METHOD

In order to evaluate these effects, erythrocyte aggregation was produced *ex vivum* by the addition of fibrinogen to freshly drawn aliquots of venous blood mixed with balanced oxalate as anticoagulant. Fibrinogen analysis, by the method of Ratnoff and Menzie, was carried out and sufficient fibrinogen (freshly prepared) added to provide a uniform concentration of 725 ± 25 mg%; a level insuring erythrocyte aggregation and settling in all samples (normal plasma fibrinogen 0.25–0.45 g%). Dextran (10% solution of molecular weight 40,000) was added to the control samples and also to those with added fibrinogen in a volume to produce a $1:5$ dilution (1 part dextran, 4 parts blood). This dilution was chosen on the basis of the peak volume effect of a rapid infusion 500 ml into man. Fibrinogen was added to control samples and to samples in which dextran had been added. This plan, therefore, allowed evaluation of effects of dextran before (prophylaxis) and after the addition of fibrinogen (therapy). Control studies were carried out with physiological saline (0.9 g%) and albumin 7.5 g%. Measurements were made of blood and plasma viscosity, hematocrit, sedimentation rate and microscopy of cell suspensions for character of aggregates. All studies were made at 37°C. Viscometry was carried out in a G.D.M. viscometer[4].

RESULTS

The addition of fibrinogen produced profound cell settling. Sedimentation rates, corrected for dilution of cell concentration, averaged 60 ± 10 mm/hr. Dextran added to controls had a negligible effect on corrected sedimentation rates. Sedimentation samples, with fibrinogen added before and after dextran addition, were not influenced by the dextran, and dextran added to samples with fibrinogen previously added also developed very high sedimentation rates. Sedimentation rates were all markedly elevated to the degree of the control values whenever fibrinogen was introduced. Photomicrography of these cell suspensions, during the settling phase, all revealed large aggregates whenever fibrinogen was present. The addition of saline or albumin, in volumes equal to those of dextran, resulted in less accelerated settling than that of fibrinogen added to the controls (average was 42.5 mm/hr or a reduction in effect of about 25%).

Viscosity values of whole blood were reduced by 40% at low rates of shear (0.1–$1 \sec^{-1}$) and by 10% at higher rates of shear (10–$20 \sec^{-1}$) when dextran was added to control samples. Albumin reduced these values by 55 and 15% respectively and saline by 60 and 20% respectively. Blood viscosity was increased from 10 to 40% by the addition of fibrinogen. The effect of dextran upon the fibrinogen added samples was to reduce viscosity, but again to a lesser degree than albumin or saline. Plasma viscosities, increased with the addition of dextran, were slightly (10%) reduced with albumin and moderately (25%) reduced by the saline.

DISCUSSION

The influence of dextran upon viscosity appears to be principally one of dilution. Erythrocyte aggregation, as created by these *in vitro* techniques, did not appear to be influenced by the action of dextran or by dilution *per se*. Albumin and saline appear to have a greater viscosity reducing effect. These interpretations must be qualified by the facts that the viscosity of dextran is considerably greater than that of saline and albumin. Equally pertinent are the effects of the interaction between dextran and fibrinogen[5] and that this reaction is one of precipitation, especially at the fibrinogen concentrations dealt with here[6].

The many observations of the effects on dextran upon aggregation or sludging *in vivo* might well have been due to hemodilution or improved flow, secondary to the viscosity effects of hemodilution. Couch, in his review of these matters of interpretation, comments on the paucity of evidence regarding specific disaggregating properties of dextran[7]. But these and other criticisms of the enthusiasm of the early dextran reports should not suggest a restriction of the use of dextran. There are valuable hemorheologic advantages of intravenous dextran, most of which relate directly to this hemodilution effect. Saline has no significant oncotic force; albumin is expensive, limited in supply and carries the threat of viral transmission.

Finally, the pros and cons of which type of dextran to use (molecular weight 75,000 and molecular weight 40,000) will be decided on the duration of action. In our hands they both have had similar effects. Dextran 40 is excreted within a few hours, Dextran 75 within a few days.

SUMMARY

Dextran (molecular weight 40,000) was evaluated in regard to its effects upon erythrocyte aggregation *in vitro*. Albumin and saline were similarly studied. Erythrocyte aggregation was produced by the addition of fibrinogen to freshly drawn blood. One part dextran added to four parts of blood reduced viscosity and hematocrit by 20% but did not influence erythrocyte aggregation, when in solution prior to the addition of fibrinogen or when added after the addition of fibrinogen. The problems of interpretation of *in vitro* studies of dextran whose action depends upon semi-permeable membranes are discussed. Dextran leads to significant hemodilution and it is likely the majority of its effects upon flow are via this mechanism.

ACKNOWLEDGMENTS

Author is Investigator for the Howard Hughes Medical Institute. This work is supported by grants from U.S. Public Health Service; NIH He 06424 and GRS 5-S01-FR-5489-03 to Peter Bent Brigham Hospital.

REFERENCES

[1] GELIN, L. E. *Proc. Conf. on Evaluation of Low Molecular Weight Dextran in Shock*. Natl. Res. Council, Washington, D.C., 1963, p. 6.
[2] ROTHMAN, S., ADELSON, E., SCHWABEL, A. and LANGDELL, R. D. *Vox Sang.* **2**, 104, 1957.
[3] BERNSTEIN, E. F., CASTENADA, A., EVANS, R. L. and VARCO, R. L. *Surgical Forum* **13**, 193, 1962.
[4] GILINSON, P. J., JR., DAUWALTER, C. R. and MERRILL, E. W. *Trans. Soc. Rheol.* **7**, 319, 1963.
[5] KROLL, J. and DYBKAER, R. *Scand. J. Clin. Lab. Invest.* **16**, 31, 1964.
[6] WELLS, R. E. *Int. Surgery* (in press).
[7] COUCH, N. P. *Clin. Pharm. Therapeutics* **6**, 656, 1965.

DISCUSSION

HINT (*Sweden*):

I feel that I ought to say something about the disaggregating effect of Dextran 40, because Thorsen and I were the first to describe this effect, both *in vitro* and *in vivo*. At that time, more than fifteen years ago, we did not consider this effect to be of therapeutic interest, and our studies were therefore not very extensive. If we did not have more data, today I could agree with Dr. Wells' findings and accept that we made some mistake fifteen years ago, especially because I know that the next speaker presents data which are in agreement with Dr. Wells' findings. We have, however, repeated our experiments several times and we have found consistently that Dextran 40 has a disaggregating effect on heavily aggregated human red cells. Recently DR. RICHTER in our laboratories has published data (*Acta Chir. Scand.* **131**, 1–8, 1966) which not only confirm our findings, but also show that the disaggregating effect of dextran is maximal when fractions with a molecular weight of 30,000–40,000 are used, while both higher and lower molecular weight fractions have lower or no effect in this respect. There are additional papers where our findings have been confirmed. (J. ENGESET, A. L. STALKER and N. A. MATHESON, *The Lancet,* May 21 (1966), pp. 1124–7 and CARL GUSTAV GROTH, dissertation Stockholm 1965.)

I am not convinced that the *in vitro* effect of Dextran 40 on erythrocyte aggregation is directly related to its clinical effects. The *in vitro* findings, however, certainly gave us reason for *in vivo* studies. After we and many other workers had shown that Dextran 40 has a red cell disaggregating effect *in vivo*, in experimental animals, clinical trials were justified. Furthermore, the disaggregating effect of Dextran 40, is of theoretical interest in regard to the mechanism of red cell aggregation. I think it is therefore important that we try to find out the reason for the difference in our and Dr. Wells' and Dr. Meiselman's results by personal communications. There may be for example, differences in dextran fractions or differences in techniques which may explain the discrepancies.

WELLS (*U.S.A.*):

Thank you, Dr. Hint. We are surely all aware of your classic contributions in this area. I have one question I might ask you or a biochemist. In your studies, aggregation is usually produced with a high molecular weight dextran. There may be certain possible differences due to our using fibrinogen to cause aggregation, even though its molecular weight is 330,000. This may be one reason, but we have always had a question as to whether, from the literature on dextran, the aggregation was equivalent. We chose fibrinogen, since that is the presumed leading cause of aggregation, according to Ham and others.

HINT:

This paper you refer to concerns studies with high molecular weight dextran. We have also found aggregation with horse blood and with human blood taken from patients with a sedimentation rate of more than a hundred. In early times, I did some experiments with fibrinogen, but I do not recall if aggregation was present. We have not tried to repeat these experiments.

LONG (*U.S.A.*):

Well, I want to join everyone in congratulating Dr. Wells on the marvelous work he presented today, and on many of the other pieces of work that have preceded this. I have several questions to ask and I must say that many of these questions arise from some previous studies that I made on Dr. Wells' work, and some of the ideas that I have developed from reading his material. First of all, it is my impression, Dr. Wells, from reading some of your previous papers, that you do not believe that these viscosity changes *per se* are terribly important when one comes down to considering the circulation through the small vessels, because we have other kinds of changes such as anomalous viscosity taking place. So that one can really not use the shear rate-vicosity curves to predict anything that is going on in the microcirculation. I have another question, and I think it is important, and that is whether one can, in the viscometer that you are using, adequately control the mixing of the materials, particularly when severe aggregation is present. Certainly in the microcirculation, if one studies it *in vivo*, at least this has been my impression and the impression I have gained from seeing many movies, the problem that we encounter when aggregation is present, is not a change in viscosity so much as plug flow. We see plugs of large aggregates of various types of corpuscles and chylomicrons plugging up vessels. This has nothing at all to do with changes in viscous flow properties. Now I want to ask two more questions. One: How often do you see this level of fibrinogen clinically? I see it very rarely in the patients I deal with. I deal with a large number of patients who have intravascular aggregation, patients with burns, trauma and shock; I have rarely seen this level of fibrinogen. We see different severities of aggregates, which I think have been emphasized several times here, and I think we must distinguish between these. In patients *in vivo* and *in vitro*, the addition of low molecular weight dextran is extremely critical in the disintegration or disaggregation of these aggregates. These are patients with apparently spontaneous intravascular aggregates, or at least aggregation has developed as the result of some injuries. Hemodilution *per se* appears to have little effect *in vivo* or *in vitro* on severe aggregation. I think one must emphasize the fact that if one attempts to study the effects of low molecular weight dextran, or Dextran 40, or hydroxyethyl starch on the disaggregating phenomenon, he must be certain that aggregation is indeed present. There have been a lot of errors made in the literature where people have reported that the only effect that dextran has is the effect of hemodilution, when in fact they were dealing with an experimental or clinical situation that was very unlikely to have any aggregation.

WELLS:

Thank you Dr. Long. The first point you made concerns microvascular flow. My main point, in earlier writings, was that the the low shear rheology of blood is especially pertinent to the microcirculation, but is not of great significance to the hemodynamics in the larger vessels. There, due to the high shear rate regimes, viscosity can be considered a relatively narrow and fixed value if hematocrit does not change. I think viscosity phenomena are very critical and have argued that viscous resistance in the peripheral microcirculation is as important as the vascular pressure resistance. Your second point is quite pertinent as regards the technical aspects of studying blood rheology. When you study blood, under conditions in which you either cause aggregation or, say, use blood from a patient with myeloma, with tremendous settling, you have got to move very fast. Some patients' blood will sediment so fast, one gets an artifact or a falsely high shear stress at the bottom of the container. After two or three viscosity determinations you go back and remix, or start at the other end of the shear rate scale. We used the rare human level of 700 mg% fibrinogen because we wanted to insure a uniform degree of aggregation. You are right, this fibrinogen level is not common. We chose this number because it was twice our mean value of about 350 mg%. Your third point, which I have trouble digesting, concerns the hemodilution phenomenon not occurring with dextran. Both *in vivo* and *in vitro*, we get a tremendous hemodilution. The hematocrit will always drop. A normal hematocrit of 42 will always, after a pint of dextran, go down to 35, with an associated dilution of all the other blood elements. We always get a very good hemodilution whenever we administer dextran. Whether hemodilution and aggregation are interrelated, is a question we are working on. I agree one must be careful in regard to interpretations of sedimentation. All sedimentation involves aggregation, but not all aggregation involves sedimentation.

GELIN (*Sweden*):

I would like to make a couple of points with regard to the experimental situation which I think are very important to consider here. It is an *extra vivum* study and you add a most powerful oncotic material which has a viscosity that increases with concentration. Of course, you can repeat exactly the same data with dextrose, for example. Just add a high concentration of it. Such *extra vivum* studies have no physiologic meaning at all. What is worrying me, however, in the clinical application of hemodilution is that people will use sometimes several bottles of 10% molecular weight dextran, undiluted, to prime a heart-lung machine. It is fantastic and I never could believe that people were so unaware of oncotic power. It has to be used, of course, related to the oncotic power we wish to produce. The rheological property of low molecular weight dextran will only act with the aid of water.

OBSERVATIONS ON THE RHEOLOGY OF HUMAN BLOOD: EFFECT OF LOW MOLECULAR WEIGHT DEXTRAN

H. J. Meiselman† and E. W. Merrill*

Department of Chemical Engineering, Massachusetts Institute of Technology, Cambridge, Massachusetts, U.S.A.

INTRODUCTION

The use of synthetic colloidal solutions for infusions is not new, but dates back, at least, to studies made during World War I[13]. These solutions, known as plasma volume expanders, have as their basic purpose the restoration of fluid to the circulatory system when blood is lost, as in severe burns, accidents, internal hemorrhaging, or during surgical procedures. They are not intended to serve as complete substitutes for whole blood, but rather as a method to restore fluid volume with an appropriate "colloid osmotic pressure" until the body can replace the loss.

Dextran, a polyglucose, is presently in wide use as a colloidal infusion medium. This macromolecule is produced by the microbiological polymerization of sucrose, usually by the bacteria Leuconostoc mesenteroides[14]. The dextran molecule consists of long chains of glucose units, normally joined by the alpha 1:6 type of linkage. In the manufacture of dextran, the cultures used produce molecular weights up to several million. However, by sulfuric acid hydrolysis followed by fractionation with alcohol, relatively narrow molecular weight fractions can be obtained[7]. Whereas almost any molecular weight fraction is possible, present clinical applications of dextran make use of only two:

1. "Flow Improver Type" — a low molecular weight dextran (LMWD), having an intrinsic viscosity of about 0.19 dl/g; $\bar{M}_w$ about 40,000.
2. "Plasma Expander Type" — a higher molecular weight dextran (HMWD), having an intrinsic viscosity of about 0.30 dl/g; $\bar{M}_w$ about 80,000 or higher.

The amount of published material covering both *in vivo* and *in vitro* usage of dextran is extensive[12]. Gelin has presented numerous examples of the effect of dextran on *in vivo* blood flow[2]. Using LMWD infusions, significant increases in flow in smaller vessels were observed. These results, which are similar to those reported by others, are interpreted to indicate a flow improving effect produced by LMWD and imply a reduction in red cell–red cell interaction. These measurements do not include corrections for the effect of simple dilution (resulting in a lowered hematocrit and plasma dilution) caused by the infusion, and thus are difficult to interpret with regard to any changed cellular aggregation.

†Present address: Department of Engineering Science, California Institute of Technology, Pasadena, California, U.S.A.

421

Rheological measurements relating to LMWD which are made *in vitro* are also difficult to interpret. Pre- and post-infusion blood samples have been examined, and a decrease in apparent viscosity was noted[3]. Suspensions prepared totally *in vitro* have also been investigated[5, 6]. However, these measurements either fail to compensate for the dilution effect of LMWD or do not report on the yield value of the resulting red cell suspensions. Thus, while blood viscosity does appear to be lowered, the basic question remains unanswered: What effect, if any, does LMWD have in addition to acting as a blood diluent?

METHOD

Viscometry

Both a Couette and a capillary viscometer were used to measure the rheological properties of red cell suspensions, and a brief description of each follows:

(a) GDM Couette Viscometer — Detailed sectional drawings of the Couette viscometer used in this study, designated the GDM viscometer, are shown in Fig. 1. The unique features of this particular viscometer[4] are that the stationary outer cylinder (2), the "cup", is mounted on an air bearing, and that the torque is measured by a "torque to balance" system which permits torques to be measured to a precision of ± 0.0001 dyne-cm or 0.1%, whichever is larger, in the torque range from 0.0100 to 1999 dyne-cm. Because of the dimensions of the viscometer cylinders, this corresponds to shear stresses from 3.7×10^{-4} to 7.3×10 dynes/cm². The inner cylinder (1), the "bob", is rotated at speeds from 0.1 to 20 rpm, which corresponds to shear rates of approximately 0.1 to 21 inverse seconds. The viscometer bob, constructed of coin silver, is hollow and is attached to a hollow shaft (4); water at a chosen constant temperature is circulated through the shaft and bob at a rate of about 2 liters per minute. Since the viscometer cup is constructed of lucite, the differences in thermal conductivity between the coin silver and lucite assure that the temperature of fluid in the gap is within 0.05°C of that of the water passed through the bob. A stationary guard ring (9), which penetrates the surface of the fluid in the viscometer, prevents the mechanical transfer of a torque from the rotating viscometer bob to the viscometer cup by any protein layer which might form at the liquid–gas interface. As shown in Fig. 1, the surfaces of the cup and bob are vertically grooved to minimize wall slip; the gap width (1.5 mm) is large in comparison with the red cell size.

(b) Capillary Viscometer — The capillary viscometer[8] shown schematically in Fig. 2, consists of two reservoirs interconnected in parallel by the experimental capillary fiber and the pressure-measuring transducer (Sanborn Model 270). The transducing element is a hollow metal bellows, the internal volume of which changes very slightly and linearly with pressure difference in the range 0–400 mm H_2O. The bellows is completely filled with water and immersed in water so that there exists a gas-free liquid connection between the experimental fiber and the transducer element; surface tension effects are eliminated. The apparatus is operated by connecting the left reservoir to a micro-metering pump (Harvard Apparatus Company, Model 900) which consists of a small glass syringe, the plunger of which is moved by a synchronous motor and movable carriage. As

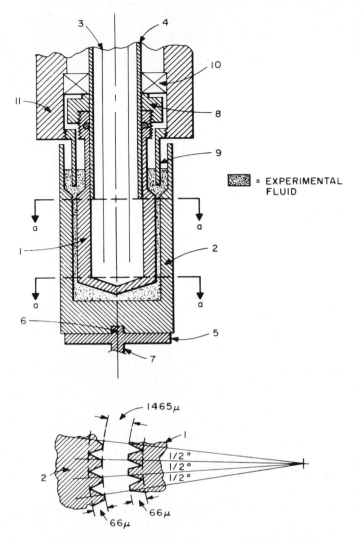

= EXPERIMENTAL FLUID

FIG. 1. COAXIAL CYLINDER ASSEMBLY AND CROSS-SECTIONAL VIEW OF GDM VISCOMETER.

soon as a steady state pressure reading is observed, all flow must occur through the experimental fiber. Under these steady state conditions the transducer measures the frictional pressure drop, and the flow rate is deduced from the syringe size and the rate of travel of the driving system.

Blood Samples

Blood samples were obtained from type O Rh$^+$ male donors in good health, drawn into standard ACD solution in Fenwall transfusion bags, and stored at 4°C until used. Samples were studied within 48 to 72 hr of withdrawal.

The procedure for preparing a suspension of red cells was as follows: (1) the sample was centrifuged at 4°C to separate the red cells and buffy coat from plasma; (2) the buffy coat was removed and discarded; (3) the red cells were either resuspended in

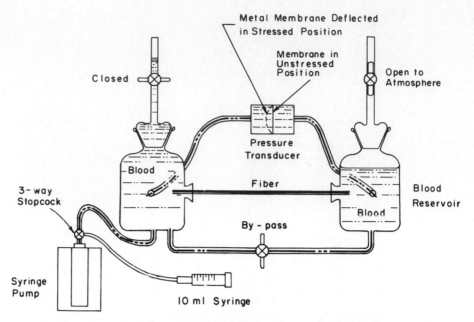

FIG. 2. SCHEMATIC DRAWING OF CAPILLARY VISCOMETER.

citrated plasma at a desired hematocrit (taken as the ratio of the red cell pack length to total sample length after centrifugation in micro-hematocrit tubes) or in plasma–dextran or plasma–saline mixtures. When other than citrated plasma was used as the final suspending medium, cells were washed twice in fresh aliquots of the particular liquid employed. LMWD stock solutions were prepared from dry, powdered dextran* and 0.15 M NaCl and added to the citrated plasma to give the desired final concentration.

RESULTS AND DISCUSSION

Correlation of Viscometer Data

The rheological model on which this study is based is that of blood acting as a homogenous medium obeying the CASSON[1] equation: $\tau^{1/2} = S\dot{\gamma}^{1/2} + \tau_y^{1/2}$, where τ_y is the yield shear stress and S is a constant. This expression has been shown to give excellent empirical fits to shear stress–shear rate data for normal blood samples undergoing Couette flow up to shear rates of about 20 inverse seconds[10]. Therefore, data in the low shear region are conveniently plotted on a double square root coordinate system (i.e. $\tau^{1/2}$ vs. $\dot{\gamma}^{1/2}$). For normal human blood, nearly straight lines result, with the ordinate intercept being the square root of the yield shear stress. The magnitude of τ_y, as well as the apparent viscosity of red cell suspensions, has been shown to be related to hematocrit and plasma composition.

The Casson model is also applicable to capillary blood flow, when it is used to describe the shear stress–shear rate rate interrelation in the fundamental equation for laminar flow[8]. Employing the usual assumptions, one obtains as an excellent approximation of the steady state flow in a circular tube the following equation:

*LMWD: $\bar{M}_w = 39,800$, $\bar{M}_N = 24,600$, obtained from Pharmacia Company, New Market, New Jersey.

$$\tau_w^{1/2} = 2\sqrt{2S}\,U^{1/2} + \tau_y^{1/2},$$

where

$$\tau_w = \frac{\Delta PD}{4L} \text{ and } \bar{U} = \frac{4Q}{\pi D^3}.$$

Thus, this model predicts that Couette viscometer data, as well as steady state pressure–flow data, should show linear behavior on square root coordinates, and that both data should extrapolate to an identical value of yield shear stress.

GDM viscometer data for red cells in citrated plasma at various hematocrit levels, shown in Fig. 3 as Casson plots, agree well with this linear prediction. As would be expected, higher concentrations of particles (higher hematocrit) increase both the

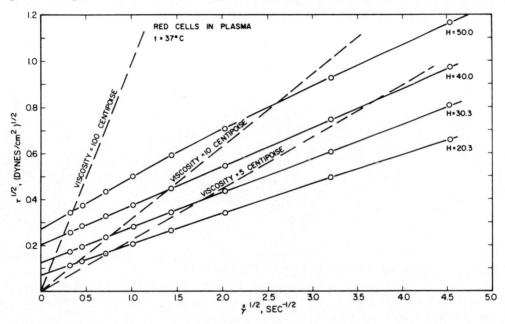

FIG. 3. CASSON PLOT FOR RED CELLS IN PLASMA — EFFECT OF HEMATOCRIT.

shear stress at a given shear rate (thus an increase in the apparent viscosity) and the yield value of the suspension. For example: (a) at a shear rate of 21 inverse seconds, a decrease in hematocrit from 50.0 to 40.0 produces a 30% decrease in viscosity (based on the initial higher hematocrit value); (b) the yield shear stress varies by more than tenfold from 0.08 (hematocrit = 50) down to 0.006 dynes/cm² (hematocrit = 20).

The rheological behavior of red cell suspensions is also markedly influenced by the type and concentration of plasma proteisn present in the liquid phase[9, 11]. While Casson plots for citrated plasma–red cell suspensions indicate the expected non-Newtonian behavior and yield shear stress, red cells suspended in isotonic saline (0.15 M NaCl) show lower apparent viscosities at all shear rates and a marked curvature in the low shear region extrapolating to the origin – i.e. *no* yield stress. Thus, cell–cell interactions such as exist in the presence of plasma proteins (particularly fibrinogen) profoundly influence the rheology of human blood.

The interrelation between the GDM and capillary viscometer is illustrated in Fig. 4. Red cells in citrated plasma were examined in a 818 μ polyethylene capillary; a separate aliquot of this suspension was also measured in the Couette instrument at the temperature existing during the capillary experiment. The ordinate is the square root of the

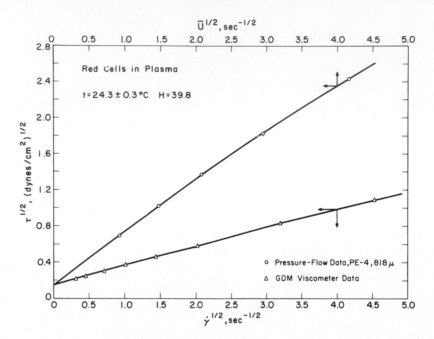

FIG. 4. CAPILLARY AND GDM VISCOMETER DATA ON SQUARE-ROOT COORDINATES — RBC IN PLASMA.

shear stress, obtained either from the electromagnetic torque readout for the GDM or from the steady state pressure drop (as τ_w) for the capillary viscometer.

It can be seen from Fig. 4 that the data from both viscometers exhibit linear behavior on square root coordinates, with some curvature at higher rates of shear. Since $\bar{U}$ is related, but *not* equal to $\dot{\gamma}$, the vertical displacement of the curves at finite rates of shear is to be expected. The most important aspect of this plot, however, is the fact that both the pressure–flow data and the rotational viscometer data extrapolate to the same value of yield shear stress. Note that in addition to the double square root plot agreement, Couette data can also be used to predict capillary pressure-flow relations[8].

From the preceding discussion, the following statements appear to be relevant:
1. Dilution of human blood (for example, by the use of a colloid infusion fluid), and the accompanying decrease in hematocrit and protein concentration have profound effects on its apparent viscosity and yield shear stress, and thus upon its resistance to the flow.
2. Unless both hematocrit *and* plasma protein composition are held constant, analysis of the specific effect of blood additives is very uncertain.
3. Measurements of human blood using both rotational and capillary viscometers are in good agreement, and experimental and interpretational artifacts seem to be absent.

Low Molecular Weight Dextran

In order to observe the effect of LMWD on the rheology of red cell suspensions, samples were examined in both the Couette and capillary viscometers. Plasma diluted by a solution of dextran was always compared to plasma diluted to an equal protein concentration by simple isotonic (0·15 M Na Cl) saline. The absolute level of plasma dilution was 10% (nine parts citrated plasma plus one part diluent), and the final, liquid phase concentration of LMWD was 1%. Hematocrit levels were identical for each suspension in a given set.

Representative data for both the LMWD and saline control suspensions are shown in Figs. 5–7, as follows: (1) Fig. 5 indicates typical shear rate–shear stress data obtained in the GDM viscometer at 37°C, 39.5% hematocrit; (2) Fig. 6 presents pressure–flow capillary viscometer data, as τ_w and $\bar{U}$, for a set of suspensions at $26.3 \pm 0.2°C$ 40.3% hematocrit. Note that two hollow fibers were used, having internal diameters of 443 and 818 μ and lengths of 13.55 and 13.34 cm, respectively; (3) Fig. 7 is the double square root plot of the data shown in Fig. 6, together with GDM measurements made on separate aliquots of the suspensions used for the capillary experiment. The temperature of the GDM was adjusted to the level existing during the capillary run, i.e. 26.3°C.

Analysis of these data leads to the following observations: (1) Compared to an equivalent saline dilution control, a 1% concentration of LMWD increases the apparent viscosity of a red cell suspension at all shear rates. For example, at 0.1 inverse seconds, a 33% increase is noted while at 21 inverse seconds the LMWD suspension has an apparent viscosity which is 16% greater than the saline control. (These values are taken from Fig. 5, but are similar to values that would be obtained from Fig. 7.) (2) Red cell–red cell interaction, as indicated by the magnitude of the yield shear stress, is increased in the presence of LMWD. The LMWD suspension presented in Fig. 5 shows a 40% increase of τ_y when compared to the corresponding isotonic saline dilution control.

Erythrocyte sedimentation rates were also observed in order to investigate the "suspension stabilizing effect of LMWD". These studies, done in standard Westergren tubes, again demonstrated the increased cellular aggregation caused by dextrans of MW = 40,000 and above. LMWD caused an increase in the sedimentation tendency of red cells, as compared to cells in a saline control, and the suspension stabilizer properties of this molecular weight fraction were only noted when it was used at concentrations high enough to increase markedly the viscosity of the suspending medium. This increase in viscosity results in a decreased sedimentation rate, but not a decrease in red cell–red cell interaction.

The *in vitro* measurements described in this study do not indicate any flow improving properties of LMWD, at least by the mechanism of reduced cellular aggregation. In fact, supplemental data indicate that at the dilution and concentration level used here, a LMWD suspension is slightly more viscous and has a somewhat higher yield value than a sample prepared with undiluted citrated plasma. It would appear, therefore, that the flow improvements noted after infusions of LMWD solutions must be related to the reduction of hematocrit and plasma protein concentration produced by hemodilution. Since an increase in shear rate is concomitant with increased flow rate, prevously existing aggregates may be dispersed; this type of de-aggregation, however, is a result rather than a precursor of increased flow.

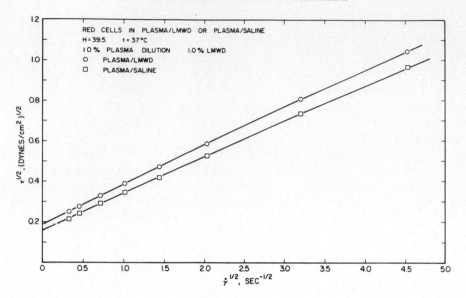

FIG. 5. RED CELLS IN PLASMA/LMWD OR PLASMA/SALINE — GDM VISCOMETER.

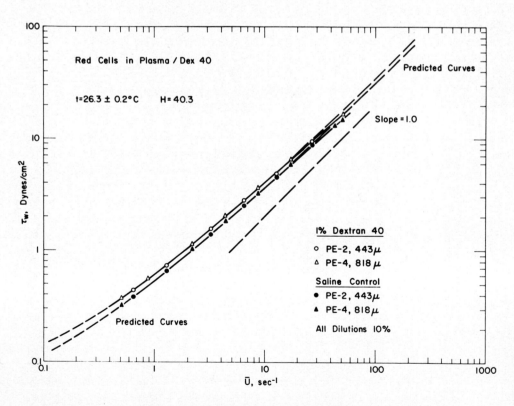

FIG. 6. RED CELLS IN PLASMA/LMWD OR PLASMA/SALINE — CAPILLARY VISCOMETER.

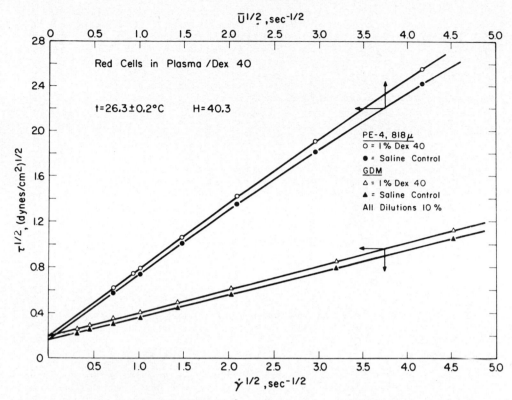

FIG. 7. RED CELLS IN PLASMA/LMWD OR PLASMA/SALINE — DOUBLE SQUARE-ROOT COORDINATES.

SUMMARY

The effect of adding low molecular weight dextran (LMWD) to human blood was observed in both Couette and capillary viscometers to explore whether or not LMWD possesses any flow improving properties. All measurements were performed on freshly drawn, ACD treated blood, and isotonic saline controls were used to provide comparable plasma protein dilutions. Employing constant hematocrit suspensions, LMWD is shown to increase both the apparent viscosity and yield shear stress of red cell suspensions. It is suggested that flow improvements noted after infusions of LMWD do not result from reduced cellular aggregation, but rather must be related to the reduction of hematocrit and plasma protein concentration produced by hemodilution.

REFERENCES

[1] CASSON, N. *Rheology of Disperse Systems*, MILL, C. C. (Editor), Pergamon Press, London, 1959, p. 84.
[2] GELIN, L. E. *Acta Chir. Scand.* **122**, 287, 1961.
[3] GELIN, L. E. and INGELMAN, B. *Acta Chir. Scand.* **122**, 294, 1961.
[4] GILINSON, P. J., JR., DAUWALTER, C. R. and MERRILL, E. W. *Trans. Soc. Rheol.* **7**, 319, 1963.
[5] GREGERSEN, M. I., USAMI, S., PERIC, B., CHANG, C., SINCLAIR, D. and CHIEN, S. *Biorheology* **1**, 247, 1963.
[6] GREGERSEN, M. I., USAMI, S., PERIC, B. and CHIEN, S. *Bibl. Anat.* **4**, 58, 1964.
[7] GRONWALL, A. *Dextran and Its Use in Colloidal Infusion Solutions*, Academic Press, New York, N. Y., 1957.
[8] MERRILL, E. W., BENIS, A. M., GILLILAND, E. R., SHERWOOD, T. K. and SALZMAN, E. W. *J. Appl. Physiol.* **20**, 954, 1965.

[9] MERRILL, E. W., COKELET, G. C., BRITTEN, A. and WELLS, R. E. *Circulation Res.* **13**, 48, 1963.
[10] MERRILL, E. W., GILLILAND, E. R., COKELET, G. C., SHIN, H., BRITTEN, A. and WELLS, R. E. *Biophys. J.* **3**, 199, 1963.
[11] MERRILL, E. W., GILLILAND, E. R., LEE, T. S. and SALZMAN, E. W. *Circulation Res.* **18**, 437, 1966.
[12] ANON. *Bibliography on Rheomacrodex and Some Related Problems*, Pharmacia International, Uppsala, Sweden, 1965.
[13] SEGAL, A. *The Clinical Use of Dextran Solutions*, Grune and Stratton, New York, 1964.
[14] WOLFF, I. A. *Ind. and Eng. Chem.* **46**, 2605, 1954.

DISCUSSION

HINT (*Sweden*):

I wonder if your and Dr. Wells' experiments may be performed with an unhappy batch of Dextran 40. The batches of Dextran 40 produced for laboratory use by Pharmacia are not tested with respect to erythrocyte aggregation. Usually, however, there is good correlation between the erythrocyte aggregation and physico-chemical characteristics of dextran.

MEISELMAN (*U.S.A.*):

I am sorry. May I interrupt? Are you implying that a particular batch that I used caused aggregation?

HINT:

Yes.

MEISELMAN:

No, I used several different batches and these were prepared from dry powders which Pharmacia sold us, as well as Rheomacrodex, which is a liquid prepared by Pharmacia. There are various lot numbers and they are all the same.

HINT:

Obviously there are discrepancies in our experimental results regarding the disaggregating effect of Dextran 40 and, therefore, I propose that we try to find out the reason for these by personal communications later on. I agree, however, entirely with you regarding the effect of aggregation on whole blood viscosity. Actually, at the Second European Conference on Microcirculation, in Pavia, 1962, I read quite a similar paper. I used the isolated rabbit ear as a biological viscometer because I hoped that the effect of aggregation would be easier to demonstrate in a normal vascular tree than it would be in a viscometer. I found that the effect of aggregation on whole blood viscosity was small. It was interesting, however, that the effect of agglutination on viscosity also was unexpectedly small using incompatible blood corpuscles and plasma. There is of course no doubt that incompatible blood has deleterious effects on microcirculation, but these effects seem not to be primarily viscosity effects.

The *in vitro* studies of erythrocyte aggregation show that aggregation can be produced with any water soluble polymer over a critical molecular weight, and that the relationship between the colloid concentration and the degree of aggregation is identical to all colloids tested. This suggests that aggregation is a result of a physico-chemical interaction between the colloids and erythrocytes. It is, however, quite possible that *in vivo* effects of colloids, including the disaggregating effect of Dextran 40, are much more complicated. I personally think that the *in vivo* effects of Dextran 40 may be mediated through the effects of dextran on prothrombin-thrombin conversion, described by Seegers, and comparable effects.

To summarize: *In vitro* effects are of great theoretical interest, but *in vitro* findings do not necessarily prove or disprove the *in vivo* effects of Dextran 40. The main part of the clinical work with this substance is based on *in vivo* experiments. Thank you.

KOCHEN (*U.S.A.*):

There will be much discussion on the subject of red cell aggregation, rouleau formation and elevation in red cell sedimentation rates at this conference. To place this subject in a proper clinical perspective, it is necessary to point out that we frequently perform a procedure which reproduces these phenomena to a considerable extent. I refer to the intravenous infusion of anti-hemophilic globulin-enriched fibrinogen into patients with hemophilia. This may result in circulating fibrinogen levels of over 1000 mg%, marked rouleaux formation and a markedly elevated sedimentation rate. These patients do not develop any complications, thrombotic or otherwise, from this therapy except for infrequent occurrence of a mild degree of hemolysis.

CHARM (*U.S.A.*):

The comment I have to make does not have to do with dextran. It has to do with your failure to pick up a marginal gap at your low velocities. I have estimated that if you had high enough velocities you should have picked up a ten micron gap. But I think perhaps this would have been what I consider an asymptotic gap for your 523 μ tube with a 20% hematocrit. On the other hand, you were working at very low velocities in the range where the yield stress effects were quite considerable and your gap width was probably within the error of your pressure measurements and probably for this reason you did not pick it up. Now the $C/V^2\rho$ was well below the number that I suggested.

MEISELMAN

The capillary viscometer data, that I presented, have an overall accuracy of about plus or minus 5%. Thus, if the magnitude of your plasma layer is less than this, its effects would not have been seen. However, the numerical value of your dimensionless group - yield shear stress divided by the product of the velocity squared times the density — varied from 10^{-4} to 10^1 and no plasma layers could be seen. I should point out, however, that we met with the usual problems one has with this optical system: differences in refractive index and illumination through a round tube. Thus, one could make a plasma layer appear by moving the substage condenser up and down while varying the intensity of illumination. But, as I said, we never had any indication of a true plasma layer.

LEE (U.S.A.):

I certainly do not want to prolong this unduly, but it seems to me that the matter has been too generalized. We are not so much interested in viscosity–hematocrit relationships, as we are interested in the relationship between viscosity and the character and proximity of the material, which is on the surfaces of the red blood cells. Hematocrit, of course, is a direct reflection of the proximity only. We are creating artificial circumstances in an *in vitro* system to define one specific erythrocyte capsule property, and then we are varying the proximity of these capsules and implying that this situation should then apply in any type of RBC aggregation. This is obviously untenable. I think that the experiments which have been described in the previous two papers are very interesting and throw considerable light on the behavior of these capsules at low shear rates under very specific circumstances: (1) with an induced fibrinogen capsule; (2) in "normal" blood. Similar circumstances need not obtain *in vivo* in healthy nor diverse disease states.

MEISELMAN:

That certainly is an argument that I cannot refute. We did all the work *in vitro*.

GELIN (*Sweden*):

I'll be very short. I think it is possible to explain your data if you relate them to the amount of relative water concentration in your suspending medium, because it is not the same in all these if you dilute with saline. However, if you wash out the aggregate itself with a 40% solution, you get a drop again, and I think the explanation is that it is this water in the samples.

MEISELMAN:

Your comment is an interesting one, and may be involved in my experimental results. The colloid osmotic pressure of pure saline is, of course, totally different from that of any of the dextran solution diluents. However, my interest in these experiments was to determine the specific effect of dextran under controlled plasma dilution, and thus isotonic saline seemed the obvious diluting agent. I do not think that the relative water concentration concept is applicable to the effects of various molecular weight dextrans at a given concentration. For example, at 37°C and 1% concentration:

$\bar{M}_w$	$\bar{M}_n$	Colloid osmotic pressure, mm H_2O
21,800	14,500	200
39,800	25,600	120
74,500	48,000	70

Thus, the lowest molecular weight dextran has the highest colloid osmotic pressure, and therefore, water in a solution of this dextran would have the lowest chemical potential. This would indicate that DEX 20 ($\bar{M}_w \approx 20,000$) should most strongly aggregate red cells.

GELIN:

This should also produce it.

MEISELMAN:

No, DEX 20 does not aggregate red cells at all.

COMMENT SUBMITTED BY EHRLY (*Germany*):

I can fully agree with Dr. Wells and Dr. Meiselman. We have done similar work that has just been published in *Medizinische Klinik* **61**, 989, 1966. We have not seen a disaggregation of rouleaux *in vitro*. *In vivo*, on the contrary, there is a dynamic disaggregation, induced mainly by hemodilution. Concerning the slide of Dr. Ritter that Dr. Hint showed us, I agree that the inhibition of a high ESR is a good sign for disaggregation. In the case of low molecular weight dextran (M.W. 40,000) added *in vitro*, however, there is also an inhibition of the ESR, but without disaggregation of rouleaux. The inhibition of the ESR in this case, I think, is due to the increased plasma viscosity, when LMW.-dextran is added in concentrations from 1 to 39% to blood.

STUDIES OF SHEAR-DEPENDENT BLOOD VISCOSITY IN EXTRACORPOREAL CIRCULATION

EUGENE F. BERNSTEIN* and ALDO R. CASTANEDA

Department of Surgery, University of Minnesota Medical School, Minneapolis, Minnesota, U.S.A.

INTRODUCTION

Among the critical factors controlling blood pressure and tissue perfusion are cardiac output, peripheral resistance, relative blood volume, and blood viscosity, the importance of which has been recognized since the time of POISEUILLE[13]. However, the effect of non-Newtonian fluid viscosity in such complex hydraulic systems as the vascular tree, with its distensible, tapering and branching tubes, is still not fully understood. Recent studies by DINTENFASS[3], GELIN[9, 10], GREGERSEN[11], MERRILL[12, 18, 19] and others have emphasized the importance of shear rate in studying blood viscosity, particularly when considering flow in the small vessels critical to tissue perfusion.

Shear stress is the tangential force per unit area (dynes/cm^2) on a fluid plane caused by the relative motion of adjacent planes. The shear rate is the velocity (cm/sec) of a moving fluid plane in relation to another fluid plane a finite distance away (cm) and is expressed as cm/sec/cm, or sec^{-1}. Merrill has estimated the major anatomic vessel shear rates as approximately 500 sec^{-1} in arterioles and 0–1000 sec^{-1} in the capillaries. In the center of the parabolic velocity curve of major arteries and veins the shear rate will be very low, as it will in capillaries and post-capillary venules when flow is slow. It is at the low shear rates of slowly flowing fluid in the capillary and post-capillary venule that the anomalously high viscosity of blood is most important. Dintenfass has demonstrated that the "critical" shear rate appears to be about 6 sec^{-1}, below which the viscosity of blood is strikingly increased. With disease, and abnormally elevated plasma protein concentrations, such increases may be magnified.

With the development of hemodilution techniques for extracorporeal circulation, first popularized by ZUDHI[20], the cardiovascular surgeon learned it was permissible markedly to dilute blood, and to diminish or eliminate the need to prime the pump-oxygenator with donor blood. More recently, evidence has begun to accumulate that such dilution is not only permissible, but actually desirable. Discussions concerning the most satisfactory blood diluents, as well as the effects of varying degrees of hypothermia on such flow systems have been published[2, 4, 6, 14–17]. It is the purpose of this report to present low shear rate viscosity data from a series of patients undergoing total cardiopulmonary by-pass with varying hemodiluents.

METHOD AND MATERIALS

In 25 patients undergoing total cardiopulmonary by-pass with the Lillehei–DeWall bubble oxygenator and Sigmamotor TM-2 finger pump, samples were obtained for study (1) from the femoral artery prior to the institution of by-pass, (2) from the mixed inferior and superior vena cava blood just at the start of the by-pass, and then (3) from the venous return line at 5 min, 15 min, and then at 15 min intervals throughout the period of cardiopulmonary by-pass. An additional sample was obtained from the femoral artery just prior to decannulation. Peripheral venous samples were obtained in several patients postoperatively for as long as 17 days following surgery. Viscosity was measured at shear rates of 1.3, 13 and 130 sec^{-1} and, in addition, measurements of oxygen tension, carbon dioxide tension, pH, plasma hemoglobin and hematocrit were performed. The temperature of the patient was recorded from inlying rectal thermistors at the time each sample was drawn, and appropriate corrections made in the pO_2, pCO_2 and pH measurements. The viscosities were determined at the temperature at which the samples were obtained. It is therefore important to consider the state of hypothermia in the patient when interpreting the results.

TABLE 1. SUMMARY OF CLINICAL DATA AND PRIMING SOLUTION COMPONENTS IN 25 PATIENTS IN WHICH STUDIES OF LOW SHEAR RATE VISCOMETRY WERE PERFORMED DURING TOTAL CARDIOPULMONARY BY-PASS

Case	Age	Wt(kg)	Diagnosis	Priming solutions
1	62	66	Thoracic aortic aneurysm	Dx*; Bld†
2	28	94	Cong. sub-aortic stenosis	3-D$_5$W‡
3	28	65	Aortic insufficiency	2-Dx; Osm**
4	23	62	Aortic insufficiency	Dx; Osm; Bld
5	47	48	Mitral stenosis	Dx; Osm
6	46	68	Mitral insufficiency and stenosis	Dx; Osm
7	43	75	Mitral insufficiency	Dx; Osm
8	51	70	Aortic insufficiency	Dx; Osm
9	39	80	Mitral insufficiency	Dx; Osm
10	12	48	VSD	D$_5$W(850 μ)
11	43	56	Aortic stenosis	Dx; Osm
12	56	65	Mitral stenosis	Dx; Osm; Bld
13	51	40	Mitral stenosis	Dx; Osm (300 μ)
14	40	71	Mitral stenosis and tricuspid insufficiency	Dx; Osm; Bld
15	18	65	IVSD	2-D$_5$W
16	57	73	Aortic stenosis	D$_5$W; Osm
17	38	72	Mitral insufficiency	D$_5$W; Osm; Bld
18	23	66	Sinus venosis	D$_5$W; Osm
19	47	56	Mitral and tricuspid insufficiency	D$_5$W; Osm; Bld
20	35	73	Aortic insufficiency	D$_5$W; Osm; Bld
21	50	52	Mitral stenosis	D$_5$W; Osm
22	30	69	Aortic insufficiency; Marfan's synd.	2-Bld; Osm
23	29	63	Tetralogy of Fallot; Prev. Blalock	D$_5$W; Osm; Bld
24	32	53	IASD	3-Bld
25	6	17	VSD and Anom. Muscle	2-Bld; Osm (100 u)

*Dx = Rheomacrodex, 500 cc.   ‡D$_5$W = 5% Dextrose in water, 500 cc.
†Bld = Blood, 500 cc.   **Osm = Osmitrol, 500 cc.

Thirteen of the 25 patients studied underwent hemodilution perfusion with low molecular weight dextran* and mannitol† as the primary diluents in the pump-oxygenator. In nine others, hemodilution with 5% dextrose in water, alone or with mannitol, was employed. In three patients, whole blood was used to prime the pump-oxygenator.

*Rheomacrodex, Pharmacia, Inc., Piscataway, N.J.
†Osmitrol, Travenol Laboratories, Morton Grove, Ill.

In all cases, whole blood was added to the system during the perfusion to replace blood losses. Perfusions were generally carried out with moderate systemic hypothermia, to 30–31°C. A list of the patients studied, with an indication of their principal pathologic lesions, and the type and amount of priming solutions used for by-pass is summarized in Table 1.

Low Shear Rate Viscometry Technique

Viscosity was measured in a specially modified cone-and-plate type Brookfield LVT Viscometer‡ (capable of eight gear speeds varying from 0.3 to 60 rpm, with resultant shear rates of 1.3–261 sec^{-1}). Water bath temperature control of the outer cup in which the specimen was placed was maintained within 0.3°C of the temperature at which the specimen was obtained. The blood sample is placed into a steel cup with a

TABLE 2. LOW SHEAR RATE VISCOSITY (1.3 SEC^{-1}) IN 25 PATIENTS UNDERGOING CARDIOPULMONARY BY-PASS

| | | Control | | | 5 min. of perfusion | | End of perfusion | | Postoperative 24–48 hrs. | |
| | | Viscosity (cps) | | Hct. | Visc. | Hct. | Visc. | Hct. | Visc. | Hct. |
Priming solutions	Case*	Art.	Vein	(%)	(cps)	(%)	(cps)	(%)	(cps)	(%)
A. Dextran	1	18.7	—	38	14.7	37	14.0	36	—	—
	3	15.3	—	48	5.3	27	4.0	26	—	—
	4	13.3	8.7	38	5.3	20	3.3	21	—	—
	5	11.3	10.7	37	3.3	21	2.7	20	—	—
	6	12.0	16.0	44	2.7	20	5.3	31	—	—
	7	13.3	14.7	45	3.3	27	8.0	28	—	—
	8	14.7	12.0	50	2.0	29	4.0	29	11.3	34
	9	32.0	24.0	60	8.7	36	6.0	38	23.3	46
	11	7.3	8.6	35	2.0	19	0.7	19	17.0	25
	12	12.0	14.0	43	4.6	28	4.0	28	12.0	—
	13	14.0	11.0	42	2.0	24	2.7	24	—	—
	14	12.0	9.3	41	4.0	28	3.3	27	—	—
	17	14.0	18.0	51	4.7	32	10.0	38	—	—
	Mean	14.6	13.2	44	4.8	27	5.2	28		
B. Dextrose	2	12.0	—	45	11.3	36	10.7	38	—	—
	10	12.0	10.0	41	1.3	32	1.0	32	10.7	—
	15	13.0	13.0	48	6.0	38	8.0	49	13.0	37
	16	15.0	16.0	40	2.6	25	4.7	29	—	—
	18	10.0	10.0	48	3.3	31	4.7	40	—	—
	19	14.0	13.5	42	6.6	26	2.7	31	—	—
	20	54.0	42.7	66	3.3	35	17.3	42	—	
	21	13.0	14 0	35	1.3	17	2.0	27	12.0	40
	23	39.0	43.0	64	5.3	40	14.7	48	—	—
	Mean	20.2	20.2	48	4.6	31	7.3	37		
C. Blood	22	14.0	14.0	46	4.0	32	4.7	35	—	—
	24	12.7	12.7	42	10.0	32	8.0	30	11.3	38
	25	4.0	4.0	38	5.0	36	5.0	36	—	—
	Mean	10.2	10.2	42	6.3	33	5.9	33		

‡Brookfield Engineering Laboratories, Inc., Stoughton, Mass.

flat, or plate-like bottom. A steel disc (the cone) is rotated in the test sample by a beryllium-copper spring driven by an electric motor and gear system. The deflection of the spring is read on a dial, and the dial reading is multiplied by a simple constant to obtain the resulting viscosity at the particular rotational speed. The model is claimed to be accurate within 1%, and to have a reproducibility of 0.2%. The machine was calibrated with standard viscometric solutions obtained from the Brookfield Laboratories.

Other Laboratory Methodology

Oxygen and CO_2 tension and pH were measured in an Instrumentation Laboratories 113 Cuvette. These determinations were performed at 37°C and suitable temperature corrections then introduced. Plasma hemoglobin was determined by the method of FLINK and WATSON[8]. Hematocrits were measured following centrifugation at 3000 rpm for 30 min.

RESULTS

Striking variability was observed in control blood samples obtained from patients just prior to cardiopulmonary by-pass. In some patients remarkably high viscosities were recorded at low shear rates. There was generally good correlation in measured viscosity between the control arterial and mixed venous samples (Table 2).

Following the institution of hemodilution by-pass, there was a sharp decrease in

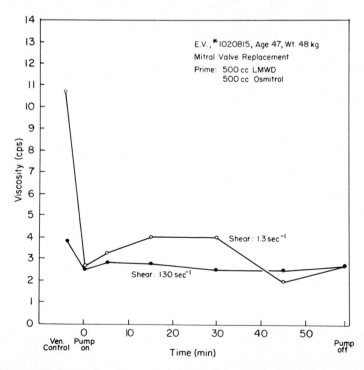

FIG. 1. LOW AND HIGH SHEAR RATE VISCOSITY DATA OBTAINED FROM A PATIENT DURING MITRAL VALVE REPLACEMENT (HEMODILUTION WITH DEXTRAN AND OSMITROL). THE MARKED IMMEDIATE DROP IN LOW SHEAR RATE VISCOSITY IS CLEAR. THE CHANGES IN VISCOSITY MEASURED AT LOW SHEAR RATES ARE CONSIDERABLY GREATER THAN THOSE MEASURED AT 130 SEC⁻¹.

viscosity, particularly at low shear rates (Fig. 1). When Rheomacrodex was used as the priming material, mid-perfusion viscosities were often as low as 20–30% of control values. This is attributed not only to the colloidal osmotic effect of low molecular weight dextran, and resulting movement of interstitial and intracellular water to the extracellular compartment, but also to the specific ability of low molecular weight dextran to increase the electronegative charge of the red blood cells, increasing their mutual repellancy[1].

Similar striking decreases in low shear rate viscosity were observed in patients undergoing hemodilution with 5% dextrose in water (Fig. 2). In general, however, these

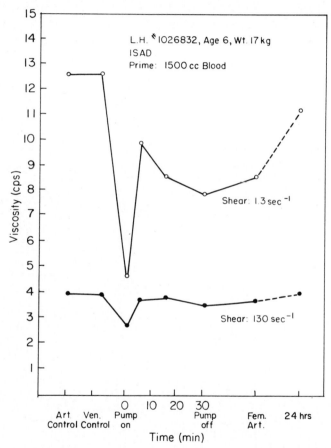

FIG. 2. VISCOSITY DATA OBTAINED FROM A PATIENT UNDERGOING CLOSURE OF AN INTERATRIAL SEPTAL DEFECT (BLOOD ALONE FOR PRIME). DECREASE IN VISCOSITY IS NOT GREAT, EXCEPT FOR THE INITIAL "PUMP ON" SAMPLE, IN WHICH THE RELATIVELY LOW HEMATOCRIT OF THE PRIMING BLOOD WAS A SIGNIFICANT FACTOR.

changes were not as persistent. In the course of longer perfusions, gradually increasing viscosity (at low shear rates) was noted when dextrose alone was used as the priming material.

As might be expected, when whole blood was used as the pump-oxygenator prime, decreases in viscosity were minimal, and probably related to the hematocrit of the blood used as a priming material.

In general, viscosity alterations tended to parallel hematocrit changes. In some instances, however, the decrease in viscosity seen with hemodilution perfusion was greater than that which would have been predicted by dilution alone (Fig. 5). Both forms of hemodilution consistently decreased the low shear rate viscosity to less than 10 cps. Final perfusion samples generally remained low when dextran was used as the hemodiluent. However, in those cases in which dextrose alone was used as the diluent, immediate post-perfusion samples tended to be higher than early perfusion specimens.

Postoperative data were obtained in eight patients, and demonstrated a return of low shear rate viscosity to figures ranging from 10.7 to 23.3 cps, which are similar to the preoperative controls in these patients (Fig. 3 and Table 2). In Fig. 4, parallel viscosity and hematocrit changes are depicted from a patient undergoing hemodilution perfusion with 5% dextrose and water. Low shear rate viscosity followed the changes in hematocrit very closely, while viscosities measured at a shear rate of 130 sec^{-1} changed comparatively little.

DISCUSSION

Viscosity of a pure, or crystalloid, solution is independent of the shear rate at which the viscosity is studied, and is equal to the shear stress ÷ shear rate. Such perfect liquids

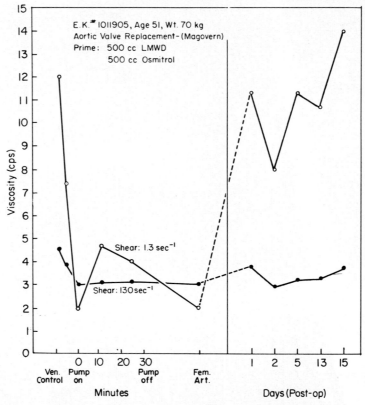

FIG. 3. VISCOSITY DATA OBTAINED FROM A PATIENT UNDERGOING DEXTRAN HEMODILUTION DURING AORTIC VALVE REPLACEMENT. A MARKED IMMEDIATE AND CONTINUED DECREASE IN LOW SHEAR RATE VISCOSITY IS APPARENT. MEASUREMENTS DURING THE POSTOPERATIVE PERIOD DEMONSTRATE A RETURN OF LOW SHEAR RATE VISCOSITY TO CONTROL LEVELS.

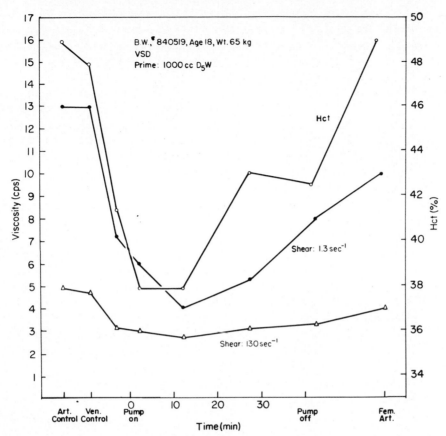

FIG. 4. HEMATOCRIT AND VISCOSITY DATA FROM A PATIENT UNDERGOING CLOSURE OF VENTRICULAR SEPTAL (DEXTROSE IN WATER PRIME). NOTE THE PARALLEL CHANGES OF HEMATOCRIT AND LOW SHEAR RATE VISCOSITY, WHICH ARE NOT WELL DEMONSTRATED BY VISCOSITY MEASUREMENTS AT 130 SEC^{-1}.

are called Newtonian. Blood, however, is non-Newtonian, since at low shear rates it has an abnormally *high* viscosity[19]. In addition, FÅHRAEUS and LINDQUIST[7] demonstrated that blood has an abnormally *low* viscosity in tubes of small radius (less than 0.5 mm diameter). Under these circumstances, it would appear that plasma skimming occurs, and that the important viscosity factor is that of the plasma alone. The Fåhraeus–Lindquist effect undoubtedly pertains to blood flowing in vessels of capillary, arteriole and venule size. Under biologic conditions of relatively slow flow in small vessels, however, it is difficult to predict whether the non-Newtonian high viscosity or the Fåhraeus–Lindquist tendency towards a lower viscosity will prevail.

Among the earliest studies concerning the effects of low molecular weight dextran upon blood flow during extracorporeal circulation are those of DRAKE, MACALAD, and LEWIS[4]. DEWALL[2] demonstrated the effectiveness of dextrose hemodilution in decreasing viscosity in extracorporeal circulation. REEMSTSMA and CREECH[15] clearly showed that *in vitro* dilution of blood with low molecular weight dextran did not decrease, but rather increased, plasma viscosity, since the dextran itself is approximately twice as viscous as plasma. They also demonstrated the effects of hematocrit and temperature on viscosity, using an ultrasonic viscometer (Bendix). EISEMAN and SPENCER[6], too, were concerned with the effects of hypothermia on flowing blood, and cited the additive factors of hemoconcentration, red blood cell aggregation, blood vessel spasm, opening of A-V shunts, decreasing flow rate and increasing viscosity as responsible for less effective tissue perfusion during hypothermia.

Adequate and effective tissue perfusion must be the final criteria of any cardio-pulmonary by-pass system. Although a single measure of perfusion adequacy is not presently available, the effects of hypothermia, hemodilution, toxic and metabolic breakdown substances in the perfusate, and effective shear rate all contribute to the final effective viscosity of the fluid perfusing tissue capillaries. The present studies have attempted to emphasize the importance of several of these factors.

Hemodilution produces relatively minor changes in viscosity when measured at high shear rates, but has a profound effect when measured at shear rates of 1.3 sec^{-1}. Such comparisons are documented in these patient studies (Fig. 1–4). Hypothermia, generally to 30–31°C, was employed during these perfusions and the viscosities were determined at the patient's temperature; the viscosity decreases would have been even greater if the measurements had been performed at 37°C. Finally, the profound clinical and experimental depression of viscosity observed in these experiments with low molecular weight dextran must be due to large movements of free water from the interstitial and intracellular spaces to the intravascular compartment. In preliminary studies in our laboratory it appears that the infusion of a given volume of low molecular weight dextran results in the additional movement of an essentially equivalent volume of water into the plasma compartment, approximately doubling the volume of diluting fluid.

The only previous report with shear-dependent measurements of viscosity during extracorporeal circulation is that of RAND[14], in which 31 patients undergoing open

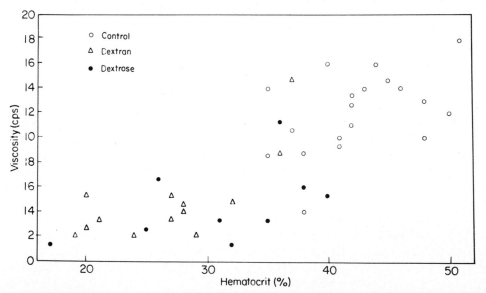

FIG. 5. PLOT OF VISCOSITY AND HEMATOCRIT DATA FROM 25 PATIENTS UNDERGOING TOTAL CARDIO-PULMONARY BY-PASS. THE MARKED CHANGES ACHIEVED BY HEMODILUTION WITH EITHER DEXTRAN OR DEXTROSE ARE OBVIOUS. THE RELATIVELY PROLONGED DEPRESSION OF BOTH HEMATOCRIT AND VISCOSITY WITH LOW MOLECULAR WEIGHT DEXTRAN HEMODILUTION IS EVEN MORE SIGNIFICANT WHEN THE IN-CREASING LENGTH OF PERFUSION IN MANY OF THE DEXTRAN CASES IS CONSIDERED.

heart surgery were studied with both Brookfield and Ostwald viscometers. However, the data in their report are limited to measurements made at high shear rates. In 17 of their patients blood alone was used as the priming fluid, while in the other 14 a mixture of $\frac{2}{3}$ blood and $\frac{1}{3}$ dextrose and water was employed. Decreases in viscosity were demonstrated with the relatively modest degree of hemodilution which they employed, and it was their opinion that viscosity decreased more than would be predicted by the observed changes in hematocrit. Rand's studies are quite consistent with those in this report, which extends the observations to patients undergoing considerably greater degrees of dilution, and to studies at much lower shear rates.

SUMMARY AND CONCLUSIONS

Whole-blood viscosity was studied in 25 patients undergoing cardipulmonary by-pass, with a cone-and-plate viscometer, employing shear rates of 1.3–130 sec^{-1}. Hemodilution with both dextrose and dextran was effective in lowering viscosity, even in the face of moderate hypothermia. Dextran appeared to have a somewhat more profound and more prolonged effect. Since *in vitro* dilution of blood with dextran causes an *increase* in viscosity, the clinically observed effects of dextran hemodilution are likely to be caused by the concurrent movement of large volumes of water from the interstitial and intracellular tissues to the plasma compartment.

The significance of measuring viscosity at low shear rates (which pertain to the physiologic situation in small blood vessels at low flow rates) and with appropriate temperature control, is emphasized.

ACKNOWLEDGMENT

This work was supported by Grant He 08981, National Heart Institute, U.S. Public Health Service.

REFERENCES

[1] BERNSTEIN, E. F., CASTANEDA, A. R., EVANS, R. L. and VARCO, R. L. *Surg. Forum* **13**, 193, 1962.
[2] DeWALL, R. A., LILLEHEI, R. C. and SELLERS, R. D. *N. Eng. J. Med.* **266**, 1078, 1962.
[3] DINTENFASS, L. *Biorheology* **1**, 91, 1963.
[4] DRAKE, C. T., MACALAD, F. and LEWIS, F. J. *J. Thor. Cardiovasc. Surg.* **42**, 735, 1961.
[5] ECKSTEIN, R. W., BOOK, D. and GREGG, D. E. *Am. J. Physiol.* **135**, 772, 1941.
[6] EISEMAN, B. and SPENCER, F. C. *Surgery* **52**, 532, 1962.
[7] FÅHRAEUS, R. and LINDQUIST, T. *Am. J. Physiol.* **96**, 562, 1931.
[8] FLINK, E. B. and WATSON, C. J. *J. Biol. Chem.* **146**, 171, 1942.
[9] GELIN, L. E. and LOFSTROM, B. *Acta Chir. Scand.* **108**, 402, 1955.
[10] GELIN, L. E., RUDENSTAM, C. M. and ZEDERFELDT, B. *Third European Conference on Microcirculation*, Jerusalem, 1964, *Bibl. Anat.* **7**, 368, HARDERS, H. (Editor), S. Karger, Basel, 1965.
[11] GREGERSEN, M. I., CHIEN, S., PERIC, B. and TAYLOR, H. *Third European Conference on Microcirculation*, Jerusalem, 1964, *Bibl. Anat.* **7**, 383, HARDERS, H. (Editor), S. Karger, Basel, 1965.
[12] MERRILL, E. W., GILLILAND, E. R., COKELET, G. C., SHIN, H., BRITTEN, A. and WELLS, R. E., Jr. *Biophys. J.* **3**, 199, 1963.
[13] POISEUILLE, J. L. M. *Comptes. Rend. Acad. d. Sc.* **11**, 961 and 1041, 1840.
[14] RAND, P. W., LACOMBE, E., BARKEN, N. and DERMAN, V. *J. Thor. Cardiovasc. Surg.* **51**, 616, 1966.
[15] REEMTSMA, K. and CREECH, O., Jr. *J. Thor. and Cardiovas. Surg.* **44**, 674, 1962.
[16] SHENK, W. G., Jr., DELIN, N. A., DOMANIG, E., HAHNLOSEV, P. and HOYT, R. K. *Arch. Surg.* **89**, 783, 1964.
[17] SHOEMAKER, W. C. *Arch. Surg.* **187**, 355, 1963.

[18] WELLS, R. E., Jr. and MERRILL, E. W. *Science* **133**, 763, 1961.
[19] WELLS, R. E., Jr. and MERRILL, E. W. *J. Clin. Invest.* **41**, 1591, 1962.
[20] AUDHI, N., McCOLLOUGH, B., CAREY, J. and GREER, A. *Arch. Surg.* **82**, 320, 1961.

DISCUSSION

SWANK (*U.S.A.*):

We have made measurements of the screen filtration pressure during extracorporeal circulation. I would like to mention an experience which, I think, has some bearing on this point. Heparinized whole blood, when approximately 24 hr old, contains large numbers of tightly aggregated platelets. These are not removed by a routine transfusion filter and these blood samples as they were mixed in the pump before starting the by-pass, usually had a screen filtration pressure that would be four or five times the normal value. Within one circulation of this blood, through the patient's body, the screen filtration pressure had dropped almost to normal and by the end of 30 min, the screen filtration pressure of all of the blood in the system was normal. This indicated, I believe, that these aggregates had been removed from the circulation by filtration. We have also had some experience using mannitol and dextran as a diluent. In these instances, we rarely have a big increase in screen filtration pressure. A day or so after operation, however, there is quite a marked increase in the screen filtration pressure in the patient himself, and the cerebral complication rate in these patients is just as high as in those in which we used heparinized blood without additional diluents to fill the extracorporeal system.

LONG (*U.S.A.*):

I am glad you mentioned your screen filtration test, Dr. Swank, because I think that in the confusion of attempting to measure a great many things, particularly when we are talking in terms of aggregation, we cannot neglect the fact that you have developed a technique that clearly in a qualitative way measures the amount of aggregation that is present. So I think it is important for us all, doing this type of viscosity study or *in vivo* microcirculation studies, to keep in mind the fact that if we really want to look for aggregates, probably the only test, at least that I know of, available today is the screen filtration test. I have been using recently, the packed cell viscosity measurements that Dr. Gregersen alluded to a few minutes ago in the previous discussion, packing cells up to a 95 hematocrit. This packed cell "viscosity" measurement seems to correlate well with the presence or absence of aggregation. Measurements of whole blood viscosity and plasma viscosity, in my hands, had no positive correlation whatsoever with the presence or absence of aggregation.

SWANK:

I would like to comment on that briefly, too. We have had experience with animals in shock, in which the screen filtration pressure was greatly increased, often as much as a thousand per cent. In these animals, we did not find any increase in viscosity using the Brookfield viscometer.

WELLS (*U.S.A.*):

You are referring to your screen filtration for the testing of platelet aggregation, and I think, Dr. Swank, you told me earlier, you cannot test erythrocyte aggregation with this. Is this correct?

SWANK:

Not completely correct, but in the main correct. The method is very sensitive to platelet aggregation, but probably much less sensitive for red cell aggregation.

WELLS:

I think Dr. Long was equating your "aggregation" with his erythrocyte aggregation, and it is important to keep this separate. I think the screen filtration may give some indication of this, but not to the degree that aggregated platelets will.

LONG:

I guess that is a good point, Dr. Wells. I think that is certainly true. I think, probably as I see it, Dr. Swank's test will pick up the rigid erythrocyte aggregates.

WELLS:

Let us clarify this. Is he willing to say that if you have rigid cells, and I am not sure how you are going to prove "rigid", but let us say, there are rigid erythrocyte aggregates; will his system define this with reliability?

SWANK:

My system will not determine between red cell and platelet aggregation.

WELLS:

The platelet-free sample was rigid?

SWANK:

If we remove the platelets, the screen filtration pressure is normal.

WELLS:

Right. This is my point.

PALMER (*Australia*):

I just want to remark briefly that there is a very simple, qualitative method of looking for platelet aggregates and that is to flow the blood through a flat channel, say 30 μ thick, under the microscope; you can see the platelet aggregates standing out very nicely against the red cells.

CHARM (*U.S.A.*):

I would just like to comment on this screen filtration test of Dr. Swank. The wall shear stresses involved in that test are in the order of 20,000 dynes/cm^2. The type of stresses involved in red cell aggregation, as we think of it, are in the order of tenths of a dyne per square centimeter. So he certainly would not pick up, on a screen filtration test, any of the stresses involved in red cell aggregation. I recall I got this information from a paper that was given in Israel, in which you mentioned screen filtration pressures and the size of your screen. As I recall, I estimated that the shear stresses were about 20,000 dynes/cm^2. I think I mentioned it to you at the time.

SWANK:

I do not know the shearing stresses in the SFP machine — perhaps in the neighborhood of 2500 sec^{-1}. I think the SFP and viscosity tests probably depend on somewhat different principles. For example, concrete has a great stress against compression, but you can pull it apart relatively easily. The sensitivity of the screen filtration pressure method, is probably due to sudden crowding of a large number of units through an opening which is too small for them to go through easily. You have a compression factor to deal with, which is quite different from the ordinary shearing factor, which is measured by other viscometry measurements.

PLASMA EXPANDERS AND THE FLOW PROPERTIES OF BLOOD

CARL-GUSTAV GROTH*

Departments of Anaesthesiology, Clinical Physiology and Surgery, Karolinska Institutet, Serafimerlasarettet, Stockholm, Sweden, and Veterans Administration Hospital, Denver, Colorado, U.S.A.

THE realization in recent years that trauma and a large number of diseases give rise to disturbances in the flow properties of the blood has led to a search for means of counteracting such disturbances. An agent that would seem to be able to counteract disturbances in some of the factors governing the flow properties is albumin. It is established that this protein reduces erythrocyte aggregation *in vitro*[1–4] and LONG and co-workers[5] have shown that the use of albumin solution reduces the intravascular erythrocyte aggregation occurring in extracorporeal circulation.

In the present study the effect of infused 10% albumin solution on haematological factors governing flow properties of the blood was studied in man. For comparison another group was given an infusion of 10% Rheomacrodex^R, that is dextran with a mean molecular weight of 40,000, a solution intended for use as an improver of the blood flow properties[6].

The study was performed on patients with various diseases, selected as to represent varying degrees of elevation of the plasma viscosity and/or erythrocyte sedimentation rate. They did not display any clinical signs of acute hypovolemia. Each patient was given one of the infusion solutions, 7 received albumin and 7 Rheomacrodex, 10 ml per kg bodyweight were given over 1 hr. Before the infusion, immediately afterwards, and 2 and 4 hr later venous blood was collected for the determination of the plasma and blood viscosities, the haematocrit, the erythrocyte sedimentation rate (ESR) and the albumin and dextran concentrations, respectively.

The plasma and blood viscosity were determined with a cone-plate viscometer (Brookfield LVT)[7] at 37°C and 23 sec^{-1}. The ESR was determined by WESTERGREN'S method[8], and the reading was corrected to a standard haematocrit (43%) using GRAM's chart[9].

The albumin solution lowered the viscosity of the plasma and the blood and at the same time the haematocrit and ESR were also lowered; all the changes were highly significant ($P \leqslant 0.001$). After the infusion there was a gradual return towards the pre-infusion values, and after 4 hr only a small part of the decrease in the plasma viscosity remained; but about one half of the decrease in the haematocrit and the greater part of the decrease in the ESR and blood viscosity. Immediately after the infusion the albumin concentration in serum had increased significantly ($0.001 < P \leqslant 0.01$); 4 hr later it had returned almost to the pre-infusion level (Fig. 1).

The Rheomacrodex solution increased the viscosity of the plasma when it was less than 2.0 but had no effect when it was between 2.0 and 2.2. There was a significant fall in the blood viscosity and at the same time there was a highly significant lowering

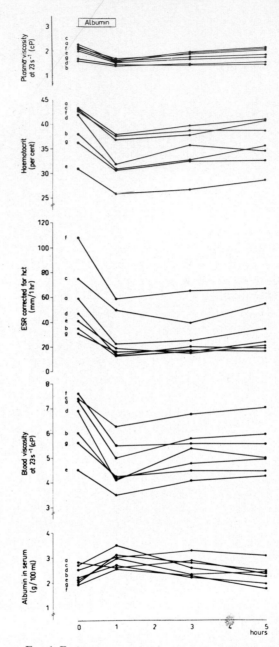

FIG. 1. EFFECT OF INFUSION OF ALBUMIN IN MAN.

of the haematocrit and ESR. Four hours after the infusion about one half of the decrease in the haematocrit, ESR and blood viscosity still remained. Immediately after the infusion the mean dextran concentration in plasma was 1.50 g/100 ml. 4 hr later this had diminished to 0.83. There was no statistically significant difference between the effects of albumin and Rheomacrodex except as regards the plasma viscosity (Fig. 2).

The recorded effects of infusion of Rheomacrodex are consistent with earlier

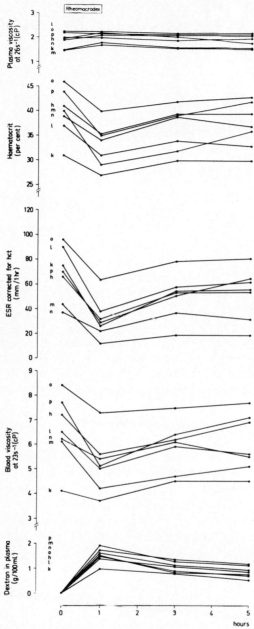

FIG. 2. EFFECT OF INFUSION OF RHEOMACRODEX IN MAN.

findings[10, 11]. The findings on infusion of albumin indicate that haemorheological disturbances may be counteracted by infusion of albumin as well as Rheomacrodex. The more beneficial effect of infused albumin on the plasma viscosity might be of considerable significance *in vivo* if a Fåhraeus–Lindquist effect exists[12].

The difference in the effect on the plasma viscosity must be related to the colloids;

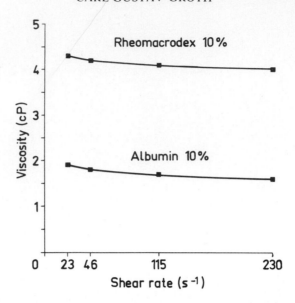

FIG. 3. THE VISCOSITY FOR 10% ALBUMIN AND RHEOMACRODEX SOLUTIONS AT DIFFERENT SHEAR RATES. MEANS OF FIVE DETERMINATIONS.

that the colloids in fact affect viscosity to a different degree is evident from the viscosities of the infusion solutions (Fig. 3).

Thus there are at least two infusion agents available for clinical use that not only are efficient plasma expanders but can also counteract disturbances of the flow properties of blood, namely Rheomacrodex and albumin. In a study on rabbits the effect of Rheomacrodex and albumin was compared with that of blood and a conventional plasma expander, Macrodex[R]. Two series of animals were studied; in one the animals had induced disturbances in the flow properties of the blood and hypovolemia, in the other only hypovolemia. In view of the assumed importance of the flow properties of the blood for the nutrition of the tissue, the tissue oxygen tension was the parameter studied. As the tissue oxygen tension is highly dependent on the microcirculation, where the plasma viscosity and erythrocyte aggregation probably are of particular significance, the disturbances induced were increased plasma viscosity and erythrocyte aggregation. These disturbances were achieved by an exchange transfusion with a mixture of 10% dextran with a mean molecular weight of 236,000, and erythrocytes.

	Before	After	Difference ± SE
Blood viscosity (cP)	5·00	6·62	+ 1·61 ± 0·05*
Plasma viscosity (cP)	1·48	2·46	+ 0·99 ± 0·02*
Haematocrit (%)	37·1	32·2	− 4·9 ± 0·2*
ESR (mm in 30 min)	0	79·5	+ 79·5 ± 3·3*

*Significant ($P \leqslant 0·01$).

FIG. 4. EFFECT OF EXCHANGE TRANSFUSION WITH DEXTRAN 250 AND ERYTHROCYTES IN RABBITS. MEAN VALUES, $n = 83$.

This exchange transfusion increased the blood and plasma viscosities and the ESR while the haematocrit diminished; all the changes were significant (Fig. 4). Since the dextran 250 solution used was of 10% strength, and therefore colloid hypertonic, the exchange transfusion must have increased the volume of circulating plasma. However, since the concurrent erythrocyte aggregation will have reduced the volume of circulating erythrocytes[13, 14], the net effect on the blood volume was presumably small. The molecular weight of the macromolecular dextran fraction and the amount infused were chosen to produce disturbances in the flow properties of blood commensurate with those occurring in pathological conditions.

Hypovolemia was induced by withdrawing 10·5 ml of blood per kg bodyweight. This moderate degree of hypovolemia was chosen in an attempt to avoid the effect of changes in the flow properties of the blood from being masked by the effect of the changes in blood volume; all the infusion agents used are known to increase the blood volume and hence the flow in hypovolemia[15].

The Rheomacrodex and albumin were given as 10% solutions in isotonic saline. The albumin was prepared from rabbit serum by fractionation, the final product consisted of 98–99% of albumin. The blood given was rabbit ACD blood. Macrodex, that is dextran with a mean molecular weight of 70,000, was given as a 6% solution in isotonic saline.

The oxygen tension of the tissue was examined in muscle and skin, using polarography. A bare-tipped platinum electrode which is inserted into the tissue was used. Examinations were also made of the arterial blood pressure, and the oxygen tension of the arterial blood. The blood and plasma viscosities, haematocrit and ESR were studied with the same methods as in the patients. However, the ESR reading for rabbit blood could not be corrected to a standard haematocrit.

Seventy-five animals with disturbed and 75 with normal flow properties of the blood were examined. The various infusion agents were given to groups of 15 rabbits, while 15 control animals of each series received no infusion.

Figure 5 summarizes the effects of the infusion agents, that is the difference between the changes found on infusion of the agent and those in the corresponding group that did not receive any infusion. The means in the groups are given, the broken line separates significantly different means. In the series with disturbed flow properties of the blood all the infusion agents increased the blood pressure, but Rheomacrodex and albumin caused a greater increase than blood and Macrodex. In the series with normal flow properties all infusion agents again increased the blood pressure but there was no significant difference between the agents. The oxygen tension of muscle was also increased by all the infusion agents and in both series the increase was greater for Rheomacrodex and albumin than for blood and Macrodex. The findings in the oxygen tension of skin are omitted from the discussion for reasons given later. There were no significant changes in the arterial blood oxygen tension. In the series with disturbed flow properties Rheomacrodex, albumin and Macrodex all decreased blood viscosity significantly while blood caused no significant change. In the series with normal flow properties, on the contrary, Rheomacrodex, albumin and Macrodex caused no significant change while blood gave a significant increase. The plasma viscosity was significantly decreased by Rheomacrodex and albumin in the series with disturbed flow properties while in the other series Rheomacrodex and Macrodex increased the plasma viscosity. In both series Rheomacrodex, albumin and Macrodex decreased

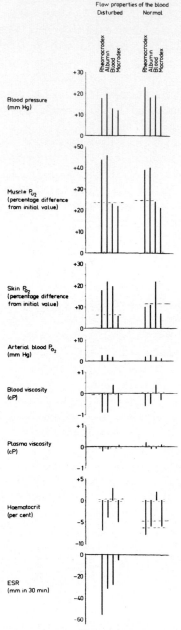

FIG. 5. EFFECT OF RHEOMACRODEX, ALBUMIN, BLOOD AND MACRODEX IN RABBITS. MEANS IN THE GROUPS.
---- SEPARATES SIGNIFICANTLY DIFFERENT MEANS.

the haematocrit, the decrease being most marked after Rheomacrodex; while blood increased the haematocrit. In the series with disturbed flow properties Rheomacrodex, albumin and blood decreased the ESR, the decrease being larger after Rheomacrodex. While the fall in ESR produced by infusion of blood might have been due to both a decrease in erythrocyte aggregation and the rise in haematocrit, the fall following infusion of Rheomacrodex and albumin must have been due to marked disaggregation, since it occurred at the same time as a decrease in haematocrit.

Comparison between the effect of a particular infusion agent in the groups with disturbed or normal flow properties showed that the reduction or increase in plasma viscosity produced by Rheomacrodex was significantly different, and that the lowering of haematocrit on infusing albumin and Macrodex was significantly greater in the group with normal flow properties. Otherwise there were no significant differences.

While the oxygen tension of muscle invariably increased on infusion of the various agents that of the skin sometimes decreased. As it is possible that this was due to vasoconstriction due to vasomotor reflexes, the measurements in skin were probably a less reliable basis than those in muscle for the evaluation of the relationship between tissue oxygen tension and the flow properties of the blood.

The considerably greater effect of Rheomacrodex and albumin than of blood and Macrodex on the oxygen tension in muscle in the series of rabbits with disturbed flow properties of the blood might be ascribed to the favourable effect of the former media on the plasma viscosity and erythrocyte aggregation, while there was no apparent relationship between the effects of the infusion agents on blood viscosity and the oxygen tension in muscle. On the other hand, in the series with normal flow properties the greater effect of Rheomacrodex and albumin on the oxygen tension in muscle was unassociated with any favourable effect on the flow properties. This, together with the fact that the respective infusion agents increased the oxygen tension of muscle to the same extent in the two series would indicate that the difference in the effect on the oxygen tension was not due primarily to the observed difference in their effects on the flow properties of blood.

This would seem not to accord with the findings of earlier experimental studies, in which Rheomacrodex has been found to exert a favourable effect on the blood flow or oxygen tension of tissue mainly by counteracting erythrocyte aggregation and increased plasma viscosity[16, 17]. In these studies, however, the disturbances in the flow properties of the blood were more pronounced than in the present study, and in consequence the favourable effect of Rheomacrodex on the flow properties was much greater.

Unlike blood and Macrodex, 10% Rheomacrodex and albumin are strongly colloid hypertonic. In vivo, this difference is offset by the fact that the albumin as well as the Rheomacrodex can easily pass from the blood stream to the extravascular compartment[18, 19]. However, Rheomacrodex and albumin presumably render the plasma colloid hypertonic during the infusion. This would result in an uptake of extravascular fluid and a dilatation of the microvasculature, and hence an increase in the blood flow and the tissue oxygen tension[20, 21]. At the same time this would make the increase in the plasma volume greater on infusion of Rheomacrodex and albumin than on blood and Macrodex and this would again increase the blood flow. However, the behaviour of the haematocrit was consistent with a greater plasma-expanding effect of Rheomacrodex but not of albumin. But the haematocrit is a poor measure of changes in plasma volume in the groups with disturbed blood flow properties because the number of circulating erythrocytes is dependent on the degree of erythrocyte aggregation.

The present investigation has shown that 10% Rheomacrodex and albumin are superior to 6% Macrodex and blood in effecting a recovery of the oxygen tension of muscle in hypovolemia. This applied whether or not the hypovolemia was accompanied by erythrocyte aggregation and an increase in plasma viscosity. Further investigation is required to ascertain the cause of this beneficial effect.

ACKNOWLEDGMENT

This investigation was supported by a grant from the U.S. National Institute of Health H–4909.

REFERENCES

[1] von Zarday, I. and von Farkas, G. *Z. ges. Exp. Med.* **78**, 367, 1931.
[2] Gray, S. J. and Mitchell, E. B. *Proc. Soc. Exp. Biol. Med.* **51**, 403, 1942.
[3] Thorsen, G. and Hint, H. *Acta Chir. Scand. Suppl.* 154, 1950.
[4] Wells, R. E., Jr., Perera, R. D., Gawronski, T. and Shahriari, A. A. *J. Clin. Invest.* **42**, 991, 1963.
[5] Long, D. M., Sanchez, L., Varco, R. L. and Lillehei, C. W. *Surgery* **50**, 12, 1961.
[6] Gelin, L. E. and Ingelman, B. *Acta Chir. Scand.* **122**, 294, 1961.
[7] Wells, R. E., Jr., Denton, R. and Merrill, E. W. *J. Lab. Clin. Med.* **57**, 646, 1961.
[8] Westergren, A. *Ergebn. inn. Med.* **26**, 577, 1924.
[9] Gram, H. D. *Acta Med. Scand.* **68**, 108, 1928.
[10] Gelin, L. E. and Thoren, O. K. A. *Acta Chir. Scand.* **122**, 303, 1961.
[11] Groth, C. G. and Thorsen, G. *Acta Chir. Scand.* **130**, 507, 1965.
[12] Fåhraeus, R. and Lindquist, T. *Amer. J. Physiol.* **96**, 562, 1931.
[13] Gelin, L. E. *Acta Chir. Scand.* Suppl. 210, 1956.
[14] Shoemaker, W. C. *Arch. Surg.* **87**, 355, 1963.
[15] Schenk, W. G., Delin, N. A., Domanig, E., Hahnloser, P. and Hoyt, R. K. *Arch. Surg.* **89**, 783, 1964.
[16] Gelin, L. E. and Shoemaker, W. C. *Surgery* **49**, 713, 1961.
[17] Groth, C. G. and Löfström, B. *Acta Chir. Scand.* **131**, 275, 1966.
[18] Gelin, L. E., Sölvell, L. and Zederfeldt, B. *Acta Chir. Scand.* **122**, 309, 1961.
[19] Wasserman, K. and Mayerson, H. S. *Amer. J. Physiol.* **165**, 15, 1951.
[20] Marshall, R. J. and Shepherd, J. T. *Amer. J. Physiol.* **197**, 951, 1959.
[21] Hint, H. C. *2nd Europ. Conf. Microcirculation*, Pavia, 1962, *Bibl. Anat.* **4**, 112, Harders, H. (Editor), S. Karger, Basel, 1964.

BLOOD CELLULAR ELEMENTS I

14 July, p.m.

Chairmen: STANLEY G. MASON, Canada
ROE E. WELLS, U.S.A.

VISCO-ELASTIC PROPERTIES OF THE RED CELL MEMBRANE

Joseph A. Kochen*

Department of Pediatrics, Albert Einstein
College of Medicine, New York, New York, U.S.A.

Investigations of the deformability of the red blood cell utilizing high-speed cine-photomicrography and micromanipulation have clearly demonstrated the remarkable plasticity of the normal red cell[1–6]. Recent studies from this and other laboratories have indicated that the red cell contents are thixotropic in character[7, 8]. This has led to the suggestion that the reversible deformation of the red cell may depend on the transfer of stresses across the red cell membrane with a resulting decrease in the viscosity of the red cell interior. The transfer of stresses across the red cell membrane could be accomplished with minimal impedance if the membrane were itself a thixotropic system[9]. This type of non-Newtonian system might be expected to exhibit not only a high degree of fluidity under conditions of shear stress, but also a high degree of spinnability under conditions of tensile stress.

Spinnability is the characteristic property of many polymer solutions to be drawn into long, thin, liquid threads or filaments. As described by Lodge[10], this property is due to the stability of the lengthening liquid filament to local changes in diameter. A Newtonian liquid would not possess this stability because the stress (tension per unit cross-sectional area) in an extending filament is proportional to the rate of increase in length per unit length. Since the tension must be the same at all points along the filament irrespective of diameter, the tension per unit cross-sectional area, or stress, must increase whenever the cross-sectional area decreases. The rate of increase of length per unit length must therefore increase in such regions, with the result that the thin places in the filament will extend more rapidly than the thick places and the filament will break. Good thread-forming properties would be obtained if thick places in the filament extended more rapidly than thin places. This has been shown to occur in polymer solutions and has been attributed to a rapid increase of the Trouton viscosity of the fluid as the tensile stress is increased. The rapid increase of Trouton viscosity with increasing tensile stress stands in marked contrast to the decrease of viscosity with increasing shear stress.

If the red cell membrane is indeed a non-Newtonian system, then in addition to thixotropy and spinnability, it may be expected to exhibit evidence of elastic recovery. Elastic recovery is the property of polymer solutions to reverse their direction of flow when a stress that has resulted in a steady flow is suddenly discontinued[10]. The combination of thixotropy, spinnability and elastic recovery would result in the capacity of the red cell membrane to be drawn into a long, thin, contractile filament under conditions of tensile stress. The present study demonstrates that the red cell membrane behaves in this manner and suggests that the molecular organization of the membrane may be analogous to that of other non-Newtonian systems.

For the purpose of this investigation, red cells adherent to a glass surface by a single point on their membranes were subjected to the deforming stress of a moving fluid–air interface. This was accomplished by transferring a small drop of a 1% human red blood cell suspension in plasma or isotonic saline buffered at pH 7.4 to a glass slide positioned on a microscope stage. A glass cover-slip with its concave surface facing downward, was then gently placed on the drop. Light pressure was momentarily brought to bear on the center of the cover-slip to flatten it. This caused increased spreading of the drop and facilitated the adherence of some of the red cells to the glass surface. On release of the pressure, the cover-slip resumed its original concave–convex shape with the result that the drop between the cover-slip and slide contracted, producing a moving air–fluid interface.

Examination of the moving air–fluid boundary under phase-contrast microscopy revealed that many of the red cells attached to the glass surface were transformed in a characteristic manner by the tensile stress of the moving interface. As these cells were pulled from their point of attachment they lost their biconcave form and became tear-drop in shape, with the spherical portion in the fluid phase and the tail of the drop and its point of attachment to the glass in the air phase (Fig. 1). Under the progressive

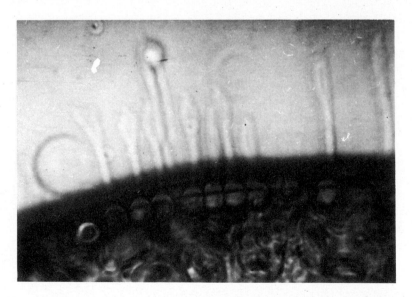

Fig. 1. Human red blood cells at the air–fluid interface. Note that cells located in the fluid phase are connected by membrane filaments to their points of attachment in the air phase.

tensile stress of the moving air–fluid boundary, the tail of the drop elongated to form a steadily lengthening filament of relatively constant caliber. As this process continued, the spherical portion of the cell became smaller and at a critical yield point, ruptured, with the release of hemoglobin and the deposition of the remainder of the membrane on the glass surface in the air phase (Fig. 2).

The addition of Alizarin Red S to the medium permitted visualization of the emerging

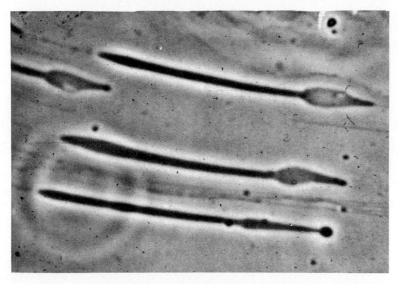

FIG. 2. RED CELL FILAMENTS IN THE AIR PHASE.

hemoglobin[8] and showed that the region of membrane breakdown occurred in the spherical portion of the cell and not in the filament. Continuity between the filament in the air phase and the spherical portion of the cell in the fluid phase could be clearly demonstrated by fixing the cells before filament formation had progressed to the point of hemolysis. This was accomplished by flowing an isotonic formalin solution under the cover-slip. This permitted visualization of both the filament and the fixed spherical portion of the cell (Fig. 3). The introduction of a hypotonic formalin solution under the cover-slip resulted in lysis of the spherical portion of the cell and fixation of the resulting

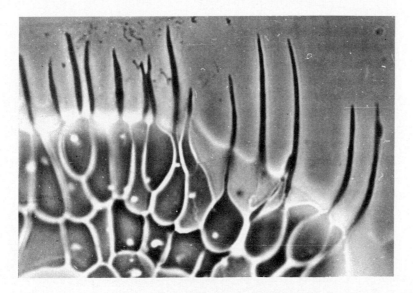

FIG. 3. FORMALIN-FIXED RED CELLS AND FILAMENTS. NOTE CONTINUITY BETWEEN FILAMENTS AND SPHERICAL PORTIONS OF THE CELLS.

red cell ghost. This procedure clearly revealed the membranous continuity between the filament and the remainder of the red cell membrane (Fig. 4). In order to determine whether the filaments consisted of a full thickness of membrane, similar experiments

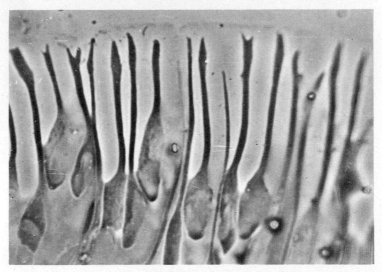

FIG. 4. FORMALIN-FIXED RED CELL GHOSTS AND FILAMENTS. NOTE MEMBRANE CONTINUITY BETWEEN FILAMENTS AND GHOSTS.

were performed with red cells containing intracellular inclusions (Heinz bodies produced by the action of acetylphenylhydrazine) adherent to the inner membrane surface. The use of these cells resulted in the formation of filaments containing Heinz bodies along their length and suggested that the filaments were indeed composed of a full thickness of membrane.

Reintroduction of red cell membrane filaments into a fluid phase by flowing isotonic saline solution under the cover-slip, resulted in a rapid contraction of many of the filaments into fluid-filled spheres with a marked morphological resemblance to red cell ghosts. Alteration in the tonicity of the suspending medium resulted in swelling and shrinking of the spheres, indicating that the spheres were osmotically intact and that reconstitution of the hemolytic membrane defect had occurred.

The width and the length of the membrane filaments deposited on the glass surface in the air phase were measured by means of a Cooke-A.E.I. image-splitting measuring attachment to the phase-contrast microscope. A total of 135 membrane filaments derived from normal red cells were measured. Their mean length was found to be $24.6\,\mu$ and their mean width was found to be $1.6\,\mu$. The width determinations were made in the mid-section of the filaments where the cross-sectional diameters were relatively constant (Fig. 2). On the over-simplified assumption that these filaments were perfectly cylindrical in shape, their mean surface area was calculated and was found to be $115\,\mu^2$. This value may be compared to a value of $137\,\mu^2$ for the mean surface area of maximally swollen red cells, as computed from volumes determined by the use of a Coulter Counter. The similarity in the values for the approximate surface area of the membrane filaments and the maximally swollen prelytic cells may be interpreted to indicate that little actual stretching of the membrane had occurred despite the marked degree of membrane deformation.

Of particular interest was the finding that the length of the membrane filaments did not vary significantly over a wide range in straining time. The rate of filament formation was determined by cinematography at 24 frames per second and subsequent counting of individual frames. Filaments formed in a period of less than 2 sec were indistinguishable in length from filaments formed over a 20 sec period. The finding that the degree of maximal membrane deformation is independent of the rate of straining is difficult to reconcile with the concept that the red cell membrane behaves as a purely visco-elastic rheological body as suggested by KATCHALSKY and co-workers[11], and may suggest the presence of a membrane component with the properties of a more rigid solid.

The possible presence of a more rigid membrane component may also offer an explanation for an otherwise perplexing phenomenon observed in the course of these studies. It was noted that some of the cells that had been maximally distorted by filament formation (Fig. 5(1)) developed an outpouching or protrusion in the spherical portion of the cell immediately prior to hemolysis (Fig. 5(2) and (3)). As the cell hemolysed and the spherical portion of the cell faded from view, the protrusion broke away in the

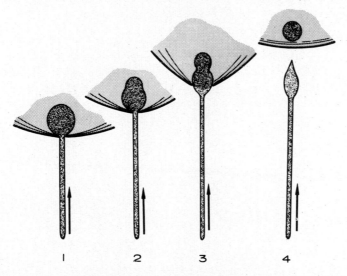

FIG. 5. DIAGRAMMATIC REPRESENTATION OF RED CELL FILAMENT AND MICROSPHERE FORMATION.

form of a spherical or discoid body (Fig. 5(4)). This microsphere ranged up to $2\,\mu$ in size, was osmotically very fragile and contained hemoglobin (Fig. 6). Of particular interest was the observation that microspheres formed from Heinz body-containing red cells were devoid of Heinz bodies and that the Heinz bodies remained with the membrane filaments. This finding suggests that the microspheres may be deficient in an inner membrane layer to which the Heinz bodies adhere in the intact cell and that this inner membrane layer is present in the membrane filament.

The deduction that the red cell membrane is a multi-layer structure may offer an explanation for the formation of microspheres and the anomalous behavior of the red cell under conditions of stress. It is proposed that the red cell membrane is composed of an outer structure consisting of a micellar arrangement of lipids and proteins and

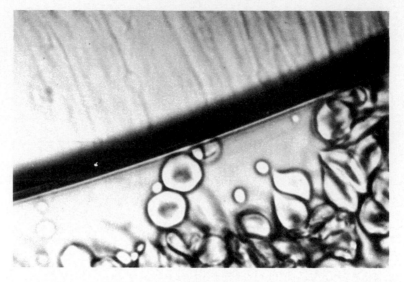

FIG. 6. APPEARANCE OF MICROSPHERES SHORTLY AFTER FORMATION AT THE AIR–FLUID INTERFACE. THESE
MICROSPHERES WERE DERIVED FROM THE RED CELLS SHOWN IN FIG. 1.

an inner structure consisting of a protein network[9]. By virtue of its paracrystalline
state the outer component combines the fluidity of a liquid while preserving the possibility of the structural characteristics of a crystalline solid. Because of its non-
Newtonian character this layer is capable of thixotropy, spinnability and elastic
recovery. The property of thixotropy is responsible for the low surface viscosity of the
red cell under conditions of shear stress. This characteristic confers on the red cell

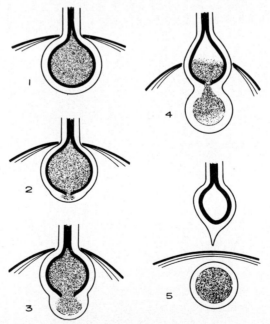

FIG. 7. DIAGRAMMATIC REPRESENTATION OF THE MECHANISM OF FILAMENT AND MICROSPHERE FORMATION.

membrane a high degree of deformability, the capacity to offer little resistance to the transmission of stresses to the red cell interior and the remarkable capacity of the membrane to reconstitute itself following injury. By virtue of its non-Newtonian character, this phase is also capable of a rapid increase in Trouton viscosity and this confers on the red cell a high capacity for filament formation. The second layer is close to or may actually represent the inner aspect of the cell membrane. This component may be responsible for the shape of the cell and the maintenance of the integrity of the membrane under conditions of stress when the thixotropic phase is highly fluid.

It is proposed that under conditions of the present study, the red cells are maximally deformed at the point where maximal elongation of the filament has been achieved (Fig. 7(1)). Further tensile stress results in a break in the inner protein network responsible for maintenance of the integrity of the cell (Fig. 7(2)). The development of a break in this layer leads to the forceful protrusion of the contents of the red cell through the resulting defect (Fig. 7(3)). However, the outer thixotropic phase is highly fluid under these conditions and forms a layer which surrounds the protruding contents of the cell (Fig. 7(4)). With further movement of the air–fluid boundary, the protruding part, no longer restrained by the presence of the inner membrane phase, breaks away and assumes an independent existence as a microsphere composed of hemoglobin surrounded by a single phase thixotropic layer (Fig. 7(5)).

In conclusion, these direct micro-rheological studies of the red cell support the concept that the red cell membrane is a heterogeneous structure which under conditions of stress exhibits many of the characteristics of a non-Newtonian system.

ACKNOWLEDGMENT

This work was supported by U.S. Public Health Service Grant ROl HE–07234.

REFERENCES

[1] PALMER, A. A. Quart. J. Exp. Physiol. 44, 149, 1959.
[2] BLOCH, E. H. Amer. J. Anat. 110, 125, 1962.
[3] GUEST, M. M., BOND, T. P., COOPER, R. G. and DERRICK, J. R. Science 142, 1319, 1963.
[4] RAND, R. P. and BURTON, A. C. Biophys. J. 4, 115, 1964.
[5] BRÅNEMARK, P–I. In Symposium on Biorheology, COPLEY, A. L. (Editor), Proc. 4th Int. Cong. Rheol., Interscience Publ. John Wiley, New York, 1965, part 4, p. 459.
[6] MONRO, P. A. G. Bibl. Anat. 7, 376, 1965.
[7] DINTENFASS, L. Angiology 13, 333, 1962.
[8] KOCHEN, J. A. In Symposium on Biorheology, COPLEY, A. L. (Editor), Proc. 4th Int. Cong. Rheol., Interscience Publ. John Wiley, New York, 1965, part 4, p. 193.
[9] DINTENFASS, L. Acta Haemat. 32, 299, 1964.
[10] LODGE, A. S. In Flow Properties of Blood and Other Biological Systems, COPLEY, A. L. and STAINSBY, G. (Editors), Pergamon Press, Oxford, New York, 1960, p. 5.
[11] KATCHALSKY, A., KEDEM, O., KLIBANSKY, C. and DE VRIES, A. In Flow Properties of Blood and Other Biological Systems, COPLEY, A. L. and STAINSBY, G. (Editors), Pergamon Press, Oxford, New York, 1960, p. 155.

DISCUSSION

BURTON (Canada):

I am simply delighted with these observations, particularly since they confirm our own, many of which have not been published. So this is no criticism. But we have observed these microspheres by sucking parts of red cells quickly into pipettes. With many of the things you said, I would agree completely. I wondered whether you had perhaps missed the confirmation of Katchalsky's values for the viscosity, which Rand did in his second paper on the viscoelastic properties. It was a different method; and yet we came out with very much the same value for the viscosity of the membrane which Katchalsky had obtained. The absolute values, I think you agree, for the viscosity of the membrane are uncertain, because in getting the coefficient of viscosity, you have to divide by a thickness of the membrane which, of course, is not well known. Apart from that, I think, there is very firm information now as to this viscosity. I would not say that either Katchalsky's or our work had contemplated the thixotropic property which you speak of, which is obviously there, but we have the simple coefficient of viscosity. So I am not really asking a question but complimenting you on this beautiful work which is most interesting.

KOCHEN (*U.S.A.*):
Thank you for your comments.

STEWART (*U.S.A.*):
I would like to congratulate Dr. Kochen on this piece of work and say that the paper I am presenting later provides some ultra-structural explanation for exactly what he has seen. I am very delighted with it.

SIRS (*England*):
They are very intriguing, these very beautiful experiments, although I cannot quite understand a lot of them. What does intrigue me is that in stretching the cells in this way, you must very considerably alter the volume of the cell. Under these circumstances the concentration of hemoglobin must get rather high. Now this can account for quite a lot of what you are suggesting, in the change of the viscoelastic properties. Have you looked at this sort of problem?

KOCHEN:
There is considerable difficulty in accurately measuring the size of the spherical portion of the cell located at the air–fluid interface, because of the difference in the refractive index of the air and fluid phases. It is our distinct impression that the spherical portion of the cell becomes smaller as the filament lengthens, and it may be assumed that there is a concomitant increase in concentration of hemoglobin within the cell. The effect of this increase in intracellular hemoglobin concentration on the rheological properties of the red cell membrane remains a problem.

LONG (*U.S.A.*):
I certainly want to add my compliments to Dr. Kochen's work; and I wonder if he has been describing in a great deal more sophisticated way and with greater accuracy some of the things that some of us have described in terms of the stretching of the red cell envelope, which we see particularly in patients with intravascular aggregation, patients with trauma, shock, myocardial infarction, and so forth. I wonder if he thinks that it is conceivable that this spherical body is coated with this gelatinous, proteinaceous red cell envelope, rather than a portion of the red cell membrane itself.

KOCHEN:
The integrity of the microsphere must be predicated on the presence of a surface boundary, which prevents the outward diffusion of the hemoglobin contained in the microsphere. Our morphologic observations on the formation of microspheres leads me to believe that this surface boundary is derived from a component of the red cell membrane.

WELLS (*U.S.A.*):
Dr. Kochen, could you help me? You may have a reference to give me regarding the thixotropy of the membrane. That is, do you, or Dr. Burton, or Dr. Murphy know of the reference regarding membrane thixotropy as opposed to that of hemoglobin, which has been defined. That is very interesting.

KOCHEN:
There have been very few direct micro-rheological studies of the red cell membrane. The outstanding studies of RAND and BURTON[4] on the deformability of the red cell membrane, under conditions of a highly controlled stress, have contributed much to our understanding of red cell membrane behavior. On the basis of studies of RAND and BURTON[4] on the deformability of the red cell membrane under conditions of a highly controlled stress, have contributed much to our understanding of red cell membrane behavior. On the basis of the hemolytic behavior of red cells, KATCHALSKY and co-workers[11] concluded that the red cell membrane behaves as a visco-elastic body. DINTENFASS[9], on the basis of viscosity studies of packed red cells, deduced that the red cell membrane exhibits considerable fluidity under conditions of shear stress.

RUBINOW (*U.S.A.*):

In order to clarify the question as to whether the extruded sphere is surrounded by membranous material, I wonder whether Dr. Kochen has made some estimate of the area of the ghost membrane that is left.

KOCHEN:

There appears to be no significant difference in the length or cross-sectional diameters of filaments derived from cells which have or have not given rise to microspheres. The irregularity in the shape of the membrane residue, derived from the collapse of the more spherical portion of the cell, precludes an accurate determination of its surface area. Our deduction that the microsphere is bounded by a component of the red cell membrane leads me to believe that microsphere formation would result in no difference in the surface area of the red cell membrane residue deposited on the glass surface.

RUBINOW:

I just was not clear whether you had estimated the area of those elongated red cells before they had extruded the sphere or afterwards.

KOCHEN:

Our measurements were made on the total membrane deposited on the glass.

LÄNGSPOLARISIERTE FLUORESCENZ GEDEHNTER STROMATA VON ERYTHROZYTEN MIT BEZUG AUF IHRE HÄMORHEOLOGISCHE BEDEUTUNG

Hans H. Pfeiffer*

Laboratorium für Polarisations-Mikroskopie,
Bremen 1, Germany

1. Die folgende Mitteilung befaßt sich mit einem erst wenig in Angriff genommenen Arbeitsfelde, nämlich *rheooptischen* Methoden und Messungen durch Studium rheologischer Deformationen im besonderen mittels Doppelbrechung bzw. Dichroismus.

Zur Untersuchung dienten frisch gewonnene, teils heparinisierte (50 mg/100 ml), teils zur Koagulation gebrachte *Erythrocyten*, welche bei Phasenkontrast oder in polarisiertem Lichte wie nach Mazerieren, Fixieren, Imbibieren oder nach zahlreichen Färbungsversuchen auf den morphologischen Aufbau aus Fasern und Fibrillen geprüft und dissektorisch zwischen Mikronadeln experimentellen Dehnungen unterworfen wurden.

2. Das Stroma dieser Erythrocyten stellt nach gängiger Auffassung einen zweiphasigen Wienerschen *Mischkörper* dar[1]. So wird in 1% NaCl mit $\lambda/30$-Glimmerplatte peripher ein negatives *Polarisationskreuz*, durch Glycerin oder Harnstofflösung ein durch nicht zu intensive OsO_4-Behandlung als Kompensation der Formdoppelbrechung des Proteins ein Umschlag in positive Anisotropie gefunden. Nach Zerstören der lipoiden Komponente durch Alkohole oder Chloroform resultiert das negative Polarisationskreuz oder nach vorheriger Glycerinbehandlung die Reduktion der Negativität.

3. Eine abweichende Analyse der negativen Eigendoppelbrechung und positiven Formdoppelbrechung des Erythrocytenstroma wird von Mitchison[2] vertreten. Nach seinen Befunden rührt die Doppelbrechung des Stroma roter Zellen allein vom Protein her. Die Deutung verlangt dann eine Anordnung der Proteinleptonen in *fortlaufenden Schleifen* mit micellaren Achsen in tangentialer, molekularen Achsen in radialer Erstreckung. Um die optischen Befunde mit voller Sicherheit auf die indirekt erschlossene Anordnung der Proteine zurückführen zu können, reichen die bisherigen Versuche des Imbibierens, Fixierens und anderer Agentien nicht aus, sondern es ist erforderlich eine unabhängige Methode, wenn auch gleichfalls rheooptischen Vorgehens, anzuwenden und die leptonische Analyse zu bestätigen oder zu verwerfen. Durch färbungsdichroitische Messungen[3] der nur für Proteine, nicht für Lipoide nachweisbaren *längspolarisierten Fluorescenz* wird die Deutung Mitchisons wahrscheinlicher als die verbreitete Anschauung. Über die terminologische Bezeichnung s. Pfeiffer[4].

4. Bei *dichroitischen Phänomenen* variiert die Absorption durch ein transmittierendes Objekt bestimmter Wellenlänge des Lichtes mit dem Polarisationszustande des transmittierten Lichtes. In der Mikroskopie hängt der Nachweis von linearem

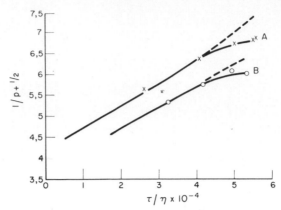

ABB. 1. POLARISATION $1/p+\frac{1}{2}$ DER CONJUGATE DES ERYTHROCYTENPROTEIN GEGEN $\tau/\eta \times 10^{-4}$.

Dichroismus vom Wechsel des Azimuths durch das Objekt gelieferten linear polarisierten Lichtes ab. Beobachtet wird eine Veränderung einer Farbnuance oder einer lokalisierten Aufhellung beim Fokusieren nacheinander auf die beiden Schwingungsrichtungen des linear polarisierten Lichtes. Ein einfacher Detektor dafür ist das *Dichroskop-Ocular*, eine vor dem letzten Kriege durch E. Leitz zu beziehende, gegenwärtig nicht mehr allgemein erhältliche Vorrichtung, welche gegen das Huyghens sche Ocular ausgetauscht wird. Die exakte quantitative Behandlung des Phänomens hängt von der Messung eines Paares von Absorptionskoeffizienten mittels *spektroskopischer* Technik ab[3]. Im sichtbaren Wellenbereich zeigen viele biologische Objekte nicht generell Dichroismus, doch kann solcher oft durch geeignete Färbung hervorgerufen werden. Gewisse organische Farbstoffe, beispielsweise vorzüglich Rhodamin B, bilden mit Proteinen (sogen.) stabile Conjugate, d.h. werden durch bestimmte Komponenten des Stromaprotein chemisch derart gebunden, daß sie wie orientiert angelagerte Leptonen Dichroismus hervorrufen.

5. Zu ausreichender Stabilität der *Conjugate* zwischen organischem Farbstoff und Stromaprotein sollte bei der Bildung ein Minimum chemischen Wandels und, soweit möglich, ein einziger Bindungstyp gewährleistet sein. Analysator und Kompensator dürfen das Fluorescenzlicht nicht zu stark absorbieren.

Nach dem Stande der Versuche, nämlich behindert durch eigene Erkrankung, sind erst wenige *Gesetzmäßigkeiten* der längspolarisierten Fluorescenz erfaßt worden. So wächst der Wert mit zunehmender experimenteller Deformation der gedehnten Stromata durch *Beschleunigung des Ausstreichens* der Blutproben, bleibt aber die *Konzentration* des färbenden Fluorochrom ganz oder nahezu ohne Einfluß auf die Polarisation. Läßt man den Ausstrich so langsam *koagulieren*, daß die Leptonen sich ausrichten können, so wächst die Polarisation ebenfalls. Dagegen scheint sie im neutralen Bereich kaum von der C_H abhängig zu sein, hingegen sinkt sie, vielleicht infolge reversibler Dissociation, zu stark erniedrigten Werten im Sauren und im Hochalkalischen.

6. Die Werte der längspolarisierten Fluorescenz bewegen sich umgekehrt proportional mit zunehmender *Temperatur* (Abb. 2). Die Werte folgen zwischen 30 und 40° oft dem Gesetze der Depolarisation PERRIN's[5]. Bezeichne p die Polarisation, T die absolute Temperatur und η einen für die relative Viskosität angenommenen Wert, so resultiert beim Auftragen von $1/p$ gegen T/η innerhalb jener Temperaturamplitude eine Gerade (Abb. 1). Das Ausbleiben einer Krümmung kann als Hinweis auf flache oder nur schwach verlängerte Leptonen interpretiert werden. In allen Fällen linearer

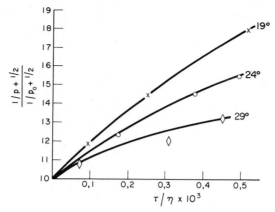

ABB. 2. LÄNGSPOLARISIERTE FLUORESCENZ A DES RINDERSERUMPROTEIN $p_0 + \frac{1}{2}$ GEGEN 0,1 MOL. NaOH BZW. B BEI ZIMMERTEMPERATUR.

Abhängigkeit ergibt sich eine ausgezeichnete Übereinstimmung zwischen der durch Extrapolation erhaltenen *Grenzpolarisation* p_0 und dem mit Ringer gefundenen Werte p_r. Differenzen der p_0-Werte verschiedener Conjugate von Stromata roter Zellen können mit wechselndem Drehungsgrade gedeutet werden. Zusatz von aq.dest. oder verdünnten Salzlösungen gestattet höhere T/η-Werte (Abb. 1), während für deren Verringerung eine Zunahme der Viskosität durch Zufügung weiterer Substanz erforderlich wird.

7. Bemerkenswert bleibt nicht allein die unerwartete Interpretation der Doppelbrechung nach dem leptonischen Buaplane nach MITCHISON[2], sondern auch der Umstand, daß die untersuchte Polarisation $p = \eta/cT$ (mit c Konstante) nach GREGERSEN et al.[6] proportional dem *mittleren Korpuskularvolumen* des Blutes (in %) zu $H = [(\ln\eta - a)/b]^{-2}$ variiert (a, b Konstanten, welche bei mittleren Schergeschwindigkeiten zu 0,45 bzw. 0,047 zu setzen sind). Auch nach jüngst veröffentlichten Untersuchungen VON BECKER und SPENGLER[7] regulieren sich Konzentration der Erythrocyten und Blutvolumen gegenseitig. Jeder Wechsel des Plasmavolumen beeinflußt die Zellkonzentration durch Verdickung oder Verdünnung des Blutes. Die Rate der O_2-Versorgung der Gewebe ist damit abhängig von der Konzentration der Zellen oder des Hämoglobingehaltes des Blutes und beeinflußt die Erythropoiese im Knochenmark. Folglich führt jede zahlenmäßige Reduktion der roten Zellen des Blutes bei konstantem Volumen zu verstärkter Erythropoiese. Diese von den genannten Autoren[7] an Verdünnungsanaemie erfolgreich geprüfte *Hypothese* läßt vielleicht eine Vorstellung von hämorheologischer Bedeutung selbst derart ausgefallener rheooptischer Studien an Erythrocyten entstehen.

LITERATUR

[1] PFEIFFER, H. H. *Naturwissenschaften* **52**, 432, 1965.
[2] MITCHISON, J. M. *Nature* **166**, 347, 1950.
[3] PFEIFFER, H. H. In *Symposium on Biorheology*, COPLEY, A. L. (Editor), *Proc. 4th Int. Cong. Rheol.*, Interscience Publ. John Wiley, New York, 1965, part 4, p. 535.
[4] PFEIFFER, H. H. *Biorheology* **3**, 211, 1966.
[5] PERRIN, F. *J. Phys. Radium* **7**, 390, 1926.
[6] GREGERSEN, M. I., PERIC, B., CHIEN, S., SINCLAIR, D., CHANG, C. and TAYLOR, H. In *Symposium on Biorheology*, COPLEY, A. L. (Editor), *Proc. 4th Int. Cong. Rheol.*, Interscience Publ. John Wiley, New York, 1965, part 4, p. 613.
[7] BECKER, H. und SPENGLER, D. *Acta Haematol.* **35**, 1, 1966.

ERYTHROCYTE SHAPE AND BLOOD VISCOSITY

JOHN R. MURPHY*

Department of Medicine, Western Reserve University and University Hospitals, Cleveland, Ohio, U.S.A.

CHANGES in erythrocyte shape resulting from changes in the surface area to volume relationship of the cell were found to be associated with changes in rheological properties of erythrocytes. Previous studies indicated that pH influences the surface area of the erythrocyte membrane[1] as well as the volume[2] of the cell. Thus the surface area to volume relationship of erythrocytes was altered at various pH's, 8.0, 7.4, 6.8 and 6.4. The influence of these shape changes on viscosity and filterability of erythrocytes will be described. Similar studies of abnormally shaped erythrocytes from patients with two different diseases will also be described. Hereditary spherocytosis is an inherited condition in which there is an abnormal membrane with less surface area and a normal volume resulting in a spheroidal cell associated with a hemolytic state. In hereditary spherocytosis the cells are trapped or sequestered in the spleen and eventually destroyed in the spleen. The mechanism of splenic sequestration has not been defined. In hemoglobin CC disease the surface area of the erythrocyte membrane is probably normal but the cell volume is small. These cells appear as target cells on dried blood films. The mechanism of the hemolytic anemia in Hb CC disease has not been defined.

The methods employed in these studies have been published[1]. All studies were done at 37°C on fresh erythrocytes from defibrinated blood. The buffy coat was removed and the cells suspended in serum. pH was adjusted by varying the pCO_2 in an equilibrating gas. In the viscosity studies the hematocrit (hct.) was adjusted to 60% at pH 8.0. Viscosity was determined on a Wells-Brookfield viscometer (LVT $\frac{1}{2}$) previously flushed with the equilibrating gas and surrounded with a water jacket for temperature control. Hemolysates for viscosity determinations were prepared by packing cells at 39,000g for 1 hr, freezing and thawing × 6 and centrifugation for 2 hr at 39,000g. Filtration studies of erythrocytes were carried out with Millipore filters of the SC type with pore sizes of 8.0 to 8.8 and 8.8 to 9.4 μ. The pore size refers to the pore opening on the surface of the filter as determined by the manufacture and not pore diameter within the filter. The time (seconds) required to filter 2.0 ml of a suspension of cells, hct 2.0%, was observed. Previous determinations of erythrocyte filtration have been reported[3], but temperature and pH were not controlled.

The influence of pH on surface area, volume, and the appearance of normal cells, is shown in Fig. 1. The surface area of erythrocytes was estimated by means of the hemolytic volume[4]. The hemolytic volume is a measure of the degree of swelling or volume change the cell undergoes in osmotic shock lysis and is in terms of the cell volume at pH 7.4. Since the cells are sphered at the time of shock lysis a difference in volume indicates a change in the surface area. The surface area was maximal at pH 6.8 and was less at higher or lower pH's. The influence of pH on cell volume is shown by the hematocrit changes. There is a direct linear relationship between pH and cell

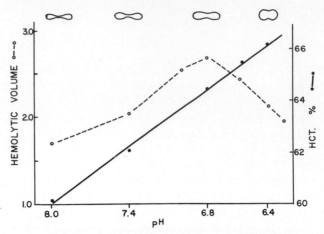

FIG. 1. INFLUENCE OF pH ON SURFACE AREA AND VOLUME.

volume. Shown in the upper portion of the figure are schematic drawings of cells in cross section as observed on wet films at different pH's by phase microscopy. The cell maintains its usual shape as pH is decreased to pH 6.8. Below pH 6.8 there was progressive sphering.

The influence of pH on viscosity of normal erythrocytes is shown in Fig. 2. The mean viscosity $\pm$ S.D. for ten normal samples at a shear rate of 2.3 inverse seconds are shown. The samples were adjusted to a hematocrit of 60% at pH 8.0. pH adjustment was by increasing pCO_2. The increase in viscosity with decreasing pH is evident.

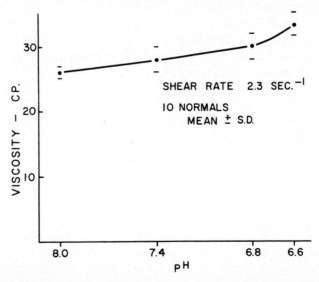

FIG. 2. INFLUENCE OF pH ON VISCOSITY OF NORMAL ERYTHROCYTES.

The change in viscosity below pH 6.8 was greater per unit change in pH than the change in viscosity above pH 6.8.

The influence of tonicity on viscosity is shown in Fig. 3. The center bar depicts the

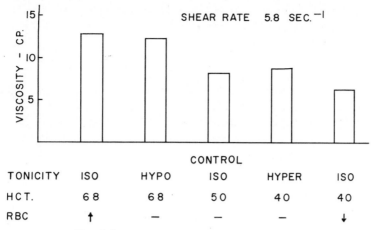

FIG. 3. INFLUENCE OF TONICITY ON VISCOSITY.

control sample. In hypotonic media with the hematocrit increased to 6.8 the viscosity was increased. A similar increase in hematocrit in isotonic media by increasing the number of cells resulted in a similar increase in viscosity. In hypertonic media the viscosity was also increased and the cell volume as shown by the hematocrit was reduced. In contrast the viscosity was decreased in isotonic media when the hematocrit was adjusted to a similar level by decreasing the number of cells. Similar results were obtained when cells were suspended in salt solution or a mixture of serum plus salt solutions. Thus viscosity was increased when cell volume was either increased or decreased.

In order to emphasize the importance of the shape change influencing the viscosity of the intact cell, control studies of hemolysate viscosity were performed and are shown in Fig. 4. A change in pH from 7.2 to 6.6 or deoxygenation did not alter the viscosity of the hemolysate from normal erythrocytes. A 5% dilution of the hemolysate resulted in a 20% decrease in viscosity. A 10% dilution decreased the viscosity 30%. Thus the increase in viscosity of intact cells at low pH's was not the result of pH *per*

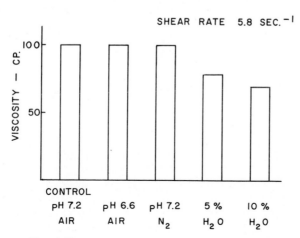

FIG. 4. HEMOLYSATE VISCOSITY, pH AND DILUTION.

se influencing internal viscosity and the increased viscosity of the intact cells at a low pH occurred in association with a decreased intracellular viscosity resulting from the dilution with the increase in cell volume.

The changes in surface area to volume relationships at different pH's also influenced the filtration of normal erythrocytes; this is shown in Fig. 5. The points represent the mean times from ten normals for the filtration of two ml of an erythrocyte suspension through the two different size filters. Filtration was slower at the lower pH's.

Figure 6 shows the influence of tonicity on filtration. The filtration time was increased when the cell volume was either increased in hypotonic media or when the volume was decreased in hypertonic media.

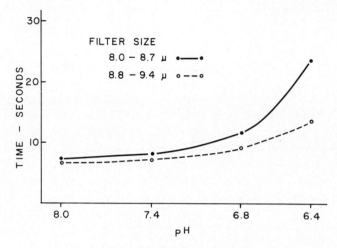

FIG. 5. INFLUENCE OF pH ON FILTRATION.

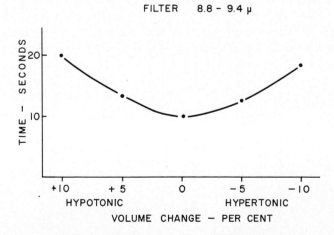

FIG. 6. INFLUENCE OF TONICITY ON FILTRATION.

Figure 7 summarizes the effects of pH and tonicity on the rheological properties of normal erythrocytes. pH alters both surface area and volume resulting in changes in the deformability of cells. The increase in volume in hypotonic media alters

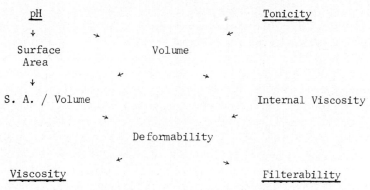

FIG. 7. EFFECT OF pH AND TONICITY ON RHEOLOGICAL PROPERTIES OF ERYTHROCYTES.

deformability by changing the surface area to volume relationship. Hypertonic media alter deformability probably by increasing internal viscosity. The increase in viscosity and prolonged filtration time with a low pH or in hypotonic media occurred in the presence of a lower internal viscosity emphasizing the importance of the surface area to volume relationships in regard to deformability.

The changes in volume at different pH's occur immediately upon changing the pH of the cell suspension. This phenomenon suggests that factors other than cation content in the cell determine cell volume. The mechanism of pH influencing the surface area of the membrane has not been defined. Previous studies indicated that the degree of saturation of cholesterol binding sites with cholesterol also changed the surface area of the membrane[5].

Erythrocytes from patients with hereditary spherocytosis have less surface area and demonstrate abnormal rheological properties. Viscosity values of blood from patients

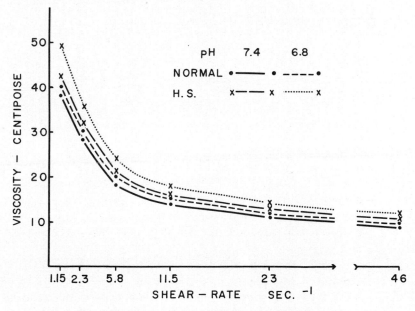

FIG. 8. BLOOD VISCOSITY — HEREDITARY SPHEROCYTOSIS.

with hereditary spherocytes and normals at varying shear rates and two pH's, 7.4
and 6.8, are shown in Fig. 8. The lower curves represent normal blood at pH 7.4 and 6.8.
These data are the mean values from 10 normals and 8 patients with hereditary spherocytosis. At pH 6.8 the viscosity of hereditary spherocytes is significantly greater than for
normal cells at pH 6.8. ERSLEV and ATWATER[6] have reported an increased viscosity
for blood from patients with hereditary spherocytosis and attributed this to the higher
concentration of hemoglobin in the hereditary spherocytes[6]. Their studies were
done at high shear rates without pH control. The mean ±S.D. MCHC value in the
10 normal bloods shown here was 35.5 ± 1.9 g% and in the hereditary spherocytosis
patients 38.6 ± 1.3 g%. It is not possible, on the basis of these studies, to separate
the influence of shape (surface area to volume relationship) from the effect of the
higher MCHC in erythrocytes from patients with hereditary spherocytosis. However,
the increase in viscosity resulting from the decrease in pH probably is related to the
shape change.

Erythrocyte filtration studies of hereditary spherocytes compared to normal cells
are shown in Fig. 9. The hereditary spherocytes showed an increased filtration time at
pH 8.0 and 7.4. However at pH 6.8 or lower the suspension of spherocytic cells
did not flow through the filter. Thus at pH 8.0 or 7.4 cells from patients with hereditary
spherocytosis show minimal changes in viscosity and filtration. However at pH 6.8

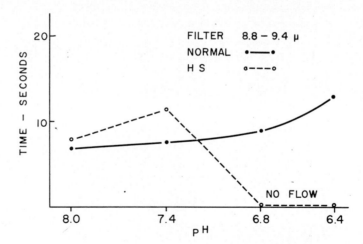

FIG. 9. ERYTHROCYTE FILTRATION–HEREDITARY SPHEROCYTOSIS.

or lower there were significant differences in viscosity and filterability. The importance
of these abnormal rheological properties at this low pH is related to the pH in the spleen.
Other studies[7] indicate that the pH in the human spleen is 0.4 to 0.8 pH units below
the pH of arterial blood. Thus the unusual rheological properties of the hereditary
spherocyte would be accentuated in the spleen. These abnormal cells are sequestered
or trapped by the spleen and subsequently undergo metabolic degeneration in the
spleen[8, 9].

Figure 10 demonstrates the separation of hereditary spherocytes from normal
erythrocytes by filtration. A mixed population of normal cells and ^{51}Cr labeled hereditary spherocytes were filtered at various pH's. The filtration of the normal cells was
not altered by suspension in the patients serum. The chromium labeling of the heredi-

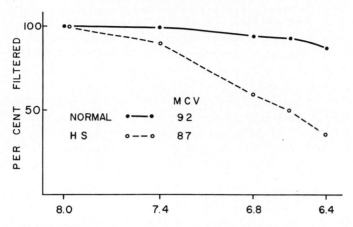

FIG. 10. SEPARATION OF HEREDITARY SPHEROCYTES FROM NORMAL ERYTHROCYTES BY FILTRATION.

tary spherocytes did not alter the filtration of these cells. At pH 8.0 and 7.4 over 90% of both kinds of cells were filtered. At pH 6.8 less than 60% of the hereditary spherocytes were filtered. At pH 6.4 less than 40% of the spherocytes were filtered whereas over 90% of the normal cells were filtered. These differences were not due to differences in the cell volume as shown by the MCV data. It is proposed that the spleen acts similar to the Millipore filter and that the ability of a cell to pass through the spleen is related to its rheological properties at a low pH.

The viscosity of blood from patients with Hb C was found to have an abnormal viscosity. CONLEY[8] has suggested that the viscosity of Hb C would be abnormal

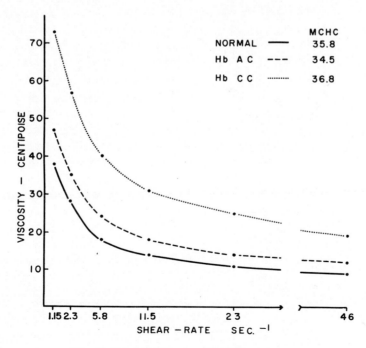

FIG. 11. BLOOD VISCOSITY—Hb. C.C. DISEASE.

because of the formation of hemoglobin crystals in cells from patients with Hb C disease when the cells were dried on blood films. In Fig. 11 the viscosity of normal blood (Hb AA) is compared to blood from patients with Hb AC and Hb CC. The presence of Hb C in erythrocytes was associated with an increase in viscosity. The viscosity of Hb CC responded normally to changes in pH and was not influenced by O_2. Similar increases in viscosity were observed in the hemolysate from cells with Hb CC.

The results of erythrocyte filtration studies in Hb CC disease are shown in Fig. 12. These data represent the mean values from 10 normals, 5 patients with Hb AC and 5 patients with Hb CC. The presence of CC hemoglobin was found to result in an increase in the filtration time. The differences were not due to variation in cell volume.

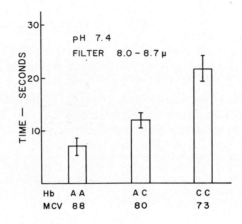

FIG. 12. ERYTHROCYTE FILTRATION–Hb CC DISEASE.

In summary the small surface area of the erythrocyte membrane in hereditary spherocytosis influences the surface area to volume relationship of the cell, particularly at low pH's, and this was associated with a less deformable cell, with an increased viscosity and decreased filterability. It is proposed that spleen sequestration of the hereditary spherocyte is related to the low pH in the spleen and the unusual rheological properties of this cell. In Hb CC disease the abnormal hemoglobin has a greater viscosity than normal hemoglobin and results in an increased internal viscosity, decreased deformability and increased blood viscosity with a decrease in cell filterability. The abnormal rheological properties of erythrocytes with Hb CC probably are related to the mild hemolytic state in this disease[11] and to the removal of these cells *in vivo* by the spleen[12]. Surface area to volume relationships and internal viscosity were found to be important factors in rheological properties of erythrocytes.

ACKNOWLEDGMENT

This work was supported by U.S. Public Health Service grants AM–02189 and GM–21,856.

REFERENCES

[1] MURPHY, J. R. *J. Lab. and Clin. Med.* **69**, 758, 1967.
[2] HAMPSON, A. C. and MARZELS, M. *J. Phys.* **62**, 16, 1926.
[3] JANDLE, J. H., SIMMONS, R. L. and CASTLE, W. B. *Blood* **18**, 133, 1961.
[4] HOFFMAN, J. F., EDEN, M., BARR, J. S., Jr. and BEDELL, R. H. S. *J. Cell. and Comp. Phys.* **51**, 405, 1958.
[5] MURPHY, J. R. *J. Lab. and Clin. Med.* **60**, 86, 1962.
[6] ERSLEV, A. J. and ATWATER, J. *J. Lab. and Clin. Med.* **62**, 401, 1963.
[7] MURPHY, J. R. (to be published).
[8] EMERSON, C. P., SHEN, S. C., HAM, T. H., FLEMING, E. M. and CASTLE, W. B. *Arch. Int. Med.* **97**, 1, 1956.
[9] WEISMAN, R., Jr., HAM, T. H., HINZ, C. F., Jr. and HARRIS, J. W. *Trans. Amer. Assoc. Phys.* **68**, 131. 1955.
[10] CONLEY, C. L. *Med.* **43**, 785, 1964.
[11] DACIE, J. V. *The Hemolytic Anemias*, Grune and Stratton, New York, 1960, part 1, p. 272.
[12] WHEBY, M. S., THORUP, O. A. and LEAVEL, B. S. *Blood* **21**, 266, 1956.

DISCUSSION

SIRS (*England*):

I would agree with a lot of what you said about the effects of pH and tonicity. I'd like however to direct you to another aspect of this problem that I have been looking at; and maybe you can help me with it. It also applies I think, to some of the studies that have been reported at this meeting. When you store blood in acid-citrate dextrose, the pH immediately drops to about 7 and then progressively falls below it with time. So if you take the blood out of the refrigerator about five days after it has been stored, its pH is about 6.8. In these circumstances, as you reported here, the red cells in this blood are relatively inflexible. At the same time their respiratory function is low. They do not transfer oxygen efficiently. Now when the pH is increased to 7.4 again, you get an improvement in the performance of these cells; but they are not completely flexible. This suggests that the internal viscosity is not the decisive factor here because if it was, just altering the pH with hemoglobin should restore the cells to normal. I have tried various aspects of changing these cells back. In particular I am interested in how long it would take, in the blood stream, for a return to normal to occur. No doubt, it does, because the life span is not particularly altered. But one would like to know how long it takes after a transfusion, particularly massive transfusion, for cells to be restored to their normal flexibility and normal function. Have you any thoughts on this matter?

MURPHY (*U.S.A.*):

I have some ideas, but no data. I should emphasize that these studies, reported here, were done on fresh cells from defibrinated blood with no added anticoagulant, which is considerably different than storing cells for five days in ACD solution in which there has been a considerable change in cation content and volume, in addition to the changes in the pH. Because of the metabolic changes, I do not think studies of ACD stored blood are comparable to these studies of fresh defibrinated blood. I would like to add that the studies which we have done and the pH changes that we have produced are completely reversible. In heparinized blood there were changes in the plasma at a pH below 6.8 that were not reversible. In a serum suspension these changes are completely reversible. I can only speculate that in five-day-old ACD blood there is a considerable change in sodium and potassium content; and a change in cell volume which has occurred because of the pH itself, as well as because of the cation changes.

SIRS:

This question of ACD is not altogether the only part. I can get similar effects relatively quickly by altering pH without waiting for five days for the solution in the refrigerator. I agree with you to some degree, the sodium-potassium problem is implicated. With the stored cells I have tried washing, cleaning, and adding various agents such as glucose, to try and restore their flexibility. I wonder if there is some surface phenomena, that you might be aware of, that could account for this?

MURPHY:

There are some studies which indicate that during storage at five degrees in ACD, there is degeneration in the membrane. It would be well to point out at this time, that most of the studies reported indicate that once a stored cell has survived the first 24 hr after having been returned to a recipient, its survival thereafter is probably normal, as related to its cell age at the time it was collected.

REES (*U.S.A.*):

In answer to Dr. Sirs, the collection of blood in ACD alone introduces a traumatic pH of 5.0 in the initial collection medium. Dr. John Gibson and I described in 1956 the so-called "lesion of collection" which was directly related to the initial insult of this extremely low pH (*Am. J. Clin. Path.* **262**, 855, 1956). This has given rise to various modifications of the ACD (GIBSON, REES *et al.*, *Am. J. Clin. Path.*, **28**, 569, 1957.) which do prevent some of the damage that is directly due to a very high hydrogen ion content of the conventional ACD collecting media. I think it was wise, in your study, to eliminate this problem by working essentially with defibrinated blood.

MURPHY:

Our pH adjustments were done by varying the concentration of the CO_2 in the equilibrating gas.

CHARM (*U.S.A.*):

I was just wondering about the packed volume. When you determined hematocrit, would you expect a difference for the same number of cells?

MURPHY:

In the manner in which we determined the hematocrit for these studies, there were no differences in the trapped plasma as determined with ^{131}I labeled albumin. It was 2.2% plus or minus 1/10 of 1% of the red cell mass. These hematocrits were determined at 11,500 g, spun for 10 min.

CHARM:

Your limiting apparent viscosity seemed unusually high, even for the normal case seen. It seemed to be about 10 cp which is extremely high even for normal blood.

MURPHY:

These viscocities were all done at a hematocrit of 60 and at a pH of 8.

CHARM:

Well, your high hematocrit would account for that. The other point concerned the changes in apparent viscosity: I wondered if these are merely reflections of changes in yield stress in your blood. In other words, is this an aggregation characteristic separate from the change in the so-called Casson viscosity? Have you considered that?

MURPHY:

I have considered it, but I do not have an answer to it.

CHARM:

Well, have you plotted your data in a square root plot?

MURPHY:

No, I have not.

CHARM:

That would probably have given us some information.

MURPHY:

The reason that these were done in serum in the absence of fibrinogen is that there would be little agglutination or rouleaux formation.

ATTRACTIVE FORCES BETWEEN RED CELLS AND WITHIN A RED CELL

Alan C. Burton* and B. B. Shrivastava

Department of Biophysics, University of Western Ontario, London, Ontario, Canada

THE problem of the normal biconcave shape of the adult erythrocyte has, of course, been the subject of much comment and speculation, but not much has been written from the point of view of the biophysicist. Some have fallen back on teleology, stating that the shape allows diffusion of gases to all regions of the interior, for the reactions with Hb, with maximal speed. This is not true, for a thinner disc would serve this function even better, so that other considerations as to maximum diameter must be added. Again, we know now that in proceeding through capillaries, where diffusion is all important, the contents of the red cell, as well as the plasma between cells, are "churned up". Even in a large artery, as Mason and his colleagues have shown, there will be motion in the interior of the red cell, so that diffusion is not the limiting, or even the important factor. If teleology is to be used (and why not?) we would rather emphasize the importance of *non-sphericity* of the red cell to allow it to be deformed without stretch of the membrane, which results in hemolysis[1]. The shape (as well as the size) of red cells determines, for instance, the size of a quasicylindrical channel through which they could pass without hemolysis[2].

THE NEED FOR ATTRACTIVE FORCES

The biophysical problem remains. How can the biconcave shape, and indeed the whole family of shapes that red cells assume in altered environments, represent a physical equilibrium of the membrane under the existing forces that act upon it? We can clarify this problem, though not solve it at present, by summarizing what we know of the mechanical properties of the membrane of the red cell, and the known forces acting on it. This knowledge is largely due to the work of RAND[3, 4] in our laboratory. The properties were deduced from experiments where portions of the red cell membrane were "sucked", by very small negative pressures, into micropipettes of different diameters. KATCHALSKY and his colleagues[5] have also worked in this field, with comparable results, obtained by very different methods. Electron microscopy has also contributed, particularly as to the uniformity and thickness of the membrane (probably between 100 and 200 Å).

The properties of the membrane appear to be:

1. The *resistance to "bending"* is very slight indeed, though not negligible. Expressing the modulus of the resistance to bending in terms of a surface energy (ergs/cm²) or interfacial tension (dynes/cm), it has a value of only about 0·013 dynes/cm (surface tension of water is 75 dynes/cm). This very low value allows the changes in shape

or deformation that are so necessary in the life of the red cell in the crowded and "bumping" circulation.

In addition, there is an "interfacial tension", or surface energy, of about equal magnitude ($0{\cdot}014$ ergs/cm^2) which tends to resist change of area of the membrane (like the surface tension in a soap-film).

2. In contrast, the *resistance to stretch* of the membrane, i.e. to increase in area, is quite high. The Young's Modulus is of the order of magnitude of that of biological fibres (10^7 dynes/cm^2), less than that of collagen, more than that of elastin. As little as 15% increase in the area of the membrane produces structural change, which is reversible, and hemoglobin leaves the cell. This is seen in osmotic swelling. As the cell becomes spherical, further volume increase results in hemolysis. The cell becomes rigid. The resulting "ghost" usually reverts to the biconcave form (Fig. 1).

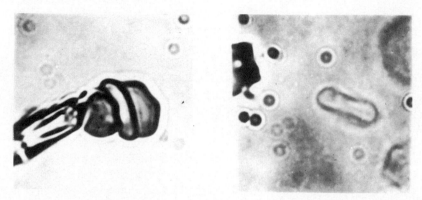

FIG. 1. *Left:* PART OF A BICONCAVE RED CELL HAS BEEN DRAWN INTO A MICROPIPETTE, UNTIL THE PART STILL OUTSIDE BECAME SPHERICAL. IT IS THEN RIGID, AND WILL DEFORM ANOTHER CELL (FOLDED) AGAINST WHICH IT IS PUSHED, WITHOUT ITSELF BEING DEFORMED. *Right:* A "GHOST" WHICH HAS RETURNED TO THE BICONCAVE SHAPE, CF. ABSENCE OF CONTRAST OF INTERIOR WITH CELLS ON LEFT.

3. The membrane is *visco-elastic,* for the time to hemolyse on application of a stretching stress depends on the magnitude of that stress. The membrane "creeps" under stress (Fig. 2). It can also rejoin itself, or another membrane (Fig. 3), so that a broken cell can be "healed". The coefficient of viscosity is of the order of 10^7 poises. The experiments revealed two other facts of great importance to the discussion of the equilibrium shapes.

4. No difference could be found between the behaviour of the membrane at the "rim" or in other parts of the cell, as at the "axis" (i.e. the "dimple" region)[3]. The membrane appeared to be uniform, and probably of uniform thickness (as the electron-microscopic results indicate).

5. Astonishingly, there appeared to be a positive excess hydrostatic pressure within the red cell, amounting to about 2.3 mm H$_2$O pressure, not only in the biconcave shape but also in cells osmotically swollen to biconvex shapes (short of the sphere). In cells shrunken by hypertonic solution, this pressure is absent. However, if the volume of the spherical cell is increased, the tension in the membrane rises, the cell becomes rigid, and without doubt, the internal pressure rises greatly. The existence of the para-doxical positive excess pressure, even in the biconcave shape, makes the problem of the physical equilibrium much harder, as we shall see.

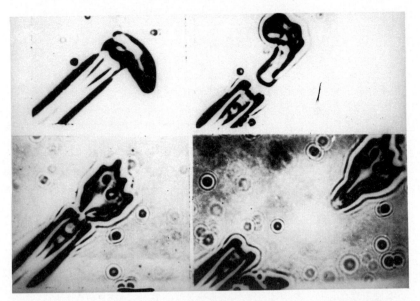

FIG. 2. DEMONSTRATION OF VISCO-ELASTIC BEHAVIOUR OF THE RED CELL MEMBRANE. PARTS OF A NORMAL RED CELL (ABOVE) AND A CRENATED, SHRUNKEN CELL (BELOW) HAVE BEEN DRAWN QUICKLY INTO A MICRO-PIPETTE, ON THE LEFT, THEN EXPELLED (RIGHT). THE DEFORMED SHAPE PERSISTS FOR SEVERAL SECONDS BEFORE THE FORMER SHAPE IS RESUMED.

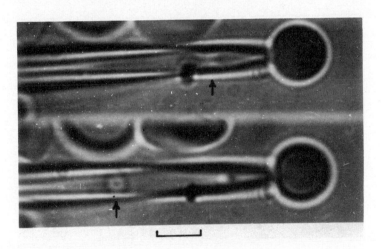

FIG. 3. DEMONSTRATION OF THE ABILITY OF THE RED CELL MEMBRANE TO JOIN ITSELF. A PORTION OF THE CELL HAS BEEN PINCHED OFF AND (BELOW) HEALS TO BECOME A "MICROERYTHROCYTE", APPARENTLY CONTAINING HB. FROM REF. 4.

Thinking that the pressure might be associated with the activity of a "metabolic pump" in the membrane, RAND[6] repeated the measurements on sheep erythrocytes of the varieties "High-K" and "Low-K," discovered by TOSTESON[7], but found that the pressure was identical. Since the activity of the "metabolic pump" is known to be very different in the two varieties of sheep cell, we abandoned associating the pressure with this. Maybe the internal pressure, rather, is evidence of an attractive force between the two sides of a red cell, across the axial region. The possibility of such an attractive force is the subject of this paper.

Of course, all these ideas depend on acceptance of our interpretation of the results of the "sucking" experiments of RAND[3, 6]. All we can say is that we used every device we know to check the method, on oil-droplets of different sizes, even on rubber balloons, where the results for pressure and tension were known; with very good agreement from the "sucking experiments". We also spent many hours arguing about alternative views of the mechanics of the membrane, e.g. that the membrane was not isotropic, of different thickness in different parts, in tension at the rim, compression near the axis, and so on. We even built many rubber models, cast in the biconcave shape, but the behaviour of these as we blew them up never imitated that of the red cell as it is osmotically swelled (Fig. 4). For example, these models never became

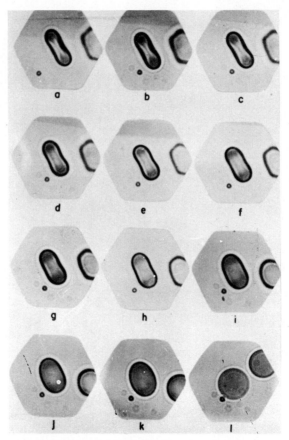

FIG. 4. THE SERIES OF SHAPES ASSUMED BY A SINGLE RED CELL AS IT WAS SWOLLEN BY INFUSION OF HYPOTONIC SALINE FROM A NEARBY MICROPIPETTE. EACH SHAPE REPRESENTS EQUILIBRIUM UNDER THE FORCES THAT ACT ON THE MEMBRANE. FROM R. P. RAND, Ph.D. THESIS, UNIVERSITY OF WESTERN ONTARIO (1964).

perfectly spherical, even with high pressures inside, and showed the "oil-can" phenomenon, snapping from biconcave to biconvex shape at a critical pressure. Red cells never show the "oil-can" effect, at least in our experience, and when swollen to spheres, appear to be geometrically perfect.

We would not advise anyone who can avoid it to enter the field of mechanics of thin shells, much less of thick shells. Even the simplest cases, such as cylinders with hemispherical caps, so important to engineers, offer almost intractable mathematics, and complicated solutions with multiple peculiar points. Perhaps our incompetence to understand the few textbooks on the subject (e.g. TIMOSHENKO[8]), is the real reason, rather than the indications given above, why we have, instead, thought about the problem of the equilibrium of the red cell membrane in terms of "soap-film" physics, as if the membrane were thin (it is), isotropic, uniform (probably it is) and with a uniform tension in it. Even this idealized case can offer very complicated analysis, but it is familiar at least, since the pioneer work of Laplace. This approach inevitably leads to the search for an attractive force between the different parts of a red cell membrane.

If we can apply "soap-film" physics, the law of Laplace should be satisfied at all points on the membrane for the red cell in all of its equilibrium shapes (Fig. 4), not only for the normal biconcave shape, i.e.

$$\Delta P = T \left(\frac{1}{R_1} + \frac{1}{R_2} \right)$$

dynes/cm²   dynes/cm   cm⁻¹

where ΔP is the transmural pressure, inside minus outside the curved membrane, T is the tension in the membrane, and R_1 and R_2 are the "principal radii of curvature" at any point on the membrane. Even this equation can lead to very difficult mathematics indeed. So much so that aerodynamicists, finding that some of their equations could be transformed to this form, have actually resorted to using soap-films to tell them what solutions may exist.

Applying this to the red cell in the biconcave form, we see immediately that the equation cannot possibly apply, *without the addition of another force*. The tension, at the rim region, produces an inward force which could balance the excess pressure, but at the axial region where the membrane is concave outwards, the tension would produce an outward force that would add to the pressure, tending to push out the membrane (Fig. 5). We therefore add, hopefully, a normal inwardly directed "attractive" force P'. (dynes/cm²)

$$\Delta P = T \left(\frac{1}{R_1} + \frac{1}{R_2} \right) + P'$$

$\Delta P = T \left(\frac{1}{R_1} + \frac{1}{R_2} \right)$ cannot apply

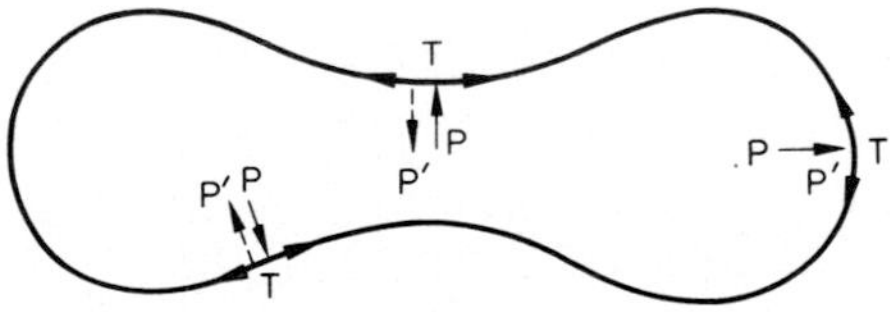

$\Delta P = T \left(\frac{1}{R_1} + \frac{1}{R_2} \right) + P'$

P'= Normal attractive force/area

FIG. 5. DIAGRAM TO ILLUSTRATE THE MISSING NORMAL FORCE REQUIRED TO EXPLAIN THE EQUILIBRIUM IF THE RED CELL OBEYS "SOAP-FILM" PHYSICS.

Obviously, this attractive force P' needs to be greatest at the axis, and need not be very great, if it exists at all, at the rim. With the data of Rand, and the interpretation given, we can quantatively estimate the magnitude of this normal inward force per unit area, and how it must vary over the profile of the red cell membrane. Calculation of the principal radii of curvature over the profile of the cell has been made by many. We had

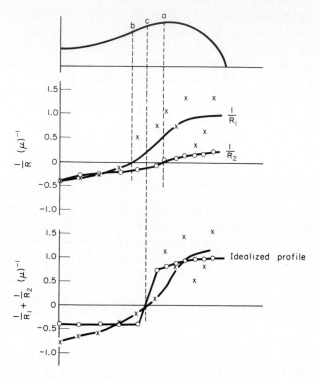

FIG. 6. RESULTS OF CALCULATION OF THE PRINCIPAL RADII OF CURVATURE OVER A QUADRANT OF THE MEMBRANE OF A BICONCAVE RED CELL. ONE OF THE CURVATURES IS ZERO AT B, THE OTHER AT A, AND BETWEEN IS THE ISOCLASTIC POINT. THE 'IDEALIZED PROFILE' IS ONE WHERE PONDER FITTED TWO CIRCLES TO THE PROFILE. FROM R. P. RAND, PH.D. THESIS, UNIVERSITY OF WESTERN ONTARIO (1964).

recalculated it from our own cell profiles (Fig. 6). The best value for excess pressure in the cell was 2·32 mm H_2O (of course, with considerable uncertainty). For the tension we might use the total found in normal and osmotically swollen cells, i.e., 0·037 dynes/cm or the lower one found in shrunken, crenated cells, i.e., 0·013 dynes/cm. Our

TABLE 1.

Point on membrane	$\left(\dfrac{1}{R_1}+\dfrac{1}{R_2}\right)$ μ^{-1}	$T=0.037$		$T=0.013$	
		$T\left(\dfrac{1}{R_1}+\dfrac{1}{R_2}\right)$	P' mm.H_2O	$T\left(\dfrac{1}{R_1}+\dfrac{1}{R_2}\right)$	P' mm.H_2O
Axis	−0·75	−2·55	4·87	−1·00	3·32
Isoclastic	0	0	2·32	0	2·32
Rim	1·30	4·88	(−2·56)	2·24	0·08

preference would be to use the smaller one, representing a sort of surface or interfacial energy, and to think that the extra tension encountered in sucking experiments on the normal cell included also the contribution of the "resistance to bending" which does not apply here. However, let us use both of these figures to see what happens (Table 1). Points on the membrane of special interest are on the rim, at the axis and at the "isoclastic point" (where $1/R_1 + 1/R_2$ is zero). We see that using the higher figure for the tension (including the resistance to bending) would require an attractive force on the axis, but an outward, *repulsive* force at the rim to balance the pressure. For this additional reason, we reject the higher value for T. In contrast, the lower value for T requires a negligible inward force at the rim, and an alternative force of the order of 3 mm H_2O, or 300 dynes/cm^2 at the axis. The values from the sucking experiments that have been used in the calculation are quite independent of the values for the curvature in the table. Surely the agreement shown in the table is more than coincidence!

THE ORIGIN OF ATTRACTIVE FORCES

What could be the origin of this postulated attractive force of the membrane on one side of the red cell for its own membrane on the other side? The existence of such an attraction is more plausible when we remember that the membrane of one red cell evidently attracts the membrane of another red cell, as shown in rouleaux formation (but only if long chain molecules like fibrinogen are present in the medium). We are suggesting that the membrane similarly attracts the membrane, not only of another cell, but its own membrane across the 1 micron distance at the axis.

LONG-RANGE ATTRACTIVE FORCES IN BIOLOGY

Here we enter the field of speculation and what follows is mostly the exercise of imagination, that stubbornly refuses to give up in the face of real theoretical difficulties. There is no doubt that in biology there is much evidence that *identical* cellular membranes tend to cohere, but do not cohere to membranes that are different. For example, in a mixed population, cells will aggregate with their own kind. Leaders in the field are such as PAUL WEISS, LEONARD WEISS, ABERCROMBIE and MUSCONA, who have written many reviews on the subject[9–12]. The specific attraction forces exist, and often over very large distances, yet the nature of the forces is very controversial. The two main difficulties are (1) How can "like" membranes have a specific attraction for each other? (2) How can the attractive forces extend over long distances (cf. molecular dimensions)? At distances up to 200 Å Van der Waals–London (quantum mechanical) forces are a satisfactory explanation, but cannot operate at greater distances.

If the forces are electrostatic in origin, logic forces us to answer question 1 in terms of a regular pattern of spacing of positive and negative charges. Figure 7 shows this for a line of charges; you must imagine instead the pattern in two dimensions on the membrane surface. This gives the necessary specificity, for if the spacing is not nearly identical, there will be very little attraction. To get a significant force of attraction, the

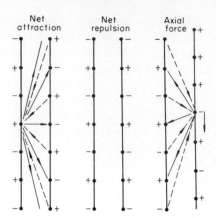

FIG. 7. DIAGRAM TO ILLUSTRATE THE SPECIFIC ATTRACTION BETWEEN TWO LINES OF EQUALLY SPACED, ALTERNATE POSITIVE AND NEGATIVE CHARGES.

spacing distance between charges of opposite sign must be comparable to the distance between the two membranes. For our problem of the red cell, the charges would have to be of the order of 1 micron apart.

We are encouraged in following this line of thought (which may well be called Burton's folly) in that we have reached the opinion that the membrane of a red cell is not uniform in its plane, but has discontinuities ("spots") regularly spaced over the surface about 1 micron apart. This comes from our work on crenation of the red cell in environments of changed pH, or in electrical fields[13]. Crenation "spots" are limited in number (20–25 per cell) and appear and disappear at the same spot on the same cell quite reversibly (Fig. 8). Also, in conditions of pH approaching those that

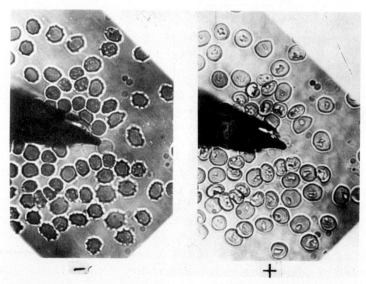

FIG. 8. REVERSIBLE CHANGES IN RED CELL SHAPE NEAR A MICROELECTRODE (OTHER ELECTRODE OUT OF FIELD SHOWN) WHEN ITS POLARITY IS CHANGED. THE CHANGES ARE DUE PROBABLY TO THE CHANGES IN pH CONSEQUENT TO THE CURRENT, RATHER THAN DIRECTLY TO THE ELECTRICAL FIELD. FROM REF. 13.

cause crenation, the cells often show regular polygonal forms, with sides of about 3 microns length, so that we do not think the "spots" or vertices of these polygons represent merely a random folding of the membrane, but rather, pre-existing points of discontinuity. They could be centres of charge. We have started to compute whether an array of charges spaced over the surface of a wooden model, of the shape of the erythrocyte, about 1 micron apart, would give the distribution of normal inward force required. There are two requirements. The resultant at each point must be zero in the plane of the membrane, and of the required value along the normal. It is obvious from symmetry that the normal force will be small at the rim. In our first attempts at computing, which is no small task, we realized that we did not know whether we ought to use an inverse square law with distance apart of individual charges, or not, and this led to the small amount of experimental work on a model that we can report.

We come to the second question of whether electrostatic forces of sufficient magnitude could be produced over distances up to 1 micron and more. If the intervening medium were non-conducting, we could calculate how much charge density on the plates of a parallel plate condenser would be needed to obtain a force of $3 \cdot 30$ mm H_2O (about 300 dynes/cm²) at a distance of 1 micron. The formula is:

$$F = \frac{2\pi}{K} \text{ (charge density)}^2,$$

where K is the dielectric constant (note that the distance does not appear in this formula, but, of course, the surfaces must be close enough to imitate a parallel plate condenser). Using the value $3 \cdot 32$ mm H_2O (320 dynes/cm²), the charge density required would be, for water ($K = 80$), 575 e.s.u. per cm². Now the surface charge density of the erythrocyte, deduced from electrophoretic studies, has been found to be of the order of 5000 e.s.u./cm² (many times greater than required). On this score, the electrostatic forces seem reasonable. However, there is a very serious consideration that most would consider as eliminating the possibility of electrostatic forces of sufficient magnitude. It is that in a *conducting* medium, the force between charges is very drastically reduced by the "ionic atmosphere" effect as shown by Debye. Instead of $e_1 e_2 / d^2$ it becomes $(e_1 e_2 / d^2) \times e^{-kd}$ where the k is related to the conductivity of the medium. If only we can remove this objection, the electrostatic attraction between membranes with a pattern of positive and negative charges might be worth pursuing. If we cannot surmount the ionic atmospheric effect, our case is lost. The biological facts seem to call for bold speculation.

Now one way of obtaining "action at a distance" is to "specialize" the medium between the two points concerned (this is the method used by the less old-fashioned chimney-sweep; instead of sending up a small boy, he fitted a succession of rods together). There is abundant evidence, particularly from the electron-microscope, of "fibres" of oriented protein molecules within cells. There is considerable doubt whether these are, in life, the "condensed" fibres of E-M photographs. Rather, they may represent dynamic organization of oriented fibres, linear arrays of dipoles, with long chain molecules from the medium joining and leaving the array freely. The phenomena occurs in what is called "tactoid" organization. This is the view reached for the spindle-fibres in cellular mitosis by INOUÉ[14] from very accurate studies of birefringence in the living cell. Could the orientation of chains of protein molecules (stromatin) within the red cell, between groups of charges distributed over the surface, account for the long range attractive forces necessary to explain the equilibrium shapes of the red cell? Would this orientation of dipoles take place even in saline? At any rate, we know that such orientation does take place in the cytoplasm of cells. Again, what happens to the force between charges if they are connected by "bridges" of oriented long molecules? In particular, how would the force vary with the distance between charges? Since we could find no theory that gave us the answers, we decided to start attacking this problem by experiments of the most elementary kind on crude models. Whether the results have any possible connection with the biological problem remains debatable, but at least we have learned some unexpected features of the model, for which we doubt that the experts have any simple explanations.

MODEL EXPERIMENTS

The apparatus is a parallel plate condenser, with an applied voltage of some 500 volts between the plates. The upper plate is divided into a fixed guard-ring and a central disc that is suspended from a balance, so that the attractive force upon it may be measured. The weight with no voltage in the plates is, of course, subtracted from that with the voltage applied, to give this attractive force, which is measured with the disc accurately at the same distance from the lower plate in each instance. The weighing is repeated with varying distances between the plates, and varying amount of fibrous material.

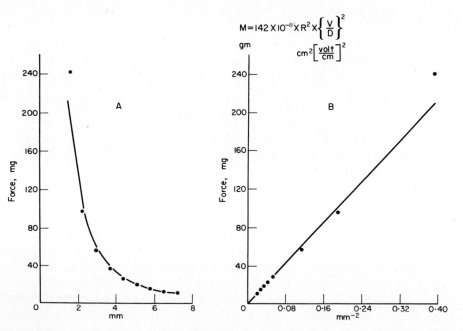

$$M = 142 \times 10^{-11} \times R^2 \times \left\{ \frac{V}{D} \right\}^2$$

$$\text{gm} \qquad \text{cm}^2 \left[\frac{\text{volt}}{\text{cm}} \right]^2$$

FIG. 9. ATTRACTIVE FORCE VS. DISTANCE BETWEEN PLATES, WITHOUT FIBRES BETWEEN. THE GRAPH ON THE RIGHT SHOWS THAT THE INVERSE SQUARE LAW IS OBEYED. THE LINE IS CALCULATED FROM THE VOLTAGE BETWEEN THE PLATES.

The results with nothing but air between the plates (Fig. 9) serve to indicate the degree of accuracy of the experiments. The lines on the graphs are those from theory, which gives the force as:

$$F/A = \frac{E^2}{8\pi} = \frac{(V/d)^2}{8\pi}$$

where

$$\text{dynes/cm}^2 = \left(\frac{\text{e.s.u. of voltage}}{\text{cm}}\right)^2$$

The fit of the straight line in the plot vs. $1/d^2$ is excellent, except for the point where d is so small that it cannot be measured with much percentage accuracy.

Known amounts of nylon fibres, of three different lengths, were then placed between the plates. Three samples of nylon were available, of different mean lengths and scatter about the mean. When the voltage was applied, the fibres were oriented, and tended to form chains between the plates. (We are told that this is a new commercial method of making artificial fur coats!)

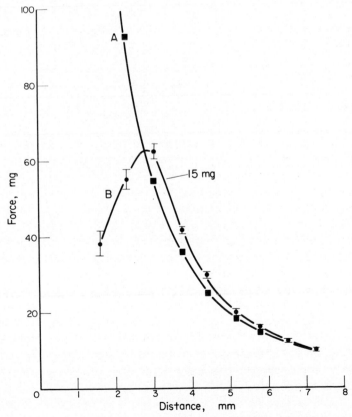

FIG. 10. FORCE VS. DISTANCE WITH NYLON FIBRES BETWEEN. THE TOTAL QUANTITY OF FIBRES BETWEEN THE PLATES WAS KEPT CONSTANT. CURVE A IS WITHOUT THE FIBRES, B WITH FIBRES. VERTICAL LINES INDICATE THE STANDARD ERROR OF THE MEANS.

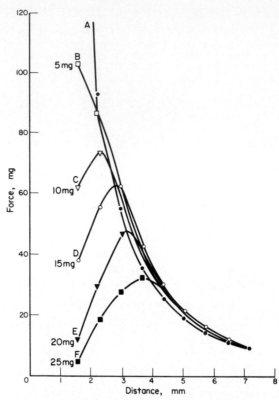

FIG. 11. FAMILY OF CURVES OBTAINED WITH DIFFERENT TOTAL QUANTITIES OF FIBRES BETWEEN PLATES.
CURVE A IS WITH NO FIBRES.

When the force was measured with increasing distance between the plates, but with
the same total quantity of fibres (this would give a decreasing *concentration* of fibres
per unit of space between the plates), the results were most unexpected (Fig. 10). The
force actually increases to a maximum as the distance between the plates is reduced.
At greater separation distances of the plates, the force follows the inverse square law
obtained for the "empty" experiment, but remains slightly higher. Repeating with
different total amounts of fibres between the plates gives the family of curves of Fig. 11.
With increasing numbers of fibres, for a given distance, the force is decreased.

From the family of curves, by interpolation, it can be deduced how the force would
vary if we had kept the *concentration*, rather than the total *amount* constant. (If we
had added half the total quantity when the distance was doubled, and so on.) We
conclude that with the same concentration of fibres, the force tends to be *independent
of distance* up to the "breaking point" of the curves, after which it declines according
to the inverse square law. Similarly, what would happen if the charge on the plates,
rather than the voltage, had been kept constant, may be deduced from theory. The
effect of the length of the fibres on the results is shown in Fig. 12.

To explain these curious results, it is necessary to know, descriptively, what is
happening to the fibres between the plates. Figure 13 shows photographs of the fibres
with a fixed distance between the plates, but with increasing number of fibres (or
increasing concentration). Two observers independently estimated how many intact

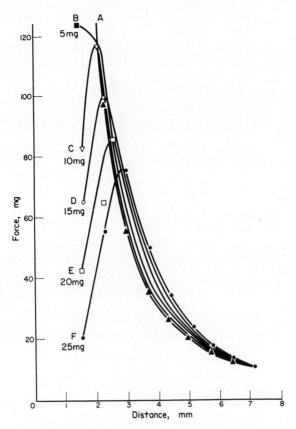

FIG. 12. AS IN FIG. 11, BUT USING SHORTER FIBRES.

chains between the plates could be counted as the quantity increased (Fig. 14). While the bias of the observers is, as to be expected, different, both agree that the number of "bridges" does not increase proportionately, but tends to a maximum. It looks as if there is an energy of interaction between parallel bridges, as well as an energy of formation of each bridge, so that a final "stationary" pattern of organization results as the quantity of fibres is still further increased.

The reason for the break in the curves of force vs. distance between plates is apparent when we look at the photographs made with the same quantity of fibres, with increasing separation of the plates (Fig. 15). The point of break in the curve of force vs. distance corresponds to the occurrence of breaks in the middle of bridges, so that each plate has a palisade of fibres with an air gap in the middle. The curve for the empty apparatus is then followed, but with the distance between plates effectively reduced by fibres attached to it, i.e. the curve is shifted on the distance axis by a constant amount.

We see, then, that chains of oriented molecules, while they could not greatly increase the force between charges at a considerable distance from another (except for the effect of broken chains described above), they could *perhaps make possible electrostatic forces of attraction between charges at considerable distance even in a conducting environment, and greatly modify the law of variation of force with distance apart*. This means that we should go back to our computation of the resultant normal

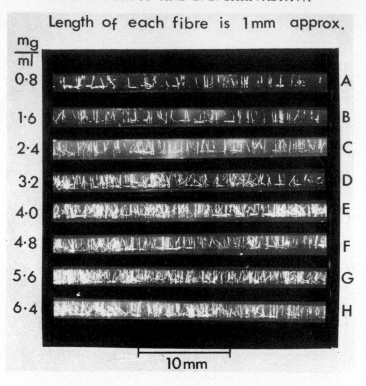

FIG. 13. PHOTOGRAPHS OF FIBRES ORIENTED BETWEEN THE PLATES, WITH CONSTANT DISTANCE BETWEEN PLATES BUT INCREASING QUANTITIES OF FIBRES.

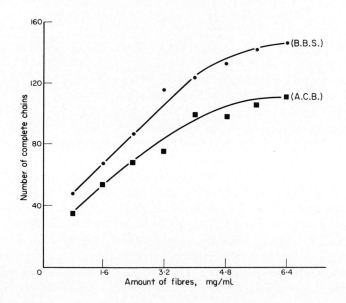

FIG. 14. RESULT OF ESTIMATES BY TWO OBSERVERS OF THE NUMBER OF INTACT CHAINS BETWEEN THE PLATES WITH INCREASING QUANTITY OF PORES. BOTH ESTIMATES SHOW TENDENCY TO "SATURATION" IN THE NUMBER OF CHAINS.

Length of each fibre is 1 mm approx.

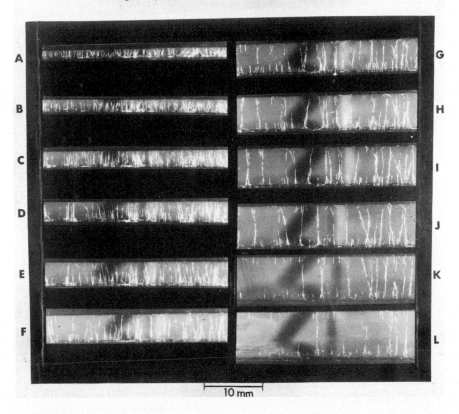

10 mm

FIG. 15. PHOTOGRAPHS OF FIBRES ORIENTED BETWEEN PLATES AS THE DISTANCE BETWEEN PLATES IS INCREASED, WITH THE QUANTITY OF FIBRES KEPT CONSTANT. AT A CRITICAL DISTANCE, BREAKS IN THE CHAINS APPEAR.

forces on a membrane, having the shape of the biconcave red cell, with approximately equidistant +Ve and −Ve charges distributed over its surface. However, we should try a variety of variations of force with distance, even including forces independent of the distance.

All this, as was admitted earlier, is unfettered exercise of the imagination. We must search for the best possible apparatus for detecting polarization, to give evidence of oriented molecules within the red cell; and we can always hope that electron-microscopy of sectioned red cells, or of rouleaux, may reveal the presence of "fibres". Certainly, the argument that there is not enough "stromatin" inside the red cell, excluding the membrane, for such fibrous bridges, does not carry weight. The concentration of nylon fibres in our model that produced very large effects on the force is very low indeed (a few mg %), and would correspond to amounts of stromatin protein below that at present detectable biochemically. Even if all this speculation and the model experiments prove to have no application, some physical-chemist may find that he was stimulated to new discoveries by these perhaps "childish" observations. The problem of long-range specific forces in biology will not "go away" simply because we ignore it.

ACKNOWLEDGMENT

The support of the Life Insurance Medical Research Fund over many years is gratefully acknowledged.

REFERENCES

[1] RAND, R. P. and BURTON, A. C. *J. Cell. and Comp. Physiol.* **61**, 245, 1963.
[2] BURTON, A. C. *Federation Proceedings* **25**, No. 6, 1753, 1966.
[3] RAND, R. P. and BURTON, A. C. *Biophysical J.* **4**, 116, 1964.
[4] RAND, R. P. and BURTON, A. C. *Biophysical J.* **4**, 303, 1964.
[5] KATCHALSKY, A., KEDEM, O., KLIBANSKY, C. and DE VRIES, A. In *Flow Properties of Blood and Other Biological Systems*, COPLEY, A. L. and STAINSBY, G. (Editors), Pergamon Press, Oxford, New York, 1960, p. 155.
[6] RAND, R. P. and BURTON, A. C. *Biophysical J.* **4**, 491, 1964.
[7] TOSTESON, D. and HOFFMAN, J. F. *J. Gen. Physiol.* **41**, 243, 1957.
[8] TIMOSHENKO, S. *Theory of Plates and Shells*, McGraw-Hill, New York, 1940.
[9] WEISS, P. In *Int. Review of Cytology* VII, BOURNE, G. H. and DANIELLI, J. F. (Editors), Academic Press, New York, 1958, p. 391.
[10] WEISS, L. In *Int. Review of Cytology* IX, BOURNE, G. H. and DANIELLI, J. F. (Editors), Academic Press, New York, 1960, p. 187.
[11] ABERCROMBIE, M. *Canadian Cancer Conference* **4**, 101, Academic Press, New York, 1964.
[12] MOSCONA, A. A. *Int. Rev. Exper. Path.* **1**, 371, 1962.
[13] RAND, R. P., BURTON, A. C. and CANHAM, P. *Nature* **205**, 977, 1965.
[14] INOUÉ, S. *Organisation and Function of the Mitotic Spindle. Primitive Motile Systems in Cell Biology.* Academic Press, New York, 1964, p. 549.

DISCUSSION

KOCHEN (*U.S.A.*):

We have been able to demonstrate the presence of a morphologically distinct structure which bridges the biconcavities of individual red cells that have been exposed to reducing conditions. These findings are consistent with your observations and may provide additional evidence for the presence of intracellular organization within the red cell.

BURTON (*Canada*):

Thank you very much. This is why I came to an International Congress.

SILBERBERG (*Israel*):

I think that your idea of a bridge between the two opposite sides of the narrow portion of the red cell is very logical; and I am very impressed by the conclusions that you have drawn. I think also that it would be possible to think of macromolecular models which could do just this. These would be polyelectrolytes or just loose gel-like interactions. I think either of these mechanisms could easily give rise to the type of interaction that you need in order to account for this missing force. I think it might be worthwhile to consider also the possibility of non-electrostatic interactions, involving macromolecular bridges extending across the gap.

BURTON:

I do not know where the limit of macromolecular and non-protein polymers really comes. I would point out that we did investigate the effect of the length of the nylon fibres. As the fibres are shorter, it seems that the part of the curve we want occurs only up to shorter distances: and the chains break more easily. Perhaps this would suggest that you have to have a certain length of molecule. I think that the long molecules we know of in the red cells and in the membrane would be long enough to fit these results with nylon. But I would recall then that fibrinogen, as a macromolecule, is not a polymer.

SILBERBERG:

If it goes up to one million molecular weight by association, then you could easily get such length extended?

BURTON:

Does anybody know of experiments on birefringence, which is the way to show oriented molecules, which have shown something lined up inside the red cell?

SIRS (*England*):

This point has been considered by PERUTZ (*Nature,* **161,** 204, 1948.) who considers the structure to be one of freely rotating Hb molecules arranged in a close-packed lattice.

BURTON:

Yes, but this has been shown just of hemoglobin, not of the red cell.

TAYLOR (*Australia*):

I am wondering, in your model, Dr. Burton, what happens if the cell is deformed? As I understand it, the red cell, as it is, has a definite top and bottom; and if you deform it, it will go back to having the same shape, the dimple and so on. The rim does not become the dimple. Now your model is such a one that if you pushed it around, the rim could become the dimple and the dimple could become the rim. You would have to have some kind of specific location of these charges, if they are charges, to make your model work, I think.

BURTON:

This is a key experiment. The crux of the matter is: Can one consider "soap-film" physics for the red cell? Is it a uniform membrane? If so, we need these extra forces. The key experiment would be to have some kind of a marker that is stuck to a red cell of normal shape at some place, swell the cell up to the sphere (short of hemolysis) shrink it back, and see if the marker is in the same place.

TAYLOR:

Well, I think Ponder's book on hemolysis discusses this. I cannot remember the exact experiments, but I think his view was that the things have a top and bottom and that you can determine this. But there are probably people here who know this much better than I.

BURTON:

I would like to hear from them. We have searched the literature, and we are not convinced that this point is settled.

ROWLANDS (*England*):

Dr. Furedi in Jerusalem has described some experiments which have a bearing on this. He was able to mark, I forget how he marked, but he did mark a specific point on the surface of red cells, then applied a high-frequency electric field and these red cells turned in a most peculiar way. But when the red cell field was switched off, this marker was no longer in the same position on the red cell membrane. So it would appear to me that your theory would have to be adapted so that the fibers, if there were such, were not anisotropic but were in fact isotropic and could elongate and contract in different directions.

BURTON:

I think you would be amused that in the days when we made rubber models, we used to buy from Woolworths' all kinds of rubber balls. We obtained a rubber ball which was made from two hemispheres with a very slight thickening around the circumference, where they were stuck together. When we used a syringe to reduce the pressure inside, the ball would become biconcave. If then one tried to press out one side of the concavity by force on the other side, the model insisted on being biconcave. The ball would "flip" back into biconcavity. But if you pressed the original ball on the rim, it would never do anything but become cup-shaped, and resisted being biconcave. This shows how complicated the mechanics of shells is. The slightest reinforcement along the rim, caused it to prefer, when pressed in one direction, to be cup-shaped, and when pressed in the direction at right angles to become biconcave. This is a very difficult field of mechanics, even for spherical shells.

MASON (*Canada*):

I would like to terminate, Professor Burton, by drawing your attention if you were not already aware of it. to related sets of principles. One is that the idea of a mosaic charge on a particle has been established in other fields. For example, there are a number of plate-like clay particles which have one charge on the face and another charge on the edge; and the rheological properties of such systems are very dependent upon the distribution of charge. Secondly, the idea of a pressure, either positive or negative, between two adjoining surfaces has been very well developed by the famous Russian colloid chemist Deryagin, who refers to this pressure as the "disjoining pressure", and who has done a great deal of work in this field. It occurs in many situations including soap-films. Soap-films assume an equilibrium thickness at which this disjoining pressure becomes zero; i.e. there is a balance between the repulsive electrical charges and the Van der Waals attractive forces.

BURTON:

Thank you very much.

REVERSIBLE DEFORMABILITY AND MECHANICAL FRAGILITY AS A FUNCTION OF RED CELL AGE

DAVID DANON*

Section of Biological Ultrastructure, Weizmann Institute of Science, Rehovoth, Israel

INTRODUCTION

Of all the alterations that are known to take place in the aging erythrocyte, the reduction in the capacity of this cell as it ages to survive the mechanical stress to which it is exposed in the circulation is one which has been least studied. The increased density and osmotic fragility, the change of form and reduced diameter, the modified Na:K equilibrium and the reduced activity of several enzymes are valuable indications of structural changes that occur in the cell membrane of the aging erythrocyte. The altered ultrastructure is more directly evidenced by electron microscopy[1] and measurements of the electric surface charge[2] of old and young cells. However, the capacity of the cell as a whole to yield to mechanical stress and recover its original form after deformation is probably a criterion that would determine, to a great extent, the overall capacity of the cell to remain in circulation[3–6].

The various mechanical fragility tests and filterability tests for red blood cells have originally been designed for diagnostic purposes. However, STEWART et al.[7] have used the rolling beads mechanical fragility test to demonstrate increased mechanical fragility of old red cells in dogs, and STAUFFER[8], has found a relation between the life span of red cells of different vertebrates and their mechanical fragility, using the FLEISCH method[9]. In the present paper, an attempt is made to analyse the principal available tests for mechanical fragility and filterability in order to clarify which of them demonstrates the closest relationship between the approximate chronological age of the red blood cells and their mechanical fragility. The method of FLEISCH[9] was not included in this study, because of lack of equipment.

METHODS

Rabbit erythrocytes were separated into age groups according to their specific gravity, using non water miscible phthalate ester mixtures of predetermined specific gravity as separating fluids[10]. Young red cells were labelled *in vivo* with ^{59}Fe[11]. The mechanical fragility of the separated young and old age groups of red blood cells was compared, using two variations of the conventional rolling glass beads method, that of SCHUBOTHE and PO-TUN-FOK[12] and that of DACIE and LEWIS[13]. The capacity for reversible deformability of red cells was estimated by passing the cells under pressure through a filter of 5μ mean pore diameter (Porvic, Essex, England) using BERGENTZ and DANON's[6] variation of the method of JANDL et al.[4]. The filterability through ordinary cellulose filters according to TEITEL and RĂDULESCU[14] and

497

P. TEITEL[15] was also measured. The fragility of the erythrocytes when injected through a needle of 0.2 mm internal diameter against a teflon wall, a test developed in our laboratory[16], was also examined. The proportion of cells that were broken in the various procedures was measured by the amount of hemoglobin liberated, the hemoglobin released from the same concentration of cells by total hemolysis providing the reference base of 100%. When ^{59}Fe labelled cells were tested, the radioactivity of the free hemoglobin from totally hemolysed cells was compared to that of the hemoglobin liberated by the broken cells during the test. The proportion of young labelled cells that were lysed during the test, as a percentage of the whole labelled population, could therefore be estimated.

In reversible deformability tests by passage through a filter of 5μ mean pore diameter, or by filterability through cellulose filters, the morphology of the deformed cells in their passage through the filters was analysed electron microscopically.

RESULTS

Old red blood cells were found to be less resistant than young ones to the mechanical trauma caused by the rolling beads method (Table 1). This finding was confirmed in the experiments in which young cells of up to 5 days of age were labelled *in vivo* with ^{59}Fe (Table 2).

When the filterability of old cells passed under pressure through a filter of 5μ mean pore diameter is compared to that of similarly treated young cells, it was found that old cells are preferentially lysed in a single passage through the filter[6], and the phenomenon is even more marked on repeated passage (Fig. 1). When cells of up to the age of

TABLE 1. MECHANICAL FRAGILITY OF YOUNG AND OLD AGE GROUPS OF ERYTHROCYTES SEPARATED ACCORDING TO THEIR SPECIFIC GRAVITY

Method	No. of exps.	Old cell fraction	% lysis	Young cell fraction	% lysis	% lysis total blood
Schubothe & Po-Tun-Fok	5	*ca.* 20%	13.5	*ca.* 25%	8.6	10.1
Dacie & Lewis	4	*ca.* 15%	5.14	*ca.* 15%	3.56	not done

TABLE 2. MECHANICAL FRAGILITY OF WHOLE RED CELL POPULATION WITH CELLS UP TO THE AGE OF 5 DAYS LABELLED *in vivo* WITH ^{59}Fe

Method	No. of exps.	% lysis in whole population	% lysis in young population	Mean* difference
Schubothe & Po-Tun-Fok	7	10.7	8.4	2.3
Dacie & Lewis	6	2.7	1.4	1.3

*Preferential lysis of old cells was found in all the experiments.

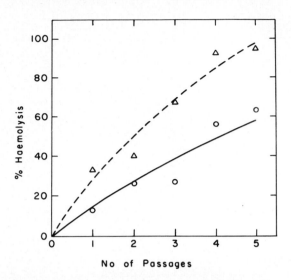

FIG. 1. REPEATED FILTRATION UNDER PRESSURE THROUGH A FILTER OF $5\,\mu$ MEAN PORE DIAMETER OF SEPARATED OLD (---) AND YOUNG (——) PACKED RED CELL FRACTIONS, SUSPENDED IN SALINE (1:400). THE FILTER DISK WAS CHANGED AFTER EACH PASSAGE.

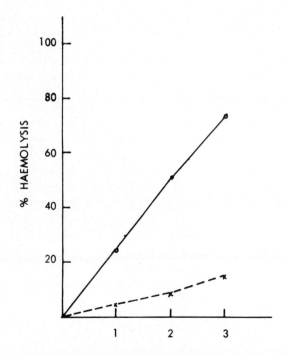

NUMBER OF PASSAGES THROUGH THE FILTER

FIG. 2. REPEATED FILTRATION UNDER PRESSURE OF RABBIT WHOLE RED BLOOD CELL POPULATION LABELLED *in vivo* 5 DAYS PREVIOUSLY WITH ^{59}Fe. CONDITIONS AS IN FIG. 1. ——% HEMOLYSIS OF TOTAL POPULATION, ---% HEMOLYSIS OF CELLS UP TO 5 DAYS.

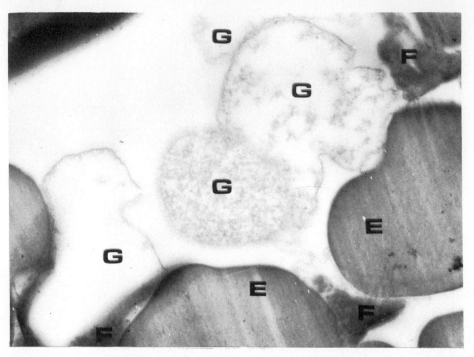

FIG. 3. ELECTRON MICROGRAPH OF A FRAGMENT OF A "PORVIC" FILTER OF 5 μ MEAN PORE DIAMETER THROUGH WHICH AN OLD RED BLOOD CELL FRACTION WAS PASSED UNDER PRESSURE. TWO INTACT ERYTHRO- CYTES (E) CAN BE SEEN IN CLOSE CONTACT WITH THE FILTER MATERIAL (F) AND FOUR GHOSTS (G) CAN BE SEEN. ×15,000.

5 days were labelled, it was confirmed that the young cells are proportionally less lysed[16] (Fig. 2). Electron microscopical analysis of the filters through which the blood suspension was passed[17] demonstrated that some cells were broken in passage (Fig. 3) while others were extremely deformed without breaking (Fig. 4), especially in the young cell fraction.

The Teitel "filterability" or "plasticity" test[15] surprisingly showed a higher rate of filtration for the old cell fraction (Fig. 5). The morphological analysis of the filter showed that the pores of the filter are large enough to accommodate groups consisting of several cells, so that the cells do not necessarily have to undergo deformation in order to pass through the filter (Fig. 6). In a new test[16] in which red cell suspensions were injected under pressure through a small bore needle against a teflon surface, old cells were also lysed preferentially (Fig. 7 and 8). This method revealed the greatest difference in mechanical fragility between young and old cell populations.

DISCUSSION

The intermediate circulation of the spleen commits arterial blood to passage through the highly cellular and compartmentalized cordal zone before emptying into the sinusoids and the venous circulation[18, 19]. One function of the cords, their action as a mechanical filter retarding the passage of prelytic, sphered erythrocytes and ex- perimentally injured cells, was demonstrated by RIFKIND in an electron microscopical

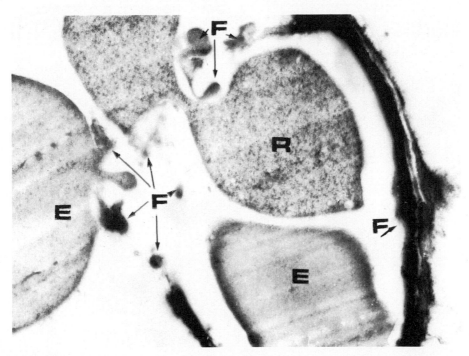

FIG. 4. AS IN FIG. 3 WITH YOUNG CELL FRACTION. TWO INTACT ERYTHROCYTES (E) CAN BE SEEN. ONE RETICULOCYTE (R) IS EXTREMELY DEFORMED WITHOUT BEING BROKEN IN ITS PASSAGE THROUGH THE FILTER STRUCTURE (F). × 15,000.

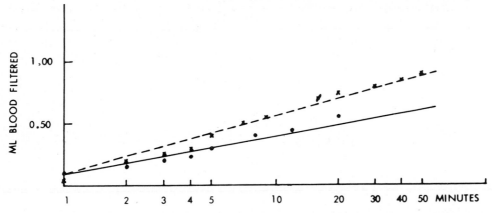

FIG. 5. RATE OF FILTRATION AT ATMOSPHERIC PRESSURE OF RABBIT RED BLOOD CELLS SEPARATED INTO OLD (- - -) AND YOUNG (——) FRACTIONS. TEITEL'S METHOD, 1:1 PACKED CELLS IN SALINE PASSED THROUGH CELLULOSE FILTER PAPER S & S 589.

study[20] which confirmed in general terms the experimental model of JANDL *et al.*[4]. Furthermore, the splenic cords seem to "recognize" physico-chemical alterations of the red cell surface[5].

The filterability test, in which a blood suspension is passed under pressure through pores smaller than the diameter of the cells[4, 6] submits the cells to severe deformation which old cells cannot resist as effectively as young ones. They are therefore

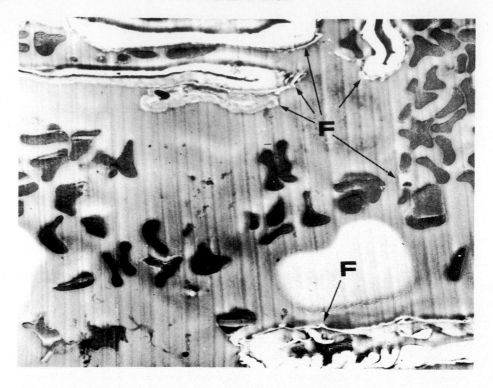

Fig. 6. Electron micrograph of a fragment of cellulose filter paper after passage at atmospheric pressure of a suspension 1:1 packed red cells in saline. Teitel's method. Spaces between the filter cellulose fibers (F) are in some places so wide that a number of cells can pass simultaneously without necessarily being deformed. ×2000.

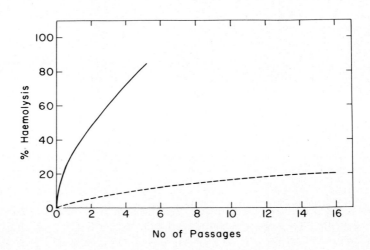

Fig. 7. Hemolysis produced by injecting repeatedly a suspension of old (- - -) and young (———) red cell fractions through a needle of 0.2 mm internal diameter, the jet impinging on a teflon surface.

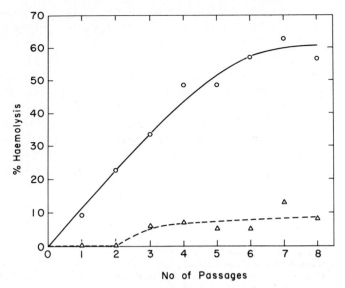

FIG. 8. AS FIG. 7, HEMOLYSIS OF RABBIT WHOLE RED BLOOD CELL POPULATION LABELLED *in vivo* 5 DAYS PREVIOUSLY WITH ^{59}Fe. ——% HEMOLYSIS OF TOTAL POPULATION - - -% HEMOLYSIS OF CELLS AGED UP TO 5 DAYS.

preferentially destroyed in the process, as demonstrated in the present study. These observations confirm that JANDL'S[4] experimental model for testing the capacity of the cell to be reversibly deformed is satisfactory for detecting alterations associated with red cell aging.

GUEST *et al.*[3] have provided evidence from high speed cinephotomicrography that the shape of red blood cells is changed during the flow of blood through capillaries from a biconcave disk to a paraboloid with a hollow bell-like center. The degree of deformation is dependent upon the velocity of flow in the capillaries. STAUFFER[8] has found, in analysing the relationship of velocity of blood in the aorta of several vertebrates to the mechanical fragility of their erythrocytes, that the higher the natural velocity of flow the more resistant are the cells. The injection of a blood suspension through a needle of small internal diameter roughly simulates high velocity blood flow. The higher the speed at which the injected suspension impinges on the teflon surface and the greater the repetition of injections, the higher the degree of hemolysis obtained.

The fact that the greatest difference between the fragility of old and young cells was demonstrated by this method is indicative that here the cells are submitted to a stress imitating but to an exaggerated degree, the stress in circulation which old cells can hardly resist without lysing. This test therefore, may be considered as a model system for the study of alterations associated with red cell aging. It is obviously advantageous in the study of hemolytic phenomena following cardiovascular surgery in which plastic components have been implanted, and might even be useful in predicting which patient would have a tendency to this kind of post operative hemolysis.

The rolling beads mechanical fragility test of SCHUBOTHE and PO-TUN-FOK[12] revealed a smaller difference in the lysis of old and young cells than the method of DACIE and LEWIS[13]. Since the mechanism by which the cells are broken in the two procedures is very different from what occurs in the circulation and the difference in resistance between old and young cells is comparatively small, these methods cannot be considered wholly adequate as models to reveal alterations occurring in red cells with physiological aging.

Passage through cellulose filters[15] does not seem to submit the cells to the stress of deformation. This is apparent from the more rapid passage of old cells and from the large space between the fibers of the filter. The reported reduced filterability of blood samples of patients with certain diseases[15] may be due to increased adhesivity or agglutinability of these cells. This test does not seem to reveal alterations in the "plasticity" due to aging of the cell and hence cannot be considered as a model for the study of such alteration. It does indicate however, the reduced diameter of old cells and their tendency to become spheroid which results in a more rapid filtration of old cells in this test.

REFERENCES

 [1] DANON, D. and MARIKOVSKY, Y. *C.R. Soc. Biol.* **CLV**, 12, 1961.
 [2] DANON, D. and MARIKOVSKY, Y. *C.R. Acad. Sci.* **253**, 1271, 1961.
 [3] GUEST, M. M., BOND, T. P., COOPER, R. G. and DERRICK, J. R. *Science* **142**, 1319, 1963.
 [4] JANDL, J. H., SIMMONS, R. L. and CASTLE, W. B. *Blood* **18**, 133, 1961.
 [5] JACOB, H. and JANDL, J. H. *J. Clin. Invest.* **41**, 779, 1962.
 [6] BERGENTZ, S. E. and DANON, D. *Acta Chir. Scand.* **130**, 165, 1965.
 [7] STEWART, W. B., STEWART, J. M., IZZO, M. J. and YOUNG, L. E. *J. Exp. Med.* **91**, 147, 1950.
 [8] STAUFFER, R. *Nouv. Rev. Fran. Hematol.* **2**, 340, 1962.
 [9] FLEISCH, H. and FLEISCH, A. *Sweiz. Med. Wschr.* **8**, 186, 1960.
[10] DANON, D. and MARIKOVSKY, Y. *J. Lab. Clin. Med.* **64**, 668, 1964.
[11] HAHN, P. F., BALE, W. F., ROSS, J. F., HETTIG, R. A. and WHIPPLE, G. H. *Science* **92**, 131, 1940.
[12] SCHUBOTHE, H. and PO-TUN-FOK, F. *Brit. J. Haematol.* **6**, 350, 1960.
[13] DACIE, J. V. and LEWIS, S. M. *Practical Haematology*, 3rd ed., Churchill, London, 1963, p. 144.
[14] TEITEL, A. and RĂDULESCU, I. *Medicina Interna* **5**, 32, 1952.
[15] TEITEL, P. *Sangre*, **9**, 421, 1964.
[16] BARZILY, M. and DANON, D. (in preparation).
[17] MEISELMAN, N. and DANON, D. (in preparation).
[18] WEISS, L. *Am. J. Anat.* **111**, 131, 1962.
[19] WEISS, L. *Am. J. Anat.* **113**, 51, 1963.
[20] RIFKIND, R. A. *Blood* **26**, 433, 1965.

HEMORHEOLOGICAL ASPECTS OF THE RESPIRATORY FUNCTION OF ERYTHROCYTES

JOHN A. SIRS*

Department of Physics, St. Mary's Hospital Medical School, University of London, London, England

INTRODUCTION

Any attempt to formulate biological processes in terms of mathematics and physics is fraught with difficulties. The essential problem has been aptly stated by Peek in the form, "Give me three constants and I can describe an elephant, give me four, and I will make it wave its trunk." While in physics the limitation of changes to two or three variables is relatively straightforward, no such restriction can be placed on biological systems. The innumerable and inaccessible constants then involved allow sufficient mathematical freedom that any approach or theory can be adjusted to fit the experimental data. It is therefore not suprising that no comparable development of mathematics in biology has occurred of the magnitude of say Maxwell's theory of electromagnetic radiation.

The best any biophysicist can hope to attain is to choose as simple a biological system as can be found, systematically attempt to measure the various constants involved, and compare the overall experimental data with a limited theory. The particular appeal of the respiratory exchange of O_2, CO and NO by haemoglobin in erythrocytes is that it satisfies these criteria. With gaseous ligands there are no complications of electric charge or extraneous binding, and the red blood cell, with no nucleus, is relatively simple, easy to obtain and handle. Techniques are available for observing these processes, in particular the rapid-mixing method of HARTRIDGE and ROUGHTON[1], and ROUGHTON and co-workers[2, 3] over a period of more than thirty years have systematically examined and measured the variables involved. On the basis of these data they suggested that O_2 was taken up by a process of diffusion through the cell membrane, followed by diffusion through and chemical reaction with the internal haemoglobin. The system appeared admirably suited, as a precursor of more complex cells, to further investigation of the influence of a number of biophysical factors of general interest. As this objective has been pursued I have come to appreciate PONDER's[4] remark, "I have been told that I tend to speak of the red cell as if it were a microcosm, and as if an understanding of its nature and properties would include an understanding of nearly everything else in the cellular world." The supposedly simple process of gaseous exchange has not proved so amenable to detailed physico-chemical analysis after all. There is however a compensatory side to this complexity: with so many factors involved it is not suprising that if you study one aspect of cell function you at the same time study some other physical process. The main theme of the data I wish to present in this paper is that a study of the respiratory efficiency of the erythrocyte in turn involves and is a measure of the cell flexibility.

THE UPTAKE OF O_2, NO AND CO BY Hb IN ERYTHROCYTES

The original application of the rapid-mixing technique of Hartridge and Roughton to the respiratory exchange of erythrocytes was restricted by technical difficulties to the constant-flow method. Though this method provided a great deal of basic data its use to study a wide range of variables was limited by the amount of reagents required. This problem was overcome by the introduction of the stopped-flow technique.[5] In principle the red blood cells are suspended in an isotonic media and all oxygen removed so that only reduced haemoglobin is present within the cell. The suspension is then rapidly mixed, within 2 msec, with an isotonic media equilibrated with O_2, CO or NO as required. The rate at which these gases then enter the cell is followed by spectrophotometrically observing the change of Hb $\rightarrow$ HbO$_2$ etc. The initial rate of uptake has proven amenable to theoretical analysis[1, 6] in terms of diffusion through the red cell membrane, followed by diffusion through and reaction with the internal haemoglobin. By observing this initial rate of uptake under a variety of experimental conditions it is possible to relate the differences to changes of these basic parameters. The fluid economy of the stopped-flow method allowed a record to be obtained of the initial rate of uptake of oxygen on the same suspension, at different time intervals after collection of the blood sample. This proved to be a variable factor[7] as indicated in Fig. 1. By contrast, under the same conditions the uptake of CO

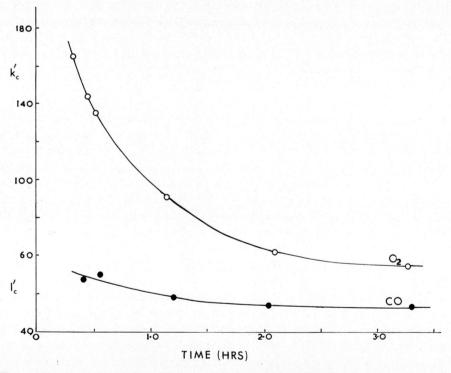

FIG. 1. THE VARIATION OF THE INITIAL RATES OF UPTAKE OF O_2 AND CO WITH TIME BY REDUCED HAEMO-GLOBIN IN A 1 : 100 SUSPENSION OF HUMAN (J.A.S.) ERYTHROCYTES IN RINGER–LOCKE SOLUTION (9 g NaCl, 0·42 g KCl, 0·2 g NaHCO$_3$ AND 0·24 g CaCl$_2$ PER LITRE). TEMPERATURE 22°C AND pH 8·0. ZERO TIME CORRESPONDS TO THE TIME OF REMOVAL OF THE WHOLE BLOOD FROM STORAGE AT 4°C FOR 48 HR. OXYGEN CONCENTRATION 0·197 mM AND CARBON MONOXIDE 0·174 mM AFTER MIXING.

remained slow and constant over this period. Experiments with cells at the lower rate of uptake, indicated that in these circumstances the ROUGHTON physico-chemical theory was valid.[1, 5, 8]. On this basis the faster rate obtained with fresh cells could only be explained if the membrane permeability had initially been higher[7]. This proposition was tested further by utilizing nitric oxide. In this case the chemical reaction of NO with Hb is effectively instantaneous and the advancing-front theory[9] of uptake can be applied. A consequence of this is that when the membrane permeability is high (i.e. offers little resistance to gaseous passage) the initial rate of uptake should be proportional to the square-root of the NO concentration. If the cell membrane had resistance it would be relatively linear with concentration. The initial rate of uptake of NO was found in fact to vary with time after collection of the blood sample in a similar manner to O_2[10], and so NO provided a means of proving whether a simple change of membrane permeability was all that was involved. While again at lower rates the physico-chemical advancing front theory proved applicable[11], the rates of uptake at the higher values did not vary with the square-root of the NO concentration. This implied that though a change of membrane permeability had occurred, the overall process was more complex. In order to explain these results it was proposed that the change was one of flexibility of the red blood cell membrane[10]. It was suggested that when all the oxygen was removed from the cell it became relatively inflexible, and for a given period the flexibility could be restored upon mixing with oxygen or nitric oxide, but not with carbon monoxide. During these experiments, the decay time over which O_2 or NO could reactivate the cell was found to be affected by a number of factors and it is now possible to correlate these effects with recently published data on the flexibility of the red blood cell.

Before it was realized that the removal of oxygen *per se*, led to inflexibility of the erythrocyte several different treatments were tried in an attempt to maintain the cells with the very fast rate of uptake. It was found that at 37°C the rate of decay to the slow state was much faster than at 20°C[12]. Cooling the cells quickly was therefore advantageous. A further extension of this procedure, by rapidly cooling the whole blood and storing at 4°C overnight proved even more effective. In this case the cells were found to exhibit an induction period, of the order one hour, during which the high rate of uptake was maintained, before decaying to a lower value[12]. Independent observations have since been reported by JACOBS[13] of the flexibility of packed red blood cells after storage at 4°C, with remarkably similar effects. The transport of Na^+ by cat erythrocytes was found by DAVSON and DANIELLI[14], in 1939, to be faster after storage at 4°C. The rates of uptake of K^+ by human red blood cells under normal conditions, as reported by SOLOMAN[15], are one-third slower than those obtained by PONDER[16] after cold storage. It might be that a more general correlation occurs between the flexibility of the erythrocyte membrane and its permeability. The oscillatory transfer of water, proposed to account for the rapid phase of the uptake of O_2 and NO, and the possible link with cation transfer are consistent with the unstable pressure and voltage fluctuations in charged membranes proposed by TEORELL[17].

The earlier observations of the decay of the initial rate of uptake of O_2 with time also suggested it might be influenced by metabolic processes. Suspending the cells in a glucose media[12] indicated that some advantage could be obtained, but the cells still reached the lower rate within 4 hours at 33°C. The addition of 2mM adenosine to a cell suspension, 80 min after starting the series of experiments and when the rate of uptake had fallen by half, restored a significantly faster rate for a further 40 min[12]. TEITEL[18] has made observations of the flexibility of red blood cells by measuring the rate at which they pass through filter paper. Application of this technique to the influence of metabolism on incubated cells[19] has indicated a significant reversal of inflexibility with adenosine, whereas after the addition of glucose the cells still remained relatively rigid.

More recently measurements on the flexibility of red blood cells sphered by heating to 49°C, have been reported by TEITEL[20], which indicated they became rigid. The experiments of CARLSEN and COMROE[21], confirmed the theoretical calculation of ROUGHTON[22], that there was no difference between the rate of uptake of CO (or NO) by discoidal cells and cells which had been sphered by heating. The mode of collection, the time elapsed in the preparation of the large volume of reagents necessary with the constant flow technique, and the rates of uptake observed, all indicate that the discoidal cells corresponded to the lower passive form indicated in Fig. 1. If the sphered cells are inflexible this would imply the discoidal cells are similarly rigid at this stage. This has more recently been confirmed by fixing discoidal cells with formaldehyde[23], after which no change of the rate of uptake of CO occurred.

Upon the addition of 2 mM iodoacetic acid to the reduced cell suspension, some 30 min after starting a series of experiments, immediate depression from a fast to slow rate of uptake of O_2 was observed[12]. Further investigation revealed that a similar effect could be obtained by addition of 1 ml of 0.5 M HCl to the cell suspension, changing the pH from 8·0 to 6·3. With neutralized iodoacetate no change was observed. Investigation of the effect of pH on the rate of filtration of red blood cells by TEITEL[19] has indicated a marked decrease of flexibility in the range pH 5·5–6·5. Again the evidence would appear to indicate a direct correlation of the respiratory function of the erythrocyte with the flexibility of its membrane.

Most of these experiments on the rates of uptake of gaseous ligands by reduced haemoglobin were made with the objective of assessing the rates that are applicable *in vivo*. This must at least be as fast as the initial rates obtained before decay. All attempts to prolong this phase, and so obtain data under a wider range of experimental conditions more likely to be applicable *in vivo* failed. The reason for this, as stated earlier, is that the complete removal of oxygen on its own leads to inflexibility. Teitel mentioned that a small effect on flexibility was obtained with deoxygenation, but more recent measurements by the author (unpublished data) have proven that the cells are effectively rigid when O_2 is completely absent. Further observations have therefore been made with oxygenated cells under conditions more comparable with those occurring *in vivo* and some aspects of these results will now be discussed.

THE EGRESS OF O_2 FROM HbO_2 IN ERYTHROCYTES

The first observations of the rate of egress of oxygen from HbO_2 in erythrocytes were made by rapid mixing of the cells with $Na_2S_2O_4$[6,24]. Though dithionite is not believed to penetrate the cell membrane[3, 24], and so denature the internal haemo-globin[25, 26], its use still presents difficulties of optical inhomogeneity[27], which have to be carefully controlled. Alternative techniques have been developed using the stopped-flow method by reducing the O_2 concentration with 1:20 dilution in an oxygen-free media and by rapid-mixing with a high concentration of CO[28]. The $Na_2S_2O_4$

method and dilution technique both, in theory, involve the back-reaction of $O_2 + Hb$ within the cell. The lower the diffusion constant of O_2 through the internal haemoglobin the higher must be the oxygen gradient and in turn oxygen concentration within the cell, and because the recapture rate is then increased the slower will be the overall rate of egress. Alternatively if the internal contents are considered to be efficiently stirred, i.e. the diffusion constant is infinity, for a cell with no membrane resistance the O_2 concentration will be the same inside as outside the cell. After mixing with $Na_2S_2O_4$ this is effectively zero, and analysis of this situation indicates that the rate of egress would be solely controlled by the chemical rate of dissociation of $HbO_2 \rightarrow Hb$. The simple dissociation of HbO_2 within the cell is thus relatively sensitive to the oxygen concentration and, in turn, the diffusion constant. The technique of mixing oxygenated

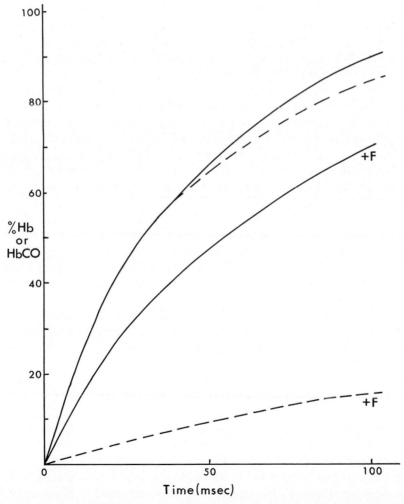

FIG. 2. STOPPED-FLOW SPECTROPHOTOMETRIC OBSERVATION OF THE RATE OF EGRESS FROM SHEEP ERY-THROCYTES, TYPE HbB, AT pH 7·4 AND 24·8°C. FULL CURVES, AFTER 1:20 DILUTION IN AN ISOTONIC SOLUTION EQUILIBRATED WITH 110 cm Hg PARTIAL PRESSURE OF CO. BROKEN CURVES AFTER DILUTION 1:20 IN AN ISOTONIC SOLUTION CONTAINING 5 g/l $Na_2S_2O_4$. THE CURVES "+F" WERE OBTAINED AFTER ADDING 5 CC OF 10% FORMALDEHYDE SOLUTION TO 100 CC OF THE HbO_2 CELL SUSPENSION (15 MIN LATER).

cells with a high concentration of CO, is not so affected. In this case the haemoglobin is maintained fully saturated as HbO_2 is converted to $HbCO$ and the rate of the process is determined by the chemical reaction rate constant, r, deduced by GIBSON and ROUGHTON[29] as:

$$r = \frac{k_4}{4(1 + k_4'[O_2]/l_4'[CO])}$$

The ratio of the rate constants k_4'/l_4' is approximately 3, so that if the CO concentration is made high, r is equivalent to $k_4/4$, the rate constant of the dissociation of $Hb_4O_8 \rightarrow Hb_4O_6$. A change from an efficiently mixed system, where $[O_2]$ is low, to an inflexible cell, where the diffusion constant is low and $[O_2]$ relatively high, would not affect r to the same degree as the rate is altered with simple dissociation.

Measurements of the rate of egress of oxygen from freshly collected cells, first after dilution and mixing with a high concentration of CO, and then by dilution of the oxygenated cells in an isotonic $Na_2S_2O_4$ medium are shown in Fig. 2. The CO curve has been proven, by variation of the CO concentration, a measure of the rate constant $k_4/4$, within the cell. The agreement of the rate of the simple dissociation of $HbO_2 \rightarrow Hb$ after mixing with dithionite would appear to indicate that the cell membrane offers no effective resistance to the passage of O_2 and the cell contents are efficiently mixed.

Further confirmation of this interpretation has been obtained by fixing the cells and making them relatively inflexible by suspending them in a formaldehyde solution as shown in Fig. 2. The simple rate of egress falls dramatically, while the rate after mixing with CO, though slower, is not altered to the same extent. There is another aspect of these results in that it has always been difficult to prove decisively, in previous experiments, that the membrane resistance was in fact due to the membrane and not a stagnant layer of water surrounding the cell. In this case there is no obstruction to a dithionite ion moving up to the true cell membrane through any such water layer and thereby reducing its effect. That an effective membrane resistance is still necessary to account for the very slow rates after the addition of formaldehyde indicates that this must be a true membrane barrier.

Similar retardation of the rates of egress have been found with other physical agents known to reduce the cell flexibility. Heating of sheep erythrocytes to 49°C for half an hour, though it has not proved possible to turn the cells into spheres in this case, considerably lowers the rates of egress as indicated in Fig. 3.

The effect of alkaline pH 8·0 is relatively slight, there is only a small decrease upon mixing with CO, consistent with the alteration of the chemical reaction rate found in solution[29]. The simple dissociation, after mixing with $Na_2S_2O_4$, is a further 10% lower. A small decrease of the cell flexibility at pH 8·0 was observed by TEITEL[19]. Increasing acidity leads to an increase of the CO rate, as $k_4/4$ increases, and a lowering of the $Na_2S_2O_4$ rate.

An investigation of the effect of tonicity on the rates of egress proved rather surprising. Decreasing the tonicity leads to a decrease of the respiratory efficiency as indicated in Fig. 4. Similar data are again available by TEITEL[19] on the reduction of flexibility of the erythrocyte. Increasing the tonicity by adding increments of 1, 3, 5 and 7 g NaCl per litre to the isotonic media in which the cells were suspended had no effect, within the experimental error of ±7%, on either the CO or $Na_2S_2O_4$ rates. RAND and

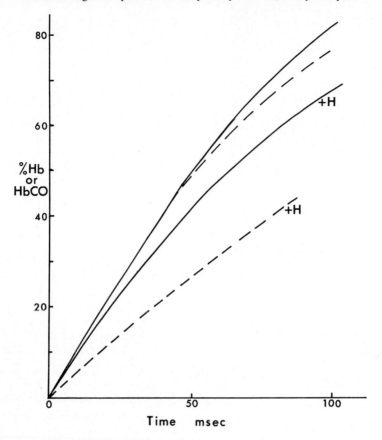

FIG. 3. THE EGRESS OF OXYGEN FROM SHEEP ERYTHROCYTES, TYPE HbA, AT pH 7·4 AND 23°C. FULL
CURVES: AFTER MIXING AND DILUTING THE CELLS WITH AN ISOTONIC SOLUTION EQUILIBRATED WITH 110 cm
pCO. BROKEN CURVES: AFTER MIXING AND DILUTING WITH 4 g/l Na$_2$S$_2$O$_4$ SOLUTION. THE CURVES "+H"
WERE OBTAINED ON A SECOND EQUIVALENT SUSPENSION WHICH HAD BEEN WARMED TO 48·5°C FOR 30 MIN.

BURTON[30] found that if anything the red blood cell membrane had less resistance to
deformation in hypertonic solutions than a normal biconcave disc. There is a difficulty
however in that their measurements were made at pH ≃ 6. The present data are more
consistent with the observations of MITCHISON and SWANN[31], and it is interesting to
note that no residual internal pressure was indicated by these measurements. A
further interesting implication of this observation relates to the question of how
effective mixing of oxygen with the internal haemoglobin occurs. PERUTZ[32] from
X-ray observations has determined the volume of the haemoglobin molecule and then
from the concentration of internal haemoglobin and erythrocyte volume calculated
that there is just sufficient space around each Hb molecule for it to rotate, but the trans-
latory motion must be negligible. If the cell is further reduced in size the haemoglobin
molecules must be even more constricted and it is unlikely that sufficient energy can be
imparted to produce any effective stirring. How is it then that the diffusion constant of
O$_2$ through the haemoglobin can be maintained so large? The only mechanism would
appear to be an oscillatory movement of water[10], carrying the O$_2$ molecules through
and among the relatively immobile haemoglobin. Some additional impetus to this water

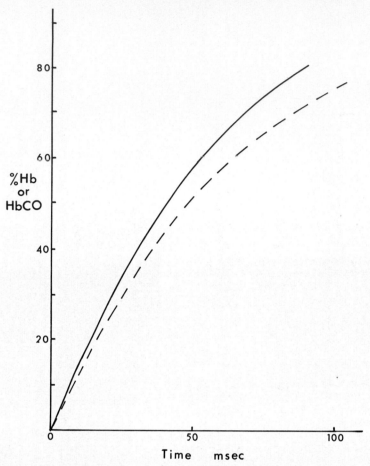

FIG. 4. THE EGRESS OF OXYGEN FROM HUMAN (J.M.) ERYTHROCYTES AFTER SLOWLY ADDING 25 ml OF DISTILLED WATER TO 100 ml OF CELL SUSPENSION AT pH 7·4 AND 25·3°C. THE EGRESS AFTER MIXING WITH 100 cm pCO (FULL CURVE) WAS UNCHANGED, WHEREAS THE RATE AFTER MIXING WITH AN ISOTONIC 4 g/l Na₂S₂O₄ SOLUTION WAS LOWERED, AS INDICATED BY THE BROKEN CURVE.

movement is probably provided by the large configuration change of the haemoglobin structure as $Hb_4O_8 \rightarrow Hb_4O_6$.

It may perhaps be added in ending this survey of the inter-relation between flexibility and respiratory function of the erythrocyte, that, to date, on every occasion the cell has been shown to be inflexible a corresponding reduction of the respiratory efficiency has been observed.

REFERENCES

[1] HARTRIDGE, H. and ROUGHTON, F. J. W. *Proc. Roy. Soc. London*, Ser. A. **104**, 376, 1923.
[2] ROUGHTON, F. J. W. *Progr. Biophys. Biophys. Chem.* **9**, 55, 1959.
[3] ROUGHTON, F. J. W. *Brit. Med. Bull.* **19**, 80, 1963.
[4] PONDER, E. *Haemolysis and Related Phenomena.* Grune and Stratton, New York, 1948.
[5] SIRS, J. A. and ROUGHTON, F. J. W. *J. Appl. Physiol.* **18**, 158, 1963.
[6] ROUGHTON, F. J. W. *Proc. Roy. Soc. London*, Ser. B, **3**, 1, 1932.

[7] SIRS, J. A. *J. Appl. Physiol.* **18**, 175, 1963.
[8] SIRS, J. A. *Biochim. Biophys. Acta* **90**, 90, 1964.
[9] HILL, A. V. *Proc. Roy. Soc. London*, Ser. B, **104**, 39, 1929.
[10] SIRS, J. A. *Biochim. Biophys. Acta* **90**, 108, 1964.
[11] SIRS, J. A. *Biochim. Biophys. Acta* **90**, 100, 1964.
[12] SIRS, J. A. *Biochim. Biophys. Acta* **66**, 378, 1963.
[13] JACOBS, H. R. *Biorheology* **1**, 129, 1963.
[14] DAVSON, H. and DANIELLI, J. M. *The Permeability of Natural Membranes*, Cambridge Univ. Press, 1943, p. 158.
[15] SOLOMAN, A. K. *J. Gen. Physiol.* **36**, 57, 1952.
[16] PONDER, E. *J. Gen. Physiol.* **33**, 745, 1950.
[17] TEORELL, T. *Biophys. J.* **2**, 27, 1962.
[18] TEITEL, P. *Sangre* **9**, 421, 1964.
[19] TEITEL, P. *Proc. Symp. Molecular Biol. and Path.* NICOLAU, C. (Editor), Bucharest, 1964, p. 57.
[20] TEITEL, P. *Nature* **206**, 409, 1965.
[21] CARLSEN, E. S. and COMROE, J. H. *J. Gen. Physiol.* **42**, 83, 1958.
[22] ROUGHTON, F. J. W. *Proc. Roy. Soc. London*, Ser. B, **140**, 203, 1952.
[23] SIRS, J. A. *Biorheology* **3**, 169, 1966.
[24] LEGGE, J. W. and ROUGHTON, F. J. W. *Biochem. J.* **47**, 43, 1950.
[25] ROUGHTON, F. J. W., LEGGE, J. W. and NICOLSON, P. *Haemoglobin* (Barcroft Memorial Conference), Butterworth's Scientific Publications, London, 1949, p. 67.
[26] DALZIEL, K. and O'BRIEN, J. R. P. *Biochem. J.* **49**, xlvii, 1951.
[27] SIRS, J. A. *Biochim. Biophys. Acta* **126**, 28, 1966.
[28] SIRS, J. A. *Biochim. Biophys. Acta*, **112**, 538, 1966.
[29] GIBSON, Q. H. and ROUGHTON, F. J. W. *Proc. Roy. Soc. London*, Ser. B, **143**, 310, 1955.
[30] RAND, R. P. and BURTON, A. C. *Biophys. J.* **4**, 115, 1964.
[31] MITCHISON, J. M. and SWANN, M. M. *J. Exp. Biol.* **31**, 461, 1954.
[32] PERUTZ, M. *Nature* **161**, 204, 1948.

DISCUSSION

BURTON (*Canada*):

I would like to ask whether it has ever occurred to you to work on sickle cell anemia cells? Here is a most interesting case because when they are oxygenated, the whole cell is very flexible in the normal shape; but when they are reduced, they go into the sickle form which is very inflexible. Now, I do not know that this implies that the membrane itself has changed and become inflexible; the whole cell has. But this would be most interesting, because one should notice a break in the oxygen uptake curves according to the oxygen tension, should one not? Have you worked on the sickle cell anemia?

SIRS (*England*):

Not in this particular way. This is one of the problems that would be interesting to tackle, but has been relegated for later study. The sickle cell is interesting from a slightly different point of view. One of the problems, is the difference between the uptake of carbon monoxide and oxygen. If it is due to decreased solubility of HbCO relative to HbO$_2$, one would expect with sickle-hemoglobin that the HbCO cells would still be sickled. No such difference has been found. This suggests that the use of carbon monoxide might be advantageous in these cases. A small quantity would prevent the amount of Hb formed from becoming sufficient to sickle. It is also a reason for eliminating hemoglobin as the possible source of the inflexibility. I agree with you that there is a whole field to study here, of the kinetics of sickle-cell formation and oxygen egress.

SILBERBERG (*Israel*):

I am actually asking for some elucidation. I seem to have missed an important point in your conclusion. In one of your curves, in the case of oxygenated cells, irrespective of the method by which you allowed oxygen to go out (that is whether you were exchanging this carbon monoxide or diluting it) no effect on the rate arises. Now I missed your conclusion. Do you conclude from this that the membrane plays no role in the process. Surely there is no reason why these two rates should be identical, as they are representative of different processes by which the exchange takes place. One might even say that this indicates the opposite to be true and that there is a common factor which is rate determining. This might be the membrane.

SIRS:

No, this depends on the carbon monoxide concentration. If the carbon monoxide rates had been determined by anything else but the reaction rate, $k_4/4$, they would have varied with carbon monoxide concentration. However, in the range that this is measured, there is no such variation. So all that determines this is simply the chemical reaction rate of dissociation of oxyhemoglobin. Again, if the membrane had resistance to the passage of O_2, or the coefficient of diffusion through the internal hemoglobin was finite, the rate after mixing with dithionite would have been slower than this chemical reaction rate. In fact, it agrees with it, which suggests that the membrane has no resistance and there is some internal mixing.

SILBERBERG:

So to summarize for myself: the rate that you have observed is simply the dissociation of the oxyhemoglobin?

SIRS:

Yes!

ULTRASTRUCTURE OF THE HUMAN RED CELL INTEGUMENT

GWENDOLYN J. STEWART*

Department of Biology, Boston University, Boston, Massachusetts, U.S.A.

RED blood cells function as mass exchangers of gases in supplying oxygen to, and removing carbon dioxide from tissues. In performance of this function the shape of the cell, permeability characteristics of the membrane, and the viscoelasticity are of vital importance. Since the advent of electron microscopy, various attempts (PONDER, 1952, 1961; RITCHIE, 1962; HILLIER and HOFFMAN, 1953; GLAESER et al., 1966) have been made to demonstrate the ultrastructural characteristics responsible for these properties of the red blood cells, with only limited success. The present paper presents results, which indicate that the red cell integument is composed of two layers with different properties.

EXPERIMENTAL

Heavy plasma suspension of essentially pure red cells were examined under phase contrast oil immersion optics. The cells were quite well dispersed and in every way typical. After a short time of grinding with a 5μ abrasive, a few knobby cells were observed and a few rouleau composed of 3 or 4 cells were present. As grinding progressed, the number of such cells increased until perhaps 25% of all the cells were knobby. The remainder of the cells appeared to be intact under phase optics. The number and the length of rouleau increased until most of the non-knobby cells were involved.

When these cells were sedimented, fixed with buffered gluteraldehyde, stained with iron hemotoxylin and again examined, many appeared as double domes enclosing a smaller, densely stained disc. The knobby cells contained pleomorphic, densely staining sheets.

Electron microscopic examination of the same material after osmium fixation and shadow casting with platinum (STEWART, 1965, 1966a) confirmed and extended the light microscopic observations.

After examining hundreds of cells broken by grinding with a 5μ abrasive, it became evident that breakage was not random but fell into a few basic types. Some of these will be illustrated by the accompanying figures.

The rarest observation was the cell with little breakage (Fig. 1). This cell is typical in shape, with electron dense contents which appeared to be in intimate contact with the limiting membrane around most of its periphery. However, there are two protrusions of the electron dense material. Close examination of these protrusions reveals that they are surrounded by an integument (I) of lesser electron density, which may be followed for a considerable way around the periphery. The cell contents and the extreme variability in density make it difficult to see exactly what is going on; however, it seems that the periphery is delimited by a fine but strong, flexible hoop over which is stretched a rather transparent, extremely thin envelope. Underneath this, there seems to be another envelope which is shrinking away and moving all the contents before it. At points

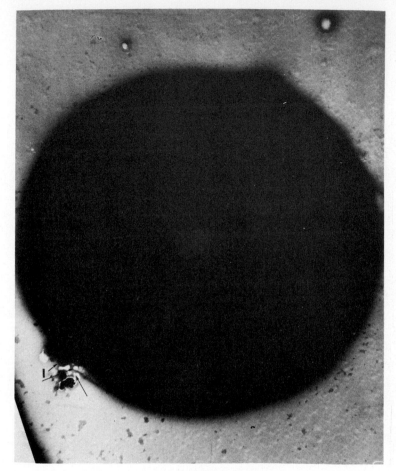

FIG. 1.

there seem to be filaments which extend between the two layers. The nature of these attachments is not clear from this figure. The material to the right of the second protrusion appears to be a part of the cell with attachments at arrows. Its mode of formation is difficult to visualize, but may be by a means similar to that by which microspheres are formed (KOCHEN, 1966).

The most frequent type of breakage is shown in Fig. 2. Here, what appears to be an internal layer of the integument has shrunk away from the outer layer over most of the surface of the cell. What appears to be a thin peripheral hoop is evident in some areas and concealed in others.

The clean separation of two layers of an integument would account for the appearance of a third of the circumference (CS), while separation by a ragged tearing, leaving part of the inner layer attached to the outer layer would account for the appearance of the rest of the circumference. At two points it appears that patches of inner membrane may have remained attached as the rest of the membrane shrunk away, thus forming tapered, "tubular ducts" (TD) through which cell contents could escape. Clear evidence of this type of behavior has been observed in cells insulated by other means (STEWART, 1966b). What appear to be broken filaments (BF) of attachment are clearly evident around nearly a fourth of the circumference.

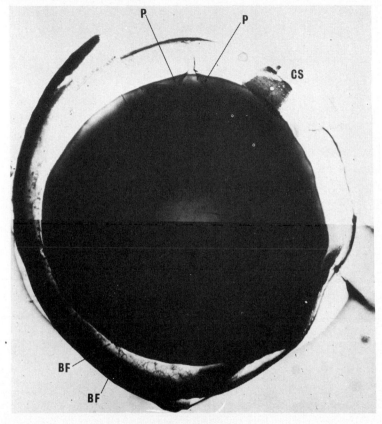

FIG. 2.

In some instances (Fig. 3) it appeared that both layers of the integument had remained attached or closely apposed to each other and had broken nearly along the same lines. The jagged edges (JE), well in from the discrete periphery of the cell, are revealed where a round portion is broken from the central area of the top dome. Along these edges, it appears that the inner layer was broken or had shrunk slightly under the edge of the outer layer. The edges of both layers are visible against the inner surface of the other dome. The electron dense disc (D) which is slightly eccentrically located could be the shrunken inner part of the area which was torn away, or it could have originated from another cell.

In this type of breakage the electron dense disc was frequently missing, revealing the entire inner surface of the other dome (Fig. 4). There is considerably more breakage of the peripheral area with both layers of the integument in this particular specimen.

The identity of the two layers of the integument is clearly indicated in some areas (arrows). The inner surface shows some indication of ordered substructure (arrows).

The typical ultrastructural features of the knobby cells are shown in Fig. 5. The peripheral hoop covered by the thin membrane is again evident, in this instance in some knobs (arrow). In some, the inner layer of the integument has shrunk away only a

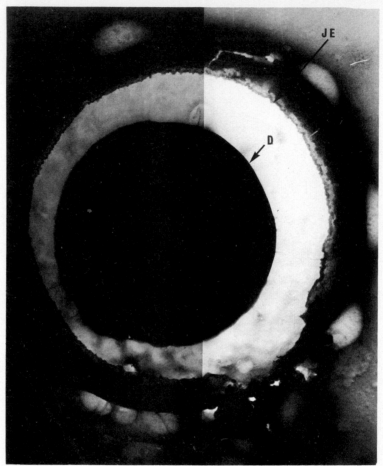

Fig. 3.

short distance, leaving numerous filaments (F) between it and the hoop. In other knobs (double arrow) the inner layer is gone and there are no filaments, while in others the electron dense layer of the integument extends entirely to the periphery (triple arrow). There appears to be a hole torn in the inner layer of the integument through which the internal surface of this layer is visible. Long tapering, tubular ducts (TD) appear to be still anchored at some places, while at others they have snapped.

In ghosts which were prepared by freezing red blood cells in their own plasma then processing without washing, the inner part of the integument was usually gone (Fig. 6).

Thin sections of these cells support the impression of an integument composed of two layers which can, under some circumstances, function as independent membranes (STEWART, 1966c).

DISCUSSION

This study has clearly indicated that the integument of the human red cell is much more than a ghost. It seems to be composed of two distinct layers which have different properties. The external layer, which seems to represent the well-known ghost, is thin

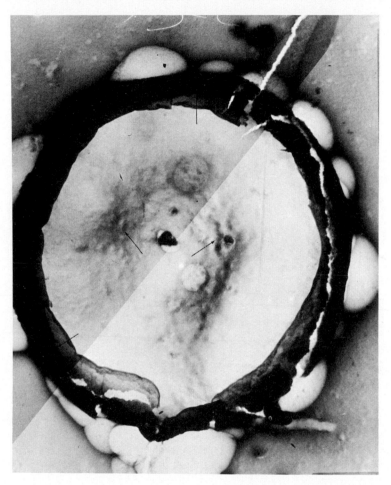

FIG. 4.

and without contractility. The inner layer, which to our knowledge has not been demonstrated before, is much thicker and capable of great contraction under various conditions such as grinding and exposure to naturally produced thrombin (STEWART, 1966b). In some cases the shrinkage which was produced during grinding resulted in the formation of discrete discs which would arise from the unrestricted, uniform shrinkage of the inner layer. The thin outer layer of the integument appeared to be supported by a "peripheral hoop". In knobby cells, the inner layer of the integument frequently followed the contours of the cells, either closely apposed to the outer layer or only a short distance from it. There appeared to be a flexible but strong hoop which was located between the layers and which formed the knobs. This arrangement would provide a means of maintaining the thin outer layer in shape while allowing the inner layer to contract.

The type of cell deformation, either discrete disc or knobby cell, might depend upon: how tightly the inner layer of the integument was attached to a supporting structure, and the uniform elasticity of the inner layer. If the attachment between hoop and inner layer is uniformly weak, the inner layer could separate from it and shrink rather uniformly over its entire expanse, despite potential differences in elasticity in different

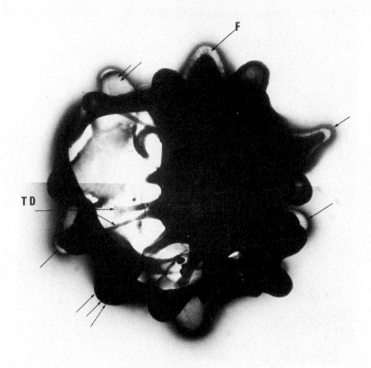

Fig. 5.

areas. If, on the other hand, the attachment of the hoop and inner layer are strong, and the elasticity of the layer is not uniform, then an area of the layer may undergo extensive contraction, pulling the flexible hoop along with it. The contraction of the inner layer observed in some knobs may represent areas of loose attachment. The possibility of a highly organized supportive structure was observed early in the study but has not been clearly confirmed in later work. This raises the possibility that the highly organized structure was a contaminant, possibly algal. But it does not eliminate the possibility that a high degree of organization exists when the two layers of the integument remain properly attached. There is evidence, which is only suggestive, of the remains of such structure in some of the discs formed by contraction of the inner layer. Hopefully, further study will enable us to identify the factors which cause contraction of the inner layer and further clarify the structural details of the integument.

The possibility that what has been described in this paper as an inner layer of the integument might in reality be the surface of the hemoglobin mass of the cell has been raised (FUNG, 1966). It is difficult to see how a material with sufficient cohesion to shrink away as a mass (Fig. 1) would also be adhesive enough to form a rather uniformly thick coating (Figs. 3 and 4) over a thin membrane, the ghost (Fig. 6). Therefore, based upon the information presently available, it would appear that the red cell integument is a complex structure composed of two layers with different properties.

Fig. 6.

REFERENCES

Fung, B. (personal communication), 1966.
Glaeser, R., Hayes, T., Mel, H. and Tobias, C. (1966) Membranes and Transport Phenomena. Discussion. *Biophysical Society, 10th Annual Meeting*, Feb. 1966, Boston, Massachusetts.
Hillier, J. and Hoffman, J. F. *J. Cell. and Comp. Physiol.* **42**, 203, 1965.
Ponder, E. *J. Exp. Biol.* **28**, 1952.
Ponder, E. *The Cell*, Academic Press, New York and London, vol. II, 1961.
Ritchie, A. A. *5th Int. Cong. for Electron Microscopy*, Academic Press, New York and London, vol. 2, p. WW–10, 1962.
Stewart, G. J. *Proceedings 23rd Annual Meeting of the Electron Microscopy Society of America*, 1965, p. 4.
Stewart, G. J. (unpublished reported data), 1966(a).
Stewart, G. J. (unpublished observation), 1966(b).
Stewart, G. J. (unpublished observation), 1966(c).

DISCUSSION

GOLDSMITH (*Canada*):

Needless to say your electron micrographs are very beautiful. Have you any idea what relation these structures have to the biconcavity of the cell? Is not the difference that you notice in the structure between red cell ghosts and red cells surprising, in view of the fact that you can reconstitute biconcave red cell ghosts in isotonic media?

STEWART (*U.S.A.*):

Well, I think the first thing we have to find out is what reconstituted ghosts really are. At this point, I have absolutely no idea of how much of the structure is left in reconstituted ghosts. As for an analysis of the structural elements, as to their shape, I am not enough of an engineer to do this.

STEHBENS (*Australia*):

I was very interested in your early electron micrographs with the network, as Dr. Wayland called it. Have you any idea what exactly would mask the appearance of this network in ordinary electron micrographs, that is, in sectioned material? Secondly, have you any sections of any of these hemolysed cells?

STEWART:

In answer to the second part of the question: We have not done thin sections. In answer to the first, we would theorize that it is because the condition of fixation has not been proper for their demonstration. If you remember, microtubules were overlooked for some 10 years before proper conditions for their demonstration were finally discovered. Unfortunately at present, we do not know how to demonstrate these in thin sections. We are currently working on this, but I cannot tell you what it would take.

STEHBENS:

The microtubules in other nucleated red cells can be demonstrated.

STEWART:

I am speaking of microtubules in cells in general.

STEHBENS:

I think one of the reasons for that, is because of the short fixation time in osmium. Most have been using a very short fixation time in osmium, whereas if you use either endothelial cells, or otherwise nucleated red cells from amphibia such as the gecko, you can demonstrate microtubules in osmium fixed material after prolonged fixation, or otherwise by combined glutaldehyde and osmium. I would have thought that if these are microtubules, they should be demonstrable by current techniques. If they are masked by hemoglobin, or whatever it is within the cell, and if these are microtubules in the lysed cells, I would expect them to be demonstrable in sections of ghosts.

STEWART:

We expect that they will be, too. At this time, we do not know the proper technique for doing so . It is possible that one may have a marginal band or compression band here that would not be microtubule. I would tend now to think they probably will be and that they can be with proper technique demonstrated.

PHIBBS (*U.S.A.*):

It would be of interest to know what you think this complicated structure is made of. There is a great deal of information on the quality and quantity of the contents of the red cell. Calculations have been made which indicate that within the normal red cell there is barely enough volume to contain the known contents. It must be assumed that the structure you describe is made up of an arrangement of the known constituents of the red cells and is not some new, previously unidentified protein. Is this a particular arrangement of the hemoglobin molecules?

STEWART:

I doubt that it is a particular arrangement of hemoglobin. Of course, now when you propose any arrangement, it is purely speculative because as you know, such calculations based on surfaces that are not rigid and are variable, are certainly subject to considerable error. My feeling would be that the cytoskeleton would be a fibrous protein rather than lipoprotein.

BLOOD CELLULAR ELEMENTS II

15 July, a.m.

Chairmen: WILLIAM E. STEHBENS, Australia
HAROLD WAYLAND, U.S.A.

THE CELL AND THE RED BLOOD CELL

Jerome J. Wolken*

Biophysical Research Laboratory, Carnegie Institute of Technology, Pittsburgh, Pennsylvania, U.S.A.

ALL cells are involved in energy transfer in carrying on their metabolic processes so necessary for their maintenance, growth, and reproduction. The living cell, therefore, is a complex, dynamic system enclosed within a semi-permeable, cell membrane. Most cells contain highly specialized organelles dispersed throughout their cytoplasm, for example: a nucleus, mitochondria, endoplasmic reticulum, ribosomes, and chromatophores, which are schematized in Fig. 1.

The cell or plasma membrane must allow for differential diffusion of ions and the exchange of gases, therefore, the molecular structure of the cell membrane is of considerable importance. It is believed to be a lipid- or lipo-protein bi-molecular structure (see models in DANIELLI and DAVSON, 1935; FREY-WYSSLING, 1948; and VANDENHEUVEL, 1966). Such a molecular structure, as schematized in Fig. 1a, is believed to hold for most biological membranes, as can be observed by the electron micrographs which illustrate the membrane structures, of the retinal rod outer segment,

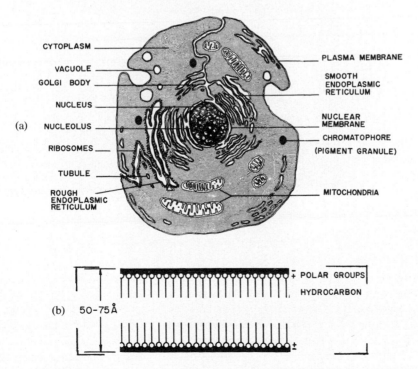

FIG. 1. (a) SCHEMATIC OF A CELL. (b) MOLECULAR MODEL OF THE MEMBRANE STRUCTURE.

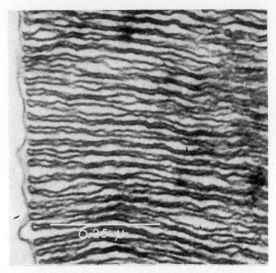

FIG. 2. ELECTRON MICROGRAPH OF A SECTION OF A FROG RETINAL ROD OUTER SEGMENT, THE PHOTO-RECEPTOR STRUCTURE, A DIFFERENTIATED ORGANELLE OF A RETINAL CELL OF THE EYE.

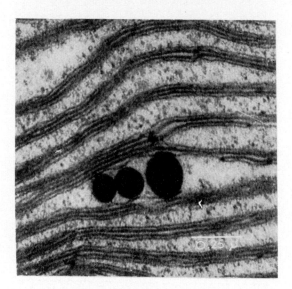

FIG. 3. ELECTRON MICROGRAPH OF SECTION OF A CHLOROPLAST (*Euglena gracilis*).

Fig. 2; the chloroplast, Fig. 3; myelin, Fig. 4; and the mitochondria, Fig. 5 (WOLKEN, 1961, 1962, 1966a).

The ordered lamellar structure observed for these biological membranes as revealed by electron microscopy appears to be associated with the lipids, which are found in relatively high concentration of the order of 30% or greater in these biological membranes. The lipids of the red blood cell membrane consist mostly of phosphatides and cholesterol. The lipids have the unique property of forming uniform (mono- or bimolecular) layers. This is due to the presence of hydrophobic groups at one end of the molecule and hydrophilic groups at the other end of the molecule and allows the

FIG. 4. ELECTRON MICROGRAPH OF A SECTION OF A MYELIN FIGURE.

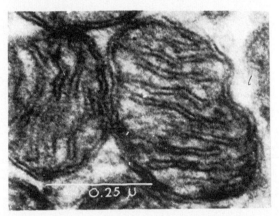

FIG. 5. ELECTRON MICROGRAPH. MITOCHONDRIA FROM THE INNER SEGMENT OF THE RETINAL ROD CELL.

lipids to form molecular layers. Such molecular layers then can serve in separating one part of a reaction from another (Fig. 1b). These layers when folded greatly maximize the surface area and minimize the volume. Lipids, their biosynthesis, and function in membrane formation should be of considerable interest in the quest to understand their rôle in these highly ordered structures.

These kinds of biological membranes exhibit structural properties of liquid-crystals for they are temperature dependent and concentration dependent on a specific molecule for their stability, for example, a dye: chlorophyll, retinene, or heme (WOLKEN, 1966a, 1966b).

Optical technics such as phase, interference and polarizing microscopy are helpful in resolving the cell structures. Electron microscopy, X-ray diffraction, and spectroscopy, however, have brought us closer to the molecular structure of the cell and its molecules. Newer developments such as Mössbauer, electron spin resonance, ESR, and nuclear magnetic resonance, NMR, should tell us more about the cell molecules. In this active field of research, it is important to develop new microanalytical instrumentation to elucidate the molecular structure and biochemistry of cells in the living state.

INSTRUMENTATION

One such microanalytical instrument is the microspectrophotometer. This instrument is being applied to study by spectroscopy the pigments of plant and animal cells (WOLKEN and STROTHER, 1963; WOLKEN, 1966a; WOLKEN et al., 1966).

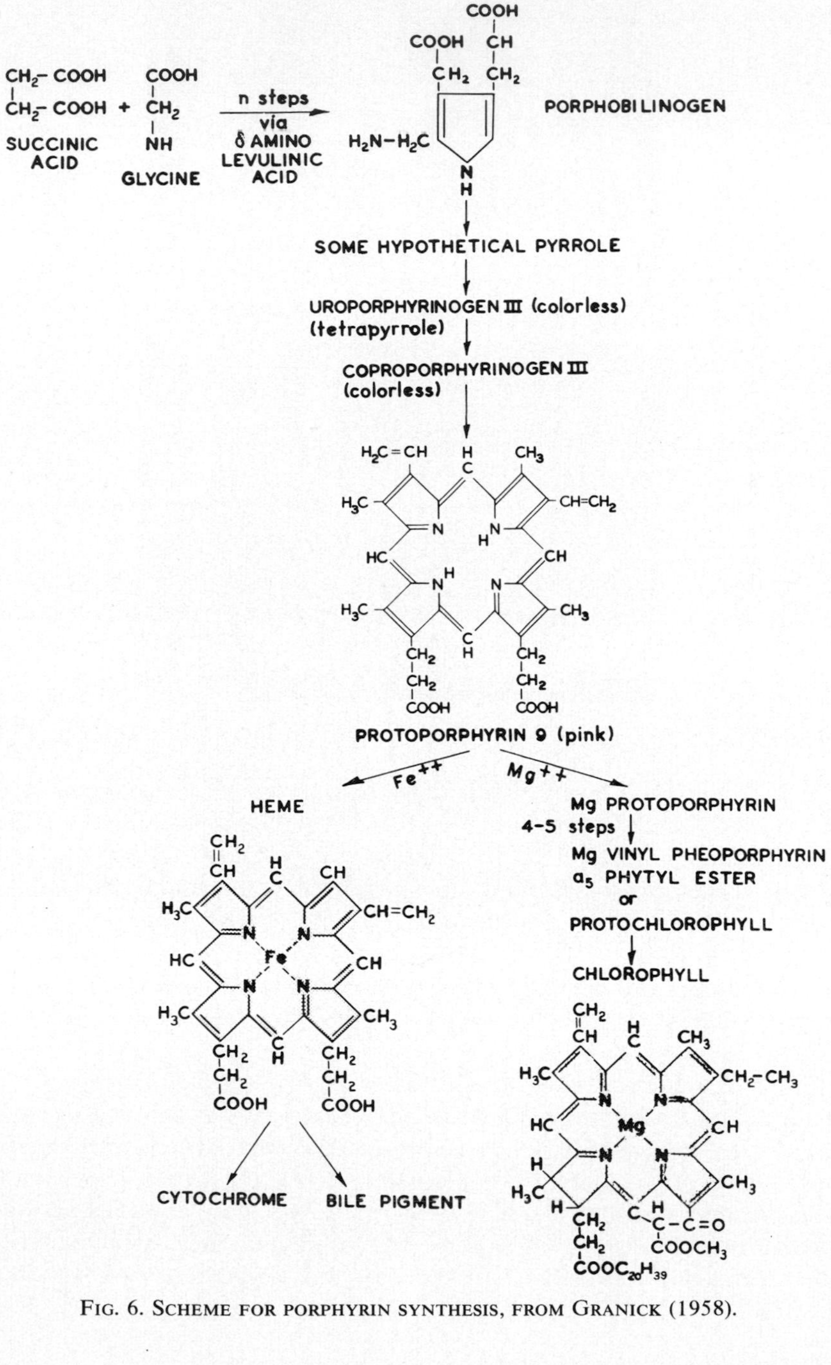

FIG. 6. SCHEME FOR PORPHYRIN SYNTHESIS, FROM GRANICK (1958).

The design of the instrument developed in our laboratory was directed towards obtaining rapid spectral data in the visible range (350–750 mμ) for the identification of pigment molecules, e.g. porphyrins, chlorophyll, hemoglobins, carotenoids within specific areas or organelles of living cells. These pigments are directly related to the energetics of the living cell and therefore, the ability to identify them and to follow their

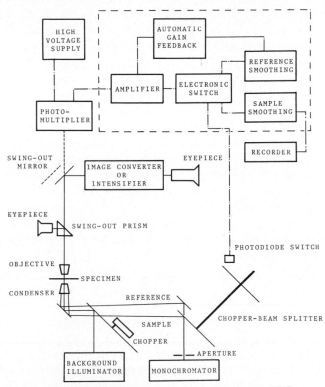

FIG. 7. DIAGRAM OF MICROSPECTROPHOTOMETER, M-5.

FIG. 8. PHOTOGRAPH OF MICROSPECTROPHOTOMETER, M-5, IN OUR LABORATORY.

biosynthesis and chemistry has much to tell us about these kinds of organic molecules and the life processes. For example, living cells synthesize specific pigments—chlorophyll for photosynthesis—carotenoids for phototropic reactions and vision—cytochromes for energy transfer—hemoglobin for oxygen transport. All of these pigments have certain precursors and structural properties in common; observe for example the molecular structure of these molecules as is illustrated in Fig. 6 (GRANICK, 1958, GRANICK and MAUZERALL, 1958; and KEILIN, 1966). To study the biosynthesis and to identify these pigments the microspectrophotometer was employed.

The microspectrophotometer M-5 used in our studies is illustrated in a schematic diagram of the instrument (Fig. 7) and in the photograph (Fig. 8). The instrument consists of an optical microscope base in which the optics are Zeiss ultrafluar objectives, and a special eyepiece. Additional attachments are necessary to view specimens which are photosensitive (and we use in this case an infrared image converter which is attached to the eyepiece for specimen location and focusing), and a cell for the stage of the microscope makes it possible to study different temperatures and to follow physical-chemical environment changes, the kinetics (WOLKEN and STROTHER, 1963).

The detector is an EMI 9558Q Photomultiplier Tube which enables us to make measurements at very low light levels. It also improves the sensitivity of the instrument. The EMI 9558QA Photomultiplier Tube has a spectral response from 162 mμ to 840 mμ, with a quantum efficiency of about 20% from 200 to 420 mμ, 10% efficiency at 480 mμ, and 1% efficiency at 758 mμ. The dark current noise is extremely low, and with cooling ($-12°C$) is almost negligible.

The monochromator used is a Canalco rapid-scanning one, which has 600 line/mm grating and has ten different speeds, from 2 sec to 1000 sec, over a 200–800 mμ range. Its dispersion is 4 mμ/mm and peaks at 500 mμ.

The accuracy in measuring the relative percentage of absorption (as far as the electronics) depends on the relative heights of the two pulses; the sample and reference areas are not measured simultaneously but alternately in time. Therefore, if the overall accuracy is to stay within 1%, any change in the relative height of the pulses due to relative spectral quantum efficiency of the photocathode, the relative spectral distribution of the light source, or the gain of the amplification would be within 1% during the time for one pair of pulses. Consequently, a short-scanning time requires a correspondingly short pulse pair-time. The desired short pulse pair-time required the development of a precision, high-speed chopper and special electronic circuits in the amplifier.

The electronics consist of a preamplifier mounted on the case of the photomultiplier tube, a main amplifier, an electronic switch, an automatic gain amplifier, a feedback circuit, and an integrating circuit for each sample and reference pulse. The recorder for the M-5 is a D'Arsonval-type pen drive, rather than a servomechanism-type recorder.

The microspectrophotometer M-5, will scan the visible spectrum, 400–700 mμ in less than 10 sec or 100 wave numbers in 0.33 sec (WOLKEN et al., 1966).

The Blood Cell and Hemoglobins

The blood contains plasma and blood cells. The blood cells are of three basic types, *red cells* (erythrocytes), *white cells* (leucocytes) and blood platelets (thrombocytes). HENDERSON (1928) has stated that—"The blood of vertebrates is a physico-chemical system of great complexity–and methods of studying and describing it are sometimes roughly approximate.''

Therefore, a brief review of some of the properties of blood will be helpful before we describe a method, microspectrophotometry, for detecting the heme pigment of various red blood cells by its most characteristic property, the spectrum. For a more comprehensive review of the spectra of heme and hematin compounds reference should be made to the studies summarized in LEMBERG and LEGGE (1949) and KEILIN (1966).

Cells are found in a variety of shapes and sizes depending on their environment and function. The red blood cells also vary in shape and size in different animal species, and are relatively structureless when compared to a typical cell, Fig. 1. However, the shape does provide it with a large surface to volume ratio in order to facilitate the rapid transfer of oxygen and carbon dioxide.

In human blood the red cells are biconcave circular discs about 7μ in diameter and about 2μ in thickness as schematically illustrated in Fig. 9. The structure and properties of the red blood cell may tell us about its behavior in flowing through the vessels. The volume of the human red cell is of the order of $100 \mu^3$ or larger. The size of the red blood cells of man, whale, elephant, and mouse are all within an order of magnitude of each other. In the chicken and the frog the red blood cells are nucleated and have the

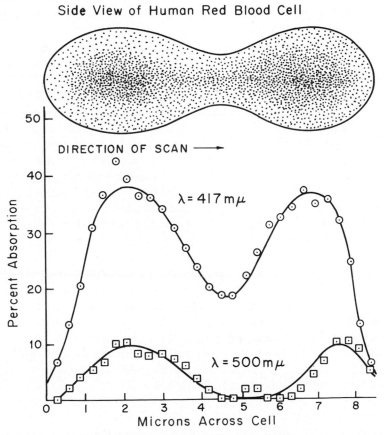

FIG. 9. SCAN ACROSS HUMAN RED BLOOD CELL (G.K.S.) AT 417 mμ NEAR THE ABSORPTION MAXIMUM, AND AT 500 mμ NEAR THE ABSORPTION MINIMUM.

shape of oval discs. The chicken red blood cell is of the order of 10 μ and the frog red blood cell 20 μ in diameter. A cubic millimeter of human blood contains 5×10^6 red blood cells.

The transfer of oxygen from the external environment into the tissue cells is accomplished in animals, from the invertebrates to the vertebrates, by specialized pigment molecules (Table 1) capable of forming a combination with oxygen when the

TABLE 1. OXYGEN CAPACITY OF SOME BLOODS

Pigment	Color	Animal	ml O$_2$ per 100 ml blood
Hemoglobin	Red	Mammals	25.0
		Birds	18.5
		Reptile	9.0
		Fish	9.0
Hemerythrin	Red	Annelids	2.0
Hemocyanin	Blue	Mollusc cephalopod	8.0
(in plasma)		Crustacean	3.0

Data taken in part from E. Baldwin, 1964. *Comparative Biochemistry*, Cambridge University Press, Cambridge, p. 95.

partial pressure is raised, and giving it up when the pressure is lowered. The proportion of oxygen taken up by the hemoglobin depends on the concentration of the oxygen or oxygen tension; some examples are given in Table 1.

Hemoglobin is present in large quantities in the cytoplasm of the red blood cells and makes up about one-third the weight of the cell. Hemoglobin is the oxygen carrier of most vertebrates and takes up oxygen to form *oxyhemoglobin*. Hemoglobins are the red pigments of vertebrates and of some invertebrates. Other invertebrate pigments are chlorocruorin, a green blood pigment that is dissolved in the blood of certain annelids; hemocyanin, a blue blood pigment that contains copper and is found in many crustaceans and molluscs; hemerythrin, a red-violet pigment that is found in annelids; and there are perhaps other respiratory pigments not as yet identified. These pigments can be detected by their spectra and all have the common property of functioning as oxygen carriers (see Table 1). These heme pigments and their functional rôle as well as their relationship to the evolutionary pattern of animal development are discussed by ALLEN (1966), BALDWIN (1964), and FLORKIN (1949).

Heme is a substance with the formula $FeC_{34}H_{32}O_4N_4$ (see Fig. 6). The heme molecule is nearly planar. The property of planarity is ascribed to the many double bonds in the molecule. In the heme molecule the iron atom forms bonds with the four nitrogen atoms of the heme. Heme with an attached oxygen molecule is responsible for the red color of the oxygenated blood. The hemoglobin molecule contains four hemes which are bound to the protein globin, this gives a molecular weight of the order of 68,000; however, the molecular weight is dependent on the protein.

As we have indicated, the heme pigments can be identified by their absorption spectra. Using the microspectrophotometer, the absorption spectrum for single human and other vertebrate and invertebrate blood cells were obtained. The average cross-section of surface of the cell was about 10 μ^2. In Figs. 10–13 examples of these spectra are illustrated and the maximum absorption peaks are summarized in Table 2. A scan across the human red blood cells at 417 mμ near the maximum absorption peak and near the

TABLE 2. RED BLOOD CELLS

Major Absorption Peaks

Human	415	541	577
Rabbit	407	534	572
Mouse	416	544	577
Chicken embryo (14 days)	413	543	576
Frog			
(*Rana pipiens*)	415	539	572
Turtle			
(*Pseudemys scripta elegans*)	408	539	574
Earthworm (plasma)	414	538	567
Water flea (plasma)			
(*Daphnia pulex*)	415	541	574

Major absorption peaks obtained with the recording micro-spectrophotometer, M-5, of single oxygenated red blood cells. Average cross section of surface viewed: 10 μ^2.

minimum absorption peak at 500 mμ (Fig. 9) shows the distribution of the hemoglobin in the red blood cell and its concentration. In Fig. 10, the absorption spectrum obtained of a red blood cell using the microspectrophotometer is compared to a sample of blood

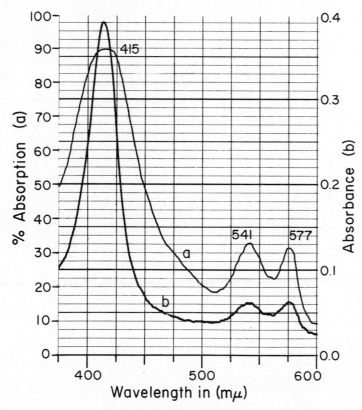

FIG. 10. ABSORPTION SPECTRA OF HUMAN RED BLOOD CELLS (G.G.). ABSORPTION SPECTRUM OF A RED BLOOD CELL (a) OBTAINED WITH MICROSPECTROPHOTOMETER, M-5, COMPARED TO SPECTRUM (b) OBTAINED WITH CARY-14.

obtained with the Cary-14 recording spectrophotometer. Their maximum absorption peaks are practically identical, but there are differences in the sharpness of the peaks.

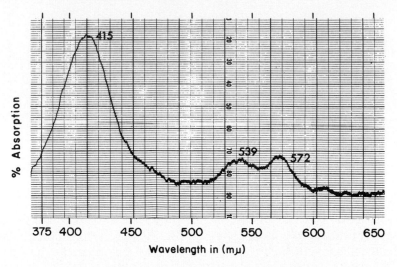

FIG. 11. ABSORPTION SPECTRUM OF FROG RED BLOOD CELL, WITH MICROSPECTROPHOTOMETER, M-5.

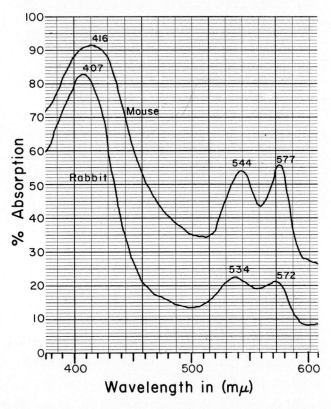

FIG. 12. ABSORPTION SPECTRA OF MOUSE AND RABBIT RED BLOOD CELLS OBTAINED WITH MICROSPECTRO-PHOTOMETER, M-5.

The small differences which are observed in the position of the absorption peaks of the oxyhemoglobins (Table 2) are most probably associated with the different globin proteins, to which the heme is complexed, in these animal species.

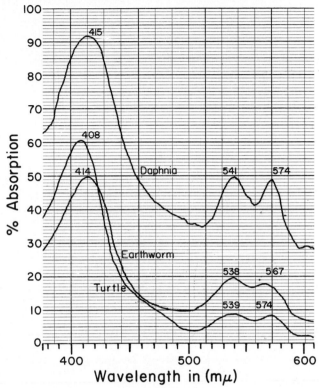

FIG. 13. ABSORPTION SPECTRA OF THE PLASMA AND RED BLOOD CELLS OF THE CRUSTACEAN, *Daphnia pulex*, THE EARTHWORM, AND THE TURTLE, OBTAINED WITH MICROSPECTROPHOTOMETER, M-5.

The application of microspectrophotometry, therefore, permits us to analyse more precisely the spectra of various hemoglobins in single cells. The location of the hemoglobins within the cell and concentration can also be determined. Information relative to the lipids and proteins should also be possible from ultraviolet and infrared studies. In addition any anomalies in the spectra of the blood cells, for example, as in the proteins and hemes that are reflected by changes in the blood cells due to diseased states may be now more amenable to attack.

ACKNOWLEDGMENTS

This research was supported in part from the National Aeronautics and Space Administration, NGR-39-002-011.

REFERENCES

ALLEN, G. E. *Bioscience* **16**, 325, 1966.
BALDWIN, E. *An Introduction to Comparative Biochemistry*, Cambridge University Press, Cambridge, 1964.

DANIELLI, J. F. and DAVSON, H. *J. Cell. Comp. Physiol.* **5**, 495, 1935.

FLORKIN, M. *Biochemical Evolution*, Academic Press, New York, 1949.

FREY-WYSSLING, A. *Submicroscopic Morphology of Protoplasm and Its Derivatives*, Elsevier, New York, pp. 110, 166, 1948.

GRANICK, S. *J. Biol. Chem.* **232**, 1101, 1958.

GRANICK, S. and MAUZERALL, D. *J. Biol. Chem.* **232**, 1119, 1958.

HENDERSON, L. J. *Blood: A Study in General Physiology*, Yale University Press, New Haven, 1928.

KEILIN, D. *The History of Cell Respiration and Cytochrome*, Cambridge University Press, Cambridge, 1966.

LEMBERG, R. and LEGGE, J. W. *Hematin Compounds and Bile Pigments*, Interscience, New York, 1949.

VANDENHEUVEL, F. A. *J. American Oil Chemists' Society* **43**, 258, 1966.

WOLKEN, J. J. *Euglena: An Experimental Organism for Biochemical and Biophysical Studies*, Rutgers University Press, New Brunswick, New Jersey, 1961.

WOLKEN, J. J. *J. Theoret. Biol.* **3**, 192, 1962.

WOLKEN, J. J. *Vision: Biophysics and Biochemistry of the Retinal Photoreceptors*, Charles C. Thomas, Springfield, Illinois, 1966(a).

WOLKEN, J. J. *J. American Oil Chemists' Society* **43**, 271, 1966(b).

WOLKEN, J. J. and STROTHER, G. K. *Applied Optics* **2**, 899, 1963.

WOLKEN, J. J., FORSBERG, R., GALLIK, G. and FLORIDA, R. Eleventh Annual Report of the Biophysical Research Laboratory, Pittsburgh, Pa. The National Aeronautics and Space Administration Report, N66–24968: Development of New Microspectrophotometric Instrumentation, 1966.

DISCUSSION

SILBERBERG (*Israel*):

I wondered whether your found differences within the same population of red cells when you scanned, let us say, 10 or 20 of them.

WOLKEN (*U.S.A.*):

Generally, all the human normal red blood cells that we have obtained spectra for (from at least forty different human subjects), look alike in regard to the positions of their three major absorption peaks. Occasionally small shifts (of 1 to 3 mμ) are noted in the positions of these peaks, but until many more spectral studies are made, we can draw no special significance from these shifts which could be the result of specimen handling or instrumentation errors.

SILBERBERG:

Thank you.

WHITMORE (*England*):

Following on from Professor Silberberg's question, do you think that the differences in the characteristics you get for the different mammalian cells are significant or not at this stage?

WOLKEN:

Perhaps they could be very significant if we knew more about the cell proteins. We have the same problem in the spectral studies of the pigment of the chloroplast of plant cells which are chlorophyll-protein complexes and the retinal rods and cones of the eye, which are retinene$_{1 \text{ or } 2}$-protein complexes.

SIRS (*England*):

I am fascinated with your techniques, having done some spectrophotometry with red cells. These are really a tremendous stride forward. There is a little problem, though, that we have, that you do not seem to have been involved in. This is that the cell is not stationary. You seem to be scanning with a single beam of light, while the cell can flex and move. We get over this problem of avoiding optical density changes with the movement of the cell by splitting the beam, after it has been through the cell, into two wave lengths which balance out these dimensional changes. Have you ever tried anything like this?

WOLKEN:

No, we have not tried splitting the beam after it has gone through the red blood cell. It would be very interesting to learn more of your technique. By our method the red blood must be in the field of view and in sharp focus. In order to keep the cell quiet it is usually suspended in solutions of higher viscosity, e.g. plasma, vitreous, glycerin, etc., and in some instance by lowering the temperature. What we are actually doing is getting the difference between the sample and the reference, in other words an absorption spectrum.

JOLY (*France*):

When you observe, for instance, at a wave length of 500 mμ, an absorption curve with two maxima and a minimum almost equal to zero, what is the physical meaning of such a curve, from point of view of composition or cell structure?

WOLKEN:

When we are scanning with the instrument at a particular wavelength, i.e. 500 mμ, and moving across the cell, any compound which absorbs at that wavelength, e.g. *rhodopsin* (as in the outer rod segments of the retinal cell), will show an increase in absorption. In other words, we can detect where a particular compound is located within the cell structures.

Of course, there is much more to be done, but this is one method which begins to bring us closer to what the living cell is doing chemically. I am not completely convinced that we have all the tools yet to attack the biochemistry of the living cell. I would like to know more about how the cell functions in its physical and chemical environment.

EVALUATION OF DEFORMABILITY OF RED CELLS BY SIEVING TESTS

Magnus I. Gregersen* and Cyrus A. Bryant

Laboratory of Hemorheology, College of Physicians and Surgeons,
Columbia University, New York, N.Y., U.S.A.

INTRODUCTION

There is abundant visual evidence that red cells undergo deformation in the blood stream especially in their passage through narrow capillary channels[1, 2]. Prothero and Burton[3] reported that red cells in dilute suspensions of Ringers solution passed through Millipore filters of 5 and 3 μ nominal pore size at pressures of 1 cm H_2O, appearing in the filtrate at essentially the same concentration as in the original suspension. We were unable to repeat these observations. When this was reported verbally to Dr. Burton he informed one of us that for some unknown reason he too had been unable to reproduce their earlier results with currently available Millipore filters. We subsequently noted that if a 5 μ Millipore filter was pretreated with diluted human plasma ($\frac{1}{10}$ in Ringers solution) red cells appeared in the filtrate for a brief period after which the filtrate was clear and contained no cells. We have not been able to detect intact cells in filtrates from 3 μ Millipore filters at any filtration pressure. The object of the present experiments was to obtain flow rates of washed erythrocytes suspensions through several types of filters and study their relationship to pressure gradient, cell concentration, and nominal pore size.

FILTER MATERIALS

Sieving tests were made with (1) Silver Flotronic filters (Selas Corp., Spring House, Pennsylvania) of 5 μ nominal pore size and 25 or 50 μ thick, (2) Nuclepore Polycarbonate sieves (General Electric Co., Pleasanton, California)[4], 10–12 μ thick, having randomly spaced cylindrical pores. Pore density was kept sufficiently low that incidence of multiple holes was less than 1%. The sieve material was supplied in several pore diameters ranging from 1 to 10 μ. (3) Nickel sieves (Buckbee Meers Co., Minneapolis,

TABLE 1.

Filter	Nominal pore size (μ)	Measured pore size (μ)	Pore density (μ)	Thickness μ
Nuclepore	6	6.8 ± 0.4	4×10^5	12
Nuclepore	5	4.2 ± 0.3	4×10^5	12
Nuclepore	4	3.5 ± 0.5	4×10^5	12
Buckbee Meers	5	7.2 ± 1.5	3.8×10^4	25

Minn.) 25 μ thick with nominally 5 μ square holes evenly spaced. The porosity of all
these sieves was such that the total pore area was a few per cent of the filter area.
Table 1 summarizes data on sieves used to obtain data reported here.

PREPARATION OF RED CELL SUSPENSIONS

Initially the tests were made on red cells washed three times in Ringers solution
adjusted to pH 7.4 with bicarbonate. It was then noted that a large proportion of red
cells from freshly drawn human blood so treated looked like "prickle balls", i.e. the
cells were crenated[5, 6]. Eventually it was found that this modification in the appearance and shape of the cells could be prevented by washing and suspending them in a
modified Eagles solution containing 0.25 mg% human albumin (Merck, Sharpe, and
Dohme, Rahway, N.J.).

Figure 1 shows the simple filtering apparatus, with an insert giving details of the filter
holder and collector. The cell suspension was stored in the jar (A) held over the magnetic stirrer (B). Measured volumes (usually 2 ml) were withdrawn with the syringe and

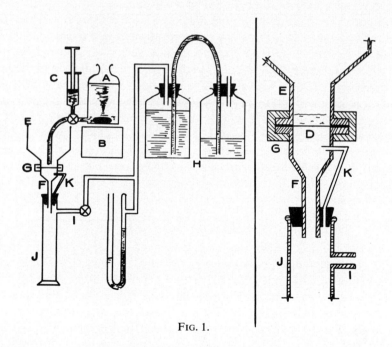

FIG. 1.

three way stopcock (C), spread uniformly over the filter (D), and their passage timed. The
time required for this amount to be filtered was noted visually by observing the filter
rather than by measuring the drops below in order to avoid the errors involved in the
dead space between the filter and the exit of the funnel into the graduate. Upper (E)
and lower (F) sections of the Millipore stainless steel filter funnel sandwiched the filter
and its fine metal screen support by means of the bayonet clamp (G). The pressure in
the lower section (F) was reduced by means of a siphon (H) through the line (I) taped
into the graduate (J) sealed to the funnel. An air bleeding line (K) ensured that the pressures in (F) and (J) were the same, even if the narrow drain from (F) contained fluid.

Before a new filter was installed it was soaked in the suspension vehicle (Ringer or Eagle solution) until wet. Immediately after installation, flow rate of the cell-free vehicle was timed. Discrete volumes of suspension were then run through the filter at a constant pressure difference between 0.5 and 20 cm of water. From data on flux vs. time, one could obtain flow rate as a function of volume, time, pressure, cell concentration, and pore size.

In the initial stages of the investigation, it was assumed that filters had uniform characteristics, and in fact tests of filtration rate of Ringers indicated that this assumption was fairly accurate. However, the Nuclepore and Buckbee Meers filters could be used repeatedly by washing with Eagles solution under vacuum suction, thereby restoring their original porosity and allowing repetition of tests on the same filter.

RESULTS

A simple exponential function fits most of the flow rate data R when plotted against accumulated volume v passed by a filter:

$$R(v) = R_0 \exp(-\lambda v) \tag{1}$$

R_0 is the initial rate and λ is a constant having the dimension of reciprocal volume which we may call the flow decrement. R_0 and λ together characterize a given experiment except when the data are no longer fit well by (I), as sometimes happened when $R(v)$ became much less than R_0. The decrement will be plotted against the pressure p and concentration c in an effort to find meaningful relationships.

Figure 2 shows typical plots of the flow decrement, λ, as a function of p at constant c. In two cases, $\lambda \sim p^{-3/4}$ is a good empirical fit to the data, but this is not generally true. The decrement is at least a factor of two higher for crenated cells than for normal looking cells. (It is virtually infinite for hardened cells[6].) Figure 3 compares $\lambda(p)$ for a 5 μ

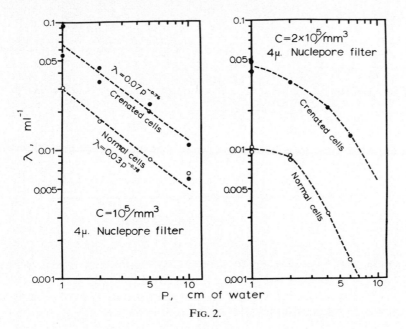

FIG. 2.

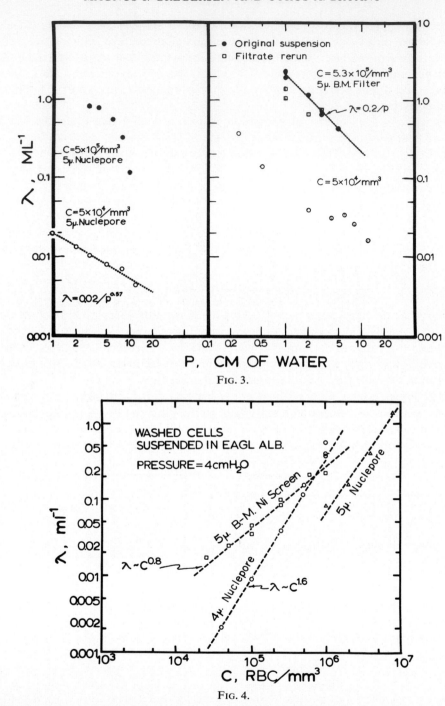

Fig. 3.

Fig. 4.

Nuclepore filter and a 5 μ B.M. nickel screen at two different concentrations. For the Nuclepore, $\lambda \sim p^{-0.57}$ at the lower c, while for the B.M. $\lambda \sim p^{-1}$.

In Fig. 4, λ is plotted against c at a constant pressure of 4 cm of water. For the 4 μ Nuclepores, $\lambda \sim c^{1.6}$, while for the 5 μ B.M. Ni screen filter $\lambda \sim c^{0.8}$.

At very high concentrations, only small volumes could be filtered before flow was so slow that settling and drying became important. Therefore, R_1, the average flow rate through $6\,\mu$ Nuclepore filters for the first 2 ml has been plotted against pressure in Fig. 5 for several hematocrits. A hematocrit of 45% corresponds to $c = 5 \times 10^6$ RBC/mm^3. Straight lines have been fitted to the points for each hematocrit. At 40%, the rate is linearly proportional to pressure, as the line has unit slope, but as the hematocrit

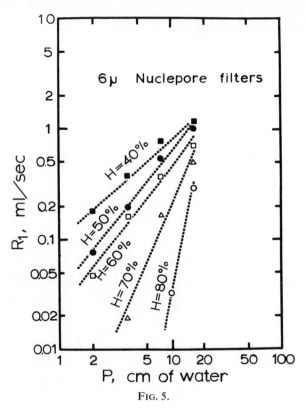

FIG. 5.

rises above 40%, the lines become superlinear. If the straight lines are extrapolated toward higher pressures, they appear to converge near the point 2 ml/sec at 30 cm water. It is tempting to say that 30 cm appears to be the pressure at which flow rate becomes rather independent of concentration.

The data in Table 1 show that the actual pore sizes (based on photomicrographs) of the 4 and 5 μ Nuclepore filters are not very different. We found that the values of $R_1(p)$ lie only slightly higher for the 5 μ than for the 4 μ filter. They are much higher for the 6 μ Nuclepore.

In Fig. 6 are compared the data $R_1(p)$ for human (MCV = $92 \pm 2\ \mu^2$) and Indian elephant cells (MCV = $119 \pm 2\ \mu^3$). The MCV (mean corpuscular volume) was measured for each suspension using a Coulter Counter and MCV computer. From the straight lines which have been fitted to the logarithmic plots in Fig. 6, we learn that at 20% hematocrit, human cells pass through each filter at about twice the rate of elephant cells. Further, $R_1(p)$ is decidedly superlinear only for elephant cells at 40% hematocrit passing the 4 and 5 μ pores.

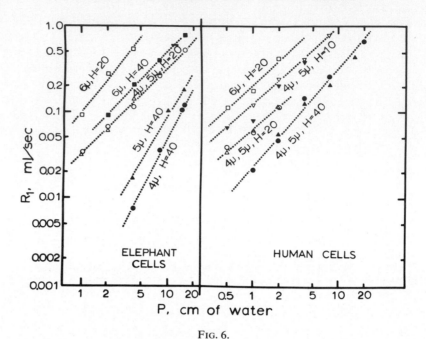

FIG. 6.

CONCLUSION

In the foregoing description of experimental results and in the simple analysis in the Appendix, we have implied that single cells in suspensions traverse filter pores independently of other cells. If, however, there is interaction between cells, such as clumping or rouleau formation, we may expect it to affect some of the functional relationships connecting R_0, λ, p and c. The form of $\lambda(c)$, for instance, will reflect any dependence frequency of cell aggregation on concentration. Similarly, the existence of aggregates which are broken up by sufficient pressure difference across the filter might be revealed in the form of $\lambda(p)$ or $R_0(p)$.

More definitely, we have evidence of cell deformability. The concentration of cells in filtrates with sieves down to the 4 μ pore size is not significantly different from that in the original suspension. (Hardened cells, which behave viscometrically like hard spheres, do not pass 4 to 7 μ filters at all.) If filtrates are re-run, the resulting filter decrements, λ, are somewhat lower than for the original suspension (see Fig. 3B). Further, the viscosity of the filtrate, as measured in a Couette viscometer is ~ 10% lower than for the original. These results suggest that there is a component of the suspension which competes with the typical cell in contributing to the filter decrement and to viscosity. This unknown component could be unusually large cells or some substance which increases cell–cell or cell–filter cohesive forces. In the Appendix it is shown that in the approximation of small volumes the speed of cells in filter pores (assuming a single value of s at a given pressure) is nearly $R_0/N_0 a$, the initial flow rate per unit pore cross-section area. If this were true throughout an experiment, the filter would not clog completely, and R would approach a steady state value greater than zero (A in eq. (7)). The experimental result, eq. (1), indicates that R tends to zero, as though an unrecognized component finally completes the obstruction. The filter decrement increases with cell hemolysis, as though a clogging substance were produced by hemo-lysis, in agreement with the observations of PROTHERO and BURTON[3] with Millipore filters.

APPENDIX. DERIVATION OF A FILTER EQUATION

We can make a simple approximate analysis of the cell filtering based on the following model. Let a filter having N_0 pores, each of area, a, pass a cell suspension of uniform concentration, c. Once a cell enters a pore, it passes along its length, l (the filter thick-ness), at a constant speed, s. We assume s is the same for all cells, i.e. we ignore distributions in cell and pore size. Let filtering begin at time $t = 0$ and $n(t)$ be the number of pores containing cells at time t; $n(0) = N_0$.

Now we will obtain the function $n(t)$. The number of cells entering $(N_0 - n)$ open pores in the time dt is

$$(N_0 - n)(cR_0/N_0)dt \tag{1'}$$

where R_0 is the initial flow rate through the N_0 pores. The number of filled pores which discharge cells in the same time is $(ns/l)dt$. If, during the passage of a cell, another cell has not entered, such a pore will reopen. The chance of this happening for one closed pore is exp $(-cal)$, the anti-coincidence probability based on a Poisson distribu-tion. Therefore, the number of filled pores which empty in the time dt is

$$(ns/l) \exp (-cal)dt \tag{2'}$$

The net rate of change in n is the difference between (1') and (2'),

$$dn/dt = (1 - n/N_0)cR_0 - (s/l) \exp (-cal)n \tag{3'}$$
$$= -\lambda'n + cR_0$$

where

$$\lambda' = cR_0/N_0 + (s/l) \exp (-cal). \tag{4'}$$

The net rate of fluid flow through the filter is the sum of the fluxes through closed and open pores,

$$R^*(t) = nas + R_0(N_0 - n)/N_0 \tag{5'}$$

The solution of our differential eq. (3) is

$$n(t) = (cR_0/\lambda')(1 - e^{-\lambda't})$$

Substituting this in (5) yields

$$R^*(t) = A + Be^{-\lambda't} \tag{6'}$$

with

$$B = (cR_0/\lambda')(R_0/N_0 - as) \tag{7'}$$

and

$$A = R_0 - B.$$

Note that $R^*(0) = R_0$ and $R^*(\infty) = A$, which means that according to this model, the flow will attain a steady state value, A, which may be different from zero. However, $A \to 0$, if $S \to 0$, as we should expect. Differentiating (7') yields

$$dR^*/dt = -cR_0(R_0/N_0 - as) \exp(-\lambda't) = K \exp(-\lambda't). \qquad (8')$$

If the experimental points are used to obtain a plot of dR^*/dt against t on semi logarithmic paper, we can find empirical values of K and λ', either of which should yield a value for the cell speed, s, in a pore. In particular we have

$$\lim_{t \to 0} (dR^*/dt) = -cR_0(R_0/N_0 - as). \qquad (9')$$

Furthermore, a good empirical fit of most of the data near the beginning of a filtering run is given by

$$R(v) = R_0 e^{-\lambda v} \qquad (10')$$

or

$$dR/dt = (dR/dv)(dv/dt) = -\lambda R^2 \qquad (11')$$

While (11) does not have the same form as (8), a comparison of the two expressions in the limit as $t \to 0$ or $v \to 0$ gives the value of s which corresponds to the initial decay of filter flow. Thus,

$$(R_0/N_0 - as) = \lambda R_0/c \qquad (12')$$

or

$$s = (R_0/aN_0) - R_0\lambda/ac \qquad (13')$$

The first term in (13) is the initial mean flow speed through a pore, the order of 2 cm/sec. The second term is the amount by which s is less than that rate. Typical values for a 5μ Nuclepore filter operating at a pressure equal to 4 cm of water are: $R_0 = 1.5$ ml/sec, $a = 1.5 \times 10^{-7}$ cm^2, $N_0 = 4 \times 10^6$, $\lambda = 10^{-2}$ ml^{-1}, $c = 10^8$ ml^{-1}, so $s \sim 2$ cm/sec. The second term is very much smaller: $R_0\lambda/ac \sim 10^{-3}$ cm/sec. Evidently a substantial filter decrement can result from a very small decrease in flow rate due to presence of a cell. Finally, it is instructive to consider that the cell count in filtrate and original suspension is the same in most cases. Hence, the number of cells per filter pore passing through with each ml of suspension is just c/N_0, or about 25. The flow rate decreases very little during the passage of 1 ml, implying that a typical cell obstructs a pore very little.

ACKNOWLEDGMENTS

The authors thank Elizabeth Luhr, Dieter Klaus, and John Febles for their able assistance with the experiments and calculation.

This work was supported by U.S. Army Medical Research and Development Command Contract DA-49-193-MD-2272. The generous support of several private donors including Mrs. Alan M. Scaife, Mrs. George W. Perkins, the Alexander Angus McDonnell, Jr. Foundation, and the Maxwell M. Upson Foundation is gratefully acknowledged.

REFERENCES

[1] BRÅNEMARK, P-I. and LINDSTRÖM, J. *Biorheology* **1**(2), 139, 1963.
[2] GUEST, M. M., BOND, T. P. and COOPER, R. G. *Science* **142**, 1319, 1963.
[3] PROTHERO, J. W. and BURTON, A. C. *Biophys. J.* **2**, 213, 1961.
[4] FLEISCHER, R. L., PRICE, P. B. and WALKER, R. M. *Science* **149**, 383, 1965.
[5] PONDER, ERIC, *Hemolysis and Related Phenomena*, Grune and Stratton, New York, 1948, p. 30.
[6] BESSIS, MARCEL. *Cytology of the Blood and Blood-Forming Organs*, translated by Eric Ponder, Grune and Stratton, New York and London, 1956.
[7] TAYLOR, H. M., CHIEN, S., GREGERSEN, M. I. and LUNDBERG, J. L. *Nature* **207**, 77, 1965.

DISCUSSION

SEAMAN (*England*):
I would like to ask Dr. Gregersen *vis-à-vis* the hardened cells whether he had corrected for the trapping factor, because presumably in this case, the packing of the hardened cells will be very much less than that of the normal pliable red cells when one can expect about a 95% packing.

GREGERSEN (*U.S.A.*):
The trapping factor for hardened cells is about 0.6 compared with 0.95–0.98 for normal fresh red cells. That is to say, in the hematocrit value obtained with a microcentrifuge, roughly 40% of the packed cell column is fluid trapped between the cells. We have measured this trapping factor by several means; with dextran of 16,000 molecular weight tagged with carbon 14, with albumin ^{131}I, and with polyvinylpyrrolidine, also tagged with carbon 14. The results agree fairly well with measurements made with the Coulter counter MCV meter for determining mean corpuscular volume. We were unable to measure the trapping with the dye T-1824. With hardened cells a brown color appears which interferes with spectrophotometric determinations. I think Dr. Seaman had the same trouble with T-1824 for this purpose.

SEAMAN:
May I just come back again. My point was really whether you had applied any correction to these results, or whether they were uncorrected results for the hardened cells in the particular slide which you showed.

GREGERSEN:
Well, that is right. These were corrected.

ROWLANDS (*England*):
Mr. David Phillips and I have frittered away quite a lot of time in playing around with Millipore filters and Nuclepore filters. We had a great deal of trouble with Millipore filters when we attempted to do similar experiments. We did find this successive clogging, but rather more severely than you have. After a great deal of difficulty we managed to section a Millipore filter and look at them. We could get no information out of the manufacturers as to what they looked like in section. When we did succeed in taking sections of these filters, contrary to what the manufacturers said, (they claimed that they were nearly parallel-holed) when we looked at these sections, it seemed to be that the Millipore filters were almost a random arrangement of fibers; and red cells were trapped in all sorts of places in this random arrangement of fibers. On the other hand, when you come to a Nuclepore filter, you now have a series of clearly punched out round holes which you can see under a microscope without any difficulty. The snag with the Nuclepore filter is that its filtrability area is only about 5% as against about 85% for a Millipore filter.

GREGERSEN:
Is it that much?

ROWLANDS:
Well, it is very much higher.

GREGERSEN:
With Ringer's or Eagle's solution, the Nuclepore filters are pretty fast.

ROWLANDS:
Well, it is supposed to be only 5%. You still get fluid coming through quite well. Now I have wondered whether you have actually tried to calibrate your Nuclepore filters with water because we did this; and to our surprise we found that, using the manufacturer's data of diameter with the Nuclepore filter, which gives you, in fact, tubes which are almost as long as they are broad, it appeared to us that Poiseuille's law held to within about 10% for these filters. I just wondered whether you had done that. The other point of interest is the point that in your slides, at 30 cm of water, the flow rate was virtually independent of the concentration. When Prothero and Burton published their results on the 5μ capillary, they found this extraordinarily small change in apparent viscosity with hematocrit; and I wondered whether we could drag Professor Burton into this.

GREGERSEN:
Yes, we did pressure flow curves with Ringer's or Eagle's solution, not water. Also, with red cell suspensions, the initial flow rate (R_1) seems to be dependent on concentration and/or hematocrit at a given pressure.

ROWLANDS:
Well, I think it rose by about 10%. Perhaps Professor Burton had better talk about this, but his work is what led me, as I mentioned earlier in the week, to propose that in these very narrow tubes water could in fact be passing across the red cell from front to back in appreciable quantities.

BURTON (*Canada*):
I am glad to have the opportunity of apologizing and I think we should, for the lack of ability of other people to reproduce the work that Prothero did with Millipore filters.

GREGERSEN:
Dr. Burton and I agree that the Millipore filters we have now may not be the same as formerly.

BURTON:
I assure you that Prothero repeated it on many filters. He tried a whole run of boxes of Millipore filters, and he did it again and again. Results fitted his mathematics perfectly. Then when Prothero used new boxes, evidently they were quite different. For one thing they were not consistent, as shown by a simple wetting test of just putting a drop of water on and watching how it spread. Within any given box of filters, some spread easily and others not. So we have reached the point of view that there is too much which can go wrong using any such kind of filter. I am not slandering any particular manufacturer. They are certainly themselves very embarrassed about this. But it seems to me that future work has got to be done with geometric filters. I would agree with what was said about the microscopic appearance when you look in your high power microscope; these filters are a meshwork of threads, which appear to be sort of a string of pearls; and I cannot see how they can claim that the pores are in any sense cylindrical. However, extrusion data certainly shows that they do have an equivalent pore size which is in a very narrow range. As to the viscosity, I think the "effective viscosity", if you use Poiseuille's law in what is bolus flow, is obviously a fiction; it is that of plasma. I think this would connote that the hematocrit would not affect the effective viscosity, because what you are measuring is that of plasma and apparently not that of the cells. Thinking teleologically, this is another place where "God the engineer" knew his business, because he achieved in this bolus flow, in the capillaries, a great improvement in the diffusion relations by "mixing", at an energy cost which seems to be quite negligible. Actually it is easier to push blood through these tiny tubes in "bolus flow" than without this type of flow.

GREGERSEN:
What astonished me was that you can pour packed cells over a Nuclepore filter of 4, 5μ pore size at 1–2 cm H_2O pressure and have the cells go through. We tried in the beginning to determine the minimum pressure required for the red cells to pass through the sieves, even 5 mm water pressure. When you increase cell concentration, as you saw from our figures, you can go up to the most astonishing concentrations and get away with it. Here, evidently, is a different engineering problem from that in larger vessels.

ROWLANDS:

May I just add one word of practical point. If anybody is taking this up, they must use the Swank technique of removing the aggregates with Dacron wool before they attempt these experiments.

GREGERSEN:

I quite agree. You noticed that we washed our cells. We have not tried anything more complicated than a washed cell suspension. We stayed away from everything else, because the problem with these suspensions of washed cells was already technically difficult.

THE RÔLE OF ELECTRICAL CHARGE IN THE STABILITY AND FLOW PROPERTIES OF RED CELL SUSPENSIONS

G. V. F. SEAMAN* †

Department of Radiotherapeutics, The University, Cambridge, England

INTRODUCTION

In 1929 FÅHRAEUS[1] suggested that electrostatic factors were important in the formation of rouleaux or Geldrollen. Since then the possible relevance of cell charge has been suggested by a number of other workers[2, 3]. In electrolytic media under approximately physiological conditions, both the plasma proteins and the red blood cells carry net negative electrokinetic charges. Alteration in the electrokinetic charge carried by any of the components of blood may, therefore, be of significance as regards its flow properties.

Changes in the electrokinetic charge carried by red blood cells in suspension could lead to changes in their flow properties as a result of:

1. Changes in electroviscous effects: At physiological salt concentrations where the effective thickness of the electrical double layer surrounding the red blood cells is about 8 Å electroviscous effects are unlikely to be of any significance. Electroviscous effects only become appreciable when the electrolytic suspending solution is very dilute and the particles small.

2. Increased agglomeration, flocculation or aggregation of cells because of changes in the electrostatic forces of repulsion between the cells: such forces are only important over molecular distances and will be considered more fully in a later section.

3. Changes in the adsorption of components from the suspending medium at the interface with the cells: this could lead to a non-localized aggregation, an example of which would be massive rouleaux formation.

4. Alteration in the deformability of the cells: WEISS[4] has shown that Murine Sarcoma 37 and Ehrlich ascites tumour cells may be sucked into a hemispherical bulge in a micropipette using significantly less negative pressure after they have been treated with neuraminidase. This enzyme is known to produce a significant decrease in the electrophoretic mobility of Sarcoma 37 and Ehrlich ascites tumour cells[5, 6]. WEISS[4] was using essentially the cell elastimer devised by MITCHISON and SWANN[7]. The negative pressure/deformation relationship is normally linear and its slope is known as the "stiffness" which is related to the ease of deformation of the membrane[8]. Unpublished data by Horwitz and Weiss suggest that reduction in the surface charge of erythrocytes may also be accompanied by an increase in their deformability. In this particular case, the enzyme neuraminidase removes terminal N-acylated neuraminic

† Present address: Division of Neurology, Department of Medicine, University of Oregon Medical School, Portland, Oregon, 97201, U.S.A.

acids from the peripheral region of the red blood cell[9, 10]. Also in this connection GOTTSCHALK[11] has suggested on the basis of his studies on the physical properties of ovine submaxillary gland mucoprotein that the presence of the charged carboxyl groups of the N-acylated neuraminic acids confers "structural rigidity" on the underlying protein core. Similarly the ionized carboxyl groups of acids, such as the sialic acids, may confer "structural rigidity" to the mucoprotein moieties at the periphery of red blood cells.

Changes in the mechanical or rheological properties of the membrane may be interpreted in a number of different ways. One unanswered question is the dimensions over which such processes are operative. Interactions or contacts between cells are probably very superficial so that the outermost portions of the membrane may tend to behave as a monolayer, although the rheological properties of the cell surface may be determined to a greater or lesser extent by the intracellular contents. Surface rheology is relevant to cell behaviour in that the surface of a cell is subjected to shear, whenever it moves or is moved. The surface viscosity of protein monolayers has been extensively studied by JOLY[12, 13, 14]. The transmission of shear stresses to the interior of the red blood cell would be expected to be inhibited by the presence of the membrane, but the ease of distortion of normal erythrocytes during flow[15] and their ready indentation by leucocytes[16] would suggest that under shear they behave more like fluid droplets.

Structure of the Erythrocyte Membrane

The human erythrocyte membrane is probably 150 to 300 Å in thickness[17]. Electron microscopical evidence suggests that about 75 Å of this thickness is occupied by a more or less continuous bimolecular lipid leaflet[18]. The structure of the portion of the membrane exterior to the lipid region has been investigated mainly by means of a combination of chemical and enzymatic treatments of the erythrocyte, coupled with electrophoretic measurements, the latter being a convenient means of detecting changes in the ionic composition and structure of the cell surface. The surface will be defined from an electrophoretic point of view as the envelope described through a set of the outermost terminal ionogenic groups, where their numerical density is such that a significant change from the optical and rheological properties of the aqueous phase thereby results[19]. Under physiological conditions of pH and ionic strength, only anionic groups are detectable on the surface of the erythrocyte by electrophoretic methods[20]. An appreciable proportion of these groups have been shown to be the carboxyl ions of N-acetyl neuraminic acid[9, 10]. There is evidence for the presence of other anionic groups which have not so far been conclusively identified[10, 21]. It is also uncertain if the ionogenic groups on the surface of the red blood cell can account for all of its electrokinetic charge, although any net charge arising from the redistribution of the ions of the suspending medium seems to be unlikely[21].

Apparatus, Materials and Methods

Blood was obtained from dogs anaesthetized with sodium pentobarbital and from normal human donors of various blood groups. The blood was taken into either acid-citrate-dextrose medium under routine blood transfusion conditions, the disodium salt of diaminoethane tetra-acetic acid (1 mg per cc of whole blood) or heparin. No significant differences were found in the behaviour of the bloods obtained by the use of different anticoagulants. The volume concentrations (haematocrits) were determined in Wintrobe tubes after centrifugation at $2000\,g$ for 60 min. Normal red blood cells were assumed to be 95% packed, but aldehyde-hardened red blood cells may be only 60% packed after this procedure. No reliable method is available for the estimation of the "trapping factor" for the hardened erythrocytes, so that only the uncorrected haematocrits are given.

The red blood cell suspensions, either fresh or aldehyde-modified, were prepared as described previously[22]. The washing and treatment of red cells with neuraminidase was carried out as given in an earlier publication[23].

All reagents were of analytical grade. The solutions of standard saline (0·15 M aqueous sodium chloride solution made 3×10^{-4} M with respect to sodium bicarbonate, pH $7\cdot2 \pm 0\cdot2$), and other reagents were made up in water which had been distilled twice in Pyrex-ware. Adjustments of the pH of solutions were effected with solutions of hydrochloric acid or sodium hydroxide corresponding in ionic strength to the solution undergoing adjustment in pH.

Neuraminidase from *vibrio cholerae* filtrate was obtained from "Behringwerke", Marburg a.d. Lahn, Germany, as a purified aqueous solution low in protease activity.

Microelectrophoresis was performed in a cylindrical tube apparatus equipped with Ag/AgCl electrodes[24, 25]. Each mobility was calculated from the mean of at least ten individual estimations of the rate of migration of red blood cells, with reversal of the polarity of the applied electrical field after each measurement. Correct alignment of the apparatus was checked by the determination of the mobility of washed human erythrocytes suspended in standard saline. The electrophoretic mobilities were expressed in μ/sec/V/cm.

Viscosities were obtained by means of Brookfield Cone-plate viscometers (standard LVT and RVT models and also $\frac{1}{2}$ LVT model), fitted with beryllium-copper springs for maximum torques at respectively 336,673·7 and 7187 dyne cm. The cones had an angle of 1·57°, and a radius of 2·4 cm. Measurements were made at either 25°C or $37° \pm 0\cdot05$°C. Coefficients of viscosity were obtained over the shear rate range 1·90–384 sec^{-1}, but mainly between 5·80 and 230 sec^{-1}. Duplicate determinations were made using the procedure outlined by WELLS, DENTON and MERRILL[26].

Unless stated otherwise all physico-chemical studies were made at 25°C.

Theoretical Considerations

Red blood cells in physiological media possess dimensions which are large compared to the effective thickness of the electrical double layer which surrounds them. The electrophoretic mobilities will depend mainly therefore upon the nature of the cell envelope, and not upon its shape or orientation in the applied electrical field[27, 28]. The electrophoretic mobility of erythrocytes suspended in a buffer solution is reproducible for a given species of animal but varies from one species to another[10, 23, 27].

Ideally it should be possible to deduce the net electrokinetic charge density at the surface of a red blood cell by calculation of zeta potentials from the electrophoretic mobilities and then to compute a surface charge density from a form of either the Gouy–Chapman or Debye–Hückel equations[29]. In the case of red blood cells suspended in a medium of high ionic strength the zeta potentials (ζ) may be calculated from the Helmholtz-Smoluchkowski equation:

$$\zeta = \frac{4\pi\eta}{\epsilon} \cdot u \tag{1}$$

where η and ϵ are respectively the viscosity and dielectric constant within the double layer (assumed to be equal to the values for the bulk of the suspending medium) and u is the electrophoretic mobility. The zeta potentials may be converted into surface charge densities (σ) by means of the Gouy–Chapman equation for uni-univalent electrolytes.

$$\sigma = 2\left(\frac{NekT}{2000\pi}\right)I^{1/2}\sinh\left(\frac{e\zeta}{2kT}\right) \tag{2}$$

where I is the ionic strength, N Avogadro's number, k the Boltzmann constant, T the absolute temperature, and e the electronic charge. At 25°C for suspensions of red blood cells, eq. (2) reduces to:

$$\sigma = 3\cdot52 \times 10^4 \cdot I^{1/2} \cdot \sinh\left(\frac{\zeta}{51\cdot3}\right) \tag{3}$$

Recent work by POLLACK, HAGER, RECKEL, TOREN and SINGHER[30] suggests that the bulk dielectric constant properties of plasma or serum may be very different from those of aqueous media such as standard saline. The revelance of dielectric constant may be seen by examination of the relationship between the zeta potential and surface charge density:

$$\zeta = \frac{4\pi\sigma}{K\epsilon} \tag{4}$$

for $Ka \gg 1$ and

$$K = \left(\frac{8\pi ne^2v^2}{kT\epsilon}\right)^{1/2} \tag{5}$$

where n is the number of ions of each kind in the bulk solution per unit volume and v their valence. At 25°C eq. (5) reduces to:

$$K = \frac{I^{1/2}}{3\cdot45 \times 10^{-9}\epsilon^{1/2}} \tag{6}$$

Combining eqs. (1) and (4), it is seen that:

$$u = \frac{\sigma}{\eta K} \tag{7}$$

which upon substitution for K from eq. (6) becomes

$$u = \frac{3\cdot45 \times 10^{-9} \cdot \sigma \cdot \epsilon^{1/2}}{\eta \cdot I^{1/2}}$$

so that the viscosity-corrected mobility:

$$u\eta = \frac{3\cdot45 \times 10^{-9}\sigma\epsilon^{1/2}}{I^{1/2}} \qquad (8)$$

Thus it is seen that the viscosity-corrected mobility should vary as the square root of the dielectric constant.

Results and Discussion

Figure 1 shows the linear relationship between the applied potential and the observed rate of migration (μ/sec) of human red blood cells suspended in citrated plasma. Similar linear relationships were found for red blood cells suspended in standard saline or serum. The results indicate that over these rates of shear (approximately

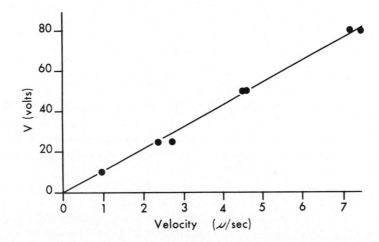

FIG. 1. RELATIONSHIP BETWEEN THE RATE OF MIGRATION OF HUMAN RED BLOOD CELLS IN CITRATED PLASMA AND THE APPLIED ELECTRIC FIELD.

$0\cdot5$–5 sec^{-1}), plasma, serum and standard saline behave as Newtonian fluids. The volume concentration of red blood cells used for electrophoretic studies is extremely low (about $0\cdot05\%$ v/v) and the effect of the erythrocytes in suspension on the total viscosity of the suspension is insignificant. The use of a microelectrophoresis apparatus as a means of assessing the flow properties of systems is limited, however, to situations where the electrokinetic charge density remains unaltered.

The mobility of human red cells in physiological saline or isotonic phosphate buffer has been shown to be independent of the method of collection of the blood, anticoagulant used, age, sex, blood group and race of the donor[27, 28, 31]. The electrophoretic mobility of human red blood cells in standard saline at pH $7\cdot4$ and $25°$C is $-1\cdot08 \pm 0\cdot04$ μ/sec/V/cm. A similar figure is obtained for the mobility of the cells in serum provided that corrections for the viscosity and bulk dielectric constant are applied. Similarly, for canine red blood cells the mobility in serum or standard saline reduces to $-1 \cdot 28 \pm 0 \cdot 06 \, \mu/\text{sec}/\text{V}/\text{cm}$.

These mobility values correspond respectively to charge densities of 6250 and 7400 esu/cm² after application of a correction factor for the ion penetrable nature of the surface[23].

As has already been mentioned, the negative electrokinetic charge carried by red blood cells arises mainly from the ionization of N-acylated neuraminic acids at their surfaces. In the case of canine and human erythrocytes, the particular sialic acid is N-acetylneuraminic acid[23]. The general structure of the sialic acids is given in Fig. 2.

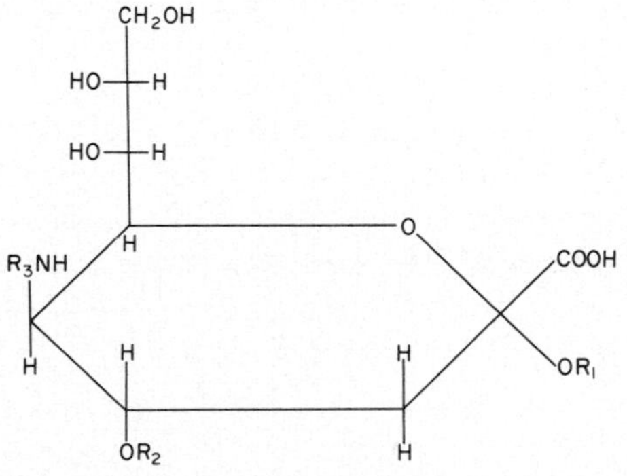

FIG. 2. GENERAL STRUCTURE OF THE SIALIC ACIDS.

The structure corresponds to N-acetylneuraminic acid when $R_1 = $ H, $R_2 = $ H and $R_3 = $ CH$_3$CO-. Treatment of red blood cells with neuraminidase, a specific α glycosidase which liberates the terminal sialic acid from their ultrastructure produced about an 80% decrease in the mobility of normal human erythrocytes[9] and a 75% decrease in the mobility of canine erythrocytes[23].

Both human and canine red blood cells are essentially macropolyanions[20, 23] so that their fixation with 2% aqueous acetaldehyde solution at pH 7·4 in a phosphate-buffered saline leads to no significant change in their respective electrophoretic mobilities, shape or mean corpuscular volumes. Treatment of red blood cells with aldehydes thus offers a means of drastically altering their deformability without affecting many other parameters which might affect the flow properties of a suspension of cells.

The flow properties of the normal, neuraminidase-treated and aldehyde-fixed canine or human red blood cells were examined over a wide range of volume concentration from a rate of shear of 11·5 up to 230 sec^{-1}. The flow properties of a suspension of canine erythrocytes in standard saline after treatment with acetaldehyde, uranyl nitrate and neuraminidase are shown in Fig. 3, the shear rate in these instances being either 23 or 230 sec^{-1}. No significant differences were detectable between the flow properties of suspensions of normal and neuraminidase-treated erythrocytes down to 11·5 sec^{-1} (the minimum reliable rate of shear for the Brookfield $\frac{1}{2}$LVT Cone-plate viscometer) for the range of haematocrits studied.

Suspensions of aldehyde-fixed red blood cells showed a much greater increase in resistance to flow with increasing volume concentration above haematocrits of about

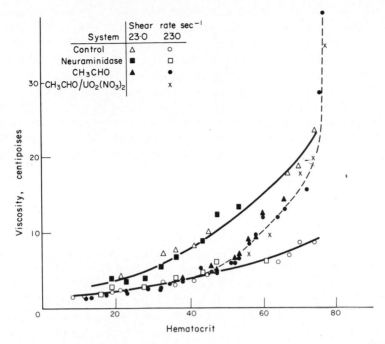

System	Shear rate sec^{-1}	
	23·0	230
Control	△	○
Neuraminidase	■	□
CH$_3$CHO	▲	●
CH$_3$CHO/UO$_2$(NO$_3$)$_2$		x

FIG. 3. FLOW PROPERTIES OF CANINE RED BLOOD CELLS SUSPENSIONS IN STANDARD SALINE.

50% than did normal red blood cells(Fig. 3). The actual volume concentration of the hardened erythrocytes is much less than is suggested by the haematocrit, since the packing corresponds to only about 60% compared with 95% for normal red blood cells. Packed, normal canine red blood cells previously washed in standard saline had a "viscosity" of about 50–60 cP at a shear rate of 23 sec^{-1}. The rheological behaviour of neuraminidase-treated red blood cells, whose charge had been approximately halved was similar, although haemolysis made the values somewhat variable.

It is possible to assess the rate of shear to which a suspension of erythrocytes must be subjected for the apparent viscosity to become independent of the rate of shear. On this criterion, aldehyde-modified red blood cells appeared to be monodisperse at a rate of shear of approximately 20 sec^{-1}, whereas normal red blood cells in plasma require a rate of shear of about 50 sec^{-1} before dispersion is complete. The force required to separate a pair of red blood cells is considered to be the most difficult stage in the process of redispersion. The quantitative aspects of the shearing of aggregates has been considered by ALBERS and OVERBEEK[32] and essentially their treatment will be followed. In their derivation, F_α, the shearing force between red blood cells will produce separation if it exceeds the Van der Waals forces of attraction (V_A), between the cells. If the angle between the direction of the shear gradient and a line joining the centres of a pair of adherent cells is designated α, then during rotation of the pair from $\alpha = 0°$ to $\alpha = 90°$, the shearing force F_α increases from zero to a maximum value at 45° and then returns to zero again at $\alpha = 90°$. ALBERS and OVERBEEK[32] have shown that

$$F_{\alpha crit} = \tfrac{3}{2}\pi\eta a(2a+H)D\sin(2\alpha_{crit})$$

where $F_{\alpha\text{crit}}$ is the force developed at the critical angle, α_{crit}, whose precise value is not too important for angles $\geqslant 27°$, since the force varies as $\sin 2\alpha$ and at angles $\geqslant 27°$, $\sin 2\alpha$ is $\geqslant 0\cdot 8$. In this analysis α_{crit} was assumed to be $30°$, η is the coefficient of viscosity of the continuous phase, a the radius of the cell, H the minimum distance between the surfaces of the cells and D the rate of shear. Neglecting H and assuming values of $0\cdot 01$ poise for η and $2\cdot 5 \times 10^{-4}$cm for a, then $F_{\alpha\text{crit}}$ corresponds to approximately 1×10^{-7} dynes at a shear rate of 20 sec^{-1} and 2.5×10^{-7} dynes at 50 sec^{-1}, or for an intercellular contact area of 10 μ^2, to 1 and 2.5 dynes/cm^2 respectively. These values are in reasonable agreement with the figure of 1–3 dynes/cm^2 deduced by COKELET, MERRILL, GILLILAND, SHIN, BRITTEN and WELLS[33] from Casson plots.

Consideration of the Intercellular Forces likely to be relevant to Adhesion and Disaggregation of Cells

Many of the possible forces of attraction and repulsion between cells have been reviewed by PETHICA[34]. The most important forces would seem to be the "long range" London–Van der Waals forces of attraction and the electrostatic forces of repulsion arising from surfaces of like charge. Cell to cell contact and separation will be considered, therefore, in terms of DERJAGUIN–LANDAU[35] and VERWEY–OVERBEEK[36] theory of the stability of hydrophobic colloids. In this application of Derjaguin–Landau–Verwey–Overbeek theory, the red blood cells were regarded as spherical particles. The potential at the surface of the cells ($\psi = \zeta$) was taken as 18 mV, the radii (a) as equal to 5×10^{-4} cm, the ionic strength of the suspending medium (I) as $0\cdot 15$ g ions per litre, $1/K$ as $7\cdot 8$ Å and T as $298\cdot 2°$K. VERWEY and OVERBEEK[36] deduced theoretically that the Hamaker constant, A, should have a value of about 10^{-12} ergs. Most values of A which have been derived from experimental data are considerably less than this and are usually in the range 1×10^{-14} to 1×10^{-15} ergs.

The basis of the Derjaguin–Landau and Verwey–Overbeek theory is the use of a total potential energy curve (V_T), composed of an electrostatic repulsive potential energy (V_R) and an attractive potential energy (V_A). Combination of the appropriate attraction and repulsion expressions leads to an equation for the variation in total potential energy of interaction (V_T) between two charged cells with respect to the distance between them.

$$V_T = V_A + V_R \tag{9}$$

For red blood cells V_R is given in an approximate form for large Ka values by

$$V_R = \frac{\epsilon a \psi^2}{2} \ln \left[1 + \exp\left(-KH\right)\right] \tag{10}$$

For spherical particles of equal size, as assumed for red blood cells, the potential energy of attraction can be considered by means of the approximate equation

$$V_A = \frac{-Aa}{12H} \tag{11}$$

Strictly speaking, the calculation of V_A for large particles should include a correction for the effects of electromagnetic retardation. This effect arises because a finite time is required for an electromagnetic wave to be propagated through the medium. If the time is long, compared with the time of rotation of a molecule, the electrons on return of the wave may have assumed a less favourable position for attraction. The omission of this correction leads to an overestimate in the values of V_A calculated from eq. (11), but does not materially affect the conclusions obtained by the use of this simplified model.

Differentiation of the potential energy of attraction and repulsion expressions yields equations for the variation of force of repulsion (F_R) and attraction (F_A) with respect to distance of separation thus:

$$F_R = \frac{\partial V_R}{\partial H} = \frac{-\epsilon a K \psi^2 \exp(-KH)}{2[1 + \exp(-KH)]} \tag{12}$$

and

$$F_A = \frac{\partial V_A}{\partial H} = \frac{Aa}{12H^2} \tag{13}$$

In order for red blood cells to maintain both a stable separation and a force of adhesion, the total potential curve must exhibit a positively directed maximum of sufficient height to oppose any thermal translational energy which the cells might acquire from molecular bombardment. A potential energy barrier of height $>10\,kT\,(kT \approx 4 \times 10^{-14}$ ergs) is considered to be sufficient to keep cells separate and a negative secondary minimum to provide a position of stable equilibrium to which a cell will tend to return if displaced by thermal agitation or external forces. The general form for a V_T versus H relationship which will fulfill these requirements is shown schematically in Fig. 4. A depth of 10–15 kT for the secondary minimum should be sufficient to provide stability.

The V_T versus H relationships show positive maxima and negative secondary minima for values of Hamaker's constant of the order of 1×10^{-14} ergs. Cells under these circumstances could be stabilized at about 45 Å separation with 15–20 kT stabilization energy as is shown in Fig. 5. The effect of changing the radius, a, will be merely to

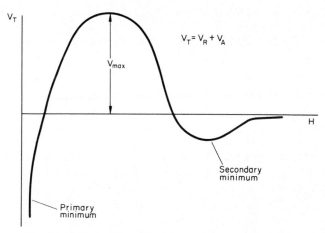

FIG. 4. DIAGRAM OF A V_T VERSUS H RELATIONSHIP SHOWING THE FEATURES NECESSARY FOR MAINTENANCE OF A STABLE DISPERSION AND ALSO A FORCE OF ADHESION.

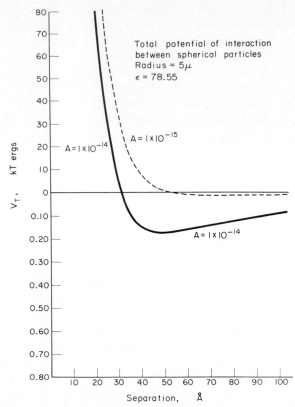

FIG. 5. VARIATION IN THE TOTAL POTENTIAL ENERGY OF INTERACTION IN kT UNITS BETWEEN IDENTICAL CHARGED SPHERES, WITH MINIMUM DISTANCE OF SEPARATION BETWEEN THEM FOR HAMAKER CONSTANTS OF 1×10^{-14} AND 1×10^{-15} ERGS.

alter the energy scale. If the red blood cells for example are not smooth, and possess microcrenations, protuberances, etc., of low radii of curvature, these portions of the membrane could approach one another much more easily. Once contacts over small areas have been made, the energy of these "bridges" will assist the running together of the membranes[34].

In Fig. 6 is shown a plot of the total force curves derived from total potential curves, for Hamaker constants of 1×10^{-13}, 5×10^{-14}, 1×10^{-14}, and 1×10^{-15} ergs. These curves are considered to be applicable only down to intercellular separations of about 10Å, as the validity of the equations is doubtful at atomic distances. In addition the presence of surface irregularities at the molecular level would be likely to necessitate the use of much smaller radii of curvature in such calculations. It is estimated that the maximum force required to dislodge cells from their equilibrium positions in the secondary minima varies between 2×10^{-7} and 9×10^{-7} dynes for values of A between 1×10^{-14} and 5×10^{-14} ergs. These values correspond reasonably well with values for the dispersion of red cells of 5–10×10^{-7} dynes derived from cone-plate viscometric measurements. The correspondence between the experimental and theoretical values, taken in conjunction with the ready reversibility of red cell association, supports the conclusion that the Derjaguin–Landau and Verwey–Overbeek type of analysis may well be applicable to red blood cells, which are normally in free suspension.

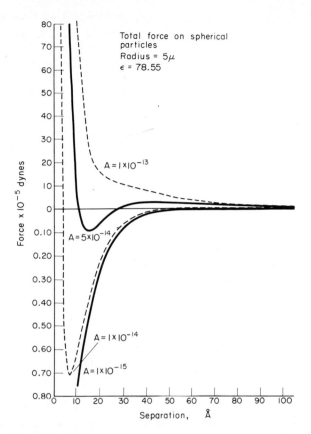

FIG. 6. VARIATION IN THE TOTAL FORCE IN DYNES BETWEEN IDENTICAL CHARGED SPHERES WITH MINIMUM DISTANCE OF SEPARATION FOR HAMAKER CONSTANTS OF 1×10^{-13}, 5×10^{-14}, 1×10^{-14}, AND 1×10^{-15} ERGS.

SUMMARY

The electrophoretic mobilities of human and canine red blood cells have been determined in 0·15 M aqueous sodium chloride solution and also in homologous plasma and serum. After correction for the effects of changes in the dielectric constant and viscosity produced by the presence of plasma or serum proteins, the electrophoretic mobilities were found to be essentially the same, namely $-1·08 \pm 0·04$ for human red blood cells and $-1·28 + 0·06$ μ/sec/v/cm for canine red blood cells. Fixation of the washed red blood cells with 2% w/v aqueous acetaldehyde in a phosphate-buffered saline at pH 7·4 led to no significant change in the respective electrophoretic mobilities. Treatment of the red blood cells with neuraminidase however, produced marked decreases in their electrokinetic charge.

The flow properties of the normal, neuraminidase-treated and aldehyde-fixed canine or human red cells were examined over a wide range of volume concentrations and a range of shear rates from 11·5 to 230 sec^{-1}. The decreases in the electrokinetic charge produced by treatment of the red blood cells with neuraminidase were without effect on the bulk flow properties of the suspensions. It was estimated that suspensions of aldehyde-treated canine red blood cells appeared to be monodisperse at a shear rate of about 20 sec^{-1} (1 × 10^{-7} dynes), whereas normal red blood cells in plasma required a shear rate close to 50 sec^{-1} (2·5 × 10^{-7}dynes) to effect complete dispersion.

The forces required to separate adherent erythrocytes were computed by application of Derjaguin–Landau and Verwey–Overbeek theory to a spherical model in which the red blood cells were assumed to possess equal surface potentials of 18 mV, radii of 5 × 10^{-4} cm and to be suspended in an electrolytic medium of ionic strength 0·15 g ions per litre at 298·2°K. For values of Hamaker's constant between 1 × 10^{-14} and 5 × 10^{-14} ergs, the forces required to separate adherent red blood cells were calculated to be between 2 × 10^{-7} and 9 × 10^{-7} dynes. These results are in reasonable agreement with the experimental values derived from cone-plate viscometry.

ACKNOWLEDGMENT

I am most grateful to Mr. D. E. Brooks, of the Department of Physics, University of British Columbia, who carried out the calculations and programming for the total potential and forces curves. These were made on the I.B.M. 7040 computer at the University of British Columbia Computing Center.

REFERENCES

[1] Fåhraeus, R. *Physiol. Rev.* **9**, 241, 1929.
[2] Knisely, M. H. *Tans. Soc. Rheol.* **6**, 13, 1962.
[3] Shin, H., Cokelet, G., Merrill, E. W., Gilliland, E. R., Britten, A. and Wells, R. E. *Biophys. J.* **3**, 199, 1963.
[4] Weiss, L. *J. Cell Biol.* **26**, 735, 1965.
[5] Simon-Reuss, I., Cook, G. M. W., Seaman, G. V. F. and Heard, D. H. *Cancer Res.* **24**, 2038, 1964.
[6] Cook, G. M. W., Seaman, G. V. F. and Weiss, L. *Cancer Res.* **23**, 1813, 1963.
[7] Mitchison, J. M. and Swann, M. M. *J. Exp. Biol.* **31**, 443, 1954.
[8] Wolpert, L. *Int. Rev. Cytol.* **10**, 164, 1960.
[9] Cook, G. M. W., Heard, D. H. and Seaman, G. V. F. *Nature* **191**, 44, 1961.
[10] Eylar, E. H., Madoff, M. A., Brody, O. V. and Oncley, J. L. *J. Biol. Chem.* **237**, 1992, 1962.
[11] Gottschalk, A. *Nature* **186**, 949, 1960.
[12] Joly, M. *Biochim. Biophys. Acta* **2**, 624, 1948.
[13] Joly, M. *J. Coll. Sci.* **5**, 49, 1950.
[14] Joly, M. *J. Coll. Sci.* **11**, 519, 1956.
[15] Dintenfass, L. *Angiology* **13**, 333, 1962.
[16] Palmer, A. A. *Quart. J. Exp. Physiol.* **44**, 149, 1959.
[17] Wolpers, C. *Klin. Wochschr.* **34**, 61, 1956.
[18] Robertson, J. D. *Biochem. Soc. Symp.* Cambridge, England, 1959.
[19] Haydon, D. A. and Seaman, G. V. F. *Proc. Roy. Soc.* **B, 156**, 533, 1962.
[20] Seaman, G. V. F. and Heard, D. H. *J. Gen. Physiol.* **44**, 251, 1960.
[21] Seaman, G. V. F. and Cook, G. M. W. In *Cell Electrophoresis*, Ambrose, E. J. (Editor), J. & A. Churchill, London, 1965, p. 48.
[22] Heard, D. H. and Seaman, G. V. F. *Biochim. Biophys. Acta* **53**, 366, 1961.
[23] Seaman, G. V. F. and Uhlenbruck, G. *Arch. Biochem. Biophys.* **100**, 493, 1963.
[24] Bangham, A. D., Flemans, R., Heard, D. H. and Seaman, G. V. F. *Nature* **182**, 642, 1958.
[25] Seaman, G. V. F. and Heard, D. H. *Blood* **18**, 599, 1961.
[26] Wells, R. E., Denton, R. and Merrill, E. W. *J. Lab. Clin. Med.* **57**, 646, 1961.
[27] Abramson, H. A., Moyer, L. S. and Gorin, M. H. *Electrophoresis of Proteins and the Chemistry of Cell Surfaces,* Reinhold, New York, 1942, p. 307.
[28] Seaman, G. V. F. *Microelectrophoresis of Red Blood Cells*, Ph.D. Dissertation, University of Cambridge, Cambridge, England, 1958.
[29] Haydon, D. A. *Proc. Roy. Soc. A*, **258**, 319, 1960.
[30] Pollack, W., Hager, H. J., Reckel, R., Toren, D. A. and Singher, H. O. *Transfusion*, **5**, 158, 1965.
[31] Ruhenstroth-Bauer, G. and Sachtleben, P. In *Medizinische Grundlagenforschung*, Bauer (Editor), Thieme, 1959, p. 639.

[32] ALBERS, W. and OVERBEEK, J. Th. G. *J. Coll. Sci.* **15**, 489, 1960.
[33] COKELET, G. R., MERRILL, E. W., GILLILAND, E. R., SHIN, H., BRITTEN, A. and WELLS, R. E. *Trans. Soc. Rheol.* **7**, 303, 1963.
[34] PETHICA, B. A. *Exp. Cell. Res.* Suppl. **8**, 123, 1961.
[35] DERJAGUIN, B. and LANDAU, L. *Acta physiochim.* **14**, 633, 1941.
[36] VERWEY, E. J. W. and OVERBEEK, J. TH. G. *Theory of Stability of Hydrophobic Colloids*, Elsevier, Amsterdam, 1948.

DISCUSSION

BURTON (*Canada*):

May I ask a question for my own personal information? It is very important to me. After treatment with neuraminidase, did you ever see red cells crenate? Either by violent changes of pH or shrinking by osmotic hypertonic solutions? Have you ever seen a crenated cell after treatment with neuramidase?

SEAMAN (*England*):

Yes, we have!

BURTON:

Does it look much like an ordinary crenated cell?

SEAMAN:

As far as I could tell, yes!

SCOTT BLAIR (*England*):

My own work has been largely concerned with the action of a different enzyme, renin on sodium caseinate; and in some way, the behaviour is so closely parallel to that of the action of enzymes on blood components that I would like to ask whether blood or its components show two phenomena which we found striking in the case of the sodium caseinates. When we acted on the sodium caseinate with the enzyme, the first thing that happened was quite a measurable fall in viscosity. When the lactopeptide was broken away from the protein, this lactopeptide was evidently positively charged relative to the protein and must have screened the negative charges which were producing an electroviscous effect on the protein itself. So there is quite a big fall in the viscosity. Is anything parallel to this happening in blood? The other thing, is that we found that in the case of sodium caseinate, if we got practically electrolyte-free sodium caseinate, (checked by conductivity measurements) we were able to get very good straight lines plotting the Arrhenius plot, i.e. the logarithm of the relative viscosity against the concentration and that, as we added increasing quantities of electrolyte, successive curves became not only flatter, but also bent. But we could straighten them, by introducing the Vand–Mooney correction which, of course, depends on the taking up of the continuous phase by the addition of the suspended phase. By doing this, we were able to get a series of straight lines but the slopes were arbitrary, in that we selected our values for the Vand–Mooney correction; then we found that they were not so arbitrary after all because these corrections themselves were strictly proportional to the intrinsic viscosity. Now I am asking whether in fact any of these phenomena are paralleled in the case of blood; I have not done such an experiment for blood, but I cannot help wondering whether in this case there may not be comparable similarities.

SEAMAN:

Treatment of red cell suspensions with proteolytic enzymes or neuraminidase, unlike the action of renin on sodium caseinate, is without significant effect on the flow properties (viscosity). The effects which you observed are certainly very interesting. I have not examined the effect of such enzymes on whole blood, but an experiment which does come to mind is that of hamsters treated *in vivo* with a neuraminidase. The mobility of the red blood cells was sharply decreased, but the hamsters remained quite healthy and the circulation was apparently normal with no significant aggregation of the blood elements.

SILBERBERG (*Israel*):

I want to find out about the calculations that you did not mention. Do you, on the basis of these calculations expect that there should be an effect on viscosity, taking charge and ionic strength as one would find in blood?

SEAMAN:

Under physiological conditions one would not expect electroviscous effects to be significant because, of course, these would be of very short range.

WHITMORE (*England*):

Did you find any evidence, in the case of the cells with different surface charges, of different degrees of aggregation? Were you able to look at the suspensions under shear or their general appearance outside the viscometer? In other words, do you think that there were similar degrees of aggregation while you were taking viscosity measurements on the differently treated cells?

SEAMAN:

Normal and neuraminidase treated cells in plasma appeared to be similar microscopically. There was not a tremendous increase in aggregation in the case of neuraminidase-treated cells. I should mention that these were probably not good experiments, in as much as the neuraminidase treatments did not reduce the electrokinetic charge of the red cells to zero, although it was reduced by perhaps 70 or 80%. There was, therefore, still an appreciable charge present. Probably a basic series of experiments to carry out would be ones involving diazomethane treated cells. I have in fact started these, but one is limited to working with aldehyde-fixed cells, which again is unsatisfactory. If one could in fact find suitable treatments for fresh red blood cells which would reduce the charge of the cells in effect to zero, then this would be a better system to study rather than one in which the charge has been reduced by only 70–80%.

TAYLOR (*Australia*):

I remember, it must have been back about 1954, I think, Alexander and I, in Sydney, did some measurements on the migration of red cells in the same way. Our problems at that time were the questions of whether the cells were repelled from the glass wall of the capillary and whether the charge of the cells had anything to do with the marginal zone. We came to exactly the same conclusions, of course, that you arrived at; that the effective radius of this charge is so small that it would not repel anything from anything much. My question was, just for fun, I mean that it is quite irrelevant to the biological situation, but just for fun: what would happen if you made up a suspension of these cells in a non-conductive iso-osmotic system such as in sucrose, for instance? Can you give the charges full rein in a non-conductive system, in a non-ionic suspension? Have you done that?

SEAMAN:

I have considered this, but I have not done so because one of the problems with red blood cells in this type of medium, where the electrolyte concentration is low, say about 10^{-3} or 10^{-4} molar, is that one tends to get hemolysis and a very marked aggregation of cells. This is a serious difficulty both from the point of view of electrophoretic measurements or indeed any other measurements.

UPTAKE OF METAL COLLOID PARTICLES BY EHRLICH ASCITES TUMOR CELL INDUCED BY HISTONE

S. SENO,* E. YOKOMURA, T. KIMOTO, K. SOGABE and N. ITOH

Department of Pathology, Okayama University Medical School, Okayama, Japan

THE iron colloid particles, chondroitin-sulfuric acid-iron colloid, and gold colloid particles, which were supplied by Dainihon Seiyaku Co. Ltd. for this experiment, proved to be selectively taken up by macrophages when they came into contact with animal tissue cells *in vitro* as well as *in vivo*. The Ehrlich tumor cells and macrophages found in the tumor ascites of mice were no exception. The iron or gold colloid particles added to the tumor ascites *in vitro* were solely taken up by macrophages but not by the tumor cells so far as the observations were made for one hour at 37°C. This fact suggests a difference in the molecular structure of the cell membrane between the macrophages and tumor cells, though electron microscopy revealed no appreciable difference between them. In the presence of histone, however, the tumor cell phagocytizes the colloid particles very actively.

The histone used in this experiment was obtained from calf thymus by the method of BUTLER[1] and finally divided into two fractions, one, arginine-rich and the other, lysine-rich. These fractions were added to the tumor cell suspension in Hanks' solution, 30 μg/ml, respectively, and then was added the colloidal iron solution, 4 mg Fe/ml, or colloidal gold, 0.7 mg Au/ml, drop by drop stirring the cell suspension gently to avoid the formation of gross coagulated masses. Finally it was incubated for an hour. The cells for control were treated similarly without adding histone and incubated for an hour. After incubation a drop of the cell suspension incubated with iron colloid was smeared, dried, fixed with methanol and stained by Perls' reaction for iron with the post-staining by Kernechtrot. The other part of the cell suspension and that incubated with colloidal gold were used for electron microscopy, i.e. after incubation the cells were fixed with glutaraldehyde followed by osmic postfixation[2]. The fixed cells were washed, dehydrated, embedded in Epon, sectioned and stained with alkaline lead solution[3] and observed by a Hitachi electron microscope, HU-11 A.

On the cell smear it was found that among the cells incubated with histone-free medium only the macrophages gave a strong positive Berlin blue reaction and no tumor cells gave visible reaction, while in the medium containing histone the tumor cells showing a marked positive reaction were frequently encountered.

The electron microscopy revealed the picture of active phagocytosis of the colloid particles by the tumor cells incubated with the histone fractions (Fig. 1), while absolutely no phagocytosis was observed in the tumor cells incubated without histone (Fig. 2E).

In histone-free medium both iron and gold colloid particles appeared as dense granules under electron microscope. These were found on the surface of macrophages

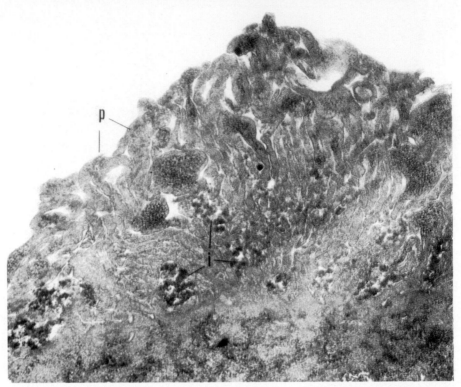

FIG. 1. ELECTRON MICROSCOPE PICTURE OF THE EARLY PHASE OF PHAGOCYTOSIS OF IRON COLLOID PARTICLES
BY AN EHRLICH ASCITES TUMOR CELL INCUBATED WITH ARGININE-RICH HISTONE AND SULFURIC ACID IRON
COLLOID FOR 10 MIN AT 37°C. *i*, IRON COLLOID PARTICLES AGGLUTINATED WITH HISTONE; *p*, PSEUDOPODS.
× 40,000.

or in their phagocytic vesicles. In the histone containing medium the metal colloid particles formed gross aggregated masses combining with histone. These masses were found adhering to the cell surfaces or in the phagocytic vesicles of the tumor cells as well as of macrophages.

The lysine-rich histone fraction was effective, and the arginine-rich fraction also. The contaminated macrophages found in the histone-containing medium also showed a retained phagocytic activity.

The result shows clearly that the phagocytosis is not the specialized function of macrophages but it can be demonstrated on the non-phagocytic cells by conditioning the environments.

Careful observation revealed that the colloid particles were adsorbed selectively on the surface of macrophages but not on the tumor cell surfaces, if the medium contains no histone. On the surface of macrophages small engulfings of cytoplasm were often encountered just at the area where the colloid particles were adsorbed (Fig. 2 M). These engulfings will be the initiation of phagocytosis and may develop to large phagocytic vesicles with the pseudopod formation on the surrounding cytoplasm.

The preincubation with papain, 5 mg/ml, for 30 min at 37°C, resulted in the loss of adsorbing capacity of macrophages to the colloid particles, probably by discharging some substance which will be on the surface of macrophages and be responsible for the adsorption of the colloid particles. Such macrophages were depressed in

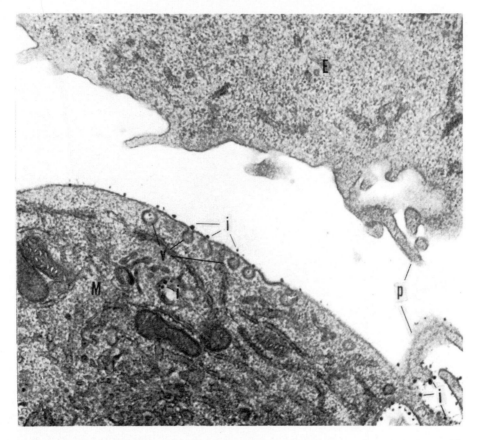

FIG. 2. ELECTRON MICROSCOPE PICTURE OF THE CELL SURFACES OF A MACROPHAGE (M) AND AN EHRLICH ASCITES TUMOR CELL (E) INCUBATED WITH THE IRON COLLOID IN THE HISTONE-FREE MEDIUM FOR 10 MIN AT 37°C. IRON COLLOID PARTICLES (*i*) WERE FOUND TO BE ADSORBED SOLELY ON THE SURFACE OF MICRO-PHAGE BUT NOT OF THE TUMOR CELL. *v*, ENGULFINGS FORMED AT THE AREA TO WHERE THE COLLOID PARTI-CLES WERE ADHERED. *p*, PSEUDOPODS. × 35,000.

their phagocytic capacity. They could take up the colloid particles but much less so compared to the control as revealed by further incubation with the colloid particles.

In the medium containing histone, where the tumor cell phagocytized the colloid particles very actively, the colloid particles were adsorbed on the surface of the tumor cells and the cells showed the engulfing on their surfaces with the formation of cyto-plasm bristle on the area where the colloid particles were adhered (Fig. 1). The process seemed to be almost the same as that found on macrophages, though the tumor cells predominated in the formation of pseudopod clusters. The findings show that the adsorption of the colloid particles to the cell surface is an essential factor of phagocytosis.

The histone added to the medium will be adsorbed on the surface of the colloid particles, which are charged negative in the media, as well as on the surface of the tumor cell, which is also proved to be rather negative in charge[4], and will act as the bridge to conjugate the colloid particles and tumor cell surface.

The mechanism of engulfing and related projections of the cytoplasm at the site where the colloid particles are adsorbed is completely obscure at present.

It will be reasonable to suppose, however, that the chemical bonds among the molecules constituting the cell membrane and cytoplasm are dissociated largely by adsorbing some substance, as may be understood by the concept of "cooperative phenomenon" in the sense of high molecular physics. The cytoplasm may react to such a damaging force from the outside of the cell by forming engulfing and related projections on cell surface. As the living cell cytoplasm is highly organized and of compact molecular structure and has a structure which should be supported by the high energy level provided by the metabolism of living cell, the restoration of the locally induced dissociation of molecular arrangement of the cytoplasm will require energy and this repairing process will be related to the final process of phagocytosis. This observation may help to explain the mechanism of the enhancing effect of histone for membrane permeability[5].

CONCLUSIONS

In spite of the remarkable pinocytotic activity the Ehrlich ascites tumor cell hardly shows any phagocytic activity for non-protein solid particles. Histone stimulates the phagocytosis of the tumor cell for the colloidal metal particles. The mechanism seems to be the enhanced adsorption of the colloid particles on the tumor cell surface.

ACKNOWLEDGMENT

This work was supported by the Ministry of Education of Japan.

REFERENCES

[1] BUTLER, J. A. V. In *The Nucleohistones*, BONNER, J. and Ts'o, P. (Editors), Holden-Day, London, 1964.
[2] SABATINI, D. D., BENSCH, K. and BARNETT, R. J. *J. Cell Biol.* **17**, 19, 1963.
[3] KARNOVSKY, M. J. *J. Biophysic. Biochem. Cytol.* **11**, 729, 1961.
[4] TERAYAMA, H. *Exp. Cell Res.* **28**, 113, 1962.
[5] RAYSET, H. J.-P. and HANCOCK, R. *Science* **150**, 501, 1965.

THE TRAPPED SUPERNATANT IN THE PACKED RED CELL COLUMN ON CENTRIFUGATION OF BOVINE RED CELL SUSPENSIONS AND ITS RELATION TO THE DEFORMABILITY OF THE RED CELL

H. W. Thomas* and D. E. Janes

Physics Department, The National Institute for Research in Dairying, Shinfield, Reading, England

INTRODUCTION

We are currently studying the wall effects that arise when suspensions of bovine red cells are allowed to flow through narrow tubes of sub-millimetre bore. For such studies it is essential to control accurately the volume concentration of the red cells. The most convenient way of achieving this close control is to centrifuge aliquots of the suspension in calibrated tubes, provided one is able to make an adequate correction for the amount of supernatant trapped between the cells in the packed red cell column. In the case of whole human blood, several investigators have determined the trapped plasma, and a fairly definitive picture has emerged [Refs. 1–15, in particular Refs. 1–3 give extensive references to earlier literature]. After 30 min centrifugation at a reduced centrifugal force (RCF) of 1500 g referred to the bottom of a Wintrobe tube, the trapped plasma for blood at normal physiological concentrations is about 0·04 when expressed as a proportion of the apparent red cell column. In recent years the use of microhaematocrit tubes with special centrifuges, giving an RCF of the order of 12,000 g and with spinning times of about 5 min, has become very common, and under these conditions, the trapped plasma can be as low as 0·01[14, 15]. Such values can, for most practical purposes, be neglected. Some information is also available for bovine blood[16–23] and this indicates quite clearly that the trapped plasma for this species can be about threefold greater than that obtaining for human blood under the same conditions of centrifugation. We wished to achieve a smaller variance in the measurement of volume concentration than seemed possible on the basis of the published data, and, in addition, we anticipated that the trapped supernatant would be significantly smaller for a suspension of red cells than for whole blood at the same concentration (a supposition which was later confirmed by Chien et al.[23]). Hence we decided to determine the trapped supernatant for our own suspensions, and to ascertain the variability that might be encountered from sample to sample. This preliminary calibration revealed certain features which might be of general interest.

METHOD

Blood samples were withdrawn from healthy cows by puncture of the external jugular vein. Heparin, at a concentration of 15 units per ml of blood was used as an anticoagulant. After centrifugation at about 1000 g, the plasma and white cells were removed, and the cells consecutively washed with the suspending phase and centrifuged two or three times until there were no significant traces of white cells. The red cells were then suspended at the chosen concentration in the same suspending phase (Eagle's solution: NaCl 6.20 g/l., KCl 0.36 g/l., NaH_2PO_4 . H_2O 0.13 g/l., $NaHCO_3$ 2·00 g/l., $CaCl_2$ 0·18 g/l., $MgCl_2$. $6H_2O$ 0·15 g/l., dextrose 0·90 g/l., modified by the addition of crystallized bovine albumin to a concentration of 10 g/l). Radioiodinated human serum albumin (preparation 1B.17P from the Radiochemical Centre, Amersham) was obtained as a solution in physiological saline at an albumin concentration of 20 g/l. and with an activity of about 1 mC/ml. This solution was diluted twofold with saline so as to bring the albumin concentration to the same value as that of the above suspending phase. This diluted solution was passed through an ion-exchange column (Permutit "Deacidite FF") in order to remove any traces of radioactive-free iodide: it is known from our own observations and those of other authors[3, 5, 24, 25] that iodide enters the red cell extremely readily, and any radioactive iodide in our preparation would lead to grossly high values for the measured trapped supernatant. Very small amounts of this material were then added to the prepared suspension to give a final activity generally in the range 20–30 μC per ml.

Aliquots of the prepared suspensions were taken in standard Wintrobe tubes (BS 2554 (1954), internal bore 2·55 mm, length 111 mm) and after sealing the open ends with small pieces of "Parafilm" (Lindsay and Williams, Ltd.) in order to limit loss due to evaporation, the tubes were centrifuged at the desired RCF for the desired period of time (Martin Christ, Junior III Centrifuge). The electrical tachometer fitted to the centrifuge was calibrated stroboscopically against a neon lamp. The effective radius of the swing-out head was measured directly by means of a dip-stick inserted down to the origin of an empty Wintrobe tube placed in position in the swung-out position. The centrifuge required a finite time to accelerate and to deaccelerate to and from the set working speed. A preliminary calibration was carried out of the variation of speed and hence of the RCF during these periods. One could then calculate the times of centrifugation at the set working conditions which would be necessary to give the same area under the RCF–time curves. These times were then used to correct the experimental periods of centrifugation: the corrections amounted to the addition of between 1 and 3 min to the time between switching on and switching off of the centrifuge motor, and were in fact insignificant except for the shorter periods of centrifugation.

Each Wintrobe tube was then read and cut at a point a millimetre or two below the red cell–supernatant interface. Since the top of each tube had been sealed with "Parafilm", the contents of the top section were retained within the tube, and it was possible to transfer the contents of the two separate sections without any spill into two separate graduated flasks. After making the flasks up to volume (25 ml for cells, 100 ml for the supernatant) 5 ml aliquots were counted in a conventional 2 inch well-type thallium-activated NaI crystal. Counting rates in excess of 1000 c.p.m. were generally obtained, and they could easily be determined to an accuracy of a few percent.

The red cells were frequently observed under a microscope in order to ensure that they remained in good condition.

Figure 1 illustrates the method of calculating the trapped supernatant. If C_r and C_s are the total activities derived respectively from below and above the cutting

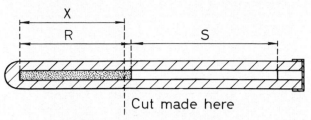

Cut made here

FIG. 1. DIAGRAM TO ILLUSTRATE THE METHOD OF DETERMINING THE TRAPPED SUPERNATANT IN THE PACKED RED CELL COLUMN.

point, if r is the activity contained per unit length of the packed red cell column, s the activity per unit length of the supernatant column, R the total length of the red cell column, X the length of the red column remaining below the cut, and S the length of the supernatant column, then

$$C_r = rX$$
$$C_s = r(R-X) + sS$$

On dividing and rearranging we get

$$(r/s) = (S/X)\{[C_s/C_r] - [(R-X)/X]\}^{-1} \tag{1}$$

The ratio (r/s) is the proportion of the red cell column that is, in fact, trapped supernatant. In order to determine the true volume concentration one must apply a correction $-(r/s)R$ to the apparent red cell column length R.

In addition to direct determination of the trapped supernatant (r/s) in the above manner, values were also obtained indirectly as follows. The length of the red cell column was observed at different times during centrifugation, and then the tube was finally cut to obtain the direct value as above. This enabled the true concentration for the particular sample to be calculated. This true concentration was subtracted from the earlier apparent values of the red cell column length to give a series of values of the trapped plasma. These indirect values were acceptable only for the lower values of the RCF or for shorter periods of centrifugation, when the absolute corrections $-(r/s)R$ were sufficiently large compared to the uncertainty of reading the haematocrit tubes.

RESULTS

Figure 2 shows the results obtained for one sample of red cells at three different volume concentrations 0·206, 0·419 and 0·621, for different periods of centrifugation up to 12 hr at a reduced centrifugal force of 3500 g. Beyond this time there were indications that some cells disintegrated. As one would naturally expect, the value of (r/s) decreases with increasing time of centrifugation, and increases with an increase in volume concentration. This particular experiment was extended over such a long period of time in order to determine whether the trapped supernatant (r/s) attains an asymptototic value, since such an equilibrium state would provide a useful starting point for any possible physical analysis of the problem. Clearly such an asymptotic value is not attained within a reasonable period of time.

The results of Fig. 2 present a completely consistent set, but as soon as measure-

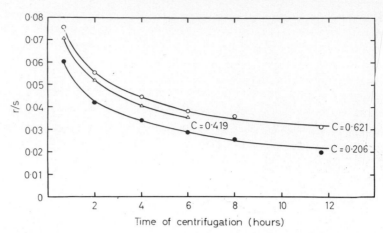

FIG. 2. VARIATION OF THE TRAPPED SUPERNATANT (r/s), DETERMINED AT 3500 g, WITH TIME AND VOLUME CONCENTRATION FOR A SINGLE SAMPLE OF CELLS (COW S37).

ments were extended to a wider range of conditions, horrible inconsistencies appeared. The (r/s) value obtained at any one particular concentration could be much greater than that obtained at a much higher concentration on a previous occasion under identical conditions of centrifugation. Whereas we were initially concerned that we had failed to master the fairly elementary techniques involved, it soon become clear that these anomalous results were due to consistent differences between samples of red cells taken from different animals. This is well illustrated in Fig. 3 which gives the values obtained for (r/s) after 2 hr centrifugation at 3500 g for a range of values of the volume concentration c. Although results deriving from nine different animals are recorded in this figure, the most striking feature is that the points for the two cows

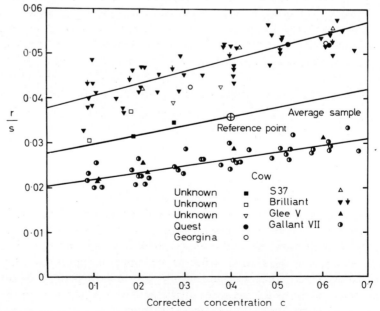

FIG. 3. VARIATION OF THE TRAPPED SUPERNATANT (r/s), DETERMINED AFTER 2 HR CENTRIFUGATION AT 3500 g, WITH VOLUME CONCENTRATION, FOR VARIOUS SAMPLES OF BOVINE RED CELLS.

Brilliant and Gallant fall into two distinct groups. The trapped supernatant in the case of cells from Brilliant is almost twice that obtained for Gallant, and this pattern was maintained consistently for samples drawn on thirteen separate occasions over a period of 11 months. It is easy to see from Fig. 3 how the inconsistencies in our earlier results arose: the difference between samples from two different animals can be much greater than the total variation of (r/s) over the complete experimental range of concentration.

From Fig. 3, for cells from both Brilliant and Gallant, it seems that there is a linear relation between the trapped supernatant (r/s) and the volume concentration c. The upper and lower lines in the figure are the calculated regression lines for the experimental points obtained for the two animals Brilliant and Gallant. Throughout the whole range of concentration 0 to 0·7, the ratio of the ordinates of the two regression lines is effectively constant, varying only from 1·85 to 1·84. This fact is taken advantage of in the reduction of the results to be described in the next two paragraphs. The points indicated by the symbol ▼ were obtained with one sample withdrawn on one single occasion: they also indicate a linear relation, but a slightly different one from the regression line based on all the results.

The third and central line in Fig. 3 is the geometric mean of the two drawn regression lines for cells from Brilliant and Gallant and can be taken to represent a fairly average sample. We have attempted to reduce the effect of sample variation on the results by relating them to the hypothetical results one would obtain for such an "average sample". All experimental values of r/s obtained at 3500 g at various times of centrifugation and at various volume concentrations have been multiplied by a "sample factor". This "sample factor" is the ratio of the (r/s) value for the "average sample" to that of the actual sample at the 2 hr point: these "sample factors" may be read from Fig. 3, and as we have already noted in the previous paragraph, they are independent of the volume concentration c. Applied generally to results drawn from all animals, this treatment results in a consistent set of (r/s) — time curves for different values of c such as those shown in Fig. 2 for a single sample. Applied only to the results of Fig. 3, this treatment results in all points being grouped closely around the line representing the "average sample": this suggests a further adjustment to eliminate the effect of the volume concentration on the value of (r/s). Taking $c = 0·4$ as a reference concentration, one multiplies all the results which have been corrected by the "sample factor" by a "concentration factor", which is the ratio of the (r/s) value of the "average sample" at 0·4 concentration to that of the "average sample" at the concentration c, in both cases taking the values at 2 hr. Since the equation for the "average sample" line is $(r/s) = 0·0278 + 0·0204c$, the concentration factor can be shown to be $0·0360/(0·0278 + 0·0204c)$. In fact, the simultaneous application of both the "sample" and "concentration factors" is equivalent to multiplying the raw data by the ratio of the (r/s) value for the "average sample" at 0·4 concentration to the (r/s) value of the actual sample at the actual c, both values being taken at the 2 hr point. When this procedure was carried out, all the adjusted experimental values of (r/s) fell close to a single smooth curve (that labelled 3500 g in Fig. 4), at least for times of centrifugation of 1 hr and above. The agreement deteriorated rapidly with the time of centrifugation below this value. The vertical lines in Fig. 4 indicate the scatter of the experimental points (which numbered between 12 and 17 at each experimental time of observation) and this scatter lies, in general, within the limits ±0·0025. By simple reversal of the above

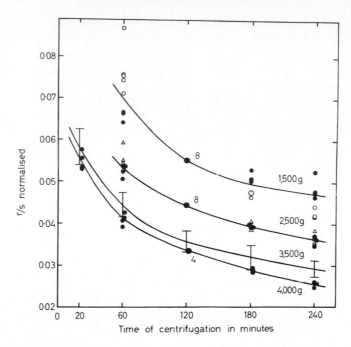

FIG. 4. VARIATION OF THE TRAPPED SUPERNATANT (r/s) WITH REDUCED CENTRIFUGAL FORCE AND TIME OF CENTRIFUGATION, AFTER NORMALIZATION WITH RESPECT TO AN AVERAGE SAMPLE AT VOLUME CONCENTRATION 0.4 (SEE TEXT) (CLOSED CIRCLES — BRILLIANT, OPEN CIRCLES — GALLANT, OPEN TRIANGLES — GLEE).

procedure this "master" curve could, in principle, be used for deriving the trapped supernatant at any values of the volume concentration, and of the time of centrifugation, within the experimental ranges. It would be necessary, however, to determine the "sample factor" for every sample in question, directly, and hence this possibility is unlikely to have practical utility.

The treatment described above has also been extended to the rather fewer results obtained at reduced centrifugal forces of 1500; 2500; and 4000 g. (At 4000 g it was necessary to deduce some (r/s) values by extrapolation from the values obtained at lower RCF.) The corresponding "master curves" are shown in Fig. 4. It is important to point out that both the "sample factors" and the "concentration factors" are dependent on the value of the RCF. At the RCF values 1500, 2500, 3500, and 4000 g the "sample factor" in the case of cells withdrawn from Gallant are respectively 1·26, 1·30, 1·36 and 1·41. (Since the geometric mean of the ordinates was used to construct the regression line for the "average sample", the "sample factor" for cells withdrawn from Brilliant must be 1/1·26, 1/1·30, 1/1·36 and 1/1·41 respectively.) For the same values of the RCF the regression lines for the "average sample" are respectively:

$$(r/s) = 0·039_9 + 0·038_3 c$$

$$(r/s) = 0·033_5 + 0·027_2 c$$

$$(r/s) = 0·027_8 + 0·020_4 c$$

$$(r/s) = 0·027_3 + 0·017_3 c$$

and from these equations one can calculate the "concentration factor" at $c = 0$ to be respectively 1·38, 1·33, 1·29 and 1·25. However, the curves given in Fig. 4 give a clear indication of the effect of the variation of the RCF and of the time of centrifugation on the value of (r/s) after elimination of the influence of both the sample variation and of the volume concentration.

DISCUSSION

First, it may be well for us to examine critically the methods we have chosen for our measurements, and the possible sources of systematic error.

Radioiodinated serum albumin is a favoured choice as a plasma label[1, 3, 5, 6, 10, 13, 18, 19, 20, 23]. It is readily available, and is believed not to enter the red cell, or to be adsorbed on the red cell membrane to any significant degree. LEESON and REEVE[1] conclude from electrophoretic observations that iodinated bovine albumin did not attach itself to human or rabbit red cells. On the other hand, the evidence presented by the detailed study of HUGHES-JONES and GARDNER[26] would not allow one to be so categorical, but they do give several indications that the adsorption of iodinated human albumin by human red cells is likely to be so small that experiments such as our own should not be subject to serious errors on that score. For instance, they found that the adsorbed labelled albumin which resists several washings of the cells with saline has a maximum value of 5 μg/ml of red cells; in our experiments with a minimal value of (r/s) of 0·02, the total albumin in the packed red cell column would be 200 μg/ml of cells, and the labelled albumin would be of the order of 20 μg/ml. They show further that the adsorbed labelled albumin which resists washing with saline exchanges readily with non-labelled albumin. They maintain that the adsorption characteristics of iodinated proteins do not differ from those of the unlabelled protein, and demonstrate this in the case of γ-globulin. It would seem to us unlikely that there should be preferential adsorption of labelled human albumin on the bovine cells of our experiments to the high concentration of 20 μg/ml of red cells, and certainly a total adsorption of albumin to a concentration of 200 μg/ml of red cells seems a very remote possibility. We ourselves have also carried out one measurement of the trapped supernatant for cells taken from the animal Gallant after centrifugation for 2 hr in a shortened Wintrobe tube placed in an ultra centrifuge capable of giving an RCF at the bottom of the tube of 18,000 g, and have obtained a value of 0·008 for (r/s). This certainly presents an upper limit to the error arising from the adsorption of labelled albumin on the red cells. In presenting our results above, we have not made any correction to allow for adsorbed labelled albumin.

Some authors have used an indirect method of determining the trapped supernatant in the packed red cell column. They have compared the dilution of a small quantity of a supernatant label (dye or radioisotope) by a known volume of blood or red cell suspension, with the dilution observed when a small quantity of the same label is diluted by a known volume of the clear supernatant. From the data they can calculate a "plasmocrit" and hence the haematocrit. The trapped supernatant is then calculated from the difference between this value and the apparent haematocrits read from centrifuge tubes. We ourselves have chosen the direct method of determining the amount of the labelled material within the packed red cell column, since a scanning of the literature [1–23] makes it clear that much more consistent results are thereby obtained.

In deriving eq. (1) we have assumed that the mean value of (r/s) is the same for the two portions of the red cell column above and below the cutting point. However, some authors have already shown that the trapped supernatant varies within the red cell column, increasing from the bottom to the top[1, 5, 6, 11]. If we allow for such a variation, and let r' be the mean activity per unit length in that part of the red cell column transferred to the supernatant flask, and r'' the mean activity per unit length in the remainder of the red cell column, then eq. (1) must be modified as follows:

$$(r''/s) = (S/X)\{[C_s/C_r] - (r'/r'')[(R-X)/X]\}^{-1} \tag{2}$$

If r is the mean activity per unit length over the whole of the red cell column, we must have:

$$(r/s)R = (r''/s)X + (r'/s)(R-X) \tag{3}$$

From eq. (2) and (3) by rearrangement we get:

$$(r/s) = (S/X)\frac{\{1 + [(r'/r'') - 1][(R-X)/R]\}}{\{[C_s/C_r] - [(R-X)/X] - [(R-X)/X][(r'/r'') - 1]\}} \tag{4}$$

Equation (4) differs from eq. (1) only in the extra final terms within the curly brackets in both the numerator and the denominator. If $(r'/r'') = 1$, then the two equations are identical as expected. CLARK and WALSH[11] determined the trapped plasma in 12 mm sections taken from the top and bottom of the red cell column at a volume concentration (we presume) of about 0·4. After 30 min centrifugation at values of RCF in the range 617–2055 g, the ratio of trapped plasma at the top to that at the bottom of the red cell column varied between 1·55 and 1·62. Although Clark and Walsh investigated whole human blood, the mean value of (r/s) for the whole red cell column that they obtained under these conditions varied between 0·044 and 0·069, which is comparable to or greater than most of the values we have reported in the results section. Hence a value <1·6 is not unreasonable for (r'/r'') in eq. (4). At a volume concentration of 0·4, the correction terms in eq. (4) result in less than a 3% change in the numerator and a change of less than 0·25% in the denominator. The terms $(R-X)/X$ and $(R-X)/R$ become significant at low volume concentrations, and were as high as 0.2 for measurements at about 0·1 volume concentration. In this case, assuming $(r'/r'') <$ 1·6, the correction in the numerator of eq. (4) is <12%, and that in the denominator <0·1%. However, at this low volume concentration (as will be discussed in the following paragraph) one would not expect such a large variation of (r/s) within the red cell column as is observed at 0·4 volume concentration. We have noted in the results section that at low RCF and short times of centrifugation we were also able to obtain good values for the trapped plasma indirectly. It is in this region of flow conditions that we would expect the corrections for the variation of (r/s) within the red cell column to be greatest. The indirect values are not subject to an error arising from this variation, and yet we have never been able to observe a significant systematic difference between the direct and indirect values of (r/s). We conclude that under the conditions of the experiments reported in the results section, there are no significant errors as a result of neglecting the variation of (r/s) within the packed red cell column.

In discussing Fig. 3 we noted that at a given set of conditions of centrifugation, the trapped supernatant (r/s) increases linearly with volume concentration. This is an observation already reported by other authors[4, 7, 8, 9, 11]. Since it has also been shown that the trapped supernatant increases from the bottom to the top of the red cell column, it is generally assumed that the increase in mean (r/s) with volume concentration is due to the fact that the RCF decreases appreciably with the height of the red cells from a maximum value at the bottom of the centrifuge tube. CLARK and WALSH[11] hint that the results do not correlate well with the actual variation of the RCF and although the position is improved by extending the period of centrifugation, they suggest that other factors must be operative. As a result of our measurements we are in a position to look closer at this point. From Fig. 3 and from the similar plots for values of the RCF of 1500, 2500 and 4000 g we are able to read off the values of (r/s) in the limit as c tends to zero, and to construct a corresponding $(r/s)_{c=0}$-RCF curve for a time of centrifugation of 2 hr. This curve would presumably give the true value of the mean (r/s) if the total volume of red cells was subjected to the RCF obtaining at the bottom of the tube, and if the extrusion of intercellular fluid from between the cells at any level was not hindered by the presence of red cells at higher levels. The effective radius of the centrifuge was 16·60 cm and the RCF at any level within the tube is given by the equation $g/g_0 = (16\cdot60 - 10c)/16\cdot60$, where g_0 is the RCF at the bottom of the tube, and c is the volume concentration of the red cell suspension that would give a completely packed cell column reaching to the level in question. From the (r/s)-RCF curves one may now calculate the value of r/s one would expect at each level within the tube, and on numerical integration of this data, one obtains the mean (r/s)-volume concentration curve. We have carried out this analysis on the data available on the cells of the animal Brilliant, which happened to be the most comprehensive available. The final plot was slightly curved due to the curvature of the (r/s)-RCF plot, but gave a very good fit to the regression line $(r/s) = 0\cdot0378 + 0\cdot0071c$. The actual data obtained for cells deriving from Brilliant were shown in Fig. 3 to fit the regression line $(r/s) = 0\cdot0378 + 0\cdot0274c$. Clearly the increase of the mean (r/s) value with increase in volume concentration is far in excess of that which can be accounted for by a decrease in the RCF with height within the tube. There must be an additional crowding effect, the extrusion of fluid from between the cells at any level being hindered by the presence of the cells at the higher levels. This analysis was carried out on data obtained after 2 hr centrifugation. It is probable that after a longer period of centrifugation, or with a higher value of the RCF, the agreement between analysis and experiment would be better. Perfect agreement may not be possible unless the mean value of r/s attains an asymptotic value after long periods of centrifugation and this we have shown to be probably unattainable (see Fig. 2).

It is only possible to make a limited comparison between our results and those of other authors. CHIEN et al.[23] have determined the trapped supernatant on centrifuging suspensions of red cells of various species in Ringer's solution at 1500 g for 30 min. Unfortunately, they made no measurements on bovine cells. However, they present a curve relating the trapped plasma to the mean corpuscular volume in the case of whole blood, and a similar plot can be constructed for the cells suspended in Ringer's solution. On interpolation of this data for a mean cell volume of 50 μ^3 for the bovine red cell[27] one obtains a value of about 0·06 for the trapped supernatant (r/s). In the case of our measurements at the same conditions of centrifugation, (r/s)

had a value 0·10 for cells taken from Gallant, and 0·12 for cells taken from the animal Brilliant, these two animals representing extremes in results. The findings are in considerable disagreement, but it is well to note that Chien *et al.* used wider bore centrifuge tubes, and that we ourselves have added a significant amount of albumin to our suspending phase. Interpolation of the data given by Chien *et al.* for whole blood on the basis of mean corpuscular volume would result in a trapped plasma of about 0·065 whereas JENNINGS *et al.*[18] quote a value of $0·125 \pm 0·048$ under the same conditions of centrifugation (except for the bore of the centrifuge tube). It would seem to us that bovine blood is a definite exception to the otherwise excellent correlation found by Chien *et al.* between the trapped plasma and mean corpuscular volume.

In all our future experiments on the flow properties of bovine red cell suspensions we shall centrifuge aliquots for 2 hr at 3500 g and make use of the data of Fig. 3 for correcting for the amount of supernatant trapped in the red cell column. An inspection of the results on cells withdrawn from Gallant indicates that, if in calling on a sample from this animal in the future, one makes use of the corresponding regression line, one will obtain a value of (r/s) which will certainly be correct to within $\pm 0·0035$. The volume concentration at about the 0·4 level could be determined to an accuracy of $\pm 0·001$. Likewise, for Brilliant, c at the 0·4 level should be determinable to a precision of $\pm 0·002$. Such precision is almost superfluous, since greater errors will arise from uncertainties in reading the lengths of the red cell and supernatant columns, and from variation of the volume concentration of successive samples. In our experience, when taking several haematocrits from a large volume (>20 ml) of well-stirred suspension and taking the greatest care in reading the haematocrit tubes (including the correction for the zero errors on the engraved scales), it is possible to achieve values of volume concentration consistent to $\pm 0·002$.

The consistent contrast in results for the trapped supernatant on centrifugation of red cell suspensions derived from different animals deserves some further comment. Examination of the pedigrees, which were available for most of the animals, did not yield any evidence that there was any genetic basis to the pattern of results obtained. The red cells from the two animals Brilliant and Gallant showed essentially the same size distribution when measured on several occasions by means of a Coulter counter. We have some evidence that the red cells from the animal Gallant, which gave the lower (r/s) values, are sometimes, but not always, prone to slight hemolysis after several hours handling, and sometimes exhibit a very small proportion of bowl forms. The results are, however, very reminiscent of the finding of EVANS and PHILLIPSON[28] that the potassium concentration in bovine red cells shows little variation during successive measurements over a period of 17 months, but vast differences between individual animals.

To obtain a packed red cell concentration of the order of 0·95 to 0·98 requires the application of considerable accelerations several thousand times that of gravity. Human red cells have a specific gravity of about 1·09[27] and bovine red cells are probably not far different. Hence at such accelerations they would be subject to forces of the order of several hundred times the force of gravity. Further, at such high volume concentrations the cells must be considerably deformed from their normal biconcave shape. The contrast in the results for the trapped supernatant for cells from the different animals, may be presumed to imply a difference in the mechanical properties of the red cell membrane. One is tempted to talk of a difference in the "deformability" of the various samples of red cells, although we do so hesitatingly since we are not clear about the mode of the deformation, and have no direct measure of either a stress or a strain.

The ability of red cells to deform has been mentioned in a variety of contexts. RAND and BURTON[29] have determined the resistance to deformation of the red cell membrane by measuring the pressure required to suck a portion of the cell into a micropipette. The deformability of red cells has often been cited in connection with studies where blood or red cell suspensions are forced through filters or very narrow tubes with bore comparable to the diameter of the cell[30–33]. There is much direct evidence that red cells are deformed appreciably *in vivo* due to hydrodynamic forces and due to both cell–cell and to cell–wall interactions[34–36]. SIRS[37] has proposed that a difference in flexibility of the red cells resulting in a change in amounts of water pumped across the membrane when a suspension of the cells is subjected to turbulent flow, is necessary to account for the difference between the high initial rate of uptake of NO by fresh sheep cells, and the low rate of uptake observed a few hours later. The deformability of red cells has been suggested by GOLDSMITH and MASON[38] to be the major element in the development of radial migrations of red cells in tube flow.

Finally, the flow properties of very concentrated suspensions are known to depend quite markedly on the deformability of the suspended particles. Rigid spheres in open packing have a volume concentration of about 0·52, and it is difficult to envisage a suspension at a higher concentration than this being sheared at all. In practice with a more random packing of particles, one would expect flow to cease at a lower concentration, and experimental results confirm this[39, 40]. The particles must be deformable for flow to be possible at concentrations above 0·52, as is possible with red cell suspensions. This picture is also confirmed by the experimental findings of certain workers who have compared the flow properties of normal and hardened red cells [40, 41], but some caution may be required in detailed interpretation of these results

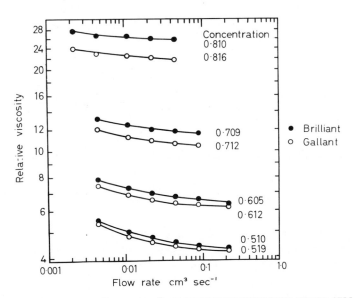

FIG. 5. VARIATION OF THE RELATIVE "APPARENT" VISCOSITY OF SUSPENSIONS OF RED CELLS FROM THE TWO ANIMALS BRILLIANT AND GALLANT WITH FLOW RATE AND VOLUME CONCENTRATION.

since at very high concentrations, the particle–particle interactions dominate the phenomenon, and differences in the surface properties of the cells could affect the flow behaviour. It is of interest to know whether concentrated suspensions of cells drawn from the two animals Brilliant and Gallant exhibit a sharp contrast in flow properties as they did, so startlingly, for the trapped supernatant on centrifugation.

For the measurement of the flow properties a capillary viscometer arrangement of our own design was used[42]. The capillary bore used was 0·058 cm, and the pressure developed across a length 6·0 cm was detected by means of a pressure transducer at various flow rates fixed by a worm-driven syringe. The results obtained for the "apparent" viscosity relative to the viscosity of the suspending phase, at various flow rates and volume concentrations are shown in Fig. 5. All the experimental points lie within 1% of the best smooth curves. The concentrations of the suspensions from the two animals do not match exactly, since it is difficult and tedious to arrange this experimentally. However, by plotting the smoothed data on relative viscosity–concentration plots at a number of flow rates, it is possible to interpolate the values which would be obtained at the precise volume concentrations 0·5, 0·6, 0·7 and 0·8 (at the 0·5 concentration a slight extrapolation was necessary). These derived values are plotted in Fig. 6. There is an obvious contrast between the apparent viscosities of samples

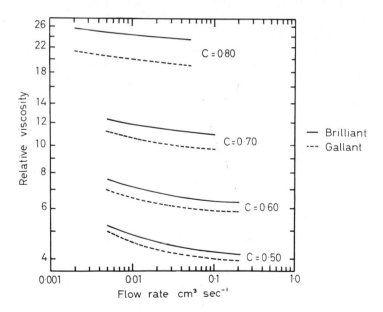

FIG. 6. VARIATION OF THE RELATIVE "APPARENT" VISCOSITY OF SUSPENSIONS OF RED CELLS FROM THE TWO ANIMALS BRILLIANT AND GALLANT WITH FLOW RATE AND VOLUME CONCENTRATION, AFTER ADJUSTMENT TO COMMON VALUES OF THE VOLUME CONCENTRATION.

drawn from the two animals, and at the concentrations 0·8, 0·7, 0·6 and 0·5 the differences amount to 20, 12, 8 and 5% respectively. After centrifugation for 2 hr at 3500 g the trapped supernatant for red cell suspensions from these two animals differed by as much as 59%. The trapped supernatant obtained on centrifugation seems to give a much more sensitive index to the sample difference in mechanical properties of the red cell membrane, than does the relative viscosity in the concentration range up to 0·8.

SUMMARY

In all experiments on the flow properties of red cell suspensions, it is essential to control accurately the volume concentration of the cells. This can be measured by centrifuging aliquots of the suspension in calibrated (Wintrobe) tubes, provided one knows the amount of supernatant fluid trapped between the red cells in the packed column. In order to evaluate this trapped supernatant, radioiodinated human serum albumin has been used as an indicator. During the course of this investigation remarkable and consistent differences were discovered between the red cell samples taken from different cows, and the trapped supernatant values varied over a twofold range. We surmise that these systematic differences are due to variation in the physical properties of the red cell membrane, in so far as they govern the ease with which the red cells can be deformed into a packed column. These differences are also reflected in the measured flow properties of concentrated red cell suspensions.

ACKNOWLEDGMENTS

We are grateful to Mr. B. B. Brown for assisting us in securing the samples of bovine blood, to Dr. R. F. Glascock and to Mr. S. H. Phillips for making the equipment for the radioactivity assaying available to us, and to Mr. F. A. Glover for determining the volume distributions of the red cells on the Coulter counter.

This investigation was supported in whole by the Public Health Service of the U.S.A. Research Grant, HE 05732 from the National Heart Institute.

REFERENCES

[1] LEESON, D. and REEVE, E. B. J. Physiol. 115, 129, 1951.
[2] JACKSON, D. M. and NUTT, M. E. J. Physiol. 115, 196, 1951.
[3] VAZQUEZ, O. N., NEWERLY, K., YALOW, R. S. and BERSON, S. A. J. Lab. Clin. Med. 39, 595, 1952.
[4] CHAPLIN, H. JR. and MOLLISON, P. L. Blood 7, 1227, 1952.
[5] OWEN, C. A. JR. and POWER, M. H. J. Appl. Physiol. 5, 323, 1953.
[6] HEAD, C. J. JR. and HOLMES, J. H. J. Appl. Physiol. 5, 457, 1953.
[7] EBAUGH, F. G. JR., LEVINE, P. and EMERSON, C. P. J. Lab. Clin. Med. 46, 409, 1955.
[8] FURTH, F. W. J. Lab. Clin. Med. 48, 421, 1956.
[9] WADSWORTH, G. R. Experientia 13, 149, 1957.
[10] HODGETTS, V. E., Austral. J. Exp. Biol. 37, 97, 1959.
[11] CLARK, P. and WALSH, R. J. Austral. J. Exp. Biol. 38, 451, 1960.
[12] JONES, R. F. J. Clin. Path. 14, 198, 1961.
[13] CHIEN, S. and GREGERSEN, M. I. In Physical Techniques in Biological Research, Vol. IV, Special Methods, NASTUK, W. L. (Editor), Academic Press, New York, 1962, p. 22.
[14] GARBY, L. and VUILLE, J.-C. Scand. J. Clin. Lab. Invest. 13, 642, 1961.
[15] RUSTAD, H. Scand. J. Clin. Lab. Invest. 16, 677, 1964.
[16] REYNOLDS, M. Amer. J. Physiol. 173, 421, 1953.
[17] BUNCE, S. A. Brit. Vet. J. 110, 322, 1954.
[18] JENNINGS, F. W., LAUDER, I. M., MULLIGAN, W. and URQUHART, G. M. Vet. Rec. 66, 155, 1954.
[19] JENNINGS, F. W., LAUDER, I. M. and MULLIGAN, W. Biochem. J. 59, iii, 1955.
[20] JENNINGS, F. W., LAUDER, I. M. and MULLIGAN, W. Analyst 81, 441, 1956.
[21] FISHER, E. W. Brit. Vet. J. 118, 513, 1962.
[22] LEPHERD, E. E. Aust. Vet. J. 41, 380, 1965.
[23] CHIEN, S., DELLENBACK, R. J., USAMI, S. and GREGERSEN, M. I. Proc. Soc. Exp. Biol. Med. 119, 1155, 1965.
[24] RALL, G. E., POWER, M. H. and ALBERT, A. Proc. Soc. Exp. Biol. Med. 74, 460, 1950.
[25] BOATMAN, J. B. and MOSES, C. Amer. J. Physiol. 164, 783, 1951.
[26] HUGHES-JONES, N. C. and GARDNER, BRIGITTE. Biochem. J. 83, 404, 1962.

[27] ALTMAN, P. L. and DITTMER, D. S. *Blood and Other Bodyfluids*, Fed. Amer. Soc. Exp. Biol. Washington, D.C. 1961.
[28] EVANS, J. V. and PHILLIPSON, A. T. *J. Physiol.* **139**, 87, 1957.
[29] RAND, R. P. and BURTON, A. C. *Biophysical J.* **4(2)**, 115, 1964.
[30] SWANK, R. L., ROTH, J. G. and JANSEN, J. J. *J. Appl. Physiol.* **19**, 340, 1964.
[31] TEITEL, P. *Nature* **206**, 409, 1965.
[32] PROTHERO, J. W. and BURTON, A. C. *Biophysical J.* **2**, 213, 1962.
[33] BRAASCH, D. and HENNIG, W. *Pflüger's Archiv.* **286**, 76, 1965.
[34] BLOCH, E. H. *Amer. J. Anatomy* **110**, 125, 1962.
[35] BRÅNEMARK, P-I. and LINDSTRÖM, J. *Biorheology* **1(2)**, 139, 1963.
[36] GUEST, M. M., BOND, T. P., COOPER, R. G. and DERRICK, J. R. *Science* **142**, 1319, 1963.
[37] SIRS, J. *Biochim. Biophys. Acta* **90**, 108, 1964.
[38] GOLDSMITH, H. L. and MASON, S. G. *Biorheology* **3**, 33, 1965.
[39] TAYLOR, H. M., CHIEN, S., GREGERSEN, M. I. and LUNDBERG, J. L. *Nature* **207**, 77, 1965.
[40] SEAMAN, G. V. F. This volume, p. 551.
[41] KURODA, K., MISHIRO, Y., WADA, I. *Tokushima J. Exp. Med.* **4**, 73, 1958.
[42] THOMAS, H. W., JANES, D. E. and BARNES, H. A. Abstracts, *4th Europ. Conf. on Microcirculation*, Cambridge, 26th June–2nd July, 1966, p. 72.

DISCUSSION

BURTON (*Canada*):
Do you think that it was possible that there were differences in lipid concentration in the blood of these two cows that might conceivably explain the discrepancies? We have heard that lipid changes can change the viscosity, and perhaps the packing properties also.

THOMAS (*England*):
Are you referring to differences in lipid on the red cell membrane?

BURTON:
Well, we heard earlier in the week that certain lipids in the blood can change the nature of the surface membrane. They coat the red cell, and so could change the viscosity and also perhaps change the ability to pack very tightly.

THOMAS:
This I cannot say.

BURTON:
Did you ever do a bull? Is there a sex difference?

THOMAS:
No, we have not taken samples from bulls.

GREGERSEN (*U.S.A.*):
Did I understand correctly that you found a trapping factor of 12% or what?

THOMAS:
In fact, I was quoting the work of JENNINGS *et al.*[18] who centrifuged their samples for 30 min only, at a value of the reduced centrifugal force of only 1500 *g*. We have reported results obtained at 3500 *g*, and of course obtained much lower values for the trapped supernatant. However, a handful of results which we have obtained at 1500 *g* are consistent with those of Jennings *et al.*

GREGERSEN:
That is a high *g* for ordinary centrifugation. Your curves, of course, look very much like those of Millard, some time back in the twenties, when he centrifuged for long periods of time. It is a disturbing thing, in doing trapping factors, when you know that you have a variable dependent upon the force and time of centrifugation; it is not an absolute value. But you evidently could not get an asymptotic value even if you went out far, could you? No matter how much you spin, you still have possibilities of reducing it. Is that not right?

THOMAS:

We centrifuged one sample for 12 hrs and there was indication of intercellular fluid still being egressed slowly. We do not think one would wish to repeat the experiment often.

GREGERSEN:

I have really not seen any longer centrifugations. We have tried them for 3, 4, 5 hr, but never for 12. Does that mean that you are squeezing stuff out of the cells or do they remain the same? I wonder what shape or size they are after long hard centrifugation.

THOMAS:

I would not expect water to be pressed out from within the cells. A very high pressure exists at the bottom of the centrifuge tube, but this is hydrostatic pressure which applies both within and outside the cells. An attempt has been made to check this point by VAZQUEZ et al.[3], who compared the activity of radioiodinated albumin in the supernatant before and after centrifugation. Within their level of precision of about 1%, they found no evidence of any dilution due to egress of water from within the cells.

SILBERBERG (Israel):

I just wondered whether there is any chance of absorption of the radioactive indicator and in this way perhaps faking some of your results. Have you checked this calibration with, let us say, marked cells in a complementary study?

THOMAS:

This should not cause a serious error unless you are maintaining that the radioactive albumin is adsorbed preferentially. It is difficult to check this point. We have centrifuged one sample at 18,000 g, and managed to reduce the trapped supernatant to 0·008. This result sets an upper limit for the error due to the adsorption of albumin. From the point of view of controlling the concentration of suspensions, this error is probably insignificant.

BURTON:

I am trying to picture a bit of trapped plasma that reached the bottom early. Later on, with the whole column of tightly packed cells on top, it becomes a severe rheological problem to emerge: it is like a volcanic problem. This perhaps is the reason why you do not have a asymptote. And also it would mean that the final slow slope would be very variable. But it is difficult to visualize when you have been centrifuging for 3, 4 hr, and there is still some plasma at the bottom of the packed column, how it is ever going to get out, even if you spin a lot longer. Is that not right?

THOMAS:

The evidence of Fig. 2 is that intercellular fluid was still being egressed after several hours centrifugation. One curve in Fig. 2 stops short of the others, since the 12 hr point had to be rejected, due to appreciable disintegration of the red cells. When hemolysis begins, the experiment has to be closed.

PALMER (Australia):

Could I ask whether you tried blood from these two different animals, centrifuged at the high speed?

THOMAS:

No. We deliberately chose the one animal which always gave the lowest value for the trapped supernatant, since we were interested in establishing a maximum limit for the error due to adsorption of albumin on the red cell membrane.

IN VIVO HEMORHEOLOGY I

14 July, a.m.

Chairmen: LEONARD M. LIBBER, U.S.A.
STANLEY ROWLANDS, England

THE SIGNIFICANCE OF APPARENT BLOOD VISCOSITY IN CIRCULATORY HEMODYNAMIC BEHAVIOR

WILLIAM H. LEE, JR.,* ABBRAM NAJIB, MICHEAL WEIDNER,
GEORGE H. A. CLOWES, JR., EMMA S. MURNER, VESSELIN VUJOVIC

Division of Thoracic Surgery, Medical College of South Carolina, Charleston, South Carolina, U.S.A.

THE application of the basic physical concepts of hydrodynamic theory to the flow of blood in a living organism has evolved the biological subdiscipline of "hemorheology". The unique viscoelastic properties of blood flow in the healthy organism have been intensively rescrutinized over the past decade and several significant major contributions to an understanding of blood flow and tissue perfusion have evolved. The apparent viscosity of blood, and its "anomalous" behavior especially at low rates of shear, have been recognized as potentially profoundly important factors in the maintenance of adequate microvascular perfusion of the body tissues, as a factor in cardiac energy requirements in the stressed organism, and as a potential pathophysiologic parameter in various clinical states of disease (e.g. shock).

The development of refined instrumentation and technology has enabled many investigators to study the mechanics of apparent blood viscosity at extremely low rates of shear, and such studies have led to the conclusion that alterations in apparent blood viscosity are determined primarily by the relative concentration of erythrocytes (e.g. the hematocrit). The previously observed hematocrit–viscosity interdependence in blood from normal healthy organisms would suggest that many of the viscoelastic flow properties of the blood might logically be based upon intercellular coherence forces between the erythrocytes suspended in the plasma medium. Such forces are quite complex, and have been only partially defined: (a) intercellular charge effects (zeta potential); (b) the state of intermolecular polymerization of the protein matrix which is adsorbed to the surface of any of the particulate elements of blood.

The viscous drag which blood displays as it flows through the microvasculature at low shear rates, and the yield stress value for such flow, should be a complex function of several events—i.e. (at least) deformability of the red blood cell, cross-sectional area of the vascular bed, viscoelastic behavior of the walls of blood vessels in the vascular tree, the relative intrinsic degree of solvation and cross-linking in the colloid moiety of plasma, and the *character and proximity* of the colloid moiety adsorbed onto the particulate elements of the blood (especially the erythrocytes). Many previous studies have provided data which suggest that the last of these factors may be a major parameter (if not the single most profound factor) in determining the viscoelastic behavior of blood flow *in vivo*.

One hypothesis[10] suggests that denaturation of plasma globular proteins, (especially high molecular weight globulins which are least stable in their tertiary steric configuration) may occur in several states of trauma or disease; the globulin may be partially unfolded into random coils, exposing normally masked non-polar groups, producing free —SH groups, and creating unsatisfied H+ bonds (which in the native state bridge portions of the molecular chains to stabilize the tertiary configuration, and in the denatured state may function as intermolecular aggregatory bridges).

Such unfolded molecules may adsorb onto the red blood cell surface and subsequently (depending upon the environment of the salt concentration, solvation, pH, temperature, and kinetic intermolecular shearing forces resulting from flow velocity) may aggregate by intermolecular (thus intercellular) bridging (H+, —SH, S═S) to produce red blood cells (and other particulate) aggregates. The *rigidity* of such aggregates (or resistance to de-aggregating forces, either physicochemical or mechanical) will depend upon the nature and force of the intermolecular bridging bonds.

The studies reported herein comprise an effort to examine the complex inter-relationships, and the possibility of correlations between changes in blood proteins and blood viscosity with deleterious changes in cardiovascular hemodynamics (in terms of cardiac output and vascular resistance) and finally with evidence of altered metabolic economy of the organism (in terms of disturbance in aerobic glucose metabolism).

Materials and methods.   The disease states selected as models for these experiments included thermal burn, hypovolemic shock, endotoxin shock, and acute ethanol intoxication. The endotoxin shock and burn experiments were conducted in experimental animals (dogs). Studies in hypovolemic shock and alcohol intoxication were carried out in human patients or volunteers. The endotoxin shock and burn experiments were selected to represent severe states of disease imposing compromise of tissue perfusion and known or highly suspected alterations in plasma protein. The alcohol intoxication study was carried out in a small group of human volunteers, (medical students), and was selected as a mild reversible clinical disease known to produce overt but readily reversible changes in the suspension stability of erythrocytes in the microcirculation. The hypovolemic shock series constituted a small but intensively studied group of patients having a mild to moderate blood-volume deficit, treated by the infusion of a new colloidal plasma expander made from hydroxyethyl starch.

Viscosity determinations in these studies were made with a Cannon-Fiske capillary tube pipette of small bore, (less than 1 mm) determining kinematic viscosity (37°C) at selected driving pressure-stresses from 8 mm of mercury to 48 mm of mercury. These ranges of pressure were chosen to simulate those which may be expected to exist in the human arteriolar and venular portions of the vascular tree. The obvious inherent disadvantage of such a viscometry system is the inability to make observations of apparent viscosity at rates of shear that would be expected in the capillary portion of the vascular tree[6, 12]. However, the system should minimize the inherent disadvantages of interface protein denaturation and the resultant wall adherence effects which may occur to a greater extent in the cone-plate and G.D.M.-type viscometer systems. In addition, the relative ease and lesser expense of this type of system rendered it much more practical for the large numbers of clinical observations which were contemplated.

Cardiac output studies were performed by the standard method of cardiogreen dye-dilution densitometry. Analysis of plasma proteins was performed by several techniques. Total protein was determined by the Biuret method, and by employing refractometry, using an AO refractometer. Electrophoretic analysis was carried out by both the Durrum macrocell and the Beckman microzone techniques, and the concentrations of protein fractions calculated from the quantitative total protein measurement. Blood pressure was measured either clinically with the use of standard clinical manometers, or in experimental animals with a standard pressure transducer-recorder assembly. Vascular resistance was calculated according to the formulae which are indicated in the figures. Acid base studies for blood were carried out by the method of ASTRUP[2]. Fibrinogen concentration was estimated by the partially saturated salt fractionation technique of PARFENTJEV[3]. (Additional extensive studies of the coagulation mechanism were carried out in these experiments, but these data are not considered to be within the scope of this report, and will not be reviewed.) Hematocrit was determined by the standard macro and micro centrifuge methods. Finally, the protein capsules from red blood cells were analysed by extracting the protein material by a modification of the method of DITZEL[5], subjecting the final saline and low molecular weight dextran washes to analysis and microelectrophoretic analysis.

The protocol in all models studied was similar: a control set of samples was obtained in the experimental series prior to the induction of thermal burn or endotoxin. Both of these series also included a group of animals which were simply anesthetized and followed. In the clinical shock studies, control samples could not be obtained prior to the patient's insult of course. However, controls were obtained before the induction of any therapeutic procedure. Follow-up samples were obtained at periods varying from 30 min to six days, as explained in the text.

RESULTS

I. *Alcohol Intoxication Model*

Four human volunteers were allowed to imbibe drinks consisting of 44 cc of 100 proof bourbon whiskey containing two standard ice cubes at a frequency of one drink every 15–30 min. This was continued until the subjects became clinically inebriated. Observations of the conjunctival microcirculation were carried out, before, during and after the period of inebriation, and were repeated 12 hr later. In addition, blood samples were drawn before, during the height of inebriation and the following morning. Figure 1 demonstrates the behavior of hematocrit and apparent blood viscosity during this experiment.* A statistically significant drop in hematocrit from the control to the acute period of inebriation is noted without any statistically significant variation in viscosity at any of the pressure ranges examined. Figures 2 and 3 demonstrate the changes in fibrinogen and other coagulation factors, protein concentration, and protein-capsule washings from the red blood cells. All four subjects exhibited rather marked degrees of intravascular erythrocyte aggregation after intoxication, and for 24 hr thereafter. The hemagglutination formed was of the elastic deformable type in two subjects and a rather inelastic, more rigid type in the other two subjects. Statistically significant increase in the low molecular weight dextran wash was apparent the morning following the intoxication.

---

*All of the viscosity determinations reported in this article should be corrected as follows: 2 mm of mercury should be 8 mm of mercury, 10 mm of mercury should 18 mm of mercury, 40 mm of mercury should be 48 mm of mercury.

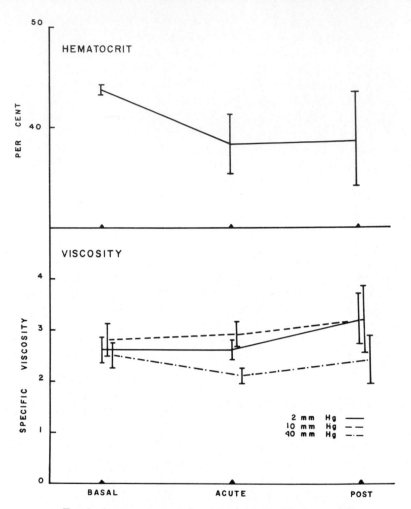

FIG. 1. ALCOHOL STUDY, 4 HUMAN SUBJECTS. MEAN AND S.E.

The dextran-extracted erythrocyte protein washings appeared to correlate most closely with the sequential alteration in apparent blood viscosity. Total serum globulins increased during the period of acute inebriation but declined as the dextran-extractable protein capsule material reached its maximum values the morning following. From these experiments, the conclusion was drawn that acute alcoholic intoxication produced an alteration of plasma protein coagulation factors, in individual cases a significant change in the apparent concentration of total globulins, a change in the extractable protein capsule material of erythrocytes, intravascular aggregation of erythrocytes of variable degrees of rigidity, and a variable effect on apparent blood viscosity. No consistent interdependence between hematocrit and viscosity was evident.

An additional individual clinical case further demonstrates the possibility of profound changes in blood viscosity which seem to be more related to the nature of plasma protein present in the circulating blood rather than the relative concentration of erythrocytes. Figures 4 and 5 display the hematocrit, viscosity, and plasma protein data for an elderly male suffering with complaints of multiple organ systems originating

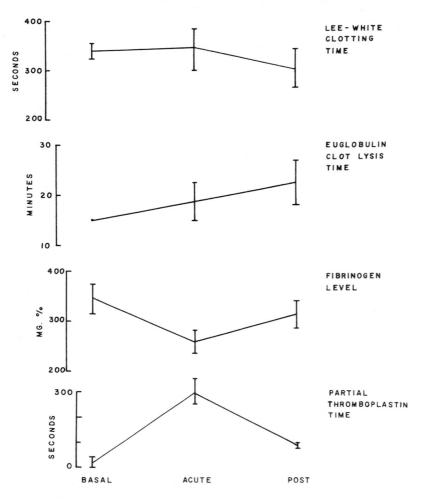

FIG. 2. ALCOHOL STUDY, 4 HUMAN SUBJECTS. MEAN AND S.E.

from deficient function. This patient displayed the highest blood viscosities which have been recorded in a series of over 100 patients. The control blood samples are noted in Fig. 4, demonstrating an unusually high total protein of almost 10 g% with a plasma globulin of almost 6 g%. The fibrinogen-plus-macroglobulin fraction was in the range of 1800 mg%. An infusion program of 500 cc of 10% low molecular weight dextran in saline every 12 hr was begun. Within 48 hr the apparent blood viscosity dropped to about 25% of the control value (Fig. 5). There was a concomitant slight decrease in hematocrit, but the hematocrit returned to levels above the control value by three days after the infusions were begun, whereas blood viscosity remained at values approximating 50% of the control after 3 days. The behavior of sequential changes in apparent blood viscosity more nearly paralleled the concentration of macroglobulins plus fibrinogen rather than concentration of red blood cells. This instance is thought to represent a diffuse alteration in the colloidal matrix of blood, corresponding to the alterations seen with the infusion of high molecular weight polysaccharide colloidal solutions. Such high concentrations of plasma macroglobulins would be expected to

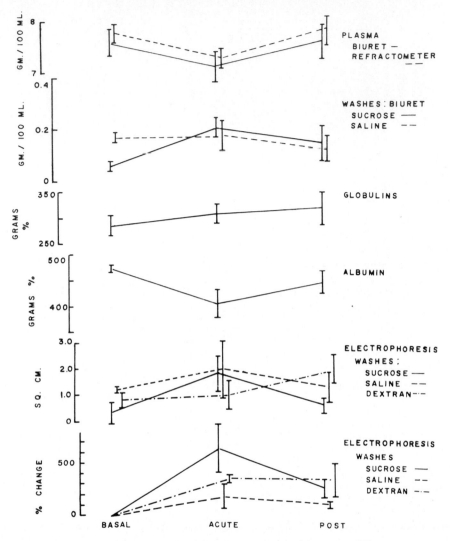

FIG. 3. ALCOHOL STUDY, 4 HUMAN SUBJECTS. MEAN AND S.E.

increase the concentration of colloid in the adsorbed surface layer on the erythrocyte, and also to drive the sol–gel relationship toward a more highly polymerized state of gelation.

II. *The Endotoxin Shock Model*

Three groups of 20 dogs each were used for this study. Series I received 2 mg per kg of body weight of Difco purified endotoxin (*E. coli*). Control samples and followup samples at intervals for 24 hr were obtained. Series II and III consisted of 20 dogs each, receiving the same dose of endotoxin. In these animals 30 min after the endotoxin was administered a treatment program was begun. The treatment program for series II and III consisted of the administration of digitalis, methyl prednisolone, vasodilator (phenoxybenzamine), exposure to 100% oxygen in a hyperbaric chamber at 3 atm

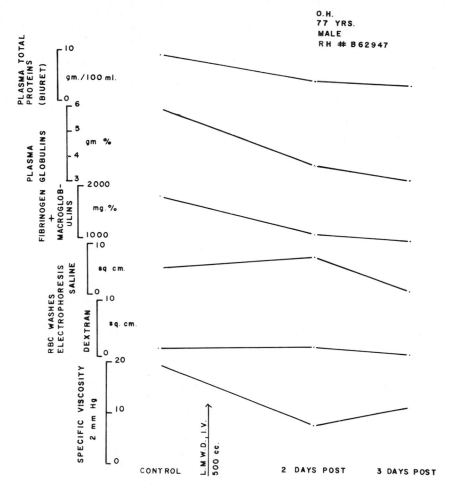

FIG. 4. HYPERVISCOSITY SYNDROME DUE TO MACROGLOBULINEMIA.

(absolute), and an infusion of 15 cc per kg of body weight of 10% low molecular weight dextran in saline. Series III was similarly treated but received an inotropic agent as well as a vasodilator (nylidrin HCl plus azepatine HCl instead of phenoxybenzamine). Of these therapeutic maneuvers most clearly significant in affecting apparent blood viscosity was that of the infusion of low molecular weight dextran every 12 hr. The behavior of the apparent blood viscosity, the central venous hematocrit, and the arterial pH of the blood are displayed in Figs. 6, 7, and 8. In Fig. 6, one notes a significant increase in apparent blood viscosity by 4 hr after endotoxin in the untreated group. In series II, however, this increase in viscosity was prevented. Series III displayed a slight increase in blood viscosity of borderline statistical significance despite the therapy program. Examination of the hematocrit behavior of the two treated series, however, reveals that there is no significant alteration in hematocrit in the treated groups over the 4-hr time period. A possible explanation for the slight increase in viscosity at 4 hr in series III may be found in Fig. 8, depicting changes in blood pH. The animals of series II which did not receive an inotropic drug, did not develop acidemia. Series

III, however, which did receive an inotropic drug (nylidrin) developed progressive acidemia. This is to be expected since one of the pharmacologic actions of the sym-

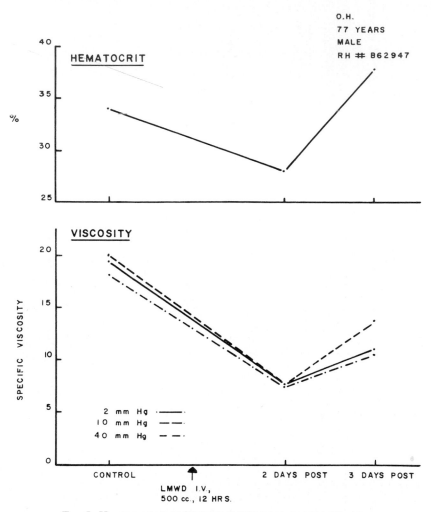

FIG. 5. HYPERVISCOSITY SYNDROME DUE TO MACROGLOBULEMIA.

pathomimetic inotropic agents (as nylidrin) tends to stimulate anaerobic glucolytic metabolic pathways to produce progressive acidemia. It seems logical that this state of acidosis may have played a significant role in the mild elevation of viscosity demonstrated in this group. All of the animals which received endotoxin exhibited rather marked degrees of intravascular hemagglutination in these studies. This was subjectively estimated to be ameliorated (although inconsistently) by the infusion of low molecular weight dextran. Despite the observed behavior of viscosity-increase in untreated animals and a reduction of this increase in treated animals, there was no statistical difference in the mean survival time or overall survival of the animals in the three series.

Nor could any correlation be established in individual cases between hyperviscosity,

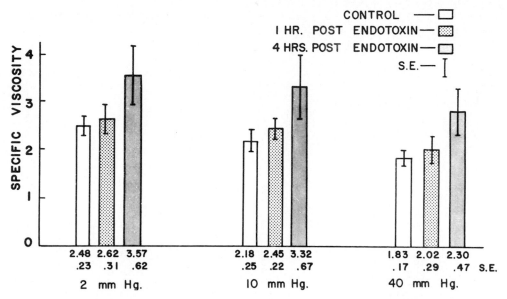

FIG. 6. APPARENT BLOOD VISCOSITY ENDOTOXIN SHOCK. UNTREATED 20 DOGS.

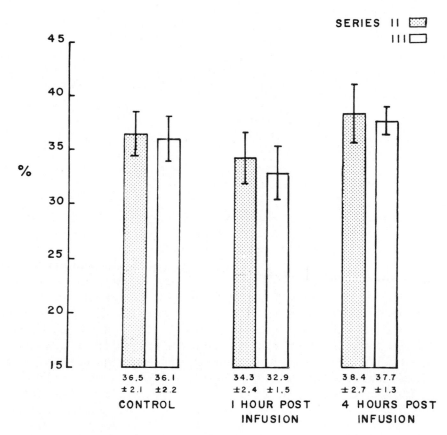

FIG. 7. HEMATOCRIT ENDOTOXIN SHOCK. MEAN AND S.E.

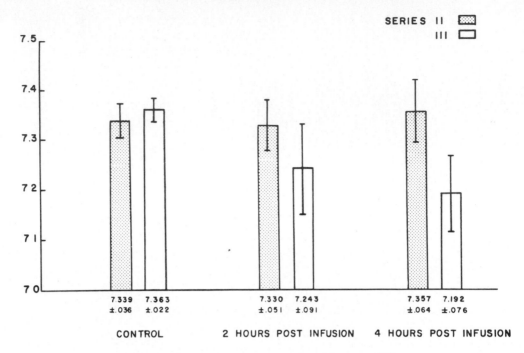

FIG. 8. BLOOD pH ENDOTOXIN SHOCK. MEAN AND S.E.

control of hyperviscosity, and survival. Studies of the protein red blood cell wash material are displayed in Fig. 9. Of special interest is the observation that a statistically significant increase in the amount of protein material in the saline and dextran erythrocyte washings of the *surviving* animals in the two treated groups was observed. Further, examination of the ratio of

$$\frac{\text{dextran-washing protein}}{\text{saline-washing protein}}$$

for the treated and untreated groups reveals a highly significant elevation of this value in the treated animals which died, but not in the untreated animals, nor in the survivors.

This observation suggests that loosely bound abnormal capsular protein may be removed by simple hydration with saline, whereas the more tightly bound capsular material (e.g. higher order of cross-linkage), which may be associated with more rigid aggregation, and the greater impediment to effective microvascular tissue perfusion, may be somehow released in the treated groups of animals with the dextran (but not saline) washings.

Examination of the changes in plasma globulin and albumin concentration leads to the conclusion that the treatment program employed in these experiments allows a progressive decline in the concentration of both globulins and albumins. This decrease in plasma protein cannot be explained on a basis of simple hemodilution, since there was no concomitant decrease in central venous hematocrit. It is intriguing to speculate that the rheologic action of LMWD allowed improved capillary perfusion in the insulted animals, thus facilitating the seepage of protein from the intravascular compartment.

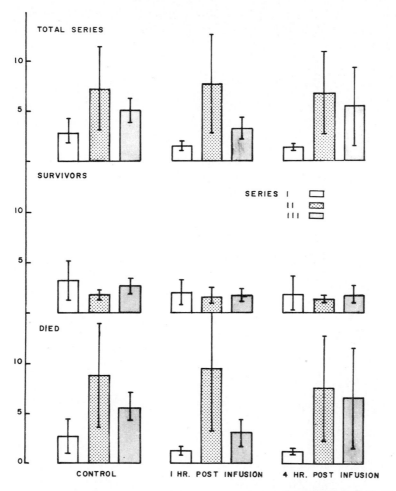

FIG. 9. ENDOTOXIN SHOCK ELECTROPHORESIS RATIO OF $\dfrac{\text{DEXTRAN (LMWD) R.B.C. WASHES.}}{\text{SALINE R.B.C. WASHES}}$

III. *Clinical Hypovolemic Shock*

A group of 10 patients who had sustained mild hypovolemic shock was selected for a clinical study to assess the effectiveness of a new colloid plasma expander derived from hydroxyethylated starch. These patients were mildly to moderately hypotensive, and had sustained blood losses estimated to be less than 1000 cc. Close clinical observation and extensive laboratory evaluations were carried out. Although there was a mild significant decline in hematocrit attributed to hemodilution, no significant changes in apparent blood viscosity were observed (Fig. 10). There was a moderate decrease in total peripheral vascular resistance, of borderline statistical significance (Fig. 11). This occurred gradually over 48 hr following the infusion. In addition, there was an immediate increase in cardiac output which was sustained for 48 hr after the infusion (Fig. 12). An increase in saline RBC washings at 24 hr, and dextran washings at 48 hr was observed, but did not appear to be of statistical significance. A significant apparent increase in fibrinogen concentration over 48 hr was observed, but showed no correlation with changes in apparent blood viscosity. Additional *in vitro* experiments were carried out, measuring apparent blood viscosity of blood aliquots which were

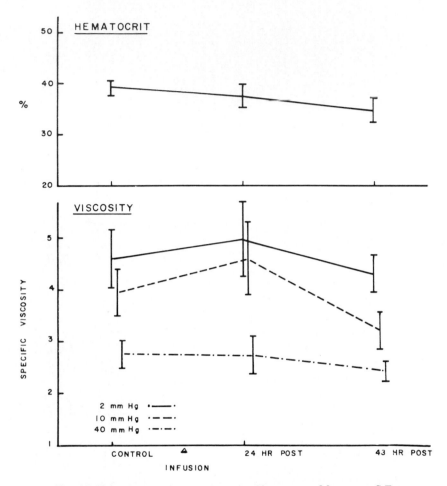

FIG. 10. HYDROXYETHYL STARCH STUDY, 10 PATIENTS. MEAN AND S.E.

undiluted, diluted with one part of HES solution in 20 parts of blood, one part of HES in 10 parts of blood, and finally the simple addition of purified endotoxin to achieve a blood concentration of 4 mg%. The results of this experiment are demonstrated in Fig. 13.

Two interesting observations are made: (1) The 10% dilution of whole blood with this well-tolerated medium molecular weight polysaccharide plasma expander failed to reduce apparent blood viscosity. If anything, there was a slight, though statistically not significant, increase in blood viscosity in the diluted aliquots. (2) The addition of endotoxin to blood *in vitro* did not result in an elevation in apparent blood viscosity. This suggests that some interaction between the endotoxin and the red cell or its protein capsule must occur *in vivo* to account for the previously observed elevations in blood viscosity which occurred in the endotoxin shock series after 4 hr.

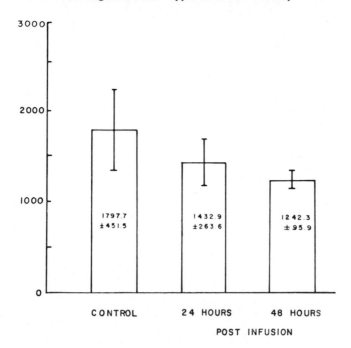

FIG. 11. HYDROXYETHYL STARCH STUDY, 10 PATIENTS. TOTAL PERIPHERAL RESISTANCE. MEAN AND S.E.

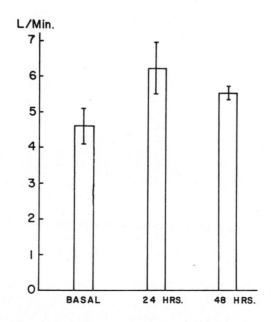

FIG. 12. HYDROXYETHYL STARCH PATIENTS, 10 PATIENTS. CARDIAC OUTPUT. MEAN AND S.E.

IV. *The Thermal Burn Model*

Six groups of 10 dogs each were utilized in this study. The code which appears on the illustrations is identified as follows: Group CN is a control group of animals which

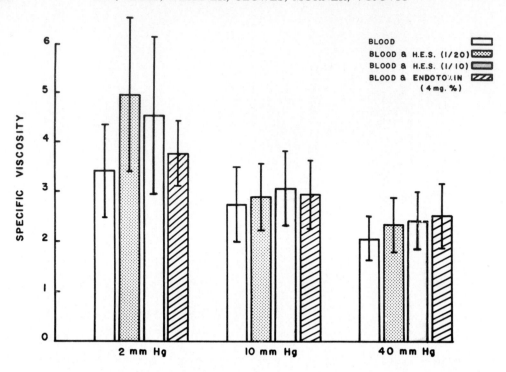

FIG. 13. APPARENT BLOOD VISCOSITY. H.E.S. AND ENDOTOXIN DILUTION. MEAN AND S.E.

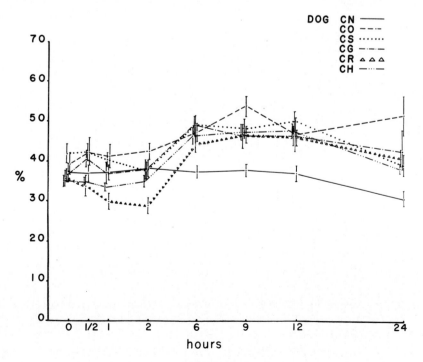

FIG. 14. HEMATOCRIT.

were anesthetized, and followed for 24 hr without burns or treatment. Group CO received a third-degree thermal burn from scalding water over the hindquarters. Group CS received a similar burn and was treated by the infusion of 30 cc per kg of body weight, of 0.85% sodium chloride 30 min after the burn. Group CG was treated with

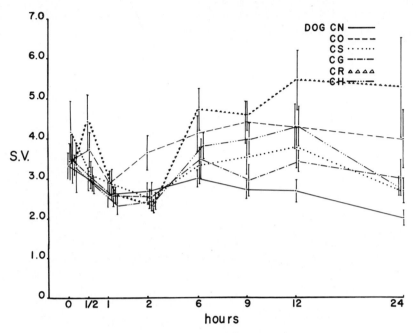

FIG. 15. MEAN VISCOSITY 1 MM Hg PRESSURE.

5% glucose in water following the burn, and Group CR received a similar volume of 10% low molecular weight dextran in saline. Group CH was burned and treated by the infusion of a similar volume of 6% low molecular weight hydroxyethyl starch in saline. The molecular weight distribution of the hydroxyethyl starch solution as determined by intrinsic viscosity was in a similar range to that of the low molecular weight dextran solution. Figure 14 displays the summary of changes in hematocrit and Figs. 15, 16 and 17 illustrate the behavior of apparent blood viscosity, cardiac output, and vascular resistance in these experiments.

Casual inspection of these data would suggest a fair correlation of changes in hematocrit and viscosity. Indeed, this is true for many of the samples studied. However, notable exceptions are apparent at closer scrutiny, and in fact, multiple covariance analysis of the data suggests that there is no consistent valid correlation between hematocrit and viscosity. For example, the saline infused group shows a hematocrit level at 2 hr unchanged from control, while viscosity decreases by 25%. Viscosity behavior of the low molecular weight dextran and hydroxyethyl starch groups is most intriguing: although depressed for about 4 hr, the colloid-infused group displayed remarkable elevations of viscosity by 6 hr. This does not appear to relate to hemodynamic changes however, since the colloids appear to have exerted a lasting (24 hr) effect in *depressing* vascular resistance (both pulmonary and systemic), and raising cardiac output (despite the high apparent viscosity).

Figure 18 demonstrates the pulmonary arterial oxygen saturation for these groups of animals. This measure provides a useful index of adequacy of general tissue perfusion, in that under circumstances of compromised microvascular perfusion oxygen extraction will be high, and mixed venous O_2 saturation (P.A.) should be correspondingly reduced. One may note good correlation of this index with cardiac output and vascular resistance, generally, with a marked depression (P.A.O_2 saturation) in the burned untreated group. Correlation with viscosity again is inconsistent.

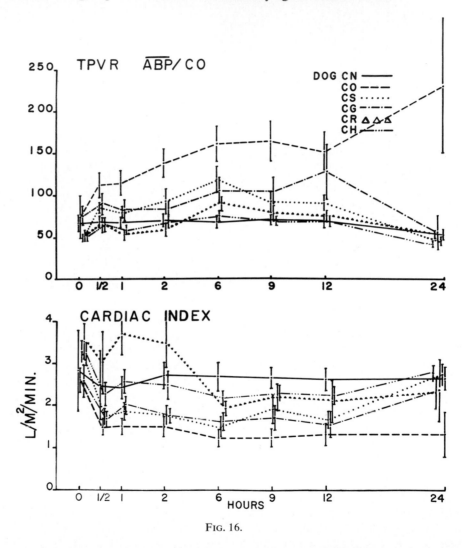

FIG. 16.

Observations of changes in plasma protein and coagulation factors in these groups of animals revealed several points of interest to this report: (a) a consistent decrease in plasma protein, measured by both Biuret and refractometer techniques. The colloid-infused groups sustained the lower levels of proteins. This would suggest simple hemo-dilution as a major mechanism, but the progressive hemoconcentration evidenced by hematocrit changes (Fig. 14) does not support this suggestion. Again, it is intriguing

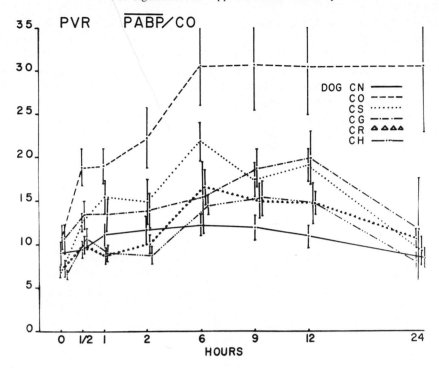

FIG. 17.

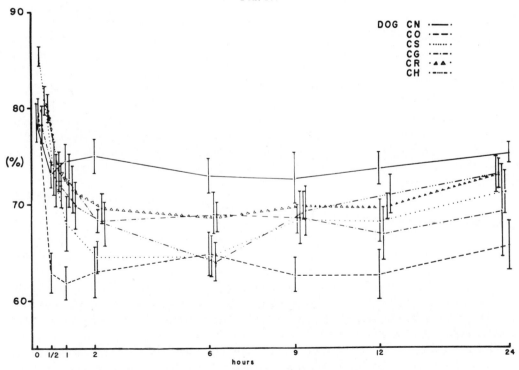

FIG. 18. OXYGEN SATURATION (PULMONARY ARTERY).

to speculate that the colloid-infused animals maintained better perfusion of burned tissues, allowing protein seepage from the damaged vascular beds. (b) The overall decrease in plasma protein represents mainly a loss of albumin, thus *increasing* the relative concentration of globulins. This would tend to shift the sol–gel moiety of the RBC capsules toward gelation, and produce erythrocyte aggregation. (c) Changes in coagulation mechanics generally suggested a transient hypercoagulable state following thermal burn, which is improved or reversed by infusion therapy, with maximal benefit apparently reached in the colloid-infused groups. The data upon which these observations were based could not be included in this report because of space limitations, and will be published elsewhere.

DISCUSSION

The theoretical concepts of the biophysical character of globular plasma protein, the interfacial behavior of such materials when partially denatured[1, 4, 8, 16] and the observed data from these experiments are concluded to support the hypothesis that the character of the protein moiety of blood may be a powerful determinant in the viscoelastic properties of blood flow. Erythrocytes have been demonstrated to possess a protein coating comprised of mainly alpha and beta globulin, and fibrinogen molecules in normal states of health[13, 14]. The denaturation of globular plasma proteins by several states of trauma has been previously documented[7, 9, 10]. It would appear that neither hematocrit *per se*, nor alterations in protein composition or structure (as determined by available methods of analysis) are of *sole* primary import in influencing apparent blood viscosity[11, 15]. Further, the significance of apparent blood viscosity as measured by those techniques currently available, would seem to represent exceedingly complex concepts, varying with the repeatable artefacts induced by the techniques of measurements. No firm relationship has been yet established which describes concisely the clinical significance of altered blood viscosity to the metabolic economy or energy demands sustained by an organism in serious states of disease. Many profound questions remain unresolved, frustrating the understanding of marvelously complex phenomena which must comprise the flow of blood in the circulatory system of the living organism in health and disease. From the fragmentary evidence accumulated, however, a working hypothesis may be evolved to serve as a "straw man", the target for other investigators:

Theorogam

(1) The fluidity of blood is a significant aspect of circulatory homeostasis, in that diminished fluidity requires a greater energy expenditure in the stressed organism to meet the demands imposed by the metabolism of the tissues of the body.

(2) The fluidity of the blood is to a large extent dependent upon the proximity of the particulate elements suspended in its plasma, and the relative strength of the forces of attraction between the colloid envelopes which enshroud the particulate elements of blood, especially the erythrocyte.

(3) Intercellular coherence forces may be due to (a) net charge effects, as manifested by zeta potential and electromagnetic attractive forces; (b) the relative density of intermolecular bonds (especially hydrogen, sulfhydryl and disulfide bonds), which may

develop as a sol–gel shift due to the disruption of the tertiary molecular configuration of globular protein molecules adsorbed onto the red cell membrane, with subsequent repolymerization by disulfide or hydrogen bridging.

(4) Some states of disease or trauma may induce by mechanisms as yet unknown in some cases and partially identified in others, various degrees of disruption of plasma protein molecules, resulting in the above described change.

(5) Chemotherapeutic agents, especially neutral polysaccharide colloids, may profoundly influence the characteristics of the adsorbed protein capsules of erythrocytes by entering the protein matrix, altering the states of hydration of the solvation shell of the erythrocyte, or biophysically decreasing the forces of attraction inherent in such abnormal intermolecular bonds.

These concepts need to be studied, to be probed, to be upheld or disproved. Such investigations must be carried out by highly trained competent scientists with special capabilities in the disciplines of physiology, biochemistry, physical chemistry, biorheology, and hemorheology. The clinician will await eagerly the products of their labor to apply in the care of the sick and injured patient.

ACKNOWLEDGMENTS

The authors would like gratefully to acknowledge the invaluable technical assistance of Mr. S. Yoakum, Mrs. S. Mercurio, Mrs. M. Brady, and Miss M. Barnes.

This work was supported in part by grants from the U.S. Army Medical Corps, Research Education, and Development Command, The National Heart Institute, The John and Mary R. Markle Foundation (Dr. Lee).

Low molecular weight dextran employed in these studies was generously supplied as "Rheomacrodex" by the Pharmacia Laboratories. Hydroxyethyl Starch solutions were provided by the Don Baxter Laboratories, Glendale, California.

REFERENCES

[1] ANSON, M. L. *Adv. in Prot. Chem.* **2**, 361, 1945.
[2] ASTRUP, P. *Clin. Chem.* **7**, 1, 1961.
[3] PARFENTJEV, I. A., JOHNSON, M. L. and CLIFFTON, E. E. *Arch. Biochem. and Biophy.* **46**, 470, 1953.
[4] CHEESMAN, D. F. and DAVIES, J. T. *Adv. in Prot. Chem.* **9**, 439, 1954.
[5] DITZEL, J. *Acta med. scandinav.*, Suppl. **343**, 1959.
[6] GREGERSEN, M. I., USAMI, S., PERIC, B., CHANG, C., SINCLAIR, D. and CHIEN, S. *Biorheology* **1**, 247, 1963.
[7] JACKSON, T. M. and LEE, W. H., JR. *Am. Surg.* **30**, 26, 1964.
[8] KAUZMANN, W. *Adv. in Prot. Chem.* **14**, 1, 1959.
[9] KRUMHAAR, D., LEE, W. H., JR. and MALONEY, J. V., JR. *Transfusion* **2**, 398, 1962.
[10] LEE, W. H., JR., KRUMHAAR, D., FONKALSRUD, E. W., SCHJEIDE, O. A. and MALONEY, J. V., JR. *Surg.* **50**, 29, 1961.
[11] LEE, W. H., JR. *et al.* Presentation, *Committee on Plasma Expanders*. Cleveland, Ohio, October, 1965.
[12] MERRILL, E. W., GILLILAND, E. R., COKELET, G., SHIN, H., BRITTEN, A. and WELLS, R. E., JR. *J. Appl. Physiol.* **18**, 255, 1963.
[13] PIROFSKY, B., CORDOVA, M. and IMEL, T. L. *Vox Sang.* **7**, 334, 1962.
[14] THOMPSON, L. (personal communication).
[15] THORSEN, G. and HINT, H. *Acta chir. scandinav.* **154**, 1, 1950.
[16] WAUGH, D. F. *Adv. in Prot. Chem.* **9**, 325, 1954.

DISCUSSION

SILBERBERG (*Israel*):

You may be interested to learn that we have evidence that a bond can be formed involving one molecule of alcohol and one of water between two methyl groups or aliphatic side chains in macromolecules; this might be a factor in the cases that you have looked at. What is the evidence that these adsorbed gel-like covers to the cells are globulins?

LEE (*U.S.A.*):

In all of the studies that we have conducted in this area for the past four or five years, the material has had the electrophoretic mobility of globulins. Thompson and his group, working at the Johns Hopkins University Medical School have analysed this material, at least under the circumstances which are induced by the infusion of relatively high molecular weight hydroxyethyl starch, and they found that the material consisted, in that particular instance, of both fibrinogen and globulin. Specifically which globulins are involved? By electrophoretic mobility studies and by substraction studies from plasma, we found that there is a good deal of variance in this depending upon the individual and the disease syndrome; and I do not think that there is very much specificity of this at all. In fact, I could show you slides which demonstrate several species of proteins in this capsular material, depending upon the clinical case and depending upon the technique of extraction. I believe the adsorbed material is comprised mainly of those plasma globulins which are least stable in their tertiary configuration. These are generally alpha 2, alpha 3 and beta globulins.

GELIN (*Sweden*):

I think Dr. Lee's work here really focuses on some very important aspects of the study of rheology *extra vivum*. All our materials interfered with the proteins of the plasma more or less. Not as much, of course, as the oxygenator or the bubble oxygenator, but what he stresses, using the extracorporeal circulation is something, which we have to assume, also occurs in many other *extra vivum* systems. Therefore, some skepticism must be given to all *extra vivum* measurements. And you had one observation here which interests me very much, indeed. You decreased with low molecular weight dextran both the viscosity and the hematocrit. But the viscosity stayed low even if the hematocrit rose; and may I have a chance to show just a quick slide stressing that point? It is taken from a burned patient; to the right you can see the viscosity readings. Curve A with a hematocrit of 56 showed these viscosity values with the Brookfield technique. Then this patient was given 100 g of low molecular weight dextran, and curve B was recorded. There was a drop of the hematocrit from 56 to 38, and the viscosity curve shows a drop. Curve C, however, was taken 2 hr after the infusion; then the hemodilution is less; hematocrit had increased to 44, but the viscosity stayed low. Hemodilution increased flow and decreased peripheral resistance. Viscosity stayed low even after the 2 hr when the hematocrit rose to 44. So the *in vivo* relationship here is different from the *extra vivum* recordings.

LEE:

I think we see that quite often, Dr. Gelin. I believe that it would be of immense value if those people who are using GVM viscometers would study some of these clinical disease states rather than "native" blood or artificially-induced aggregation. I think Dr. Long (and Dr. Wells) have been working in this area; and I am sure he already has the data on it. But I think that there are many instances in which the low molecular weight dextran is lost fairly rapidly from the circulation of a shocked organism, and the hematocrit may come back to control value; yet the viscosity effect persists some time thereafter.

HARDAWAY (*U.S.A*):

If one subjects a dog to hemorrhagic shock, the results can be influenced to a great extent by what one does with the blood while it is out of the animal. In other words, if one exposes that blood only to plastic, one can retain recovery rates almost indefinitely. It is reversible rather than irreversible preparation. However, if one subjects this blood to the surface of glass or of air or of a disc oxygenator or any other foreign surfaces, then this blood, when given back to the animal, will result in mortality and a marked coagulation defect.

LEE:

That is quite true.

BARNHARD (*U.S.A.*):

I would like to report on our experience with extracorporeal circulation in man because, I think, the finding that we have of an increased amount of circulating fibrinogen related material that is non-clottable may possibly relate to the stickiness of the platelets and the cells. In our experience thus far on some 20 or 30 people with extracorporeal circulation, we have found that the non-clottable fibrinogen related molecules, as determined immunologically, frequently rise during this exposure to the extracorporeal circulation. It may in some cases rise as high as 4 or 5 mg per ml in contrast to the normal circulating level of this material which is $\frac{2}{10}$ mg. We have had little experience with the platelets and leucocytes in these patients, but we do know that they drop during the course of this treatment. However, it does seem reasonable from the work with dogs reported previously, that the increase in altered fibrinogen, or actually the fibrinolysis which we know exists in these patients, may create material to surface on the platelets, leucocytes and red cells and might be responsible for their aggregation.

LEE:

I think it is difficult to determine precisely what is sticking these particles together. We need more discrete information on this. We analysed our last 300 pump cases not very long ago, and observed a significant incidence of clinical fibrinolysin syndrome in these patients. I think there were thirteen cases in which serious hemorrhages were associated with marked fibrinolytic activity. I was very interested in your data earlier because of this. I think that the concept of enzymatic degradation or enzymatic denaturation, if you will, is certainly an important one as a possible etiologic mechanism for the production of denatured protein *in vivo*. This sort of question demands highly sophisticated knowledge of physical and biological chemistry of proteins. More of Dr. Silberberg's and Dr. Eirich's type of work will be needed to provide the answers here. I think this requires an expert in these fields, and I do not think that clinicians like myself are generally equipped to attack the problem.

LONG (*U.S.A.*):

I only want to make one short comment about this business of hematocrit and viscosity differences and the unpredictability in their relationship. We noticed in some of our studies, recently, that patients with a leucocytosis will not have a correlation between viscosity and hematocrit when viscosity is measured with the cone in cone viscometer. Removal of the buffy coat, which obviously takes more than just the leucocytes, will seriously affect the viscosity, and some people doing viscosity with the rotational viscometers have been routinely removing the buffy coat. I think this may have a very profound influence on the whole blood viscosity, which is what we are interested in *in vivo*.

QUESTION SUBMITTED BY EHRLY (*Germany*):

I would like to know the rates of shear in your experiments with a capillary viscosimeter at different pressure stresses. In earlier experiments with our type of capillary viscosimeter we could not have low rates of shear which are really interesting.

LEE:

Shear stress/shear rate relations were not calculated, as the determinations made in the pipette viscometer represent kinematic viscosity. The pressure ranges employed are mentioned in the text, and calculated conversions of shear rate are in a range much higher than those obtained with the GVM-type viscometer. The advantages and disadvantages of various methods of measuring the "viscosity" of blood is a topic too broad in scope to discuss here. I refer you to the text of this paper for my limited comments regarding this question.

A COMPARISON OF BLOOD FLOW IN A LIVING VESSEL AND IN GLASS TUBES

G. S. KURLAND*

Departments of Medicine, Harvard Medical School and Beth Israel Hospital, Boston, Massachusetts, U.S.A.

S. E. CHARM, S. L. BROWN and P. TOUSIGNANT

Department of Physiology, Tufts University Medical School, Boston, Massachusetts, U.S.A.

THE understanding of flow in the microcirculation remains a difficult problem in physiology. In the attempt to develop useful models of the circulation, a vast literature, since Poiseuille, has described flow in glass capillary tubes. From such studies have come a recognition of the importance of shear stress, shear rate, volume fraction of suspended particles, laminar flow, vessel diameter, and the marginal plasma gap at the wall. However, the relevance of these observations in glass tubes to intravascular flow in small vessels remains speculative. No intravascular viscometer has yet been constructed and only limited studies of pressure–flow relationships in the microcirculation of intact animals are reported. HINKE and WILSON described a system for studying the excised long artery of the rat's tail, but noted that efforts to use the preparation as a viscometer had failed[1]. The present studies were undertaken to use this vessel *in situ* in the living anesthetized rat as a model of factors affecting blood flow in vessels approximately 300 μ in diameter.

METHODS

Male Wistar rats 400–500 g in weight were anesthetized lightly with intraperitoneal 10% pentobarbital sodium. A tracheotomy was performed for regular suctioning of mucus. Two areas of the tail artery about 5 cm apart were exposed. A $\frac{1}{4}$ in. 25 gauge blunt needle with a tri-beveled trochar was mounted in a needle holder on an adjustable arm(Fig. 1). The artery was punctured in the proximal exposed area, the adjustable arm was tightened, the tri-beveled insert was removed and the artery was firmly attached with a silk suture. When the distal end of the artery was severed, a heparin solution was slowly injected through the needle. After satisfactory flow had been obtained a jacketed calibrated reservoir maintained at 37°C was attached (Fig. 2). The vessel was perfused with isotonic saline for an hour to permit adequate relaxation.

Pressure and flow measurements were made as saline, plasma, whole blood, and, finally, a radiopaque solution were passed successively through the vessel. The volume of flow was determined from the fall of the meniscus in the calibrated reservoir. A variety of opaque media were tried. The most frequently used was methylglucamine diatrozate USP (Renografen-60) diluted with an equal volume of normal saline. A 20% suspension of micropaque was also useful. X-rays of the tail were made while

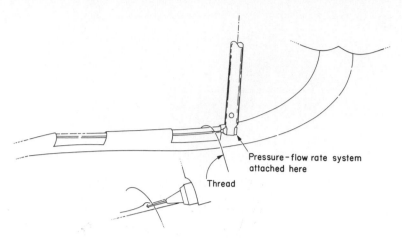

FIG. 1. PUNCTURING OF RAT-TAIL ARTERY WITH 25 GAUGE BLUNT NEEDLE WITH A TRI-BEVELED TROCHAR.

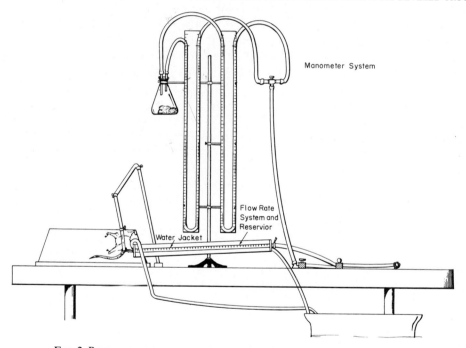

FIG. 2. PRESSURE-FLOW MEASURING SYSTEM ADAPTED TO RAT-TAIL ARTERY.

the opaque solution was in the artery. The X-rays were projected on a screen and measurements of arterial diameter were made at several places. The needle of known diameter which appeared in the X-ray standardized measurements. There were usually no branches through which fluid could escape; occasionally, however, these branches were noted. It was determined experimentally that less than 5% of the perfusing fluid could be lost through these branches. The diameter determined from the X-rays was compared to the diameter obtained by studies of plasma flow as follows. Whole human blood was drawn into ACD as anticoagulant. Part was rapidly centrifuged and used as plasma. The viscosity of the plasma was determined in a

FIG. 3. OPAQUING SOLUTION IN RAT-TAIL ARTERY.

Brookfield cone and plate viscometer. From the plasma viscosity, the average diameter of the vessel was determined at each pressure by the use of Poiseuille's equation assuming laminar flow, negligible yield stress and ignoring the taper. There was no change in the flow properties of the vessel system during the course of the study prior to the injection of opaque medium which was always done last. This was demonstrated by repeating the plasma flow studies early and again later in the experiment. Upon the death of the animal, there was a dramatic increase in resistance to flow over the course of 30 sec.

The viscometry of whole blood or a dilution of blood was measured in the Brookfield viscometer. Utilizing the diameter calculated from plasma flow a theoretical line relating pressure to flow was constructed for whole blood and blood of diminished cell content. These were compared to the actual pressure and flow data (Figs. 4, 5). In drawing the theoretical line a Poiseuille relation was assumed with no consideration of taper or cell-poor gap at the wall.

RESULTS

The calculated average diameter of the segments of the rats' tail artery ranged from 212 to 358 μ. The segments varied from 3.5 to 6.3 cm in length.

The taper of a typical vessel drawn from the enlarged X-ray is shown in Fig. 3. At a pressure of 4.66×10^4 dynes/cm^2 and a flow of 0.00572 ml per sec the widest segment was 0.0447 cm in diameter and the narrowest, 0.0235 cm. The effective diameter

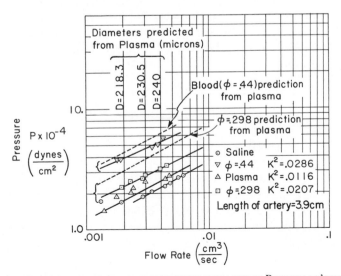

FIG. 4. TAIL ARTERY EXPERIMENTAL DATA AND PREDICTED DATA USING POISEUILLE'S EQUATION WITHOUT GAP CONSIDERATION. DIAMETERS CALCULATED AT VARIOUS PRESSURES FROM PLASMA FLOW DATA.

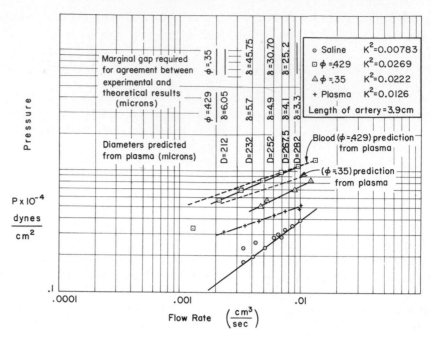

FIG. 5. MARGINAL GAP REQUIRED TO BRING EXPERIMENTAL AND CALCULATED RESULTS TO AGREEMENT IN TAIL ARTERY.

calculated from plasma flow data was 0.0247 cm confirming that the narrowest segment is responsible for the greatest pressure drop.*

When the pressure–flow relationships for blood flowing in a living vessel were compared with the theoretical value obtained using a Poiseuille equation, the experimental pressure drop was equal to the anticipated value once and less than it in seven of eight studies (Figs. 4, 5). The difference was as large as 30%. In two experiments in which blood of decreased hematocrit was also studied the discrepancy between theoretical and actual values was greater in the dilute specimen than in the whole blood.

DISCUSSION

WHITAKER and WINTON[2] who attempted to construct a "biologic viscometer" concluded that the apparent viscosity of blood flowing in the vessels of the hind limb of the dog was about one-half that of the same blood flowing in a glass viscometer of a high-velocity type. They ascribed this difference to the hemodynamic effect of a marginal zone of relatively clear plasma and the increasing importance of the gap in small vessels like the arterioles in the hind limb in which the main pressure fall occurred and which are of smaller bore than the glass tubes in which *in vitro* studies could be made. Our data utilizing a single vessel similarly show a smaller pressure drop in the living system than in glass tubes. We have considered a number of explanations for this difference.

*Since this was written, it has been possible to calculate the experimental pressure-drop of the opaque solution from its viscosity and knowing the artery shape from X-ray.

Since we had already studied extensively the cell-poor gap at the wall in glass capillaries, we attempted to see whether the discrepancy could be explained by this method. The vessel of the rat tail used in the study ranged from 212 to 358 μ average diameter. The contribution of the plasma gap to the dynamics of blood flowing in glass tubes of this size is known[3]; the application of this correction reduces but does not eliminate the discrepancy between predicted and observed value for flow. When blood with a hematocrit of 0.4 flows in a glass tube, our previous data indicate that the ratio of gap to vessel diameter (δ/D) should not exceed 0.02[3]. We calculated the δ/D which would be necessary to eliminate the difference between the theoretical and actual curves. The δ/D values of 0.05–0.10 which we calculated are beyond the expected values. With a decreased hematocrit the difference between the actual and the theoretical pressure drop was increased. Previous studies on the plasma gap in blood flow in small glass tubes have demonstrated that the marginal gap is related inversely to hematocrit. This may be considered evidence that the cell-poor gap at the wall plays some role in explaining the differences which we have observed. Since consideration of the cell-poor gap at the wall did not entirely eliminate the differences in flow between the anticipated values and the actual pressure drop, we have speculated on other factors which may also play a part: the taper of the vessel, irregularities in the vessel and wall factors. Our data on tapered glass tubes indicate that it is reasonable to use the dimensions of the plasma gap obtained in straight tubes in calculating flow in tapered tubes[4]. However, we are unable to take into account the effect of tiny irregularities in the living vessel such as projections which we have seen on X-ray and which might throw cells into the central stream and increase the size of the gap at the wall.

One other possibility which we have considered is plasma slip at the wall. It has been suggested that apparent viscosity and wall adherence of blood plasma or serum is always less in contact with a surface of fibrin than with glass and that studies in tubes yielded data perhaps not applicable to the circulation in living blood vessels[5]. Since the calibration of vessel diameter was performed with plasma, this possibility has already been discounted. Thus, some part of the differences in pressure drop between blood flow in glass capillaries and in the living vessel remains unexplained.

SUMMARY

1. The tail artery of the anesthetized rat was used to study blood flowing in a living vessel.

2. When the pressure drop in this system was compared to values calculated from flow characteristics in glass tubes, the calculated pressure drop was greater than the experimental.

3. Application of a correction for a cell-poor gap at the wall reduced, but did not entirely eliminate the discrepancy.

ACKNOWLEDGMENT

Aided by a grant from the United States Public Health Service (HE–08783–02).

REFERENCES

[1] HINKE, J. A. M. and WILSON, M. L. *Am. J. Physiol.* **203**, 1153, 1962.
[2] WHITAKER, S. R. F. and WINTON, F. R. *J. Physiol.* **78**, 339, 1933.
[3] CHARM, S. E., KURLAND, G. S. and BROWN, S. This volume, p. 403.
[4] CHARM, S. E. and KURLAND, G. S. The Flow of Blood in Non-uniform Tapered Glass Tubes. *Biorheology* (in press).
[5] COPLEY, A. L. In *Flow Properties of Blood and Other Biological Systems*, COPLEY, A. L. and STAINSBY, G. (Editors), Pergamon Press, Oxford, New York, 1960, p. 97.

DISCUSSION

ROWLANDS (*England*):

I would like to begin by asking Dr. Charm: has he compared his results directly with those of Whitaker and Winton, and those of Prothero and Burton, to see how his results lie in respect to their results?

CHARM (*U.S.A.*):

As a matter of fact, we have not compared them quantitatively. They have just been compared qualitatively. The differences between their calculated and experimental results were greater than ours. However, in order of magnitude, they were about the same as ours. We considered they had about 50% difference between what they expected and what they found. I think ours were of the order of perhaps half that, 25 or 30%. I do not think we have compared ours with Prothero and Burton.

WHITMORE (*England*):

Was it possible, in the experiment, to ascertain in any way, the possibility of fluid from the tissue somehow coming into the blood stream through the walls or through small side vessels and thus altering the effective hematocrit or general flow pattern characteristics?

CHARM:

Yes, this was, of course, the first thing that occurred to us, and as a result we did take samples of blood to determine the viscometry, samples of blood which had passed through the system and compared it with the blood which was in the reservoir, and this was not the case. Note, we did use a plasma and not saline, for example, to calibrate our vessels. If you use saline, it leaks through the wall, but plasma does not. One of the things we have attempted, but with which we have not been entirely successful, is in taking pressure velocity measurements with an opaquing solution and comparing these directly with the X-rays. Unfortunately, we have had very few runs in which we had a complete set, in other words, where we have been able to get a good set of X-ray data and pressure–velocity measurements on opaquing solution as well as the plasma and blood dilutions. Usually, we were able to get one without the other before the animal died. This is just what we are working on now.

MEISELMAN (*U.S.A.*):

I was curious about your use of an apparent Casson viscosity in your mathematical modeling. K^2 in your terminology is really the square of the slope of the line at a given point. This is opposed to what one normally thinks of as an apparent viscosity which is, of course, the square of the slope from zero zero to any point. Are you assuming then that the viscosity becomes Newtonian in a higher range? You mentioned that you were at a higher shear rate.

CHARM:

Yes. Our flow rate in the range that we measure pressure drops is such that yield stress effects are very small. Negligible!

MEISELMAN:

Rheological data generated in our laboratories for human blood indicates that the Casson type plot shows curvature above 5–10 inverse seconds. Thus, the value of K (and thus K^2) would not be constant. In your modeling system, can you use the portion of a log-log plot of shear rate vs. shear stress diagram where the slope equals unity? Is there a difference between this type of calculated viscosity and your K^2 with respect to the model?

CHARM:

There should not be any difference. Now K^2 is, in effect, the limiting apparent viscosity, if you were to plot apparent viscosity against the shear rate. This would be equivalent to the apparent viscosity on a log-log plot where you have a slope of one.

TAYLOR (*Australia*):

I am sorry I missed the first part of this. I was not expecting it to come along quite so soon, but I am sorry. You may have covered what I am about to raise. As I understand these results, the discrepancies are not really terribly large.

CHARM:

Yes, they are very large. I'd like to put back one of the slides because I can show you how large they are.

TAYLOR:

20% or something like that?

CHARM:

Well, it depends on what flow-rate range we are in. It varied.

TAYLOR:

Because the point I am sort of working around to, is the assumptions on which the calculation of marginal zone thicknesses are made. One of the most important, of course, is the assumption of what the viscosity of the central core is. There is almost no way of measuring that. One has to assume what the hematocrit might be and what the effect of shear is. I think this could have given rise to discrepancies which would be otherwise unaccountable.

CHARM:

I cannot fully agree with you on that. Actually you can estimate the core viscosity by knowing what the viscometry is of different dilutions of your suspension. You can estimate what the central core viscometry would be, considering you know what the gap is and what the concentrations of cells are. If I understand you correctly, it *is* possible to estimate what the central core viscometry associated with any particular gap width would be. Is that what you meant?

TAYLOR:

That is what I meant. I wonder whether in fact it is as exact as all that, whether one can safely estimate this within, well, 10%, shall we say. If your things are out by a factor of say 15 or 20%, this might very well lie in the calculations and not in the data!

CHARM:

We were talking about a 30% difference, let us say, in these dilute solutions. I do not think that we could be out that much.

PALMER (*Australia*):

I would like to ask Dr. Charm about the sudden change which he found after the animal died.

CHARM:

Yes. The pressure we had imposed on the reservoir was forcing blood through the artery. When the animal died, we observed that although the pressure remained constant, the flow rate diminished to practically zero within 30 sec; very rapidly.

PALMER:

That presumably suggests that the vessel contracted?

CHARM:

Yes, that is right.

PALMER:

So that there might be differences in vasoconstriction when you are using plasma and when you are using a blood solution, that might perhaps, account for some of the differences?

CHARM:

Well, I do not see why. If you are using blood as compared with plasma, I think the vessel wall would still essentially see plasma. Perhaps I am wrong, perhaps some physiologist could help me. But that was the way I looked at it. There would not be any difference in that respect, because the vessel would not know whether it was blood or plasma that was going through. It would only see plasma.

ORIENTATION AND DISTRIBUTION OF ERYTHROCYTES IN BLOOD FLOWING THROUGH MEDIUM-SIZED ARTERIES

RODERIC H. PHIBBS*

Department of Pediatrics and the Cardiovascular Research Institute,
University of California, San Francisco Medical Center,
San Francisco, U.S.A.
With an appendix by
ALAN C. BURTON
Department of Biophysics, University of Western Ontario,
London, Ontario, Canada

THIS is the description of a study of the arrangement of erythrocytes in blood flowing through rabbit arteries of 1 mm diameter. Vessels in three living animals and five arterial segments perfused *in vitro* were frozen ultrarapidly. By this method, if the freezing is rapid enough, the cells become fixed in the arrangement held during flow and, on cross-sectioning, present an "end-on" view of the blood as it flows through the artery.

PROCEDURE

For the *in vivo* study, the femoral artery of anesthetized rabbits was exposed above and below the knee, where there are few branches and the diameter changes very little for 4–5 cm. The adventitia was cleared, the branch arteries tied off, and 5–6 cm of the vessel freed and suspended in a trough. The artery was bathed in warm isotonic saline and 1% lidocaine hydrochloride to relieve spasm produced by handling. When the vessel was dilated and pulsating well, the warm fluid was removed and the trough quickly filled to overflowing with liquid propane cooled to $-175°C$ in liquid nitrogen[1]. The animal was killed and the frozen segment of its artery severed and transferred to liquid nitrogen. Blood flow was not measured before freezing the arteries. However, in other rabbits of the same size and under comparable conditions, the flow in this portion of the femoral artery varied from 0.4 to 1.5 ml/min when measured with a bubble flow meter.

For the *in vitro* studies, the same portion of the femoral artery was exposed, the branches were tied off and then the segment was removed. Both ends of the arterial segment were cannulated with polyethylene catheters, the internal diameters of which approximated the artery's diameter in the distended state. The segment was stretched to its *in vivo* length on a wire spreader. The "upstream" catheter led to a reservoir of heart blood that had been drawn from the animal just before the arterial segment was removed, anticoagulated with disodium ethylenediaminetetra-acetic acid, and maintained at 37°C. The artery was mounted in a horizontal position 130 cm below the level of the fluid in the reservoir and blood flow was regulated by a screw clamp on the "downstream" catheter. When the desired flow was obtained, the artery was frozen by lowering it into a container of liquid propane. The flow through these arteries was not pulsatile and varied from 0.01 to 2.6 ml/min.

In one of these arteries, a suture placed around one of the branches very close to its origin accidentally produced a short regional stenosis in the middle of the segment to be frozen. As the suture was tightened, a short length of the main artery narrowed to about 80% of its normal diameter. This produced about a 50% increase in the velocity of the flowing blood at the stenosis.

From experiment to experiment the hematocrit of the blood (heart blood *in vivo*, reservoir blood *in vitro*) varied from 32 to 35%.

With these methods of freezing, the blood in the center of the vessel reached −20°C and solidified in less than 0.1 sec from the onset of cooling. The more peripheral blood was immobilized more rapidly. After freezing, all vessels were freeze-substituted, embedded, cut cross-sectionally in 5–7 μ thick sections and prepared for microscopic examination[1].

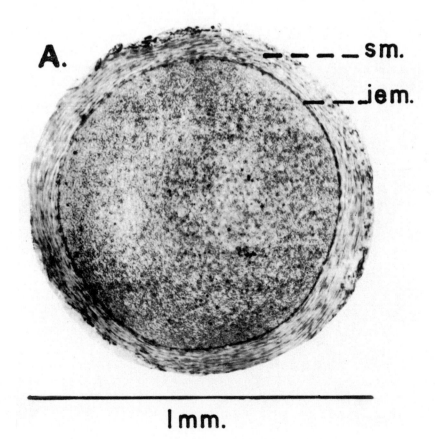

FIG. 1. (a) 7 μ THICK CROSS-SECTION OF ARTERY FROZEN *in vivo*. × 17 BEFORE ENLARGEMENT. SM, SMOOTH MUSCLE OF ARTERIAL WALL; IEM, INTERNAL ELASTIC MEMBRANE.

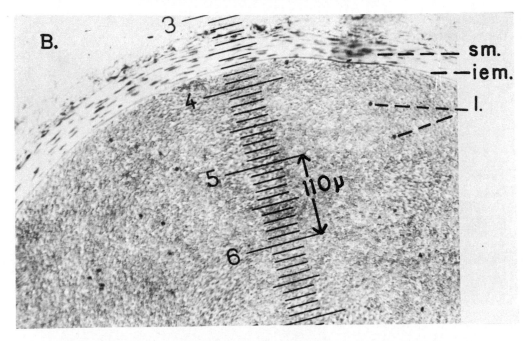

(b) SAME SECTION, × 33 BEFORE ENLARGEMENT, REDUCED TO $\frac{8}{10}$. L, LEUCOCYTES.

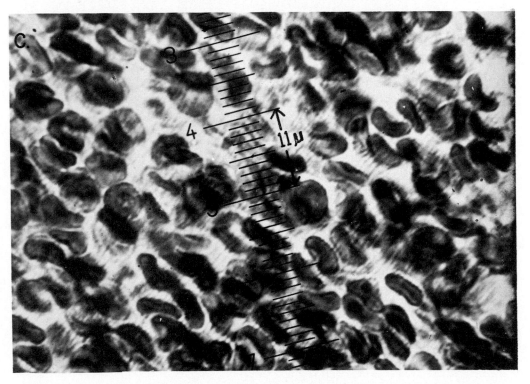

(c) PHOTOMICROGRAPH OF $5\,\mu$ THICK CROSS-SECTION $\frac{1}{3}$ RADIAL DISTANCE IN FROM PERIPHERY OF SAME ARTERY, × 333 BEFORE ENLARGEMENT, REDUCED TO $\frac{8}{10}$. (10 SMALL UNITS = $11\,\mu$).

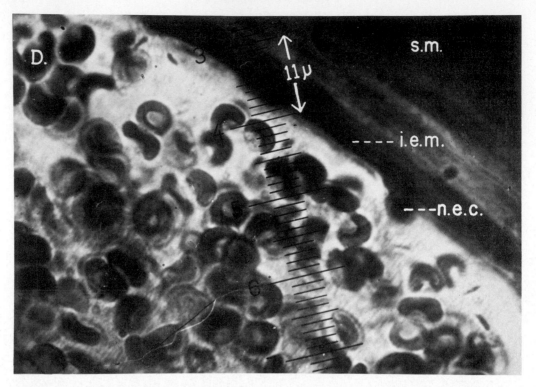

(d) Photomicrograph of same region as (c) at periphery. Note deformed erythrocytes and irregular cell-free zone of plasma adjacent to arterial wall, × 333 before enlargement, reduced to $\frac{8}{10}$. NEC, nucleus of endothelial cell.

RESULTS

On microscopic examination, the arteries were round and appeared to be distended by the transmural pressure (Fig. 1a, b). The internal elastic membrane was smooth, not wrinkled as in arteries preserved by the usual histologic methods. A fairly homogeneous mass of closely packed erythrocytes filled the lumen of the vessels and leucocytes were distinguishable[1].

High-power magnification (Fig. 1c, d) showed the erythrocytes to be closely crowded. Many were deformed, like those seen by high speed cinematography of the micro-circulation[2]. At the periphery of the flowing blood (adjacent to the vessel wall) there was a definite but very irregular and narrow zone of cell-free plasma. Many of the erythrocytes were in contact with the endothelium. Between these cells there were irregular patches of cell-free plasma. Most of the erythrocytes appeared to be on edge and oriented so that their biconcave surfaces were parallel to the adjacent vessel wall (parallel to the plane of shear of laminar flow).

The radial distribution of erythrocytes was measured by counting the number of erythrocytes within a circle on a reticule mounted in a microscope eyepiece. This described a circle of 35 μ diameter on the image of the artery viewed at × 1000 magnification. Counts were done at 0.05-mm intervals across the equator of the cross-section of the artery and the cell concentration at each interval expressed as the percentage of all the cells counted.

There was no consistent change in erythrocyte concentration radially except in the outermost 0.05-mm interval (Fig. 2). From the edge to the region of 0.05 mm from the edge, there was an increase in concentration. The mean change in concentration

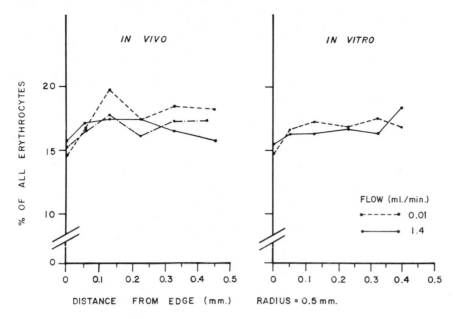

FIG. 2. RADIAL CONCENTRATION OF ERYTHROCYTES.

between these two points varied from +7 to +17% and was statistically significant ($p = <0.05$ evaluated by the t-test) in only two of five arteries so studied. The direction of the change, however, was the same in all five arteries (Fig. 2), so that there was a significant tendency for the concentration to decrease peripherally.

The width of the marginal zone of cell-free plasma was measured with the microscope micrometer. The radial distance from the endothelium to the nearest erythrocyte measured varied from 0 (where the erythrocyte was in contact with the endothelium within the limits of microscopic resolution) to 16 μ, with mean distance from 2.5 to 6.5 μ. The variation from vessel to vessel depended upon the thickness of the cross-section, so that it was not possible to know if a small change in width was dependent upon flow.

The orientation of the long axes of the erythrocytes was assessed by the method diagrammed in Fig. 3. The slide with the cross-section of the artery was moved so that the axis of the grid in the reticule was tangent to the vessel wall. The long axis of any erythrocyte on edge was scored as being in one of the four sectors (I—parallel or nearly parallel to the plane of shear through IV—most nearly perpendicular to the plane of shear) (Fig. 3a). The number of cells in each angle sector was then scored. The grid was moved across the artery horizontally and the scoring process repeated in the four radius domains (Fig. 3b).

The results of a set of measurements on a vessel frozen *in vivo* are shown in a histo-gram (Fig. 4) of the distribution of the cell axes at different points across the vessel, from the periphery to the center. Orientation of cell axes appeared to be related to

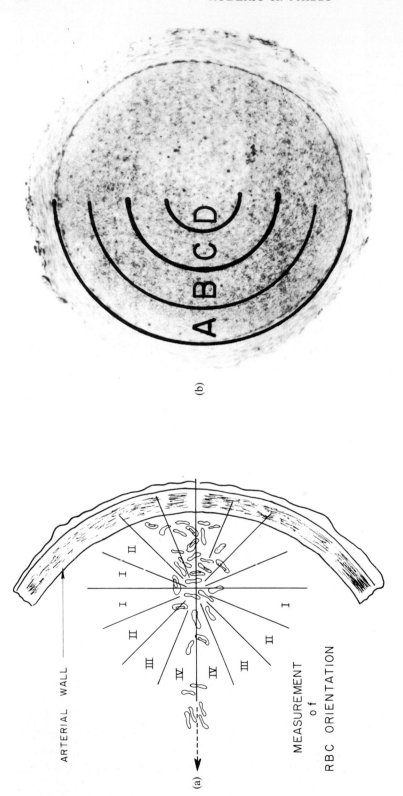

Fig. 3.(a) Cross-section of artery with superimposed grid for measuring orientation of long axis of erythrocytes, which are scored as having their long axis in one of four angle sectors. Arrow indicates movement of grid across artery (actually, artery moves in opposite direction under grid) so that the center of the grid passes through the center of the artery. (b) Radial domains in which orientation was measured and compared.

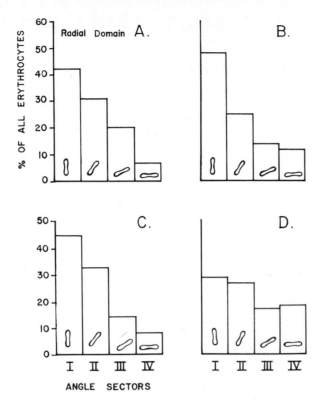

FIG. 4. ORIENTATION OF ERYTHROCYTES IN THE FOUR RADIAL DOMAINS OF ARTERY FROZEN *in vivo*. LOCA-
TION OF RADIAL DOMAINS AND ANGLE SECTORS AS IN FIG. 3.

shear — greater in the more peripheral zones where shear was greater — and no evident
orientation in the center of the vessel.

In order to assess the degree of orientation, a numerical term which expresses the
degree of orientation was used. This index of orientation is:

$$X = \frac{[(O-E)^2/n(n-1)]^{1/2}}{E}$$

X = index of orientation
E = number of cells expected in angle sector
O = number of cells observed in angle sector
n = number of angle sectors.

This is a new term based upon the chi square. It is a dimensionless number, varying
from 0 to 1, which expresses the degree to which the cells in a given radius domain
are oriented toward one angle sector rather randomly distributed among the four angle
sectors. When the index is 0, the long axes of the cells in the radius domain under
consideration are evenly distributed among the four angle sectors. When the index
equals 1, there is maximum orientation — all the cells in the radius domain are then
in one angle sector, none in the other three. The index by itself does not indicate in
which angle sector the cells are oriented; that is found in the data. Because the index
is derived from the chi square, a minimum value can be defined, depending upon the

number of cells scored in the sample. The index must exceed this minimum value for the orientation to be significantly different from 0.

Figure 5 shows the index of orientation plotted for all the vessels frozen. Where there was significant orientation, the cells tended to be more nearly parallel to the plane of shear (i.e., in angle sectors I and II) rather than perpendicular to the planes

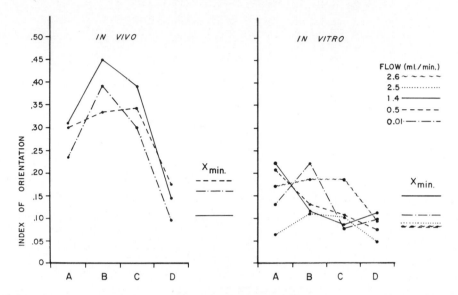

FIG. 5. PLOT OF INDEX OF ERYTHROCYTE ORIENTATION FROM PERIPHERY TO CENTER IN ARTERIES FROZEN *in vivo* AND *in vitro*. X_{min}, MINIMUM VALUE WHICH X (INDEX OF ORIENTATION) MUST EXCEED TO BE SIGNIFICANTLY DIFFERENT FROM 0 (WHERE THERE IS NO ORIENTATION INTO ONE OR ANOTHER ANGLE SECTOR). X_{min} VARIES FROM ARTERY TO ARTERY, DEPENDING UPON THE NUMBER OF CELLS SCORED IN EACH ANGLE SECTOR.

of shear. The orientation was least in the center of the vessel and increased peripherally

For the vessels frozen *in vivo,* the orientation appeared to be related to shear, but not linearly, since the maximum orientation occurred at a quarter of the radial distance from the periphery. The vessels frozen *in vitro* had the same general pattern, except for the vessel frozen at the highest rate of flow (approximately twice that *in vivo*) in which there was significant orientation all the way across the vessel, and no tendency

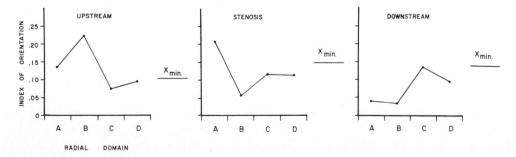

FIG. 6. ARTERY WITH SHORT REGIONAL STENOSIS FROZEN *in vitro*, PLOTTED AS IN FIG. 5. ORIENTATION MEASURED IN A GROUP OF CROSS-SECTIONS UPSTREAM OF THE STENOSIS AND REPEATED ON GROUPS OF CROSS-SECTIONS AT, AND WITHIN 1 MM DOWNSTREAM OF THE STENOSIS.

to increase peripherally. The orientation was much greater *in vivo*, where the flow was pulsatile, than *in vitro* where the flow was steady.

Figure 6 shows the index of orientation for the artery with the stenosis measured upstream, at, and downstream of the stenosis. Again, where the orientation was significant, it was toward angle sectors I and II (i.e. parallel to the plane of shear). Above the stenosis, the pattern of orientation was similar to that in the other arteries frozen *in vitro*. This pattern was maintained at the point of stenosis but downstream, where one might expect the pattern of streamline flow to be somewhat disrupted, the orientation disappeared.

DISCUSSION

The process of freezing flowing blood and potential changes in cell distribution have already been discussed[1]. Since the center of the artery is cooled last, the more peripheral blood is immobilized in much less time than the 0.1 sec required to cool the center from 37 to −20°C. It is not known if some force tending to change the distribution of the cells develops during the cooling process but the time available for the cells to respond to such a force is limited.

The striking differences in erythrocyte orientation with different patterns of flow (steady vs. pulsatile and proximal vs. distal to a stenosis) suggest that the observed patterns of cell distribution bear a relationship to the patterns present before the onset of freezing. This does not rule out the possibility, however, that there may be a freezing artefact superimposed upon all of the patterns of cell distribution.

The only significant radial change in erythrocyte concentration is at the most peripheral 0.05 mm of the vessel, which includes the irregular narrow zone of marginal cell-free plasma. This is the region most rapidly frozen and, hence, least likely to change during the freezing process. This is similar to the irregular patches of marginal cell-free plasma seen by high speed cinematography in smaller vessels *in vivo*[3]. This might be expected by the "wall effect" described by VAND[4] and MAUDE and WHITMORE[5] and does not indicate any significant degree of radial migration of the cells. This is enough, however, to provide blood of lower viscosity where shear is greatest. The width of the cell-free marginal zone has been measured indirectly by light transmission in blood flowing through glass tubes and inferred from viscometry data[6, 7]. Such methods have generally estimated a cell-free zone in blood with a hematocrit in the range of 35%, of the same order of magnitude as the "mean" width we have measured.

The lack of a generalized migration of erythrocytes inward from the periphery of the flowing blood is not surprising. In the close crowding of erythrocytes evident on microscopic examination (Fig. 1c, d), many appear to be in contact with each other. Any axial migration would increase the crowding and would have to overcome the dispersive forces produced by this crowding[8].

The orientation of the erythrocytes with respect to shear is expected on the basis of observations made on erythrocyte orientation in suspensions *in vitro*[9]. Some orientation has been observed repeatedly (but not quantitated) by high-speed cinematography in the microcirculation where the arteries are much narrower than those reported in this study. The erythrocytes tend to be oriented so that each cell is exposed to the least possible shear. However, this is an unstable position, for if the cell deviates so that the leading edge moves into a slower flowing lamina, the cell will rapidly tumble 180°. The orientation and orbital rotation of single rigid discs exposed to shear has been studied by GOLDSMITH and MASON[10].

In the arteries described here, however, the case is more complex because the cells are not rigid and the concentration of cells is great enough so that orientation might be expected to be enhanced by interactions between neighboring cells. From the degree of crowding observed in these arteries, it is evident that few cells are free to spin about their long axes without colliding with their neighbors. In most of the vessels studied, the degree of orientation does not directly correspond to the degree of shear across the vessel radius. Maximum orientation tends to occur in the next-to-the-most peripheral radial domain rather than in the most peripheral where shear is greatest. The slightly lower hematocrit at the periphery may partly explain the decrease in orientation there.

A second possible explanation is that, if the leading edge of one of the most peripheral erythrocytes adheres to the vascular endothelium even briefly it will be swung in an 180° arc by the passing blood stream. This tumbling phenomenon has been observed repeatedly in microcirculation and could produce a disorienting effect which might be transmitted several cell widths inward from the periphery.

The orientation is much greater in the vessels frozen *in vivo* than *in vitro*. The decrease in orientation or tendency for the peak orientation in the next-most peripheral rather than the most peripheral zone is more marked *in vivo* than *in vitro*. These differences may be due to the much more complex pattern of shear throughout a complete cardiac cycle in pulsatile flow[11]. The heart rate of those animals whose arteries were frozen *in vivo* was from 100 to 120 beats/min at the time of freezing. It is not known in what phase of the cardiac cycle the vessels froze, if the erythrocytes changed their orientation through each cardiac cycle or if they responded to the "mean" shear of the pulsatile cycle. If the cells maintain this high degree of orientation it may result in a considerable reduction in the viscosity with pulsatile flow. Other differences between *in vivo* and *in vitro* conditions include the presence of anticoagulant, possible injury and change of the vascular endothelium in *in vivo* and *in vitro* experiments. However, the difference in the type of flow seems to be the most likely cause of the difference in orientation.

ACKNOWLEDGMENTS

This work was supported by National Institutes of Health Grant GM 18275, USPHS HE–06285, and Life Insurance Medical Research Fund.

I am grateful to Professor Alan C. Burton for guidance and encouragement during the course of this work, and to Mrs. Dorothy Elston and Dr. David Rowed for valuable technical assistance.

REFERENCES

[1] PHIBBS, R. H. *Am. J. Physiol.* **210**, 919, 1966.
[2] BRÅNEMARK, P-I. and LINDSTRÖM, J. *Biorheology* **1**, 139, 1963.
[3] BLOCH, E. H. *Am. J. Anat.* **110**, 125, 1962.
[4] VAND, V. J. *J. Phys. Colloid Chem.* **52**, 277 and 300, 1948.
[5] MAUDE, A. D. and WHITMORE, R. L. *J. Appl. Physiol.* **12**, 105, 1958.
[6] TAYLOR, M. *Austral. J. Exp. Biol. Med. Sc.* **33**, 1, 1955.

[7] HAYNES, R. H. *Nature* **185**, 679, 1960.
[8] BAGNOLD, R. A. *Proc. Roy. Soc.*, Ser. A, **225**, 49, 1954.
[9] KURODA, K. and FUJINO, M. *Biorheology* **1**, 167, 1963.
[10] GOLDSMITH, H. L. and MASON, S. G. *J. Fluid Mech.* **12**, 88, 1962.
[11] HALE, J. F., McDONALD, D. A. and WOMERSLEY, J. R. *J. Physiol.* **128**, 629, 1955.

APPENDIX

ALAN C. BURTON

Department of Biophysics, University of Western Ontario, London, Ontario, Canada

Development of Index of Orientation

This index should be "dimensionless" in the sense that it does not tend to rise or fall if more or less cells are counted in each sector, and "normalized" so that the maximum value of the index for absolutely complete orientation (all the cells in a given radius-domain, e.g. parallel to the wall or at 45°—none at other angles) should be 1.0.

Since chance gives an index that is not zero, but has some small value, there must also be a measure of confidence in the value of the index as being greater than that which chance might produce.

Consider the case of using four sectors of angles; the results for a given radius domain might be:

Sector 1	61
2	42
3	20
4	21
	4) 144
Mean	36

If there were no tendency to orientation other than random, we would expect about equal numbers in each angle sector (this is for one radius domain, so that axial accumulation does not enter into the argument).

The measure of degree of orientation is based on the standard deviation, i.e.

$$\left(\frac{\Sigma d^2}{n-1}\right)^{1/2}.$$

To make this dimensionless so that it does not rise if more cells are counted it should be divided by the mean, giving the "variation"

$$\frac{\text{S.D}}{\text{M}}.$$

However, this is not "parametric" but "contingency" statistics, dealing with numbers of occurrences not values of parameters. Instead of the "mean" we talk of the expected number "E" (as in the chi-square test), and the observed number "O". The equivalent of the standard deviation becomes

$$\frac{\Sigma(E-O)^2}{n-1}$$

and the "variation" becomes

$$\left(\frac{\Sigma(E-O)^2}{n-1}\right)^{1/2} \Big/ E.$$

This equivalent of "variation" appears to be the best index of "degree of orientation". It is dimensionless, and does not tend to change with the number of cells counted. However, it has to be normalized, as indicated by investigation of how high the value of this index can go.

Normalizing the index: If we adopt the index of orientation as

$$X = \left(\frac{\Sigma(E-O)^2}{n-1}\right)^{1/2} \Big/ E$$

how great would this be if we had the most complete orientation imaginable? If we have, not four, but n categories or sectors of angle (the same n as in the formula for X), and if every cell in that radius domain is at one angle, one of the categories of angle would contain a high number "a" while the other $(n-1)$ categories would contain a low number, which we may assume to be the same, "b". The total number counted then is

$$a + (n-1)b.$$

The expected value E is

$$\frac{a + (n-1)b}{n}$$

$(E-O)$ for the category with "a" cells is

$$a - \frac{a + (n-1)b}{n} = \frac{(n-1)(a-b)}{n}.$$

$(E-O)$ for the $(n-1)$ other categories is

$$\frac{a + (n-1)b}{n} - b = \frac{(a-b)}{n}.$$

Therefore,

$$\Sigma(E-O)^2 = \frac{(n-1)^2(a-b)^2}{n^2} + \frac{(n-1)(a-b)^2}{n^2} = \frac{(n-1)}{n}(a-b)^2$$

and the index

$$X = \frac{1}{E}\left(\frac{(n-1)(a-b)^2}{n(n-1)}\right)^{1/2} = \frac{1}{E}\frac{(a-b)}{n^{1/2}} + \frac{(a-b)}{[a+(n-1)b]} \cdot \frac{n}{n^{1/2}}.$$

If we now make $a \gg b$

$$X \to n^{1/2}.$$

If we adopt the original formula for X as the index of degree of orientation, perfect orientation would give an index of $n^{1/2}$, i.e. for four angle sectors it would be 2, for nine angle sectors 3, etc. To normalize the index, therefore, we must define it as: Index of orientation

$$X = \left(\frac{\Sigma(E-O)^2}{n(n-1)}\right)^{1/2} \Big/ E.$$

This index would be 1.0 for absolutely complete orientation, whatever the number of angle sectors used. Note that the index is exactly analogous, in parametric statistics, to the

$$\frac{\text{(standard error of the mean)}}{\text{mean}}$$

and though this reminds one of the "critical ratio" (or its reciprocal) of the t-test, its meaning here is very different.

Minimum Value of the Index of Orientation

This will not be zero, but the values which might occur by chance are different — according to the number of cells counted, the number of angle categories, and to the "level of confidence" required.

The probability that the observed distribution of cells in the angle sectors occurs by chance is determined by the "goodness of fit" or chi-square test.

$$X^2 = \frac{\Sigma(E-O)^2}{E}$$

in our case, since the expected values E are the same for each angle sector. If there are four angle sectors, the number of degrees of freedom is three, and for 5% confidence level ($p = 0.05$), chi square must be greater than 7.815; for $p = 0.01$, greater than 11.345. Since the same sum $\Sigma(E-O)^2$ occurs in the normalized index of orientation, we can estimate the least value of the index which is likely not to be chance, from the value of the index.

Index of orientation

$$X = \left(\frac{\Sigma(E-O)^2}{n(n-1)}\right)^{1/2} \Big/ E$$

where n is the number of angle categories. Therefore

$$X^2 = \frac{\Sigma(E-O)^2}{E} = \frac{n(n-1)X^2E^2}{E} = n(n-1)X^2E.$$

But $E = N/n$ where $N = $ total number of cells, in all angle categories.

$$X^2 = \frac{n(n-1)X^2}{n}N = (n-1)N.X^2.$$

If X_{Pn}^2 is the minimum value of X^2 for a level of confidence P, and number of categories $n(n-1$ degrees of freedom), then the minimum value of the index X that is significant is given by

$$X_{\min} = \left(\frac{X_{Pn}^2}{n-1}\right)^{1/2} \cdot \frac{1}{N^{1/2}}.$$

For our particular case:

$$X_{P=0.05, n=4}^2 = 7.815 \quad \text{and} \quad X_{\min P=0.05} = \frac{1.61}{N^{1/2}}$$

and

$$X_{P=0.01, n=4}^2 = 11.345 \quad \text{and} \quad X_{\min P=0.01} = \frac{1.94}{N^{1/2}}$$

Effect of having more angle categories. Suppose eight angle categories are used instead of four. Then $n-1 = 7$ and

$$X_{P=0.05, n=8}^2 = 14.067 \quad \text{and} \quad X_{\min P=0.05} = \frac{1.42}{N^{1/2}},$$

$$X_{P=0.01, n=8}^2 = 18.475 \quad \text{and} \quad X_{\min P=0.01} = \frac{1.62}{N^{1/2}}.$$

These are lower than for the four angle categories, but not much. There would be, therefore, only a slight advantage of using more angle categories than the four we used, so long as the number in each category was not reduced below the necessary number for a chi-square test (5, Yates correction, etc.). This advantage would be offset by the disadvantage of making it harder to decide in which category to put any given cell. The four categories chosen here are about the optimum.

DISCUSSION

WELLS (*U.S.A.*):

This is very interesting. I have just one question that you may have answered as regards the technique. When your microtome cuts across this vessel, if an erythrocyte is, let us say, 45° away from you, and you cut across this, you may then have an elliptical cross section that looks as if the cell was on edge. Now perhaps you are able to determine the slightly different degrees of the concave surface to tell whether this occurred. If that is the way you did, can we be sure that freezing might not change the surface enough to make this a difficult interpretation?

PHIBBS (*U.S.A.*):

The sections were deep enough so that, by focusing up and down, one could see whether the cell was completely on edge or partially rotated. A number of the cells were rotated and, as you suggested, may have been turning over. When the rotation was slight and the long axis of the cell could be measured easily, with respect to the tangent of the adjacent vessel wall, this was done and included in the scoring of the orientation.

WELLS:

You mean your depth of field was more than say 4 microns?

PHIBBS:

The thin sections were 5 microns. What needs to be done in order to evaluate this rotation is to section the vessels longitudinally. We now have a number of frozen vessels which we plan to section in this way.

WHITMORE (*U.S.A.*):

Just one short question: Was it possible to determine the time in the pulse cycle at which the freezing operating took place?

PHIBBS:

We did not determine this for the arteries frozen *in vivo* but have, since then, frozen another group of vessels, recording the arterial pulse with a small plethysmograph just downstream of the segment and will have this information. However, these vessels are not completely processed yet.

CHARM (*U.S.A.*):

I was wondering if you would make a comment about the possible expansion in the course of freezing?

PHIBBS:

When blood is cooled very rapidly to these low temperatures there is probably no ice crystal formation at first. The water in the blood becomes what Luyet calls "vitreous water". The initial expansion of water, due to this type of cooling, is a 1 or 2% increase in volume rather than the greater expansion expected with ice formation. With subsequent warming to $-78.5°C$, as done for freeze-substitution, a slow growth of both intra- and extra-cellular ice crystals will occur. However, this would be a slow uniform process across the entire artery, so that intercellular relationships should be preserved. Furthermore, when the vessels were warmed to $-78.5°C$ they were undergoing freeze-substitution, so that some of the water would have been removed and replaced by acetone before it had crystallized. We do not know how much water remained in the tissue to be crystallized into ice, but some certainly did. Under high power magnification one can see the fine deformation in the red cell membrane, which is characteristic of the intracellular ice crystal formation seen with very rapid cooling of tissue.

CHARM:

One other point: Would you say that the gap widths that you estimated in *extra vivum* and *in vivo* were about the same?

PHIBBS:

They were similar, but because of the differences in thickness of the cross-sections, no strict comparisons could be made. The gap widths are in the range of 2–6 microns, which I believe is the same order of magnitude as your measurements of gap width.

CHARM:

This sounds like a technique we ought to adapt to the rat-tail artery studies that we have been doing.

BUGLIARELLO (*U.S.A.*):

I am extremely delighted with this technique. I think it is a very powerful technique and certainly has provided us with a great deal of information. I would like particularly to call attention to two problems. First of all, the fact that the type of configuration that you have obtained from this type of technique tallies very well with what has been observed by high speed cinematography. This means that even if we are doing cine-photomicrography *in vitro*, we are still getting some relevant and important information, because the peripheral layer configuration appears to be very much the same and to have the same characteristics. Secondly, one aspect that puzzles me: some of the results we have obtained by high speed cinephotomicrography. We measured the velocity profiles *in vitro* and found that if, from these velocity profiles, we attempted to derive a viscosity profile, there was a peak in viscosity which was rather close to the boundary. Now it appears that from your measurements *in vivo*, there is also a peak of hematocrit, particularly at low speed, which is a little bit away from the wall. In other words, the hematocrit is low, then goes up, and then goes down again. And this is an interesting coincidence. Mine is really not a question, just a comment.

PHIBBS:

The hematocrit does not consistently change that much *in vitro*. The changes in hematocrit, both *in vivo* and *in vitro* are too small to affect viscosity significantly, except at the edge. The orientation does increase and then decrease from the edge to the center. I do not know to what extent the orientation affects the viscosity. *In vivo*, the effect of orientation upon viscosity would also depend upon whether the cells are oriented throughout the cardiac cycle or are changing with each pulse. If the latter, they must be changing very rapidly—twice per second.

MASON (*Canada*):

In connection with these measurements which are extremely interesting and extremely important, I would like to mention that we are able to infer orientation distributions in very dilute suspensions of disc-like particles, flowing down tubes in both steady flow and pulsatile flow, from an analysis of Jeffrey's theoretical equations, which Dr. Goldsmith described in the model particles session. The orientation distribution which we infer is very similar to those which you described for the pulsatile *in vivo* flow. I would like to ask whether you attempted any kind of correlation analysis between near neighbor particles to see if there was any evidence of aggregation or rouleau formation? If not, is it evident to the eye that there is any correlation between the organization of adjacent particles or cells?

PHIBBS:

No, we did not. This is a good suggestion.

MASON:

We have done analogous experiments in which the medium was polymerized and subsequently sectioned, and have found that rigid discs do indeed aggregate and form rouleau-like structures. I realize that this technique will not provide the answer, but from a rheological point of view it would be very interesting to know whether or not the particles are rotating as they flow. Since you do not find any preferred orientation in the steady flow measurements *in vivo*, I would infer that the particles are not rotating, and that you have a condition of plug flow; in other words, no velocity gradients which cause rotation. Whether you have simultaneous rotation in your pulsating flow, or in *in vivo* experiments, is uncertain. They may be rotating; on the other hand, the preferred orientation which you get may be produced as an entrance effect and the subsequent orientations frozen by the entrance conditions. I would like to draw attention to the rheological importance of rotation, which in many situations may be much more important than translation.

PHIBBS:

In regard to rotation: on the photomicrographs, if you look in from the edge of the vessel a little bit, it is clear that very few of those cells could rotate without colliding with their neighbors. Few could flip in the fashion you have described with your discs without colliding, so that there is a secondary orienting effect from the adjacent particles. At the edge, where the hematocrit is a bit lower, the cells are freer to rotate and this is where less orientation is seen. There may also be some interaction between the erythrocyte membrane and the endothelium which might produce a flipping effect that could be transmitted a couple of cell layers toward the center. I do not think many of the cells in the center could rotate very far individually without colliding. Of course, a whole column could also rotate.

MASON:

In that case you got an orientation effect that could be fixed by some entrance condition upstream, which occurred before you made your observations.

PHIBBS:

That is right.

RHEOLOGICAL PATTERNS IN THE MICROCIRCULATION

GEORGE P. FULTON,* HERBERT J. BERMAN,* ROBERT F. SLECHTA,
ARTHUR M. BROOKS

Biological Science Center, Boston University, Boston, Mass., U.S.A.

INTRODUCTION

The microarchitecture of the terminal vascular system is an important factor in determining the rheological properties of the microcirculation[1]. In studies using mechanical models of the circulation, basic rheological phenomena have been established for Newtonian fluids and for blood flowing in rigid straight-walled tubes. Blood is non-Newtonian and to compound the problem, the living blood vessels are not mere rigid straight-walled tubes but are constructed in the form of tapering cones decreasing in diameter from larger arterioles to capillaries and increasing again in the venules. In addition, the blood vessels have elastic walls which may distend or retract changing vessel diameters and concomitantly alter the blood pressure and flow characteristics in these vessels. The fundamental tenets of rheology therefore should not be applied without modification to blood and blood vessels because of the anatomical and physical arrangements of the microvasculature. For this reason, we have made a photographic comparison of selected capillary beds including both arterioles and venules with respect to the microarchitecture in each tissue and the rheological properties inherent in each pattern.

COMPARISON OF BLOOD FLOW AND VESSEL PATTERN IN VARIOUS TISSUES

By means of cinephotomicrographic recording at normal and high speeds (32–3000 frames per second), rheological patterns and flow characteristics of the microcirculation have been investigated *in vivo* in normal and pathological states in several representative tissues in the frog and hamster. The tissues exposed and visualized in the frog were the retrolingual membrane, lung, web of the foot, skin, mesentery and bladder; and in the hamster, the cheek pouch and mesocaecum.

The comparative microarchitecture of the terminal vascular system is an important factor in determining the rheological properties of the microcirculation found in each blood vessel pattern. In the retrolingual membrane beneath the tongue of the frog, the pressure differential existing between capillaries is well illustrated. The pressure found in the precapillary vessels frequently equals the pressure found in the post-capillary vessels, resulting in a cessation of flow within that particular capillary bed (Figs. 1, 2). This stoppage of flow is usually temporary; however, in some instances it may persist for hours dependent on several factors such as sphincter activity in the precapillary and postcapillary bed, metabolic need of the tissue, and pressure differential

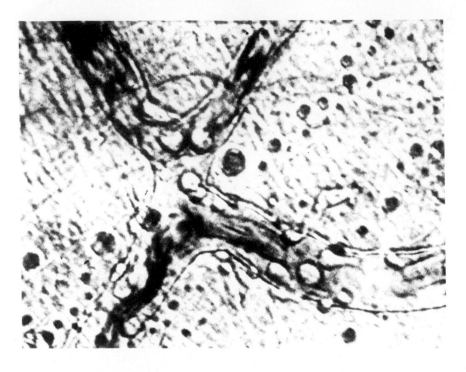

FIG. 1. Two V-shaped anastomosing venules in frog retrolingual membrane. Note large RBC and smaller thrombocytes in the anastomosis × 200.

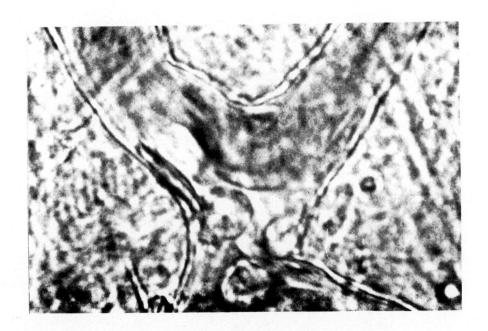

FIG. 2. Same preparation. × 500.

which is affected by the general blood pressure of the organ involved. Thus flow characteristics in the capillary bed are quite variable and do not necessarily reflect general patterns of flow found in the larger precapillary and postcapillary vessels.

An important factor which may affect patterns of flow in the microcirculation is the characteristic right angle branching of the capillary from the supplying arteriole[1]. Because of this unique feature, blood corpuscles and plasma must execute an abrupt ninety degree angle turn in order to enter the capillary. This maneuver carries with it inherent hemorheological attributes which may possibly lead to turbulence, plasma skimming and distortion of red cells.

Within the capillary bed it is possible to find two columns of blood approaching each other from opposite directions that abruptly, upon meeting, execute a right angle turn, and enter the precapillary arteriole as two relatively distinct streams which blend slowly. This flow phenomenon may continue indefinitely or the stream may shift to the right or the left. This change in direction of flow is such that the opening of the capillary may be by-passed resulting in a condition where the peripheral plasma layer may be "skimmed" from the main vessel (Fig. 3). Plasma skimming may concentrate the red cell flow by removing the plasma from the main column of blood and result in an increase in hematocrit.

A common feature of blood flow in the microvasculature is the buffeting received by the red cells as they enter the capillary. Many of the red cells are caught or "impaled" on the bifurcation of the capillary and precapillary arteriole (Fig. 4). The red cell is usually considerably deformed; however, it does not rupture but continues to circulate. In addition, in this particular situation, flow characteristics may create eddying of formed elements when pressure differentials permit this to occur (Fig. 3).

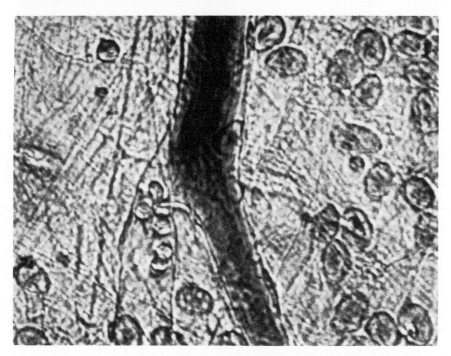

FIG. 3. FROG. PLASMA SKIMMING. × 200.

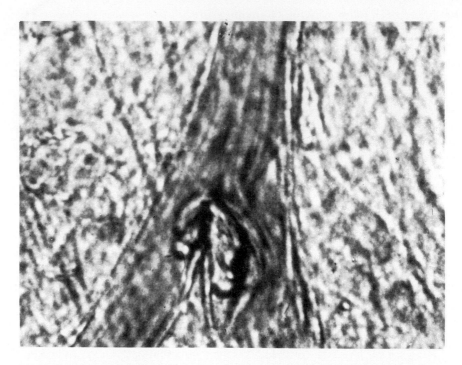

FIG. 4. FROG. RED CELLS "IMPALED" ON BIFURCATION OF ARTERIOLE.

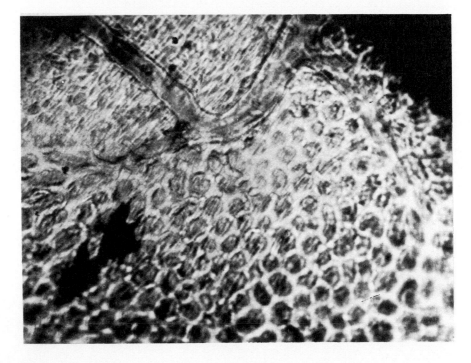

FIG. 5. FROG LUNG. NOTE ABRUPT EMERGENCE OF CAPILLARY FROM LARGE ARTERIOLE. STREAKING IS
CAUSED BY RAPID BLOOD FLOW IN CAPILLARIES AROUND THE ALVEOLI BUT IN A DIFFERENT FOCAL PLANE.

A unique feature found in lung tissue is the abrupt exit of capillaries from arterioles into the lung capillary network (Fig. 5)[2, 3]. This anatomical arrangement permits an enormous blood volume to flow into the lung capillary bed in a relatively short time. The capillary bed of the lung has an unusual pattern. Each capillary divides and subdivides to form a "basket-like" structure over and around the alveoli of the lung, presenting the greatest surface area possible for gaseous exchange. In this organ the red cell does not flow through direct capillary vessels as in the retrolingual membrane, but must "trickle" through a series of pathways around the alveoli before emerging into the postcapillary network (Fig. 5). The formed elements are subjected to considerable but more gentle buffeting in this tissue, and because of the nature of the vascular pattern emboli may possibly have a greater opportunity to become lodged within the maze of capillaries.

The web of the foot of the frog has a peculiar vascular pattern, since no obvious direction of flow from arteriole to venule is evident. A multilayered vascular bed with a rapid blood flow is seen favoring the respiratory function attributed to this organ.

The pattern of vessels found in the frog urinary bladder is well adapted to its function. The general impression obtained upon viewing the microcirculation of the bladder is that of complexity. The vessels are numerous and are highly twisted and tortuous (Figs. 6, 7). Flow rates appear to be rapid and arterio-venous anastomoses are found; however, capillaries *per se* are not numerous. This highly tortuous pattern is ideally suited for the function of the bladder, that is distension. Thus when the bladder is empty the marked twisting of the vessels is obvious while when the bladder is filled with urine or experimentally inflated with air the twists in the vessels become straight.

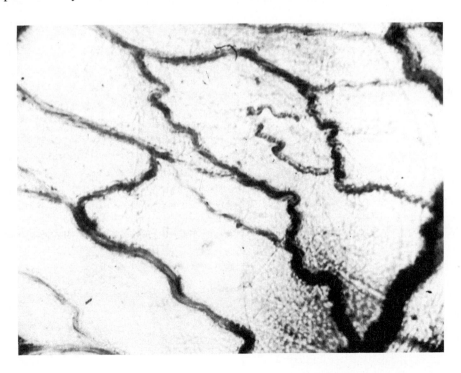

FIG. 6. FROG BLADDER. TORTUOSITY IS FOUND IN A HIGH DEGREE. × 100.

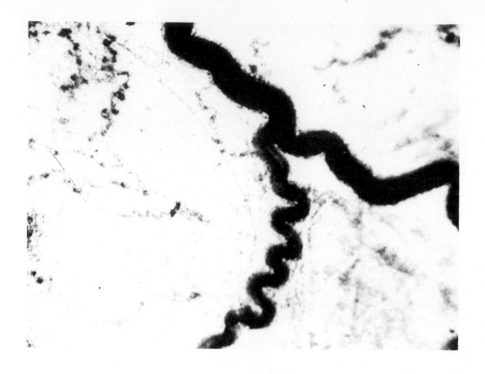

FIG. 7. SAME PREPARATION. × 200.

The cheek pouch of the golden hamster is an opportune site in which to study the microarchitecture of the blood vessels of a mammal. Also the preparation reveals very clearly the rheological problems present in blood flow[6]. The cheek pouch exhibits almost all of the rheological phenomena, but lacks arterio-venous anastomoses. Arteriole to arteriole anastomoses and venule to venule anastomoses are prevalent. The rheological effects of thrombus and/or embolus formation may be studied experimentally in this preparation. Red cell diapedesis may be evaluated, evidenced by petechial formation[4], and the rheological changes associated with white-cell "pavementing" of the lumen of the vessels in bacterial infection may be observed. All of the classical architecture of the microvasculature is present, namely, artery, arteriole, precapillary arteriole, capillary, venule, vein. Spontaneous sphincter activity may be seen or contraction of sphincters may be induced by topical application of chemical reagents or electrical stimulation. The resultant effects on flow characteristics have been recorded on motion picture film. The extensive capillary network found in the cheek pouch lends itself ideally to analysis of the physiological factors related to rheological phenomena. The mesocaecum of the hamster has a microcirculatory pattern similar to that of the cheek pouch. In addition to the usual anatomical characteristics found in the pouch, the mesocaecum contains large deposits of fat possessing extensive capillary networks. Generally, the arrangement of the microvasculature of the mesocaecum is fan-shaped with the larger vessels making up the ribs and outer periphery of the fan and with a limited capillary bed found interspersed between the ribs.

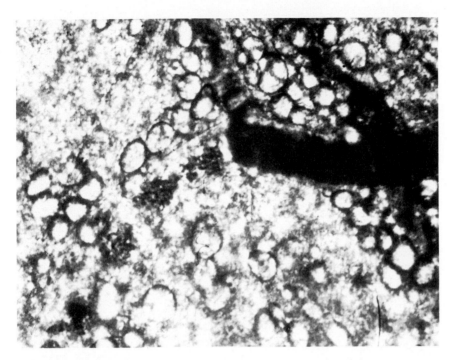

FIG. 8. HAMSTER CHEEK POUCH. AGGREGATES OF RBC MAY BE CLEARLY SEEN IN VENULE. × 200.

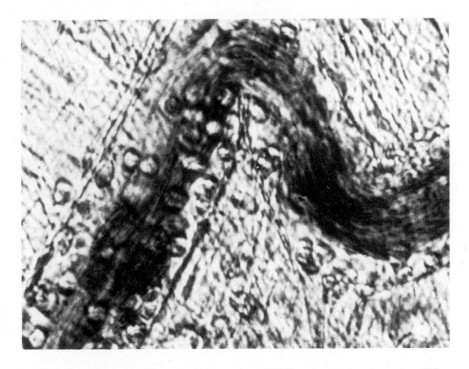

FIG. 9. HAMSTER CHEEK POUCH. ADHERENCE OF WBC TO ENDOTHELIAL WALL. × 500.

SUMMARY

The quantitative study of blood flow in small living blood vessels and the techniques and instrumentation required for such quantitative studies are still in their formative stages[3–6]. The paper by its illustrations and the film it describes, displays some of the variations in vascular patterns and flow inherent in any one vertebrate species, and between two relatively widely separated vertebrate species, the frog and the hamster. The variables, such as local variations in vasomotor tone, different vascular patterns, thromboembolic phenomena, rotation of cells, erythrocytic aggregation (Fig. 8), white cell adherence to the endothelium (Fig. 9), petechial formation, and flow and pressure variation can affect blood flow, vascular permeability, Starling's variables and therefore transvascular exchange.

ACKNOWLEDGMENT

This work was supported by Grant HE-902, DA-49-193-MD-2696, and Frostbite Grant, PHS-HE-06984-04 U.S. Public Health Service.

REFERENCES

[1] BERMAN, H. J. *Bibl. Anat.* **7**, 29, 1965.
[2] IRWIN, J. W., BURRAGE, W. S., AIMAR, C. E. and CHESTNUT, R. W., JR. *Anat. Rec.* **119**, 391, 1954.
[3] IRWIN, J. W., VINEYARD, P. A. and MARR, E. M. *J. Roy. Micro. Soc.* **83**, 37, 1964.
[4] FULTON, G. P., LUTZ, B. R., SHULMAN, M. H. and ARENDT, K. A. Moccasin venom as a test for susceptibility to petechial formation in the hamster. Reprint from *Venom*, American Association for the Advancement of Science, Washington, D.C., p. 303, 1956.
[5] BROOKS, A. M. and FULTON, G. P. *Angiology* **16**, 470, 1965.
[6] WELLS, R. E. *New Eng. J. Med.* **270**, 832, 889, 1964.

DISCUSSION

MEISELMAN (*U.S.A.*):

I have two questions, Dr. Berman. The first relates to the platelet and white cell emboli that you noticed after slight mechanical injury. I am relating this now to some micro-occlusion techniques that have been used to measure permeability through the capillary wall by watching movement of red cells. Do you feel that emboli could form here? Is there a change in the adherence or stickiness of the formed elements, caused by the micro-occlusion technique of bringing a fine needle down on the vessel?

BERMAN (*U.S.A.*):

I would suspect that gentle placement of a fine needle or hair across a capillary, such as done recently by Drs. Intagliata and Zweifach, would not injure the blood vessel, or if it did, not sufficiently to produce adherence to the endothelium. True capillaries do appear to be comparatively resistant to thrombosis while venules are much more susceptible.

MEISELMAN:

My second question relates to observations made when using very high molecular weight dextran—I think you mentioned 500,000 molecular weight. You observed sludging (or aggregation, if you will) of red cells. The vessels where normal flow began to return first were the arteries, that is, in regions of higher shear. I think this is related to some of the material that was presented yesterday. Increased shear forces may reduce aggregate size when, in fact, there still may be strong aggregating forces in existence. Do you have the feeling that this is what you have been seeing? Have you been able to stop flow in these arteries and observe if there really is aggregation which is in a dynamically deaggregated state?

BERMAN:

I believe that you are right. I would suspect that high shear stress would tend to break up red cell aggregates. I have not stopped flow in such arterial vessels, but, since the red cells reaggregate in venous vessels, an area of relatively low shear, after passing as more or less discrete units through the capillary bed, I suspect that if flow were stopped in arterial vessels they would reaggregate there.

WAYLAND (*U.S.A.*):

I was most interested in your statistics on the various areas as you go down the tree. I was wondering whether in the true capillaries your figures represent the number or the area that is available at any particular moment or if you have taken into consideration the fact that there appears to be a statistical movement of blood among a group of capillaries, some of which are open and some of which are not, at any particular time?

BERMAN:

The vascular tree was reconstructed by camera lucida drawings at 60–1200 magnifications. All capillaries that could be seen were included, whether flow was present in them or not. We estimated that at any one time flow was present in about one third of the capillaries in the hamster cheek pouch. (LITTON, A., BERMAN, H. J. and WALTERS, C. W. *Anat. Record.* **154**, 472, 1966).

COPLEY (*U.S.A.*):

My question is more a matter regarding terminology. As I understand you, you talk about capillaries; you mean the true capillaries, is this correct? I think, in general, if you cannot identify the capillary vessel, then you should use the term "capillaries" in a generic way, similar to what Landis had proposed and what is also my contention. Thus, capillary blood vessels, up to about 20 microns in diameter, I think, should be called capillaries, except if you really can identify the capillary as "true" capillary, postcapillary, precapillary, etc.

BERMAN:

In the hamster cheek pouch most true capillaries can be readily identified. The first postcapillary vessels commence at the confluence of two or more true capillaries. There, rather abruptly, the diameter of the vessel just about doubles.

GELIN (*Sweden*):

I, as well as Dr. Copley, was very interested in your quantitation of the intravascular volume. You emphasize here that the venous system is the most volume-consuming compartment of the circulation, which is of utmost importance for the understanding of the rheological properties in venous return compared to cardiac output. I will come back to that point another time. It is very important to elucidate what is a true capillary compared to the onflow and offflow capillary, using, for example, Copley's definition, because the shear rate is quite different in the $20\,\mu$ arteriole compared to the $20\,\mu$ venule. So I think we have to be sure we mean capillaries as true capillaries. I think that definition is very important.

BERMAN:

Dr. Gelin, I fully agree with you. Since the vascular pattern differs in different tissues and organs, the problems of identifying each type of vessel in each of these tissues and organs may differ. I believe that the cheek pouch vasculature is pretty well worked out. I hope that the others can be quantitated in a similar or better manner.

TRANSIT TIMES OF CELLS AND ALBUMIN THROUGH THE VASCULAR BED OF SKELETAL MUSCLE

A. C. Groom* †

St. Mary's Hospital Medical School,
University of London, London, England

THERE are two distinct and complementary approaches to the study of events taking place in the smaller blood vessels. Either we may look with a microscope at the small vessels contained in a very small area of a vascular bed, or we may examine the overall behaviour of the bed by looking at the input and the output of some marker substances flowing through the system.

Ideas from direct observations of small vessels help us to interpret what we find when using the second approach; quantitative measurements using the second approach enable us to see how important in the overall scheme of things are the processes which we observe with the microscope.

Axial streaming of cells, plasma skimming, and a slow accumulation, in the extravascular space, of albumin conjugated with fluorescein have all been observed directly *in vivo*; on the other hand radioactive tracer studies have shown that red cells travel slightly faster than plasma in traversing the heart and lungs[1, 2], the kidney[3, 4, 5], and the liver [6]. A similar effect has also been demonstrated in blood flowing through nylon tubes of $200\,\mu$ bore[7], but it would be unfortunate if the differences observed *in vivo* were attributed exclusively to one particular mechanism, for there is as yet an absence of data, obtained *in vivo* under a sufficient variety of conditions, on the ratio of mean velocities of cells and plasma in the vessels where temporal separation occurs.

This ratio of the mean velocities is difficult to measure *in vivo*, because we are dealing with a closed loop and recirculating "indicator" masks the decaying concentration corresponding to a single passage through the vascular bed under study. In the conventional dye dilution method for measuring blood flow the descending limb is extrapolated on the arbitrary basis of a single exponential decay. Whilst this extrapolation may sometimes be reasonable for estimating the total area under the curve, it can lead to large errors where the first moment of area is concerned, as in determination of mean transit time.

A further problem, particularly serious in the case of the heart and lungs, arises from the dead space of large vessels in series with the smaller vessels in which temporal separation occurs. Because of this the difference from unity of the ratio of measured mean transit times is small.

We are faced also with two technical difficulties:
1. Sampling by withdrawal at constant rate from a blood vessel may mask changes in flow rate during passage of indicators.

---

†Present address: Department of Biophysics, University of Western Ontario, London, Ontario, Canada.

2. Considerable interpolation is necessary where clearance curves are derived from
   a set of discrete samples, as with a faction cutter.

Axial streaming, molecular diffusion, and extravascular passage of albumin may
all contribute to an observed difference in transit times of cells and albumin. As has
been stressed previously[8], accurate measurements of mean transit times are essential if the contributions of these various mechanisms are to be assessed.

Many of the difficulties associated with the determination of mean transit time have
been overcome by the use of a vascularly isolated gastrocnemius preparation.

Cats were anaesthetized with chloralose and urethane and the left gastrocnemius
group of muscles was exposed. All branches of the left femoral artery and vein, except
those running to and from the gastrocnemius, were ligated. All other vessels running
between the gastrocnemius and elsewhere were ligated. The sciatic nerve was divided. Blood was routed from the right femoral artery to the left popliteal artery via the
cannula shown in the lower portion of Fig. 1. This cannula consisted of siliconed glass,

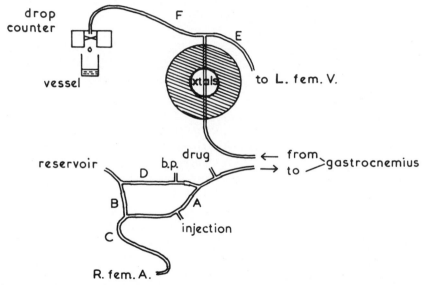

FIG. 1. ARRANGEMENT OF ARTERIAL AND VENOUS CANNULAE. DURING OBSERVATIONS THE MUSCLE IS
PERFUSED AT CONSTANT FLOW WITH BLOOD FROM A RESERVOIR AND THE VENOUS OUTFLOW IS DIVERTED
TO A COLLECTING VESSEL (SEE TEXT).

silicone rubber, and polythene tubing, and enabled the muscle to be supplied with
blood at a constant flow rate from a thermostat-controlled reservoir during the period
of observations. At the same time a vasodilator drug, chloral hydrate, could be infused
via a T-junction, and the arterial blood pressure or the perfusion pressure measured
with a Statham transducer. A volume $0 \cdot 03$ ml of autologous blood containing red
cells labelled with ^{32}P and human serum albumin labelled with ^{131}I could be injected
from a siliconed glass $0 \cdot 25$ ml tuberculin syringe into the lower branch and circulate
through the vascular bed of the muscle. It is essential that the syringe be siliconed,
otherwise plasma kinin formation gives rise to a tremendous vasodilatation during
passage of the labelled blood. To avoid a transient increase in flow rate the blood was
injected into the lower branch while it was occluded at A and B and open at C. C was
then clamped and the flow diverted from the upper to the lower branch.

The entire venous return from the muscle was routed via a cannula, shown in the upper part of Fig. 1, between two scintillation counters and then back into the femoral vein or else via a branch to a photoelectric drop counter the outflow from which was collected in a siliconed weighing bottle. Under these conditions there was no recirculation of labelled blood. The height of the outflow point could be varied above or below the level of the muscle. The blood in the reservoir was kept at 37°C and the muscle was kept moist and warm by wrapping loosely a thin polythene sheet three or four times around the limb.

One of the scintillation detectors measured the areal concentration of ^{32}P and the other that of ^{131}I in the venous blood. When therefore labelled blood was injected into the artery, a record such as that in Fig. 2 was obtained. The injection was made at time

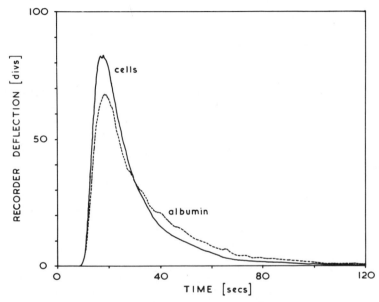

Fig. 2. [Exp. 6508. Trace 2.] Concentration – time records of ^{32}P-labelled cells and ^{131}I-labelled albumin in the venous outflow from the muscle. Both labels were injected simultaneously into the arterial cannula at time zero. The curves have been normalized to have the same area.

zero and here the two indicator curves, normalized to have the same area, are shown superimposed. It is clear that there will be a difference of mean transit times, the cells travelling the faster.

These curves were recorded at a ratemeter time constant of 1 sec using Leeds & Northrup potentiometric recorders with a response time of 0·25 sec and a maximum deflection of 10 in. The paper used had lines ruled at 0·1 in. intervals along both ordinate and abscissa, and the chart speed was 15 in./min. An event marker gave a record of the instant of injection. Before the injection the baselines were adjusted to be at the zero position precisely, so that it was a simple procedure afterwards to read off the deflections at regular intervals and calculate the integral curves as a function of time.

The successive integral values were expressed as percentages of the total area under the curve and plotted as shown in Fig. 3. Perhaps the difference in transit times can be seen even more clearly from the integral curve; the mean transit time is, of course,

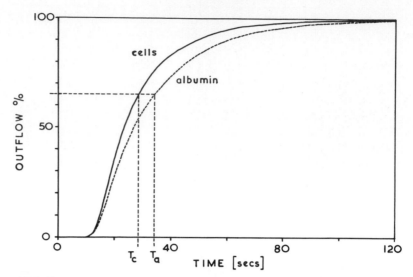

FIG. 3. [EXP. 6508. TRACE 2.] PERCENTAGE OUTFLOWS OF LABELLED CELLS AND ALBUMIN, PREPARED BY NUMERICAL INTEGRATION OF THE RECORDS SHOWN IN FIG. 2. FOR EXPLANATION OF CORRESPONDING TIMES, T_c AND T_a, SEE TEXT.

derived from measuring the area between the graph and the percentage outflow axis. By deducting from each mean transit time the time corresponding to flow through the cannulae, the values relating to flow through the muscle vascular bed may be obtained.

From an examination of such curves it became clear that in most cases the temporal separation of cells and albumin ($T_c - T_a$) at the same value of percentage outflow increased linearly with transit time up to about 90% outflow. For this reason values of T_c were plotted against the values of T_a corresponding to the same percentage outflow, as shown in Fig. 4.

The data of Figs. 3 and 4 represent the actual analysis of the pair of clearance curves shown in Fig. 2. The relation between T_c and T_a is remarkably linear; deviation occurs here at 96% outflow. This diagram is typical of almost all the curves examined. For instance, in a recent experiment deviation from linearity occurred at 95·5, 98, 98, 98, 94, 98, and 97% outflow respectively in seven pairs of clearance curves. At 98% outflow the recorded deflection on the original curves is less than one-tenth of an inch, so that errors of measuring very small ordinates account for some of the deviation from linearity. Nevertheless there have been isolated instances where deviation has occurred much earlier, either towards, or away from the line of identity, and one of these cases will be discussed in connection with Fig. 5.

What does this linear relationship mean?

Firstly, the intersection at T_0 of the experimental curve with the line of identity must represent a zero time for separation of the labelled constituents by whatever mechanisms are responsible. Measured from this point, the transit times of cells and albumin for corresponding fractions of the outflow are in a constant ratio given by the slope of the graph. A mean transit time (measured from the instant of injection) minus T_0 will represent the mean transit time through the vessels responsible for the temporal separation of cells and albumin.

Secondly, we should not expect that the first 1% of each label at the inflow to the

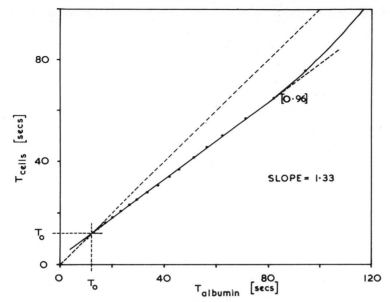

FIG. 4. [EXP. 6508. TRACE 2.] T_c VERSUS T_a FOR CORRESPONDING FRACTIONS OF THE OUTFLOW OF LABELLED CELLS AND ALBUMIN, MEASURED FROM THE INTEGRAL CURVES OF FIG. 3. THE RELATIONSHIP (SOLID LINE) IS LINEAR TO 96% OUTFLOW AND THEN DEVIATES SLIGHTLY TOWARDS THE LINE OF IDENTITY (DOTTED LINE).

THE INTERSECTION OF THE TWO LINES DEFINES A ZERO TIME T_0 FOR THE TEMPORAL SEPARATION OF CELLS AND ALBUMIN, AND THE SLOPE MEASURES THE RATIO OF TRANSIT TIMES (ALBUMIN/CELLS) THROUGH THE VESSELS IN WHICH SEPARATION OCCURS.

muscle would be the first 1% to appear at the outflow, for some of the vascular paths may involve longer transit times than others. However, the fact that a linear relationship exists between cell and albumin transit times for corresponding fractions of the outflow must mean that both labels are distributed to the available vascular channels in the same proportions. If certain channels were available to plasma only an asymmetry would necessarily arise.

The value of T_0 seems to be the same for longer as for shorter paths within the limits of the experiment. This was actually not quite true for the particular experiment to which Fig. 4 refers because the upper branch of the cannula was not clamped after the lower one was opened, and this led to an increased washout time of labelled blood from the lower branch of the cannula. This omission has since been remedied and a vibrator produces turbulence in the injection branch; under these circumstances the relationship is linear from the appearance time, and T_0 is at, or else very close to, the appearance time.

The inference that T_0 corresponds to the mean transit time through the cannulae and larger vessels was checked as follows. The volumes of cannulae between the muscle and the points of injection and detection respectively were measured by displacement from a 1-ml syringe, and the flow rate during an observation was measured by collecting the venous outflow over a known time interval. Hence the mean transit time through the cannula could be determined. When the venous pressure was between 5 and 10 cm saline, the value of T_0 was slightly greater than the cannula transit time. When the venous pressure was raised to 30–35 cm saline, the value of T_0 increased by a small amount (corresponding to an increased muscle blood volume) but the slope of the graph remained substantially the same. This indicates that the increase of blood volume with venous pressure in the fully vasodilated muscle occurs predominantly in the larger vessels.

We may then conclude that if the relationship between corresponding transit times were linear up to 100% outflow, then the slope would be exactly equal to the ratio of mean transit times through the vessels responsible for the temporal separation. Further, the slope may be determined more precisely than the ratio of corrected mean transit times. What then are the ratios of transit times encountered in vasodilated skeletal muscle?

TABLE 1. VALUES FROM THIRTY COMPARISONS OF CORRESPONDING CELL AND ALBUMIN TRANSIT TIMES (SEE FIG. 4) IN THE ISOLATED CAT GASTROCNEMIUS VASODILATED WITH CHLORAL HYDRATE

Mean flow rate	$= 7 \cdot 80$ ml/min/100 g
Mean haematocrit	$= 20 \cdot 4\%$
Mean slope $\dfrac{\Delta T_a}{\Delta T_c}$	$= 1 \cdot 27 \pm 0 \cdot 09$ (S.D.) $\pm 0 \cdot 02$ (S.E.M.).

It may be seen from Table 1 that the mean value from thirty comparisons is $1 \cdot 27 \pm 0 \cdot 09$ (S.D.), giving a standard error of less than $0 \cdot 02$. This value is much higher than those reported for the heart and lungs where the considerable dead space almost certainly accounts for the small difference of the ratio from unity. The present ratio is comparable with values reported for the kidney and liver where, because of the high ratio, the presence of an extravascular pathway for albumin has been inferred. The question then arises: does albumin cross the capillary wall in skeletal muscle also to a significant extent during a single transit? If this is considered on histological grounds to be unlikely and that the separation found in the present experiments is due entirely to intravascular mechanisms, we must then turn the question and ask whether it is necessary to postulate that the difference in transit times is entirely due to an extravascular mechanism in the case of kidney and liver. GORESKY has developed an elegant analytical approach to the passage of diffusible indicators through the liver,[6] in which differences between the clearance curves of a diffusible substance and of labelled cells injected simultaneously are interpreted as entirely due to extravascular exchange. It is then found that the differences between albumin and cells can be explained in the same way; perhaps some caution is now necessary regarding this last conclusion.

If one can measure accurately the transit time ratios, then there is the exciting possibility in the isolated perfused preparation of determining the relative importance of intravascular and extravascular mechanisms in producing a temporal separation of cells and albumin.

For example, consider the variation with flow rate. If the separation is predominantly of intravascular origin, then we may expect a shear-dependence and the ratio should increase with increasing flow rate. However, if the principal mechanism is extravascular exchange then some degree of diffusion-limitation would result in a less complete equilibration at higher flow rates, that is, the separation should decrease with increasing flow rate. The results to date do not allow any firm conclusion to be drawn, because of the variability of transit time ratios as between repeated observations on the same preparation. The origin of these differences is not yet clear, but it may be that varying degrees of red cell aggregation are being produced.

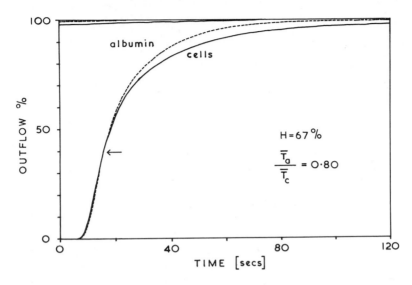

FIG. 5. [EXP. 6609. TRACE 1.] INTEGRAL OUTFLOWS OF LABELLED CELLS AND ALBUMIN AT HAEMATOCRIT 67%. NOTE THAT ALBUMIN CLEARED MORE QUICKLY THAN CELLS IN THIS PARTICULAR CASE. THE TAILS OF THE CLEARANCE CURVES ARE CONTINUED IN THE TOP LEFT CORNER OF THE DIAGRAM. RATIO OF CORRECTED MEAN TRANSIT TIMES 0·80 (SEE TEXT).

We may also examine the variation with haematocrit, for an intravascular mechanism would be increasingly opposed by cell–cell interactions as the haematocrit increased. The real situation may however be more complicated than this, as shown in three sets of integral outflow curves (Figs. 5, 6 and 7) taken at the same flow rate but at different haematocrits during a recent experiment.

At haematocrit 67% (Fig. 5) the cells were initially very slightly ahead of the albumin, but at 38% outflow a cross-over occurred and we have the surprising observation that thereafter the albumin cleared more quickly than the cells. The prolonged tail of each clearance curve is shown in the top left hand portion of the diagram. On the graph of corresponding transit times a tremendous departure from linearity occurred so early that the only way of examining the data quantitatively was to measure the mean transit times directly from the integral outflow curves. The ratio of mean albumin to cell transit times, corrected for the mean time of transit through the cannulae, proved to be 0·80.

When the haematocrit of the perfusing blood was reduced to 49% the cells were ahead of the albumin until 82% outflow, at which point a cross-over occurred, and thereafter the albumin cleared earlier than cells. The ratio of corrected mean transit times was now 0·99 (Fig. 6).

At haematocrit 27% the cells were ahead of the albumin throughout, and the graph of corresponding transit times was linear to 92% outflow. The ratio of the albumin to cell corrected mean transit times now became 1·12 (Fig. 7).

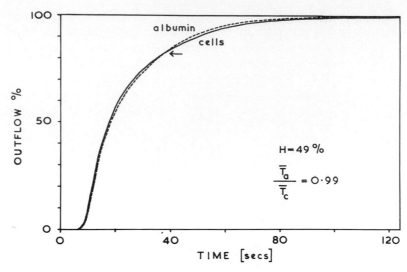

FIG. 6. [EXP. 6609. TRACE 5.] INTEGRAL OUTFLOWS OF LABELLED CELLS AND ALBUMIN AT HAEMATOCRIT 49%. THE CLEARANCE CURVES ARE VERY SIMILAR, GIVING A MEAN TRANSIT TIME RATIO 0·99.

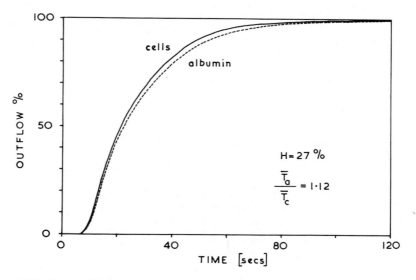

FIG. 7. [EXP. 6609. TRACE 6.] INTEGRAL OUTFLOWS OF LABELLED CELLS AND ALBUMIN AT HAEMATOCRIT 27%. THE CELLS CLEARED MORE QUICKLY THAN ALBUMIN, GIVING A MEAN TRANSIT TIME RATIO 1·12.

One can only speculate at present about what these data may mean but one thing is clear, no loss of either label occurred in transit through the muscle. The early departure from linearity on the graph of corresponding transit times must indicate that at high haematocrit some pathway was available to albumin but not to cells.

The results reported here are of a preliminary nature. When the causes of the variability in the present experiments have been eliminated we may be able to assess *in vivo* the relative importance of the various factors which give rise to a difference in the mean velocities of cells and their suspending phase.

REFERENCES

[1] RAPPAPORT, E., KUIDA, H., HAYNES, F. W. and DEXTER, L. *Am. J. Physiol.* **185**, 127, 1956.

[2] GROOM, C., MORRIS, W. B. and ROWLANDS, S. *J. Physiol.* **136**, 218, 1957.

[3] OCHWADT, B. *Arch. Ges. Physiol.* **265**, 112, 1957.

[4] LILIENFIELD, L. W. and ROSE, J. C. *J. Clin. Invest.* **37**, 1106, 1958.

[5] CHINARD, F. P., ENNS, T. and NOLAN, M. F. *Am. J. Physiol.* **207**, 128, 1964.

[6] GORESKY, C. A. *Am. J. Physiol.* **204**, 626, 1963.

[7] THOMAS, H. W., FRENCH, R. J., GROOM, A. C. and ROWLANDS, S. In *Symposium on Biorheology*, COPLEY, A. L. (Editor), *Proc. 4th Int. Cong. Rheol.*, Interscience Publ. John Wiley, New York, 1965, part 4, p. 381.

[8] ROWLANDS, S., GROOM, A. C. and THOMAS, H. W. In *Symposium on Biorheology*, COPLEY, A. L. (Editor), *Proc. 4th Int. Cong. Rheol.*, Interscience Publ. John Wiley, New York, 1965, part 4, p. 371.

DISCUSSION

PALMER (*Australia*):

I think this is a most interesting method of study; and it seems to be a very sensitive one. There is one thing that I'd like to comment on, and that is the conclusion that if reducing the flow rate increases the separation, this necessarily indicates an extravascular pathway, because at lower flow rates the aggregation of the cells may be greater and this will cause an increased axial drift. Hence, increased separation at reduced flow rate could also be consistent with intravascular phenomena.

GROOM (*England*):

Yes, thank you Dr. Palmer; I accept your point. I have not made any particular observations on degrees of aggregation, for I have been working single-handed, and, if aggregation is increased at low flow rate, then of course, we can only discover this by direct microscopic examinations of the vessels; one cannot tell anything from looking at a sample of blood outside the muscle. This has been my rationale so far.

GELIN (*Sweden*):

I really congratulate Dr. Groom for a most, most wonderful study. We have, since Professor Rowlands described his transit time curves some years ago, been very interested in this kind of experiment, trying to get a quantitation of how much aggregation will mean for the difference in transit times for the cells and the plasma. Over the lung, these studies have been done by Dr. Lewis and Dr. Bergentz in my laboratory; they were, however, unable to show more than a delay in the peak. What we had hoped to see was that the cell would travel more slowly than the plasma in the slowest moving part of the circulation. I think that is just what you have demonstrated here. We have been unable to see this because we have had recirculation too early to detect this late phase which probably would be the most important way to quantitate the stasis produced by aggregation in the postcapillary flow bed. From our capillary model studies this should be expected if there is a severe aggregation. Therefore I was extremely delighted to see your curves showing that cells are traveling more slowly than the plasma in the slowest flowing part of the circulation in your system.

GROOM:

Thank you, Professor Gelin. I think there are two things we have to distinguish here; Dr. Palmer was just drawing my attention to the first, which is that if you have aggregation in the vessels which normally produce the temporal separation of cells and plasma, then you will get an enhanced temporal separation. The second, is that if aggregation is present; and if the aggregates do not break up too easily, then we may have them temporarily lodging in capillaries or in some other way being slowed up at the later stages of the journey. So, I think that your comments and Dr. Palmer's comments in fact could both be true at the same time.

GOLDSMITH (*Canada*):

In connection with Goresky's theory and experiments, it should be pointed out that there is a great deal of circumstantial evidence to support the fact that his results cannot be explained, except in terms of an extravascular space and the diffusion of substances into it. Thus, his results with bromosulphothalein, a substance which goes into the liver cells and is removed from the vascular system, showed an additional delay in transit times and further distortion of the outflow curves. Could you also comment on the rather surprising 20% difference in transit times which you find and the previous results of Groom, Thomas and Rowlands in rigid tubes where the difference was so much smaller.

GROOM:

I admire Dr. Goresky's work tremendously and I accept the validity of this approach. What bothers me is that Goresky compares the clearance curves for diffusible indicators with the red cell curve, assuming that this is a suitable marker for what would happen if you had an indicator which did not leave the circulation. Now the sort of things I have been finding cause me to ask whether this is true. Should one compare a diffusible indicator curve with the red cell curve or the albumin curve or something in between? This is the point I wanted to make. I accept his experimental results and his analytical procedure with respect to diffusible indicators. The problem is: Is albumin diffusible out of the capillary at all? If you assume, as Goresky has done, that the entire difference between the curves for cells and albumin is due to an extravascular exchange of albumin, then you would compare your diffusible indicator curve with the red cell curve. If, on the other hand, this is not true and the albumin does not go out of the vascular system, then you should not compare the diffusible indicator curve with the red cell curve, but with the albumin curve. Regarding your second point; the work that Dr. Thomas, Dr. Rowlands, and I did with narrow-bore nylon tubes was with tubes of 200 micron diameter. This was the smallest we could get at the time. I realize that you now have polypropylene tubes going down well below that. I think we got a mean transit time ratio of the order of 1·078. Now if you have vessels of smaller diameters, which certainly occur in the blood circulation, you would expect to get an increased ratio of transit times.

MEISELMAN (U.S.A.):

I am very much interested in your observations of the differences in clearance based on the hematocrit. At 20% you appear to have the maximum differences. I recall that by increasing the hematocrit from about 20 to 60%, the two curves were almost identical. Doing some rather simple minded calculations of velocity profiles, one finds the velocity profile is very much a function of the ratio of the shear stress at the wall to the ultimate yield shear stress of the suspension. Thus, comparing the 60 to the 20% sample, large differences in the yield shear stress are to be expected. I wonder if part of the identity of the clearance curves may be due to pseudo plug flow or flow in your system with a very blunted velocity profile and an almost unsheared core in the center. Would this explain any of it or is it more complicated?

GROOM:

I am sure it is more complicated than that, because we are dealing, as Dr. Berman has emphasized, with a branching network of vessels where all possible things are happening, and I am looking at the gross summation of all these different processes. You will recall that in the outflow curves taken at 67% hematocrit, the red cells were just slightly ahead until about 40% outflow, then crossed over, and lagged behind with a very long tail which extended for roughly another minute and a half beyond the two minutes to which this graph referred. So I am sure it is more like the situation Dr. Gelin was referring to.

SWANK (U.S.A.):

During use of the extracorporeal system, you produce many aggregated platelets, which microembolize the tissues being studied. You may not have increased permeability of albumin before microembolization, but you certainly will have it after microembolization. Four years ago, in Pavia, we described a glass wool filter. At the present time we are using a dacron wool filter which removes these aggregates from the blood. It does not remove red cell aggregates. In any event, circulation after filtration of the blood has been much more effective than before. It might be helpful to repeat this type of work using such a filter to see if, under these circumstances, you get the same results as you get here. What I am really asking is: Could microembolism explain the differences which you have seen?

GROOM:

Thank you very much. I am extremely interested. In fact, I have been tackling people at this conference about platelets ever since Dr. Stehbens began talking about them at Cambridge. So I would like very much to know more about this. If microemboli were occurring, and perhaps depending on where they were occurring, one would expect to find an increase of perfusion pressure with time for constant flow in a fully vasodilated muscle. There is one experiment, the first of six on which I was basing these results, in which there is some evidence of that. There was a rise, of something like 16 mm.Hg in perfusion pressure towards the end of the experiment; so that certainly is a possibility. In the later experiments, where perhaps my technique had improved, the muscle, even after 6 hours, seemed to be in splendid condition and there was no change in perfusion pressure. There was no sign of obvious deterioration, and no systematic trend of the transit time ratio up or down.

BERMAN (U.S.A.):

Dr. Meiselman has more or less stated what I wanted to say. In addition, I should also like to set right any inaccurate impressions that I may have made during my presentation. A plasma gap can be seen in arterial vessels. In the cheek pouch of the normal hamster the gap is difficult to see. By incorrectly focusing the microscope an artifactual plasma gap of variable and even considerable magnitude can be seen. The true gap can, however, be accentuated and easily observed by diluting or partially replacing the blood with a plasma expander. The gap thus appears to vary with hematocrit. In the venous vessels in the pouch of the normal hamster, the plasma gap is still more difficult to detect. During the study of blood flow in models where infinite variation of hematocrit is possible, reference to the condition prevailing in the normal *in vivo* state may be of use.

GROOM:

I think the only point I want to make is that one thing may be happening in a few blood vessels here, but there are hundreds of vessels elsewhere where something else may be happening, and certainly my approach is just looking at the statistical evaluation of the whole.

HIGH SPEED CINEPHOTOGRAPHY OF THE MICROVASCULAR SYSTEM

EDWARD H. BLOCH*

Department of Anatomy, Western Reserve University, Cleveland, Ohio, U.S.A.

THE purpose of this communication is to indicate the development that has been made in establishing the dynamic morphology of cellular blood flow in the living microvascular system using high-speed cinephotography.

The precise manner in which red blood cells, white cells and platelets flow in the microvascular system and especially in arterioles and venules has been either interpreted incorrectly or at best it has been a controversial issue for many years[4, 15, 19]. The essential reason for this state of affairs has been due to the fact that the circulation had not been recorded either at sufficient repetition rates or magnification so that the trajectory of individual cells could be analysed. While this state of affairs still exists for much of the gross and microvascular systems a beginning has been made. This beginning occurred when the method of high-speed cinephotography, the recording of 1000 or more pictures per second (fps) was used to record blood flow. The method was applied to the gross circulation, at unit magnification, by McDONALD[20, 21] in the late 1940s, and to the microcirculation at magnifications to × 900 by BLOCH[2–4] in the early 1950s. High-speed cinephotography was found to be the first satisfactory method for analysing cellular flow in arterioles and venules when the internal diameter of these vessels was less than approximately five times the largest dimension of the species's erythrocyte ($\sim 100\,\mu$ in amphibia and $\sim 30\,\mu$ in mammals). In spite of the advantages of this method for analysing blood flow the method has been used infrequently[6, 12, 14].

Method. Successful recording of blood flow in the microvascular system with high-speed cinephotography requires the adequate simultaneous operation of the following components: illumination, optics, animal, camera and film.

The availability of light sources for securing adequate illumination of blood vessels, preferably with monochromatic light, in organs at the highest magnification of the light microscope is not the problem it was when this form of photography was begun. However, in spite of the availability of more intense light sources practical experience has been restricted to tungsten (1200 watt) and high-pressure mercury arc (Osram type HBO 100W/2) sources. These sources are barely adequate for exposing monochromatic film (Eastman Tri-X ASA 200) at framing rates of 8000 per second when recording the microcirculation in the most transparent of tissues (mesenteries) with objective magnifications of 90–100, ocular magnifications of approximately 3, and projection distances of 4–6 in. to the film plane. If the microcirculation is to be recorded in organs (lung, liver, kidney) in a similar manner the intensity of the illumination will need to be increased by at least one order of magnitude. The most promising sources for such light are the lasers[8, 26]. A pulsed gas laser with suitable filters should produce the requisite film exposure. While such lasers have been used for illuminating biological tissue they have not been utilized for high speed cinephotomicrography. The advantage in using lasers is their monochromaticity and light intensity. Such light will produce a better optical image than the white light produced by tungsten sources, and the mono-chromatic light of the laser is not attenuated by a monochromator which is required for other light sources. Another light source that is superior to continuous light sources is the Xenon flash tube[10, 11]. Such "stroboscopic" light sources may be pulsed for single flashes as short as a millionth of a second and repeated 4000 times during 0.12 sec. To date however such stroboscopic light sources have not been used to produce films of the microcirculation where their quality has compared with films that were produced by continuous light sources, where transillumination and high magnifications were used[12].

The optical requirements for high-speed cinephotomicrography are not unique. The requirements for adequate resolution of tissue are the same as those used for other forms of recording living tissue *in situ*. While these requirements have been discussed in detail elsewhere[4] it should be re-emphasized that the largest possible optical image of the desired component in the tissue that is to be *analysed,* should impinge on the film emulsion so that an adequate photographic image can be secured. Thus, when the trajectory of red cells are to be recorded in the microvascular system of small mammals, which have red cells whose maximum undistorted dimension do not exceed approxi-mately $6\,\mu$, it is desirable to use objective magnifications between 60 and 90 with numerical apertures better than 1.0.

The methods that have been used for maintaining homeokinesis of the intensely illuminated area of tissue for high-speed recording are limited to blood vessels em-bedded in thin membranes like mesenteries[5]. The vessels in these tissues have been transilluminated with white or monochromatic light sources for as long as 5 min with an intensity that was sufficient to expose film adequately at objective magnifications of 90 and framing rates of 3600 per second. At the termination of such experiments there was no visible evidence of damage to the vessel walls or their contents[4]. However the thermoregulating system that was devised for such photography has been inadequate for maintaining homeokinesis in solid organs like the liver when similar illumination was used. It is anticipated that the thermal injury to tissue that is produced by contin-uous illumination can be decreased significantly when pulsed light is used but whether or not this will be sufficient to prevent injuring organs remains to be answered.

Of the large variety of cameras that are available for recording events at picture rates from one thousand to one billion per second my experience has been limited to cameras that have maximum picture framing rates of 3600–8000 per second. These cameras are of the optical plane shutter type (Eastman Kodak Type III) and the optical prism type (Wollensak-Fastex type WF3)[1, 9, 13]. These cameras are not adequate for recording the fastest cellular linear velocity in small mammals when the micro-circulation is transilluminated with *continuous* light. As the quality of the images have been just marginal it is anticipated that but minimal improvement will be required before satisfactory images will be obtained. There are several mechanisms for solving this problem. The least satisfactory method is increasing the recording film rate be-cause the light intensity must be increased. As every increase in light intensity is attended with ever increasing problems in maintaining homeokinesis this type of solution is to be avoided. The solution lies in another direction, namely the utilization of shutterless cameras with stroboscopic light or the pulsed light from lasers. With these forms of illumination the exposure can be of very short duration, 10^{-4}–10^{-6} sec or less, while the film rate, past a shutterless aperture, can be significantly reduced.

There is yet another solution to the recording of events in very short durations of time which utilizes electron optics as exemplified by image intensifier and converter systems[16, 17]. The advantages of such systems are that the light is amplified, the images can be detected in regions of the electromagnetic spectrum which are not detectable by the human sensor and they can be registered at a rate of 10^{-3}–10^{-6} sec or less. However, the repetition rates for securing sequential images from these devices are considerably longer than those from high-speed cameras due to the image retention of phosphorescent screens.

The final component that needs to be considered for high-speed cinephotography is the film[18, 25]. Of the films that have been tested for recording blood flow with high-speed cameras, Tri-X reversal film (Eastman Kodak type 7278) and Eastman Kodak type II color film have been found useful. These films possess adequate sensitivity and have sufficiently broad spectral characteristics so that it is possible to select any wave length between ~ 410 and $610 \, m\mu$ during an experiment while the camera is loaded. These film characteristics are useful in this type of investigation as it is not always practical to load the camera after the desired scene is selected, nor is it always possible to predict the wave length that will result in the best rendition of the scene. Some of the films that have been found unsatisfactory for recording the microcirculation with high-speed photography are the commercial Ektachrome (Type 7255) film and some high-speed color films. While all color film produces more picture information, even when monochromatic light is used, it was found that the commercial color films were too insensitive in the red portion of the spectrum and the final image quality was unpredictable unless a print was made. The latter is an undesirable feature because of economic reasons. Furthermore, the difference in the quality of the best prints of the commercial film were not sufficiently superior to warrant the increased cost.

The new information of blood flow that was derived from motion pictures that were taken at picture rates of 2000 – 8000 per second was related to: the flow pattern of erythrocytes in arterioles and venules; the relationship of these cells to the vessel walls; the size and shape of the "peripheral" plasma layer; streaklines (streamlines) as an indicator of laminar flow; and the relationship of leucocytes and platelets to the erythrocytes and the vessel wall. While the bulk of the data for these components of flow has been derived from the amphibian circulation sufficient data have been secured from the mammalian circulation to indicate the extent that the data derived from the amphibian circulation can be transferred to the mammalian circulation.

High-speed photography did not add new facts about the flow of blood in capillaries as the details of cellular flow in these vessels can be ascertained readily from direct microscopy by the human sensor or from motion pictures taken at framing rates of 8 – 24 frames per second. However, high-speed photography did emphasize the similarities and differences of flow in these vessels with the flow in contiguous arterioles and venules.

When blood flow is examined directly by the human sensor with a microscope in any mesenteric arteriole whose internal diameter is about four times larger than the largest dimension of the red blood cell, where the blood pressure is normal, and intravascular aggregation is absent, a picture is presented that has been observed and agreed upon by investigators for hundreds of years. The picture consists of a pinkish column of blood devoid of cellular detail. The only detail that is noted in the blood stream consists of irregular longitudinal lines of varying degrees of opacity that are parallel to the vessel wall; these are the streaklines. These streaklines have been considered to be due to the diffraction of light from the edges of the erythrocytes while the pattern of the lines was interpreted to be due to the alignment of the cells in the flowing blood and it was deduced that their largest dimension was parallel to the vessel wall. The only other feature observed frequently was the presence of a clear layer of plasma adjacent to the vessel wall: the peripheral plasma layer. When such blood was recorded with high-speed photography at framing rates of 2500–8000 per second it was found that the cellular flow pattern was more complex and contained characteristics that had been unknown.

In discussing the data that have been secured with high-speed photography of blood flow in the microvascular system it is desirable to consider the flow of erythrocytes under the following categories: in vessels whose diameter is larger than the cell; in vessels where the diameter of the cell and vessel is about the same; and where the diameter of the vessel is less than the cell. It is also desirable to differentiate the flow patterns during systole and diastole in arterioles from the flow pattern in venules.

The most satisfactory data that have been secured for the flow pattern of erythrocytes with high-speed photography have been in the arterial system and the best data have been obtained from vessels whose maximum internal diameter in the mammal did not exceed 18μ and 80μ in amphibia. Furthermore, since 1952 more data have been secured from these vessels than from venules. Therefore it is only from the terminal segment of the arterial system that it is possible to make statements regarding cellular flow that are based on information that can be considered relatively reliable in context and volume. This cautionary attitude is required because of the technical difficulties encountered in maintaining homeokinesis as well as securing a sufficient number of records so as to be relatively certain that the images which were recorded represent a reasonable sample of reality.* The comments that follow are based on images that have been secured during the past fourteen years and during this time similar images were secured irrespective whether the blood vessels were recorded in tissues which were suspended horizontally or vertically or whether they were transilluminated with white or monochromatic light. Furthermore, no basic differences were found to exist between the amphibian or mammalian circulations. The differences between these circulations was one of degree; the mammalian erythrocytes were more flexible and thereby they were subjected more to the hydrostatic forces of the circulation than were the amphibian cells.

The images of blood flow that have been secured with high-speed photography have revealed some rather surprising images that were demonstrated best in arterioles whose diameters were larger than any single blood cell. The most interesting images were related to the position of red cells in the flowing column of blood. The preferential position of these cells was with their largest diameter at right angle to the axis of the vessel; the largest diameter of the cell moving in the same direction as the flow (Figs. 1–9). This pattern occurred in all arterioles whose internal diameter varied from about twice the largest dimension of the species' erythrocyte to a diameter that

*The series of photographs in Figs. 1–9 were selected from approximately 800 images that were recorded in 0·25 sec, which represents the events occurring in the circulation during one heart beat.

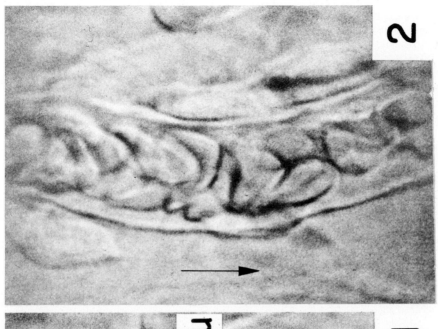

Fig. 1.

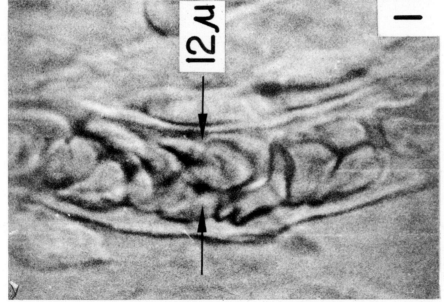

Fig. 2.

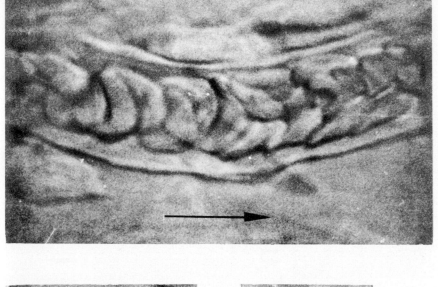

Fig. 4.

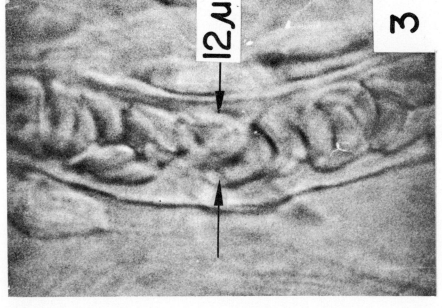

Fig. 3.

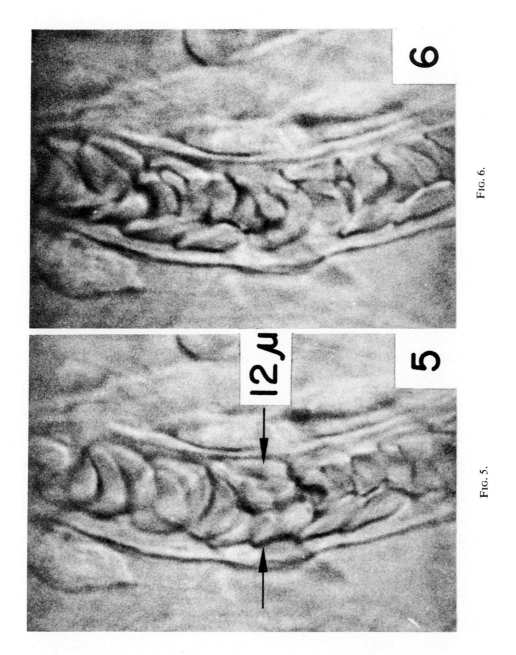

FIG. 6.

FIG. 5.

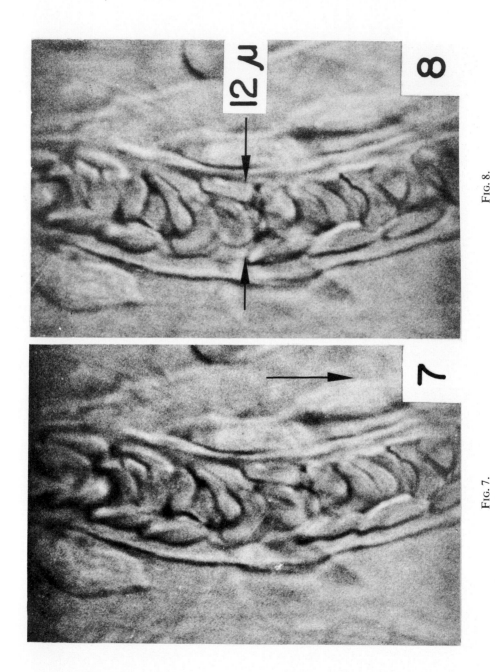

Fig. 7.

Fig. 8.

FIGURES 1–12 are unretouched images of single frames of 16-mm motion picture films (Tri-X) that were taken with an Eastman Kodak High Speed Type III camera. The images were secured from blood vessels in rat mesenteries which had been sutured to a quartz window and transilluminated with monochromatic light (~560 mμ).

FIGURES 1–9 depict the flow pattern of erythrocytes in a 12 μ arteriole (rat mesentery). The film speed was 3000 frames per second and the total elapsed time between Figs. 1 and 9 was 0.149 sec during which 484 pictures were recorded.

The elapsed time between Figs. 1 and 9 are as follows:

FIGURES 1 AND 2 : 0.021 sec
2 AND 3 : 0.033 sec
3 AND 4 : 0.021 sec
4 AND 5 : 0.006 sec
5 AND 6 : 0.021 sec
6 AND 7 : 0.007 sec
7 AND 8 : 0.007 sec
8 AND 9 : 0.033 sec

The majority of the cells are oriented at various angles to the direction of flow (indicated by an arrow). There is a tendency of the largest diameter of the cell to assume a right angle to the wall. Also note the rate of change in the orientation of the cells through the sequence of photographs; some cells change their orientation within a hundredth of a second. Finally, almost all erythrocytes are distorted.

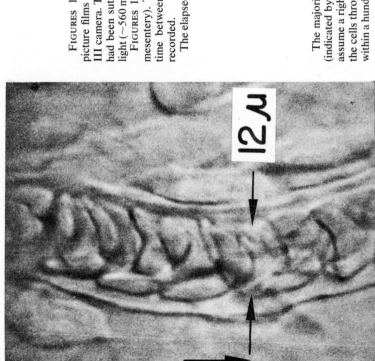

FIG. 9.

was slightly less than the erythrocyte. Other erythrocytes were either at right angle to these cells (their largest dimension parallel with the wall) or at various angles between these extremes (Figs. 1–9). The position of such erythrocytes changed frequently in milliseconds: they changed their length and thickness and while doing so they also rotated about their equatorial and polar axes. (Undistorted red cells were the exception in all vessels of the microvascular systems.) The rate of such changes may be appreciated by citing the result of one set of measurements for erythrocytes in 9–15 μ arterioles of the rat. Some cells changed their orientation 360° within a distance of 15–40 μ which is equivalent to 2–10 msec and they were lengthened to 10 or 10.5 μ which was a 50% increase in their length which occurred in 7 msec. Adjacent cells had *different* rates of spin and distortion.*

When the diameter of arterioles increased above 25 μ in the *mammal* it was not possible to secure adequate images of *every* cell in the blood stream due to the inadequate imaging properties of the optical system, the overlapping of cells, and serious blurring of the images due to the linear velocity of flow. In such vessels, during some phase of the cardiac cycle, the orientation of red cells was more in accord with the classical concept of cellular flow where it is assumed that the cells are oriented with their largest diameter parallel to the wall.

The orientation of erythrocytes in arterioles is also influenced by the various phases of the cardiac cycle. In rats, where the heart beat ranges between 250–300 beats per minute, the linear velocity of flow varies considerably from the maximum flow during systole to almost zero flow in diastole. These variations in flow have been detected with high-speed photography in arterioles whose internal diameters ranged from 30 to 8 μ. The effect of linear velocity and the attendant changes in pressure on erythrocytes were especially notable in 20–30 μ arterioles. During diastole many red cells were oriented with their largest diameter at right angle to the wall while in systole more cells were parallel to the vessel wall (Figs. 10 and 11).

Erythrocytes distort in size and shape as well as in their spatial relations with each other. Examples of this are illustrated in Figs. 1–9 and in ref. 4, Fig. 18, Plate 3, p. 151, and Figs. 2 and 3, p. 136.

Finally the flow pattern is complicated further by the "trajectory" of erythrocytes in the normal direction of flow. The forward progression of the cells in vessels whose internal diameters are two or three times larger than these cells is in the form of a spiral or helix. When an attempt is made to follow individual erythrocytes for a distance of 30–50 μ along the direction of flow they are lost from view because they have changed their position.

High-speed photography, in conjunction with monochromatic light which was used to enhance the contrast of erythrocytes to vessel walls, has assisted in defining the relationship of these cells with the peripheral plasma layer. These cells were often present in close proximity 0.5–1 μ to the wall. Conversely the "boundary" of the plasma layer often extended appreciable distances toward the center of the vessel, or to the center. These relationships changed within a few thousandths of a second or less. However, no matter how close the erythrocytes appeared to be to the wall, even when they appeared to be touching the wall, they were probably separated from the wall by a

---

*Full appreciation of the complexity of cellular flow cannot occur from study of single photographs but only from motion pictures and preferably from the study of many thousands of feet of such film as a hundred feet of film will contain an example of but a fraction of a second of the flow pattern.

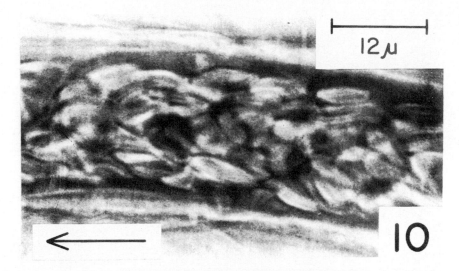

FIG. 10. A 20 μ ARTERIOLE (RAT MESENTERY) PHOTOGRAPHED AT 3500 FRAMES PER SECOND. THIS MOTION PICTURE FRAME DEPICTS THE ORIENTATION OF THE CELLS AT NEARLY ZERO FLOW DURING DIASTOLE. COMPARE WITH FIG. 11.

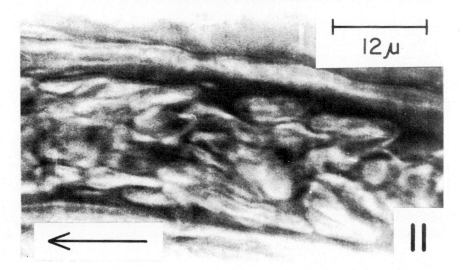

FIG. 11. THE SAME VESSEL AS DEPICTED IN FIG. 10 BUT THE IMAGE WAS RECORDED DURING SYSTOLE. MORE ERYTHROCYTES ARE ALIGNED WITH THEIR LARGEST DIAMETER PARALLEL TO THE VESSEL WALL THAN IN THE PRECEDING FIGURE.

film of plasma whose dimension was close to the resolution of the light microscope, about 0.2 μ. High-speed photography has demonstrated that the configuration of the peripheral plasma layer is complex, as compared with the spatial and dimensional data that were secured by direct visualization of this layer[4].

Too few data exist for any meaningful statement of the relation of leucocytes or platelets either in regard to their position in the blood stream or in the peripheral plasma layer in arterioles or venules.

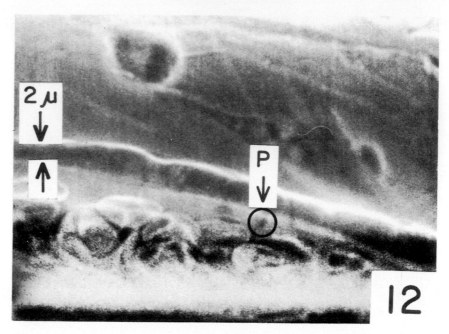

FIG. 12. A SEGMENT OF AN IMAGE OF A 30-μ ARTERIOLE (RAT MESENTERY) FROM A SINGLE FRAME OF A MOTION PICTURE FILM THAT WAS RECORDED AT 2500 FRAMES PER SECOND. NOTE THE BOUNDARY BETWEEN THE CELLS AND THE LUMEN OF THE WALL. A PLATELET (P) (JUST OUT OF CRITICAL FOCUS) CAN BE SEEN IN THE PERIPHERAL PLASMA LAYER.

The analysis of cellular flow in venules has not been as thorough as that made in arterioles. Erythrocyte distortion, spin, and orientation were often similar to the behavior of these cells in the arterial system but at reduced rates. There appeared to be a more predominant orientation of the largest diameter of the erythrocytes to the wall when the internal diameter of the vessel was three or four times greater than the erythrocyte. Boundary conditions of the cells with the wall were complex as in the arterial system (see Fig. 28, ref. 4).

The distortion of erythrocytes in capillaries has been demonstrated repeatedly by direct observation with the microscope, by motion pictures at framing speeds from 24–64 per second, as well as with high-speed cine and still photography[4, 7, 14, 22–24]. The maximum distortion of the cells in these vessels is *less* than in arterioles because the arteriolar dimensions frequently limit the minimum dimension of erythrocyte which can pass through these vessels at higher intravascular pressures than is present in capillaries for distorting the cells. The attention has been focused on the marked changes in the shape of erythrocytes in capillaries because such changes could be recognized readily in contrast to the changes of these cells in the arterial system which require high speed photography for the recognition of their changes. In both arterioles and capillaries, therefore, where the diameter of the vessel is less than the smallest dimension of the erythrocyte, cells deform in a particular manner. (As most marked changes in shape occur in the mammalian erythrocyte the description will be limited to these cells.) The cells deform to a cone with the smallest dimension of the cone in the direction of flow. The trailing edges of the cytoplasm may be very thin. Because the cells are fixed by the dimension of the vessel their change in shape is considerably *less* than in the larger vessels where they are subjected to the forces imposed by adjacent cells, the fluctuations in blood pressure, and the influences induced by the reorientation of the entire column of cells by the bifurcations of vessels.

In summary, high-speed cine photography has demonstrated that a complex flow pattern exists for erythrocytes in arterioles and venules. This cellular flow pattern does not fit the classical descriptions of flow for vessels whose diameters range between 10–30μ in the mammal. The data, for the time being, are assumed to be representative for vessels to 30μ in small mammals, and to 100μ in amphibia. The cellular flow pattern in such vessels is indeed complex, and it is difficult to characterize it, as it has been done before high-speed photography was used, as laminar or turbulent. The erythrocytes are continuously distorted within thousandths of a second, with adjacent cells responding differently in vessels whose diameters are larger than the largest dimension of these cells. Also, it is anticipated that the plasma is being agitated in a similar manner. Therefore it is not unreasonable to reach the conclusion that the total of these gyrations would make these flows "turbulent".

ACKNOWLEDGMENT

This work was supported in part by USPHS grants H-3240 and H-5300.

REFERENCES

[1] Annual Technical Bulletin, *Ind. Phot.* **14**, 104, 1965.
[2] BLOCH, E. H. *Anat. Rec.* **115**, 383, 1953.
[3] BLOCH, E. H. *Fed. Proc.* **19**, 89, 1960.
[4] BLOCH, E. H. *Am. J. Anat.* **110**, 125, 1962.
[5] BLOCH, E. H. and HASS, R. H. *Anat. Rec.* **138**, 261, 1960.
[6] BOND, T. P., DERRICK, J. R. and GUEST, M. M. *Circulation* **28**, 693, 1963.
[7] BRÅNEMARK, P-I. and LINDSTRÖM, J. *Biorheology* **1**, 139, 1963.
[8] ANON. *Applied Optics* **4**, Supplement 2, 1, 1965.
[9] CHESTERMAN, W. D., *The Photographic Study of Rapid Events*, Clarendon Press, Oxford, 1951.
[10] EDGERTON, H. E. *J. Biological Phot. Assoc.* **30**, 45, 1962.
[11] EDGERTON, H. and CARSON, J. *Applied Optics* **3**, 1211, 1964.
[12] FULTON, G. P. (unpublished observations).
[13] GARVIN, E. L. *SMPTE* **56**, 93, 1960.
[14] GUEST, M. M., BOND, T. P., COOPER, R. G. and DERRICK, J. R. *Science* **142**, 1319, 1963.
[15] HAYNES, R. H. *Trans. Soc. Rheol.* **7**, 1924, 1963.
[16] *Image Intensifier Symposium*, October 6–7, 1958, U.S. Department of Commerce, O.T.S., 151813. Superintendent of Documents, U.S. Government Printing Office, Washington 25, D.C.
[17] *Image Intensifier Symposium*, October 24–26, 1961, National Aeronautics and Space Administration, Superintendent of Documents, U.S. Government Printing Office, Washington 25, D.C.
[18] KODAK, EASTMAN. Modulation transfer data for Kodak films. Kodak Sales Service Pamphlet No. P-49, 1962.
[19] KURODA, K. and FUJINO, M. *Biorheology*, **1**, 167, 1963.
[20] McDONALD, D. A. and POTTER, J. M. Blood streams in the basilar artery (motion picture). *Am. Med. Assoc.*, 535 N. Dearborn Street, Chicago, Illinois, 1949.
[21] McDONALD, D. A. *J. Physiol.* **118**, 328, 1952.
[22] MONRO, P. A. G. *Biorheology* **1**, 239, 1963.
[23] NICOLL, P. A. and WEBB, R. L. Subcutaneous blood flow in the bat's wing (motion picture). Audio-visual Center, Indiana University, Bloomington, Indiana.
[24] PALMER, A. A. *Quart. J. Exper. Physiol. and Cognate Med. Sci.* **44**, 149, 1959.
[25] PERRIN, F. H. *SMPTE* **69**, 151, 239, 1960.
[26] Special Issue on Quantum Electronics. *Proc. Inst. Electrical and Electronic Engineering*, **51**, 3, 1963.

IN VIVO HEMORHEOLOGY II

16 July, a.m.

Chairmen: LARS-ERIC GELIN, Sweden
A. A. PALMER, Australia

QUANTITATIVE RHEOLOGICAL MEASUREMENTS IN MICROCIRCULATORY BEDS

HAROLD WAYLAND,* PAUL C. JOHNSON† and WALLACE G. FRASHER, JR.

Division of Engineering and Applied Science,
California Institute of Technology,
Pasadena, California, and
Los Angeles County Heart Association
Cardiovascular Research Laboratory at
Loma Linda University School of Medicine,
Los Angeles, California

1. INTRODUCTION

In attempting to evaluate the rôle of the rheological properties of blood and its components and of the vascular system in determining the nature of blood flow in the microcirculation we would like to have the following information:

1. Location of vessels being studied.
2. Geometry of vessels being studied, including the time history.
3. Driving forces: pressure gradients along the vessels and across the vessel walls.
4. Flow velocities along the vessels, preferably in terms of flow quantity of each of the components of blood.
5. Movement of material across the vessel walls.
6. Regulatory processes not due to purely mechanical reactions to local pressures: autoregulation, sphincter activity, control from central nervous system, etc.
7. Relationship of vessels being studied to their neighbors, including their physiological function.

Several of these items are not directly associated with purely rheological studies, but must either be eliminated or understood in order to isolate those aspects of microcirculatory flow which are controlled by rheological factors. Having called attention to this wide diversity of factors, we shall primarily confine our attention to methods for making three basic types of measurement: vessel lumen, pressure, and flow velocity.

2. VESSEL LUMEN

Direct visual microscopic examination with a measuring eyepiece can give good quantitative measurements of vessel lumen if it is not changing too rapidly. This is not practical for extended periods of observation because of fatigue of the observer, and is usually supplanted by photography. Shutter controlled exposure times for still photography, in the neighborhood of 1/25–1/250 sec, will give somewhat blurred images, whether due to vasomotion or motion of the entire bed. Not that the motions

†Present address: Department of Physiology, Indiana University School of Medicine, Indianapolis, Indiana, U.S.A.

671

in the bed are always very large, but the motion on the film is magnified by the linear magnification of the projected image. This difficulty can be eliminated with microsecond flash illumination, which has a further advantage in minimizing the total exposure of the physiological preparation to heating due to the illumination. In such photography care should be taken in choice of objective, magnification at the film, film format and film type to assure recording of all of the desired detail, balancing the actual optical resolution of the microscope with the film grain. Ordinarily one should not use empty magnification on the film, as this yields no additional information, and accentuates blurring due to motion of the object. It is relatively easy to magnify the photographic image later and, by subsequent printing operations, contrast adjustments can also be made. To obtain a good time sequence of dimensional measurements from a series of photographs is, however, tedious at best.

Instead of using a photographic film to record the image, it can be projected onto a photosensitive surface such as that in a television camera. This permits the image to be presented on a television screen, with the possibility of immediate contrast control. Since the usual television image is made up of a relatively small number of lines, care must be exercised not to lose information from the limited resolution of the television system. The principal advantage of the television system is the fact that the optical data has been converted to electrical signals, which permits a great diversity of processing. These electrical signals can be stored on video tape, which permits later projection of the pictorial image, or it can be processed on-line to study variations in a limited number of parameters. WIEDERHIELM[1] has used the intensity variations of a single line from the raster to follow changes in lumen of a microvessel; WIEDERHIELM[2] and BLOCH[3] have both used the intensity variations of a single line to study the diffusion of light-absorbing dyes through the capillary wall; and BLOCH[4] has suggested the possibility of using TV photometry to study chemical changes in individual cells, including erythrocytes.

A good photograph, and even a TV image, contains a tremendous amount of information, much of which may be irrelevant to a given experiment. For example, if we are interested in rapid changes in vessel lumen it may be sufficient to collect the data at a very few points along the length of the vessel. The general pictorial data which gives the geographical location of the vessel usually need to be gathered much less frequently. The band width required for good picture formation at 30 per second and 512 lines per picture (the normal U.S. commercial TV rate) is of the order of 6 Mc/s, which means that if we are interested only in the information in a single scan line, the signal to electronic noise ratio is very poor. Wiederhielm has been developing a slow-scan TV which will partially compensate for this, but this still does not give an optimal system. In fact, if the same number of scan lines are to be used to form the picture, the same gain in the single line to be photometered can be made by using an average of several scans. For example, if the scan rate is reduced by a factor of five, then using the original system and averaging five successive scans of the line being studied before processing the data would give the same signal to electronic noise ratio as obtained with the slow scan system. The apparent quality of an overall TV image is enhanced both by the averaging effect of the persistence of the phosphor on the receiving tube and by our ability to recognize patterns in a pictorial image in which we average information from adjacent lines. Since the overall picture is normally used merely for monitoring the general layout of the bed being observed, it would be sufficient to obtain pictorial information only every second or even every few seconds. If the entire raster could be collapsed into a single line (or two or three appropriately spaced lines) the signal noise ratio in this limited region would be greatly improved. Periodically the raster could be returned to normal and a picture formed, which could be held during the data-collecting scans.

The greatly improved signal to noise ratio obtainable by concentrating on just the information desired has been demonstrated with a flying spot microscope[5]. In this instrument a demagnified image of a luminous spot from a cathode ray tube is projected onto the microbed. The spot is moved in a straight line across the face of the tube in such a way that its image traverses the vessel being studied at right angles to the vessel axis. The scan rate has normally been taken at 25 sweeps per second. The light transmitted through the bed is imaged on a photomultiplier by means of a microscope and changes in light intensity due to preferential absorption by the hemoglobin in the blood flowing in the vessel under observation can be recorded. This information can be processed to yield the diameter of the erythrocyte column in the blood vessel, and changes monitored in real time on a visual recorder. This system gives much cleaner signals than the TV system, but it has the disadvantage that the spot diameter of the cathode ray tube limits the use of the instrument to vessels 20μ or larger; and the fact that there is no simultaneous overall picture of the bed makes it necessary to stop measurements periodically to monitor the appearance of the bed either visually or photographically. This might be overcome by using an overall illumination of the bed by a very different wave length than that emitted by the cathode ray tube, using a beam splitter to divide the light passing the image forming objective between screen or TV camera and the photomultiplier, using a suitable filter on the photomultiplier to accept only the light from the flying spot.

Another approach which we have shown to be feasible, but have not completely engineered, is to use optical scanning. Here an image of the microbed of interest is projected onto a screen penetrated by a slit. The image is adjusted so that the slit lies across the vessel to be measured and at right angles to its axis. The slit is then scanned by a rotating mirror or a system of moving slits. The scanned beam is then photometered in much the same way as is used for the flying spot system. This method has at least three potential advantages over the flying spot: a significant portion of the microbed is imaged on the screen at all times, permitting continuous visual monitoring; the slit width and magnification on the screen can be controlled to give spatial resolution compatible with the requirements of the experiment, being limited essentially by the resolution of the optical system; and a wide choice of wave lengths of light used for the photometry is available, and is not limited by the availability of phosphors on a cathode ray tube.

3. PRESSURE MEASUREMENTS

It would be highly desirable to be able to measure the pressure inside a microvessel without penetrating it. Attempts have been made to do this by a total or partial occlusion method. The oldest such method goes back to the last century when ROY and BROWN[6] placed an inflated rubber balloon in such a way as to press the microbed up against a glass surface through which the bed could be observed with a microscope. By inflating the membrane the pressure required just to stop flow in any vessel or series of vessels can be measured. The principal objection to such a method is that the amount of mechanical support given by the surrounding tissue may be a significant fraction of the total force being measured. INTAGLIETTA and WIEDERHIELM[7] have used a micro-probe instrumented to measure the force with which it is pressing against an object. When this was used partially to occlude flow in a small vessel, the pulsatile wave form compared favorably with that measured by a probe inserted into the vessel, but the absolute pressure level was seriously disturbed by the supporting tissue. In the current state of the art, it must be concluded that there is no satisfactory way of measuring pressure without vessel penetration.

WIEDERHIELM and RUSHMER[8] have developed a penetrating probe which can be used with micropipette tips as small as 0.5μ. This is essentially an automated version of the technique employed by LANDIS[9]. The probe is filled with hypertonic saline (0.6–2M NaCl) and incorporated into a servo-controlled mechanism. The tip is inserted into the vessel being studied, plasma is permitted to penetrate a small distance into the probe and the impedance of the probe is measured by means of an AC. bridge. A change in pressure inside the vessel will cause the meniscus between saline and plasma to move, unbalancing the bridge. A servo-controlled bellows pump readjusts the balance, and the pressure is measured in the bellows system. In this way the power for operating the system does not have to come from the microvessel. Because of the external source of power and the extremely small meniscus motions required to give an adequate signal to actuate the servo system, this is the only pressure gauge of which I am aware which is capable of a frequency response of the order 20 c/s with a tip small enough to use in individual mammalian capillaries.

The simplicity of a passive pressure gauge would make it desirable whenever it can be used. RAPPAPORT, BLOCH and IRWIN[10] successfully used a condenser pressure transducer hydraulically coupled to a micropipette for measuring pressure in vessels down to about 50μ. The advances in micro-strain-gauge technology have encouraged us to see how much farther down in the size scale we can push this type of instrument. We have been experimenting with a pressure sensing diaphragm 1.5 mm in diameter and 15–16μ thick, on which a solid state strain gauge bridge has been mounted, which has been furnished us by the Biomedical Instrument Department of Electro-Optical Systems, Inc., of Pasadena, California. The diaphragm tested gives an output of 50 microvolts per millimeter of mercury pressure. The compliance of the diaphragm is approximately equal to that of 15μl of water. The dynamic response of the micro-pipette–diaphragm system has not yet been obtained, but preliminary calculations indicate that we should be able to make useful dynamic measurements in vessels down at least to 30μ, and measurements of the average pressure in vessels down to 15μ or less.

With any gauge used for dynamic measurements it is essential to calibrate the system not only for amplitude response as a function of frequency, but also for phase shift if a correct reconstruction of the dynamic pressure changes is to be obtained.

4. VELOCITY MEASUREMENTS

One of the simplest methods of measuring the velocity of erythrocytes or clumps of erythrocytes is to use the fact that patterns of cells remain substantially constant for small distances of movement along the length of a small blood vessel. This fact is fundamental to all streak image methods, whether recorded on photographic film or measured visually. With photographic streak images it is possible to get reasonably good time resolution, and the measurement of the slopes of the streaks is not so tedious as measuring image displacements on successive photographs. It is, however, a time consuming operation. MONRO'S[11] visual streak device requires adjusting the angular velocity of a rotating prism until the streaks are at 45° to the direction of flow. This maximizes the sensitivity, but it is impossible to follow changes as rapid as the heart beat and, unless an automatic readout were available, it seems unlikely that one could record a measurement oftener than about twice a minute. It does, however, permit gathering of some information on velocity distribution across vessels in the 40 μ range. For individual capillaries, where the flow is generally less than 2 mm/sec, he finds a flying spot system more accurate. Any of the visual methods requires a skilled operator, observing continuously.

We[12] have used double slit photometry of the cell pattern to determine the velocity in several different ways. The possibility of using such a photometric method was pointed out by ASANO, YOSHIDA and TATAI[13] in 1964, but we were not aware of their work until after our methods were developed. In our system, the image of the blood vessel to be studied is formed on a screen penetrated by two parallel slits, such that the axis of the vessel is perpendicular to the long axis of the slits. In one mode of operation the slits are about 5 mm apart so that with a × 100 magnification on the screen, this represents about 50 μ along the vessel. The slits are each connected by a light pipe to a photomultiplier. To obtain maximum signals, we illuminated with the violet line of a high pressure mercury arc, since this lies close to the Soret absorption band of hemoglobin. Typical data for a mesenteric capillary are given in Fig. 1. We

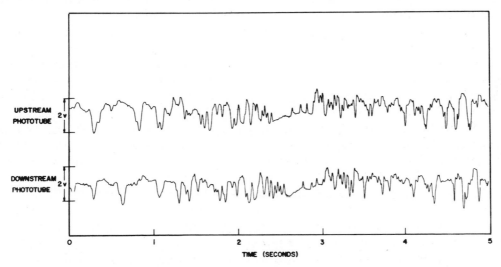

FIG. 1. SIGNAL TRACINGS FROM A MESENTERIC CAPILLARY. EQUIVALENT SLIT SPACING 50 μ.

found it most convenient to record the data on an FM modulated tape recorder at 15 in. per second and to play it back at 0·6 in. per second through a pen recorder to obtain a visual record without loss of detail. The time delays between the two channels can readily be obtained by visual inspection of similar events on the two channels, and we have found it practical to obtain three to five readings per second of real time. The analysis of the record of Fig. 1 is shown in Fig. 2.

A more convenient method of analysis is to perform a time series cross-correlation of the two records as a function of lag time. The lag time corresponding to the maximum cross-correlation gives the average transit time of the erythrocytes passing the slits in

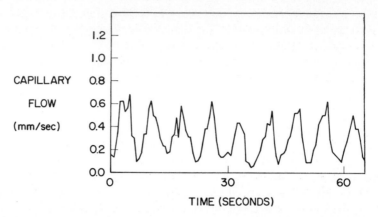

FIG. 2. VELOCITY DATA FROM THE CAPILLARY DATA OF FIG. 1 AND THEIR EXTENSION IN TIME.

the basic interval of integration. This has usually been taken to be 1 sec, and by staggering intervals a point each half second was obtained. For the computations, the analog data from the magnetic tape was digitized by means of an analog-digital converter and the cross-correlations performed on a high speed digital computer. Unfortunately cross-correlation requires a considerable amount of computing time, so that unless one has free access to computing facilities this is not too practical a method of reducing the data.

Another approach we have tried is to make a direct measure of the transit time of those events which give substantial signals. By placing the slits closer together — the equivalent of 7 or 8 μ on the vessel — we found the two signals to be remarkably similar. When a signal above a predetermined threshold comes from the upstream photomultiplier, an interval timer is started, and it is stopped on receiving a similar signal from the downstream photomultiplier. The time interval can then be recorded for subsequent analysis, or, more conveniently, its reciprocal taken and this number recorded, which is proportional to the transit velocity. With the equipment available we found it better to record the basic data on analog tape and process it later, but we are now working on modifications which will permit on-line recording of velocity. Since the signals at the two slits are not always identical, this method occasionally gives spurious signals. It is a great convenience to have a visual recording of the basic data to examine at leisure in order to check on unexpected velocities to know if they are real or merely artefacts of the recording system.

The photometric method of measuring erythrocyte velocities has proved particularly useful in studying blood flow in capillaries, as it works best for slow flow in small vessels. Also, since the erythrocytes essentially fill the lumen of the capillaries, the erythrocyte velocity should give a good measure of the volume rate of flow once the vessel diameter is known.

5. LIMITATIONS OF *IN VIVO* MEASUREMENTS

With the current state of the art we are severely handicapped in trying to make quantitative rheological measurements in the microcirculation. In the first place, the best methods are most successful in thin transparent microbeds, which limits the functional types of microcirculation available for study. Some work can also be done on the surface of certain organs, but the microvasculature on the surface is probably not particularly representative of that in depth. We can obtain volume flow rates only in vessels so small that the erythrocytes pass in single file. Otherwise we have to perform an integration of erythrocyte velocity over the cross-section and make some assumptions as to how the plasma moves. Although it is possible to measure pressures in blood vessels even down to the capillaries, the available methods require penetration of the vessel wall, introducing traumatic injury the rheological effects of which are hard to assess. We can obtain good dynamic data on vessel lumen, but we have information on the vessel width only in one plane, and lack adequate means of obtaining it in three dimensions.

We feel that a direct study of *in vivo* microbeds involves so many difficulties that it should be supplemented with other approaches. For this, we have devised a three pronged attack (we call it the three-fold way) to try to make an effective interrelation between *in vivo* and *in vitro* studies. Our approach is outlined in Fig. 3. The ultimate

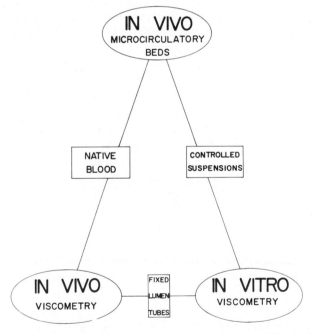

FIG. 3. SCHEME OF INTERRELATIONSHIPS AMONG *in vivo* AND *in vitro* STUDIES RELEVANT TO MICROCIRCULA-
TORY RHEOLOGY.

goal is a better understanding of the rôle of the rheological properties of blood and blood vessels in living microbeds, indicated at the top of the diagram. For this part of the program we are using all of the basic tools discussed above, both for observing the beds when perfused with the animals, own blood and when cannulated and perfused with controlled fluids and red cell suspensions.

One of the big unknowns in hemorheology today is the effect on the rheological properties of blood of removing it from an animal and treating it with various anti-coagulants. In order to try to evaluate these effects we have developed a method of outflow viscometry in which blood from a chronically implanted arterio-venous shunt can be studied in fixed lumen tubes of microvessel dimensions[13]. This method is represented by the lower left block in Fig. 3. We believe that this will give us basic information on the flow properties of native and physiologically altered blood to relate to our *in vivo* experiments, as indicated by the line tieing these two boxes together in the diagram.

We are also carrying out *in vitro* viscometry of drawn blood and artificial suspensions of erythrocytes — the box to the lower right. This includes both basic viscometry to study the bulk properties of red cell suspensions, and *in vitro* flow-out viscometry using polymer tubes identical in size and wall characteristics with those used in the *in vivo* flow-out viscometry. In this way we hope to interrelate the effect of systematic modification of blood with its properties in the native state — represented by the line joining the lower two boxes. The loop is closed by our ability to experiment with artificial suspensions — whose physical properties we know — through cannulated microbeds.

We feel that this three-fold way gives us an opportunity of taking the most effective advantage of the methods of physical science — to isolate and control a few factors at a time — without losing our perspective with respect to the basic problem: a better understanding of the living microcirculation.

ACKNOWLEDGMENTS

This work was supported by United States Public Health Service Grants HE 08977, HE 08976, HE 02500, AM 06221 and HE 07325. One of us (W.G.F.) Career Development Awardee, U.S. Public Health Service, National Institutes of Health. The academic year 1965–6 was spent by one of us (P.C.J.) at the California Institute of Technology during tenure of an N.I.H. special post-doctoral fellowship (1-F3-HE28, 675-01).

REFERENCES

[1] WIEDERHIELM, C. A. *J. App. Physiol.* **18**, 1041, 1963.

[2] WIEDERHIELM, C. A. and PELROY, G. E. *Digest of 6th Inter. Conf. on Med. Electronics and Biological Engineering*, Tokyo, 1965, p. 636.

[3] BLOCH, E. H. *Angiology* **15**, 353, 1964.

[4] BLOCH, E. H. *Am. J. Anat.* **110**, 125, 1961.

[5] JOHNSON, P. C. and GREATBATCH, W. H., Jr. *Methods in Medical Research* **11**, 220, 1966.

[6] ROY, C. S. and BROWN, J. G. *J. Physiol.* **2**, 323, 1880.

[7] Personal communication.

[8] WIEDERHIELM, C. A. and RUSHMER, R. F. *Bibl. Anat.* **4**, 234, 1964.

[9] LANDIS, E. M. *Am. J. Physiol.* **14**, 651, 1959.

[10] RAPPAPORT, M. B., BLOCH, E. H. and IRWIN, J. W. *J. Appl. Physiol.* **14**, 651, 1959.

[11] MONRO, P. A. G. Chapter in *Advances in Optical and Electron Microscopy*, BARER and COSLETT (Editors), Academic Press, London and New York, vol. I, 1966, p. 1.

[12] WAYLAND, H. and JOHNSON, P. C. *4th Europ. Conf. on Microcirculation*, Cambridge, England, 1966, HARDERS, H. (Editor), *Bibl. Anat.*, S. Karger, Basel (in press).

[13] Asano, M., Yoshida, K. and Tatai, K. *Bull. Inst. Publ. Health* **13**, 201, 1964.
[14] Frasher, W. G., Jr., Wayland, H. and Sobin, S. *Bull. Inst. Publ. Health* **13**, 1964 (companion paper).

DISCUSSION

WIEDERHIELM (*U.S.A.*):

I would just like to comment that techniques of the kind that Dr. Wayland has described today will have a profound effect on future attempts at formulating models of the cardiovascular system. Until a few years ago, relatively little quantitative information was available in virtually the whole field of microvascular physiology. Recently, a variety of techniques have been developed for measuring pressure, dimension and flow in microscopic blood vessels. The impact of these techniques is still some distance in the future, but hopefully quantitative data will begin to accumulate, which will help to establish a solid foundation for a more detailed analysis of the system.

JOLY (*France*):

With the very fine technique you used, is it possible to obtain some indication on the velocity profile in the capillary?

WAYLAND (*U.S.A.*):

With the correlation technique we have used so far, we have not been very successful with this. In principle we could. This requires using circular pin holes rather than slits. This means that a very precise adjustment along the axis of the vessel is necessary, because otherwise it would not be correlating similar events. I do not have time to go into the details, but Monro has an optical scanning device which essentially forms a slit image at an angle, depending upon the speed of rotation of this optical device. While Monro was in our laboratory last winter, he tried moving the slit of his instrument to various positions across a 40 μ vessel, and one could indeed see differences. Furthermore, one could do the same thing with a series of slits and photograph the streak images. In this way one could get some information as to the velocity profile. We have confined our quantitative work, to date, to individual capillaries, where we feel that because the red cell is about the same size as the capillary, the motion of the red cell is probably a pretty good indicator of the total flow. We have hopes that, out of this, we can eventually get some information of the local "crit" because if we do not know the local percentage of red cells to plasma, we are lacking one of the important factors in trying to describe the flow. But so far, to get good profiles in the smaller vessels has been extremely difficult. Another thing that is important: we often want "Q dot" rather than "V"; we really want volume flow rather than the velocity of the individual red cells. The only device I know of that measures "Q dot" directly, is the electromagnetic flow meter. This has at long last been miniaturized, so that one works on vessels of about half a millimeter in diameter, which is adequate for inflow and outflow of, say, a microbed, but far from getting to the microvessels themselves. If somebody has a good method for measuring profile at this level, please, let me know. We'd like it.

HARDAWAY (*U.S.A.*):

Dr. Zahn, working in Frankfort, Germany, perfected this technique to a high degree. It can draw profiles of various vessels which include anything in the objective and record their openings, closings, dilations and contractions very beautifully on paper.

WAYLAND:

What is his method?

HARDAWAY:

The flying spot method.

PALMER (*Australia*):

I should like to ask Professor Wayland about the double flash technique. Firstly, does he have any difficulty in identifying the cells in the two photographs? And secondly, might this be a method for working out the velocity profile if the photographs included the whole of the small vessel?

WAYLAND:

We have not tried to look at it in terms of getting velocity profile. That is an interesting thought. The big problem, of course, is relative absorption. If you go to a vessel that is more than about 40 μ, you just do not get enough information to quantitate because there is so much absorption in the middle that you can only work with plasma gaps between clumps of cells. Of course, this works beautifully in the venous system, but in the arterial system it is much more difficult. In the very small vessels, down below 20 microns, you have enough detail that it is probably possible to get some information on profiles. The chore of doing the measuring for the double flash method is tremendous. It would well be worth it in a few isolated cases where the information by any other method is completely lacking. This could, of course, in principle be done with some of Bloch's beautiful pictures; but I think that by having two pictures on the same frame, you can make the analysis a good deal easier than when you have to go from frame to frame.

WIEDERHIELM:

I believe it is within the capabilities of the Monro visual particle velocity meter to resolve the velocity profile in vessels down to 20–30 μ diameter. This approach is currently used in Berman's laboratory in Boston.

WAYLAND:

Yes, certainly the streak image technique, whether it be the optical or the photographic one, has a great deal of possibility. There is another point I did not bring up that I think we ought to look at. This is the question of stereoscopic viewing of these various systems. It is possible in principle to work with a 10 μ diameter tube, or smaller, and get adequate depth of field to see clear across the tube. This is accomplished by using a long range petrographic objective. You have resolution of only about a micron, but this would give one some idea of the deformation that takes place. We have built such a microscope but have not had time to use it yet. We do hope that we can get some information on the deformations of the individual red cells in three dimensions in this way. The only way I know to get three-dimensional information in much greater depth than that, is to use the hologram. A lot of work has to be done yet to make it possible.

EFFECTS OF ERYTHROCYTE ORIENTATION AND CONCENTRATION ON LIGHT TRANSMISSION THROUGH BLOOD FLOWING THROUGH MICROSCOPIC BLOOD VESSELS

CURT A. WIEDERHIELM[*][1] and LEON BILLIG[2]

Microcirculation Laboratory,
Department of Physiology and Biophysics,[1] and
Department of Mechanical Engineering,
University of Washington,[2] Seattle, Washington, U.S.A.

EXAMINATION of microvascular beds with a microscope reveals a characteristic pattern of light absorption during rapid flow (Fig. 1). In arterioles, the optical path length is maximum at the center of the vessel, but optical density is substantially lower than at positions midway between the center and the wall, giving rise to a central light streak bordered by two symmetrical darker streaks. In contrast, in venules, several alternating light and dark streaks are seen, lined up parallel with the vessel's axis.

This anomalous light transmission characteristic of rapidly flowing blood was described by TAYLOR[1], who also obtained densitometer tracings from microscopic

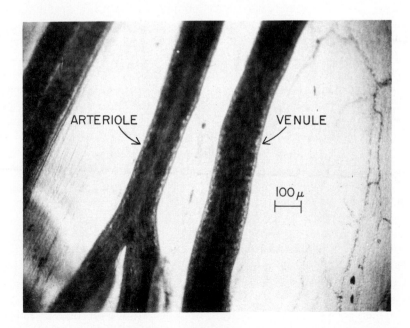

FIG. 1. PHOTOMICROGRAPH OF ARTERIOLE AND VENULE IN THE FROG MESENTERY.

blood vessels, and concluded that the observed light transmission patterns might be accounted for by orientation of erythrocytes in the shear field.

A preliminary report by PHIBBS and BURTON[2] demonstrated that erythrocytes in quick-frozen arteries tend to orient in the plane of shear, thus lending indirect support to Taylor's view. An alternative explanation must also be considered however. FÅHRAEUS and LINDQUIST[3] demonstrated that erythrocytes in a Poiseuille shear field are displaced from the wall toward the vessel's center. The axial drift of erythrocytes gives rise to a thin, cell-poor plasma sleeve adjacent to the vessel wall, whereas the erythrocytes are concentrated toward the center in a relatively cell-rich core.

SEGRÉ and SILBERBERG[4] demonstrated that, in addition to drifting radially away from the wall, particles also drifted from the center toward an intermediate position. The net result of these combined shifts of the suspended particles was to produce an annular zone of relatively high particle concentration at positions intermediate between the center and the wall, the so-called tubular pinch effect. Other model studies by GOLDSMITH and MASON[5] yielded similar results. An annular zone of high cell concentration could produce a light transmission pattern similar to that shown in Fig. 1. The studies reported here were designed to evaluate the relative importance of erythrocyte orientation and concentration gradients on this pattern in blood vessels of the frog mesentery.

METHODS

These studies were conducted in two phases: (1) Light transmission characteristics in arterioles in the frog mesentery were measured *in situ* with a TV microdensitometer system, described elsewhere[6]. (2) Blood vessels having markedly anomalous light transmission were quick-frozen, embedded and sectioned. The histologic cross-sections of vessels were used to evaluate cell orientation and concentration gradients.

The TV-microscope system provides a convenient means for obtaining quantitative information from microscopic images. The TV camera tube basically performs the function of a transducer, translating the light intensity in discrete picture elements in the microscopic image into corresponding amplitude levels of the video signal from the camera. The relationship between light intensity and video signal amplitude is logarithmic and can be calibrated by inserting neutral density filters of different optical densities in the light path of the microscope. The video signal amplitude is a linear function of optical density over a range from 0 to 1.6.

The raster in the TV system is composed of an array of horizontal lines which may be sampled individually by means of a specially designed electronic gating circuit[7]. By lining up blood vessels perpendicular to the TV raster and then sampling the video signal from a single line in the raster, densitometer tracings could be obtained as the electron beam in the camera tube scanned past the image of the vessel. Generally the video signal information was recorded on a video tape recorder for conversion to densitometer tracings at a later time. Blood vessels under observation were also photographed from the TV monitor screen, which offered the advantage that the contrast could be exaggerated by appropriate adjustment of the contrast and brightness controls on the monitor.

Quick-frozen blood vessel sections were obtained from experimental animals under Nembutal anesthesia. The animals were restrained with straps on a thin metal plate.

The exposed mesentery was pinned over a hole in the plate, permitting transillumination and observation of the preparation as well as free access of the coolant solution to both sides of the mesentery. Before the freezing procedure, the mesentery was examined under the microscope, photomicrographs were taken and arterioles and venules which displayed prominent light transmission anomalies were selected. The metal plate with the attached animal preparation was then rapidly plunged into acetone, cooled to its freezing temperature ($-95°C$) with liquid nitrogen.

The freezing time for the vessels was estimated conservatively, by the method of BAXTER[8], to be 10–15 msec for a vessel 250 μ in diameter. The thermal properties of the frozen tissue, plasma, and cellular elements of the blood were assumed to be identical to those of water. The erythrocyte velocity in the arterioles of the frog mesentery ranges from 1 to 5 mm/sec, and the maximal displacement of erythrocytes at these velocities would amount to less than three erythrocyte diameters, or 75 μ. The time required for freezing is thus sufficiently short to stop motion of the blood effectively, with minimal change in orientation or concentration within the blood stream.

The mesentery was subsequently excised, freeze-substituted, and imbedded for sectioning and staining with hematoxylin and eosin. Large, high contrast photomicrographs were obtained of cross-sections of the quick frozen vessels. Orientation of the erythrocytes was determined from the photomicrographs by measuring the angle between the axis of the erythrocyte and the radius of the blood vessel. Most histologic sections showed some shrinkage, presumably due to the relatively low hematocrit (30–35%) and plasma protein content (2–3%) of amphibian blood. Differences of cell concentration in arterioles were estimated by dividing the vessel's cross-section (excluding the shrinkage artefact) into three concentric annuli, and counting the cells per unit area. Orientation and concentration gradients were not evaluated quantitatively in venules, since the persistence of discrete flow domains from individual tributaries led to a distribution of erythrocytes which made such measurements difficult.

RESULTS AND CONCLUSIONS

A. *Transmission of Light through Terminal Arteries, Arterioles and Venules*

A comparison of the light absorption in a uniformly absorbing cylinder and in a 300 μ terminal artery is shown in Fig. 2. The light absorption in a uniform cylinder is a function of the path length. Thus light absorption is highest through the center of the cylinder, where path length is the longest (Fig. 2, left). In contrast, the light absorption in a 300 μ artery displays a relative minimum in the center of the vessel, whereas it is quite high in intermediate positions between the center and the wall (Fig. 2, right). Superimposing the two optical density tracings (Fig. 2, bottom) shows that light transmission through the center of the artery is considerably lower than predicted for a uniform cylinder. Near the wall, however, the light absorption is higher than predicted for a uniform cylinder.

The pattern of light absorption in a branching 160 μ arteriole is shown in Fig. 3. The photomicrograph (Fig. 3, left) shows the parent vessel originating at the bottom and the branches on top. The parent vessel displays the typical central light streak which is divided and located asymmetrically in the initial part of the branches, with relatively wide dark streaks on the outside, and thin dark streaks inside the branches. Further

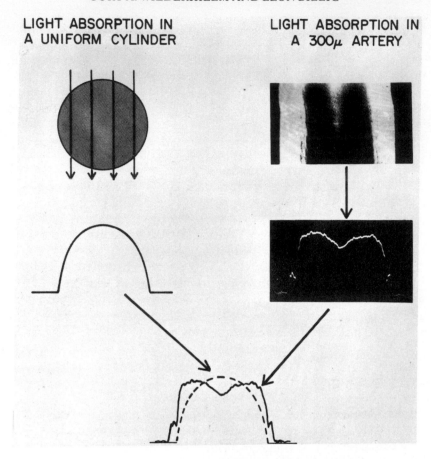

FIG. 2. COMPARISON OF LIGHT ABSORPTION IN UNIFORM CYLINDER AND 300 μ TERMINAL ARTERY.

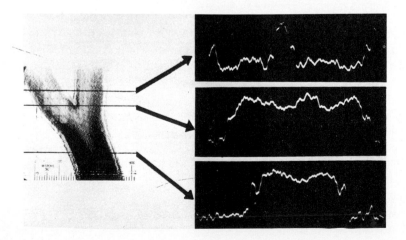

FIG. 3. LIGHT ABSORPTION IN A 160 μ BRANCHING ARTERIOLE. *Left:* PHOTOMICROGRAPH OF MONITOR SCREEN IN TV MICROSCOPE SYSTEM. *Right:* DENSITOMETER TRACINGS IN CROSS SECTION OF BRANCHING ARTERIOLE AS INDICATED BY ARROWS.

downstream the symmetric pattern is gradually re-established by an increase in the thickness of the darker zone on the medial side of the branches. Densitometer tracings were obtained from the three sites indicated by arrows (Fig. 3, left). The central region of low optical density can be clearly seen in the densitometer tracing from the main vessel. The asymmetry in light transmission in the branches is also evident in the top two oscilloscope tracings.

The light absorption pattern at the confluence of venules is markedly different from that seen in arterioles (Fig. 4). The first generation of tributaries, seen on top of the

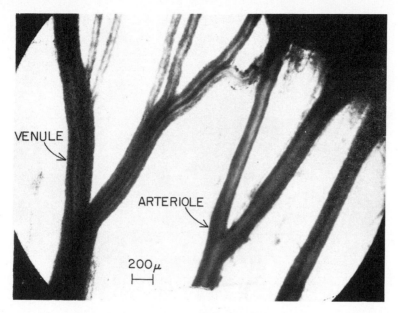

FIG. 4. LIGHT ABSORPTION IN ARTERIOLE AND VENULE IN THE FROG MESENTERY. CONTRAST WAS EXAGGERATED BY PRINTING ON HIGH CONTRAST PAPER.

photomicrograph, show light transmission characteristics similar to arterioles; i.e. a central light streak bordered by two approximately equal dark zones. Beyond the confluence of the tributaries however, the light and dark zones retain their individuality for considerable distances downstream. When traced for several millimeters, the streaks gradually blend, and a pattern similar to that seen in arterioles emerges.

The pattern of light absorption observed both in arterioles and venules might be explained either by orientation of the erythrocytes and the resulting optical anisotropy of the blood, or alternatively by radial differences in cell concentration in the blood vessel lumen.

B. *Erythrocyte Orientation and Concentration in Arterioles and Venules*

Microscopic cross-sections of quick-frozen arterioles are shown in Fig. 5. The most striking feature is the high degree of orientation of erythrocytes in a plane parallel to the cell wall. Near the vessel's center the orientation of the cells appears to be more random. Measurements of the angle of the cells' major axis with respect to the vessel's radius averaged 84° with a standard deviation of ±23° for the three cross-sections of the vessel shown in Fig. 5.

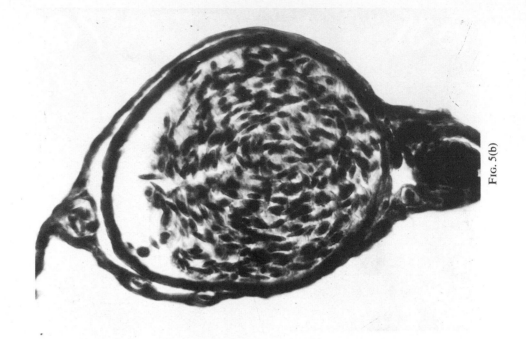

Fig. 5(a)

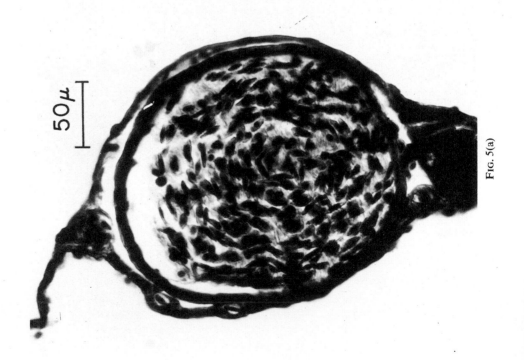

Fig. 5(b)

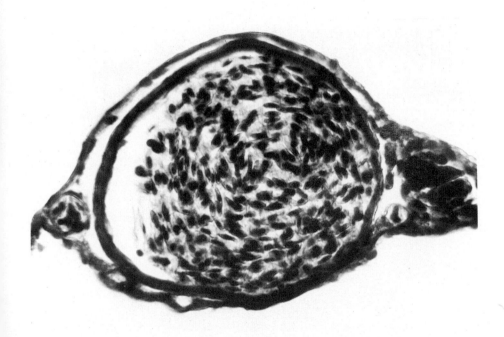

FIG. 5(c)

FIG. 5(a)–(c). CROSS-SECTIONS OF QUICK-FROZEN ARTERIOLES IN FROG MESENTERY. THICKNESS OF SECTIONS: 25 μ.

687

Another striking feature of these sections is the relatively uniform distribution of erythrocytes in the vessel. Regional hematocrits were estimated by dividing the internal areas of the arterioles, excluding the shrinkage artefact, into three annuli, and counting the red cells in each annulus. The cells per unit area totaled 26, 25 and 23 in the cross-section shown in Fig. 5a; 26, 24 and 25 in Fig. 5b; and finally 28, 27 and 26 in Fig. 5c. Sections from an arteriole with slow flow rates ($<100\ \mu$/sec) are shown in Fig. 6. Under

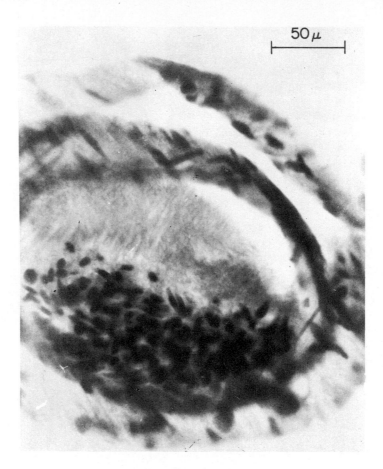

FIG. 6. QUICK-FROZEN SECTION OF ARTERIOLE. ERYTHROCYTE SEDIMENTATION ASSOCIATED WITH SLOW FLOW RATES (LESS THAN $100\ \mu$/SEC).

these circumstances the erythrocytes sediment to the bottom of the vessel, and the orientation is essentially random.

The pattern of cellular organization in venules differs markedly from arterioles as shown in Fig. 7. The orientation of the erythrocytes is in general not parallel to the wall, and in certain areas the concentration of cells is increased. At least three domains can be distinguished in serial sections (Fig. 7a, b), each retaining some orientation. These domains may represent inflow from separate tributaries upstream; the zones with high cell concentration contain blood from a segment of the vascular bed in which hemoconcentration has occurred, either by increased capillary filtration or by plasma

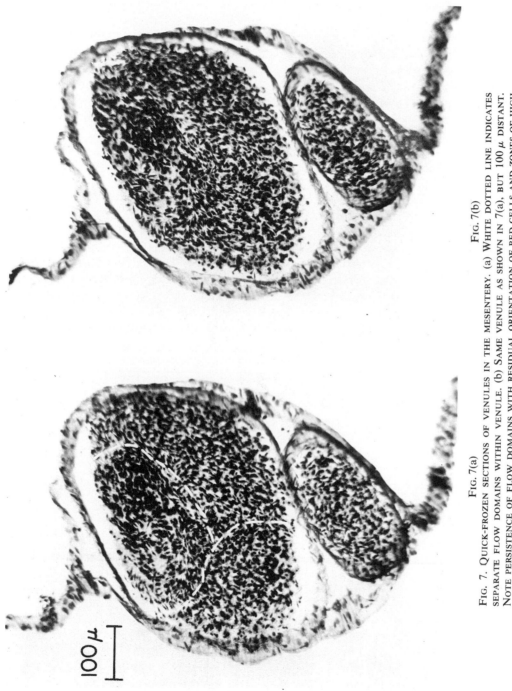

Fig. 7(a)

Fig. 7(b)

Fig. 7. Quick-frozen sections of venules in the mesentery. (a) White dotted line indicates separate flow domains within venule. (b) Same venule as shown in 7(a), but 100 μ distant. Note persistence of flow domains with residual orientation of red cells and zones of high erythrocyte concentration.

skimming. The three major flow domains with residual orientation may be traced downstream for some distance (Fig. 7b). The areas of high cell concentration are found in the same relative position in the two sections.

C. *The Relationship between Cellular Orientation and Light Transmission*

The observations on quick-frozen cross-sections of arterioles support Taylor's view that orientation of erythrocytes is a major factor in determining light transmission through the microscopic blood vessels, since the differences in cell concentration are too small to account for the observed pattern. That erythrocytes have a different index of refraction than blood plasma can be demonstrated in capillary blood flow under incident light. As erythrocytes rotate or are deformed in the capillaries, their surfaces occasionally intersect the incident light beam at less than a critical angle and totally reflect the light. The erythrocytes may then be visualized as brief scintillations of light within the capillary.

A possible explanation for the light transmission characteristics may be provided by combining the data on erythrocyte orientation and differences in refractive index of erythrocytes in plasma as shown in Fig. 8. When an arteriole filled with a highly oriented red cell mass is observed by transillumination, the light strikes the erythrocytes in the center of the arteriole at less than the critical angle, and specular transmission will occur through the erythrocytes. Toward the wall of the vessel, however, the angle between the incident light beam and the cell membrane approaches the critical angle, and total reflection occurs, leading to multiple reflections and scattering of the light. The pattern of light absorption expected under these circumstances consists of the typical central light streak, bordered by two symmetric dark streaks (Fig. 8, left). However, if the blood vessel is observed through a microscope, rotated to an angle of

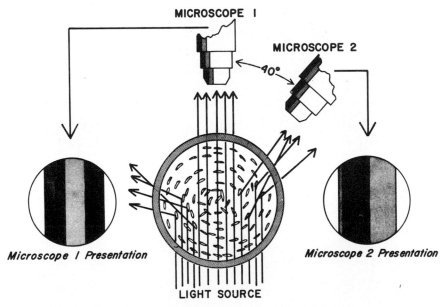

FIG. 8. LIGHT SCATTERING AND SPECULAR TRANSMISSION IN HIGHLY ORIENTED RED CELL CORE. *Left:* PREDICTED LIGHT ABSORPTION PATTERN IN TRANSILLUMINATION OF BLOOD VESSEL. *Right:* LIGHT ABSORPTION PATTERN PREDICTED WITH OBLIQUE INCIDENT LIGHT.

40–45° with respect to the direction of the incident light, the directly transmitted light in the center of the vessel does not reach the objective. Scattered light from the peripheral zone does enter the microscope, however, and the pattern of light transmission is expected to reverse as shown on the right. Thus, a central dark streak, bordered by two lighter streaks of unequal thickness, would be expected. This reversal of light pattern can actually be observed as shown in Fig. 9. The predicted reversal of the light

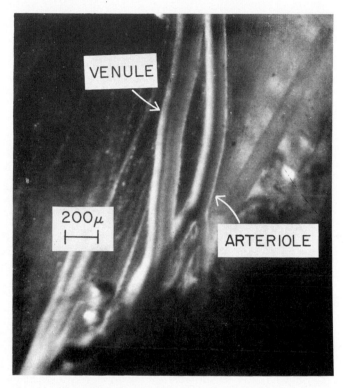

FIG. 9. ARTERIOLE AND VENULE IN FROG MESENTERY. ILLUMINATION BY OBLIQUE INCIDENT LIGHT. NOTE REVERSAL OF LIGHT TRANSMISSION PATTERN IN ARTERIOLE AND VENULE.

transmission pattern can be clearly observed in the arteriole in the center of the figure. The adjacent venule also shows multiple alternating light and dark streaks which gradually blend together downstream in the vessel. The light transmission characteristics of rapidly flowing blood in microscopic blood vessels may in this manner be explained by orientation of the erythrocytes in the planes of shear, and by the difference in refractive index of cells and plasma. The multiple streaks observed in venules and veins probably represent separate domains of flow from tributaries, with a residual orientation of cells, which progressively is dispersed in the shear field of the vessel.

ACKNOWLEDGMENTS

Technical assistance in all phases of these studies by Mr. Gary Pelroy and Mr. Burton Weston is gratefully acknowledged. These studies were supported by National Institutes of Health grants HE-07152 and 5-K3-HE-22,465.

REFERENCES

[1] TAYLOR, M. *Australian J. Exp. Biol. Med. Sci.* **33**, 1, 1955.
[2] PHIBBS, R. H. and BURTON, A. C. *Federation Proc.* **24**, 156, 1965.
[3] FÅHRAEUS, R. and LINDQUIST, T. *Am. J. Physiol.* **96**, 562, 1931.
[4] SEGRÉ, G. and SILBERBERG, A. *Bibliotheca Anat.* **4**, 83. 1964.
[5] GOLDSMITH, H. L. and MASON, S. G. *Bibliotheca Anat.* **7**, 353, 1965.
[6] WIEDERHIELM, C. A. *Federation Proc.* **25**, 6, 1966.
[7] WIEDERHIELM, C. A. *J. Appl. Physiol.* **18**, 1041, 1963.
[8] BAXTER, D. C. *Trans. ASME.* **84**, 317, 1962.

DISCUSSION

WAYLAND (*U.S.A.*):

I would like to congratulate Dr. Wiederhielm for presenting information to lay to rest some of the ghosts concerning the use of photometry in trying to establish distribution of red cells. Of course, as he points out, as originally suggested by Taylor, some of the other optical artefacts have very carefully been discussed by Bayliss and others. I would like to point out one thing in connection with the use of the TV system versus photography. If any of you have been doing this type of work and do not have a TV system or Dr. Wiederhielm's ingenuity in using it, one can actually do more precise photometry with photographic materials than you can with a TV system, provided, of course, that you are interested in a stationary or static situation or in only a few successive pictures. Most of you are in institutions where there is a spectrographic laboratory or an astronomy laboratory. Certainly the photographic materials they use are more uniform over the surface of a given plate than any Vidicon tube is apt to be over its photosensitive surface. So it is inherent that comparisons from one part of this plate to another can be made much more accurately than one can do with a TV tube unless one is prepared to do the very complicated types of corrections that the NASA people have done with respect to pictures taken on Mars. If you want to follow what is happening in one particular part of the image in time, then it is very difficult to beat the TV system. We should not feel that just because we do not have a good television system we are eliminated from quantitiative photometry.

WIEDERHIELM (*U.S.A.*):

Thank you for your comment, Dr. Wayland. Our reason for using the TV densitometer is that we had it set up in the laboratory, and used it routinely in a different study.

PHIBBS (*U.S.A.*):

How often did you find contraction of the mass of blood away from the wall in the lumen of a frozen vessel? We encountered this in a few frozen vessels and felt obliged to exclude them from the kind of analysis we were doing because we felt that, if the mass of erythrocytes did contract, this might in itself produce some orientation. It is really the plasma proteins which are fixed during freeze substitution that preserve the intercellular relationships in the frozen blood. Is a frog's plasma protein concentration much less than a mammal's?

WIEDERHIELM:

I think the reason for the difference may be two-fold: first the hematocrit of frog blood usually runs between 25 and 30%. Secondly, the plasma protein concentration is only in the order of 3%. In general, we found some degree of shrinkage in most of our preparations. Since we were not primarily concerned with the peripheral plasma sleeve, we felt that the information on cell orientation would nevertheless be useful. In slowly flowing blood in arterioles you do see random cell orientation in frozen section, even though shrinkage may still be present.

PHIBBS

What about changes in erythrocyte orientation? In the arterial side of the circulation where flow was pulsatile, did you find a change throughout the cardiac cycle in the orientation or the light reflection?

WIEDERHIELM:

I believe there may again be a fundamental difference between the flow in amphibian blood vessels and the mesenteric and femoral arteries you were studying. We never see reversal of flow in the frog mesentery even though it is pulsatile in nature. We have not observed any changes in light transmission associated with the cardiac cycle.

SIRS (*England*):

I wonder if these light absorption characteristics do in fact imply orientation. I think there are two phenomena here, one is direct absorption of the light by the erythrocyte, the other is the scattering phenomenon. Would you not get the same thing even if they were orientated in any direction with the scattering phenomena and that if you scatter at the periphery of the artery, the light can be lost out of the artery? If you scatter in the center, it is very likely, it will be scattered back again by other cells in the vicinity in much the same way as a light guide operates. I wonder in this connection whether you studied the effect of variation of the wave lengths of light and the absorption characteristics of the erythrocyte?

WIEDERHIELM:

We have not compared the light transmission pattern at different wave lengths. Your other question referred to whether the light transmission pattern is related to orientation or due to multiple reflections in the randomly orientated red cell core. A very striking change can be seen if you occlude an arteriole with a probe. Within a matter of seconds after cessation of flow the streaks disappear, and you find the type of absorption curve that you would expect in a uniform cylinder.

SIRS:

Is this possibly sedimentation of the erythrocytes in the arteriole once you stop the flow?

WIEDERHIELM:

Sedimentation could presumably be involved but the sedimentation process itself would probably also be associated with disorientation of the cells.

SIRS:

You get a more homogenous mass of material then? This is what I am getting at.

WIEDERHIELM:

A similar phenomenon can be observed when you observe pulsatile flow through a glass tube. You note that when the flow is very rapid . . . the blood has a silky appearance. In diastole the color becomes deeper red. Perhaps this represents phenomenon in the boundary between the tube and the blood.

TAYLOR (*Australia*):

This is naturally, of course, very gratifying to me after all this time to have the theory from Adelaide actually confirmed so beautifully. I think I can add a little more: one point, I am not sure whether I published this or not. If one uses the cells from the sheep, which are cup-shaped, these orientation effects disappear. There is no bright band in the middle of the stream of blood flowing, if the cells are from a sheep. So I think this perhaps answers Dr. Sirs' point. Otherwise, I am terribly pleased about this. There is one other thing that I might mention that we did. We illuminated the glass capillary with a slit of light. If the blood was flowing very slowly and presumably the orientation effects were very mild, then one saw a very diffuse image of the slit and along the axis of the tube, the slit, as it were, bulged out. This is light scattered along the long axis of the tube. And the faster the flow was made, then the clearer became the image of the slit, and this longitudinal scattering also disappeared. And this seemed to me another indication that scattering was in fact involved in this process; the scattering and of course absorption of the scattered light. But I congratulate Dr. Wiederhielm on a very beautiful demonstration.

SIRS:

This scattering phenomenon is very dependent on the shape of the red cell, I agree, especially *in vitro*.

PALMER (*Australia*):

I am very interested in these results from the veins because *in vivo* one can see a peripheral clear zone in the small venules; and, as I think Dr. Stehbens's photographs showed, at a point of confluence the clear peripheral zones unite and form streaks. I was wondering whether these cell-poor streaks outlined the regions which were defined in the cross-section of your vein. These regions seemed to show differences in concentration which may represent a persistence of the concentration pattern in the very much smaller tributary venules, because I think marked axial drift is apparent only in vessels of about the order of 50μ rather than 100μ. You may be seeing persistence of the cell concentration pattern coming from these smaller tributaries.

WIEDERHIELM:

I believe that Dr. McDonald's movies of dye in the mesenteric vessels demonstrate admirably that there is very little radial mixing in these vessels. The dye stream lines can be traced clear into discrete liver lobules. The high concentration of erythrocytes found in some of these domains represent inflow from a tributary, in which hemoconcentration has occurred either by filtration processes or perhaps plasma skimming effects. The gradual disappearance of the streaks downstream in the venules, however, is more likely due to dispersion of orientation in the separate flow domains, since radial mixing is relatively insignificant in the short distances we are concerned with.

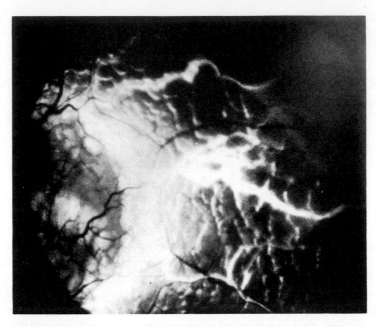

FIG. 1. DRAINAGE OF A FLUORESCEIN–SODIUM DEPOT IN THE HAMSTER CHEEK POUCH IN THE FORM OF PERIVASCULAR STREAKS. DEPOT IN LEFT HALF OF PICTURE, DRAINAGE TO THE RIGHT. FLUORESCENCE LIGHT, ×10.

have here a perivascular flow of fluid, which can be localized microscopically as lying outside of the vascular wall. The flow rate is fairly high; the streaks develop within the first 30 sec after injection of the dye depot. The direction of flow is towards the base of the cheek pouch, i.e. towards the hamster's mouth. On the basis of the good water-solubility of fluorescein–sodium, we may conclude that the aqueous phase of the extravascular system preferably flows by such perivascular channels.

The second dye employed is brillantsulfoflavin (0.1% solution in physiological saline). This dye binds *in vivo* to plasma proteins up to 0.03%. Upon local injection of brillantsulfoflavin into the cheek pouch tissue, the dye remains there unchanged for about 5–10 min. After this time, perivascular streaks also develop, as described for fluorescein–sodium.

Fluorescein–isothiocyanate, which is conjugated to plasma protein *in vitro* prior to application, is the third type of dye employed by us. All unbound dye is removed by means of chromatography before use, and the protein solution is brought to the approximate blood plasma level by ultrafiltration[5]. After local injection of this dye–protein conjugate, the fluorescent depot remains in the cheek pouch tissue stationary, without any drainage taking place within an observation period of 30–50 min.

It is of importance to note that no lymphatic vessels have been seen in the hamster cheek pouch by such fluorescence microscopic methods. The drainage of large molecular substances, such as plasma proteins, appears to be very minimal in the extravascular space of the cheek pouch. In comparison, the flow relationships in the extravascular tissue of the rat or hamster mesenterium is quite different. If one injects the same depot of dyes mentioned above into the mesenterial root of a small intestine coil, then the lymphatic vessels are visualized by the fluorescent dye, thus indicating a drain-

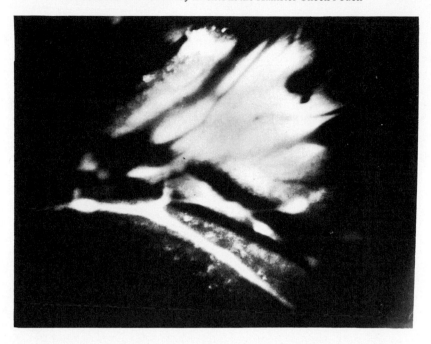

FIG. 2. DRAINAGE OF A FLUORESCEIN–SODIUM DEPOT IN MESENTERIUM VIA THE LYMPH WITH FLUORE-
SCENCE STAINING OF THE LYMPH CHANNELS. FLUORESCENCE LIGHT, ×10.

age of extravascular fluid via the lymph (Fig. 2). An intravascular or perivascular fluorescence in the efferent blood vessels does not occur. In short, drainage of fluorescence-
labelled fluids from the interstitial tissue of the mesenterium takes place via lymphatic
channels. Although aqueous and protein-conjugated dyes behave differently with
regard to flow rate, they are, in principle, quite alike in their qualitative effects. In the
hamster cheek pouch, however, other conditions prevail, for water-soluble dyes flow
perivascularly and protein-conjugated dyes remain unmoved in the connective tissue
for a long time. A drainage of fluid via lymphatic channels cannot be documented.

Such unique flow relationships probably explain, for the most part, the immunologically privileged character of the hamster cheek pouch. Consequently, the heterotrans-
plantation of tumors to this site has received much attention[1, 4, 6]. For the past two
years, we have also been studying human tumors serially transplantable in the cheek
pouch, in terms of chemotherapy[10], enzyme chemistry[3], histopathology[2], and
vascularization[9]. In the question of tumor vascularization, our initial concern has
been to document, by vital microscopic means, the early vascular reactions of the
host to tumor transplantation. After implanting tumor material, a hyperemia of the
cheek pouch vessels first results, followed by a corkscrew twisting of capillaries and
larger vessels, and finally, by the formation of new capillaries and a rearrangement of
the vascular architecture of the cheek pouch. These findings were earlier summarized
by us in Cambridge[11], where consideration was given to the early vascular reactions
resulting after the transplantation of histologically different tumor types, both of human
and hamster origin.

In conformity with the principal theme of this conference, we should like, in closing,
to demonstrate several observations we have made concerning extravascular flow

processes in tumor-bearing cheek pouches. Of main concern was whether a different extravascular fluid transport could be found in the immediate area of the tumor than in other regions of the cheek pouch. Accordingly, we injected the same dyes mentioned above both intravenously and intracardially into hamsters bearing human tumors in their cheek pouches; our transplantation technique has been described elsewhere[12]. Thereafter, the cheek pouches were everted at various periods after dye injection and examined under the fluorescence microscope. Later, the cheek pouches were cut open and spread out, so that the fluorescence phenomena could be more easily evaluated.

Figure 3 shows the border of a human sarcoma, H.S. No. 1[6], 6 min after intravenous injection of brillantsulfoflavin. One sees a bright, diffuse, fluorescence in the

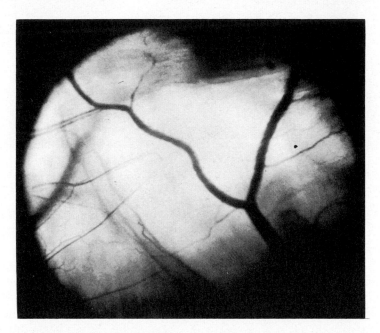

FIG. 3. BORDER OF A HUMAN TUMOR (H.S. No.1) IN THE HAMSTER CHEEK POUCH AFTER INTRAVENOUS INJECTION OF BRILLANTSULFOFLAVIN, WITH ACCUMULATION OF FLUORESCENCE AT THE TUMOR'S BORDER (UPPER HALF OF PICTURE). FLUORESCENCE LIGHT, ×10.

region immediately surrounding the tumor. For comparison, Fig. 4 shows an area in the same cheek pouch further removed from the tumor. The fluorescence here is mainly in the blood vessels, whereby the interstitial space is mostly free of dye. Only a few circumscribed exits of dye can be found perivascularly. The interstitial tissue of cheek pouches without tumors is free of fluorescence, even 15 min after injection of the dye, thus indicating that the permeability of blood vessels and interstitial tissue is minimal.

Figure 5 clearly shows the accumulation of fluorescence in the tumor itself, once again H. S. No. 1, one day after injection of a tumor cell suspension into the cheek pouch and a clearly visible tumor has developed, accompanied by marked hyperemia of the blood vessels in the area surrounding the tumor. Already 2 min after intravenous injection of brillantsulfoflavin, one sees a glowing of the tumor and its surroundings under the fluorescent light. Hence, a definitely increased fluid transport from the blood

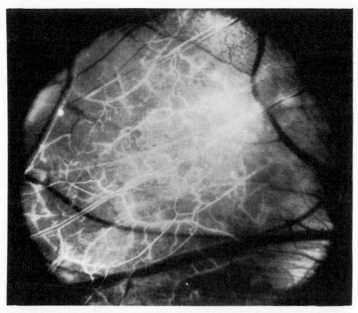

FIG. 4. SAME CHEEK POUCH AS IN FIG. 3, HERE A NON-TUMOR AREA. FLUORESCENCE PRIMARILY INTRA-VASCULAR. FLUORESCENCE LIGHT, ×10.

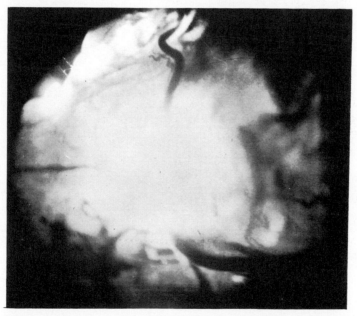

FIG. 5. CENTER OF A HUMAN TUMOR (H.S. No.1) IN THE HAMSTER CHEEK POUCH, AFTER INTRAVENOUS INJECTION OF BRILLANTSULFOFLAVIN. ACCUMULATION OF FLUORESCENCE IN THE TUMOR. FLUORESCENCE LIGHT, ×10.

vessels into the tumor is present. The fluorescence in both the tumor and its surrounding tissue can also be seen well in the dissected preparation. Lymph production, however, could not be found in any of these cheek pouches.

These findings have demonstrated the use of intravital observation in studying the movement of extravascular fluid in the interstitial tissue. In this way, the edifice of "hemorheology" can claim another sphere of investigation. When applied to the cancer problem, a knowledge of such flow phenomena in tumor-bearing tissues might very well provide the oncologist with new perspectives in the development of more selective approaches in the chemotherapy of cancer.

SUMMARY

A number of tumors, mostly of human origin, are being serially transplanted by us in the cheek pouch of the golden hamster. In vital microscopic studies, we have concentrated on the early vascular reactions in the host's cheek pouch after tumor transplantation. During the first days following transplantation, a local hyperemia can be seen. This is followed by a corkscrew deformation of capillaries and larger vessels, the formation of new capillaries and a rearrangement of the vascular architecture.

The extravascular streaming events have been examined on these tumor models. On the basis of fluorescent–biomicroscopic studies, we have found that the hamster cheek pouch shows unique properties in its extravascular transport of fluids and substances. Water-soluble substances brought into the interstitial tissue of the cheek pouch quickly spread in perivascular streaks, whereas proteins remain in the tissue for a long time as a depot without any noticeable lymph drainage being present. By means of fluorescence microscopy, the extravascular circulation in the cheek pouch bearing transplanted tumors has been examined. A concentration of the fluorescent dyes in the tumors has been documented.

REFERENCES

[1] CHUTE, R. N., SOMMERS, S. C. and WARREN, S. Cancer Res. 12, 912, 1952.
[2] GOLDENBERG, D. M., WITTE, S. and ELSTER, K. Krebsforschung u. Krebsbekämpfung, 6, 156, 1967.
[3] GOLDENBERG, D. M. WITTE, S., WÜST, H. and GOLDENBERG, H. Antimicrobial Agents and Chemotherapy—1965 (Amer. Soc. Microbiol., 1966), p. 524.
[4] LUTZ, B. R., PATT, D. I., HANDLER, A. H. and STEVENS, D. F. Anat. Rec. 108, 545, 1950.
[5] RINDERKNECHT, H. Nature 193, 167, 1962.
[6] TOOLAN, H. W. Cancer Res. 14, 660, 1954.
[7] WITTE, S. Bibl. Anat. 1, 56, 1961.
[8] WITTE, S. 4th Europ. Conf. on Microcirculation, Cambridge, England, 1966, HARDERS, H. (Editor), Bibl. Anat. S. Karger, Basel, New York (in press).
[9] WITTE, S. and GOLDENBERG, D. M. Z. ges. exp. Med. 139, 633, 1965.
[10] WITTE, S. and GOLDENBERG, D. M. Verh. dtsch. Ges. inn. Med. 72, 745, 1966.
[11] WITTE, S. and GOLDENBERG, D. M. Proc. 4th Europ. Conf. Microcirculation, Cambridge, 1966.
[12] WITTE, S., GOLDENBERG, D. M. and BREINING, H. Med. Welt 17, 1453, 1966.
[13] WITTE, S., GOLDENBERG, D. M. and SCHRICKER, K. T. Klin. Wschr. 43, 1182, 1965.

DISCUSSION

JOLY (*France*):

Is there any experimental way to demonstrate that interaction with the fluorescent dye does not modify the permeability of blood vessel?

WITTE (*Germany*):

The dye *per se,* yes. Although we have no control of what happens with permeability without dye-injection, we have a lot of experience with injecting many different dyes. Those dyes mentioned, we believe, reflect normal, or near normal, flow patterns and permeability phenomena in the vessel and in the surrounding tissue. There are other dyes that are toxic and produce quite different patterns.

BURTON *(Canada)*:

I would like to ask what type of tumor this is. Is it a kind of tumor which, as it grows, confines its blood supply to the outside? I want to know whether all that dye got into the middle through vessels and then diffused from them, or whether it had to diffuse into the whole mass. As you know, many tumors, malignant tumors, resorb their circulation as they grow so that the supply of oxygen and so on is confined to the periphery. Is this true of these tumors?

WITTE:

We have studied the vascular supply of these tumors used by us; adenocarcinomas, sarcomas, melanomas and others. These tumors are young, 1 to 4 days after injection of the tumor material into the cheek pouch. In these early stages, the vascular supply is from the vessels of the hamster cheek pouch.

BURTON:

So the dye diffuses into the interior?

WITTE:

Yes, at later stages you have necrosis in the central part of the tumor; but in these early stages, we have no necrosis. All the cells are quite well nourished in these small tumors.

GELIN *(Sweden)*:

I think that point is very important here to differentiate the age of the tumor. First of all, this is a heterologous tumor transplantation. Have you tried isologous tumors as well and been able to see this perivascular flow?

WITTE:

Yes, it is the same. I think all these phenomena point to a hyaluronidase-like activity of the tumor or, in this direction, a weakening of the ground substance of the vascular wall and surrounding connective tissue. You can observe the same thing in the cheek pouch bearing a homologous hamster tumor for instance, with Fortner's melanoma.

WIEDERHIELM *(U.S.A.)*:

I was interested in one of your slides showing a tumor transplant where the distribution of the fluorescent material was limited to the tumor tissue. It seems to imply that the capillary bed within and surrounding the tumor tissue shows an increased permeability. Also the ground substance appears to have been modified so that the material can move very rapidly within the tumor tissue itself. The fluorescent material did not appear to move into the interstitial space of the surrounding connective tissue. Have you generally observed this pattern . . . particularly of very slow spread of the fluorescent material in the connective tissue itself?

WITTE:

Yes, in the normal, non-transplanted, cheek pouch. This very slow spread of material to the surrounding tissue in the normal cheek pouch must be a special character of the interstitial space of the cheek pouch. Perhaps this is related to the reduced or absent lymph transport in this tissue.

HARTERT *(Germany)*:

I would like to ask: are you sure that this transport parallel to the vessel goes in the same direction as the vessel flow? What is your opinion about that?

WITTE:

It does not. This is striking: you can see the blood stream in one direction and flow of the extravascular material, the fluorescent dyes, in the other one. So, this streaming can occur in arteries or around arteries, because the arteries enter the cheek pouch and the fluorescence leaves the cheek pouch.

PALMER *(Australia)*:

I would like to comment that one sees sometimes in sections around malignant tumors that the tumor cells spread along the course of vessels, even apart from lymphatics. There may be looser connective tissue in the immediate vicinity of the vessels.

WITTE:

One can observe a similar event in cutaneous vessels of the forearm when you inject, for instance, a small depot of adrenalin subcutaneously. One can observe two white borders on the subcutaneous veins for a long distance, so it must be a zone with a special flow condition in the surrounding of the vessel.

SMALL PORE AND LARGE PORE SYSTEMS
IN CAPILLARY PERMEABILITY

G. E. Palade*

Department of Cell Biology, The Rockefeller University, New York, N.Y., U.S.A.

CAPILLARY PERMEABILITY AND THE TWO PORE SYSTEMS

It is generally assumed that the permeability characteristics of blood capillaries to water and water-soluble substances can be explained by the existence of two systems of "pores" or water-filled channels that penetrate the wall of these vessels to connect their lumen with the pericapillary spaces[1]. The first or small-pore system presumably consists of a population of cylindrical pores with an equivalent diameter of 80–90 Å, which occur with a frequency of ~17 units per $1\,\mu^2$ of capillary surface, and whose aggregated area does not exceed 0.1% of the total surface of the endothelium. The permeability data can be explained equally well by slit-, rather than cylindrical, pores of the same width and aggregate area. In fact, recent interpretations[1] have preferred this kind of small pores and postulated that they are located along the intercellular spaces of the endothelium. The bulk of exchanges between the blood plasma and the interstitial fluid takes place through the small pore system, primarily by diffusion and to a much smaller extent by hydrodynamic flow. Within the corresponding dimensional range, i.e. 0–90 Å, permeability coefficients drop with the increase in molecular diameter of the permeant species, because of restricted diffusion and molecular sieving effects, and the drop becomes precipitous when molecular diameters approach 60–80 Å. Yet the capillary wall remains slightly permeable to even larger molecules; moreover, for these molecules permeability coefficients appear to become independent of molecular size at least within the range so far tested. This permeability to large molecules, thoroughly studied by Grotte[2] and by Wasserman and Mayerson [3, 4] with calibrated dextrans, is generally ascribed to a system of large pores (diameter $\simeq 350$ Å) whose aggregated area may represent only a small fraction of the area occupied by the small pore system: the ratio of the two areas has been estimated to be 1:300 for liver sinusoids, and 1:30,000 for limb muscle capillaries. Molecules or particles with a diameter larger than 80 Å are expected to move exclusively through such large pores.

Electron microscopy of the capillary wall. It should be pointed out that the two pore systems represent structural interpretations arrived at on the basis of permeability data alone, at a time when knowledge concerning the structure of blood capillaries was restricted to the meager yield of light microscope observations. And it should also be stressed that the postulated pores are relatively large structures which could be easily detected by electron microscopy. Consider the small pores: the water-filled hole or slit of each pore is expected to be surrounded by a cell membrane of the usual thickness (~80 Å) and density. This would give a structure with a total diameter of

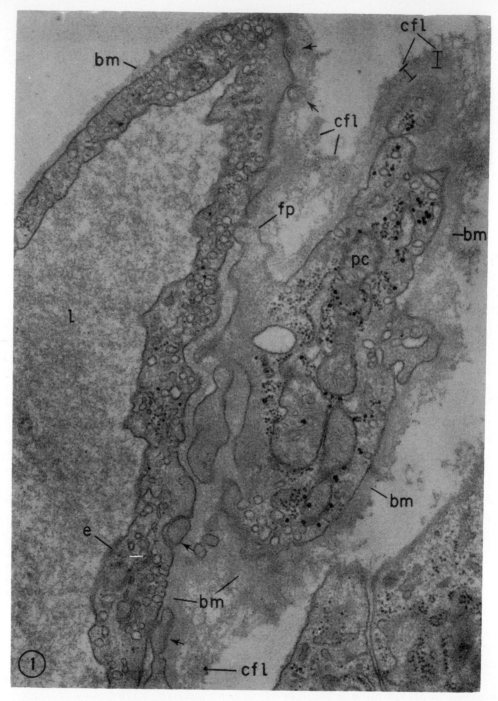

Fig. 1. Rat myocardium (right ventricle). Oblique section through a blood capillary showing the lumen (*l*), the continuous endothelium (*e*), the continuous basement membrane (*bm*), and part of the body of a pericyte (*pc*) tucked in between two leaflets of the basement membrane. A pericyte foot process (*fp*) penetrates the deep leaflet to make contact with the endothelium. Other foot processes, not connected with the pericyte body in the plane of the section, are marked by arrows. Note the variation in thickness of the basement membrane and the existence of a discontinuous, more or less distinct layer of coarser fibrils (*cfl*). The macrophages in the lower right corner are not covered by a basement membrane. × 36,000.

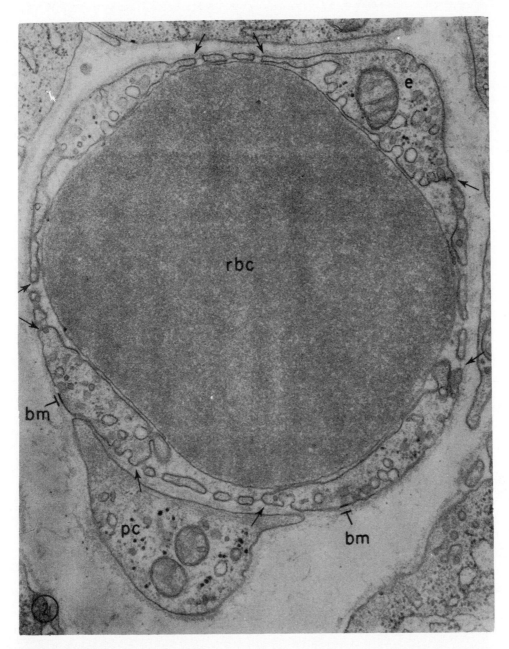

Fig. 2. Guinea pig pancreas. Cross section through a blood capillary the lumen of which is almost completely filled by a red blood cell (*rbc*). Relatively large sectors of the endothelium (*e*) are extremely attenuated and fenestrated (in between arrows). The continuous basement membrane (*bm*) is thin and in places poorly defined. A pericyte, seen at *pc*, shows the same relationship to the basement membrane and the endothelium as the pericyte in Fig. 1. × 36,000.

~240 Å. For a large pore, the corresponding figure would be ~500 Å. With such dimensions and with an anticipated, inherently favorable pattern of density distribution (light hole surrounded by a dense rim or sleeve), pores of both types should be easily detected by electron microscopy, if present.

Electron microscopical studies carried out so far (see refs. 5-8 for classification and reviews) indicate that: (a) the wall of blood capillaries is a stratified structure which consists of two or three distinct layers (endothelium, basement membrane and adventitia); (b) a series of distinct types of blood capillaries are used in the vascular system of a mammal, each type being characteristic for a given organ or group of organs. For instance, the prevalent type of capillary vessel, usually called muscular or somatic, is found in skeletal muscles, skin and connective tissues of the body wall (soma), but also in the myocardium and in smooth visceral muscle. It is characterized (Fig. 1) by a continuous endothelium, a continuous basement membrane, and a discontinuous adventitia comprised of cellular (fibroblasts, mast cells) and acellular (collagen, elastic fibrils) elements[9]. The capillaries of most viscera (Fig. 2) also have a continuous basement membrane, and a discontinuous adventitia, but their endothelial lining is also discontinuous, the discontinuities taking the form of "fenestrae" (Fig. 3) that cut

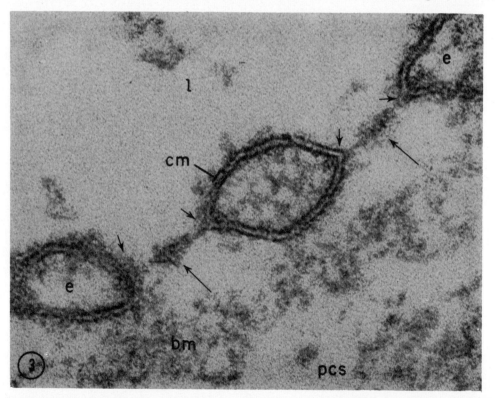

FIG. 3. GUINEA PIG PANCREAS. SMALL SECTOR IN THE WALL OF A CROSS SECTIONED BLOOD CAPILLARY. THE LUMEN IS MARKED *l*, THE ENDOTHELIUM *e*, THE BASEMENT MEMBRANE *bm* AND THE PERICAPILLARY SPACES *pcs*. THE TWO FENESTRAE MARKED BY SHORT ARROWS ARE CLOSED BY DIAPHRAGMS WHICH CONSIST OF A SINGLE, FLUFFY, UNEVEN LAYER OF DENSE MATERIAL THAT THICKENS INTO A CENTRAL KNOB (LONG ARROW). NOTE THE DIFFERENCE BETWEEN THE SIMPLE STRUCTURE OF THESE DIAPHRAGMS AND THE LAYERED (UNIT MEMBRANE) STRUCTURE OF THE CELL MEMBRANE (*cm*). NOTE ALSO THE DISCONTINUOUS LAYER OF FLUFFY MATERIAL THAT COVERS BOTH FRONTS OF THE ENDOTHELIUM. × 360,000.

through the attenuated peripheral part of the endothelial cells[10]. For a survey of other types of blood capillaries, the reader is directed to a series of recent review articles[6–8].

The features mentioned, i.e. the stratification of the vessel wall, and the diversity encountered in the structure of its layers from one capillary type to another, render the problem of structural-functional correlations in capillary permeability considerably more complex than previously assumed. It is clear that all the layers of the wall must be "porous", but the size-limiting pores could be located in a single layer which may not be the same for all types of capillaries. For instance, it is already known that the main barrier to filtration-diffusion is the basement membrane in renal glomerular capillaries[11], whereas in muscle capillaries this role is apparently played by the endothelium. Finally, the pores may be of different morphology, i.e. they may not be represented by the same structure in all types of capillaries. It follows that, in the absence of a common structural basis, a generalized treatment of structural-functional permeability correlations is no longer justified, and that such correlations should be worked out separately for each type of capillary vessel.

Muscle capillaries. The present paper discusses muscle (somatic) capillaries which are of interest for two main reasons: (a) as already mentioned, they are by far the prevalent type of capillary vessel of the mammalian vasculature; (b) to a large extent, the

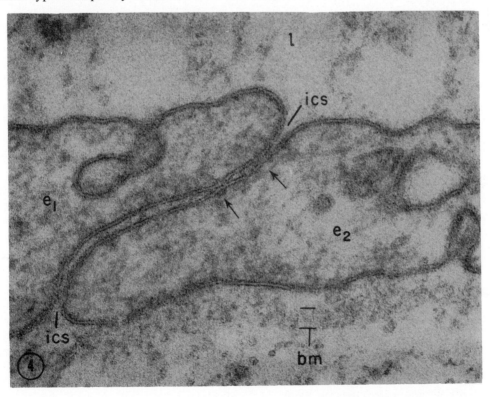

Fig. 4. Junction between two endothelial cells in the wall of a blood capillary. The lumen is marked *l*, the endothelial cells e_1 and e_2, and the basement membrane *bm*. The arrows point to limited areas of fusion of the adjacent cell membranes which result in the occlusion of the intercellular space (*ics*). × 240,000

concept of the two pore systems has evolved in relation to work carried out on this type of vessels.

Electron microscopical studies of blood capillaries in a series of skeletal muscles and myocardium have failed to demonstrate small pores of the cylindrical variety in the endothelium[9, 12]. The existence of slit pores along intercellular junctions is also questionable. It appeared likely a few years ago[1, 6] when the outer leaflet of the plasmalemma of the endothelial cells was difficult to visualize, but now, with better staining procedures[13, 14], it is clear that the membranes of adjacent endothelial cells are either fused to one another to form shallow occluding zonules (cf. ref. 15) or are in close contact with one another (Fig. 4). Open intercellular gaps are only occasionally seen and when present they are usually below the postulated 90–100 Å width; their aggregated area seems to be far below 0.1% of the endothelial surface.

All studies of muscle capillaries[5–9, 16] have pointed out the existence of a large population of vesicles located mainly in the attenuated periphery of endothelial cells. These vesicles are of relatively constant dimensions (outer diameter $\simeq$ 700 Å), occur in large numbers ($\sim$ 100 units behind each μ^2 of endothelial surface) (Fig. 5), and occupy a sizable fraction of the endothelial volume (20–30%) in regions in which the endothelium is thinner than 0.5 μ[12]. A tridimensional reconstruction from serial sections through a sector of a capillary wall[12] has shown that most of these vesicles occur as single units either in the immediate vicinity of the plasmalemma or deeper in the cytoplasmic matrix. Many vesicles are open to the cell surface on the blood-, as well as the tissue front of the cell, and around the opening the membrane of the vesicle is continuous layer by layer with the plasmalemma (Fig. 6). Both have the usual unit membrane structure. In addition to isolated vesicles, the reconstructed sector contains a few chains of two to three vesicles, but no uninterrupted channel made up of interconnected vesicles or otherwise, although four pores or channels should have been detected therein, according to the distribution figures mentioned before ($\sim$17 pores per μ^2).

Use of tracers to identify the large pore system. Direct morphological analysis of muscle capillaries has produced, therefore, negative evidence as far as pores are concerned, and has brought forward the existence of a large population of vesicles of unknown function. Preliminary experiments have shown that these plasmalemmal vesicles transport colloidal gold particles from one side of the endothelium to the other[17]. Similar results were obtained by JENNINGS et al.[18] on rat hearts perfused *in vitro* using colloidal iron particles as a tracer. More recently, the function of plasmalemmal vesicles has been systematically investigated in collaboration with R. R. BRUNS[9, 19] using cadmium-free ferritin as a tracer and the rat diaphragm as a standard specimen. The muscle was fixed *in situ* by glutaraldehyde injection into the peritoneal and pleural cavities. This procedure fixed and thereby retained the tracer-loaded plasma in the lumen of the large majority of vessels so satisfactorily that it was possible to follow the decrease with time in ferritin concentration in the plasma by counting the molecules in sections through the lumen, and by normalizing the counts to a standard lumen volume. The curve constructed on the basis of such counts showed that the tracer has a half-life of $\sim$6 hrs in the circulation, which is comparable to the half-lives of endogenous plasma proteins (cf. ref. 1).

The tracer marked relatively rapidly a sizable proportion of plasmalemmal vesicles but appeared slowly in the pericapillary spaces, where most of the ferritin molecules were picked up and concentrated in large phagocytic vacuoles by the macrophages of

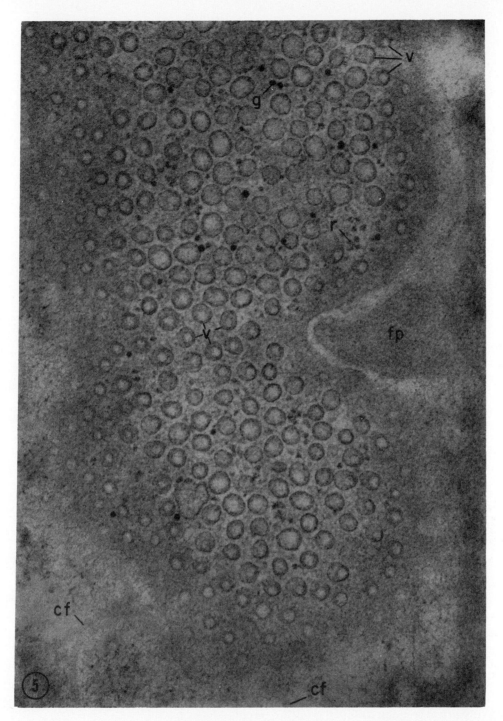

Fig. 5. Rat myocardium (right ventricle). Section grazing the outer surface (tissue front) of an endothelial cell. It demonstrates the high frequency and irregular distribution of plasmalemmal vesicles (v). The intervening cytoplasmic matrix contains a few glycogen particles (g) and a few clusters of ribosomes (r). The foot process of a pericyte (fp) indents the outer surface (tissue front) of the endothelial cell. The basement membrane is poorly outlined on account of the obliquity of the section. A few collagen fibrils (cf) appear in the adventitia. ×75,000.

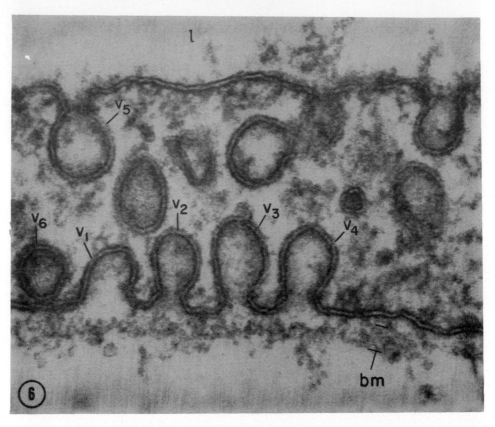

FIG. 6. SMALL SECTOR IN THE WALL OF A MUSCLE CAPILLARY (RAT TONGUE). THE LUMEN IS MARKED *l*, THE ENDOTHELIUM *e*, AND THE BASEMENT MEMBRANE *bm*. NOTE THAT THE CELL MEMBRANE AND THE LIMITING MEMBRANE OF THE PLASMALEMMAL VESICLES ARE SIMILAR IN STRUCTURE. CONTINUITY LAYER BY LAYER FROM ONE MEMBRANE TO THE OTHER CAN BE FOLLOWED CLEARLY FOR THE VESICLES MARKED v_1 AND v_2 AND LESS CLEARLY (ONE SIDE ONLY) FOR THOSE MARKED $v_3 - v_5$. A VESICLE IN THE PROCESS OF FUSION WITH THE CELL MEMBRANE IS MARKED v_6. $\times$ 210,000.

the adventitia (Fig. 7). The concentration of extracellular ferritin in the pericapillary spaces increased slowly over the first few hours and reached a maximum after 24 hrs, presumably because by that time tissue macrophages were approaching saturation. While in transit through the endothelium, the tracer was generally restricted to the cavity of plasmalemmal vesicles (Fig. 8), and only occasionally was found in uncertain locations in the cytoplasm. No ferritin was detected within cell junctions at any of the time points examined.

Since ferritin has a diameter of ~100 Å, and as such is a "specific" probe for the large pore system, it follows from our results that in muscle capillaries this system is represented by plasmalemmal vesicles. The conclusion is supported by results obtained with other tracers, e.g. colloidal gold [17] or colloidal iron [18].

Functional modulations of plasmalemmal vesicles. It should be clear that the plasmalemmal vesicles represent a novel, unexpected structural device involved in capillary permeability. They carry out the function ascribed to the large pore system but, according to the morphological evidence so far obtained, they do not form continuous channels connecting the plasma to the interstitial fluid. They appear to be closed

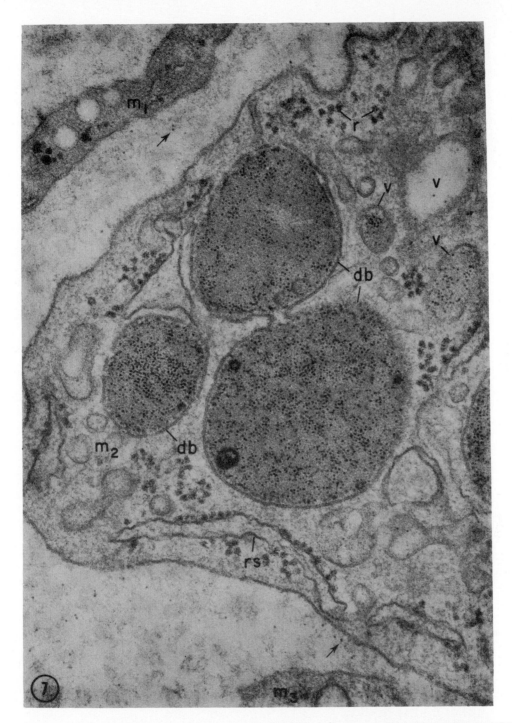

Fig. 7. Rat diaphragm. Parts of three macrophages ($m_1 - m_3$) in the interstitia of the muscle. The intercellular spaces contain ferritin in relatively high concentration (arrows). The central macrophage has incorporated a large amount of ferritin in vacuoles (v) and dense bodies (db), and has markedly concentrated the tracer within these bodies. The cytoplasm of the macrophage contains, in addition, a number of rough surfaced cisternae of the endoplasmic reticulum (rs) and clusters of free ribosomes (r). × 80,000.

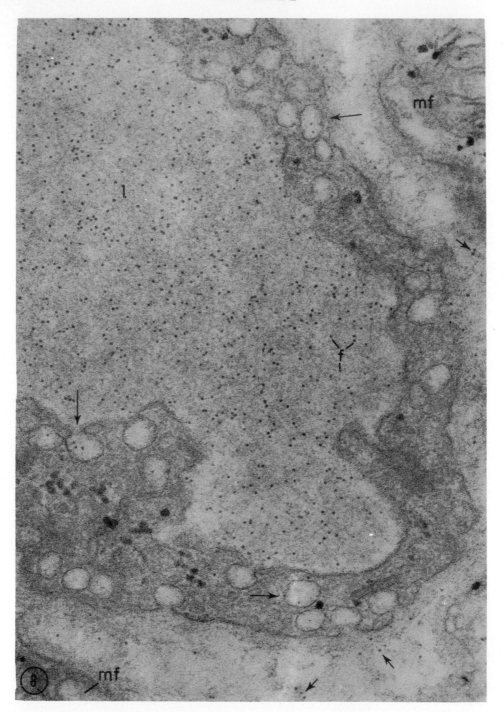

Fig. 8. Rat diaphragm. The section shows a sector of a blood capillary, the surrounding pericapillary space, and parts of two muscle fibers (*mf*). The lumen (*l*) is filled with blood plasma loaded with ferritin molecules (*f*). Several plasmalemmal vesicles on both the blood and tissue front of the endothelial cell contain ferritin (long arrows), and tracer molecules are also present in the pericapillary spaces (short arrows). × 120,000.

pockets which, in order to transport large molecules across the endothelium, must form by invagination of the plasmalemma on one front of the cell; detach therefrom, carrying within them a droplet of imprisoned fluid marked or not marked by the tracer; move across the cytoplasm; fuse with the plasmalemma on the opposite front; and discharge their content upon opening to the cell surface. The events mentioned should occur simultaneously in both directions, i.e. from the blood to the tissue front of the cell and vice versa.

Assuming that the sequence mentioned does in fact occur, we should be able to detect structural features connected with some of its postulated stages. Recent work carried out on specimens in which contrast was greatly increased by uranyl acetate treatment before dehydration[13, 14] suggests that we can distinguish vesicles which seem to be in the process of formation, from vesicles which are apparently in the process of opening to discharge their content. The former have the form of flasks or vials with a narrow, often elongated neck (Fig. 9); whereas the latter show a variety of appearances in which the content of the vesicle is separated from the external medium by a 5-layer, 3-layer, or 1-layer structure. The first is clearly the result of the fusion of the vesicle membrane to the plasmalemma (Figs. 6 and 10); the second seems to represent a partial elimination of the layers of these fused membranes so that a single unit membrane separates the content of the vesicle from the external medium (Fig. 11); finally, the third appearance may result from further elimination which reduces the unit membrane to a single dense layer, presumably a protein film that closes like a diaphragm the stoma of the vesicle (Fig. 12). Diaphragmed vesicles have been recently noted by LUFT[8] and by ELFVIN[14]. With the evidence at hand it cannot be decided whether this single layer represents a film of adsorbed protein or a film of constitutive membrane proteins left behind upon the break and retraction of the lipid layers. The diaphragms often have a thickened central knob and all around their insertion the plasmalemma is sharply bent into an angular rim that protrudes into the opening of the vesicle. This characteristic appearance suggests that the diaphragm is under high enough tension to overcome the surface tension of the plasmalemma. Of course, there is no proof that the three types of appearances mentioned are related to one another as stages in a common process in the sequence given, but this seems to be the most plausible explanation for the spectrum of vesicular images encountered. It is probable that the diaphragm finally breaks allowing the vesicle either to flatten and become aligned with the cell surface, or start invaginating so as to begin a new cycle in the opposite direction.

It is evident that the plasmalemma and the limiting membrane of open vesicles are continuous with one another layer by layer and as such seem to be parts of a common, supposedly homogeneous structure. Yet certain histochemical reactions with nucleoside di- and triphosphates as substrates show that the phosphatasic activities involved are restricted to the membrane of vesicles, open as well as closed[20]. Hence, the vesicular membrane could be a distinct membrane species, not necessarily exchangeable with the plasmalemma, and the vesicles may retain their identity while functioning as shuttles between the two fronts of the endothelium.

Basement membrane. As already mentioned, the second layer of the wall of muscle capillaries is a continuous basement membrane, an acellular stratum which in sectioned and stained specimens appears as a thin (∼ 500 Å), poorly outlined layer of fibrillar texture (Fig. 1). It is apparently a feltwork of two or three different types of fine fibrils[9, 12, 17] embedded in an amorphous matrix. The basement membrane does not retain the

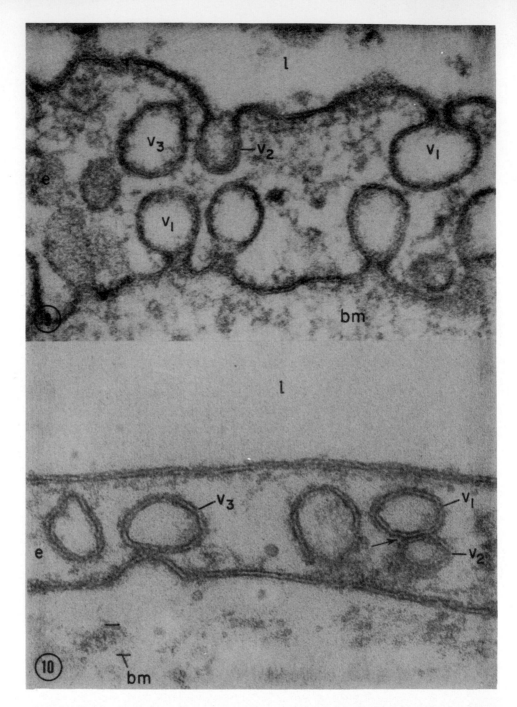

FIGS. 9 TO 12. SMALL SECTORS OF THE WALL OF BLOOD CAPILLARIES IN RAT MYOCARDIUM (FIG. 9) AND RAT TONGUE (FIGS. 10 TO 12). IN ALL FIGURES THE LUMEN IS MARKED l, THE ENDOTHELIUM e, AND THE BASEMENT MEMBRANE bm.

FIG. 9. IN THIS SECTOR, MOST PLASMALEMMAL VESICLES ARE FLASK-SHAPED AND APPEAR CONNECTED WITH THE CELL SURFACE BY A NARROW NECK AND A SMALL STOMA (v_1). A VESICLE OPENED ON THE BLOOD FRONT THROUGH A RELATIVELY LARGE STOMA IS MARKED v_2 AND AN APPARENTLY CLOSED VESICLE IS DESIGNATED v_3. × 165,000.

FIG. 10. IN THIS SECTOR, THE LIMITING MEMBRANES OF TWO PLASMALEMMAL VESICLES (v_1 v_2) HAVE FUSED IN A SUCCESSION OF 5 LAYERS (3 DENSE AND 2 LIGHT) IN WHICH THE FUSION LAYER IS MARKED BY AN ARROW. IN OTHER CASES, SIMILAR APPEARANCES ARE FOUND BETWEEN THE CELL MEMBRANE AND THE LIMITING MEMBRANE OF PLASMALEMMAL VESICLES ON BOTH CELL FRONTS. A VESICLE ALMOST IN CONTACT WITH, BUT NOT YET FUSED TO, THE CELL MEMBRANE IS MARKED v_3. AT THIS MAGNIFICATION AND WITH THIS PROCEDURE, THE BASEMENT MEMBRANE APPEARS AS A POORLY DEFINED, APPARENTLY DISCONTINUOUS LAYER. × 220,000.

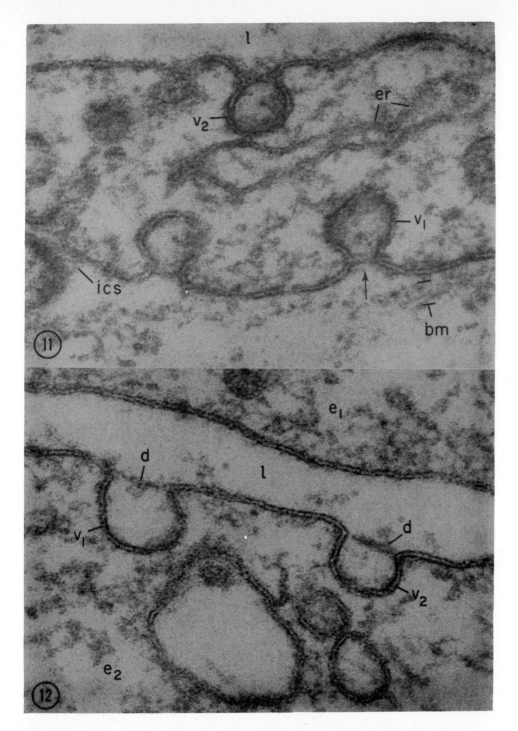

Fig. 11. In this sector, the cavity of a plasmalemmal vesicle (v_1) appears separated from the interstitial fluid by a single unit membrane (arrow); the same situation applies for the vesicle marked v_2 except that the closing unit membrane seems to be thinned out in its center. An element of the endoplasmic reticulum appears at *er* and the beginning of an intercellular space at *ics*. × 220,000.

Fig. 12. The section shows parts of two endothelial cells (e_1, e_2) separated by a narrow lumen (*l*). Two plasmalemmal vesicles (v_1, v_2) open on the luminal surface of e_2 by wide open stoma which appear to be closed by diaphragms (*d*). In the case of v_1, parts of the diaphragm seem to show some residue of stratification: while in the case of v_2, the diaphragm has no more than one dense layer. Note the layer by layer continuity of the plasma membrane with the limiting membrane of v_2 and the sharp, pointed rims at the site of insertion of the diaphragms. × 220,000.

ferritin that reaches it after having traversed the endothelium and this implies that the layer is porous and its pores are larger than 100 Å, i.e. larger than the diameter of the ferritin molecule. When focal gaps appear along the cell junctions of the endothelium, as a result of topical applications of histamine or 5-hydroxytryptamine, the denuded basement membrane is directly exposed to the plasma[21]. Under such conditions, the permeability of the basement membrane can be tested experimentally: it is fine enough to retain carbon black particles and colloidal particles of gold or mercuric sulfide [21], i.e. particles with a diameter greater than 300–400 Å, yet not sufficiently fine to retain ferritin. The results suggest that capillary permeability to large molecules is controlled by the endothelium under normal conditions, and by the basement membrane in inflammation.

Large pore system in other types of capillaries.   The findings reported apply strictly to muscle capillaries. The structural equivalent of the large pore system remains unknown in other types of capillary vessels. In visceral capillaries provided with a fenestrated endothelium the diaphragms which subtend the fenestrae may well be permeable to large molecules, but there is no clear evidence so far available on this point. In liver sinusoids, it is clear that there are no restrictions to macromolecular traffic between the lumen and the space of Disse, because of gross discontinuities in all layers of these vessels' wall[5, 22]. Whatever restrictions exist for the movement of large molecules from plasma to lymph are probably located at the periphery of of the hepatic lobule, between the spaces of Disse and the lymphatics. Yet it is worthwhile recalling that in all these cases permeability to large molecules is explained in terms of a common structural feature, i.e. the large pore, differences in permeability being ascribed to differences in the frequency of such pores [1, 2, 4].

Small pore system. At present, the main outstanding problem in capillary morphology is the identification of the structural equivalent(s) of the small pore system. Since direct morphological inquiry has been unsuccessful, the solution of this problem hinges mainly on finding an adequate tracer, i.e. a particle with a diameter of 30–40 Å which could be fixed, i.e. cross-linked to the proteins of the corresponding structure or otherwise retained *in situ,* and which could be subsequently visualized. A promising tracer seems to be horseradish peroxidase originally used by STRAUS (cf. ref. 23) in his studies of phagosomes and lysosomes, and recently applied by COPLEY[24] and KARNOVSKY[25] to investigations of capillary permeability. The exact dimensions of the molecule are not known but its diameter is estimated at ~ 40 Å, which would make it an adequate tracer for the small pore system. Since the molecule is a protein, it can be retained *in situ* by fixation and its location subsequently detected by a histochemical reaction, the product of which is opaque to electrons[26]. Using this approach Karnovsky has obtained evidence on heart capillaries that the tracer rapidly reaches the pericapillary spaces via plasmalemmal vesicles as well as intercellular spaces, which –by implication–should be open to a gap of at least 50 Å. The exact condition of the cell junctions (open or closed) in such experiments is not yet clearly established. Moreover, when tested on other muscle capillaries (diaphragm), the peroxidase appears to reach the pericapillary spaces much more slowly and to move through plasmalemmal vesicles rather than along intercellular junctions. The difference between heart and diaphragm capillaries may reflect known differences in capillary permeability: the protein concentration in heart lymph is much higher (about 5×) than in lymph collected from limbs[27], i.e. primarily from skeletal muscles, or in other words the capillaries of the myocardium are more permeable to large molecules than those of skeletal muscles.

Final comments. All this goes to say that a substantial amount of work is still required to identify reliably the structural equivalent(s) of the small pore system. For the moment, the only point which appears reasonably well secured is the identification of the large pore system in muscle capillaries: surprisingly enough it turned out to be a discontinuous type of transport, rather than a system of permanent patent channels. Even here, a lot remains to be learned about the rate at which these ferrying vesicles move from one front of the cell to the other (cf. ref. 28), about the forces involved in their movement (cf. refs. 29, 30), and about the means by which this kind of transport is controlled.

REFERENCES

[1] LANDIS, E. M. and PAPPENHEIMER, J. R. In *Handbook of Physiology*, Section 2, Circulation, **2**, 961, HAMILTON, W. F. and Dow, P. (Editors), Am. Physiol. Soc., Washington, D.C., 1963.

[2] GROTTE, G. *Acta chir. scand.* Suppl. 221, 1, 1956.

[3] WASSERMAN, K. and MAYERSON, H. S. *Cardiologia* **21**, 296, 1952.

[4] MAYERSON, H. S., WOLFRAM, C. G., SHIRLEY, H. H., Jr. and WASSERMAN, K. *Am. J. Physiol.* **198**, 155, 1960.

[5] BENNETT, H. S., LUFT, J. H. and HAMPTON, J. C. *Am. J. Physiol.* **196**, 381, 1959.

[6] FAWCETT, D. W. In *The Microcirculation.* Symposium on factors influencing exchanges across capillary wall, REYNOLDS, S. R. M. and ZWEIFACH, B. W. (Editors), Univ. of Illinois Press, Urbana, Ill., 1959, p. 1.

[7] MAJNO, G. In *Handbook of Physiology*, Section 2, Circulation, **3**, 2293, HAMILTON, W. F. and Dow, P. (Editors), Am. Physiol. Soc., Washington, D.C., 1965.

[8] LUFT, J. H. In *The Inflammatory Process*, ZWEIFACH, B. W., GRANT, L. and McCLUSKEY, R. T. (Editors), Academic Press, New York, 1965, p. 121.

[9] PALADE, G. E. and BRUNS, R. R. In *Small Blood Vessel Involvement in Diabetes Mellitus*, SIPERSTEIN, M. D., COLWELL, A. R. SR., and MEYER, K. (Editors), Am. Inst. of Biological Sciences, Washington, D.C., 1964, p. 39.

[10] FARQUHAR, M. G. *Angiology* **12**, 270, 1962.

[11] FARQUHAR, M. G., WISSIG, S. L. and PALADE, G. E. *J. Exptl. Med.* **113**, 47, 1961.

[12] BRUNS, R. R. and PALADE, G. E. (in press).

[13] FARQUHAR, M. G. and PALADE, G. E. *J. Cell Biol.* **26**, 263, 1965.

[14] ELFVIN, L. G. *J. Ultrastructure Research* **12**, 687, 1965.

[15] FARQUHAR, M. G. and PALADE, G. E. *J. Cell Biol.* **17**, 375, 1963.

[16] PALADE, G. E. *J. App. Phys.* **24**, 1424, 1953.

[17] PALADE, G. E. *Circulation* **24**, 368, 1961.

[18] JENNINGS, M. A., MARCHESI, V. T. and FLOREY, H. *Proc. Roy. Soc. Lond.* Ser. B. **156**, 14, 1962.

[19] BRUNS, R. R. and PALADE, G. E. (in press).

[20] MARCHESI, V. T. and BARRNETT, R. J. *J. Cell Biol.* **17**, 547, 1963.

[21] MAJNO, G. and PALADE, G. E. *J. Biophys. Biochem. Cytol.* **11**, 571, 1961.

[22] BURKEL, W. E. and LOW, F. N. *Am. J. Anat.* **118**, 769, 1966.

[23] STRAUS, W. In *Lysosomes, Ciba Foundation Symposium*, DE REUCK, A. V. S. and CAMERON, M. P. (Editors), J. & A. Churchill, Ltd., London, 1963, p. 151.

[24] COPLEY, A. L. and CAROL, B. *Life Sciences* **3**, 65, 1964.

[25] KARNOVSKY, M. J. *J. Cell Biol.* **27**, 49A, 1965.

[26] GRAHAM, R. C. and KARNOVSKY, M. J. *J. Histochem. Cytochem.* **14**, 291, 1966.

[27] DRINKER, C. K., WARREN, M. F., MAURER, F. W. and McCARRELL, J. D. *Am. J. Physiol.* **130**, 43, 1940.

[28] RENKIN, E. M. *The Physiologist* **7**, 13, 1964.

[29] FLOREY, H. W. *Quart. J. Exp. Physiol.* **49**, 117, 1964.

[30] SHEA, S. M. and KARNOVSKY, M. J. *Nature* **212**, 353, 1966.

FIGURE LEGENDS

All figures are electron micrographs of epon embedded tissues.

For Figures 1, 2 and 5, the specimens were fixed in 1% OsO_4 in 0.1 phosphate buffer (pH 7.6) and the sections were stained with lead hydroxide.

For Figures 3, 4, 6 and 9–12, the specimens were fixed in 1% OsO$_4$ in 0.1 M phosphate buffer, and stained before dehydration in uranyl acetate (13). The sections were doubly stained with uranyl acetate and lead citrate.

For Figures 7 and 8, the tissue was fixed *in situ* in 6% glutaraldehyde in 0.1 M phosphate buffer (pH 7.2), and post fixed in 1% OsO$_4$ in the same buffer. The sections were stained with lead hydroxide only.

Figures 1, 5, 7 and 8 have been published previously in the volume *Small Blood Vessel Involvement in Diabetes Mellitus* edited by M. D. SIPERSTEIN, A. R. COLWELL, SR. and K. MEYER and published by the American Institute of Biological Sciences, Washington, D.C., 1964. The figures were part of an article by G. E. PALADE and R. R. BRUNS and are here republished with the permission of the American Institute of Biological Sciences.

CLINICAL HEMORHEOLOGY

15 July, p.m.

Chairmen: HELLMUT HARTERT, Germany
SIGMUNDUR MAGNUSSON, Iceland

HEMODYNAMIC CONSEQUENCES FROM INCREASED VISCOSITY OF BLOOD

L-E. GELIN,* S-E. BERGENTZ, C-G. HELANDER, E. LINDER, N. J. NILSSON and C-M. Rudenstam

Department of Surgery I, University of Gothenburg, Gothenburg, Sweden

THE viscosity of whole blood is shear rate dependent. Tissue injury markedly changes the viscosity of whole blood especially at the lower rates of shear[1].

The flow characteristics of blood are also influenced by the axial orientation of the cells when streaming through tubes narrower than $300\,\mu$ as found by FÅHRAEUS and LINDQUIST[4]. This axial orientation of cells accelerated with decreasing suspension stability of blood. The narrower the tube the more the viscosity of whole blood approaches the viscosity of plasma by this separation of cell flow and plasma flow. In capillary model experiments GELIN[7] found these rules for separation of plasma flow and cell flow to be valid only for on-flow but not for off-flow capillary tube systems. In off-flow tubes stasis of cells relative to plasma (erythrostasis) occurred. This erythrostasis accelerated with decreasing suspension stability and decreasing flow rate.

The pathophysiologic significance of rheologic flow disturbances has been elaborated in experiments where increased plasma and whole blood viscosity has been provoked by the intravascular injection of dextran fractions with high molecular weights. Such experiments have demonstrated marked decrease of blood flow through hindlimb[6], liver[9] and kidney[8] despite increase in blood volume and blood pressure. Such impaired flow was accompanied by anemia[5], disturbed organ function[5], delayed healing[14] and signs of stagnation hypoxia[2] which could be prevented by injection of dextran fractions of low molecular weight.

The purpose of the present investigation was to study the influence of provoked rheologic flow disturbances on cardiac output, systemic and pulmonary vascular resistance.

MATERIAL AND METHODS

Six healthy mongrel dogs, weighing between 11 and 28 kg were anesthetized with nembutal (30 mg/kg bodyweight) or urethane ($\frac{1}{2}$ g/kg bodyweight). The dogs were intubated. They respirated air supplemented by oxygen. Anesthesia level as well as body and environmental temperature was kept constant throughout the experiment.

A Cournand No. 9 catheter was inserted in the femoral vein and passed into the pulmonary artery under fluoroscopic control. Polyethylene catheters were introduced in the abdominal aorta, the right atrium and the external jugular vein. In three dogs the left atrium was punctured by the transbronchial route[11].

Cardiac output was determined by the dye dilution technique with Cardio Green as indicator[3]. Sudden single injections of dye (2·5–5 mg) were made through a thin polyethylene catheter in the external jugular vein. Blood was sampled at constant rate and simultaneously from the pulmonary artery and the aorta. The dye concentrations were obtained with a water cuvette densitometer XC-100 A and a cuvette oximeter, especially adapted to Cardio Green and combined with Atlas Oximeter,* according to principles earlier published[12]. The dye curves were recorded on an Elema 4-channel direct writing oscilligraph.† Cardiac output was calculated from the dye curves according to STEWART-HAMILTON[13].

Pressures in mm Hg were recorded in the pulmonary artery, aorta, right and left auricles by Elema electromanometer on the same recorder and in time immediately after the dye dilution curves were recorded. Mean pressures were electrically integrated. Repeated determinations of cardiac output and pressures were made throughout the whole experiments.

Systemic vascular resistance and pulmonary vascular resistance were calculated in simple units by the ratio in pressure difference between mean aortic and right atrial pressures and between mean pulmonary arterial and left atrial pressures respectively and cardiac output in litres/min.

The flow pattern in the capillaries and the degree of intravascular aggregation was checked by vitalmicroscopy of the bulbar conjunctiva capillary network at regular intervals.

Hematocrit was determined according to Winthrop and E.S.R. according to Westergren.

Whole blood viscosity was determined at 37°C as a function of shear rate and shear stress using a Brookfield viscosimeter equipped with a special adaptor for small blood samples. The obtained values were transformed to centipoise units after comparison with distilled water.

The experiments were divided into three periods:
1. A control period of 60 min duration.
2. A period of aggregation initiated by intravenous injection of dextran of high viscosity (HVD, mean molecular weight about 1 mill. and intrinsic viscosity of 0·7 dl/g) in a dosage of 1 g/kg bodyweight. This period had a duration of 180 min.
3. A period of disaggregation of 60 min duration. Aggregation was resolved by intravenous injection of low viscosity dextran (LVD, molecular weight 39,000, intrinsic viscosity of 0·19 dl/g) in a dosage of 2 g/kg bodyweight. Supplementary dosages of $\frac{1}{2}$ g/kg BW/hour were continuously infused during the whole period to maintain the effect.

Five dogs were treated in the above-mentioned way. One dog used as control was given the same quantity of dextran but LVD instead of HVD.

RESULTS

Capillary Flow

The capillary flow in the bulbar conjunctiva was markedly changed after administration of HVD compared to normal (Fig. 1a, b). The flow rate of red cells was reduced

*Atlas-Werken, Bremen, Germany.
†Elema, Sweden.

and the cells became aggregated and stagnated in the venules. These changes increased with time after injection of HVD. In the arterioles a more axial orientation of cells was noted and arteriolo-venular shunts were seen to open up.

After the administration of LVD the flow rate increased and the aggregation and stasis disappeared (Fig. 1c).

The control dog did not show any aggregation or stasis after the infusion of LVD.

Viscosity of Blood

The viscosity changes provoked by the dextran infusions are given in Fig. 2. From this it is apparent that during the control period (sample 1) the viscosity is 4·6 at the shear rate of 230 inverse seconds but 12 at the shear rate of 23 inverse seconds. After

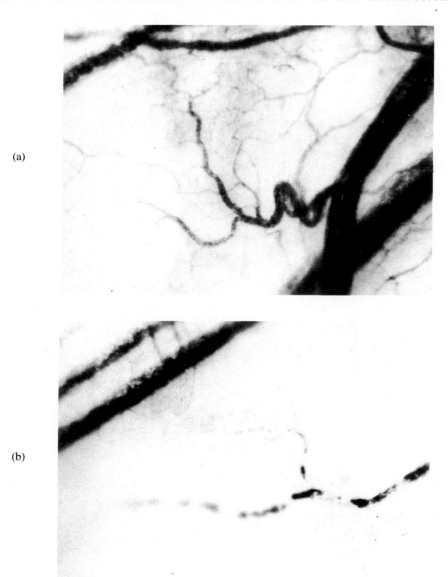

(a)

(b)

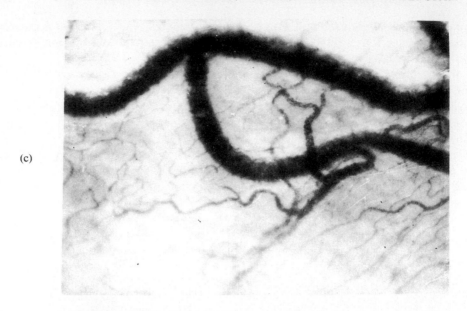

(c)

Fig. 1. Capillary flow in the bulbar conjunctiva in one experimental dog. (a) During control period. (b) After infusion of 1 g/kg bodyweight of HVD. (c) After subsequent infusion of 2 g/kg bodyweight of LVD.

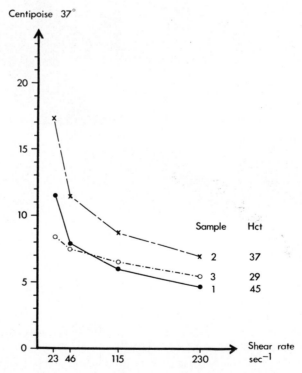

Fig. 2. Mean values on hematocrit and on whole blood viscosity at different rates of shear in the experimental dogs. (a) During control period. (b) At the end of aggregation period. (c) During disaggregation period.

HVD infusion (sample 2) the viscosity of whole blood increased at all rates of shear despite a drop in hematocrit. In the third period (sample 3) the viscosity dropped toward the initial values concomittant with a further drop in hematocrit.

Cardiac Output

Corresponding to these viscosity and microcirculatory events marked changes in cardiac output were observed. Figure 3 shows the average percentage change in cardiac output in the 5 HVD-treated animals. The values from the single control animal

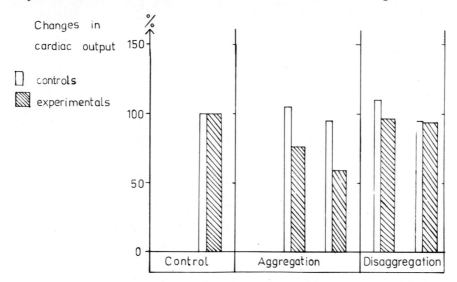

FIG. 3. CHANGES IN CARDIAC OUTPUT EXPRESSED AS MEAN CHANGES IN PER CENT OF THE VALUES OBTAINED DURING CONTROL PERIOD IN A CONTROL AND IN FIVE EXPERIMENTAL DOGS.

are given for comparison. Each column represents mean values of several determinations obtained within short time intervals as covered by the column on the abscissa. During the period of aggregation cardiac output dropped to about 60% of the original value. It increased rapidly to pre-experimental level after the administration of LVD. This is in sharp contrast to the small variations in cardiac output obtained in the control animal.

Pressures

The changes in mean pressures are graphically demonstrated in Fig. 4. During the period of aggregation mean aortic pressure increased moderately with time and reached a still higher level after the administration of LVD. Corresponding pressure elevation in the pulmonary artery did not occur until LVD was injected. The same was found regarding left atrial pressures, and could be explained by the sudden increase of flow. The right atrial pressure dropped after the administration of HVD but increased again after administration of LVD.

Resistance in Systemic and Pulmonary Circulation

In Fig. 5 the resistance changes in per cent of control values in both the systemic and the pulmonary circulation are computed. During the period of aggregation the total

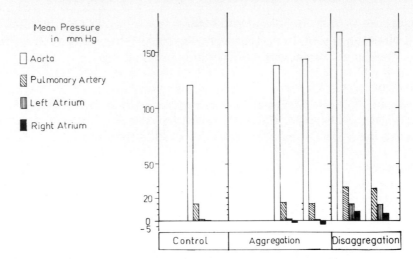

FIG. 4. CHANGES IN MEAN PRESSURES IN MM HG IN AORTA PULMONARY ARTERY LEFT ATRIUM AND RIGHT ATRIUM IN THE EXPERIMENTAL DOGS.

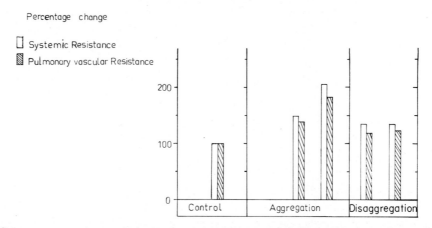

FIG. 5. CHANGES IN SYSTEMIC AND PULMONARY VASCULAR RESISTANCE EXPRESSED AS MEAN CHANGES IN PER CENT OF THE VALUES CALCULATED FROM CARDIAC OUTPUT AND PRESSURE DIFFERENCES DURING THE CONTROL PERIOD IN THE EXPERIMENTAL DOGS.

peripheral resistance became doubled but dropped promptly after LVD infusion. Somewhat less marked changes were recorded in the pulmonary circulation.

The purpose of the double sampling technique was to rule out unexpected reactions from the bronchial circulation and to get simultaneous control determinations of cardiac output. No significant differences between the values from the two sampling sites were obtained, which is in agreement with earlier reported findings in humans[10].

DISCUSSION

The observed reduction of cardiac output in the actual study might indicate a primary myocardial insufficiency. This is, however, not likely as the right atrial pressure was lowered while the systemic perfusion pressure was increased. The drop in CO is therefore consecutive to a reduced venous return.

This decreased venous return is in turn caused by a retardation of the flow of a large portion of blood on the venular side of the capillary bed as confirmed by the microscopic observations on the capillary circulation.

The retardation of blood flow in the venules and the increased perfusion pressure must both be due to the increased viscosity of whole blood.

The viscosity of whole blood depends on many factors especially the hematocrit, the viscosity of plasma, the velocity of flow, the suspension and emulsion stability of blood and the diameter of the vessels when less than 300 μ.

The data obtained on whole blood viscosity in this study show the influence of these factors except the influence of diameter of the narrow vessels. A drop in shear rate caused an increase in the viscosity of whole blood. This is due to the fact that blood is a suspension and behaves like a pseudoplastic fluid as indicated by the viscosity curves at defined rates of shear. However, a reduction in flow rate will by itself increase the viscosity if the rates of shear are within the range studied. In the actual experiments where the flow rate was lowered by a moderate increase in viscosity, this lowered flow rate will thus in itself bring about a further increase in apparent viscosity.

The progressive fall in cardiac output despite a slight increase in systemic pressure indicates an additional hindrance factor, namely the increasing aggregation of blood cells observed to produce flow obstruction in postcapillary venules.

The increased viscosity and the stasis of aggregated cells can thus explain the decrease in CO by an increased vascular resistance and a decreased venous return. This conclusion is further supported by the reversing effect of LVD.

SUMMARY

Injection of a high viscosity dextran fraction produced increased viscosity of whole blood, intravascular aggregation of blood cells, decreased cardiac output and increased vascular resistance. All these changes could be reversed by injection of a low viscosity dextran fraction.

The changes in vascular resistance can be fully understood as secondary to increased viscosity and stasis of aggregated blood cells. The decreased cardiac output must be understood as secondary to decreased venous return because of stasis in postcapillary flow.

REFERENCES

[1] BERGENTZ, S-E., GELIN, L-E., RUDENSTAM, C-M. and ZEDERFELDT, B. *2nd Europ. Conf. on Microcirculation*, Pavia, 1962, HARDERS, H. (Editor), *Bibl. Anat.* **4**, 676, S. Karger, Basel, New York, 1964.
[2] FAJERS, C-M. and GELIN, L-E. *Acta Path. Microbiol. Scand.* **46**, 97, 1959.
[3] Fox, I. J., BROOKER, L. G., HESELTINE, D. W. and WOOD, E. H. *Proc. Am. Heart Assn.* October, 1957.
[4] FÅHRAEUS, R. and LINDQUIST, T. *Amer. J. Physiol.* **96**, 562, 1931.
[5] GELIN, L-E. *Acta Chir. Scand.* Suppl. 210, 1956.
[6] GELIN, L-E. *Acta Chir. Scand.* **113**, 463, 1957.
[7] GELIN, L-E. *Biorheology* **1**, 119, 1963.
[8] GELIN, L-E., PAPPENHEIMER, J. R. and RENNIE, D. W. *Ciba Shock Symposium*, Springer-Verlag, Heidelberg, 1962.
[9] GELIN, L-E. and SHOEMAKER, W. C. *Surgery* **49**, 713, 1961.
[10] HAMILTON, W. F., MOORE, J. W., KINSMAN, J. M. and SPURLING, R. G. *Am. J. Physiol.* **84**, 338, 1928.
[11] HENSCHEL, E. O., HAMILTON, L. H. and RAINBOW, G. R. L. *J. Appl. Physiol.* **11**, 319, 1957.
[12] NILSSON, N. J. *Pflügers Archiv.* **263**, 374, 1956.
[13] STEWART, G. N. *Am. J. Physiol.* **52**, 20, 1921.
[14] ZEDERFELDT, B. *Acta Chir. Scand.* Suppl. 224, 1957.

DISCUSSION

BURTON (*Canada*):

I find the results very interesting. What astonishes me, and I wonder if it does you, are the changes in the oxygen consumption consequent to changes in cardiac output and flow. This is rather unusual, is it not? Physiologically one tends to think of the oxygen consumption as being relatively fixed, and certainly the reduced work of the heart would not be expected to reduce the oxygen consumption this much; would you comment further on this point?

GELIN (*Sweden*):

Yes, I think it is a decreased metabolic rate in the capillary because of this slow flow rate, producing hypoxia in the tissues, and that this really is the reason.

BURTON:

Well, on that point, though, the data shows that the oxygen consumption of cells surrounding the capillaries is independent of the actual oxygen tension, down to about 5 mm mercury–oxygen tension; so it is difficult to see how aggregation in flowing capillary blood could be so drastic as to result in PO_2 at the limit which affects oxygen consumption of cells.

GELIN:

The oxygen extraction is markedly increased in this situation. Apparently the flow rate is not sufficient. That is how we have interpreted this. We have to add that some of the circulation occurs in arteriolovenular shunts and does not reach the nutritional state of the capillary flow but contributes oxygen unused to the venous side.

LEE (*U.S.A.*):

It seems to me that in controlled perfusion, clinical or experimental, the oxygen consumption cannot be above what one supplies in the way of tissue perfusion. In other words, if we do not set the pump oxygenator high enough, then the oxygen consumption is depressed simply because the tissue blood flow is not sufficient to provide an adequate oxygen supply. I do not know if the range of the depression of flow is in the same order of magnitude, but certainly one sees this in clinical, low perfusion states.

GROOM (*England*):

I wondered if you had measured the circulating cell or plasma volumes after you have given high molecular weight dextran. Under many conditions, one can have an appreciable fraction of the total blood volume which is not actually circulating. If this were so, I think, the difficulty about oxygen consumption would be resolved.

GELIN:

Yes, we have. The amount of circulating red cells is decreased. Now we have to consider what this means. That includes a function of time for the equilibration of the injected labelled cells. And, therefore, it is hard to tell what is the absolute amount of circulating cells here. The decrease of total circulating cells, for example, in a 10 min sample after the injection of chromate labelled cells, may well go down to about 70% of the control value. But after 60 min the amount of cells would almost be the same as in the control period. This in turn is because of a delayed equilibration time in this stasis situation. The plasma volume increase would be about 20% after the injection of 1 g per kg bodyweight of high molecular weight dextran to these animals. The plasma volume increase would be 40–45% after 2 g of low molecular weight dextran, during this second period of the experiments. The animals were overloaded.

LONG (*U.S.A.*):

I just wondered if you noted any coagulation defects in these animals, and particularly whether the high molecular weight dextran defibrinated them.

GELIN:

We did not study this in our particular preparation. There are coagulation defects after high molecular weight dextran, but not after low molecular weight dextran.

LONG:

Are they defibrinated?

GELIN:

There is a lowering of the fibrinogen concentration.

VISCOSITY OF BLOOD WITH RESPECT TO CLINICAL DIAGNOSIS

EIICHI FUKADA*

The Institute of Physical and Chemical Research, Bunkyo-ku, Tokyo

TAKAYOSHI IBE

Rion Co. Ltd., Kokubunji, Tokyo

KAZUHIKO ATSUMI

The Institute for Medical Electronics,
Faculty of Medicine, University of Tokyo, Tokyo

TAKEHIKO OOSAWA

Hiranumabashi Clinic, Yokohama

INTRODUCTION

In order to measure the viscosity of blood for as large a number of patients as possible, it is necessary to find a viscometer by which the measurement can be made for as small amounts of blood as possible and also in as short a time as possible. It is also desirable that the measuring procedure be as simple as possible. To meet these requirements we have devised a new type of capillary viscometer[1].

Figure 1 shows an example of our capillary viscometer. A and B are syringe needles which are put in both ends of a graduated glass tube C. The capillary B is immersed in the liquid specimen and the capillary A is open to the air. D is a metal bellows attached to the upper side of tube C. If the bellows D is released from the compressed state, a negative pressure is produced inside the glass tube C. The liquid is then drawn into the tube C through the capillary B and air is also drawn into the tube C through the capillary A. The amount of liquid or the height of liquid sucked up the graduated glass tube simply is determined by the viscosity of the liquid. The theoretical analysis for this type of viscometer has been presented in previous papers[1, 2].

The measurable range of viscosity is varied by selecting a suitable combination of the size of two capillaries. The viscometer shown in Fig. 1 has been designed for the range of viscosity from 0·5 to 5 cp. The length and inner diameter of the capillary A are 52 and 0·43 mm. The length and inner diameter of the capillary B are 100 and 0·93 mm. The length and inner diameter of the glass tube C are 16 cm and 4·2 mm. The volume of the bellows is 12 cm³.

The time required for the liquid to reach its highest level in the tube is about 5 sec after which the liquid flows back gradually due to the gravitational force. The volume required for the specimen is about 1 ml. The average rate of shear is estimated to be about 10^3 sec^{-1}. The overall accuracy of measurement by this viscometer is within 5%.

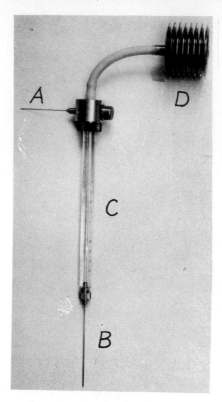

EXPERIMENT

The viscosity of each of more than 200 specimens of blood taken from the patients was investigated together with its clinical examination. About 5 ml of blood was taken from the vein of the patient with a heparinized syringe. The amount of whole blood and plasma used for the measurement of viscosity was approximately 1 ml. In addition, the hematocrit and sedimentation rate were determined. Also, the concentration of total protein, albumin, and globulin in the serum was measured by standard methods. The concentration of fibrinogen was not determined.

Figures 2 and 3 show the viscosity of whole blood and plasma for a variety of diseases. The unfilled circles illustrate the actual values of measurement and the filled circles the average values for each kind of disease. The ranges shown by the arrows indicate the 95% level of confidence according to a statistical treatment of the data. The dotted lines give the average values of viscosity in normal state for normal whole blood and plasma.

The classification of the kind of disease given in the figures is rather tentative. The assignment of the disease for each patient was sometimes difficult. The number of specimen for each disease is not yet sufficiently large. In some cases, however, a positive correlation between the viscosity and the kind of disease was actually observed. For example, the viscosity of whole blood for anaemia falls below the normal value as would be expected. However, it would still be premature to suggest a definite correlation between the kind of disease and viscosity values of whole blood and plasma.

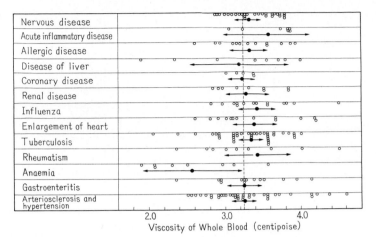

Viscosity of Whole Blood (centipoise)

FIG. 2.

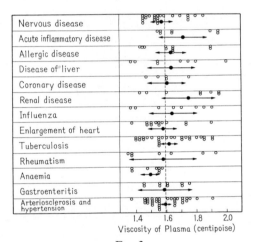

Viscosity of Plasma (centipoise)

FIG. 3.

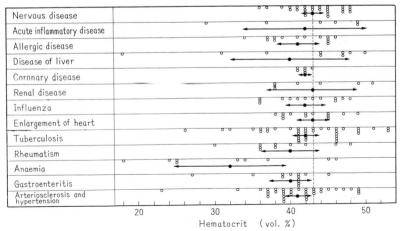

Hematocrit (vol. %)

FIG. 4.

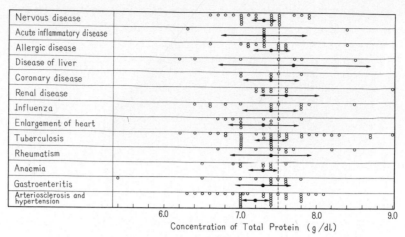

Concentration of Total Protein (g/dl)

FIG. 5.

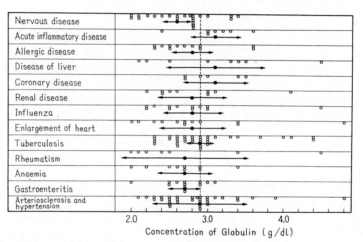

Concentration of Globulin (g/dl)

FIG. 6.

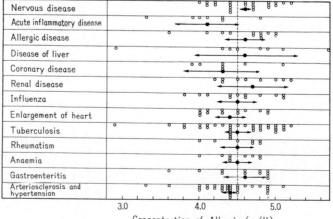

Concentration of Albumin (g/dl)

FIG. 7.

Figure 4 presents the hematocrit measured for the same specimen used for the viscosity measurement. Figures 5, 6 and 7 illustrate the concentration of total protein, globulin, and albumin for the specimens used for the viscosity measurement. Dotted lines show the average values for the normal state. When the viscosity of whole blood is plotted against the hematocrit and when the viscosity of plasma is plotted against the concentration of total protein, the correlation curves between these quantities were obtained, which were similar to those previously reported [1].

Although it is difficult to draw any conclusion from the present investigation, it seems unlikely that the viscosity of whole blood and plasma would indicate any decisive correlation with the kind of disease except for the case of anaemia. However, the sedimentation rate of red blood cells is usually measured as a clinical test to find out the indication of some kinds of disease. The rate of shear employed at the present study is about 10^3 sec^{-1}. The aggregates of blood cell would, therefore, be dispersed to independent cells due to the high rate of shear during measurement. The measurement of the viscosity at very small rate of shear would be more informative for the investigation of the correlation between viscosity of blood and kind of disease.

REFERENCES

[1] KAWAI, H., FUKADA, E., IBE, T. and SHONO, H. In *Symposium on Biorheology*, COPLEY, A. L. (Editor), *Proc. 4th Int. Cong. Rheol.* Interscience Publ. John Wiley, New York, 1965, part 4, p. 281.
[2] FUKADA, E. and IBE, T. *J. Soc. Mat. Sci. Japan* **14**, 252, 1965.

DISCUSSION

SILBERBERG (*Israel*):
We have also started to study the viscoelasticity of blood in various healthy and pathological conditions and have so far, in preliminary experiments, determined that the dynamic elasticity seems to be much more subject to pathology than the viscous components, in the dynamic analysis of the data.

FUKADA (*Japan*):
We have been measuring a dynamic elastic modulus of blood by means of a double cylinder viscoelastometer at a frequency of 10 c/s. (*Biorheology* **1**, 101, 1963.) However, it is regrettable that the data are not available for presentation at this time.

GELIN (*Sweden*):
In these diseases which you describe, was there aggregation which could decrease the viscosity reading, using the nylon capillary tube? I wonder if you have correlated the degree of aggregation to the viscosity changes observed here with this kind of viscometer?

FUKADA:
Since the shear rate in the present viscosity measurement is fairly large, about 10^3 sec^{-1}, the aggregation of blood cells would probably have been decomposed during the flow in the capillary. We are now trying to correlate the degree of aggregation to the shear-rate dependence of viscosity at a range of shear rate 10^{-1}–10^2 sec^{-1}.

CAPILLARY BLOOD FLOW AND COAGULATION IN SHOCK

ROBERT M. HARDAWAY III*

Division of Surgery, Walter Reed Army Institute of Research, Washington, D.C., U.S.A.

DISSEMINATED intravascular coagulation (DIC) is a new concept in the etiology of disease. It is defined as acute, transient coagulation occurring in the flowing blood throughout the vascular tree and which may obstruct the microcirculation. It may or may not result in an accumulation of fibrin but does involve the transformation of fibrinogen into fibrin. It includes the agglutination of platelets and red cells and the sticking of leucocytes.

Perhaps the purest example of DIC is the intravascular injection of thrombin or other agents which produce coagulation. A number of experiments in dogs showed similar results whether one injected thrombin, incompatible blood, hemolyzed blood, bacterial endotoxin, or unfiltered amniotic fluid[1].

After injection there was an immediate fall in arterial blood pressure, which occasionally resulted in immediate death but usually returned toward normal within 30–60 min. Following this there may be under certain circumstances (previous stress) a secondary fall, terminating in death usually within 24 hr. Without previous stress (surgery or other trauma) death frequently does not result. During the initial systemic arterial hypotension there was a pulmonary arterial hypertension, a right atrial hypotension, a vena caval hypotension, and a portal hypertension (Figs. 1 and 2). These pressure changes were apparently due primarily to obstruction and stagnation in the microcirculation of the lungs, liver and other tissues (Fig. 3). Obstruction was probably due to thrombi formation in the capillaries and arteriolar vasospasm. Decreased venous filling caused a low right atrial pressure and a decreased cardiac output. This in turn caused a low arterial blood pressure in spite of increased peripheral resistance.

A bleeding tendency usually developed with capillary oozing from any wound. There was a decrease in all measured blood clotting factors (Table 1) including fibrinogen (Fig. 4) and platelets (Fig. 5). There was a prolonged silicone clotting time, which may have been due to any or all of the above.

At death there was a characteristic hemorrhagic necrosis of the gastrointestinal mucosa. There was severe congestion in the abdominal viscera including liver, kidneys and gastrointestinal mucosa. Microscopically there was occlusion by thrombi of capillaries and other small vessels of the gastrointestinal mucosa, lungs, liver, kidneys, pancreas or elsewhere with resulting focal necrosis and hemorrhage in all of these organs. These thrombi may consist of: platelets, fibrin (Fig. 6), predominantly congealed, packed and lysed red cells or white cells. Characteristic changes in the lungs were not necrosis but congestion and an effusion of blood and fluid into the alveoli.

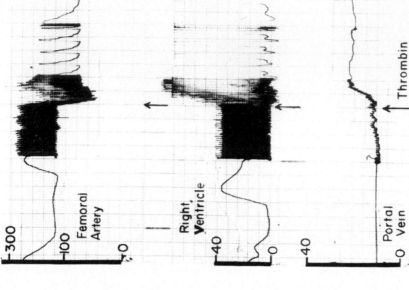

Fig. 2. Various blood pressures in a dog which was given an intravascular injection of bovine thrombin. Note that the thrombin injection caused an immediate fall in femoral artery pressure, a rise in right ventricular pressure (as in Fig. 1) and a rise in portal vein pressure.

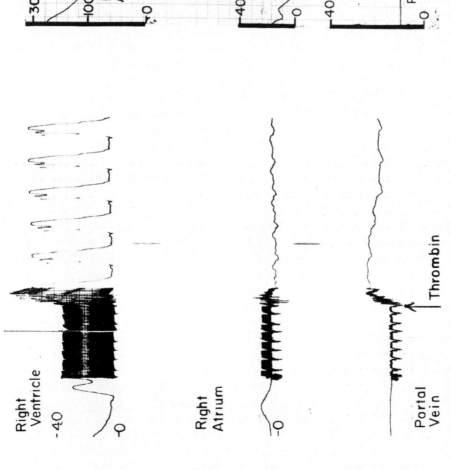

Fig. 1. Various blood pressures in a dog which was given an intravascular injection of bovine thrombin. Note that the thrombin injection caused an immediate rise in right ventricular systolic pressure (therefore a rise in pulmonary artery pressure), a fall in right atrial pressure (therefore a fall in central venous pressure) and a rise in portal vein pressure.

736

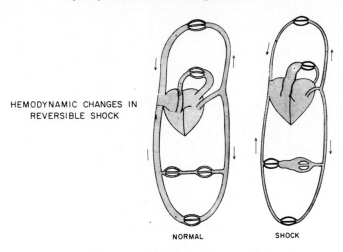

HEMODYNAMIC CHANGES IN
REVERSIBLE SHOCK

NORMAL   SHOCK

FIG. 3. DIAGRAM OF HEMODYNAMIC CHANGES AFTER INTRAVASCULAR THROMBIN INJECTION. ON THE LEFT IS THE NORMAL SITUATION. THE WIDTH OF THE VESSELS CORRESPONDS ROUGHLY TO THEIR ACTUAL DIAMETER AND BLOOD FLOW. AFTER DIC DUE TO THROMBIN (RIGHT) THERE IS RELATIVE OBSTRUCTION IN THE LUNGS, LIVER AND PERIPHERAL SMALL VESSELS. THIS CAUSES A DAMMING OF BLOOD IN THE PORTAL SYSTEM AND PULMONARY ARTERY WITH DECREASED VENA CAVAL AND PULMONARY VEIN FILLING. THIS, IN TURN, CAUSES A DECREASED RETURN TO BOTH THE LEFT AND RIGHT HEART. A DECREASED CARDIAC OUTPUT AND LOW SYSTEMIC ARTERIAL PRESSURE RESULT.

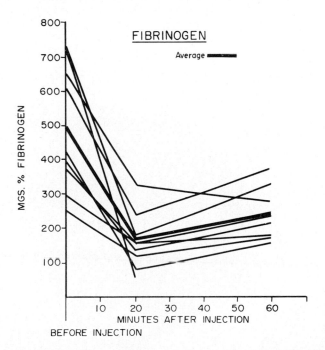

FIG. 4. FIBRINOGEN DETERMINATIONS IN DOGS MADE BEFORE INTRAVASCULAR INJECTION OF THROMBIN AND 20 AND 60 MIN AFTER INJECTION. THE HEAVY LINE MARKS THE AVERAGE; INDIVIDUAL READINGS ARE RECORDED BY LIGHT LINES. NOTE THE INITIAL MARKED DROP DURING THE FIRST 20 MIN, FOLLOWED BY A MODEST RECOVERY DURING THE SUBSEQUENT 40 MIN. ALSO NOTE A TENDENCY FOR THE DOGS WITH INITIAL READINGS OF 400 mg% OR OVER TO HAVE A MORE MARKED FIBRINOGEN FALL THAN THOSE ANIMALS WITH INITIAL READINGS OF UNDER 400 mg%.

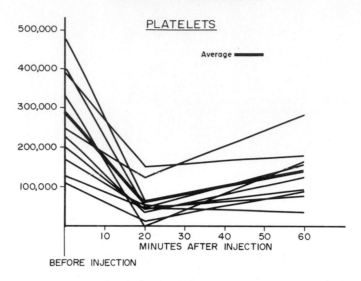

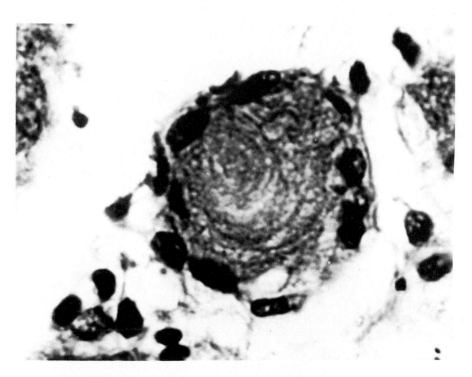

FIG. 5. PLATELET COUNTS MADE BEFORE INTRAVASCULAR INJECTION OF THROMBIN INTO DOGS AND AT 20 AND 60 MIN AFTER INJECTION. INDIVIDUAL DETERMINATIONS ARE IN FINE LINES TO SHOW INDIVIDUAL VARIATIONS. THE DARK LINE REPRESENTS THE AVERAGE OF ALL DETERMINATIONS. NOTE THE INITIAL MARKED FALL DURING THE FIRST 20 MIN AND THE SUBSEQUENT PARTIAL RECOVERY DURING THE SUCCEEDING 40 MIN. ALSO NOTE THERE IS A TENDENCY FOR THE DOGS WITH THE HIGHER INITIAL READINGS TO HAVE A GREATER PLATELET DROP THAN THOSE WITH INITIAL LOW READINGS.

FIG. 6. FIBRIN THROMBUS IN KIDNEY OF PATIENT DYING OF SEPTIC SHOCK.

TABLE 1. MEAN DECREASE IN CLOTTING
FACTOR ACTIVITY* AFTER ENDOTOXIN

Factor	5 min after	4 hr after
Fibrinogen†	58.5	99.3
Prothrombin	25%	37%
Factor V	27%	64%
Factor VII	20%	65%
Factor VIII	47%	31%
Factor IX	45%	41%
Factor X	15%	60%
Factor XI	68%	54%
Factor XII	36%	33%

*Factors V-XII expressed as the percent
of the total activity originally present on the
animal's control plasma.
†Expressed in mg%.

SHOCK

The common denominator of all types of shock appears to be an inadequate perfusion of vital capillaries. This is affected but not exclusively determined by arterial blood pressure, venous return to the heart and cardiac output, vasoconstriction or dilation, blood volume, heart failure and other factors. A factor which can dramatically affect flow of blood through capillaries is the plugging of these capillaries with clotted blood.

The application of DIC to shock is two-fold. DIC may produce shock as described above. Also shock can produce DIC. Not only can DIC produce a coagulation deficit and shock, but hemorrhage can produce shock and a coagulation deficit.

The postulated mechanism of production of DIC in shock is as illustrated in Fig. 7. Initiated by hemorrhage, trauma, infection, etc., there is vasoconstriction of arterioles brought about by an elevation in blood catecholamine level. In addition, there is possibly arterial hypotension. Accompanying this may be the opening of arteriovenous shunts. These three factors result in a decreased flow through the arterioles. Normally only a small number of the total number of capillaries are open at any one time, the capillaries opening and closing in response to the needs of the cells they serve, probably by means of a histamine mechanism[1]. With a lessened arteriolar flow, cells are not so easily satisfied with part time perfusion and may call for full time perfusion. This results in simultaneous opening of many capillaries. This results in two important changes. (1) The capacity of the vascular space is greatly increased. Even a normal blood volume is inadequate to fill all the capillaries and run through to fill the veins leaving the veins collapsed. (2) With less flow now being required to supply more capillaries, the capillary flow becomes very slow. Lactic acid production is increased by the low oxygen supply and is constantly being added to blood in the capillary. By the time the slow flowing blood reaches the venous end of the capillary, it is very acidotic, possibly pH 6.9 or below, even though arterial pH may as yet be essentially normal. This stagnant acid blood is hypercoagulable and will clot more quickly than normal if removed from the body (Fig. 8). Pure hemorrhage does not induce the blood to clot but apparently the red cell thromboplastin liberated by hemolysis, bacterial toxins and many other substances will induce coagulation in this stagnant blood[1]. If coagulation

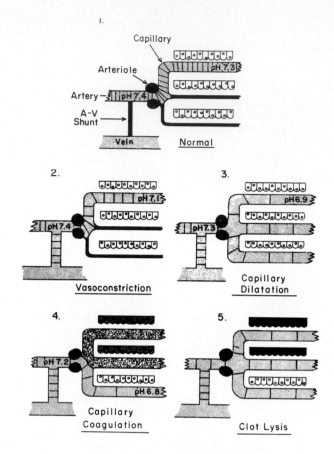

FIG. 7. STAGES IN DEVELOPMENT OF IRREVERSIBLE SHOCK. DIAGRAM REPRESENTS A SMALL ARTERY ENDING IN AN ARTERIOLE WITH SPHINCTER-LIKE ACTION. ARTERIOLE FEEDS THREE CAPILLARIES, EACH FEEDING A GROUP OF CELLS.

1. NORMAL CONDITION. ARTERIOLES FAIRLY WIDELY OPENED. ONLY ONE CAPILLARY IS BEING PERFUSED WHILE OTHERS REST. CAPILLARIES OPEN IN ROTATION ON DEMAND OF THE CELLS ADJACENT TO THEM. CONSTANT PERFUSION NOT NECESSARY. BLOOD FLOW THROUGH THE CAPILLARY IS RAPID. pH DROP ACROSS THE CAPILLARY IS MINIMAL.

2. PHASE I. SHOCK. VASOCONSTRICTION. DUE TO CATECHOLAMINES AFTER HEMORRHAGE AND TRAUMA. ARTERIOLE CONSTRICTS, LETTING LESS BLOOD THROUGH. HYPOTENSION IN THE ARTERY, CAPILLARY FLOW SLOWED.

3. PHASE II. SHOCK. CAPILLARY DILATION. (EXPANSION OF VASCULAR SPACE). ALL CAPILLARIES ARE OPEN ON DEMAND OF THEIR CELLS. BLOOD FLOW THROUGH ALL CAPILLARIES IS EXTREMELY SLOW. pH DROP ACROSS THE CAPILLARY IS MARKED.

4. PHASE III. SHOCK. DISSEMINATED INTRAVASCULAR COAGULATION. LATE SHOCK. HEMOLYSIS HAS AIDED THE SLOW FLOWING ACID BLOOD IN TWO OF THE CAPILLARIES TO CLOT, STOPPING PERFUSION COMPLETELY IN THESE CAPILLARIES. CELLS NOURISHED BY THESE CAPILLARIES ARE DYING. BLOOD FLOW THROUGH THE REMAINING CAPILLARY IS SLUGGISH. CIRCULATING BLOOD INCOAGULABLE.

5. PHASE IV. IRREVERSIBLE SHOCK. ARTERIOLE HAS OPENED SOMEWHAT AFTER REPLACEMENT OF BLOOD VOLUME. CAPILLARY CLOTS HAVE BEEN LYSED BY ENDOGENOUS FIBRINOLYSIN RESTORING CIRCULATION. HOWEVER, CELLS SUPPLIED BY THE FORMERLY CLOTTED CAPILLARIES ARE NOW DEAD. THIS PRODUCES AREAS OF FOCAL NECROSIS AND IF WIDESPREAD ENOUGH CAUSES TISSUE AND ORGAN FAILURE.

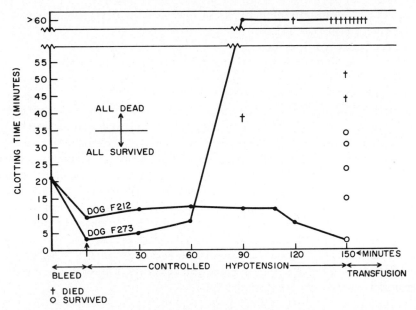

FIG. 8. SILICONE CLOTTING TIMES OF DOGS SUBJECTED TO HEMORRHAGIC SHOCK. BLEEDING PRODUCED
A DECREASE IN CLOTTING TIME. THOSE DOGS THAT LATER SHOWED A PROLONGED CLOTTING TIME (OVER
35 MIN) ALL DIED AS NOTED BY THE CROSSES. THOSE WHICH DID NOT, ALL SURVIVED, AS NOTED BY THE
CIRCLES. TWO TYPICAL ANIMALS ARE SHOWN BY THE LINES.

occurs, most frequent in capillaries, two important results occur. (1) A coagulation
defect due to the consumption of clotting factors and (2) perfusion of vital capillaries
completely halts causing lactic acid pileup around the cells and cellular death. Under
severe shock conditions blood becomes incoagulable in silicone. This marks the onset
of DIC and is a good prognosticator of death (Fig. 8).

Hemolysis is marked in any crushing injury or many other situations. The presence
of hemolysis causes an otherwise non-fatal hemorrhagic shock to result fatally. Frequently capillary clots are washed out by dissolution of the clots by endogenous
fibrinolysin. However, if they remain long enough (1 hr?) focal tissue necrosis may
result. This may be lethal if enough parenchyma of vital organs such as the liver and
kidney is destroyed.

The cause of this coagulation thus involves a combination of two major factors
(both must be present)[1].

1. Slowing of capillary flow caused by
   (a) arterial hypotension
   (b) arteriolar vasoconstriction
   (c) dilation of all capillaries simultaneously
   (d) opening of arteriovenous shunts.
2. Hypercoagulability and a stimulus to clotting of the blood. These include the
   following:
   (a) acidosis
   (b) hemolysis
   (c) high level of clotting factors
   (d) bacterial toxins

(e) surface factor activation by glass, air (or any gas) or metal surfaces as in extracorporeal circulation

(f) cancer or necrotic tissue

(g) particulate matter introduced into the blood (amniotic fluid)

(h) snake venom

(i) thrombin.

Treatment of DIC can be by attacking either of the two main component causes, i.e. (1) slow capillary flow or (2) the clotting itself. The former is most easily carried out clinically by volume addition coupled with vasodilatation (Figs. 9, 10 and 11)[1]. With the expansion of the vascular space by capillary dilatation, the vena cava fails to fill and decreased cardiac output results. By filling the vascular tree, this is remedied. Arteriolar constriction is relieved because, with adequate volume, the blood catecholamine level goes down. However, there may be some residual arteriolar spasm, particularly in the lungs causing cor pulmonale and decreased return to the left heart (Fig. 3). This may be relieved by drugs (Dibenzyline 1 mg/Kg carefully titrated).

The second approach is that of hastening dissolution of clots by exogenous fibrinolysin. It is effective in experimental animals. However, it frequently results in transient afibrinogenemia and has not been tried clinically.

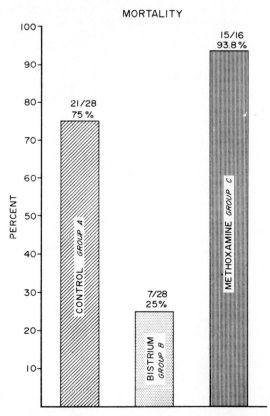

FIG. 9. MORTALITY RATES OF THREE GROUPS OF DOGS SUBJECTED TO HEMORRHAGIC SHOCK. ALL WERE MAINTAINED AT 40 mm Hg ARTERIAL PRESSURE FOR 4 HR. GROUP B WAS TREATED WITH GANGLIONIC BLOCKING AGENT AND GROUP C WITH A PERIPHERAL VASOCONSTRICTOR.

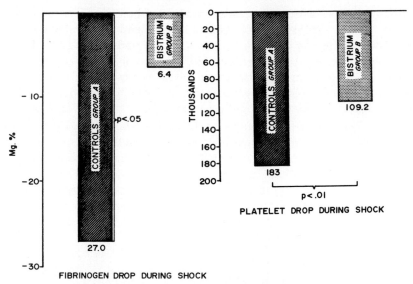

FIG. 10. FIBRINOGEN AND PLATELET DROP DURING HEMORRHAGIC SHOCK IN DOGS TREATED WITH A VASODILATOR. FIBRINOGEN VALUES WERE CORRECTED FOR DILUTION USING TOTAL PROTEIN AS AN INDEX OF DILUTION. NOTE THAT WHILE THERE WAS A SIGNIFICANT FALL IN FIBRINOGEN IN CONTROL (GROUP A) DOGS, THERE WAS ONLY A SMALL AND INSIGNIFICANT FALL IN FIBRINOGEN IN DOGS TREATED WITH A VASODILATOR. SIMILARLY THERE WAS A SIGNIFICANTLY GREATER FALL IN PLATELET COUNT IN THE CONTROL DOGS THAN IN THOSE TREATED WITH A VASODILATOR. GROUP C (VASOCONSTRICTOR GROUP) WAS SIMILAR TO THE CONTROLS.

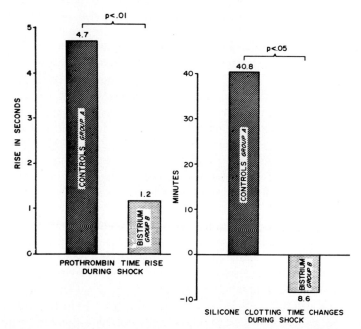

FIG. 11. PROTHROMBIN TIME RISE AND SILICONE CLOTTING TIME CHANGES DURING HEMORRHAGIC SHOCK IN DOGS TREATED WITH VASOCONSTRICTORS OR VASODILATORS. NOTE THAT THE CONTROL GROUP SHOWED A MARKED LENGTHENING OF SILICONE CLOTTING TIME AS A RESULT OF THE SHOCK WHEREAS GROUP B DOGS SHOWED AN ACTUAL SLIGHT SHORTENING. THAT OF GROUP C (VASOCONSTRICTOR) DOGS APPROXI-MATED TIME OF THE CONTROLS.

A unit for the intensive treatment and study of refractory shock in human patients was activated in late 1965 at Walter Reed General Hospital at Walter Reed Army Medical Center[1]. The unit is operated and staffed by the Division of Surgery of the Walter Reed Army Institute of Research. The mission of this unit is to admit selected shock patients, provide them with optimal medical care based on modern concepts of the pathophysiology of the shock syndrome, and through extensive monitoring facilities to gather clinical, physiological and laboratory data. The unit admits only patients in "refractory" shock. Refractory shock is defined as shock due to *any* cause which has not responded to the usual treatment of intravenous fluids, oxygen, vasoconstrictors, etc. In Walter Reed General Hospital approximately one to two cases of shock are seen each day. Of these approximately one patient a week does not respond to the usual treatment and is admitted to the special shock treatment unit. The unit accommodates only one patient at a time, who may stay there for from one day to a week. Patients are admitted from any ward in the hospital and on recovery from shock are transferred back to their original ward.

RESULTS OF STUDY AND TREATMENT

Fifteen patients have been admitted to the shock unit suffering from refractory shock. They were treated in accordance with a definite treatment plan. Of the 15, 11 were discharged from the unit recovered from their episode of shock. Seven were later discharged from the hospital as well. Four patients died later on a ward of conditions other than this shock episode. This compares with a shock mortality of about 65–70% predicted from an analysis of past cases. These 15 patients had been unresponsive on their wards to energetic treatment consisting of intravenous fluids, oxygen and vasopressors. In general the central venous pressures recorded on these patients on the wards were high, averaging 12.4 cm H_2O. However, on admission to the shock unit the central venous pressure was found to be lower averaging 6.0 cm H_2O. This was due in part to the ward catheter tip being not within the chest, or in one case being in the right ventricle. This relatively low central venous pressure as measured in the shock unit allowed the use of large amounts of volume administration in most cases. It is important that the tip of a central venous pressure catheter be inside a chest vein.

In every case it was possible to obtain a satisfactory systemic blood pressure by treatment without the use of vasopressors although 4 cases died in the shock episode. Two of these were essentially moribund on admission and died in a few hours after repeated cardiac arrests.

The following generalization in findings and treatment are possible:

1. *Adequate volume administration was effective in producing a satisfactory systemic arterial blood pressure in 10 out of 15 cases.* Administration of these fluids was governed by monitoring central venous and pulmonary pressure. It was felt that pulmonary artery pressure gave a little advance notice of adequate blood volume so that fluid could more promptly be discontinued with less chance of pulmonary edema. No problems were encountered in inserting and maintaining a pulmonary artery catheter for 3 days, which was done routinely. It was inserted by means of the portable image intensifier without moving the patient from his special radiolucent bed. When adequate volume is given causing adequate venous return to the right heart, an increased right heart output results. If there is continued pulmonary microcirculatory obstruction

due to microthrombi and vasoconstriction, this may result in pulmonary artery hypertension. It may be only with right heart failure that this increase in pressure backs up through the right heart and causes an abnormal rise in central venous pressure[1]. Usually, large quantities of fluid were required amounting up to 12 liters in a few hours. Most of the fluid given was normal saline, although blood, dextran, bicarbonate, glucose and other fluids were used. The various fluids were given to correct electrolyte or other deficiencies or defects in the blood including acidosis. Five cases showed a hyponatremia. No ill effect was seen in giving large quantities of normal saline. It was thought undesirable to give lactate because lactate levels were already abnormally high and not being properly metabolized. It was thought better to treat acidosis by sodium bicarbonate. However, the best way to treat the acidosis was by increasing capillary perfusion by volume administration. Blood was given only up to the point of a normal red cell mass. It was thought that red cell mass could be accurately measured in the presence of shock and that it should be at a relatively normal size. More than normal red cell mass would be hard to get rid of when the vascular volume contracted to normal size after adequate tissue perfusion was obtained. Excess fluid components were easily discarded by a tremendous diuresis which nearly always followed adequate perfusion. It is recognized that accurate blood volume measurements are not possible in shock. By the time tagged albumin has properly mixed in the slowly circulating blood, significant amounts have already leaked out of the vascular tree. However, red cell mass measurements are probably reasonably accurate.

2. *pO_2 was extremely low and required immediate treatment in 11 out of 15 cases.* This was sometimes accomplished by nasal oxygen, but in most cases tracheotomy or tracheal intubation with use of 95% O_2 and an Engstrom respirator was required. In two cases even this was inadequate. This was probably due to the lesion of "shock lung" or "acute pulmonary failure"[1], which seems to be associated with all severe shock. It is characterized by pulmonary congestion, hemorrhage, edema and capillary thrombi. Usually pCO_2 was very low initially even with the low pO_2 and required administration of 5% CO_2 in the 95% O_2. This reflected the body's attempt to flow off CO_2 producing a respiratory alkalosis to compensate for the increasing lactic acidemia.

3. *The above procedures failed to produce a satisfactory systemic arterial blood pressure in 5 out of 15 cases. In these cases a vasodilator, phenoxybenzamine, was given and in 3 produced dramatic improvement.* It was given in a dosage of 1 mg/kg in 1–200 ml of normal saline over a period of an hour or so. In two cases (Nos. 10 and 13) no dramatic improvement occurred. However, in no case were there any detrimental effects. In no case should a vasodilator be given without proof of adequate volume administration as determined by central venous pressure or pulmonary artery pressure. In no case was vasodilation accompanied by a systemic blood pressure drop. It is thought that this was due to adequate filling of the expanded vascular space before the drug was given. In 3 of the cases a significant rise in systemic arterial pressure resulted. Other usual effects were a fall in both pulmonary artery pressure and central venous pressure, a great (100–400%) increase in cardiac index, a decrease in peripheral resistance and a tremendous diuresis. Frequently lactic acid levels continued to rise for a short time before falling. This is probably because lactic acid accumulated in the tissues was being washed out into the bloodstream by the increased

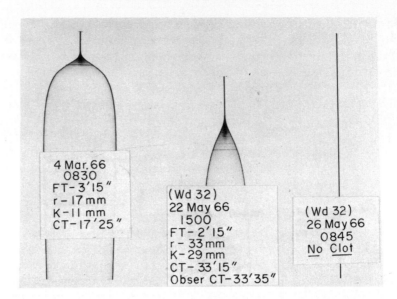

FIG. 12. SELECTED THROMBOELASTOGRAPHS. ON THE LEFT IS A NORMAL RECORDING SHOWING NORMAL
COAGULATION OF BLOOD. ON THE RIGHT ARE TWO THROMBOELASTOGRAPHS TAKEN ON A PATIENT
FOLLOWED BY THE SHOCK UNIT BUT NOT TREATED BY THE SHOCK UNIT. THE FIRST SHOWS THE THROMBO-
ELASTOGRAPH OF A SAMPLE OF BLOOD WHICH SHOWED A DEFINITE CLOTTING DEFECT. COAGULATION WAS
SLOW AND THE CLOT WEAK BUT CLOTTING STILL OCCURRED. AS THE PATIENT DETERIORATED THE BLOOD
BECAME INCOAGULABLE, NOTED ON THE THROMBOELASTOGRAPH AS A STRAIGHT LINE. THIS DEVELOPMENT
IS A PROGNOSTICATOR OF A FATAL OUTCOME[1].

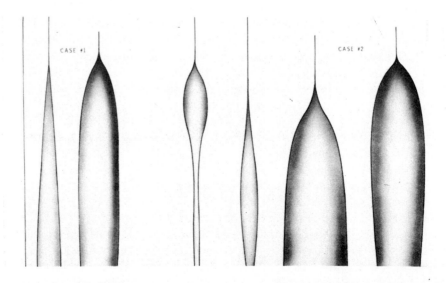

FIG. 13. THROMBOELASTOGRAPHS OF TWO SUCCESSFULLY TREATED CASES. NOTE IN CASE 1 THAT WHILE
THE INITIAL BLOOD SAMPLE DID NOT CLOT AT ALL, IT SPONTANEOUSLY REVERTED TO NORMAL AS THE
PATIENT IMPROVED. NOTE IN CASE 2 THE FIRST THROMBOELASTOGRAPH SHOWS NOT ONLY DEFECTIVE
COAGULATION BUT ENDOGENOUS FIBRINOLYTIC ACTIVITY CAUSING LYSIS OF THE CLOT. THESE DEFECTS
SPONTANEOUSLY REVERTED TO NORMAL AS THE PATIENT IMPROVED.

capillary perfusion. Phenoxybenzamine lowers systemic vascular resistance to a greater degree than pulmonary vascular resistance, thereby shifting fluid sequestered in pulmonary vessels to the systemic circulation and alleviating pulmonary hypertension and congestion. Phenoxybenzamine failed to produce any improvement in a patient with bilateral pheochromocytomas who was moribund when the drug was administered. This cannot be judged a therapeutic failure of phenoxybenzamine, which has been well known to be the drug of choice in the treatment of this disease.

Twelve out of 15 cases were on vasopressors when admitted to the shock unit. In every case they were successfully weaned off the drug during volume administration. Only one case was given Aramine in the shock unit. It was given on a trial basis before a vasodilator was tried. It was quickly discontinued when it failed to help the patient. In addition, it caused an elevation of the central venous pressure and produced alarming ECG changes without increasing cardiac output.

4. *All cases demonstrated a coagulation defect* (Figs 12, 13; Table 2). The clotting defects were always multiple and involved deficiencies of several clotting factors.

TABLE 2

Coagulation Tests from Two Patients. Note in case 2 that factors II, V, IX and X were deficient at the time of admission in refractory shock. The partial thromboplastin time was grossly abnormal and platelets descended to only 53,000. All of these defects spontaneously repaired themselves as the patient improved. In case 4 note that on admission, factor IX was only 2% of normal and factor XII only 17% of normal. Prothrombin time and partial thromboplastin time were grossly prolonged. All of these factors spontaneously reverted to normal as the patient improved. All patients have shown multiple coagulation defects. There has been no definite pattern except that all defects were multiple.

COAGULATION TESTS

Case 2 Factor	Activity = % of normal			
	Admission 17 Dec 65 (shock)	18 Dec 65	20 Dec 65	Follow-up
II	49%	100%	49%	84%
V	59%	84%	100%	—
VIII	100%	100%	100%	—
IX	57%	57%	93%	100%
X	73%	58%	54%	—
PT	14.6 (13.0)	16.0 (13)	12.7 (12.0)	12.5
PTT	56.6 (37.7)	55.2 (36)	42.4 (36.4)	47.4 (39.5)
Platelets	98,500	53,000	64,000	319,000

Case 4 Factor	Activity = % of normal	
	Admission 14 Jan 66 (shock)	Discharge 17 Jan 66
II	45%	72%
V	66%	100%
VIII	48%	77%
IX	2%	69%
X	95%	—
XII	17%	72%
PT	17 (12.7 control)	13.5 (13.0 control)
PTT	215 (41.2 control)	43.8 (42.0 control)

Fibrinogen was usually high reflecting an increase in manufacture which overtook an increase in utilization. Other factors were less fortunate and in 3 cases became extremely low, resulting in a clinical hemorrhagic tendency and serious capillary bleeding. In these 3 cases the coagulation defect was quickly and effectively treated with *rapid* administration of fresh whole blood or fresh frozen plasma. Platelet defects, which were common, were only helped by fresh whole blood. Clinical bleeding may be dangerous and require prompt treatment. However, most clotting defects result in no clinical bleeding. They are important only in documenting the onset of disseminated intravascular coagulation which means a serious prognosis. If the patient improves the clotting defect repairs itself spontaneously. If the clotting defect increases in severity, a fatal outcome is in the offing (Fig. 12). Contrariwise, the spontaneous improvement of a clotting defect presages a successful outcome.

REFERENCES

[1] HARDAWAY, R. M. *Syndromes of Disseminated Intravascular Coagulation* (With special reference to shock and hemorrhage). Charles C. Thomas, Springfield, Ill., 1966.

DISCUSSION

BARNHART *(U.S.A.)*:

Do you propose that administration of fibrinolysin or activator, improved such microthrombotic animals? Do you still feel that this is a proper kind of course to follow, or do you think it should be combined with vasodilators?

HARDAWAY *(U.S.A.)*:

We have used vasodilators after volume administration with great success clinically. We have not yet used fibrinolysin clinically, although we are now prepared to do so. Fibrinolysin has been used in Germany, for shock, with success.

GELIN *(Sweden)*:

All Dr. Hardaway's work now has accumulated to focus on the irreversibility of thrombosis on the venular side of the microcirculation. We arrived at the same conclusion starting from different view points on shock; coagulation will appear not only from hemorrhagic, but from any kind of shock. Nature does not seem to be able to distinguish between a burn injury and a hemorrhage. The first event we have observed is the formation of platelet aggregates in the venular flow from a crushed or damaged area, and brought to the lung as white emboli. I would like to ask to what extent you think these microemboli in the lung represent only white material, or if it also contains red material? Because the red material will, according to our observations, not occur in the very early stage, but only after 1 or 2 hr of injury. The first event will be just white emboli in the lung. I think it is an important step to the understanding of the whole event after injury.

HARDAWAY:

Platelets seem to be the first and most sensitive event in disseminated intravascular coagulation. The fibrinogen–fibrin mechanism seems to follow later, so that first white, then red thrombi is the typical sequence. The delay in intravascular thrombi after trauma is very interesting, because trauma seems the result in considerable hemolysis which reaches its peak perhaps 24–48 hr later; and this hemolysis apparently results in the liberation, in the bloodstream, of a red cell thromboplastin which in this slow hypercoagulable state will easily produce intravascular clotting.

GELIN:

Yes, I think that is a very important point, also for the anemia of injury; first this early aggregation and then release of hemolysing substances.

PALMER *(Australia)*:

In your illustrations where the capillaries were shown narrowed, I take it that it is purely diagrammatic and indicates reduced flow and not a physical narrowing of the capillaries.

HARDAWAY:

The narrow solid line denotes a capillary with no blood flow at all.

GELIN:

I come back to a point I just forgot about. Many shock studies, and I would specifically emphasize Wiggers wonderful book on the physiology of shock, have allowed few conclusions about the clinical shock situation. I think it depends on one fundamental error in the experimental approach, namely that the heparinized animal itself will prevent many of the events, here observed, to occur. So the one who really wants to study the circulatory disturbances following tissue injury should not work on the anticoagulated animal. And I think that is the very big contribution of Dr. Hardaway here.

HARDAWAY:

Yes, I think that with heparinized animals we mess up the entire experiment, and we do not know quite where we are. Heparin is interesting. It will not, for instance, prevent platelet agglutination, in our experience; but it will prevent fibrinogen–fibrin. It is also inactivated by acidosis.

HEMORHEOLOGICAL INVESTIGATIONS IN RELATION TO DIABETES MELLITUS AND ITS ANGIOPATHY

Jørn Ditzel* and Flemming Skovborg

Department of Medicine, Aalborg Municipal Hospital, Aalborg,
Hvidøre Hospital and NOVO Research Institute, Copenhagen,
Denmark

There is good supporting evidence that hemorheological changes in the microvasculature play a major and important role in the development of diabetic microangiopathy.

This statement is based on a number of observations of which some should be emphasized.

1. *The microaneurysms*—the most characteristic lesion in the diabetic retinopathy—almost exclusively *are confined to the venous part of capillaries and small venules*[1–6].

2. *Venous changes occur prior to arteriolar changes in the retina of diabetics* [1, 2, 7–11]. That means that the initial changes in diabetic retinopathy take place in that part of the microvasculature having the slowest linear rate of flow and in which the shearing forces are the least.

3. *The microaneurysms are* by no means specific to diabetes. Identical microaneurysms with similar hyaline thickening, lipoid and mucopolysaccharide staining may be *found in a variety of unrelated conditions which are associated with prolonged periods of retinal venous stasis*[12, 13].

In cases of central retinal venous occlusion the microaneurysms are particularly numerous[12, 14–18], and in a case of macroglobulinaemia Ashton[13] found more microaneurysms in the retina than in any previous study he had made.

The mechanisms of formation of microaneurysms in retinal vein occlusion and in macroglobulinaemia appear fairly clear and differ only slightly from each other. In retinal vein occlusion the intravascular rise in venous tension produces stasis, dilatation of the veins above the obstruction, which in turn causes anoxia of the venular and capillary walls, focal mural degenerative changes of the basement membrane, microaneurysm formation on the venous side and a breakdown of the blood-retinal barrier[12, 17]. Thus the two factors, increased capillary pressure and anoxia, appear to be responsible for the capillary injury.

In the case of macroglobulinaemia the mechanism of the microaneurysm formation is related to the presence of macroglobulins in the circulation. The plasma macroglobulins with sedimentation constants of 19S or more and molecular weights about one million make blood highly viscous, produce marked aggregation of red cells, extreme decrease in linear rate of flow and stasis in the periphery of the retina, anoxia of the venular and capillary walls, focal mural degenerative changes and microaneurysm formation. The increase in viscosity probably leads to a rise in pressure within the retinal circulation and again the combination of increased capillary pressure and anoxia appears to be the factor responsible for microaneurysm formation[19]. That the retinopathy thus formed is due to the presence of macroglobulins is strongly supported by the repeated observation of reversibility of the retinopathy after plasma-pheresis[20–23].

The earliest possible change observed in the retina of young diabetics is a general dilatation or fullness of the veins[1, 2, 7, 8, 9, 11, 24, 25]. WALKER[10] and HARDIN et al.[26] found venous engorgement without other signs of retinopathy in 13·3 and 10% respectively. Since venous dilatation and evidence of venous stasis also appear to precede the formation of microaneurysms, exudates, haemorrhages and neovascularization in diabetes, it is of importance to elucidate the mechanism for this early change. Histological studies have not revealed changes in the larger or central retinal vein which can explain the venous stasis[25].

In 1952, while working at the Joslin Clinic in Boston, I had the opportunity to observe an exceptional case. In a 15-year-old, poorly regulated, diabetic boy I observed the development of early diabetic retinopathy (i.e. dilatation of venules and micro-aneurysms) in one eye in immediate time-relationship to the occurrence of central retinal vein occlusion in the other eye and again suggesting venous stasis in the retinal circulation as a common pathogenetic factor in these two conditions[27]. It was observed, however, that the veins and venules were dilated not only in the retina but also in the bulbar conjunctiva. In this tissue the small blood vessels and the micro-circulation can be studied under a magnification of $\times 100$ in contrast to the $\times 15$ magnification provided by the ophthalmoscope. As the diabetes was regulated, it was observed that the venous changes both in the retina and in the bulbar conjunctiva slowly reversed. These observations suggested that the dilatation of the venules and veins in diabetes was a functional change, possibly a loss of tone which leads to marked slowing of venous flow. We found this observation of significance and it gave impetus to a series of hemorheological investigations which still continues in order to elucidate the mechanism of prolonged venous stasis in the microcirculation of diabetics. These studies have shown that the venous stasis and impaired capillary-venous flow are produced mainly by three factors, (1) by pathophysiological functional changes of the vessel walls, leading to a redistribution of flow and leakage of plasma components through the small venules, (2) by aggregation of erythrocytes and (3) by increased whole blood viscosity. These studies by us and other groups of investigators shall be touched upon.

PATHOPHYSIOLOGICAL FUNCTIONAL CHANGES OF THE VESSEL WALLS

Although considerable variation exists in the arrangement of the smaller blood vessels in the bulbar conjunctiva from subject to subject, certain characteristics of the vessel walls and the blood flow are invariably the same. The picture of the combined vascular and hemorheological pattern of healthy children or young individuals can be fairly well defined by these characteristics. The arterioles are often found to enter the conjunctiva parallel to larger venules. The capillaries can be seen to branch from the tip of the arterioles. Besides the "true" capillaries it is often possible to follow a terminal arteriole more directly into a venule through a non-anastomosing vascular channel, an arteriolar-venular communication, which should not be mistaken for the so-called arterio-venous anastomoses (Fig. 1). Under normal conditions the ratio between the diameter of the arteriole and that of the accompanying venules is relatively

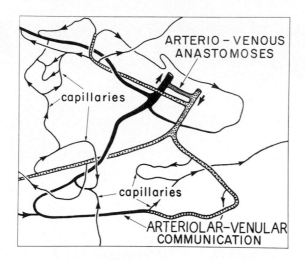

FIG. 1. THE DIFFERENT PLACEMENT OF THE "ARTERIOLAR-VENULAR COMMUNICATION" AND THE ARTERIO-VENOUS ANASTOMOSIS. ARTERIO-VENOUS ANASTOMOSIS IS A RARE FINDING IN THE VASCULAR BED.

constant and is 1:3–1:2[28–34]. In young diabetics besides the normal vascular pattern two fairly well-defined functional deviations from the normal could be observed, designated Vascular Pattern-Change I and Vascular Pattern-Change II (Figs. 2 and 3). These responses apparently manifest themselves as different stages in a rather complex reaction maintained by some blood- or tissue-borne factor in the diabetic metabolic disturbance (insulin deficiency? lactic acid? pCO_2? pH? growth hormone?). Most often (approximately 45%) Vascular Pattern-Change I occurs characterized by a general, but not universal engorgement of the venules, occasionally with fusiform sacculations in collecting venules. There occurs some redistribution of flow from the "true" capillaries to the arteriolar-venular shunts. The arteriolar-venular diameter ratio decreases. Concentration of the passing blood can occasionally be observed in smaller venules, the linear rate of blood flow decreases. As the venules become engorged, evidence of microscopic edema is observed[29, 32, 35, 34]. Other cases show Vascular Pattern-Change II, characterized by arteriolar constriction. The direct arteriolar-venular communications are open and much blood appear to be shunted through these channels [32]. Most "true" capillaries appear free of circulating red cells, leaving the tissue ischemic. The most harmful effect of the loss of venular tone is a decrease in the linear rate of blood flow through the venules and pathological permeability. The continuous seepage of plasma components through endothelium leads to edema and over prolonged time to hyaline-mucoid changes in the tissue[32, 33]. The most harmful consequence of the prolonged constriction of arterioles and capillaries and shunting of blood would be prolonged hypoxia and subnutrition. Because the small blood vessels, beyond the branched arterioles, are an integral part of the tissue in which they are imbedded, the degeneration may vary in intensity and appearance from tissue to tissue. It is conceivable that the vascular damage, the functional impairment and the subsequent tissue response are greatest in tissues with high cellular metabolism (retina), in tissues in which damaged small blood vessels cannot be replaced (kidney glomeruli) and in tissues in which the capillaries form the only vascular component (kidney glomeruli, inner

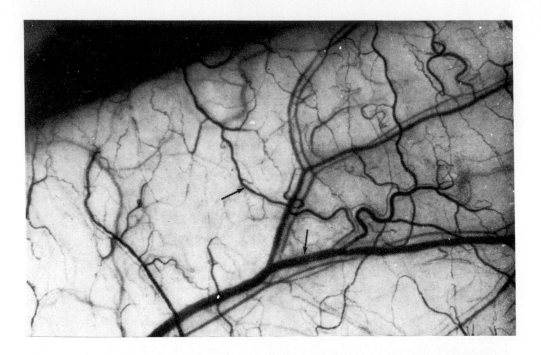

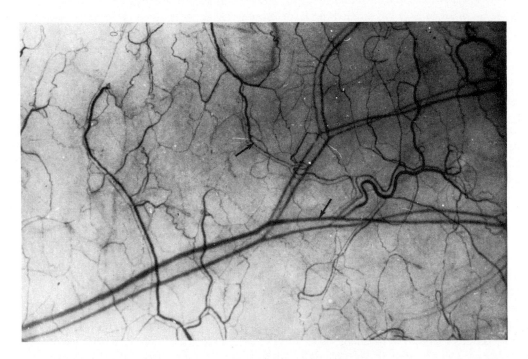

FIG. 2. THE CHANGE FROM VASCULAR PATTERN-CHANGE I TO NORMAL VASCULAR PATTERN IN A JUVENILE DIABETIC SUBJECT. NOTE THE DISAPPEARANCE OF THE VENOUS CONGESTION. (MAGNIFICATION APPROX. × 45). REDUCED TO 8/10.

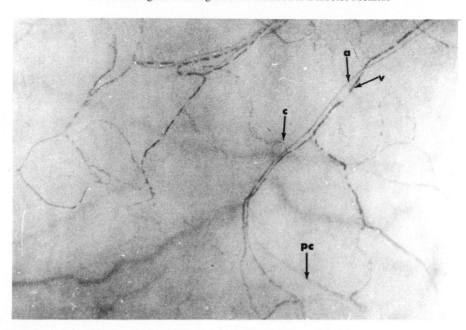

FIG. 3. THE CONJUNCTIVAL VASCULAR BED, SHOWING VASCULAR PATTERN-CHANGE II IN A YOUNG DIA-
BETIC SUBJECT. NOTE THE ISCHEMIA OF THE TISSUE. MOST TRUE CAPILLARIES ARE CLOSED BUT THE ARTERIO-
LAR–VENULAR COMMUNICATIONS ARE OPEN (PC) (MAGNIFICATION APPROX. × 70). REDUCED TO 7/10.

nuclear layer of the retina). Although the small vessel degeneration might be general, the kidneys and the retina would be more highly affected. In diabetes the "complications", appearing after long duration of the condition, are those affecting the kidney and the retina. Not recognized until recently have been the similarities in changes taking place in these and other tissues.

(For functional circulatory studies of the skin circulation of diabetics see MEGIBOW et al.[36, 37], MENDLOWITZ et al.[38], BÁRÁNY[39], SIGROTH[40]; for studies of vessel pathology of the conjunctiva see FUNAHASKI and FINK[41], PIERI and SCARPELLI[42]; peripheral nerves, FAGERBERG[43]; heart, BLUMENTHAL et al.[44]; skin and muscles, GOLDBERG et al.[45], AAGENÆS and MOE[46], PEDERSEN and OLSEN[47], HANDELSMAN et al.[48], ZACHS et al.[49]; inner ear, JØRGENSEN[50]; placenta, BURSTEIN et al.[51]; mucosa of the stomach, ANGERVALL et al.[52]; pancreas, LAZARUS and VOLK[53]; gingiva, STAHL et al.[54]; retina, ASHTON[55]; kidney, THOMSEN[56].

If the observed pathophysiological pattern deviations have to be considered of importance in the pathogenesis of the diabetic microangiopathy, the following requirements must be satisfied.

1. The pattern changes must occur considerably more frequently in a group of diabetic patients than in an otherwise comparable group of non-diabetics.
2. Their incidence in the group must increase with the duration of diabetes.
3. Their incidence in the group must increase in diabetics with retinopathy and nephropathy.

All these three requirements have been shown to be fullfilled for the pathophysiological response changes[32, 35, 57, 58, 59].

The pathophysiological response changes could be seen even in recent onset diabetics. In a selected group of children of young diabetic mothers there was found to be a correlation between the vascular change in the bulbar conjunctiva and the abnormality of the glucose tolerance test[60, 32]. This same group of children was re-examined three years later, and among 16 cases which previously had shown Vascular Pattern-Change I, 3 in the meantime had developed symptomatic diabetics[61]. REES and co-workers[58] demonstrated reversibility of the venular dilatation in the conjunctiva of young newly discovered diabetics after insulin and dietary treatment had started. By measurement of the same vessel segments over the day in 100 young diabetic and non-diabetic subjects we have shown that the diurnal variations in the diameters of the venules were far greater among the diabetics than among the non-diabetics[62, 63, 34, 58]. With increasing duration of diabetes, the venular anomaly tended to become fixed and was essentially irreversible in the majority of diabetics with diabetes of 15 or more years' standing[63].

With these new observations at hand ophthalmologists have started to make more exact studies on the retina of recent onset juvenile diabetics; patients they previously rarely saw. By doing so LARSEN[25] reported that fullness or dilatation of the retinal veins might be seen, even from the onset of diabetics. During the first years of the disease the fullness of the retinal veins seems to be related to the degree of regulation, but later on venous dilatation is prone to be more permanent. JÜTTE[64, 65] carefully measured the retinal veins by the method of Lobeck and found that the retinal veins were dilated in 43% of 100 juvenile diabetics. The dilatation increased with the duration of diabetes over the first 10 years. An increase in vein diameter occurred during periods of poor regulation, but was reversible. In many juvenile diabetics Jütte as well as THIEL[66, 67] also observed dilatation of the smaller venules (rubeosis retinae). Both Larsen and Jütte agreed that the venous dilatation appeared to be due to a pathophysiological response and that it leads to prolonged venous stasis. Thus it seems as if these response changes are of more generalized nature.

One might ask whether similar response changes take place in the kidney glomeruli?

For obvious reasons such changes are not observable. However, indirect evidence for a functional disturbance in the permeability might be obtained by measurements of the glomerular filtration rates in young diabetics with Vascular Pattern-Change I in the conjunctival vascular bed. We have recently reported such a study, using the radio-vitamin B_{12} method of measuring glomerular filtration rates and have found that the filtration rates in young diabetics with no evidence of nephropathy were abnormally high as compared to a group of healthy subjects[68](Fig. 4). Further studies with this technique are in progress.

If similar vascular response patterns are more generalized in distribution, it becomes necessary to explain why no microaneurysms develop in the bulbar conjunctiva. As has been pointed out by ASHTON[5] capillary microaneurysms are absent in any tissue other than the retina and possibly the glomeruli of the kidneys[55], and it suggests that the formation of microaneurysms is related in some way to local factors in the retina such as the high cellular metabolism in combination with the absence of lymphatics and perivascular connective tissue, high capillary pressure and fluctuating intraocular tension [69]. Also it has to be explained why no retinopathy is seen in all cases, showing Vascular Pattern-Change I. Here, of course, enters the importance of the duration of diabetes, because it allows more time for the harmful influence of venous stasis to take place. Two additional changes in flow properties appear to add to the decrease in venous-capillary flow, namely intravascular erythrocyte aggregation and the blood viscosity.

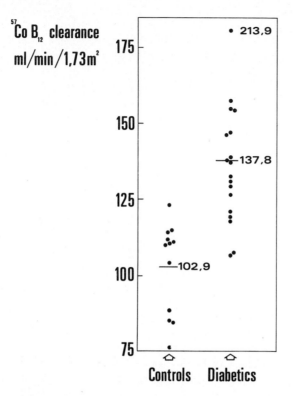

FIG. 4. THE GLOMERULAR FILTRATION RATE AS MEASURED WITH THE RADIOACTIVE VITAMIN B_{12} METHOD IN 12 CONTROL SUBJECTS AND IN 18 YOUNG DIABETIC SUBJECTS WITHOUT ANY EVIDENCE OF DIABETIC NEPHRO-PATHY AND WITH SHORT DURATION OF THEIR DISEASE. THE DIFFERENCE IN DISTRIBUTION IS HIGHLY SIGNIFICANT ($p < 0.01$).

ERYTHROCYTE AGGREGATION

The presence of prolonged significant erythrocyte aggregation in diabetic subjects have been described by several investigators [31, 57, 70, 71, 72, 58]. In short-term diabetes the degree of aggregation varies according to the disturbance in the carbo-hydrate metabolism or complicating factors (infections). In long-term diabetes the degree of aggregation is persistent. The aggregation is associated with a significant decrease of the linear rate of flow particularly in the postcapillary venules. Large heavy aggregates in static venous channels tend to sediment to the lower side of the vessels (Fig. 5).

The intravascular erythrocyte aggregation is formed by an interaction between the red cell membrane and an increase in the content of alpha₁-, alpha₂- and beta-globulins as well as fibrinogen. We have also found a correlation between the degree of aggrega-tion and the total amount of lipoproteins [72]. Evidence for a coating of the erythrocytes consisting of alpha₂-globulin and fibrinogen has been found in diabetic subjects

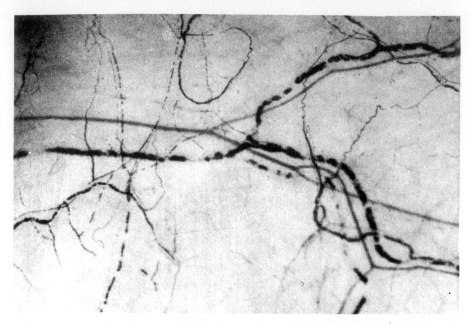

FIG. 5. HEAVILY AGGREGATED FLOW WITH SETTLING OF BLOOD CELL MASSES IN COLLECTING VENULES IN A 30-YEAR-OLD MAN, SUFFERING FROM DIABETES FOR 19 YEARS. (MAGNIFICATION APPROX. 45×). REDUCED TO 7/10.

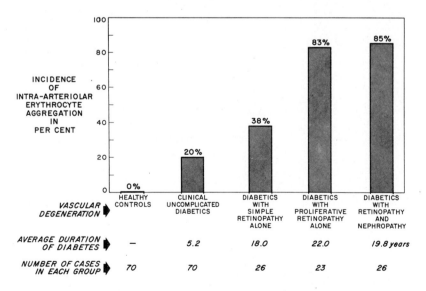

FIG. 6. RELATIONSHIP BETWEEN INTRA-ARTERIOLAR ERYTHROCYTE AGGREGATION IN VIVO AND DIABETIC MICROANGIOPATHY.

with markedly altered plasma protein pattern and marked aggregation, whereas this could not be shown in cases with smaller deviation in their protein patterns [73, 71].

In 145 young diabetics a relationship was found between the incidence and degree of severe intravascular erythrocyte aggregation and the degree of microangiopathy. Since, of the diabetics showing no clinical evidence of retinopathy or nephropathy

20% had intravascular erythrocyte aggregation, this indicates that this change by its rheological effect might be of importance in the development of diabetic micro-angiopathy (Fig. 6).

BLOOD VISCOSITY

Because of the evident similarity of venous-capillary changes in the retina of macro-globulinaemia and diabetes, Skovborg has started a study of the blood viscosity in diabetic patients. SKOVBORG [74] has just reported in Cambridge on the finding of increased blood viscosity in 40 non-acidotic long-term diabetics as compared to 25 healthy controls. The viscosity was measured with the Wells–Brookfield viscometer, and he found that the hematocrit-corrected full-blood viscosity was on an average 20% higher in the diabetic group than in the controls, and thus confirming his prelim-inary report [75]. Within the diabetic group the blood viscosity was significantly cor-related to the alpha$_1$-, alpha$_2$-, beta-globulin and the fibrinogen concentration [74]. In cases of diabetics with short duration of their disease and without evidence of retino-pathy and nephropathy I find that the hematocrit-corrected blood viscosity is not increased compared with normals (Fig. 7). The material is still rather small but the

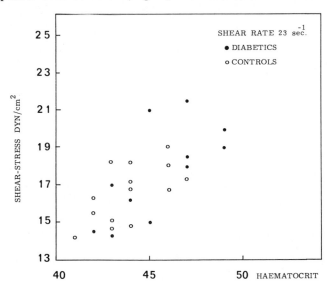

FIG. 7. PLOT FOR THE RELATION BETWEEN SHEAR-STRESS AND HEMATOCRITS FOR DIABETIC SUBJECTS AND CONTROLS AT SHEAR RATE 23 SEC^{-1}.

finding so far would indicate that high blood viscosity is a late phenomenon and it detracts from its importance in the development of the early diabetic retinal lesions. However, it might still be of some importance as a factor in the progression of already established retinopathy.

SUMMARY

Reasons have been given in support of the assumption that hemorheological changes play an important rôle in the development of diabetic microangiopathy. The importance of pathophysiological response changes leading to venous slowing of flow and a redistribution of flow in the microvasculature is emphasized. These pathophysiological response changes satisfy the necessary three requirements for considering them as having pathogenetic importance. The changes in flow properties: intravascular erythrocyte aggregation and increased blood viscosity both aggravate the tendency to stasis in the venous microcirculation of diabetics.

Emphasis purposely has been placed upon the rôle possibly played by the hemorheological factors. However, this should not detract from the importance of other significant factors, as demonstrated in the many intracellular changes which occur in the altered metabolic-hormonal environment. It is obvious that the whole problem of the pathogenesis of the diabetic angiopathy is one of great complexity.

ACKNOWLEDGMENTS

Miss Hanne Zacharias and Miss Birte Hyldgaard afforded valuable assistance for which we are thankful.

This study was supported in part by the Swedish Diabetes Association and the Danish State Research Foundation.

REFERENCES

[1] BALLANTYNE, A. J. and LOEWENSTEIN, A. *Trans. Ophth. Soc. U. Kingdom* **63**, 95, 1943.
[2] BALLANTYNE, A. J. and LOEWENSTEIN, A. *Brit. J. Ophth.* **28**, 593, 1944.
[3] FRIEDENWALD, J. S. *Trans. Am. Acad. Ophth.* **53**, 73, 1948.
[4] FRIEDENWALD, J. S. *Am. J. Ophth.* **33**, 1187, 1950.
[5] ASHTON, N. *Brit. J. Ophth.* **33**, 407, 1949.
[6] ASHTON, N. *Brit. J. Opth.* **34**, 38, 1950.
[7] BALLANTYNE, A. J. *Arch. Ophth.* **33**, 97, 1945.
[8] BALLANTYNE, A. J. *Trans. Ophth. Soc. U. Kingdom* **66**, 503, 1946.
[9] JENSEN, V. A. *Ugeskr. laeger* **111**, 1360, 1949.
[10] WALKER, G. L. *Trans. Am. Ophth. Soc.* **48**, 677, 1950.
[11] LUNDBÆK, K. In *Long-term Diabetes*. Ophthalmological section in collaboration with V. A. Jensen, Copenhagen, 1953.
[12] ASHTON, N. *Brit. J. Ophth.* **35**, 189, 1951.
[13] ASHTON, N. *Diabetic Retinopathy, in Disorders of Carbohydrate Metabolism*. PYKE, A. (Editor), Pitman Medical Publishing Co. Ltd., London, 1962, p. 195.
[14] LOEWENSTEIN, A. and GARROW, A. *Am. J. Ophth.* **28**, 840, 1945.
[15] BALLANTYNE, A. J. and MICHAELSON, I. C. *Trans. Ophth. Soc. U. Kingdom* **67**, 59, 1947.
[16] BECKER, B. and POST, L. T., Jr. *Am. J. Ophth.* **34**, 677, 1951.
[17] WISE, G. N. *Trans. Am. Ophth. Soc.* **54**, 729, 1956.
[18] WISE, G. N., *A. M. A. Arch. Ophth.* **58**, 544, 1957.
[19] ASHTON, N., KOK, D'A. and FOULDS, W. S. *J. Path. and Bact.* **86**, 453, 1963.
[20] SCHWAB, P. J., OKUN, E. and FAHEY, J. L. *Arch. Ophth. (Chicago)* **64**, 515, 1960.
[21] COYLE, J. T., FRANK, P. E., LEONARD, A. L. and WEINER, A. *Arch. Ophth. (Chicago)* **65**, 75, 1961.
[22] CONWAY, N. and WALKER, J. M. *Brit. Med. J.* **2**, 1296, 1962.
[23] KOK, D'A., WHITMORE, D. N. and AINSWORTH, R. W. *J. Clin. Path.* **16**, 351, 1963.
[24] ASHTON, N. *Brit. J. Ophth.* **37**, 282, 1953.
[25] LARSEN, H-W. *Diabetic Retinopathy*. An Ophthalmoscopic Study with a Discussion of the Morphologic Changes and the Pathogenetic Factors in this Disease, Copenhagen, 1960.
[26] HARDIN, R. C., JACKSON, R. L., JOHNSTON, TH. L. and KELLY, H. G. *Diabetes* **5**, 397, 1956.
[27] DITZEL, J. and WHITE, P. *J. Chron. Dis.* **3**, 253, 1956.
[28] GRAFFLIN, A. L. and CORDDRY, E. G. *Bull. Johns Hopkins Hosp.* **93**, 275, 1953.
[29] DITZEL, J. and SAGILD, U. *New Engl. J. Med.* **250**, 587, 1954.
[30] MEIGHAN, S. S. *Brit. J. Ophth.* **40**, 513, 1956.
[31] BLOCH, E. H. *Ergebn. Anat. EntwGesch.* **35**, 1, 1956.

[32] DITZEL, J. and DUCKERS, J. *Acta Paed.* **46**, 535, 1957.
[33] DITZEL, J. and MOINAT, P. *Diabetes* **6**, 307, 1957.
[34] DITZEL, J. *The Conjunctival Vessels in Diabetes Mellitus*, Munksgaard, Copenhagen, 1962.
[35] LABRAM, C. *L'Examen Biomicroscopique des Vaisseaux Conjonctivaux*, R. Vezin, 48, rue de la Sante, Paris, 1959, p. 2.
[36] MEGIBOW, R. S., POLLOCK, H., MEGIBOW, S. J., BOOKMAN, J. J. and OSSERMAN, K. *Am. Heart. J.* **38**, 468, 1949.
[37] MEGIBOW, R. S., MEGIBOW, S. J., POLLOCK, H., BOOKMAN, J. J. and OSSERMAN, K. *Am. J. Med.* **15**, 322, 1953.
[38] MENDLOWITZ, M., GROSSMAN, E. B. and ALPERT, S. *Am. J. Med.* **15**, 316, 1953.
[39] BÁRÁNY, F. *Acta Med. Scand., Suppl.* **304**, 125, 1955.
[40] SIGROTH, K. *Acta Med. Scand., Suppl.* **325**, 77, 1957.
[41] FUNAHASKI, T. and FINK, A. I. *Am. J. Ophth.* **55**, 504, 1963.
[42] PIERI, A. and SCARPELLI, P. T. Paper presented at the Second Annual Meeting, European Association for the Study of Diabetes. Arhus, Denmark, 1966.
[43] FAGERBERG, S. E. *Acta Med. Scand., Suppl.* **345**, 33, 1959.
[44] BLUMENTHAL, H. T., ALEX, M. and GOLDBERG, S. *Arch. Path.* **70**, 13, 1960.
[45] GOLDBERG, S. M., ALEX, M., JOSHI, R. A. and BLUMENTHAL, H. T. *Diabetes* **8**, 261, 1959.
[46] AAGENÆS, O. and MOE, H. *Diabetes* **10**, 253, 1961.
[47] PEDERSEN, J. and OLSEN, S. *Acta Med. Scand.* **171**, 551, 1962.
[48] HANDELSMAN, M. B., MORRIONE, T. G. and GHITMAN, B. *Arch. Intern. Med.* **110**, 70, 1962.
[49] ZACHS, S. I., PEGUES, J. J. and ELLIOTT, F. A. *Metabolism* **11**, 381, 1962.
[50] JØRGENSEN, M. B. *Arch. Otolaryng.* **74**, 373, 1961.
[51] BURSTEIN, R., BERNS, A. W., HIRATA, Y. and BLUMENTHAL, H. T. *Amer. J. Obstet. Gynec.* **86**, 66, 1963.
[52] ANGERVALL, L., DOTEVALL, G. and LEHMANN, K. E. *Acta Med. Scand.* **169**, 339, 1961.
[53] LAZARUS, S. S. and VOLK, B. W. *Arch. Path. (Chicago)* **71**, 44, 1961.
[54] STAHL, S. S., WITKIN, G. J. and SCOPP, I. W., *Oral Surg.* **15**, 1495, 1962.
[55] ASHTON, N. *Advanc. Ophthal.* **8**, 1, 1958.
[56] THOMSEN, A. C. *The Kidney in Diabetes Mellitus*, Munksgaard, Copenhagen, 1965.
[57] DITZEL, J. *Circulation* **14**, 386, 1956.
[58] REES, S. B., CAMERINI-DAVALOS, R. A., CAULFIELD, J. B., LOZANO-CASTANEDA, O., CERVANTES-AMEZCUS, A. TATON, J., POMETTA, D., KRAUTHAMMER, J. P. and MARBLE, A. In *CIBA Foundation*: *Colloquia on Endocrinology*, vol. 15, Churchill Ltd., London, 1964.
[59] DITZEL, J., SARGEANT, L. and HADLEY, W. B. *Arch. Int. Med.* **101**, 912, 1958.
[60] DITZEL, J., WHITE, P. and DUCKERS, J. *Diabetes* **3**, 99, 1954.
[61] DITZEL, J., WHITE, P. and SARGEANT, L. *Acta Genet.* **7**, 101, 1957.
[62] DITZEL, J. and CAMERINI-DAVALOS, R. *Proc. Soc. Exp. Biol. & Med.* **97**, 475, 1958.
[63] DITZEL, J., BEAVEN, D. and RENOLD, A. E. *Metabolism* **9**, 400, 1960.
[64] JÜTTE, A. Bericht über die 63. Zusammenkunft der Deutschen Ophthalmologischen Gesellschaft in Heidelberg, 1960.
[65] JÜTTE, A. In *Diabetisc. Angiopathie*, MOHNIKE, G. (Editor), Akademie-Verlag, Berlin, 1964.
[66] THIEL, R. *Klin. Mbl. Augenhk.* Beiheft 25, 1956.
[67] THIEL, R. 3 Kongr. Internat. Diabetes Fed. Düsseldorf 212, 1958. Stuttgart, 1959.
[68] DITZEL, J., SCHWARTZ, M. and SKOVBORG, F. *4th Europ. Conf. on Microcirculation*, Cambridge, 1966, HARDERS, H. (Editor), *Bibl. Anat.*, S. Karger, Basel (in press).
[69] LARSEN, H-W. and POULSEN, J. E. Lecture given at the 4th Congress of the International Diabetes Federation, Geneva, 1961.
[70] WEISS-FOGH, J. *Scand. J. Clin. Lab. Invest.* **9**, Suppl. 28, 1957.
[71] DITZEL, J. *Acta med. Scand.* **164**, Suppl. 343, 1959.
[72] DITZEL, J. and MOINAT, P. *J. Lab. & Clin. Med.* **54**, 843, 1959.
[73] DITZEL, J. *Acta med. Scand.* **152**, 371, 1955.
[74] SKOVBORG, F., NIELSEN, A. V., SCHLICHTKRULL, J. and DITZEL, J. *4th Europ. Conf. on Microcirculation*, Cambridge, 1966, HARDERS, H. (Editor), *Bibl. Anat.*, S. Karger, Basel (in press).
[75] SKOVBORG, F., NIELSEN, A. V., SCHLICHTKRULL, J. and DITZEL, J. *Lancet* **1**, 129, 1966.

HEMORHEOLOGIC STUDIES DURING THE PROGRESSION AND REMISSION OF DIABETIC RETINOPATHY

S. B. REES,*[1] L. SIMON,[1] G. A. PELTIER,[2] R. GLEASON,[1]
M. BALODIMOS,[1] A. MARBLE[1] and E. W. MERRILL[2]

Joslin Research Laboratory, Harvard Medical School[1] and
Department of Chemical Engineering

Massachusetts Institute of Technology,[2] Boston, Massachusetts, U.S.A.

ABSTRACT†

A G.D.M. rotational viscometer has been utilized to study the relationship between plasma protein composition and the extrapolated "yield" shear stress at zero shear rate of an erythrocyte (RBC)-plasma suspension. Fasting whole blood is collected in a citrate–phosphate buffered preservation media (CPD) and separated RBC resuspended in native plasma with a final hematocrit of 0.40. Previous studies by Merrill *et al.* have demonstrated that the fibrinogen content of normal plasma is the major determinant of variations in the yield shear stress of normal RBC-plasma suspensions at a constant hematocrit. In patients with various stages of characteristic diabetic retinopathy uncomplicated by diabetic nephropathy, ketoacidosis, infection, infarction or other pathologic processes there was no evidence of a significant increase in the yield shear stress of diabetics versus controls despite significant differences in plasma lipids, orosomucoids and sugar content. Similarly, varying degrees of RBC aggregation secondary to a reduction of capillary and venular flow in the bulbar conjunctiva could be demonstrated without evidence of globulin coating of erythrocytes or significant changes in the yield shear stress or plasma protein composition.

Fulminating progression of hemorrhagic proliferating diabetic retinopathy complicating uncontrolled diabetes, infection and the nephrotic stage of diabetic nephropathy were consistently associated with an increase in the yield shear stress of CPD blood which correlated with significant increases in plasma fibrinogen and macroglobulin content. Varying degrees of hypoalbuminemia were demonstrable but showed no significant relationship to the yield shear stress of CPD blood in the absence of a significant increase in plasma fibrinogen and macroglobulin content. From our preliminary observations to date in normal and diabetic subjects, we conclude that multiple non-specific factors can increase the yield shear stress of blood *in vitro* by increasing the net work interaction of fibrinogen and macroglobulins with normal erythrocytes. These changes in shed blood appear to be only secondary

†The paper was not received at this publication's deadline and the senior author expressed his intention to submit it for publication to the journal *Biorheology*. (Editor.)

complications of a dysproteinemia complicating late stages of diabetic microangio-pathy and other disease processes but in some instances contribute significantly to the fulminating progression of diabetic microangiopathy and erythrocyte destruc-tion—which cannot be correlated with degrees of azotemia, carbohydrate intolerance or hyperlipidemia.

A resume of a multivariate regression analysis of multiple factors contributing to the progression and remission of clinical diabetic retinopathy will be presented.

DISCUSSION

SKOVBORG *(Denmark)*:

With my experience it is very difficult to state whether the change of the vessel, which you demonstrated on the slide of the retina is pathological—at least it is difficult in the case of diabetes. We do not have any experience with prediabetes. In my opinion the picture which you showed was normal. I did not see any pathological tortuosity of the vessels. I should like to ask if you have made this evaluation as a double-blind study.

REES *(U.S.A.)*:

Yes, there are different views on the application of double-blind studies. Our incidence of capillary tortuos-ity was determined by a double-blind evaluation of both the bulbar conjunctival and retinal photographs. Photographs of control subjects were interspersed among the photographs of the diabetics, and these were graded and analysed statistically, as described. We could not show evidence of venular dilation in this carefully selected patient population which still has prediabetes. We believe that venular dilation represents a later manifestation of chemical diabetes. How do you feel about this, Jørn? This is an attempt to really dissect further some of your pioneering studies.

DITZEL *(Denmark)*:

Well, I fully agree with you that one sees, in the early cases of diabetes, venular dilation at the same time as you have increased tortuosity of your capillaries. I also observed real evidence of changes in children of diabetic mothers, at a time when these presumable prediabetics have abnormal glucose tolerance tests, indicating that there is a relationship between the abnormality in the carbohydrate metabolism and the changes in the conjunctival vascular bed.

REES:

But then they cease to be prediabetics, Jørn, i.e. if they have an abnormal glucose tolerance, we classify this group as chemical diabetics.

DITZEL:

Yes, they are chemical diabetics and not prediabetics, according to your definition.

SKOVBORG:

As you know, we have built the same type of doubleflash as the one you use. I should like to know how great your measuring accuracy is. Our measuring accuracy is about 50% of the average value. In our opin-ion such results cannot be used. Furthermore, I should like to ask: How can you measure the velocity in normals? It is our opinion that it is absolutely necessary to photograph aggregates, if you will employ this method—and to find aggregates in normals—if they are real normals—is a rare thing. So I do not under-stand how you can make any comparison with normals.

REES:

The evidence of aggregation of formed elements in the capillary and postcapillary venular bed of normal subjects is well substantiated. Jørn Ditzel and many others have described this. We measure, in normal and in our pre- and early chemical diabetic population, those areas of the capillary bed which show aggregation. The increment DS is equal to the net movement of aggregates in those vessels which have a low shear rate. We are unable to demonstrate aggregation in the arterioles, and, therefore, this method is not useful for measuring aggregate flow where it cannot be demonstrated. In our experience we are able to find aggregate flow with a precision of only plus or minus 50%, because this is the variable nature of the flow in the capillary and postcapillary venular circulation. The distribution curve of linear velocity, which I presented, demonstrated preponderance of measurements between zero and 50 microns per second, but a mean value of about 350 microns per second and a range from 0 to 1400 microns per second. Thus, we agree that there is variability in the estimate of linear capillary velocity, but this does not detract from its usefulness in estimating the low shear rates which exist in the microcirculation. Our data presented today, suggest that there is no demonstrable impairment of flow in the early stages of prediabetes. The first measurable changes appear to be in the arteriolar wall with alterations of viscoelastic properties of this wall, before there is impairment of the capillary circulation.

SKOVBORG:

I am glad to hear that you have confirmed our results concerning the viscosity in diabetic patients, but I should like to know why you talk only about the yield stress. As the blood–at least most of the time–is flowing in the vessels, I think it should also be of interest to study the viscosity.

REES:

... in Boston we feel very strongly that because of the non-Newtonian properties of blood, a yield value (yield shear stress) is much easier to agree on whether you want to use the log–log plot that Scott Blair demonstrated or the Casson plot. Actually, the yield value you get from both techniques, through one and a half decades of change of shear rate provides the same extrapolated yield value. This technique enables us to standardize our data at zero shear rate and the apparent viscosity itself is a meaningless figure without specifying the shear rate.

SKOVBORG:

In Europe it is very difficult to estimate the range of the thickness of a normal basement membrane, and it has not been possible to find any pathological thickening of the basement membrane in the case of recently diagnosed diabetes. I really wonder how you can find any pathological thickening in the case of prediabetes.

REES:

Yes, this is a question directed at my Cambridge paper for those of you who were not in Cambridge. The earliest lesions in prediabetes were, as I stressed there, evidences of accumulation of PAS positive and electron dense material between the capillary loops. I have extended this further with this paper to demonstrate the other fascinating changes in the ground tissue substance, particularly the elastic tissue. The peripheral capillary loop basement membrane in prediabetics is perfectly normal. The focal changes that have been described by our laboratory and others, appear to be secondary to the capillary tortuosity where tangential sections give you an apparent thickening, but careful cuts that are made at right angles to the basement membrane clearly indicate the peripheral loops are quite narrow. It is for that reason we are stressing the fact that the early angiopathy is evidenced by premature arteriosclerosis and involves elastic tissue before there are changes in the capillary basement membrane. Thickening of the capillary basement membrane is observed in much later stages of chemical and overt clinical diabetes.

LEHR (U.S.A.):

This is not my field of interest. But, as a member of the Department of Medicine of which Dr. Rachmiel Levine is Chairman, I have some questions for Dr. Ditzel and Dr. Rees. I think it is Dr. Levine's view that the vascular changes are a primary entity and not necessarily connected with or brought about by the metabolic disturbances. I know that there is some disagreement in that area. While Dr. Rees has described the characteristic arterial degeneration occurring in diabetes mellitus, Dr. Ditzel did not mention any arterial changes. I believe the early arterial alterations are very important and do occur in what is known as the prediabetic stage. I wonder whether Dr. Rees and Dr. Ditzel would agree that there is no causal connection between the metabolic changes and the arterial changes, although the latter might be aggravated by the metabolic disturbances and partly improved by metabolic compensation. In other words, the arterial disease is a primary disease and is part of the diabetic syndrome, unrelated to the metabolic derangement.

DITZEL:

My studies have of course been purely clinical and performed with a magnification of approximately one hundred and I have not used the electron microscope. If one observed pure diabetes, that is to say, diabetes in a child, one is impressed with the changes occurring on the venous side, as they occur much earlier than on the arterial side. Of course, if you come down and make electron microscopy studies, you may find that the arterial changes occur as quickly. But from the clinical observation on the retina and on the conjunctiva, the venous changes appear to be the first ones.

REES:

Let me answer the other part of the question which came from Dr. Lehr of New York. Even in Boston, at the Joslin Clinic, where the importance of carbohydrate control has been emphasized, there is a general agreement that all we can do is retard the progression of the vascular disease, which does appear to be a part of the underlying diabetic syndrome.

SWANK (*U.S.A.*):

I'd like to make a comment about the difficulties of measuring the speed of flow in capillaries. I found it very difficult to pick a capillary with an average flow. Even if you averaged the speed in ten vessels, one could not be certain of having an average flow. The differences which you show, depend upon the choice of vessels which you made. I would consider such measurements rather weak evidence that there was no change in blood flow at any stage.

REES:

The lack of evidence for the slowing of capillary flow, in prediabetics, could be due to the difficulties in measuring small differences in the early stages, with our crude methods. The morphologic and ultrastructural evidence does suggest that there are vascular changes, predominantly arteriolar, in this very early stage of diabetes, which can alter the viscoelastic properties of the vessel wall, before there is a significant reduction in the linear velocity of red cells in the true capillary and postcapillary venular vessels of the bulbar conjunctiva.

SWANK:

I do not think my question was answered; is it not possible you missed a real slowing? I am asking, technically, if it is not possible for you to have missed significant slowing before the anatomical changes which you described.

REES:

This is possible because of the variability in estimating the linear capillary velocity. However, actual estimates of gross renal blood flow and glomerular filtration rate during the early stage of diabetes, demonstrate that blood flow is not only normal, but that gross organ flow is actually increased. Thus, there is no evidence of impairment of large vessel flow in the early stages of the diabetic syndrome.

GREGERSEN (*U.S.A.*):

I should like to raise the same point. It is a problem which may relate to the central problem in circulatory shock, namely inadequate perfusion of tissues and stagnant anoxia. Have you actual quantitative evidence of metabolic disturbances? You spoke of that earlier, did you not? In a shock-like state, the crucial thing is not the linear velocity of the blood, but the volume flow and actual delivery of oxygen and what not to the tissues. What evidence have you in diabetes that shows that deficiency in oxygen delivery occurs?

REES:

Actually, in the earlier stages, there is no evidence of impairment of gross delivery of blood to any of the organs. The only evidence is an alteration of the pulsatile nature of the arteriolar wall, which would suggest that there are vascular events going on that are actually causing vascular damage, in this very early stage, that are a part of the early diabetic inheritance.

GREGERSEN:

This suggested to me that changes in pulsation, which are very difficult to evaluate may be important in delivery of blood to the tissues.

REES:

I agree completely.

GREGERSEN:

Because otherwise . . . I do not see the logic of your argument. You say it is a matter of metabolic deficiency, but you do not really demonstrate that you have the sort of thing we see in stagnant anoxia, in circulatory shock, if these two conditions have some similarity. I do not know that they do.

REES:

The important point is that there is no incidence of clinically significant microcirculatory stasis until we focus on later stages of diabetic microangiopathy. In this patient population, we find marked impairment of linear microcirculatory flow rates associated with an increase in the yield shear stress of blood, and a seconddary dysproteinemia. This is the only stage that is analogous to the shock-like low flow state.

GREGERSEN:

While I have the floor, may I follow up something Dr. Skovborg spoke of. It refers to my paper at Cambridge. We are concerned about what happens to blood, from zero flow upwards. That is why we have studied the low shear rates and have seen what happens to the torque response curves, in a sensitive Couette viscometer, at successively lower shear rates. At or below 1/100 r.p.m., the characteristics of these curves raise many questions about how to interpret the events below 1/10 reciprocal second. How you can calculate the shear stress or viscosity from these torque curves, I do not understand.

REES:

By exactly the same means that you and your pioneering efforts with Drs. Gibson and Evans used extrapolation techniques from dye disappearance curves to estimate the plasma volume.

GREGERSEN:

We had a demonstrable rational basis for it.

REES:

The answer is that even with the GDM equipment, there are difficulties in measuring the shear stress at shear rates below 1/10 reciprocal second, so that one has to extrapolate to get an estimate of the yield value at zero shear rate.

GREGERSEN:

I must confess that the work of Benis convinced me of the yield stress. It seemed good work. I was trying to stress how complicated the problem was when we chose the peaks of torque curves. This has a bearing upon what you are discussing, has it not, Dr. Skovborg?

CHARM (U.S.A.):

With respect to whether the yield stress exists or not, we satisfied ourselves that it exists, from sedimentation experiments. We merely found a small enough diameter capillary tube in which sedimentation did not occur, and calculated the yield stress which prevented the sedimentation in that tube, and found that this did check out with an extrapolated value from a shear stress–shear rate plot. So, from this standpoint, we felt that there was indeed a yield stress. Now the question that I want to ask you is an extension of Dr. Skovborg's question concerning your neglect in taking advantage of your Casson viscosities, which you obviously have the experimental data to determine. In doing this, you have, in essence, neglected the effect of these plasma protein changes on the plasma viscosity. I do not see where you have attempted to determine these changes on the plasma viscosity. You have not, have you?

REES:

No, actually we have not because of the early studies of Dr. Cogan and collaborators (*Diabetes,* **10,** 393, 1961.) which could not demonstrate significant changes in diabetic plasma. We have, therefore, focused on the interaction of diabetic plasma and red cells for estimating a small increase in yield values at constant hematocrit, which magnifies abnormalities attributed to the interaction of plasma constituents with erythrocytes.

DITZEL:

I do not think that this is quite correct. Cogan and co-workers did not, unfortunately, measure the plasma viscosity, but only serum viscosity in diabetics. What interest does serum viscosity have when you are talking about circulation? That is why we prefer to measure full-blood viscosity.

CHARM:

I think the one point that has to be made is that it is possible to have the same yield stress and different viscosities as it is to have different viscosities and the same yield stress. I do not think it is reasonable, really, that you should neglect this. I do not think it has been established definitely that there are not changes in your viscosities. I think this may be an important fact especially since you are dealing with circulation.

TAYLOR (*Australia*):

I quite agree that it is extremely difficult to interpret pulse waves or flow pulses one at a time. I think it is almost impossible to take a single pulse wave from an artery and say what is going on. I think this is very dangerous. One has to take at least two, so that one can make a comparison. No, this is serious. It is really very necessary to take at least two, over a stretch of artery or something like that. Granted that, looking at those waves, if that was a dog, the shape of the waves suggests to me what happens when you have peripheral vosodilation. I would not draw any conclusions about the elastic properties of the artery from a single wave. But other things being equal, I would say that there was peripheral vasodilation in the example you showed.

REES:

It is important to analyse a series of pulse waves as you well emphasized, Dr. Taylor. The differences cited in the prediabetic are not associated with vasodilation but are associated with morphologic abnormalities in the arteriolar wall.

GELIN *(Sweden)*:

Dr. Ditzel, how fast are these changes reversible concerning stasis phenomenon and dilation? Can this happen within hours or days?

DITZEL:

They are quite reversible. We measured, as I told, fluctuations in vessel calibers in one hundred young diabetics and non-diabetics from photographs. Quite remarkable changes could be observed over a period of 8 hours. So they are quite reversible.

GELIN:

That is a very important point for the whole discussion here. If it is rapidly occurring, or if it takes weeks to reverse it. Because if they are rapid changes, it should be possible to come back to metabolic quantitative studies which are fairly accurate.

ACROSYNDROMES VASCULAIRES:
STASE ET VISCOSITÉ DU SANG

J. F. Merlen* et J. Coget

La Clinique Medical Quest du Centre Hospitalier
Universitaire de Lille, Lille, France

Il est classique de dire que la viscosité sanguine est augmentée au cours de la stase veineuse, en particulier dans l'acrocyanose et la phase asphyxique du Raynaud. Le fait en aurait été vérifié sur le sang veineux central, au pli du coude, par la méthode habituelle de Hess. Pringle et col. (1965) trouvaient récemment des viscosités élevées chez 21 de leurs 22 sujets souffrant de maladie de Raynaud grâce à la technique de Pirofsky (1953). C'est la raison pour laquelle nous avons voulu le vérifier par l'étude comparative des divers acrosyndromes vasculaires des extrémités.

1. LE CONCEPT DE STASE SANGUINE

Le concept de stase est mal défini par la plupart des auteurs; il ne s'agit pas du simple ralentissement du cours du sang dans les capillaires et les veinules mais d'un *phénomène dynamique* visible au capillaroscope. La colonne sanguine circulante parait écarlate, transparente, homogène, il n'y a plus de manchon plasmatique mais une simple colonne d'hématies conglutinées, agrégées mais non agglutinées, car l'aspect normal reprend dès l'instant où le cours du sang s'accélère à nouveau. La colonne est souvent fragmentée et donne l'aspect du "spasme" surtout au voisinage des branchements vasculaires. Illig distingue la *préstase* ou ralentissement simple du sang et *la stase* ou agrégation des hématies, mail il n'y a ni thrombose ni sludge. Sous l'effet de la stase, l'hypertension veineuse en aval des capillaires inverse le sens du courant sanguin qui se fait des tissus vers la lumière vasculaire d'où une souffrance de la barrière hématotissulaire et ouvre passivement les canaux dérivatifs artério-veineux. D'où à la longue des altérations histologiques plus ou moins profondes des dispositifs de bloc. Tous phénomènes qui réalisent les tableaux cliniques d'acroasphyxie et qu'à l'encontre de Mian nous considérons comme primitifs et non secondaires. Se servant du microscope électronique les Italiens Giunta 1957 et Arcangeli 1965 voient la lumière capillaire augmenter et les mastocytes de voisinage perdre leurs granulations qui passent dans l'espace péricapillaire d'où l'oedème par inhibition et l'érythrodiapédèse par libération de facteurs protéolytiques. La stase par suite du ralentissement de la circulation et de la conglutination des hématies a pour corollaire hémodynamique l'élévation de la viscosité sanguine et ceci s'observe cliniquement au cours des états polyglobuliques, de l'acrocyanose et de la phase asphyzique du Raynaud.

2. MÉTHODE UTILISÉE

Toute méthode de mesure de la viscosité sanguine est critiquable, même celle de Couette ou de Brookfield, si elle ne porte pas sur du sang périphérique prélevé en pleine zone cutanée de stase sanguine. Or la quantité de sang capillaro-veineux prélevée ne pouvant être que minime, il nous a donc fallu utiliser une méthode simple, pratique et suffisamment valable lors d'examens comparatifs en cours de traitement. Nous nous sommes adressés à la technique de McGOVERN (1955) basée sur les corrélations de l'hématocrite et de la viscosité absolue mesurée en centipoises, la modifiant par l'emploi d'une micropipette capillaire. La centrifugation étant faite à 10.000 tours/minute pendant 7 minutes, aussitôt le prélèvement, toujours dans le même laboratoire et par le même technicien. La valeur normale est de 2,70 centipoises ±0,12 avec des limites extrêmes de 2,46 et 2,94. La goutte de sang prélevée par ponction du bout du doigt est d'origine capillaro-veineuse, or comme le fait remarquer B. Zweifach, c'est le débit de retour qui commande la rhéologie à l'étage terminal et c'est à ce niveau même que les mouvements de flux et de reflux du sang dans le lit capillaire reflètent les modifications biophysiques du sang lui-même, surtout s'il s'agit de stase. Il y a et il y aura toujours des causes d'erreur, mais il est de fait que la corrélation hématocrite-viscosité est suffisamment grande pour qu'il soit possible lors des mesures comparatives, pour des échantillons de sang de degré d'hématocrite inférieur à 50% et de teneur en protéines voisine de la normale, de tirer des conclusions valables en clinique journalière.

3. RESULTATS

Notre matériel comporte une centaine de sujets adultes suivis depuis bientôt deux ans et porteurs d'acrosyndromes vasculaires purs, dont 2 cas intriqués d'acrocyanose et de Raynaud et 3 cas de Raynaud avec sclérodactylie sans sclérodermie généralisée. Il s'agit de:

— 26 cas d'acrocyanose pure,
— 17 cas de maladie ou phénomène de Raynaud,
— 2 cas mixtes de Raynaud sur acrocyanose,
— 17 cas d'acroparesthésies de Schultze,
— 5 cas de paumes rouges de Lane,
— 5 cas de purpura vasculaire sans macroglobulinémie,
— 5 cas de sclérodermie généralisée,
— 2 cas de polyglobulie essentielle (maladie de Vaquez).

La viscosité sanguine absolue réalisée dans les meilleures conditions est élevée 15 fois sur 24 dans l'acrocyanose et 10 fois sur 17 dans le Raynaud. Elle reste par contre dans les limites normales dans le livedo reticularis ou annularis et les acroparesthésies, normale dans les paumes rouges et la sclérodermie généraliseé mais pour les 5 cas observés de purpura vasculaire elle est diminuée par rapport à l'ensemble (Fig. 1). Bien entendu elle est très augmentée dans la polyglobulie essentielle ou maladie de Vaquez. Certes de tels résultats n'apportent qu'une valeur indicative, celle de l'élévation fréquente de la viscosité sanguine à l'étage terminal dans l'acrocyanose et la maladie de Raynaud, conséquence de la stase veinulo-capillaire. Il est à penser que lorsque la viscosité n'est pas trouvée élevée, celà tient à un phénomène de compensa-

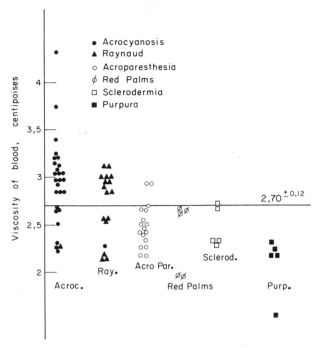

FIG. 1. DISTRIBUTION DES CAS D'ACROSYNDROMES VASCULAIRES EN FONCTION DES VALEURS EN CENTI-POISES DE LA VISCOSITÉ ABSOLUE DU SANG PÉRIPHÉRIQUE.

tion hémodynamique de la stase, l'ouverture large des court-circuits artério-veineux comme nous l'avons montré dès 1952.

CONCLUSION

Il est admis, classiquement, un accroissement de la viscosité sanguine lors de la stase et dans l'acrocyanose. Les expériences récentes de PRINGLE (1965) ont montré une viscosité élevée dans la maladie du Raynaud. Les auteurs ont utilisé la methode pratique de PIROFSKY (1953) dans un grand nombre de cas d'acrosyndrome vasculaire. Ils ont trouvé 6 fois sur 10 une augmentation de la viscosité absolue du sang périphérique dans l'acrocyanose et une diminution dans le phénomène du Raynaud. Ces résultats sont discutés.

RÉFÉRENCES

ALBERT, S. N., JAIN, S. C., SCHIBUYA, J. et ALBERT, C. A. *The Hematocrit in Clinical Practice*, Charles C. Thomas, Springfield, Illinois, 1965.

BAYLISS, L. E. In *Flow Properties of Blood and Other Biological Systems*, COPLEY, A. L. and STAINSBY, G. (Editors), Pergamon Press, Oxford, New York, 1960, p. 29.

BURTON, A. C. *Physiology and Biophysics of the Circulation*. Year Book Medical Publ., Chicago, 1965.

COPLEY, A. L. In *Flow Properties of Blood and Other Biological Systems*, COPLEY, A. L. and STAINSBY, G. (Editors), Pergamon Press, Oxford, New York, 1960, p. 97.

McGOVERN, J., JONES, A. R. et STEINBERG, A. G. *New Engl. J. Med.* **253**, 308, 1955.

HANSEN, P. F. et THORN, N. A. *Amer. J. Med. Sci.* **231**, 665, 1956.

MERLEN, J. F. *5e Journ. Internat. Phlebologie,* Aix en Provence, 1966.

PIROFSKY, B. *J. Clin. Invest.* **32**, 292, 1953.

PRINGLE, R., WALDER, D. N. et WEAVER, J. P. *Lancet* i, 1086, 1965.

WIRKUNG UND WIRKUNGSWEISE UNVERESTERTER FETTSÄUREN AUF DIE VISKOSITÄT DES BLUTES

A. M. Ehrly*

Medizinische Klinik und Poliklinik der Johannes-Gutenberg-Universität, Mainz, Germany

Die Zusammenlagerung von Erythrocyten zu Aggregaten ist vielfach in einen pathogenetischen Zusammenhang mit einer Reihe von Erkrankungen gebracht worden, die sich vom Schock bis hin zur Thrombose erstrecken. Neben der Möglichkeit, daß Erythrocytenaggregate direkt als kleine Emboli die Mikrozirkulation behindern können, ist besonders die Frage der Viskosität aggregatreichen Blutes aus hämodynamischen und hämorheologischen Gründen beachtet worden. Bereits im Jahre 1920 hatten Hess[1] und Rothlin[2] festgestellt, daß die Blutviskosität keine Konstante ist, sondern von der Fließgeschwindigkeit ganz wesentlich abhängt. Entsprechende Untersuchungen wurden 1955 auch von Krosch und Heidelmann[3] angestellt. Es ist das Verdienst von Wells und Merrill[4, 5, 6], Copley[7], Dintenfass[8, 9] und anderen[10, 11], die Gesetze der Strukturviskosität des Blutes exakt untersucht und bekannt gemacht zu haben.

Die Quintessenz dieser Untersuchungen ist die, daß die effektive Blutviskosität bei abnehmender Fließgeschwindigkeit und bei sinkendem Tangentialdruck ganz erheblich zunimmt und dann das mehrfache der Viskosität bei normalen und hohen Fließgeschwindigkeiten betragen kann. Wenn also bei verschiedenen Erkrankungen die Scherkräfte abnehmen, weil die *vis a tergo* gering ist (zum Beispiel im Kreislaufschock, bei peripheren arteriellen und venösen Durchblutungsstörungen), dann wird durch die auftretende Erhöhung der Strukturviskosität die Durchblutung der Organe noch mehr herabgesetzt und es kann sich ein circulus vitiosus entwickeln.

Auf Grund dieser Überlegungen wäre es also am einfachsten, die Fließgeschwindigkeiten in den Gefäßen zu erhöhen und damit die Strukturviskosität herabzusetzen. Im Kreislaufschock kann dies jedoch sehr schwierig sein; auch ist zum Beispiel bei peripheren arteriellen Durchblutungsstörungen bei Arteriosklerose eine Erhöhung des Durchflußvolumens pro Zeit durch eine Drucksteigerung oder eine Erweiterung der Gefäße kaum möglich. In solchen Fällen liegt oftmals schon ein erhöhter Blutdruck vor, und die Gefäß durchmesser können bei der bestehenden Wandverkalkung nicht verändert werden. Bei diesen Erkrankungen wäre der umgekehrte Weg erfolgversprechend, nämlich durch eine direkte Erniedrigung der effektiven Viskosität die Durchblutung der Organe zu verbessern.

Eigene Untersuchungen der letzten Jahre ließen erkennen, daß es möglich ist, Erythrocytenaggregate *in vitro*, d.h. unabhängig von der Strömungsgeschwindigkeit, durch Zusatz von unveresterten Fettsäuren und anderen oberflächenaktiven Substanzen zu desaggregieren[12]. Dabei kommt es gleichzeitig zur Hemmung einer vorher beschleunigten Blutkörperchensenkung[13]. Messungen mit dem Kapillarviskosimeter nach Ostwald (Kapillarradius 0,025 cm) bei konstanter Fließgeschwindigkeit, gleichem Hämatokrit der Proben und bei einer Temperatur von $37 \mp 0,1°C$ ergaben eine Senkung der Blutviskosität aggregatreichen Blutes nach Zusatz von Natrium-Oleat in Konzentrationen zwischen 20 und 60 mg/100 ml Blut[14]. Auf der Abb. 1 ist die relative

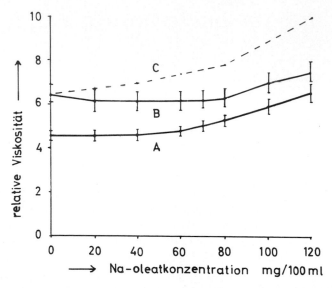

ABB. 1. WIRKUNG VERSCHIEDENER OLEATKONZENTRATIONEN (ABSZISSE) AUF DIE VISKOSITÄT DES BLUTES (ORDINATE). KURVE A: NORMALBLUT. KURVE B: ERYTHROCYTEN-AGGREGATREICHES BLUT VON PATIENTEN.

Viskosität (Wasser = 1) menschlichen Blutes nach Zusatz verschieden hoher Konzentrationen von Natrium-Oleat aufgezeichnet. Kurve A zeigt die Verhältnisse bei normalem, erythrocytenaggregatarmem Blut von 6 gesunden Probanden (Mittelwerte). Oleatkonzentrationen bis 40 mg% bewirken keine Änderung der Viskosität; hohe Konzentrationen führen zu einem Viskositätsanstieg. Bei kurve B handelt es sich um ein aggregatreiches Blut von Patienten mit erhöhter Blutkörperchensenkungsgeschwindigkeit und den gleichen Hämatokritwerten wie in Kurve A. (Mittelwerte aus Messungen bei 8 Patienten). Na-oleat in Konzentrationen bis 60 mg% bewirkt hier eine geringe, aber konstant nachweisbare Verringerung der Blutviskosität gegenüber Kontrollen ohne Oleatzusatz. Erst bei hohen Na-oleatkonzentrationen steigt die Blutviskosität an.

Da bei normalem, aggregatarmem Blut eine Senkung der Blutviskosität mit dem Kapillarviskosimeter nicht nachzuweisen war, nahmen wir an, daß die Viskositätsminderung aggregatreichen Blutes durch Zusatz unveresterter Fettsäuren oder deren Salze auf dem Wege über eine Desaggregation von Erythrocytenaggregaten zustande kommt und als Senkung der Strukturviskosität zu erklären ist. Zur Beantwortung dieser Frage wurde jetzt die Änderung der Blutviskosität nach Zusatz von Natrium-Oleat bei verschiedenen Geschwindigkeitsgradienten (shear rate) mit einem Brookfield-Viskosimeter durchgeführt. Außerdem wurde mit dem selben Gerät die Viskosität des Blutes vor und nach intravenöser Injektion von Heparin beim Menschen untersucht.

METHODE

Es wurde Normalblut und Blut von Patienten mit deutlich erhöhter Blutkörperchensenkungsgeschwindigkeit und kapillarmikroskopisch sichtbaren Erythrocytenaggregaten (Sludge-Phänomen) untersucht. Die Proben wurden morgens nüchtern aus den ungestauten Cubitalvenen entnommen und durch Zusatz von Natrium-Zitrat ungerinnbar gemacht (38 mg Na-zitrat auf 10 ml Blut). Als Prototyp einer langkettigen Fettsäure wurde Natrium-Oleat (Fa. Riedel-de-Haen, Seelze) zunächst in verschiedenen Konzentrationen in physiologischer Kochsalzlösung gelöst und dann jeweils 0,1 ml dieser Oleatlösung zu jeweils 5 ml Blut zugegeben. Die so erhaltenen Oleatkonzentrationen im Blut betrugen 20, 40, 80 und 120 mg/100 ml. Die Bestimmung der unveresterten Fettsäuren im Plasma erfolgte nach der Methode von Dole und Meinertz in einer Modifikation nach Konitzer et al.[15]. Die Inkubationszeit des Blutes mit Na-oleat betrug 10 Minuten[16]. Alle Versuche wurden unmittelbar im Anschluß an die Blutentnahmen durchgeführt.

Die Blutviskosität wurde mit einem Brookfield—micro (cone-plate)—Viskosimeter vom Typ LVT bei 5,8; 11,5; 23; 46; und 115 shear rate sec^{-1} gemessen. Die Temperatur wurde mit einem leistungsfähigen Thermostaten auf $37 \mp 0, 1°C$ konstant gehalten. Bei vergleichenden Viskositätsmessungen wurde besonders auf die Übereinstimmung der Hämatokritwerte geachtet. Erythrocytenaggregate wurden *in vitro* durch besondere Blutausstriche[12] und durch eine erhöhte Blutkörperchensenkungsgeschwindigkeit nachgewiesen. Bei den Messungen mit dem Brookfield-Viskosimeter mußte zur Erzielung reproduzierbarer Werte neben der Temperaturkonstanz besonders darauf geachtet werden, daß es während der Messung nicht zu einer Sedimentation der Erythrocytenaggregate im Gerät kam, und daß es nicht durch die Drehbewegungen des Meßtellers zu einer Verringerung des Hämatokrits infolge zentrifugal abfließender Erythrocyten kam. Außerdem wurde zur Erzielung genügend großer Ausschläge des Zeigers meist der Hämatokrit durch Abpipettieren von Plasma erhöht.

ERGEBNISSE

(1) *Einfluß von Natrium-Oleat auf die Viskosität aggregatreichen Blutes*

In Abb. 2 ist das Verhalten der Viskosität, gemessen in centipoise (cp) bei verschiedenen Geschwindigkeitsgradienten im Blut einer Patientin mit chronischer Polyarthritis dargestellt. Die Blutkörperchensenkung war mit 33/65 deutlich beschleunigt; mikroskopisch ließen sich vielfach Erythrocytenaggregate nachweisen. Der Hämatokrit betrug 42. Es sind 4 Kurven eingezeichnet, die 4 verschiedenen Oleatkonzentrationen entsprechen. Ohne Zusatz von Na-oleat (Kurve mit ausgefüllten Punkten) zeigt sich der bekannte Anstieg der Blutviskosität bei abnehmenden Tangentialdrucken. Bei einem Oleatzusatz von 20 und 40 mg% sind bei 115 und 46 shear rate sec^{-1} noch keine Differenzen festzustellen. Bei kleineren Geschwindigkeitsgradienten jedoch ist die Viskosität nach Oleatzusatz gegenüber der Kontrolle wesentlich verringert; und zwar umso mehr, je kleiner der Geschwindigkeitsgradient ist. Die Kurvenform bei der Oleatkonzentration von 40 mg% ähnelt einer entsprechend gemessenen Viskositätskurve eines normalen, nicht aggregierten Blutes. Bei hohen Oleatkonzentrationen (80 mg% und mehr) liegt die Blutviskosität bei allen shear rate—Werten über dem Ausgangswert.

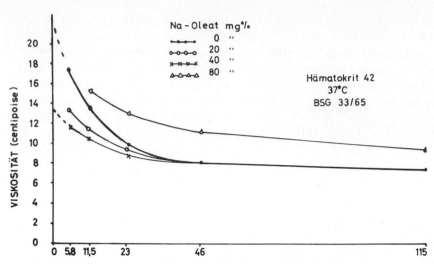

ABB. 2. EINFLUSS VERSCHIEDENER NA-OLEATKONZENTRATIONEN AUF DIE VISKOSITÄT ERYTHROCYTEN-AGGREGATREICHEN BLUTES EINES PATIENTEN BEI VERSCHIEDENEN GESCHWINDIGKEITSGRADIENTEN.

(2) *Einfluß von Natrium-Oleat auf die Viskosität normalen Blutes*

In Abb. 3 ist die Viskosität des Blutes einer gesunden Versuchsperson bei verschiedenen Geschwindigkeitsgradienten aufgezeichnet. Der Hämatokrit betrug bei diesen Proben 43, die Blutkörperchensenkungsgeschwindigkeit 2/4. Bei der Blutprobe ohne Oleatzusatz sind die Viskositätswerte, auch bei niedrigen Tangentialdrucken

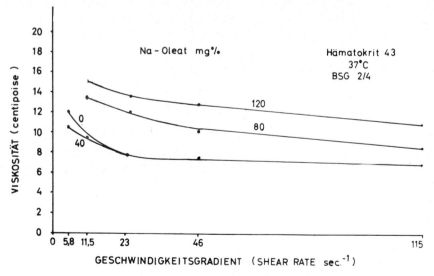

ABB. 3. EINFLUSS VERSCHIEDENER NA.OLEATKONZENTRATIONEN AUF DIE VISKOSITÄT DES BLUTES EINER GESUNDEN PERSON BEI VERSCHIEDENEN GESCHWINDIGKEITSGRADIENTEN.

relativ niedrig. Zusatz von Na-Oleat in einer Konzentration bis 40 mg% bewirkt nur eine sehr geringe Verminderung der Viskosität bei den kleinsten Geschwindigkeitsgradienten. Na-oleatkonzentrationen von 80 und 120 mg% bewirken eine deutliche Erhöhung der Blutviskosität bei allen Fließgeschwindigkeiten.

(3) *Verhalten der Viskosität eines erythrocytenaggregathaltigen Blutes vor und nach einer Injektion von Heparin*

Abb. 4 zeigt die Viskosität des Blutes einer Patientin mit einer chronischen Pyelonephritis bei verschiedenen Geschwindigkeitsgradienten. Der Hämatokrit betrug 47, die Blutkörperchensenkungsgeschwindigkeit 15/28. Unter dem Mikroskop ließen sich vielfach Erythrocytenaggregate in Form von Geldrollen nachweisen. Kurve A zeigt

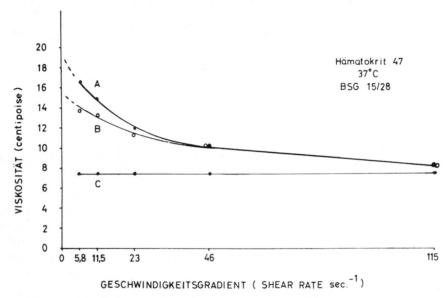

ABB. 4. EINFLUSS DER KONZENTRATION UNVERESTERTER FETTSÄUREN IN VIVO AUF DIE VISKOSITÄT ERYTHROCYTEN-AGGREGATHALTIGEN BLUTES EINER PATIENTIN BEI VERSCHIEDENEN GESCHWINDIGKEITS-GRADIENTEN. KURVE A: VOR DER INJEKTION VON HEPARIN (KONZENTRATION AN UFS 18 MG%). KURVE B: 15 MINUTEN NACH DER INJEKTION VON HEPARIN INTRAVENÖS (KONZENTRATION AN UFS 30 MG%). KURVE C: VISKOSITÄT DER STANDARDFLÜSSIGKEIT DER FA. BROOKFIELD.

das typische Verhalten der Viskosität aggregathaltigen Blutes bei verschiedenen Geschwindigkeitsgradienten: hohe Viskositätswerte bei niedrigen Fließgeschwindigkeiten. Das Blut der Patientin, das vor der intravenösen Injektion von 1o ooo I.E. Heparin untersucht wurde, hatte einen Wert von 18 mg% an unveresterten Fettsäuren. 15 Minuten nach der Heparininjektion wurde wieder Blut entnommen und sofort viskosimetriert (Kurve B). Während bei hohen Fließgeschwindigkeiten keine Differenzen der Viskositätswerte nachzuweisen ist, sind bei kleinen Geschwindigkeitsgradienten die Viskositätswerte 15 Minuten nach der Injektion von Heparin wesentlich geringer (16,2 cp vor der Injektion und 13,5 cp nach Heparin bei 5,8 shear rate sec^{-1}). Die Konzentration der unveresterten Fettsäuren im Blute war 15 Minuten nach der Heparininjektion auf 30 mg% angestiegen. Kurve C stellt die Viskositätswerte der von der Fa. Brookfield gelieferten Standardflüssigkeit bei der Temperatur 37°C dar.

DISKUSSION

Blut ist eine Suspension von Erythrocyten in Plasma. Für Suspensionen gilt das rheologische Prinzip, daß bei abnehmenden Fließgeschwindigkeiten die Viskosität zunimmt. Diese Zunahme ist besonders dann ausgeprägt, wenn die Erythrocythen, etwa durch eine Erhöhung der Fibrinogenkonzentration im Blut, zu Aggregaten zusammengelagert sind[10,6]. Auf der nächsten Abbildung (Abb. 5), die einer Arbeit von Wells entnommen ist, sieht man die shear rate—Abhängigkeit der Viskosität bei

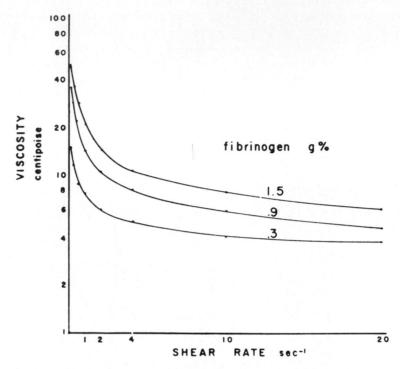

ABB. 5. ABHÄNGIGKEIT DER VISKOSITÄT DES BLUTES VON DEN RATES OF SHEAR BEI VERSCHIEDENEN KONZENTRATIONEN VON FIBRINOGEN (NACH WELLS).

verschiedenen Fibrinogenkonzentrationen. Nach DINTENFASS[9] wird die Strukturviskosität des Blutes vorwiegend von der Aggregation der Erythrocyten, in geringerem Maße auch von der Thixotropie des Plasmas und der Plastizität der Erythrocyten hervorgerufen. Wir folgerten daraus, daß umgekehrt eine Spaltung der geldrollenartigen Erythrocytenaggregate zu einer Senkung der Strukturviskosität führen müßte. Die vorliegenden Untersuchungen über den Einfluß der unveresterten oder freien Fettsäuren auf die Viskosität des Blutes im Zusammenhang mit früheren Untersuchungen scheinen diese Vermutung zu bestätigen.

Wie aus Abb. 2 hervorgeht, gelingt es, durch Zusatz von Na-Oleat *in vitro* die Blutviskosität bei niederen Geschwindigkeitsgradienten ganz erheblich herabzusetzen. Der Effekt ist dosisabhängig. Weitere, hier nicht im einzelnen aufgeführte Messungen ergaben, daß schon eine zusätzliche Oleatkonzentration von 10 mg% diesen viskositätssenkenden Effekt bewirken kann. Hohe Oleatkonzentrationen von 80 mg% und mehr ergeben eine Erhöhung der Viskosität bei allen Geschwindigkeitsgradienten. Bei normalem Blut (Abb. 3) sind die Verhältnisse entsprechend. Da hier jedoch eine erhöhte Strukturviskosität nicht vorliegt, ist auch eine Verringerung der Viskositätswerte durch Natrium-Oleat bei niedrigen Fließgeschwindigkeiten nicht oder nur in geringem

Ausmaß zu erwarten. Auf der Abb. 4 schließlich war zu erkennen, daß eine Erhöhung der Konzentration der unveresterten Fettsäuren *in vivo* (zum Beispiel durch Heparin) die Strukturviskosität des Blutes ebenfalls erheblich reduziert. Bei dem verwendeten Brookfield-Viskosimeter waren Messungen von Blut mit normalen Hämatokritwerten nur bis zu einer shear rate sec^{-1} von 5,8 möglich; darunter waren die Messungen ungenau und nicht reproduzierbar. Es ist anzunehmen, daß der viskositätssenkende Effekt unveresterter Fettsäuren noch deutlicher wird, wenn Messungen bei noch kleineren Geschwindigkeitsgradienten vorgenommen werden. Entsprechende Untersuchungen mit einem geeigneteren Viskosimeter sind vorgesehen, wobei auch die viskositätssenkende Wirkung von Natrium-Oleat und anderen oberflächenaktiven Substanzen und Pharmaka auf Blut von verschiedenen Hämatokritwerten und mit verschiedenen Fibrinogenkonzentrationen geprüft werden soll. Zur Erklärung des Wirkungsmechanismus der Senkung der Strukturviskosität durch unveresterte Fettsäuren oder deren Salze ist es erforderlich, auf einige früher erhobene Befunde einzugehen. Wir hatten

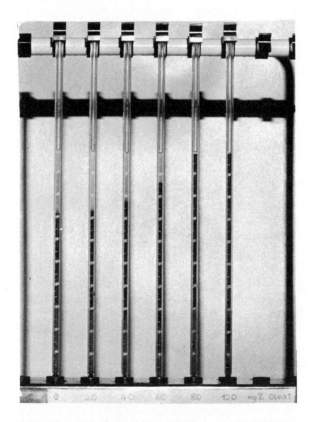

ABB. 6. HEMMUNG DER BLUTKÖRPERCHENSENKUNGSGESCHWINDIGKEIT DURCH VERSCHIEDENEN KONZENTRATION VON NA-OLEAT (0, 20, 40, 60, 80 UND 120 MG%) *in vitro*.

zunächst beobachtet, daß man Blutproben von Patienten mit einer erhöhten Blutkörperchensenkungsgeschwindigkeit durch Zusatz von Natrium-Oleat in Abhängigkeit von der zugesetzten Konzentration hemmen kann[13] (Abb. 6). Nach Zusatz von 20, 40, 60, 80 und 120 mg Oleat pro 100 ml Blut ist bei gleichem Hämatokrit der Proben die Blutkörperchensenkung nach der 1. und 2. Stunde weniger ausgeprägt; d.h. die Sedimentation der Erythrocyten ist verzögert und bei hohen Oleatkonzentrationen bleibt sie völlig aus. Betrachtet man das Blut dieser Proben mit und ohne Oleatzusatz unter dem Mikroskop, dann sind mit steigender Oleatkonzentration die vorher reichlich vorhandenen geldrollenförmigen Erythrocytenaggregate zunehmend desaggregiert, d.h. gespalten; wobei es zum Auftreten von stechapfelförmigen und sphärocytischen Zellen kommt.

Die nächsten Abbildungen zeigen das aggregatreiche Blut eines Patienten mit einem Bronchialkarzinom ohne Oleat (Abb. 7) und nach Zusatz von 40 mg% (Abb. 8), 80 mg% (Abb. 9) und 120 mg% Natrium-Oleat (Abb. 10). Die zunächst zahlreich vorhandenen Geldrollenaggregate teilen sich in kleinere Verbände auf; es finden sich zuneh-

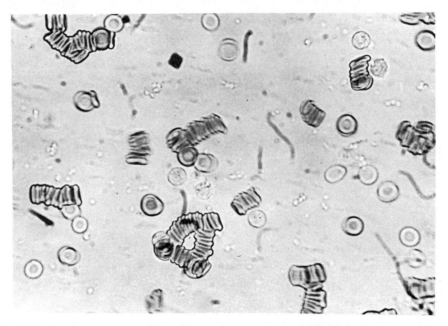

ABB. 7. TYPISCHE GELDROLLENFÖRMIGE ERYTHROCYTENAGGREGATE IM BLUTE EINES PATIENTEN.

mend mehr Einzelerythrocyten und bei hohen Oleatkonzentrationen sind alle Erythrocytenaggregate desaggregiert. Es liegen dann stechapfelförmige und sphärocytische Zellen vor, deren Durchmesser von 7 auf 5 μ herabgesetzt ist[17]. Die nächste Abbildung (Abb. 11) zeigt im Schema die Formveränderungen von Einzelerythrocyten durch Na-Oleat.

Es ist leicht, sich vorzustellen, daß die zunehmende Sphärocytose der Erythrocyten schon rein mechanisch gesehen eine Anlagerung der Zellen zu Aggregaten verhindert, bzw. daß bereits bestehende Aggregate desaggregiert werden. So ergibt sich auch eine Erklärung für die Hemmung der Blutkörperchensenkung durch Fettsäuren: die großen Erythrocytenaggregate, die zu einer erhöhten Blutkörperchensenkungsgeschwindigkeit führen, werden in Einzelerythrocyten aufgespalten. In Abb. 12 sind nochmals im Schema die Veränderungen der Erythrocytenaggregation durch Fibrinogen einerseits und Fettsäuren andererseits dargestellt.

Neben Fettsäuren und deren Salzen haben noch andere oberflächenaktive Stoffe wie

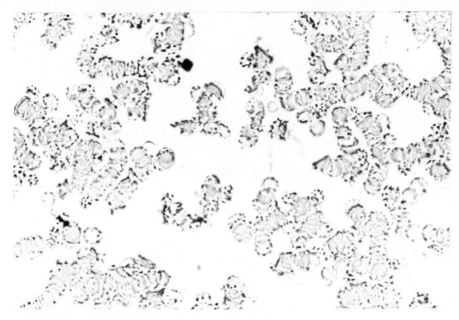

ABB. 8. BLUT DES GLEICHEN PATIENTEN WIE ABB. 7 NACH ZUSATZ VON 40 MG% NATRIUM-OLEAT. BEGIN-
NENDE DESAGGREGATION.

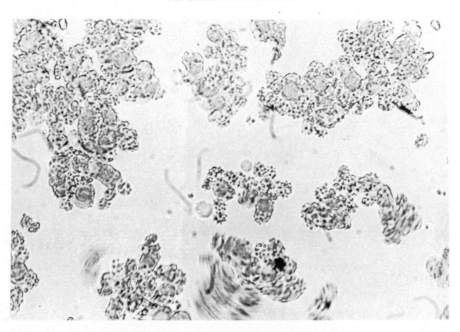

ABB. 9. BLUT DES GLEICHEN PATIENTEN WIE ABB. 7 UND 8 NACH ZUSATZ VON 80 MG% NATRIUM-OLEAT.
STÄRKERGRADIGE DESAGGREGATION.

Dodekansulfonat, Cetyltrimethylammoniumbromid, Natriumsalizylat und Phenylbu-
tazon eine desaggregierende Wirkung. Alle diese Substanzen sind oberflächenaktiv und
setzen die Oberflächenspannung des Blutes herab[18].

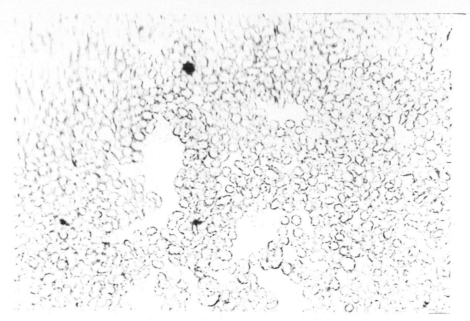

ABB. 10. BLUT DES GLEICHEN PATIENTEN WIE ABB. 7, 8 UND 9 NACH ZUSATZ VON 120 MG% NA-OLEAT.
VOLLSTÄNDIGE DESAGGREGATION DER ERYTHROCYTENAGGREGATE.

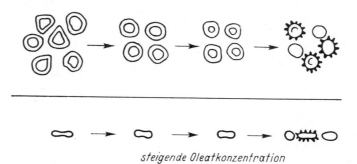

steigende Oleatkonzentration

ABB. 11.

Wir nehmen an, das der beschriebene desaggregierende Effekt oberflächenaktiver
Substanzen auch die Ursache für die Verminderung der Strukturviskosität des Blutes
ist. Auffällig ist jedoch, daß bei sehr hohen Kozentrationen von Natrium-Oleat (120
mg%) zwar die Blutkörperchensenkung vollständig gehemmt ist und alle Aggregate
aufgespalten sind, daß aber auch die Blutviskosität gegenüber oleatfreiem Blut angestiegen ist. Andererseits führt ein Oleatzusatz von 10, 20 und 40 mg/100 ml bei aggregat-
reichem Blut zu einer deutlichen Senkung der Viskosität, während dessen die Blutkörperchensenkungsgeschwindigkeit bei diesen Konzentrationen nur mäßiggradig
gehemmt wird. Zur Erreichung einer Viskositätssenkung über eine Reduktion der
Strukturviskosität des Blutes ist eine vollständige Desaggregation der Erythrocytenaggregate offensichtlich nicht erforderlich. Es ist anzunehmen, daß die geringfügi-
gen Formveränderungen der Erythrocyten via Sphärocytose durch Zusatz geringer
Konzentrationen von Natrium-Oleat ausreichen, um die vorhandenen Erythrocyten-

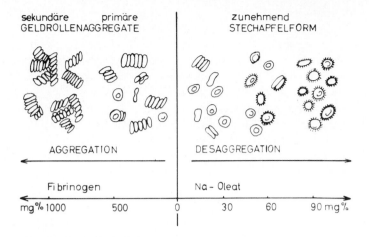

ABB. 12. EINFLUSS VON FIBRINOGEN (LINKE SEITE DER ABB.) UND VON NA-OLEAT (RECHTE SEITE DER ABB.) AUF DIE AGGREGATION VON ERYTHROCYTEN.

aggregate bei niedrigen Fließgeschwindigkeiten leichter zu sprengen. Der Anstieg der Blutviskosität bei allen Fließgeschwindigkeiten als Folge einer sehr hohen Natrium-Oleatkonzentration ist wahrscheinlich auf die erhöhte Rigidität der sphärozytischen Einzelerythrocyten zurückzuführen.

Auf der nächsten Abbildung (Abb. 13) wurde versucht, in einem Regelschema Faktoren und Mechanismen zusammenzustellen, welche zu einer Aggregation und Desaggregation von Erythrocyten sowie einer Strukturviskositätsänderung führen. Einer dynamischen Erythrocytenaggregation bzw. Desaggregation durch sehr niedrige bzw. hohe Fließgeschwindigkeiten wird eine sogenannte statische Aggregation bzw.

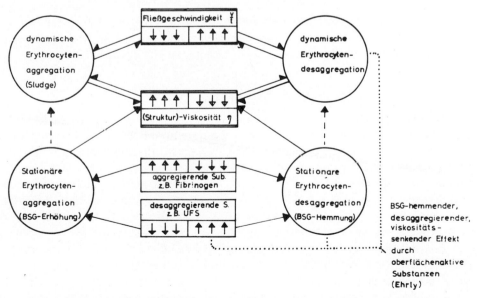

ABB. 13. REGELSCHEMA ÜBER DIE BEEINFLÜSSUNG DER STRUKTURVISKOSITÄT UNTER SPEZIELLER BERÜCK-SICHTIGUNG DER WIRKUNG VON DESAGGREGIERENDEN, OBERFLÄCHENAKTIVEN SUBSTANZEN.

Desaggregation gegenübergestellt. Eine Erhöhung der Fließgeschwindigkeit führt zu einer dynamischen Erythrocytendesaggregation, welche wiederum die Strukturviskosität herabsetzt. Umgekehrt führt eine verminderte Fließgeschwindigkeit zu einer dynamischen Erythrocytenaggregation, die dann kapillarmikroskopisch als Sludge-Phänomen nachzuweisen ist; die Strukturviskosität wird erhöht. Die Vermehrung von Fibrinogen im Blut führt *in vitro* zu einer statischen Erythrocytenaggregation, welche unabhängig von der Fließeschwindigkeit ist. Ausdruck dieser statischen Erythrocytenaggregation ist eine erhöhte Blutkörperchensenkungsgeschwindigkeit. Die verstärkte Erythrocytenaggregation durch Fibrinogen bedingt wiederum eine Erhöhung der Strukturviskosität. Oberflächenaktive, desaggregierende Substanzen z.B. Natrium-Oleat führen in erhöhten Konzentrationen zu einer von der Fließgeschwindigkeit unabhängigen Erythrocytendesaggregation und bewirken eine Senkungshemmung. Eine Desaggregation von Erythrocytenaggregaten führt direkt oder indirekt über eine Erleichterung der dynamischen Erythrocytendesaggregation zu einer verminderten Strukturviskosität des Blutes und damit zu einer Erhöhung des Durchflußvolumens pro Zeit.

Zusammenfassend kann gesagt werden, daß es möglich ist, durch eine Erhöhung der Konzentration oberflächenaktiver Substanzen z.B. der unveresterten Fettsäuren des Blutes, die Strukturviskosität wesentlich herabzusetzen. Der Wirkungsmechanismus dieses Effektes ist über eine Desaggregation bestehender Erythrocytenaggregate zu erklären. Eine Erhöhung der Konzentration an unveresterten Fettsäuren im Blut verursacht Veränderungen der Erythrocytenform, die wiederum das Zusammenlagern von Erythrocyten zu Geldrollenaggregaten bei niederen Fließgeschwindigkeiten erschweren und die Spaltung bereits bestehender Aggregate bewirken. Wie *in vitro*, so ist dieser viskositätssenkende, desaggregierende Effekt unveresterter Fettsäuren auch *in vivo* nach einer Erhöhung der Konzentration unveresterter Fettsäuren durch Heparininjektionen nachzuweisen. Die Senkung der Strukturviskosität des Blutes bei unverändertem Hämatokrit dürfte von besonderem Interesse sein, da bei einer Reihe von Erkrankungen die Strukturviskosität erhöht ist (z.B. Schockzustände, Thrombosen, Myocardinfarkt, arterielle Durchblutungsstörungen). Es ist deshalb anzunehmen, daß dieser von uns beschriebene viskositätssenkende Effekt oberflächenaktiver Substanzen in Zukunft auch therapeutisch nutzbar gemacht werden kann.

SUMMARY

The increase of blood viscosity at low rates of shear is mainly due to the aggregation of red cells in the form of rouleaux. It could be shown, that an increase of unesterified (free) fatty acids up to 40 mg% in the blood can markedly decrease the viscosity of aggregated blood at low rates of shear. The same has been seen with other substances which lower the surface tension of the blood. The mechanism of this effect was found to be as a disaggregation, that is splitting off, of rouleaux by small, reversible changes of the red cell shape. After addition of small doses of sodium oleate, the cells of the aggregates become somewhat crenated or spherocytic and therefore they are lying at a greater distance from each other and can be broken off more easily. A complete disaggregation of rouleaux, which is possible at high concentrations of sodium oleate *in vitro* is not necessary.

This disaggregating, viscosity-decreasing effect of surface active substances (Ehrly) can also be seen after the injection of heparin in man, when the concentration of free fatty acids is increased. In several diseases with aggregation of red cells (burns, shock, venous thrombosis, myocardial infarction etc.) the knowledge of this effect may be useful for therapy.

REFERENZEN

[1]   Hess, W. R. *Kolloid–Z.* **27**, 1, 1920.

[2]   Rothlin, E. *Z. klin. Med.* **89**, 233, 1920.

[3]   Krosch, H. und Heidelmann, G. *Klin. Wschr.* **33**, 947, 1955.

[4]   Wells, R. E. und Merill, E. W *Science* **133**, 763, 1961.

[5]   Wells, R. E. und Merill, E. W. *J. Clin. Invest.* **41**, 1591, 1962.

[6]   Wells, R. E., Gawronski, Th. H., Cox, P. J. und Perera, R. D. *Am. J. Physiol.* **207**, 1035, 1964.

[7]   Copley, A. L. In *Flow Properties of Blood and Other Biological Systems*, Copley, A. L. and Stainsby, G. (Editors), Pergamon Press, Oxford, New York, 1960 p. 97.

[8]   Dintenfass, L. *Kolloid–Z.* **180**, 160, 1962.

[9]   Dintenfass, L. *Circulation Res.* **14**, 1, 1964.

[10] Madow, B. und Bloch, E. H. *Angiology* **7**, 1, 1956.

[11] Haynes, R. H. und Burton, A. C. *Am. J. Physiol.* **197**, 943, 1959.

[12] Ehrly, A. M. und Müller, H. E. *Acta Haematol.* **35**, 331, 1966.

[13] Ehrly, A. M., Gramlich, F. und Müller, H. E. *Klin. Wschr.* **43**, 943, 1965.

[14] Ehrly, A. M. (im Druck).

[15] Konitzer, K., Voigt, S. und Solle, M. *Acta biol. med. german.* **12**, 502, 1964.

[16] Ehrly, A. M., Gramlich, F. und Müller, H. E *Blut* **11**. 284, 1965.

[17] Ehrly, A. M. *Med. Klinik* **59**, 1575, 1964.

[18] Ehrly, A. M. und Frese, A. (in Vorbereitung).

DISCUSSION

Lee (*U.S.A.*):

I was very interested in this. I wish I had understood the whole presentation, but I do not speak German. Some years ago, David Sachs and associates at the University of California, Los Angeles, undertook to look at the potential chemical agents which should, on the basis of the physical chemistry involved. disaggregate cells if they were indeed stuck together with protein or lipoprotein envelopes; he was interested in several types of diseases; there were a number of materials which were effective in producing disaggregation and degradation of capsular material. However, they were all for one reason or another not applicable for clinical use, mostly because of toxicity. Some of them produced hemolysis; and of the others, now in the light of knowledge which has come about in the past two or three years, some of the fatty acids, particularly, are rather destructive to pulmonary surfactants and to normal pulmonary mechanics. This has not really been a fruitful area to my knowledge. Have you found other compounds which may be effective in producing disaggregation besides sodium oleate?

Ehrly (*Germany*):

We used others too, salicylate and phenylbutazone. We also found a great number of surface active agents able to do so. From the point of suppression or destruction by fatty acids I have one slide I would like to show.

Lee:

Other compounds in this series which are also effective are some of the anionic and cationic detergents. Dr. Silberberg brought this to my attention the other day. We had known of a couple of them, for example, high molar concentrations of urea, sodium lauryl sulfate, and formaldehyde in concentrations of 1–50,000. These have all been highly toxic, and were discarded.

Ehrly:

It must be established that the concentration of fatty acids, that is necessary to disaggregate erythrocyte aggregates and to lower the viscosity, is really very small. The normal range of free fatty acids in human beings is between 7 and 30 mg%. We could show that an increase of 10% up to 40% is able to lower the apparent viscosity of blood. This is one question. The other is, if such substances can hemolyse. Curiously, we have seen, that low concentrations of free fatty acids do not increase destruction of erythrocytes; on the contrary, if you add fatty acids *in vitro*, as *in vivo*, in concentrations up to 60 mg%, there is a better osmotic resistance of erythrocytes than before. And we have used this effect in the therapy of some hemolytic diseases, by giving heparin in small doses over the day. Now, that is normal blood with a normal osmotic fragility of erythrocyte and this is the same blood to which is added 40% of sodium oleate. You see that the beginning of the hemolysis is later. That means, the erythrocytes are less fragile.

GELIN (*Sweden*):

I am very interested in this subject at the moment. It was clear that heparin decreased the low shear rate viscosity of the fatty material. Do you think this might be due to the clearing effect of heparin, or would you ascribe it to an increase of free fatty acids which always follow heparin administration?

EHRLY:

I believe the clearing effect of heparin is somewhat other than the production of free fatty acids. Zöllner and others have demonstrated this. But I believe that this effect is due to the free fatty acids following heparin administration, because we could show it also *in vitro*, quite easily. I may say that it is not heparin itself that lowers the viscosity. We think that the free fatty acids, which are released by activation of lipoprotein lipase *in vivo*, are responsible for the viscosity-lowering effect of heparin.

GELIN:

I fully agree that heparin itself will not induce these changes, it must be due to its biologic action. My next question will be: if you add fatty material, which will apparently attach to the surface of the red cell membrane, that will also mean a lowering of the specific weight of the red cell, compared with the suspending medium. How much do you think this change in specific weight will influence the drop in sedimentation rate? Do your records reflect disaggregation?

EHRLY:

We have not studied this, and I cannot say very much. I believe that in hyperlipemia, if you inject heparin, there is a higher elevation of the concentration of free fatty acids because the substrate, that is fat, is more concentrated in the blood. The concentrations of enzyme may be the same, but if the substrate is elevated, the concentration of free fatty acids will be also higher. Maybe that is an explanation for what you found.

GELIN:

From the differences we found, we draw quite another conclusion. We related it to triglycerides and not to free fatty acids.

BLOOD AND PLASMA LIPID LEVELS AFTER DIFFERENT TEST MEALS

Louis Lino and Roy L. Swank*

Division of Neurology, Department of Medicine, University of Oregon Medical School,
Portland, Oregon, U.S.A.

EARLIER work revealed *in vitro* aggregation of blood cells in dogs and human beings[1], and marked slowing of the circulation *in vivo* in hamsters[2] and rabbits[3] followed the feeding of butter-fat meals. These observations have been confirmed in man[4, 5] and cat[6]. Subsequently it was shown that butter-fat meals in hamsters were also followed by a decrease in the available oxygen in the cerebral cortex[7], by convulsions[8], by prolongation of the QT interval in EKG's[9], and by an increase in potassium excretion[10]. The peak of changes occurred about 6–8 hr after butter-fat feeding, and followed the peak of visible lipemia by about 2 hr. The changes did not occur, or were very much less marked after vegetable oil or codliver oil meals. After protein meals a slight decrease in oxygen availability in the brain was observed, but the other changes observed after butter-fat meals did not occur. After carbohydrate meals no alterations of any kind were observed.

In the present study changes in plasma and red cell lipids in hamsters after butter fat, safflower oil, protein, and carbohydrate meals are described in a continuing effort to reveal the mechanism by which butter fat so markedly affects the circulation, whereas the same amount of vegetable or codliver oil do not.

Mature golden hamsters were used. They were housed in individual cages $10 \times 6 \times 6$ in. large and were allowed fox chow and water *ad lib*. They were not fasted prior to the experimental meals. The feedings consisted of 8 g/kg of butter fat as cream (36% butter fat), or of the same amounts of safflower oil, essenamine (for protein), or sucrose. All were made up in skim milk to a concentration of 36%, except essenamine which was 30%. The control animals were fed as before[10]. They were lightly anesthetized with ether; a small tube was inserted into the stomach and a measured amount of the feeding was injected. The animals quickly recovered and resumed normal activities. Six hours after feeding, they were sacrificed as follows. They were anesthetized with ether and the abdomen opened. A #20 gauge intravenous needle was inserted into the inferior vena cava and the animal's blood was collected in heparin. Two to three cc of blood were obtained from each control, and from the oil-, protein-, and carbohydrate-fed hamsters. Slightly more than half this amount could be withdrawn from the butter-fed animals. The blood from each group of approximately 20 animals was pooled for analyses.

The chemical analyses were done as follows: 1 and 3 cc samples of whole blood, plasma, and red cells were processed identically. The samples were extracted with a 2:1 chloroform–methanol mixture (v:v) according to the method of SPERRY and BRAND[11], as modified by BRAGDON in SUNDERMAN and SUNDERMAN[12]. The

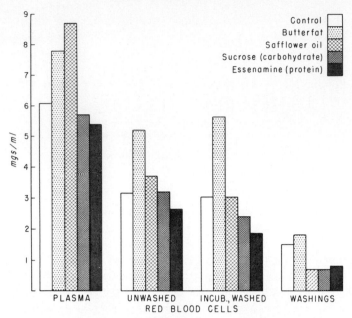

FIG. 1. TOTAL EXTRACTABLE LIPIDS FROM 1 CC SAMPLES

extracts were dried under nitrogen and weighed. The 1 cc extracts were then methylated by acid catalysis, according to the procedure of Volpenhein, and the fatty acid composition was determined in duplicate by gas liquid chromatography. These latter analyses plus results of silicic acid column separation will be reported elsewhere.

The gravimetric analyses of total extractable lipids is shown in the figure. After butter-fat and oil feedings the total plasma lipids were increased, the increase being slightly more marked after oil feedings. No significant, or slight decreases in lipid levels in the plasma followed the sucrose and protein meals.

Red cell lipids also increased sharply after butter-fat meals, but showed little or no change after the oil meals, and after sucrose and protein meals.

After incubation for 1 hr at 37°C and triple washing the red cells in normal saline, minor, and perhaps significant further changes in the lipids occurred. The total red cell lipid showed a further slight increase after butter-fat meals, but after safflower oil feedings the total red cell lipids decreased. The blood samples from carbohydrate- and protein-fed animals also exhibited a further decrease in total red cell lipids. The washings from the red cells showed a much higher concentration of total lipid in samples from control and butter-fat fed animals than in any of the others.

The curious migration of lipid to the red cell mass after butter-fat meals, and the retention of lipid in the plasma after codliver oil meals may in part be due to the electrophoretic mobility of the lipids themselves. The chylomicra from butter-fat and codliver oil fed dogs are negatively charged as are the red cells, and have about the same electrophoretic mobility. They have a tendency to repel one another. After storage at 4°C for 4 days, butter-fat chylomicra still possess the same mobility, whereas codliver oil particles have a greatly increased electrophoretic mobility and hence increased negative electrical potential. In both instances the mobility is the same as for butter-fat or codliver oil particles suspended in normal saline solution[13].

It is suggested that in the process of their metabolism the chylomicra first lose their protein envelopes and momentarily are free to become attached to the other formed elements in the blood. Although the negative charge on butter-fat particles would be small, chance collision with red cells would be expected to occur. Because of their much greater negative electrical potential, and hence greater tendency to repel the red cells, the codliver oil chylomcra without a complete protein envelope would tend to remain emulsified in the plasma.

It is unlikely that the observation described in this paper is a species characteristic since similar lipid changes have been observed in dogs.

ACKNOWLEDGMENT

Supported by Public Health Service grants He-2676 and He-6336.

REFERENCES

[1] SWANK, R. L. *Am. J. Physiol.* **164**, 798, 1951.
[2] CULLEN, C. F. and SWANK, R. L. *Circulation* **9**, 335, 1954.
[3] SWANK, R. L. *Am. J. Physiol.* **196**, 473, 1959.
[4] HARDERS, H. *Verhandl. deutsch. Gesellsch. inn. Med.* **62**, 499, 1956.
[5] WILLIAMS, A. V., HIGGINBOTHAM, A. C. and KNISELY, M. H. *Angiology* **8**, 29, 1957.
[6] MEYER, J. S. and WALTZ, A. G. *Neurology* **9**, 728, 1959.
[7] SWANK, R. L. and NAKAMURA, H. *Am. J. Physiol.* **198**, 217, 1960.
[8] SWANK, R. L. and NAKAMURA, H. *Arch. Neurol.* **3**, 594, 1960.
[9] NAKAMURA, H. and SWANK, R. L. *Proc. Soc. Exp. Biol. Med.* **105**, 195, 1960.
[10] SWANK, R. L. and JACKSON, L. *Am. J. Physiol.* **204**, 1071, 1963.
[11] SPERRY, W. M. and BRAND, F. C. *J. Biol. Chem.* **213**, 69, 1955.
[12] SUNDERMAN, F. W. and SUNDERMAN, F. W., JR. *Lipids and the Steroids Hormones in Clinical Medicine.* J. P. Lippincott Co., Philadelphia, 1960.
[13] SEAMAN, G. V. F. and SWANK, R. L. *J. Physiol.* **168**, 118, 1963.

THE EFFECT OF DIETARY FAT ON WHOLE BLOOD AND PLASMA VISCOSITY IN NORMAL AND HYPERCHOLESTEROLEMIC SUBJECTS†

Lars-Erik Gelin, Jüri Kerstell and Alvar Svanborg

Department of Surgery I and Department of Medicine II,
University of Gothenburg, Sahlgrenska Sjukhuset, Göteborg, Sweden

Experimental studies have shown that hyperlipemia induces disturbances in the flow properties of blood, which are most marked after intravenous infusions of fat emulsion. Alimentary hyperlipemia also induces flow changes but only of a slight or moderate degree[1, 6].

While infusions of fat emulsion produces increased whole blood and plasma viscosities[8] alimentary hyperlipemia has not been observed to induce viscosity changes[2, 8]. Charm, McComis, Tejada and Kurland[2] observed rather a decrease in plasma viscosity at shear rates of 230 sec^{-1} after fat meals given to normal subjects.

Regan et al.[5, 6] studied the effects of alimentary hyperlipemia on coronary blood flow and myocardial oxygen consumption. They found a significantly lower blood flow and myocardial oxygen extraction in the hyperlipemic subjects both at rest and at work. These alterations could be abolished by intravenous heparin administration. These changes in flow were interpreted as secondary to changes in the physical composition of the blood.

The present investigation was initiated to observe if there are any differences in whole blood or plasma viscosities after alimentary hyperlipemia in subjects with normal and abnormal plasma lipid patterns. For this purpose patients with essential hypercholesterolemia were chosen.

MATERIAL AND METHODS

Four patients with known essential hypercholesterolemia were compared with four healthy persons aged 23–30 years. The clinical data on the four patients with hypercholesterolemia and their initial plasma lipid values are given in Table 1. No patient had anticoagulation therapy. The patients were on an ordinary Swedish diet but cases 1, 2 and 3 had been instructed to restrict the intake of fat rich food and used corn oil in cooking.

EXPERIMENTAL PROCEDURE

All subjects were fasting overnight. Eight o'clock in the morning an initial blood sample was drawn into two dry-heparinized tubes. They were then given 100 ml of

†This paper was not listed in the Final Program; however, permission was granted to its senior author (L-E.G.) to present it. (Editor.)

TABLE 1. CLINICAL DATA

Patient No.	Age years	Sex	Coronary disease	Previous myocardial infarction	Initial plasma lipid values			
					Phospholipids mg/100 ml	Cholesterol mg/100 ml	Triglycerides mg/100 ml	FFA mM
1	58	♀	+		306	350	98	0.86
2	53	♀	+		354	352	156	1.13
3	38	♂	+		435	569	175	0.15
4	52	♀	+	+	390	372	181	0.58

Patients 1–3 had received a low fat diet for more than one year.

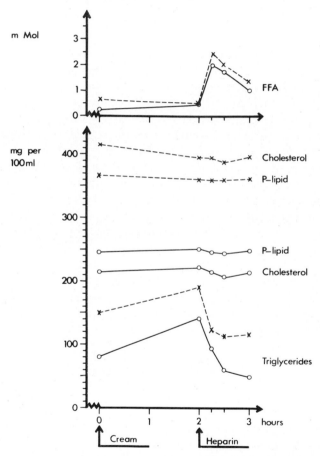

FIG. 1. PLASMA LIPIDS IN FOUR NORMAL SUBJECTS (o———o) AND FOUR HYPERCHOLESTEROLEMIC PATIENTS (x- - - - -x) FOLLOWING FAT MEAL AND SUBSEQUENT ADMINISTRATION OF 100 MG HEPARIN.

cream containing 40 g of fat. Two hours later a second blood sample was drawn and 100 mg of heparin was given intravenously. Blood samples were again drawn after 15, 30 and 60 min.

Blood samples were analysed for hematocrit, whole blood viscosity and plasma viscosity at different rates of shear using a Brookfield cone-plate viscometer. Lipid extraction and determination of total cholesterol, total phospholipids and triglycerides were performed as earlier described[7]. Free fatty acids (FFA) were analysed according to DUNCOMBE[3].

RESULTS AND COMMENTS

The changes within the plasma lipid fractions in the two groups of subjects are summarized as mean values in Fig. 1. The hypercholesterolemic patients had markedly

TABLE 2. PLASMA VISCOSITY

| Subject | Shear rate sec^{-1} | Plasma viscosity centipoise | | | | |
| | | Initial | After fat meal | After heparin | | |
				15 min	30 min	60 min
Patient 1	23	1.8	1.4	1.4	1.4	1.4
	230	1.8	1.5	1.6	1.6	1.5
2	23	1.7	1.8	1.7	1.6	1.2
	230	1.6	1.7	1.6	1.5	1.4
3	23	1.6	1.6	1.5	1.5	1.2
	230	1.7	1.6	1.6	1.7	1.5
4	23	1.6	1.6	1.4	1.5	1.3
	230	1.5	1.6	1.3	1.3	1.5
Control 1	23	1.5	1.4	1.4	1.4	1.4
	230	1.5	1.5	1.5	1.5	1.6
2	23	1.8	1.3	1.2	1.2	1.6
	230	1.5	1.4	1.4	1.4	1.6
3	23	1.3	1.3	1.3	1.3	1.6
	230	1.5	1.5	1.5	1.5	1.4
4	23	1.5	1.4	1.4	1.6	
	230	1.5	1.5	1.5	1.6	1.5

TABLE 3. WHOLE BLOOD VISCOSITY

| Subject | Shear rate sec^{-1} | Whole blood viscosity centipoise | | | | |
| | | Initial | After fat meal | After heparin | | |
				15 min	30 min	60 min
Patient 1	23	6.6	6.2	6.4	6.7	7.2
	230	4.5	4.4	4.4	4.5	4.4
2	23	7.6	8.4	7.4	7.3	6.7
	230	5.0	4.9	4.5	4.4	4.2
3	23	8.9	8.6	8.4	7.8	8.4
	230	5.8	5.2	5.3	4.8	5.4
4	23	7.3	7.6	6.7	6.4	6.4
	230	4.6	4.6	4.2	3.8	4.1
Control 1	23	6.6	6.9	6.4	6.4	6.7
	230	4.4	4.6	4.4	4.1	4.4
2	23	7.4	7.4	7.0	6.4	7.2
	230	4.8	4.8	4.5	4.4	4.5
3	23	7.8	8.1	7.9	7.7	8.0
	230	5.0	5.0	4.8	4.7	4.9
4	23	6.4	7.2	6.7	6.5	6.3
	230	4.3	4.6	4.4	4.3	4.2

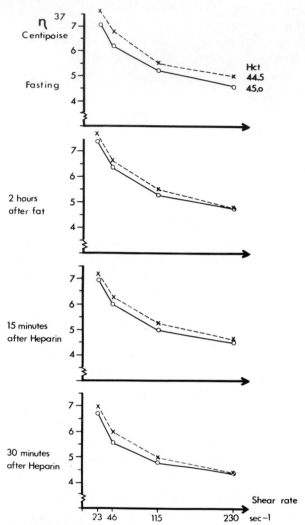

Fig. 2. Whole blood viscosity values at different shear rates in four normal (o———o) and four hypercholesterolemic subjects (x- - - - -x) at fasting, 2 hr after a fat meal and 15 and 30 min after subsequent administration of 100 mg heparin.

higher plasma values of cholesterol, phospholipids and triglycerides than the normal subjects. Fat meal caused significant increase of triglycerides in both groups. Heparin administration caused a rapid drop in triglycerides and an increase in FFA both in the hypercholesterolemic patient and in the normal subject as earlier described by HAHN[4] and many others. The cholesterol and phospholipid levels were not altered during the experiment.

The viscosity changes observed during the experiment are given in Tables 2 and 3, and summarized as mean values in Figs. 2 and 3. The hypercholesterolemic patients had a slightly higher viscosity of both plasma and whole blood than the normal subjects despite identical hematocrits. The differences in viscosity were most marked at lower rates of shear.

Fat meal caused in both groups no change or a slight decrease in plasma viscosity which is in line with the data found by CHARM *et al.*[2]. Whole blood viscosity increased very slightly in all normal subjects but not in the hypercholesterolemic patients.

Heparin administration produced a drop in whole blood viscosity in all subjects

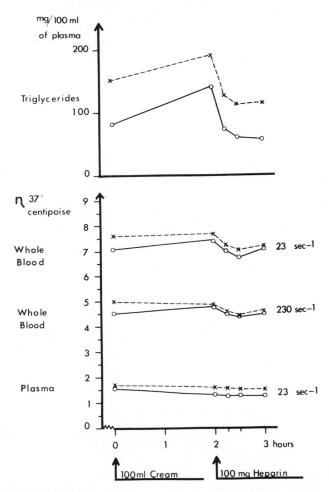

FIG. 3. ALTERATIONS IN TRIGLYCERIDE LEVEL, IN WHOLE BLOOD VISCOSITY AT THE SHEAR RATES OF 230 AND 23 SEC^{-1}, AND IN PLASMA VISCOSITY AT 23 SEC^{-1} AFTER A FAT MEAL AND SUBSEQUENT ADMINISTRATION OF 100 MG HEPARIN IN FOUR NORMAL (o———o) AND FOUR HYPERCHOLESTEROLEMIC SUBJECTS (x-----x).

except one. If the effect of heparin was studied in the total material the decrease in the viscosity of whole blood was found to be significant both at shear rate of 23 sec^{-1} ($p < 0.05$) and at shear rate of 230 sec^{-1} ($p < 0.01$).

The alterations in plasma lipid pattern and in viscosity of blood indicate a correlation between the triglyceride level and the viscosity of whole blood. The changes in the FFA level were maximal before the maximal change in blood viscosity appeared. It seems reasonable to assume that the heparin induced changes in blood viscosity are related to alterations in the plasma lipoprotein pattern.

SUMMARY

In a preliminary study on the effect of dietary fat and subsequent heparin administration on the viscosity of whole blood and plasma it was found that:

1. Four hypercholesterolemic patients had slightly higher viscosity of both plasma and whole blood compared to normal subjects.
2. A fat meal rather decreased plasma viscosity but increased whole blood viscosity especially at low rates of shear.
3. Subsequent heparin administration produced a significant decrease of whole blood viscosity parallel to the decrease in the plasma triglyceride level.

REFERENCES

[1] BERGENTZ, S-E., GELIN, L-E. and RUDENSTAM, C-M. *Acta Chir. Scand.* **120**, 115, 1960.
[2] CHARM, S., McCOMIS, C., TEJADA, C. and KURLAND, G. *J. Appl. Physiol.* **18**, 1217, 1963.
[3] DUNCOMBE, W. G. *Biochem. J.* **88**, 7, 1963.
[4] HAHN, P. F. *Science* **98**, 19, 1943.
[5] REGAN, T. J., BINAK, K., GORDON, S., DeFAZIO, V. and HELLEMS, H. K. *J. Clin. Invest.* **38**, 1033, 1959.
[6] REGAN, T. J., TIMMIS, G., GRAY, M., BINAK, K. and HELLEMS, H. K. *J. Clin. Invest.* **40**, 624, 1961.
[7] SVANBORG, A. and SVENNERHOLM, L. *Acta Med. Scand.* **169**, 43, 1961.
[8] SWANK, R. L. *Circulation Research* **4**, 579, 1956.

DISCUSSION

REES (*U.S.A.*):

Professor Edward Merrill and I have studied patients who have increases in triglycerides and cholesterol secondary to a functional insulin deficiency. Utilizing the GDM type of viscometer described by Dr. Meiselman earlier this afternoon, we have not been able to show any increase in whole blood or plasma viscosities as a function of the triglyceride level. I suspect that, as we discussed at Cambridge, there is a problem of instrumentation here that has not yet been worked out.

GELIN (*Sweden*):

Yes, we also have thought of instrumentation. But we can observe a clear effect from heparin. So I really do not believe it is a matter of instrumentation. The differences are slight; they are very slight. I do not believe they have any physiological significance. There is an influence on whole blood viscosity from the fat meal which might not be related to triglyceride level, but to something induced by the intake of fat.

GREGERSEN (*U.S.A.*):

I hesitate to insert any questions here, but it seems to me that if both of you have a point that fats stick to the red cells, it might be possible to detect the difference in the interaction among the red cells by studying the packed cells. If you were to study the differences in the viscosity at low shear rate, and very high hematocrit (packed cells) you might be able to detect some differences. We also have considered the effect of lipids on blood viscosity, but there are instrumental problems that are difficult to overcome because of the layering in the viscometer. We were working routinely at very low shear rates, supposedly equivalent to 0.01 reciprocal seconds (0.01 r.p.m.). I am not sure about the actual shear rate as I disclosed in Cambridge. One more point which may be of some interest is a paper by Murphy in Cleveland, showing that the cholesterol is located on the edges of the red cells. This might influence cell–cell interactions in the blood and conceivably bring about the changes that Dr. Swank has noted here today.

SWANK (*U.S.A.*):

Let me comment on Dr. Gregersen's statement about cholesterol. I mentioned that we had made studies of the silicic acid fractions of the lipids. The fractions containing cholesterol and triglyceride have a strong tendency to migrate the red cell after lipid meals. I would like to say that after fat meals, the blood viscosity in dogs increases slightly 2 hr after feeding, but then rapidly decreases. It is interesting that at 2 hr, you do not have a heavy lipemia. This suggests that the initial increases in viscosity may not be related to lipemia at all, but to other factors. Since people are making their study at different time intervals, they may not agree.

GREGERSEN:

There is a certain difficulty, Dr. Swank, with the experiment that you do of that sort. Have you controlled the hematocrit very accurately, because you could easily be misled by changes in hematocrit? Many years ago I saw large changes in the hematocrit in dogs after meals, simply because of the rapid exchange of fluids in the gut and reduction in plasma volume. It changes after a large meal. You probably are aware of this.

SWANK:

Yes, it is very true that two things happen which I did not mention, but which were described some fifteen years ago. First, the sedimentation rate is greatly decreased at 2, 4 and 6 hrs, and often 9 hrs after the fat meal. This observation was quite consistent in both animals and in humans. Also the hematocrit changes; it drops 5–10% 3–6 hr after a fat meal, then climbs back to the original value. These changes were taken into consideration.

WHITMORE (England):

As I mentioned in Cambridge, I think you can get a fair idea of cell interaction by dealing with relative viscosity – that is, the viscosity of the whole blood, at a given rate of shear, relative to the plasma. I was looking at Professor Gelin's figures, and wondering whether he had tried plotting them in this way. I very much suspect that any differences are going to almost disappear, and I would ask whether he has considered the method of looking at his data.

GELIN:

These changes were unexpected for us. One thing I would like to stress here: something happens when you give heparin to these patients which decreases their blood viscosity and this happens in all patients, both normal and hypercholesterolemic. There is no doubt that the hypercholesterolemic patient had a higher whole blood viscosity in this series. Maybe it is too small a series.

EHRLY (Germany):

We found that after injection of heparin the apparent viscosity is decreased, as did Dr. Gelin. And we have found that the effect is due to the free fatty acids and to a splitting off of aggregates by these fatty acids. I hope I can say something more on Friday.

You speak of the "disaggregation" in your experiments. I would like to ask you: how did you measure or estimate the disaggregation of erythrocytes? After injection of low molecular weight dextran (M.W. 40,000), we did not see any changes of erythrocyte sedimentation rate nor of the rouleaux under the microscope (Med. Klinik 61, 989, 1966). The same opinion has been pointed out by Wells and Meiselman during this congress. I fully agree with you if you mean a functional, that is, hemodynamic induced disaggregation by increased shear stresses. One other remark: on one of your slides, the viscosity of blood (ordinate) was plotted versus the rates of shear (abscissa). I wondered about the high rates of shear (230–26 sec^{-1} because the increase of viscosity at low rates of shear, as shown in this slide, will usually occur at rates of shear below 20 sec^{-1}. I could imagine that in this case, you meant turns/min of the Brookfield viscometer and not the shear rate numbers.

Part IV

CLOSING SESSION

16 July, a.m.

Chairmen: OLAFUR BJARNASON, Iceland
SYOTEN OKA, Japan
ALFRED L. COPLEY, U.S.A.

A. APPRAISALS OF THE ACHIEVEMENTS OF THE CONFERENCE

HEMORHEOLOGY THEORY

A. SILBERBERG

WHAT form of hemorheological theory has emerged out of this conference? In what way, in other words, are we now better able to cast the rheological behavior of blood into mathematical form, i.e. into expressions whose parameters are material constants clearly related to the structural elements. Formulated in this way, however, the problem invites some cautionary remarks.

Firstly, is this objective fundamentally realistic, i.e. is blood a system sufficiently inert that the biological processes which run in it can be ignored in rheological experimentation. The present thesis seems to be that, with the exception only of some regimes, there exists a wide range of practical conditions over which the rheological representations, found mainly on the basis of *extra vivum* studies, are indeed significant. Probably the best way to allay doubts and settle the issue is through the use of procedures which combine a rheologically well defined flow system with an immediate return of the blood to the living animal. By such artifices it should be possible to decide whether, where and over what range *extra vivum* results are relevant.

But even assuming that this aspect is settled and that we are dealing with the rheological behavior of blood in a regime where we are entitled to consider it as a physical system, we must still make proper and detailed allowance for its discontinuous two-phase nature. In consequence, our experimentation depends on the dimensions of the apparatus, and the rheological behavior, in terms of a continuum model, cannot be a pure function of material constants. Whether this additional parametric dependence is due to a plasmolytic zone, in the wider vessels, or to bolus or group flow, in the narrower vessels, is not the relevant issue at this level of discussion. What is important and should be remembered is that no equivalent continuum representation, as for example, the Casson equation, may ever be extended beyond the range over which its applicability has been tested. In particular, since such representations involve implicitly the geometry of the flow system, the danger of extrapolation beyond the tested range refers not only to flow rates, but also to apparatus or vessel dimensions. On the other hand, even in the most discontinuous flow regimes we may, with justice but with caution, employ equations which are averages over the many situations which can arise simultaneously or in rapid sequence.

In this spirit, the connection between fundamental rheology and hemorheology was discussed by Joly, while Rivlin, in a review of non-Newtonian fluid behavior, particularly in non-circular tubes, pointed out the necessity of considering normal stresses in the flow of blood. Comparing rheological equations relating shear stress to rate of shear, Scott Blair clearly favored the log–log Herschel–Bulkley equation over the square root formalism of the Casson plot, except for purely empirical purposes.

Despite their usefulness, however, we seem to be getting a little disenchanted with overall representations and the largest number of contributions by far dealt with models and theories which consider the two phase nature of blood, explicitly, i.e. the rheology of each of its components and the overall rheological effects resulting from changes in aggregation and other physico-chemical variations in the structure of the system.

Rheology appears in these studies in two guises, (i) as a framework in which to present the results and (ii) as a technique by which the sought-for structural information is to be established.

(i) The tendency today to discuss the rheological characteristics of each phase separately and to look for equations which will synthesize the separate rheological elements into the behavior of the overall system under various conditions of flow, is hampered, unfortunately, by the specific effects of some blood components and the high volume concentration of the particulate phase. It is clear that no simple super-position is involved.

Much very good work has been done, however, with model systems or semi-model systems, i.e. red cell suspensions in other than full plasma. In fact much of the best quantitative hemorheological information which we possess refers to semi-model systems of this kind. While it is not clear, of course, whether whole blood is adequately represented in this way, such measurements are of enormous importance for comparison with each other and against data to be obtained on whole blood.

(ii) Though the synthesis of the rheological description of the overall system from its parts is one aspect of the work, an equally, if not more, significant one is the insight which rheological methods are now beginning to provide into the structural and molecular aspects of blood; in close analogy to the use of the rheological approach made by polymer physicists over the years.

These new thoughts are also reflected in the development of measurement techniques. For *extra vivum* viscosity measurements an instrument involving a very narrow (5–60 μ) gap was described by Dintenfass, while Zimmer has developed a technique where samples are interposed into a continuous stream of saline passing through the apparatus. As the sample appears between the walls of the instrument, the changed mechanical response is recorded. The importance of meniscal resistance in tube viscometers was stressed by Jacobs.

Very interesting in particular were some *in vivo* techniques. Frasher reported on his success in introducing an arterial-venal shunt into dogs such that tube viscometers, or other devices, can be perfused with blood which derives from and returns to the intact animal, which can be maintained alive and healthy for periods of up to 6 months. A similar idea underlies the use of a cannulated artery viscometer described by Charm, while Wayland gave details of techniques which were developed to interpret flow in the transilluminated living vessels directly.

With the two-phase nature of blood uppermost in mind, great emphasis was placed, in a large number of contributions, on the red blood cell, both as a unit and as an assembly of particles in suspension.

The most remarkable rheological property of the red cell is probably the flexibility of its wall. It seems that cells can be drawn into threads, during which process, despite hemolysis, their surface area, as Kochen has shown, remains constant and their ability to form an intact ghost cell, is retained. While normal cells easily pass through 5μ wide channels, acetaldehyde-hardened cells do not (Gregersen). The puzzle of the restoration of the biconcave shape after enormous deformations was discussed by Burton, but if the latest observations of Stewart are confirmed the membrane may not be as structureless as most of the previous evidence seems to suggest. The likelihood that membrane flexibility varies considerably from sample to sample was pointed out by Thomas. Great differences in fragility and reversible deformability with cell age were indeed established quantitatively in the Fragiligraph by Danon. The correlation between flexibility and respiration, on the one hand, and pH and other environmental factors, on the other, were discussed by Sirs.

Mushroom-like deformation of single cells, completely analogous to that observed in the microcirculation, was demonstrated by Goldsmith using 10μ diameter glass tubes, and a mathematical model and a device to determine flow conditions using large-scale models of variously shaped red cells in a tow tank were described by Bugliarello. The forces giving rise to these shapes should thus become known in due course. It is indeed not unlikely that the shape-change resisting forces of erythrocytes are an important rheological element in the flow of high hematocrit samples as Dintenfass points out. Changes in temperature alter surface area, but not volume, while changes in pH affect area, volume and visco-elastic properties. This was shown by Murphy while Seaman could prove that reducing the electric charge of the cell (by neuraminidase) left the overall blood viscosity unaffected.

Treating more concentrated cell suspensions, Goldsmith demonstrated the presence of the same rouleaux which are seen in *in vivo* systems. The stability of such rouleaux to flow can now be measured. It is to be noted in this connection that Seaman finds that a force of about 10^{-7} dynes is needed to break up normal red cell aggregates at an overall shear rate of 50 sec^{-1}. An interesting observation is due to Ehrly. Na oleate addition, to a total of 20–40 mg fatty acid/100 ml, reduces aggregation in cases of pathologically aggregated blood, but leaves normal blood practically unaffected. The effect of various lipid meals on cell stickiness was discussed by Swank who pointed out that only saturated fatty acids seem to combine well with red cells. A method for determining aggregate shape from fluorescence depolarization was described by Pfeiffer.

The flow of cell suspensions through vessels only slightly larger than the cells was discussed by Whitmore, whose treatment explains why, under these circumstances, cells flow in stacked groups and why the overall viscosity is only a weak function of hematocrit. The flow of blood, or model suspensions, through wider tubes was the subject of a number of papers which were all concerned, in some way or another, with the problem of axial streaming and the presence of a plasmolytic zone. There is little doubt but that such a zone arises, at least in *extra vivum* experiments, even though only in a statistical sense. This was demonstrated in a plasma skimming apparatus by Palmer and in concentrated particle suspension experiments by Goldsmith and Mason and by Sacks. Charm, basing himself on the Casson equation, predicts a correlation of plasmolytic layer thickness and flow rates when Casson equation yield stress and velocity are large enough. A difference in transit time of cells and albumin through an isolated vascular bed in cat muscle was also demonstrated by Groom.

In wide blood vessels, however, the hematocrit seems to be uniform across the tube section and a plasmolytic layer, if it exists, is negligible. This has now been demonstrated by both Wiederhielm and Phibbs using quick freeze techniques. Both find preferred parallel orientation of the red cells to the vessel wall, no concentration changes across a diameter and no strong aggregation. Wiederhielm, moreover, has found the explanation why in tubes 10–15 times the red cell diameter maximum light absorption is apparently concentrated in two bands running parallel to and on each side of the tube axis. It has in the past been suggested that the enhanced transmission of light through the center is due to an axial outward migration of particles from the core. It now appears that the absorption there is normal, but that much of the incident light is specularly reflected in the region of the in-between band from red cells orientated parallel to the wall but at 45° to the incident beam. Wiederhielm could confirm this explanation by showing that the dark bands shifted as the inclination of the light source was changed.

Rheologically, plasma is not merely an inert suspending medium, and fibrinogen has been known for some time to be the rheologically active plasma component. Without fibrinogen, i.e. in serum, red cells do not form rouleaux. Copley has now shown that when fibrin-fibrinogen complexes are formed, their presence considerably augments aggregation. Furthermore, as Lee has constituted, blood viscosity is considerably affected by any abnormal plasma protein structure or composition despite only very minor variations in hematocrit. Similarly, it is reported by Rees that increased Casson equation yield shear stresses result when fibrinogen and macroglobulins combine in what seems to be a network interaction with red blood cells. The role of beta-2-fibrinogen D in platelet aggregation was discussed by Barnhart.

Much of the discussion of plasma was devoted to the function of dextrans as plasma expanders and blood conditioners. There seems to be general agreement on the effects of high molecular weight dextrans. These increase cell aggregation and blood viscosity and both Gelin and Meiselman independently reconfirm this result. On the other hand, while Gelin and Groth believe that the decreased viscosity when low molecular weight dextrans are administered is accompanied by deaggregation, Wells, Meiselman and Bernstein, in separate investigations, attribute the reduced overall viscosity to hemodilution alone and find no change in aggregation even in cases where aggregation was first artificially increased.

To this discussion of the cell and plasma phase of blood and the rheological interplay between them, a new element was added which has till now been largely ignored. In a series of contributions the importance of surface effects on the rheology of blood was stressed. The discussion involved not only the interfaces cell–plasma and plasma–vessel wall, but also the interfaces in the micropores which are believed to exist in the membranes of the red blood cell and the vessel wall. Such pores, as Palade has pointed out, are the presumed vehicles of exchange flow between cell and plasma and the carriers of the extravascular circulation.

Basing himself on the properties of adsorbed polymer layers, Silberberg suggested that since the thickness of such films is able to vary considerably they could act as self-regulatory pressure or composition sensitive devices controlling the instantaneous flow of red cells in narrow vessels and the flow of components through the pores of the membranes. Lee did, indeed, point out that many serum proteins, but mainly α- and β-globulins, interact with the surface and undergo partial denaturation. Eirich, as well, referred to the profound surface effects of adsorbed macromolecules particularly polyelectrolytes and the many types of interaction which may be expected. The surface effects of macromolecules were also considered by Burton, who pointed out that rouleaux were almost certainly formed by long macromolecules linking cell to cell. In addition, he attributes the biconcave structure of the red cell to an internal membrane to membrane interaction involving macromolecules.

The presence of adsorbed macromolecules on the vessel wall is implied by the coatings which Frasher found were developed in his artificial shunt capillaries in dogs and by the thickening of the vessel wall at arterial forks observed by Stehbens. Unless these coats are very thick indeed no direct effects are to be expected in wide vessels, but Oka has suggested that indirect effects such as a wall slip could account for the reduced viscosity observed in model systems with fibrin coated walls. Tamamushi, as well, discusses slip and the effect of surface forces in the transmission of flow shear stresses.

The irreversible thermodynamics of membrane transport as linked to macro-molecular transformation were discussed by Katchalsky while Seno proposed that a structural rearrangement in the membrane is involved in the transfer of macromolecular components across the cell or vessel wall.

The importance of including the vessel wall into the rheological picture is also well illustrated by the great progress which has been scored in hemodynamics where the analysis of pulsatile flow has been pushed very far. The overriding contribution of the visco-elasticity of the arterial wall in determining the nature of the system response was pointed out by Taylor, while the contributions of McDonald and of Seymour emphasize, in addition, the control asserted by the muscle component of the arterial wall. Overall mathematical models for the circulation were presented by Rubinow, and Attinger and discussed by Rouse and the usefulness of high-speed computing methods in their solution was acknowledged. It is to be noted that in these calculations the detailed rheological properties of the blood seem to play a minor role as useful, overall representations can be found with blood replaced by a Newtonian liquid.

Hemorheology is bound to remain a rather complex field for some time. Though the present working model, a two phase system, i.e. a suspension, in which surface inter-actions may be highly important, seems to be adequate for most purposes and is now generally accepted, it can be applied only qualitatively as the rheological information which would make the model quantitative is not nearly available. This is particularly true for *in vivo* situations where the complexities introduced by the vascular bed, which were described and discussed by Berman and by Joly, still have to be taken into account.

Since it appears that the rheological situations which arise in the circulation, are already sufficiently involved, the characterization of an all embracing model, valid also outside physiological flow regimes, seems at first glance to be unnecessary and ambitious. It turns out, however, that flow under non-physiological conditions may display differences and changes in the state of the blood which are indicative of a pathological variation not otherwise rheologically detectable. Such information is thus of diagnostic, clinical value. For example, in a contribution by Fukada, the possibility of disease-linked rheological changes, using both a capillary viscometer and a double cylinder visco-elastometer, has been examined; similarly Casson equation yield stress was looked at by Rees and overall blood viscosity by Merlen and by Lee.

HEMORHEOLOGICAL TECHNIQUES

M. Joly

It is always difficult to appraise exactly the real achievement of an international conference immediately at the end. It is usually much easier to give a general survey of the fruitfulness of a conference a few months later, when everybody has had time enough to think about the various results which have been discussed. This difficulty is still greater when the conference is on a subject such as hemorheology which includes so many topics, extending from pure mathematical rheology to almost pure medicine.

Nevertheless some conclusions can be drawn forthwith concerning particular sessions of the present meeting. That is why I should like to make a few comments on the technical aspects of hemorheology.

In all the sciences, the techniques play an important part. In several sciences the techniques have reached a very high level of complexity and adequacy. In the case of hemorheology such a development is not yet attained. There is still much work to do in the technical field. That is the reason why the present conference has been very important and very useful in the domain of hemorheological techniques.

The nature of blood, the complexity of the macro- and micro-circulation, and the intricate structure of blood vessels have led to the development, on a theoretical basis, of a rheology very different from the classical rheology. The scale of the constitutive elements of blood compared with the size of blood vessels, the deformability of these bodies and their variations in space and time have sometimes induced us to call in question again the assumptions used in the ordinary methods of mathematical rheology. Therefore, it has been necessary to attempt to establish the theoretical basis of a rheology valid on a microscopic scale, for heterogeneous media, the components of which vary and show physical properties depending on the state of motion.

Such a theoretical attempt can be fruitful only if the experimental data are adequately obtained. It is necessary that the experimentalist should provide the theoretician with an exhaustive set of well defined results clearly describing the various aspects of blood flow. The hemorheological techniques must be much more elaborate than in the case of classical rheology, in order to obtain a good selection of the parameters and to satisfy the exact conditions required for an accurate description of the whole rheological behaviour of very complicated systems. For these experimental data, all the parameters must be completely characterized and show the properties of steady variables as required in physics.

In some cases it is difficult to approximate to such a situation. Therefore, the techniques used in practical hemorheology may sometimes appear as rather surprising methods to a physicist not familiar with the problems of hemorheology. Indeed very often a sample of blood is put into a more or less complicated apparatus, a button is pushed, the apparatus gives a signal, figures are read or a curve is recorded and a conclusion is derived. But, what, if anything, has been measured?

The signal given by an apparatus is generally not a measurement, in the physical sense of the word. A set of very severe conditions must be satisfied by a quantity for it to be a physical measurable quantity. The limiting conditions, the presence of a stationary state with regard to the environment, the reproducibility, and so on, must be strictly verified. The separation of the various parameters is rigorously necessary if one wants to know exactly what is measured.

Unfortunately such conditions, which are trivial in ordinary physics, are not always very easy to be satisfied in rheology as well as in biophysics, and are always very difficult to attain in hemorheology because of the extreme complexity of blood, blood vessels, and, more generally, of living systems. This is the reason why the First International Conference on Hemorheology has been extremely useful and fruitful in order to promote, on a strong scientific basis, a valid development of hemorheology. Indeed, each speaker, in the various fields of hemorheology, has made a real effort to state precisely the exact conditions of his experiments.

In the Session devoted to the technical aspects of hemorheology, very interesting papers have been presented, in which various aspects of the techniques used have been described. In each of these papers it has been pointed out that particular conditions must be satisfied for the validity of the measurements.

W. G. Frasher, H. Wayland and S. S. Sobin, for instance, have shown that sampling of blood in its native condition is necessary for the physiological significance of the measurements; and they have proposed an appropriate device in the form of a chronic external arterio-venous shunt. This shunt carries between 15 and 25% of the cardiac output and functions free from clotting for prolonged periods without flushing or the use of anticoagulants. It allows one to perform outflow viscometry in artificial tubes cast in silicon resin.

The importance of direct observation *in vivo,* for instance by high-speed cinephotography has been emphasized in the paper by E. H. Bloch. The flow is recorded at frame rates from 540 to 8000 per second, and the magnification permits an adequate resolution of all the elements of the blood. With this technique it is possible to establish the cellular flow pattern and to determine the boundary conditions at the vessel wall in living animals. A similar method has been developed by G. P. Fulton, H. J. Berman, R. F. Slechta and A. M. Brooks in order to study the rheological disturbances introduced by various pathological changes.

H. Wayland, P. C. Johnson and W. B. Frasher have developed a very fine technique for the precise measurement of flow rates and shearing forces in living blood vessels. In capillary beds, vessel diameter is measured either with a flying spot microscope or with an optical scanning device. The velocity of blood cells is measured by a double-slit photometric method. For the determination of the pressure gradient two types of micro-pressure transducers have been used: the Wiederhielm active gauge and a miniature passive gauge using a low compliance pressure diaphragm fitted with solid state strain-gauge elements. They have emphasized the importance of the exact determination of the real tridimensional geometry in the studies of *in vivo* hemorheology. They have observed in the capillaries of the isolated mesentery of cats two different types of flow: a steady flow, the velocity of which is linear with pressure difference, and an oscillatory flow with a period of 6–10 sec related to the activity of precapillary sphincters. As pointed out by the authors, this type of flow and the fluid transport across capillary walls make it difficult to isolate the flow characteristics which can be attributed to the rheological properties of blood.

In his paper, H. R. Jacobs has shown the importance of the perturbations introduced by the meniscal resistance to the flow in glass capillary tubes. He emphasizes the corresponding necessity of building viscometers minimizing the meniscal resistance in order to obtain significant values of blood viscosity.

The advantages of a microcapillary viscometer made of parallel plates of glass polished to an optical tolerance of few wavelengths has been demonstrated in the paper by L. Dintenfass. In the series of microcapillary viscometers so constructed, the gaps between plates vary from 5 to 60 μ, the length of the slit-capillary varies from 15 to 95 mm and the width of the slits varies from 40 to 100 mm.

S. G. Mason and H. L. Goldsmith have shown very elaborate apparatus enabling precise measurements of the motion of particles in various types of flow. The rotation of linear and flexible chains of spheres and discs have been studied in Couette flow and compared with that of rouleaux of human red cells of various lengths. These experiments confirm the necessity of very accurate measurements, as in physics, if one wishes to test the validity of theoretical deductions, which is extremely important for hemorheology as well as for fundamental rheology.

Unfortunately the paper by K. Weissenberg could not be read. In this paper some uses of the rheogoniometer were described. The advantage of such an apparatus is the following: one knows exactly what is measured, which is not always the case with other devices.

A new kind of viscometer has been proposed by J. Zimmer. This consists of a modified Couette viscometer in the gap of which the liquid is continuously renewed. The variations of the torque as a function of time are recorded. By alternating the circulation of a reference liquid and of the medium to be tested, one can obtain with this apparatus rapid information on the influence of various drugs on the serum viscosity.

Many other technical data were given in the various sessions not especially devoted to technique. Important applications of thrombodynamography were presented. This very clever technique bears on several rheological problems. On the other hand its physical, biophysical and also biochemical significance will certainly be studied thoroughly in the near future.

It would be useful to develop the theory of a number of other techniques. For instance, the flow through discs of sintered glass or other types of filters, as described in the communication of F. R. Eirich, and systematically studied in the paper by M. I. Gregersen and C. A. Bryant, seems to be, as a first approximation, a good simulation method of study of the flow in capillary beds, and a tentative technique for the determination of the force required for the deformation of the cells entering and traversing the pores.

This rapid survey of recent progress in hemorheological techniques shows that the aim of very accurate and significative experimental data in hemorheology is not too unrealistic. The realization of this aim requires the collaboration of hemorheologists, biochemists, pure rheologists and biophysicists. Such a cooperation will be extremely useful for the rapid development of hemorheology as well as of basic rheology.

MODEL STUDIES AND PHASE SEPARATION

G. Bugliarello

The session on Model Studies comprised six papers given by Silberberg, Rouse, Goldsmith, Attinger, Sacks and Bugliarello, and the session on Phase Separation had two papers, presented by Palmer and Charm.

Clearly, the first difficulty with regard to models is to define what a model really is — a difficulty that certainly cannot be resolved here. It should be pointed out, however, that there were papers in other sessions that by all rights would have fitted the session on models, notably Professor Burton's paper. Also, of course, mathematical and physical models have played an unconscious role in the mind of many contributors to this Conference.

Be this as it may, a striking characteristic of the session on models was its very broad scope, ranging from Silberberg's model of physico-chemical boundary processes at the molecular scale to Attinger's model of the peripheral circulation. Breadth of scope was associated with diversity of methods of approach: hydrodynamic modeling, mathematical modeling, visual observations, electrical analog modeling. Such breadth, both in scope and in approach, represents a quantum advance with respect to previous symposia. This is most encouraging, since, unquestionably, the development of both the qualitative and the quantitative understanding of hemorheological phenomena in the context of the circulation can be seen only through constant interplay between prototype and model in exactly the same way and with the same conceptual difficulties that, as Rouse pointed out, obtain in the hydrodynamics of rivers. The link between model and prototype is, of course, given by *ex vivo* experiments such as those by Palmer and Charm.

What have been the specific accomplishments of the sessions on models and phase separation? It is always very difficult, as explained by Professor Joly in his remarks, to evaluate accomplishments so close to an event. Perspective can be gained only with time, and only time will tell what, in the model sessions, has been really relevant to the development of knowledge in hemodynamics and what instead has contributed to the development of physical science. The present commentary will be confined to a listing of some of the more significant points that have emerged both from the papers and the discussions.

1. We continue systematically to expand our knowledge of the behavior of model suspensions (Sacks, Goldsmith and Mason, Bugliarello).

2. In several cases, model and *ex vivo* observations have given striking qualitative predictions of what is observed *in vivo* (as remarked, e.g. in the discussion of the papers by Phibbs and Wiederhielm).

3. We are acquiring the ability to model accurately by electrical analogy entire blocks of the circulatory system (Attinger). These models require an understanding

813

of the role that the rheological characteristics of blood in the vessel wall may or may not play in the circulation.

4. We have been alerted to the possibility that under certain conditions adsorbed macromolecules on the vessel wall may play a very important role in regulating the flow in very small vessels and in influencing the resistance in other situations (Silberberg).

5. We are achieving a greater quantitative insight into the transport processes taking place in the axial plasmatic gaps of true capillaries (Bugliarello).

6. We are becoming intently aware of the importance of bifurcations as controls for the hematocrit in downstream vessels (Palmer).

7. We have obtained further information on the peripheral plasma layer in small tubes (Charm) and hopefully settled the argument as to the meaning of data for the layer deduced from pressure-flow relationships (Thomas, Bugliarello and Hershey's discussions of Charm's paper).

CELLULAR AND FIBRIN CLOTTING

S. WITTE

THE session on "Cellular and Fibrin Clotting" not only was the main topic of this week's program, but also seemed to be the central theme of the entire Conference. This is understandable when we consider that clotting processes influence most the rheology of blood. There are principally two points which may be important with regard to the process of clotting. They are (1) the aggregation of platelets and (2) the production of fibrin. Both processes may influence each other in many different ways. Thus, the rigidity of the fibrin clot and its ability to retract is brought about by the platelets, which can be shown by thromboelastographic methods, as demonstrated by Leroux. By means of the retractograph, likewise developed by Hartert, it was found that retraction begins at the same time as clotting does, and is not merely a secondary process. The molecular mechanism of retraction, which is linked to an undisturbed energy metabolism of the platelets and determined by at least one plasma cofactor, is still, for the most part, unknown. The transformation of chemical into mechanical energy, which is well documented in the retractograph, appears to resemble that taking place in muscle contraction.

The formation of a special intermediate product during fibrin formation, during which only the first step in the clotting reactions (namely, the splitting off of fibrinopeptide A) takes place, was intensively examined by Copley. These fibrin monomers can be formed in the presence of very weak thrombin activity. They complex with fibrinogen, not resulting in a solid clot, but increase rouleau formation of the erythrocytes and, in this way, are of utmost importance in hemorheology.

In this respect, fibrinolysis is another important process. It brings about a resolution of clots and can be nicely viewed in the thromboelastograph, as also demonstrated by Leroux. Fibrinolysis is likewise related to other blood clotting events. It is inhibited in the presence of platelets. On the other hand, a high molecular product of fibrinogen is able to aggregate platelets, as was shown by Marion Barnhart. This aggregation is reversible, it resembles the aggregation caused by ADP, and occurs with the production of pseudopodia when platelets come into contact with a glass surface.

The building of platelet aggregates is important for hemostasis and for thrombosis. However, it does not seem to be related to the vascular changes encountered in the early stages of arteriosclerosis, i.e. to the intimal plaques occurring preferentially at vascular forks, as shown by Stehbens in vital microscopic and electron microscopic studies. Stehbens described hemodynamic disturbances occurring at these forks, and succeeded in demonstrating a tendency of the platelets to adhere to leucocytes, but not to preferential locations in the vessel.

The paper delivered by Scott Blair stood amidst these experimental studies on coagulation. Scott Blair presented a number of different equations describing the flow of blood through artificial capillaries, and for the processes of fibrin polymerization and softening. With regard to clotting, the equations were derived from thromboelasto-graphic curves and from torsiometric values obtained from Scott Blair's own apparatus. With all respect for the mathematical and physical sophistication of this work, this appears to me as a first brave attempt at describing the whole of physiology and patho-logy of clotting from a general standpoint. I believe, however, we must admire with still greater respect the competence of nature, in her ability to balance the forces of cellular and fibrin clotting in such a way that the flow of blood is insured and the loss of blood is prevented.

PLASMA EXPANDERS

R. L. WHITMORE

THE four papers devoted to plasma expanders ranged from detailed *ex vivum* rheological studies to *in vivo* experiments on dogs and rabbits.

Taking first the *ex vivum* work, general conclusions were that all dextrans of nominal molecular weight in excess of about 20,000 are likely to cause some degree of aggregation of human red cells, and that the viscosities of solutions of dextrans at isotonic concentrations are appreciably greater than those of plasma. The yield shear stress and the sedimentation rate of suspensions of human red cells increase with increasing molecular weight of dextran, although a reversal in sedimentation rate may occur if the concentration of dextran raises the viscosity of the suspending fluid to a sufficiently high value. These results support the conclusions of many earlier workers in this field. It was also shown that additions of dextrans of 40,000 molecular weight to suspensions of human red cells which had been strongly aggregated by the presence of fibrinogen or high molecular weight dextran led to no relative improvement in flow behaviour compared with similar suspensions which were diluted with albumin or saline solutions.

The *in vivo* experiments emphasized the many additional factors which have been extensively reported elsewhere and which must be taken into consideration when plasma expanders are used in living systems. High molecular weight dextran infusions in healthy dogs led to a fall in haematocrit, the appearance of aggregation and a dramatic decline in cardiac output. A corresponding fall in oxygen consumption was also reported and is probably attributable to the blockage by aggregates of some of the vascular beds. The addition of low molecular weight dextran was followed by a further fall in haematocrit and a fall in the blood viscosity to a value comparable with the original. There followed a recovery of cardiac output and oxygen consumption. In the work on rabbits suffering from hypovolaemia the recovery of oxygen tension in muscle was much better after infusion of albumin or dextran of 40,000 molecular weight than after infusions of whole blood or high molecular weight dextran.

A suspension exhibits a yield shear stress when a complete structure which can transmit the stress is present. An increase in the strength of the structure raises the yield stress. In the case of blood, therefore, some relationship between the degree of aggregation and the yield shear stress might reasonably be expected. The addition of a dextran solution to an aggregated suspension of red cells raises the viscosity of the suspending fluid but reduces the haematocrit. The lowered haematocrit leads automatically to a fall in the viscosity of the total suspension, relative to that of the suspending fluid, and reduces the yield stress. The influence of yield stress is most marked at low flow rates so that the reduction in haematocrit of human blood from 45 to 40% lowers the relative viscosity at high rates of shear by 10 or 12%, but reduces it at low rates of shear by some 40%.

The *ex vivum* experiments described in the papers indicate that the viscosity changes in blood resulting from additions of dextran of 40,000 molecular weight are very similar to those following additions of saline or albumin. From this it might be deduced that the additives all had a similar effect on the degree of aggregation of the red cells. On the other hand, visual evidence from *ex vivum* experiments not reported at the Conference [1] is that dextran solutions of 40,000 molecular weight do give better dispersion of human red cells than saline if present in concentrations exceeding about 2 g/100 ml. The discrepancy between the conclusion reached in the Conference papers that dextran of 40,000 molecular weight alters the flow properties of blood to the same extent as saline solution, and the visual observation that the same dextran fraction disperses the red cells better than saline solution, can only be resolved by assuming that the degree of dispersion of the cells is not related in a simple, direct manner to the viscous properties (particularly the yield stress) of the suspension.

The fall in haematocrit following *in vivo* infusion of dextran is accentuated by the osmotic diffusion of tissue fluids into the circulatory system. The improved dispersion of the red cells which is generally observed following infusion of dextran of 40,000 molecular weight can be attributed to an increase in the disruptive forces to which the aggregates are exposed (which results from the increased flow rate brought about by the reduced haematocrit and modified plasma viscosity) and possibly to a reduction in the internal strength of the aggregates. Unfortunately the strength of the aggregates, and the forces between them must be deduced from yield stress measurements made *ex vivum* and, as mentioned above, the correlation with aggregation is apparently not a simple one.

Further experimental work is clearly required to confirm the *ex vivum* conclusions before the relevance or significance of viscometric measurements to the behaviour of dextran *in vivo* can definitely be established.

REFERENCE

[1] ENGESET, J., STALKER, A. L. and MATHESON, N. A. *The Lancet,* May 21, 1124, 1966.

IN VIVO HEMORHEOLOGY

M. G. TAYLOR

IT IS difficult to summarize such a conference like this except perhaps in the broadest historical terms. The thing that occurs to me is the relation between Poiseuille's work and what came before and after. Before his time, the formula for the flow of blood, or the flow of liquid rather, through a tube, was not known. The relation between rate of flow, pressure gradient and volume flow was very uncertain. This was, of course, because people were using large tubes and as soon as the flow rate got high enough, they got turbulent flow and the predictions became very uncertain. And they simply did not know what the relationship was. Poiseuille, interested in the flow of blood, studied the flow of water (thank goodness, it was water and not blood) in small tubes. We are very fortunate that it was water he studied, not blood, because he would have come against the anomalous properties of blood and we would have never learnt how even water went through anything. Now this represented a considerable advance and, I think, we are in the process now of seeing a similar advance between *in vivo* hemorheology and hemorheology *in vitro*. Now just as before Poiseuille's time no one really knew how water flowed through small tubes, nowadays we have not yet a quantitative knowledge of how blood flows through small tubes in the body. Enormous amounts of data are available on the flow of blood in various artificial systems. The thing, I think, can be divided in the body into large vessel-flow and small vessel-flow where these anomalous effects become apparent. In the large vessel-flow, I think, as has been said by previous summarizers, the situation is fairly clear and, in fact, the important rheological problem there is in the structure of the wall rather than the structure of the blood. We are now fortunately in the position of gradually accumulating more and more evidence of the measurements, direct measurements, made of the viscous properties of arteries in the animal. Large arteries with various fine calipers applied to them and smaller vessels perhaps will be accessible by microscopic technique, such as Dr. Wiederhielm has been describing. So we might be able to continue the rheological investigation of the arterial wall right down to arterioles and capillaries, and so on, and more attention is being paid to that now, which is a very good thing. As far as the small vessels are concerned, for the flow problems here, at last, the quantitation is catching up with the enormous amount of qualitative observation which has been made in the past. People have been looking at and describing the flow of blood in small vessels for many years. An enormous amount of very accurate and interesting descriptive material is available, but it has only recently become possible to establish quantitative methods for this region. I think, that just as through the big jump across the time of Poiseuille for the measurements of the flow of fluids through anything, we are about to arrive at a similar situation for the flow of blood through small vessels. There is no doubt that the proper place to measure the viscosity of blood is in the arterioles and in the capillaries. The amount of information that can be got from model studies can only contribute to this and help with its interpretation; it cannot answer the whole question. And it is now, I think, largely a matter of instrumentation, which seems to have been blossoming in the last few years, that we are finally in the position to make accurate studies of what does go on in the small vessel circulation. I think there is a very hopeful future for this, indeed, extremely hopeful. And I am sure in the next meeting of this group there will be numerous papers on dynamic measurements of viscosity in small vessels by a number of techniques. The direct observations with and without various computer attachments to the machinery, and indirect ones, such as Groom has described, surely will be very useful in the differential passage of material through the circulation, and can be subtly analysed in this way. So in conclusion, I would say that as yet the new techniques are just flying their flags and, I think, with every promise of very great achievement in the next few years. The quantitative hemorheology of the microcirculation is just about to get launched, and I think it is very exciting.

BLOOD CELLULAR ELEMENTS

A. C. Burton

THERE were two sessions of the Conference specifically under this title, with twelve interesting papers. Of course, there were a great many other papers, under different general headings, that had reference to the form, elasticity, and interaction of the "particles" in blood. For many years there was a lack of emphasis in rheology on the properties of the particulate matter, as largely determining the rheological properties of a suspension that is as closely packed with particles as is blood of normal hematocrit. Beautiful work has been done with ingenious experimental, microscopical methods and highly sophisticated hydrodynamic theory has been produced on the problem of *very dilute suspensions*. So far, no one could claim that we have mounted a real attack on the actual problem of flow of blood of 45–50% hematocrit, where obviously the inter-action (jostling, bumping, deformation) of the cells must be the dominant factor. For example, the contrast between what happens with relatively isolated cells in a shear gradient, e.g. from the beautiful work of Goldsmith and Mason, and what occurs in normal blood, e.g. from the remarkable pictures of Phibbs, is evident in the orientation of the cells. Isolated cells turn to the posture of discs with their plane at right angles to the axis of flow; whereas in blood of normal hematocrit most of the cells appear, in a cross-section of an artery, to be "edge-on".

While it may take many years to produce an adequate theoretical treatment of this dominant interaction of the cells in flow, we know now that the shape, deformability, and internal viscosity of the cell, and of its membrane will be all important in that eventual formulation. Dr. Mason and his co-workers find marked differences, even in very dilute suspensions, in the behaviour of rigid vs. deformable particles. There is some rather neglected Japanese work[1] that shows that suspensions of rigid ("tanned") crenated cells have viscosities not five, but fifty times that of water! All this means that we must learn as much about the physics of the red cell itself (and of the other cells of blood) as we can, before we can hope to formulate an adequate theory of the rheology of blood as it flows in the circulation in arteries and veins, as well as in capillaries, where obviously (in "bolus flow"), deformability is the important factor.

The Conference indicated how new methods of study of the properties of the cell itself are being added to our armament. The tendency to form rouleaux, a property of the red cell membrane surface, has been studied quantitatively by rheological methods, e.g. the work of our Chairman, Professor Copley, at low shear rates. The fascinating microscopical observations of Goldsmith on the separation of rouleaux in a shear gradient offers a new quantitative approach to the wide-spread problem of cellular cohesion in biology — important even as far afield as in cancer research. Micromanipul-ation, "poking and sucking" bits of red cells, is helping us understand what might happen to an erythrocyte in the circulation. The electron microscope is being used on the red cell membrane and its interior, with some results which we were shown that are

difficult at present to interpret. I hope that the refined and sensitive methods of birefringence and dichroism, described by Professor Pfeiffer, will enable us to learn more
about possible structure *inside* the normal red cell, for which our own analysis of the
physical equilibrium of the membrane seems to call.

The method of the "black box", so popular with those of engineering training and
with the Systems Analysts, though a powerful tool of theory, is, as it should be, most
unsatisfying to the basic scientist, who must know what is inside the black box, and, if
possible, watch the wheels go round there. The most encouraging aspect of this Conference to me has been the change in attitude of those who came to hemorheology
through rheology, rather than through biology. Ten years ago I visited the laboratories
of some of the engineer pioneers of hemorheology. I was astonished to find that there
was not even a simple microscope in their laboratories, and they actually had never seen
for themselves the "particles" of the samples of blood on which they worked. Today, I
am sure, this is not true in the laboratory of any hemorheologist. Even if only as best
evidence that the erythrocytes in our suspensions are normal, microscopic examination
of the fluid under study is essential. It has taken some time for hemorheologists to see
how important is the study of the cellular elements, but the future of our subject surely
depends upon this aspect of our research effort.

REFERENCE

[1] WADANO, K. *Tokoshima J. Exp. Med.* **3**, 111, 1956.

CLINICAL HEMORHEOLOGY

L-E. GELIN

THIS Conference has indeed been a great success for the application of knowledge from the basic science of rheology to clinical medicine. All new knowledge in hemorheology will find its immediate application both in preventive medicine and in the treatment of diseased states. From this point of view, information on the viscosity of whole blood at very low rates of shear is especially valuable. It was not very long ago that the only recordings during the treatment of a patient in shock were measurements of blood pressure and pulse rate. Today, as evidenced in this Conference, this is no longer adequate when shock is agreed upon as a condition of low flow and the goal for treatment is to establish a proper nutritional flow. The disturbed flow of blood in the microcirculation, observed under wide variations in pathology, was better understood when the physiologist and the clinician became better acquainted with the basic knowledge of rheology. It has to be emphasized, however, that we have difficulties in understanding the different languages spoken by different scientists in rheology, i.e. physicists, mechanical engineers, mathematicians. One of the most important goals of this Conference has been to bring these different scientists together with the physiologists and clinicians. The next important goal of this Society should be to work out clear definitions of the terms which are generally used in hemorheology. This will especially be valid for different terms of viscosity. Disagreements on viscosity values depend much on difficulties and variations in instrumentation. The equipment has no doubt been much improved during the last years and much more accurate measurements have been made on the shearing forces at very low rates of shear. The viscosity of blood at very low shear rates is, of course, of utmost importance for the clinician to measure, in order to adequately resuscitate a patient in profound shock, in cardiac arrest and for the protection and storage of organs for transplantation purposes, when the flow rate is zero.

There are still disagreements as to the normal viscosity values of plasma and of whole blood. This disagreement depends partly on instrumentation but mainly on how the sample for measurement is obtained. It has been emphasized earlier and I am going to reemphasize the difference in viscosity values obtained if the measurements are made *in vivo*, *extra vivum* or *in vitro*. I should, however, especially like to emphasize the *artefacts* studied when different substances (e.g. dextran, electrolytes or glucose) are *added* to plasma or whole blood *in vitro* with the belief or the conclusion that these substances influence the flow properties of blood *in vivo* in the same way as they do *in vitro*. The influences of such substances on the rheology of blood can only be studied after the administration of the substance to the patient or to the experimental animal. Here again the influence of a substance on the viscosity of blood at low rates of shear is of utmost importance.

From the clinical papers presented on flow disturbances in diabetes mellitus it is quite evident how necessary it is to distinguish between flow disturbances, arising from changes in the flow properties, changes in the vascular wall and in the vascular environment. Here again model studies have proven to be most valuable in elucidating the forces which will influence the separation of different cell particles toward different branches. The extremely important information brought forward on the influence of flow rate on distribution of cells and of plasma in on-flow and off-flow capillary tubes is greatly appreciated. This will help to understand how stasis builds up in the venules. There is now a great need for experiments which differ between total flow, flow rate, nutritional flow and also the flow rates of cells and of plasma in different vascular beds.

One of the main topics has been the relationship between clotting phenomena and flow disturbances in different clinical conditions. The primary platelet aggregation as a cause of flow obstruction and of flow disturbance after tissue injury has been stressed. The consequences of this white aggregation are to induce both clotting and lysis. The effects of fibrinogen split products have drawn special and new attention to the genesis of alterations in the flow properties of blood.

The influence of fat on the flow properties of blood in vivo and in vitro is controversial. This has only been touched on during this Conference but I think it is such an important field for research in clinical hemorheology and should be worth a main interest at a coming conference.

Hemorheology has come into clinical medicine to provide a better understanding of the dynamics in pathology. Increased knowledge in hemorheology will open possibilities for new therapeutic approaches, and the elaboration of new drugs which will be able to act at specific shearing forces to control blood flow and the distribution of different cell elements. The clinical importance of hemorheology is very great. This Conference has initiated an interest among many scientists of different disciplines and I should like to assure them that their knowledge and their contribution will come to the benefit of the patient. That is why we clinicians are so thankful for the initiative to this very successful Conference. Hemorheology will be a new discipline in medicine.

The above is a revised text and differs from the one published in *Biorheology* **4,** 115, 1968. (Editor.)

B. CLOSING REMARKS

AFTER the Chairman thanked the speakers for their appraisals, Professor Oka gave a statement, as a member of the Organizing Committee of the Fifth International Congress on Rheology, on the Biorheology Sessions planned at this Congress, to be held from 7–11 October 1968, in Kyoto. The second statement was made by Dr. Joly with regard to the Second International Conference on Hemorheology, to be held in 1969, in France. The statements and announcements by Professor Oka and Dr. Joly are not included in this volume because the information given has been published in the journal *Biorheology* (**4**, 115, 1967). This is also the case of the statement given by Professor Bugliarello, as Secretary of the International Society of Hemorheology, regarding announcements by the Council of the Society (*Biorheology* **4**, 116, 1967).

The final remarks by Professors Silberberg, Bjarnason and Copley were transcribed as follows:

COPLEY:

Thank you, Professor Bugliarello. It has just come to my attention that Professor Silberberg would like to make a statement. Professor Silberberg.

SILBERBERG:

Thank you very much, Mister Chairman. What I have to propose is something very simple. It is a vote of thanks to you, Professor Copley, for conceiving this meeting and initiating the Society and providing us not only with a very stimulating scientific meeting which was socially as much a success and where we all got to know each other extremely well. Thank you very much. I want to propose a word of thanks to you which, I hope, will be seconded and appreciated.

COPLEY:

Thank you for your most kind words. I hope really that I deserve so much credit. The last speaker will be Professor Bjarnason, our most able Chairman of the Local Committee. Professor Bjarnason, please.

BJARNASON:

Chairman, Ladies and Gentlemen. On behalf of the Local Committee, I just would like to congratulate you on the outcome of this First International Conference on Hemorheology. It has been, for us, a great pleasure to have you all here this week and I want to wish you a pleasant journey and a happy home-coming. Thank you very much.

COPLEY:

Dear Friends. As everything has a beginning, so everything appears to have an end. Now, we come to the end of this Conference. Above all, I like to thank our hosts,

Haskoli Islands, The University of Iceland, its Senate and, in particular, its Rektor Professor Armann Snaevarr for their fine hospitality. Our thanks go to Professor Bjarnason and the members of his Local Committee for helping us in every way possible to make this Conference a pleasant one and a fruitful one. We thank, as well, Mrs. Valborg Snaevarr and the other ladies of the Committee for all the generous and cordial assistance they have extended to the ladies who have been here with us. I should also like to thank our projectionist, Mr. Magnus Johannsson, for helping us to make this Conference a smooth one.

I thank every speaker and every participant in the discussions, and everyone who came here, for their contributions and for their patience. I thank the members of the Organizing Committee, and in particular those who formed the Executive Committee, our friends, George Bugliarello, Roe Wells, George Scott Blair and Ray Whitmore, who have happily shared with me the preparatory work. I hope that we have not made too many errors, but if we committed some bad ones, please blame them on me. You know we all tried to do our very best.

It is my hope that we all, who have been here this week, will be able to come to France in three years, to participate in the Second International Conference on Hemorheology, to which our friend, Joly, welcomed us a little while ago.

There is something more for me to say. It is my wish that, as long as you will stay here in Iceland, you have a most pleasant time and that you return well to the countries you came from. Only then, when we all have arrived safely back, shall I know that this has been a successful Conference.

Now, I have the duty to declare the First International Conference on Hemorheology, held here at the University of Iceland, as closed.

Thank you. Bon Voyage! Góda Ferd!

NAME INDEX

Names appearing in the text are indicated by figures in roman type; names in the References by figures in **bold**.

Wayland, H. J. ix, **51**, 182, 522, **678**, **679**, 692, 804, 810
Weaver, J. P. **771**
Webb, R. L. **667**
Weber 233
Wedell 344
Wegrzynowicz, Z. **372**
Weiner, A. **760**
Weisman, R. **477**
Weiss, G. H. **51**
Weiss, L. 485, **494**, **504**, 551, **562**
Weiss, P. 485, **494**
Weissenberg, K. **52**, **168**, 811
Weiss-Fogh, J. **761**
Wells, R. E. v, vi, **51**, **83**, **183**, **235**, **417**, **418**, **430**, 432, **442**, 443, **452**, 553, 558, **562**, **563**, **605**, **641**, 759, 773, **785**, 798, 806, 826
Wessler, S. **372**
Westergren, A. **452**
Westerhof, N. **275**
Weston, B. 691
Weymann, H. **50**, **51**
Wezler, K. 267, **274**, 276
Whang, S. H. Z. **62**
Wheby, M. S. **477**
Whetham, W. C. D. **62**
Whipple, G. H. **504**
Whitaker, S. R. F. 612, **614**
White, P. **760**, **761**
Whitfield, G. W. **208**
Whitmore, D. N. **760**
Whitmore, R. L. v, vi, ix, **50**, **51**, **83**, **84**, 85, 86, 111, 208, 398, 411, 625, **626**, 805, 810, 826
Whitney, E. **183**, 347, **358**
Whittaker 86
Whittam, R. 95, 105, 106, **110**
Wiederhielm, C. A. ix, 672, 674, **678**, 692, 694, 805, 813, 819
Wiegel **275**
Wiggers 748
Wilbrandt 95, 101, 104

Wilens, S. **329**
Wilkinson, W. L. **62**, **301**
Williams, A. V. **789**
Williams, P. S. **51**
Wilson, M. L. 609, **614**
Winslow 238, **251**
Winton, F. R. 86, 612, **614**
Wise, G. N. **760**
Wissig, S. L. **717**
Witkin, G. J. **761**
Witte, S. viii, **52**, **700**
Witzig, K. 255, **275**
Wolfe, A. **430**
Wolfram, C. G. **717**
Wolken, J. J. 526, 527, 528, 530, **536**
Wolpers, C. **562**
Wolpert, L. **562**
Womersley, J. R. J. **52**, 113, 114, 115, 121, 122, **125**, **141**, 245, 255, 256, 259, 275, **627**
Wood, B. H. **727**
Wood, G. F. 164, **168**
Woodbury, G. W. **51**
Wüst, H. **700**

Yalow, R. S. **581**
Yamamoto, M. **50**, **62**, 403, **409**
Yoakum, S. 605
Yoshida, K. 675, **679**
Young, L. E. **504**
Young, T. 152, **154**

Zacharias, H. **760**
Zachs, S. I. 755, **761**
Zahn 679
Zederfeldt, B. **441**, 452, **727**
Zia, I. Y. Z. 238, **251**
Zimmer, J. 804, 811
Zucker, M. B. 370, 371, **372**
Zuhdi, N. 433, **442**
Zweifach, B. W. 641, **717**

AUTHOR INDEX

Authors' contributions are indicated by figures in **bold** type; Discussants remarks by figures in roman.

839

SUBJECT INDEX